ORGANOBORON CHEMISTRY

Volume 1 Boron–Oxygen and Boron–Sulfur Compounds

Volume 2 Boron–Nitrogen and Boron–Phosphorus Compounds

Volume 3 Boron–Carbon Compounds

Volume One

BORON–OXYGEN AND

BORON–SULFUR COMPOUNDS

INTERSCIENCE PUBLISHERS a division of

ORGANOBORON CHEMISTRY

Howard Steinberg

Vice President and Director of Research

U.S. Borax Research Corporation

John Wiley & Sons Inc. · New York · London · Sydney

First published 1964 by John Wiley & Sons Inc.

Library of Congress Catalog Card Number: 63–20337

Made and printed in Great Britain by
William Clowes and Sons, Limited, London and Beccles

To Eve

PREFACE

The purpose of this volume and the series of which it is a part is to correlate the voluminous and rapidly growing literature dealing with the organic chemistry of boron. It is hoped that in the process a broad and firm basis can be laid which will aid in the integration of the lore on the subject which will be recorded in the future.

In order to present in a finite and manageable volume as broad a coverage as possible with full integration of the many fragmentary bits of pertinent information, it was necessary to limit the report of experimental details to only those parameters which bear directly on the chemistry under discussion. The reader is referred to the original literature for more exacting details.

The first three chapters deal with the scope of the series in general and the nature and nomenclature of the compounds involved in the first volume. However, in the main, the present volume is generically oriented on a type of compound basis. Chapters 4 through 13 treat the chemistry of trigonal coplanar boron–oxygen compounds, and Chapters 14 through 19 are concerned with tetrahedral boron–oxygen compounds. The present state of boron–sulfur chemistry is summarized in Chapter 20, and Chapter 21 correlates the available hydrolytic kinetic data for the boron–oxygen compounds. Infrared assignments, bond energy, bond distance, and heat of formation data are recorded in the Appendices.

The author is indebted to Dr. D. S. Taylor, President of the U.S. Borax Research Corporation, and Dr. C. L. Randolph, Assistant to the President, U.S. Borax and Chemical Corporation, for their vote of confidence in this venture. No less thanks are due to Drs. I. S. Bengelsdorf, J. L. Boone, J. G. Bower, G. W. Campbell, W. D. English, K. Kitasaki, H. C. Newsom, and W. G. Woods for their critical review of many of the chapters and Professors S. Winstein and R. O. Schaeffer for their advice on many points of theory. The author is indebted also to Mesdames Linda Counihan, Maxine Knudsen, Margaret McKenna, Sandra Ortega, and Esther Tedder for their excellent clerical assistance, and to Mesdames Heather Broome, Donna Croft, and Betty Robson for their very competent assistance in the library.

HOWARD STEINBERG

Fullerton, California
July, 1963

CONTENTS

chlorine atom, but in addition it itself undergoes a significant transformation as a direct result of its influence on the second functional grouping.[4]

A third path, and possibly the most intriguing, comprises catenation of the element in question. A fourth path involves the preparation of compounds with more than one of the "hetero" atoms in question.

The chemistry of boron is today enjoying simultaneous exploration of the four paths outlined. Adjacent to carbon in the first row of the periodic table, boron might be expected to be capable of forming a series of covalent compounds. Indeed, boron is capable of forming stable bonds with those atoms which also constitute most organic compounds; carbon, hydrogen, oxygen, nitrogen, sulfur, and the halogens. Thus, as in the case of classical organic chemistry, an infinite number of organoboron compounds can be envisaged. To date, the preparation and interconversion of thousands of organoboron compounds representing a wide variety of functional species has allowed the development of a systemization approaching that of carbon compounds.

The chemistry of organofunctional boron compounds is being pursued at a slower pace due to the added difficulty of preparing, maintaining, and transforming an organofunctional group in the presence of a boron atom.

The catenation of boron in non-hydridic compounds, as first demonstrated with diboron tetrachloride by Stock in 1926,[5] is being pursued vigorously by both academic and industrial chemists in the United States, England, and Germany.

The introduction of second and third "hetero" atoms has led to several unique chemistries including that of the borazines (I), boroxines (II), borthiins (III), and borphosphines (IV).

(I) (II) (III) (IV)

II. SCOPE OF SERIES

This series will treat the chemistry of the organic compounds of boron. The present volume deals with the oxygen derivatives, which are the most prevalent covalent boron compounds. In a sense they can be considered as primary derivatives of boric acid. Boron–sulfur compounds are a logical extension of the oxygen compounds and their chemistry also is included.

Volume II treats the nitrogen compounds of boron. They can be considered secondary derivatives of boric acid in that they are not usually prepared directly from boric acid but rather are derived from compounds prepared in turn from boric acid. Thus, inherent in the title of the series, *Organoboron Chemistry*, is the broader definition of "organoboron" which in its strictest sense would include only boron–carbon bonded materials. Volume III will cover boron–carbon bonded materials.

The disposition of the chemistry which concerns compounds with two or possibly three different types of bondings in the same molecule, such as the compounds in structure (V) or in reaction (1-2),

$$RO{-}B\begin{matrix} \diagup NHR \\ \diagdown CH_2R \end{matrix}$$

(V)

$$(RO)_3B + RNH_2 \rightarrow (RO)_2BNHR + ROH \qquad (1\text{-}2)$$

will be on the basis of latest position in the order oxygen–nitrogen–carbon. Thus, the chemistry of structure (V) will be found in Volume III, "Boron–Carbon Compounds," and the chemistry of reaction (1-2) would be found in Volume II, "Boron–Nitrogen Compounds." One exception to this rule will be found in Volume II which will discuss the borazines (I) as an integral unit regardless of the presence of boron–carbon bonds.

The hydro and halo derivatives of the three basic types of compounds will be found in the three volumes on the basis of the presence of B–O, B–N or B–C bonds. Thus, the chemistry of $ROBH_2$ and $(RO)_2BX$ will be in Volume I, $(RNH)_2BH$ and $RNHBX_2$ in Volume II, and RBH_2 and R_2BX in Volume III.

Complexes composed of inorganic boron compounds and organic nucleophiles, such as the ether–boron halide complexes (VI) and

$$R_2O{:}BX_3 \qquad\qquad RNH_2{:}BH_3$$

(VI) (VII)

borane–amine adducts (VII), are considered to be beyond the scope of this series. Their chemistry is included in the series only to the extent that they are either reactants or products in a system under discussion. Consideration of the chemistry of the boron halides, sodium borohydride, the fluoborates, and like compounds is on a similar basis. The boron hydrides, as characterized by the presence of bridged hydrogen three-centered orbitals, are also considered to be beyond the scope of the present series.

III. LITERATURE COVERAGE

An attempt has been made to include all significant references from the early 19th century to January 1, 1962. The validity of certain results obtained in the 19th century certainly may be discounted on the basis of questionable purity of starting materials and the choice of experimental conditions, which under scrutiny of present-day knowledge might preclude the attainment of "correct" answers; however, the intent of an experiment performed in 1867 cannot be discounted. If in 1867 Schiff attempted to prepare an alkyl metaborate from the reaction of boric acid and an alkyl orthoborate, it makes no difference at this late date whether he indeed did actually isolate the pure metaborate or not. His approach was original and his concept was correct. Thus, the series will contain pertinent references of historical interest when the data contained therein have a real relationship to what we choose to call present-day reality.

The appropriate chapters include a compilation of all reported compounds and their physical constants. In some instances, compounds are included in the table whose physical constants were not recorded in the original paper. This was done in order to present a complete compilation for use as a starting point for literature searches.

The U.S. and foreign patent literature is included in so far as it contains valid discussions or experimental details of boron chemistry. The inclusion of prophetic statements is kept to a minimum and all unsubstantiated claims of a broad and sweeping nature are ignored. Discussion of the uses of boron compounds is beyond the scope of this series.

Unclassified Government report literature is included wherever the law specifically provides for such usage.

IV. REFERENCES

1. Baker, D. B., *Chem. Eng. News*, **39** No. 29, 78 (1961).
2. Ebelman, J. J., and M. Bouquet, *Ann. chim. et phys.*, **17**, 54 (1846); *Ann.*, **60**, 251 (1846).

3. Gay-Lussac, J. L., and L. J. Thénard, *Ann. chim. et phys.*, **68**, 169 (1808).
4. Hawthorne, M. F., and J. A. Dupont, *J. Am. Chem. Soc.*, **80**, 5830 (1958).
5. Stock, A., A. Brandt, and H. Fischer, *Ber.*, **58**, 653 (1926).
6. Wöhler, F., *Ann. Physik.*, [2] **12**, 253 (1828); *Ann. chim.*, [2] **37**, 330 (1828).

2

CONFIGURATION AND GENERAL NATURE OF COMPOUNDS

I. GENERAL NATURE

Organic boron–oxygen and boron–sulfur compounds are similar in nature to ordinary organic materials. They are usually colorless liquids or white solids. Crystallinity is common. They are combustible, volatile, in general melt below 400°, and are soluble in organic solvents. Their solubility in water, with the exception of the coordination compounds derived from diols and from hydroxy acids, is due mainly to hydrolysis and not to their ability to ionize in this medium. The hydrolytic instability, coupled with their ability to complex with nucleophiles, often makes it inadvisable to expose them to the air or to work with them in many of the hydroxylic, amine or oxygen-containing solvents. With proper precautions, however, standard manipulative techniques and equipment can be employed.

Reaction rates involving organoboron compounds are in general of the same order of magnitude as organic reactions, and ultimate yields of esterification reactions, transesterification reactions, etc., are analogous.

II. CONFIGURATION

Organoboron compounds in general, and the compounds of this volume in particular, exist in two general configurations (Table 2-1).* In the majority of cases, the boron atom is trigonal coplanar with sp^2 hybridization. Vacant lobes of a $2p$-orbital lie above and below the BO_3 plane (I). Thus, most organoboron compounds are electron

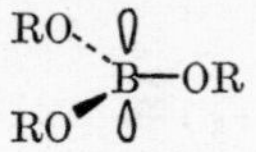

RO, RO, B—OR

(I)

* The organic derivatives of the boron hydrides clearly constitute a third configuration involving the geometry peculiar to three-centered orbitals. As stated in the introduction, the chemistry of these compounds is beyond the scope of this series.

Table 2-1. Configuration of compounds and nature of substituents

Configuration	Formal charge on boron	Y	Approximate number of compounds reported
Trigonal coplanar, BY_3	0	—OR, —OOR, —ORO—, —$OSiR_3$, —OH, —OM, —OC(=O)R, —OC(=O)RO—, —OB<, —SR, —SRS—, —SB<, H, X	850
Tetrahedral, >N—:BY_3	−1	—OR, —OOR, —ORO—, —OB<, H, X	100
Tetrahedral, $[BY_4]^-M^+$	−1	—OR, —ORO—, OH, —OM, —OC(=O)R, —OC(=O)RO—, —OC(=O)RC(=O)O—, H, X	300
Tetrahedral, 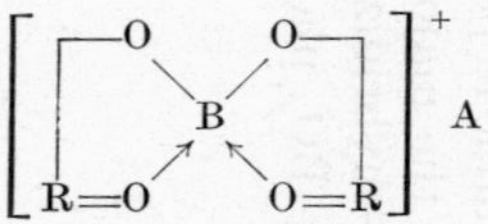 $[(O\text{—}R\text{=}O)B(O\text{—}R\text{=}O)]^+A^-$ (two rings, each O—R=O bonded to B, the R=O bond coordinating to B)	+1	RC(O⁻)=CHC(=O)R, RC(O⁻)=CHC(=O)OR	20

deficient in the sense of the Lewis octet theory and much of the recorded organoboron chemistry is related to the resulting electrophilicity of the boron atom.

In the second general configuration boron assumes tetrahedral

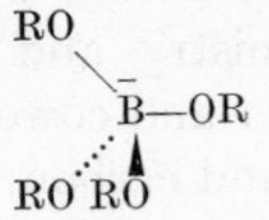

RO
B—OR
RO RO
(II)

character with sp^3 hybridization (II). Clearly, the electron deficient nature of boron is alleviated in this series of compounds.

Three types of tetrahedral compounds have been described. Addition compounds, i.e. complexes or adducts (III), are formed by

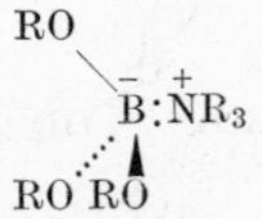

RO
$\overset{-}{B}:\overset{+}{N}R_3$
RO RO
(III)

the one to one addition of a trigonal coplanar boron derivative and a nucleophile such as an amine. In such complexes boron can be pictured as having a formal charge of -1 which is compensated by an adjacent donor atom of formal charge $+1$.

In the second type of tetrahedral species, a fourth covalent bond is present and the boron atom again assumes a full formal negative charge. A cation completes the structure (IV).

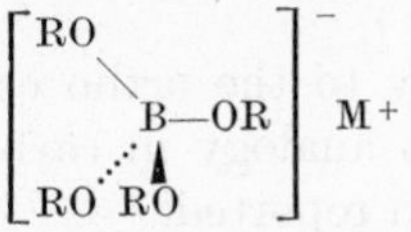

[RO B—OR RO RO]$^-$ M^+
(IV)

The third type of sp^3 hybridization involves chelate bonds and a full formal positive charge on boron. An anion completes the structure (V).

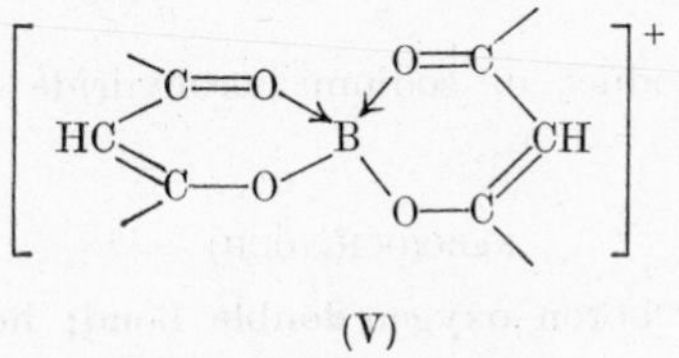

[HC(C=O)(C—O)B(O=C)(O—C)CH]$^+$ A^-
(V)

III. COMPARISON OF ORGANIC AND ORGANOBORON STRUCTURES

There is much to be learned from a simultaneous study of the disciplines of organic chemistry and organoboron chemistry. In 1938, Professor H. R. Snyder and coworkers stated: "Owing to the close relationship of boron and carbon, in so far as effective nuclear charge and atomic radius are concerned, one may expect studies of organoboron compounds to be of value in interpreting the behavior of analogous electronic systems associated with carbon."[3] Thus, esters of boric acid (VI) may be considered to be the structural counterpart of esters of carbonic acid (VII) or carboxylic acids (VIII)

$B(OR)_3$ (VI) $RO-C(=O)-OR$ (VII) $R-C(=O)-OR$ (VIII)

in which the carbonyl carbon is electrophilic by virtue of the electronic shifts as shown.

In the tetravalent series, the tetraalkoxyborate anion (IX) can

$[B(OR)_4]^-$ (IX) $[C(OR)_4]$ (X) $[B(OCH_2CH_2O)_2]^-$ (XI)

be compared structurally to the ortho esters (X). The spiroborate anion (XI) has no exact analogy in carbon chemistry; spiroorthocarbonates have not been reported.

There are other discontinuities in the structural analogies of carbon and organoboron compounds. Many simple structures which are common in organic compounds have as yet not found their counterpart in organoboron compounds. For example, boron–oxygen double bonds (XIII),* boron–sulfur double bonds (XIV),

* The reaction product of sodium borohydride and carbon dioxide, formulated as[2,4]

$$NaBO(OCH_3)(\overset{O}{\overset{\|}{C}}H)$$

could accommodate a boron–oxygen double bond; however, the trimeric and vinyloxyboranes (XV) have not yet been reported. Conversely,

—B=O	—B=S	CH_2=CHOB<
(XIII)	(XIV)	(XV)

boron is capable of forming stable structures not attainable with carbon. Thus, structure (XVI) bearing three acyloxy groups has no analogy in carbon chemistry.

$$\left(R\overset{O}{\overset{\|}{C}}O\right)_3B$$

(XVI)

IV. REFERENCES

1. Lappert, M. F., and J. K. Smith, *J. Chem. Soc.*, 3224 (1961).
2. Pearson, R. K., and T. Wartik, U.S. Pat. 2,872,474 (1959, to Callery Chemical Company).
3. Snyder, H. R., J. A. Kuck, and J. R. Johnson, *J. Am. Chem. Soc.*, **60**, 105 (1938).
4. Wartik, T., and R. K. Pearson, *J. Am. Chem. Soc.*, **77**, 1075 (1959).
5. Wartik, T., and R. K. Pearson, *J. Inorg. & Nucl. Chem.*, **7**, 404 (1958).

---

formulation below is more probable.[5]

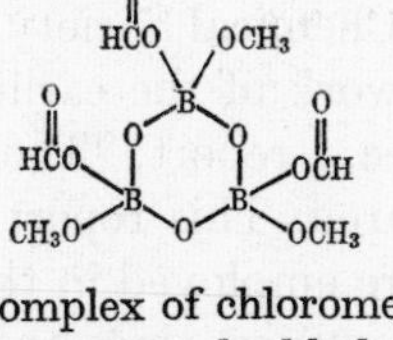

The boron oxychloride complex of chloromethyl methyl sulfide has been formulated to contain a boron–oxygen double bond.[1]

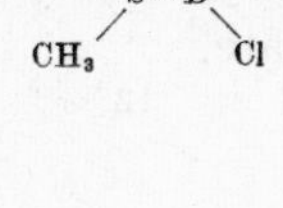

3

NOMENCLATURE

I. INTRODUCTION

The almost exponential rate of growth of boron chemistry in the past two decades has made it apparent that the existing rules of nomenclature for boron compounds[1,2] do not lead to unambiguous names for the wide variety of new compound types that have been prepared. Thus, structure (I) has been called boron acetate, tetraacetyl diborate, pyroboroacetate, tetraacetoxy boric anhydride and bis(diacetoxyboron) oxide.

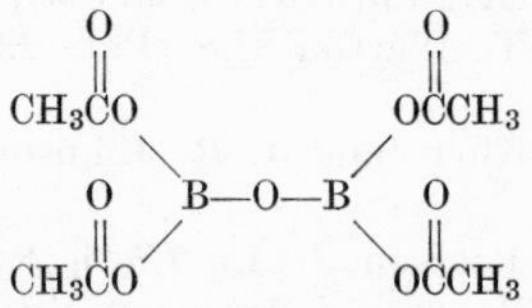

```
       O                 O
       ‖                 ‖
    CH3CO               OCCH3
          \            /
       O   B — O — B    O
       ‖  /           \ ‖
    CH3CO               OCCH3
               (I)
```

Several informal groups became concerned with the increasing confusion in the field and the need for a system capable of expansion to include new compounds and areas of knowledge. Their studies led to a paper, "The Nomenclature in Boron Compounds," presented before the Division of Chemical Literature of the American Chemical Society.[9] The paper was subsequently reviewed in *Chemical and Engineering News*.[3,7]

These and other activities of interested persons occasioned the establishment of an "Advisory Subcommittee on the Nomenclature of Organic Boron Compounds" under the Nomenclature Committee of the Division of Organic Chemistry of the American Chemical Society. The subcommittee met for the first time during the 128th Meeting of the American Chemical Society at Minneapolis in 1955.

On the basis of the work of the earlier informal groups and of the advisory subcommittee, a report, "The Nomenclature of Boron," January 1958, was prepared. This report is used as the basis and guide for the nomenclature employed in the present and subsequent volumes of this series. However, since the report has not yet been officially adopted and some changes may be introduced, the most plausible alternative names for many of the compounds are also recorded wherever appropriate.

Any systematic approach to nomenclature is oriented from the indexing viewpoint and not from the viewpoint of euphony. The name must be unambiguous or it is essentially worthless. In addition, one must be able to "translate" the structure to a set of ciphers or phrases and, conversely, be able to convert an isolated sequence of ciphers and phrases into a unique structure. A subject index cannot usually supply the reader with a picture or detailed description of the compound in question; some expediency and intangible feeling of "understanding" is lost, and the reader feels he is engrossed in an encyclopedic compilation. Thus, structure (II) is named 2,2′-(1,1,3-trimethyltrimethylenedioxy)bis-(4,4,6-trimethyl-1,3,2-dioxaborinane), and structure (III) is 3,7,10-trimethyl-2,8,9-trioxa-5-aza-1-borabicyclo[3.3.3]undecane.

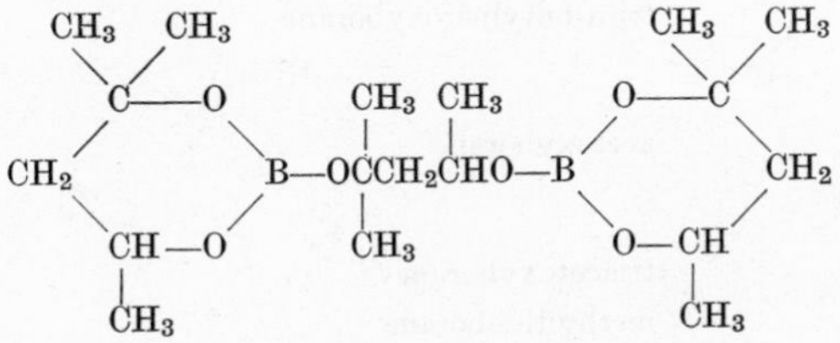

```
 CH3   CH3                           CH3   CH3
   \   /                               \   /
    C——O      CH3 CH3           O——C
   /    \      |   |           /    \
CH2      B—OCCH2CHO—B            CH2
   \    /      |                \    /
    CH—O      CH3                O—CH
    |                               |
    CH3                             CH3
                  (II)
```

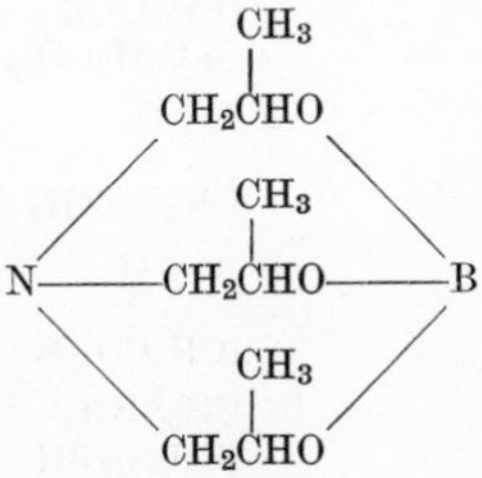

```
                 CH3
                 |
               CH2CHO
              /       \
                 CH3
                 |
N————————CH2CHO————————B
                 CH3
              \  |    /
               CH2CHO
               (III)
```

Fortunately, in a finite work such as the present volume we are not compelled to convey unambiguous titles without the aid of crutches. We can describe the starting materials together with the subtleties of the molecule in question and, if necessary, draw a picture representing the actual structure of the compound. With these written and pictorial aids, we are able to use more descriptive names which make for more attentive readership and, therefore, greater ease of understanding of the chemistry in question. In the final analysis, we are less concerned in the present volume with the search for a perfect nomenclature system than with reaching an understanding of the chemistry. Thus, structure (II) can be called hexylene glycol biborate and structure (III) can be referred to as triisopropanolamine borate.

Such practices neither detract from elaborate systems of nomenclature nor do they obviate the need for the systematic approach; they serve to complement the systematic approach. If we had to choose a single system, it would of necessity have to be the systematic one; however, we are not forced into such a choice in this work and alternative names can be used without loss of understanding. Thus, the reader will find the backbone for the systematic approach in this chapter and a blend of approaches in the other chapters.

II. TRIGONAL COPLANAR COMPOUNDS — BORON ATOM NOT IN A RING

A. Compounds Containing One Boron Atom

The trigonal coplanar compounds of boron, which comprise the majority of organoboron compounds, are named as derivatives of borane, the simplest hypothetical boron hydride, BH_3.*

CH_3OBH_2	methoxyborane
$(CH_3O)_2BH$	dimethoxyborane
$(CH_3O)_3B$	trimethoxyborane
$(n\text{-}C_4H_9OO)_3B$	tri-n-butylperoxyborane
$CH_3\overset{\overset{O}{\|}}{C}OBH_2$	acetoxyborane
$(CH_3\overset{\overset{O}{\|}}{C}O)_3B$	triacetoxyborane
CH_3SBH_2	methylthioborane
$(CH_3S)_2BH$	dimethylthioborane
$(CH_3S)_3B$	trimethylthioborane

Trimethoxyborane represents the simplest member of the most common type of boron–oxygen compounds, the boric acid esters. These compounds have been named almost exclusively as esters in the past literature.

$(CH_3O)_3B$	trimethyl borate or methyl borate
$(C_6H_5O)_3B$	triphenyl borate or phenyl borate
$(NH_2CH_2CH_2O)_3B$	tri-(2-aminoethyl) borate or 2-aminoethyl borate

The "ester" nomenclature system has little versatility and breaks down for compounds such as $CH_3OB(OH)_2$. Since the name methyl borate commonly refers to the species $(CH_3O)_3B$, one is forced to describe rather than name $CH_3OB(OH)_2$ as the monomethyl ester of boric acid. For these reasons and the sake of overall simplicity and conformity, the "trialkoxyborane" nomenclature will be used extensively in these volumes.

Consistent with this approach, the esters derived from silanols

* Reference 1 records the molecule BH_3 as "borine" and its derivatives as substituted borines. This terminology is used by many contributing workers in the field.

will be called tris(trialkylsiloxy)boranes rather than tris(trialkylsilyl) borates.

$[(CH_3)_3SiO]_3B$	tris(trimethylsiloxy)borane
$[(CH_3CH_2)_2Si(Cl)O]_3B$	tris(chlorodiethylsiloxy)borane

When two or more different substituents are present, the substituents are named in alphabetical order, as is the common practice for organic compounds.[1]

$CH_3CH_2OB(H)OCH_3$	ethoxy(methoxy)borane
$CH_3OB(H)Cl$	chloro(methoxy)borane
$CH_3CH_2OB(H)F$	ethoxyfluoroborane
$CH_3OB(H)OH$	hydroxy(methoxy)borane
$CH_3C(=O)OB(H)OH$	acetoxyhydroxyborane
$CH_3CH_2CH_2OB(H)SCH_3$	methylthio(propoxy)borane
$CH_3C(=O)OB(OCH_2CH_3)Cl$	acetoxy(chloro)ethoxyborane
$CH_3CH_2CH(CH_3)OB(OCH(CH_3)_2)OCH_3$	2-butoxy(methoxy)-2-propoxyborane

The substituents are named alphabetically regardless of the number of each substituent.

$(CH_3O)_2BOH$	hydroxydimethoxyborane
$(C_4H_9O)_2BCl$	dibutoxychloroborane
$(C_3H_7O)_2BSH$	mercaptodipropoxyborane
$(CH_3S)_2BF$	fluorodimethylthioborane
$[(CH_3)_2N-C_6H_4-O]_2BCl$	chlorobis-(4-dimethylaminophenoxy)-borane

B. Compounds Containing More Than One Boron Atom

Compounds containing more than one isolated boron atom are named as "bisboranes."

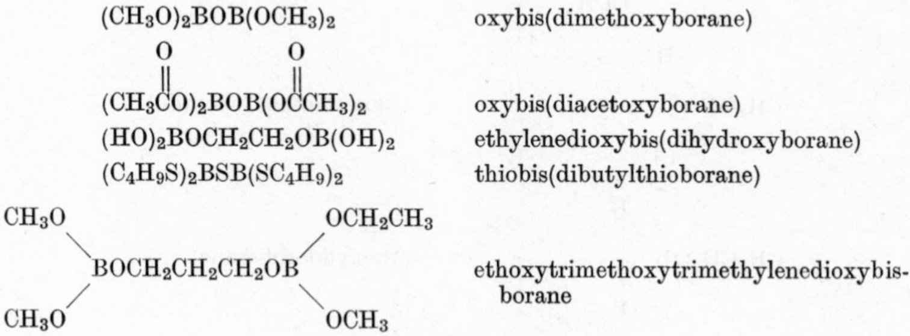

$(CH_3O)_2BOB(OCH_3)_2$	oxybis(dimethoxyborane)
$(CH_3C(=O)O)_2BOB(OC(=O)CH_3)_2$	oxybis(diacetoxyborane)
$(HO)_2BOCH_2CH_2OB(OH)_2$	ethylenedioxybis(dihydroxyborane)
$(C_4H_9S)_2BSB(SC_4H_9)_2$	thiobis(dibutylthioborane)
$(CH_3O)_2BOCH_2CH_2CH_2OB(OCH_2CH_3)(OCH_3)$	ethoxytrimethoxytrimethylenedioxybis-borane

III. BORON RADICALS

In many cases the naming of certain apparently complex boron compounds can be simplified by treating them as boron derivatives of simpler or better-known compounds.

Names of radicals:

H_2B-	boryl
$(HO)_2B-$	dihydroxyboryl
Cl_2B-	dichloroboryl
$O{=}B-$	oxoboryl

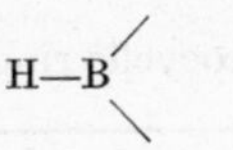

borylene

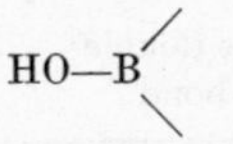

hydroxyborylene

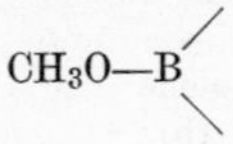

methoxyborylene

Applications:

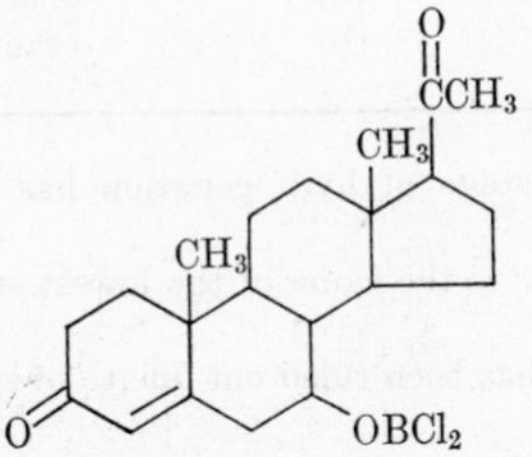

7-dichloroboryloxyprogesterone

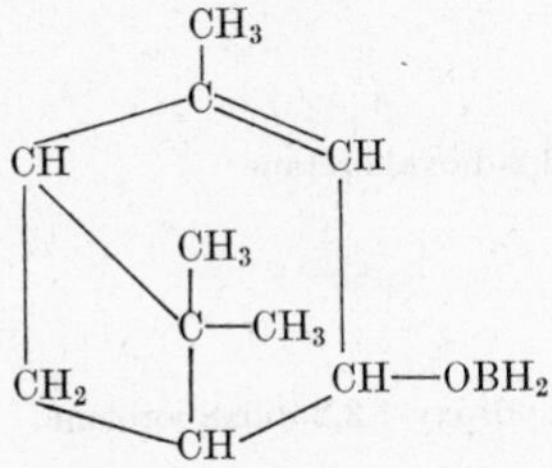

6-boryloxy-α-pinene

IV. TRIGONAL COPLANAR COMPOUNDS — BORON ATOM IN A RING

A. Four- to Ten-membered Rings

Four- to ten-membered rings are named by the practices established in the *Ring Index*.[8] Table 3-1 lists the endings of the names of the simple heterocyclic rings at various states of hydrogenation.

The numbering system starts with the heterocyclic atom other than boron (IV). The heterocyclic atoms are referred to as oxa, thia and bora. The letter "a" may be elided before a vowel.

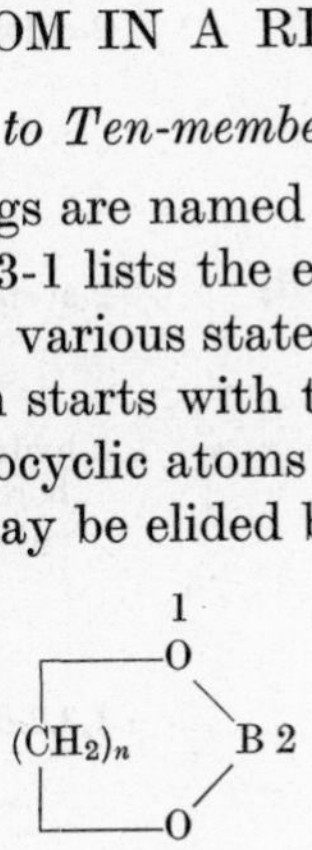

(IV)

Table 3-1. Endings of names of simple heterocyclic rings

Size of ring	Lowest stage of hydrogenation	Two double bonds	One double bond	Saturated
4-membered	—	—	—	-etane
5-membered	-ole[a]	—	-olene	-olane
6-membered	-in	(b)	(b)	-inane[c]
7-membered	-epin	(b)	(b)	-epane
8-membered	-ocin	(b)	(b)	-ocane
9-membered	-onin	(b)	(b)	-onane
10-membered	-ecin	(b)	(b)	-ecane

[a] Takes precedence over olene when the lowest stage of hydrogenation has one double bond.

[b] Expressed by prefixing dihydro-, tetrahydro-, etc., to the name of the lowest stage of hydrogenation.

[c] The alternative, -ane, as given in the *Ring Index* has been ruled out due to obvious ambiguities which would be caused by its use.

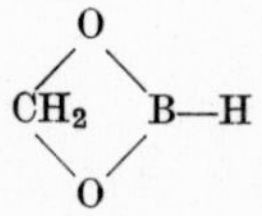

1,3,2-dioxaboretane

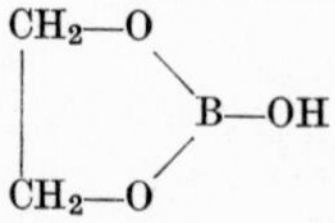

2-hydroxy-1,3,2-dioxaborolane

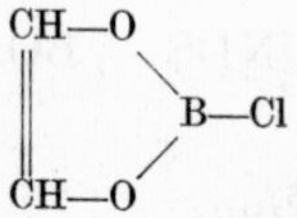

2-chloro-1,3,2-dioxaborole

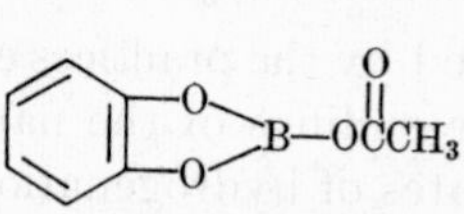

2-acetoxy-1,3,2-benzodioxaborole

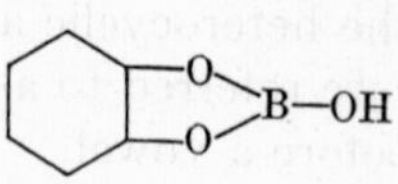

2-hydroxy-1,3,2-hexahydrobenzodioxaborole or 2-hydroxy-4,5-tetramethylene-1,3,2-dioxaborolane*

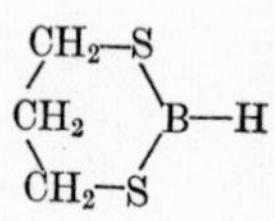

1,3,2-dithiaborinane

* Could also be named as a bicyclic compound. See Section IV-C.

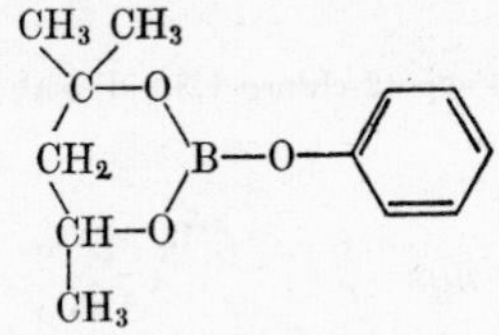

2-phenoxy-4,4,6-trimethyl-1,3,2-dioxaborinane

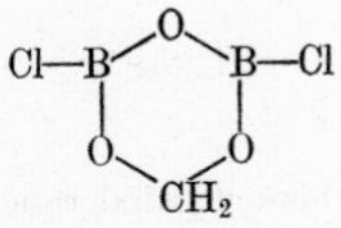

2,4-dichloro-1,3,5,2,4-trioxadiborinane

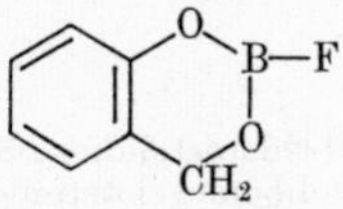

2-fluoro-1,3,2-benzodioxaborin

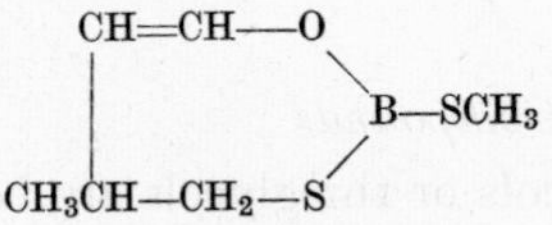

2-methylthio-6-methyl-4,5-dihydro-1,3,2-thiaoxaborepin

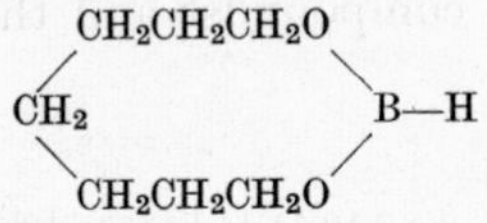

1,3,2-dioxaborecane

Two rings joined by a simple connective are named as "bisboranes" preceded by the numbers denoting the points of attachment.

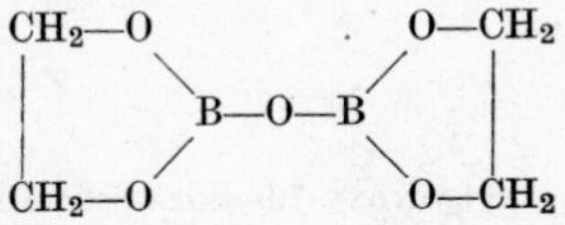

2,2′-oxybis-(1,3,2-dioxaborolane)

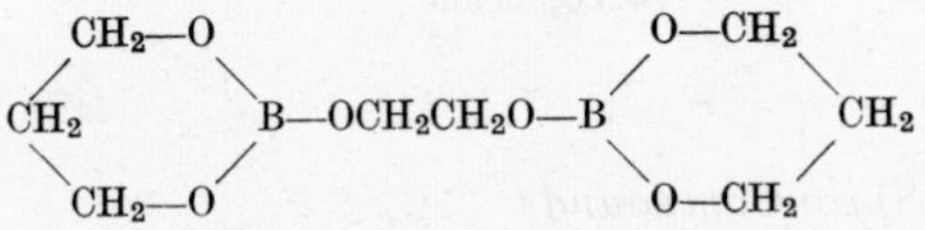

2,2′-ethylenedioxybis-(1,3,2-dioxaborinane)

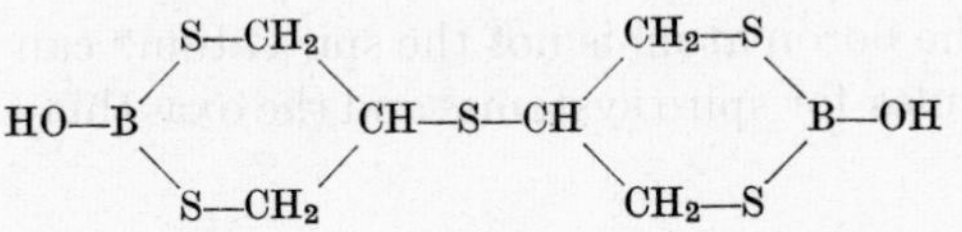

5,5′-thiobis-(2-hydroxy-1,3,2-dithiaborinane)

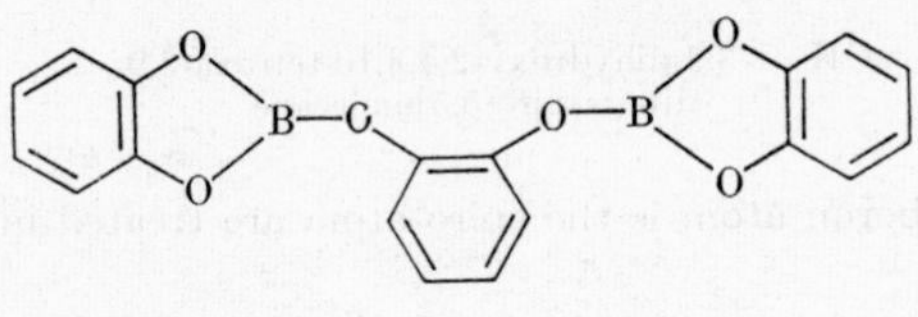

2,2′-*o*-phenylenedioxybis-(1,3,2-benzodioxaborole)

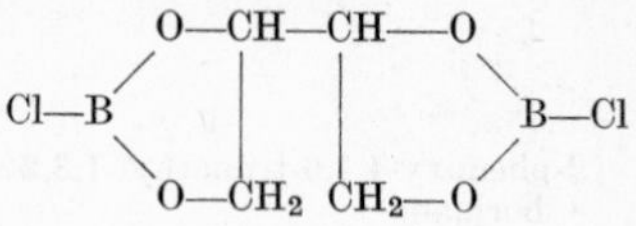

4,4′-bis-(2-chloro-1,3,2-dioxaborolane)

B. Larger Rings

Larger rings may be named as cyclic hydrocarbons denoting the hetero atoms as oxa, thia, bora, etc.[1]

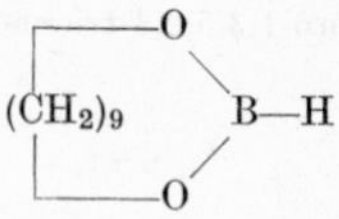

1,3-dioxa-2-boracyclododecane

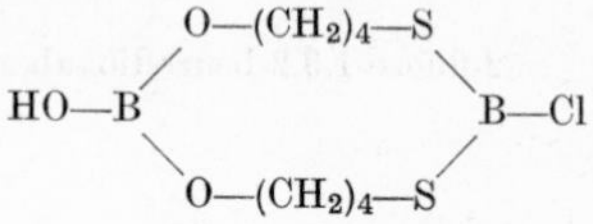

2-hydroxy-9-chloro-1,3-dioxa-8,10-dithia-2,9-diboracyclotetradecane

C. Bicyclic Compounds

Bridged systems derived from glycols or thioglycols are best named according to the rules for bicyclic compounds[8] and the oxa–thia–bora system.[1]

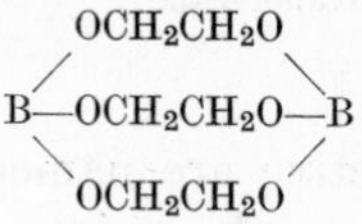

2,5,7,10,11,14-hexoxa-1,6-diborabicyclo-[4.4.4]tetradecane

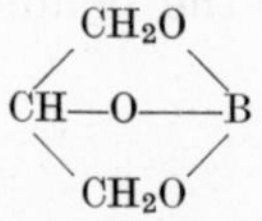

2,6,7-trioxa-1-borabicyclo[2.2.1]heptane

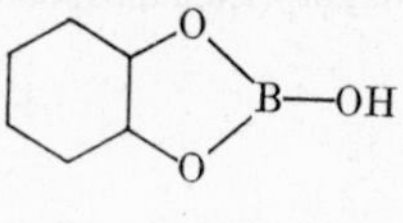

8-hydroxy-7,9-dioxa-8-borabicyclo-[4.3.0]nonane

D. Spiro Compounds

Spiro compounds in which the boron atom is not the spiro atom* can be named according to the rules for spiro systems[8] and the oxa–thia–bora system.[1]

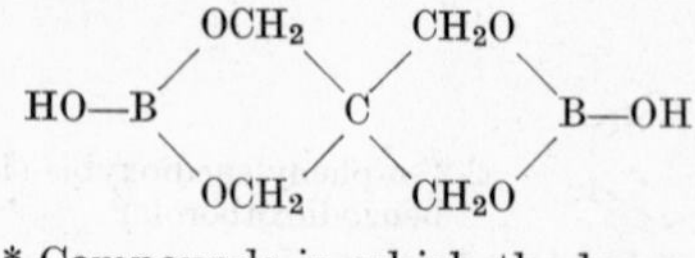

3,9-dihydroxy-2,4,8,10-tetroxa-3,9-diboraspiro[5.5]undecane

* Compounds in which the boron atom is the spiro atom are treated in Section V-B-2.

E. Sugar Derivatives

Compounds of known stoichiometry but unknown structure are simply named as polyol borates. Thus, the structurally undefined compound derived from mannitol and two moles of boric acid is given the stoichiometric name "mannitol diborate."

Derivatives of known structure also may be named stoichiometrically preceded by the positions of attachment. A more definitive alternative employing the use of boron radical terminology and sugar terminology may be used. Both approaches retain the name of the polyl or sugar in question.

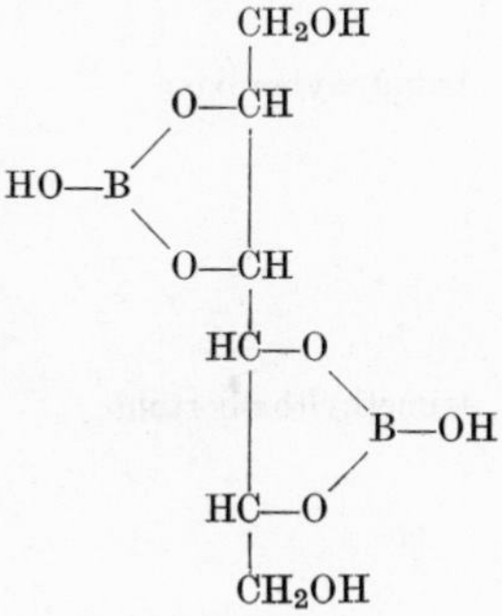

Stoichiometric name: 2,3:4,5-mannitol bisborate*

Use of boron radical and sugar terminology: 2,3:4,5-bis-*O*-(hydroxyborylene)mannitol

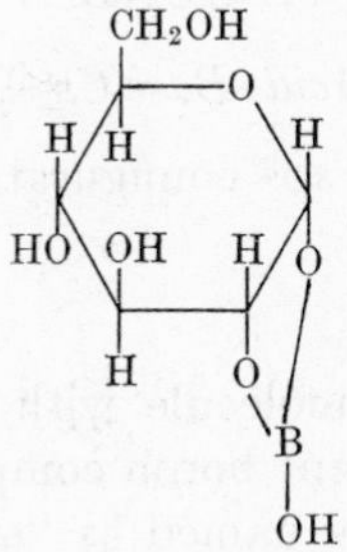

Stoichiometric name: 1,2-α-D-glucopyranose borate

Use of boron radical and sugar terminology: 1,2-*O*-(hydroxyborylene)-α-D-glucopyranose

F. Trivial Names

Certain ring systems, by virtue of their stability, appear frequently in the literature. Such systems have been assigned trivial names.

* The mannitol derivative could be named by the bisborane system as applied to two rings joined by a simple connective. However, the resulting name, 4,4′-bis-(2-hydroxy-5-hydroxymethyl-1,3,2-dioxaborolane), does not convey the stereochemical relationships or the basic polyol structure as well as does the simple term, mannitol.

The parent rings, boroxine (V) and borthiin (VI), as yet have not

```
        H                     H
        |                     |
        B                     B
      O   O                 S   S
      |   |                 |   |
   H—B     B—H           H—B     B—H
        O                     S
       (V)                   (VI)
```

been shown to have an independent existence; their derivatives, however, are well known.

```
              OC4H9
               |
               B
             O   O
             |   |
   C4H9O—B         B—OC4H9          tributoxyboroxine
               O

              SCH3
               |
               B
             S   S
             |   |
   CH3S—B          B—SCH3           trimethylthioborthiin
               S
```

V. TETRAHEDRAL COMPOUNDS

A. *Addition Compounds* (*Lewis Acid–Base Complexes*)

A large class of boron compounds with sp^3 configuration (VII) are

$$(RO)_3B\!:\!\text{base}$$
(VII)

prepared by the simple addition of a molecule with an available electron pair (Lewis base) and a tricovalent boron compound (Lewis acid). These substances are conveniently named as "addition compounds"[4] by naming the base or donor molecule first followed by a hyphen and the name of the boron compound.

$(CH_3)_2O\!:\!BH_3$	dimethyl ether-borane
$(CH_3CH_2)_2S\!:\!BF_3$	diethyl sulfide-boron trifluoride or diethyl sulfide-trifluoroborane
$(CH_3O)_3B\!:\!NH_3$	ammonia-trimethoxyborane

B. *Coordination Compounds*

1. UNIDENTATE LIGANDS

Boron forms an extended series of coordination compounds in which the boron atom assumes sp^3 tetrahedral configuration and bears a full formal negative charge (VIII). The rules generally accepted for naming coordination compounds[5,6] may be applied. The names of

$$[BY_4]^- \text{ cation}^+$$
(VIII)

the common coordinate groups or ligands and their recommended order* are as follows:

O^{2-}	oxo
HO^-	hydroxy
$CH_3C(=O)O^-$	acetoxy
$C_2H_5O^-$	ethoxy
CH_3O^-	methoxy
CH_3S^-	methylthio
HS^-	mercapto
Br^-	bromo
Cl^-	chloro
F^-	fluoro
H^-	hydro

The cation is named first, followed by the ligands in the recommended order. The prefixes di, tri, and tetra are used before simple expressions, and the prefixes bis, tris, and tetrakis before complex expressions. Complex expressions are enclosed in parentheses.

$NaB(OCH_3)_4$	sodium tetramethoxyborate†
$KBH(OC_2H_5)_3$	potassium triethoxyhydroborate
$LiB(OH)_2(SCH_3)_2$	lithium dihydroxydimethylthioborate
$HB(OC(=O)CH_3)_4$	hydrogen tetraacetoxyborate
$[(CH_3)_2N\text{—}C_6H_4\text{—}O]_3BClNa$	sodium tris(*p*-dimethylaminophenoxy)-chloroborate
$[BH(OCH_3)_3]_2Ca$	calcium trimethoxyhydroborate

* The recommended order is: (*i*) O^{2-}, OH^-, (*ii*) organic anions in order of decreasing complexity, (*iii*) polynuclear inorganic anions, and (*iv*) mononuclear anions.[5] More recently an alternative order has been recommended by the Commission on Nomenclature of Inorganic Chemistry of the International Union of Pure and Applied Chemistry:[11] (*i*) O^{2-}, OH^-, (*ii*) other one-atom anions in alphabetical order, (*iii*) polyatomic inorganic anions in alphabetical order, and (*iv*) organic anions in alphabetical order.

† The "borohydride" system of nomenclature[10] would lead to the name "sodium tetramethoxyborohydride" even though no hydride functions are present in the molecule.

$NaBO(OCH_3)(O\overset{\overset{O}{\|}}{C}H)$	sodium oxoformoxymethoxyborate*

2. BIDENTATE LIGANDS

Coordination compounds derived from diols, hydroxyacids, dibasic acids, and their sulfur analogs are named according to the rules for unidentate ligands.

Some common ligands:

$—OCH_2CH_2O—$	ethylenedioxy
$—O(CH_2)_3O—$	trimethylenedioxy
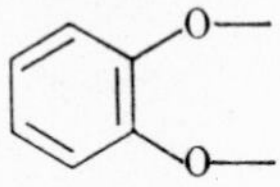	*o*-phenylenedioxy
$—SCH_2CH_2S—$	ethylenedithio
$—OCH_2\overset{\overset{O}{\|}}{C}O—$	glycolato
$—SCH_2\overset{\overset{O}{\|}}{C}O—$	thioglycolato
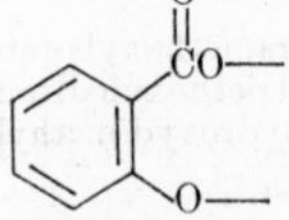	salicylato
$—O\overset{\overset{O}{\|}}{C}CH_2\overset{\overset{O}{\|}}{C}O—$	malonato

Applications:

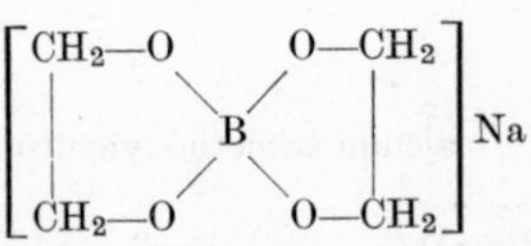 sodium bis(ethylenedioxy)borate

* The actual structure of this compound probably is the trimer.[12]

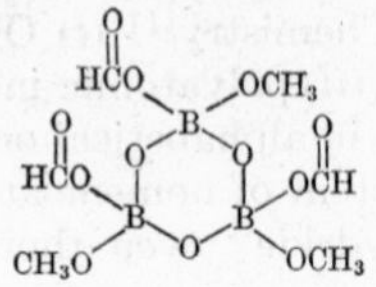

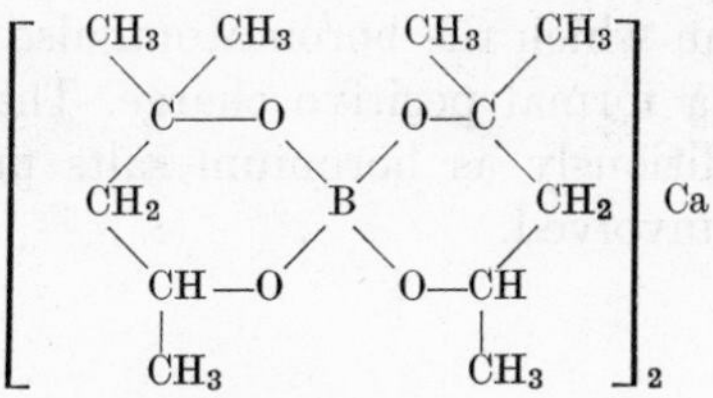

calcium bis(1,1,3-trimethyltrimethylenedioxy)borate

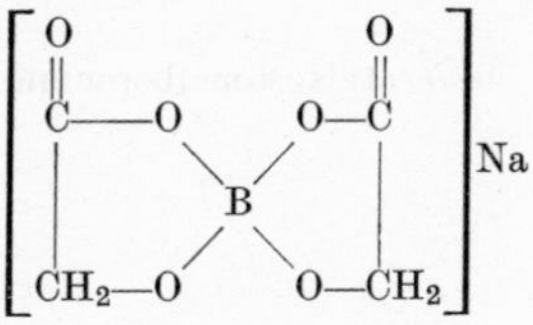

sodium bis(glycolato)borate

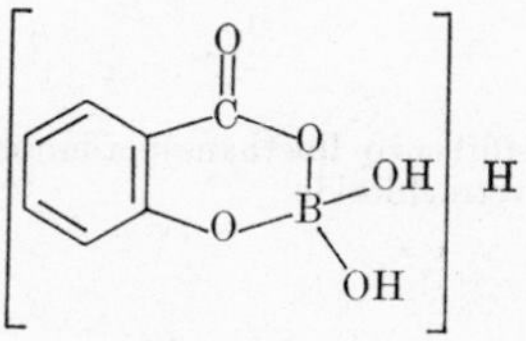

hydrogen dihydroxysalicylatoborate

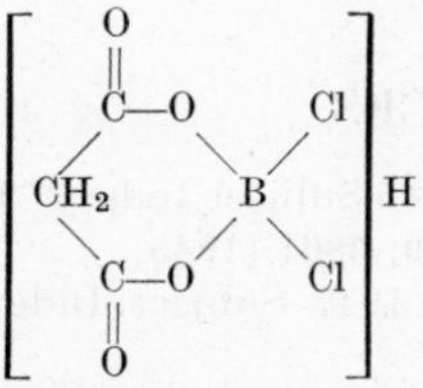

hydrogen malonatodichloroborate

3. TERDENTATE LIGANDS

Coordination compounds derived from triols, tribasic acids, etc., are named according to the rules for unidentate ligands.

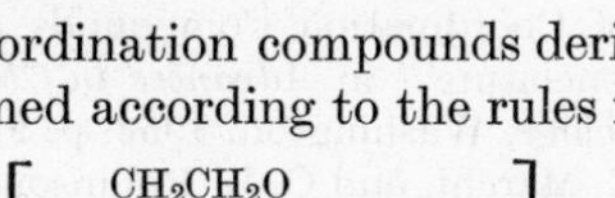

$[N(CH_2CH_2O)_3B—OCH_3]Na$ sodium (2,2′,2″-nitrilotriethoxy)-methoxyborate

C. Boronium Salts

In contrast to the coordination compounds in which boron bears a formal negative charge, a series of compounds exists derived from

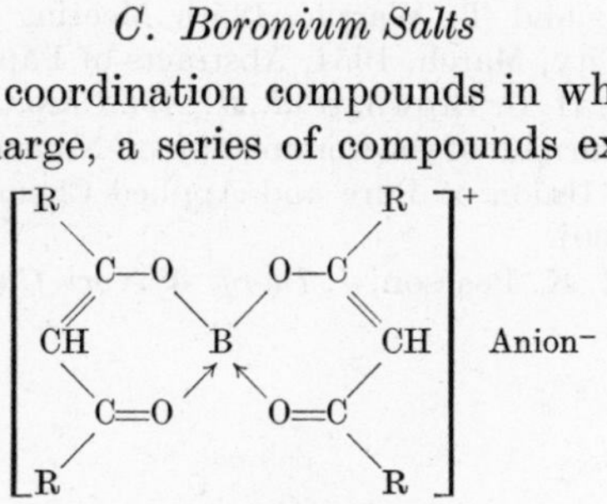

$[B(RC(O)CHC(O)R)_2]^+$ Anion$^-$

(IX)

β-diketones and β-hydroxyketones in which the boron atom, also in a tetrahedral configuration, bears a formal positive charge. These compounds (IX) are named expeditiously as boronium salts prefaced by the name of the diketone involved.

```
┌CH3               CH3┐+
   \               /
    C—O       O—C
   //   \     /   \\
  CH      B        CH    Cl-    bis(acetylacetone)boronium chloride
   \    ↗   ↖     /
    C=O       O=C
   /               \
└CH3               CH3┘

┌C6H5              C6H5┐+
   \               /
    C—O       O—C
   //   \     /   \\
  CH      B        CH    FeCl4-   bis(dibenzoylmethane)boronium ferric
   \    ↗   ↖     /                 tetrachloride
    C=O       O=C
   /               \
└C6H5              C6H5┘
```

VI. REFERENCES

1. *Chemical Abstracts*, Introduction to the 1945 Subject Index, "The Naming of Chemical Compounds for Indexing," **39**, 5867 (1945).
2. *Chemical Abstracts*, Introduction to the 1947 Subject Index, **41**, 8175 (1947).
3. *Chem. Eng. News*, **32**, 1441 (1954).
4. Davidson, N., and H. C. Brown, *J. Am. Chem. Soc.*, **64**, 316 (1942).
5. Fernelius, W. C., "Nomenclature of Coordination Compounds and its Relation to General Inorganic Nomenclature," in *Advances in Chemistry Series, No. 8*, American Chemical Society, Washington, 1953, p. 9.
6. Fernelius, W. C., E. M. Larson, L. E. Marchi, and C. L. Rollinson, *Chem. Eng. News*, **26**, 520 (1948).
7. Patterson, A. M., *Chem. Eng. News*, **34**, 560 (1956).
8. Patterson, A. M., and L. T. Capell, *The Ring Index*, Reinhold Publishing Corporation, New York, 1940.
9. Schaeffer, G. W., and T. Wartik, 125th Meeting American Chemical Society, Kansas City, March, 1954, Abstracts of Papers, p. 7-G.
10. Schlesinger, H. I., H. C. Brown, *et al.*, *J. Am. Chem. Soc.*, **75**, 186 (1953).
11. Silverman, A., Chairman of the Commission on Nomenclature of Inorganic Chemistry of the Union of Pure and Applied Chemistry, *J. Am. Chem. Soc.*, **82**, 5538 (1960).
12. Wartik, T., and R. K. Pearson, *J. Inorg. & Nucl. Chem.*, **7**, 107 (1958).

4

SYMMETRICAL ORTHOBORATES OF MONOHYDRIC ALCOHOLS AND PHENOLS

I. INTRODUCTION

Trialkoxy (I) and triaryloxyboranes (II) are the most numerous and

$$B(OR)_3 \quad \text{(I)} \qquad\qquad B(OAr)_3 \quad \text{(II)}$$

best-known of the boron–oxygen compounds. This chapter discusses the chemistry of the members derived from a single monohydric alcohol or phenol.* Aliphatic and alicyclic derivatives have been recorded with a variety of primary, secondary, and tertiary alkoxy groups substituted with fluorine, chlorine, bromine, and alkoxy, aryloxy, acyloxy, carboxy, carbalkoxy, hydroxy, keto, amino, aryl, cyano, mercapto, trialkyltinmercaptoalkyl, and nitro groups. Aldehydo substituents have not been documented.

The alkenyl borates such as the allyl, propargyl, and 3-butenyl derivatives have not included organofunctional substituents. The simplest unsaturate, trivinyl borate (III), is yet to be prepared.

$$(CH_2{=}CHO)_3B$$

(III)

Aromatic members have been described with chloro, iodo, aryl, alkyl, cycloalkyl, mercaptoalkyl, trialkyltinmercaptoalkyl, alkoxy, hydroxy, nitro, carboxy, carbamyl, and mercapto substituents.

Amine complexes of the borates (IV) also are included in the discussion.

$$(RO)_3B{:}NR_3$$

(IV)

* Diols and diphenols have been included when the product contains free hydroxyl groups, such as $(HOCH_2CH_2O)_3B$ and $(HOC_6H_4O)_3B$.

II. HISTORICAL

In 1846 Ebelman and Bouquet[140] reported to the French Academy of Science their preparation of the methyl, ethyl and amyl esters of boric acid from the reaction of the appropriate alcohol and boron trichloride. This work not only describes the first preparation of a boric acid ester but also represents the first recorded synthesis of an organoboron compound.

III. PROPERTIES

A. General

The orthoborates range from colorless volatile liquids boiling at 68.5° to polymeric solids which decompose upon heating. With the

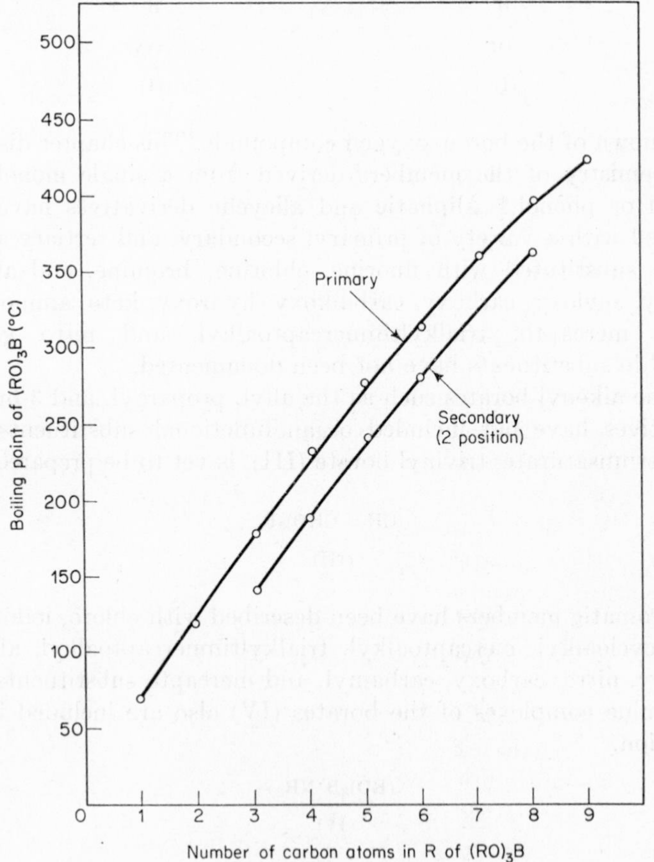

Fig. 4-1. Boiling point versus number of carbon atoms in alkyl group of $(RO)_3B$.

exclusion of the first two members of the aliphatic series, their boiling points tend to parallel their molecular weights[208] (Table 4-1 and Fig. 4-1).

Table 4-1. Comparison of boiling points and molecular weights of trialkoxyboranes

R in $(RO)_3B$	Molecular weight	B.p. (°C)
CH_3	104	68.5
C_2H_5	146	118
n-C_3H_7	188	177
n-C_4H_9	230	230
n-C_5H_{11}	272	275
n-C_6H_{13}	314	311
n-C_7H_{15}	356	358[a]
n-C_8H_{17}	398	395[a]
n-C_9H_{19}	441	445[a]

[a] Extrapolated

The esters of boric acid usually have an odor similar to the alcohol or phenol from which they are derived; this may be due in part to their ready hydrolysis. They burn with a green flame leaving a residue of boric oxide. In general, they are soluble in organic solvents and insoluble in water. The miscibility of tri-β-cyano-ethoxyborane with benzene and immiscibility with heptane has been used to separate the two hydrocarbons.[383]

The aliphatic members are somewhat less dense than water (ca. 0.85 at 25°); the aromatics in the few cases recorded have densities slightly greater than unity, and the halogenated derivatives are well above unity in density. The refractive indices of the aliphatics fall in the range 1.35 to 1.45 (Fig. 4-2). The few recorded values for the aromatics are in excess of 1.5. The viscosities of the lower aliphatic members range from about 1 to 3 centipoise at 28°;[208] the higher alkyl members range from about 25 to 120 centipoise at 20°,[15,491] and the values of the aromatic members are around 200 centipoise at 20°.[491]

Octet refractivities for a series of aliphatic and aromatic derivatives are recorded in Table 4-2. Molar refractivities and magnetic susceptibilities also have been documented.[201] Complete critical data as well as the relationship of the molar refractivity to the number of carbon atoms in the alkyl group (equation 4-1) have been recorded for a series of alkyl borates.[105]

$$R_{\text{obsd.}} = 13.87n + 10.74 \tag{4-1}$$

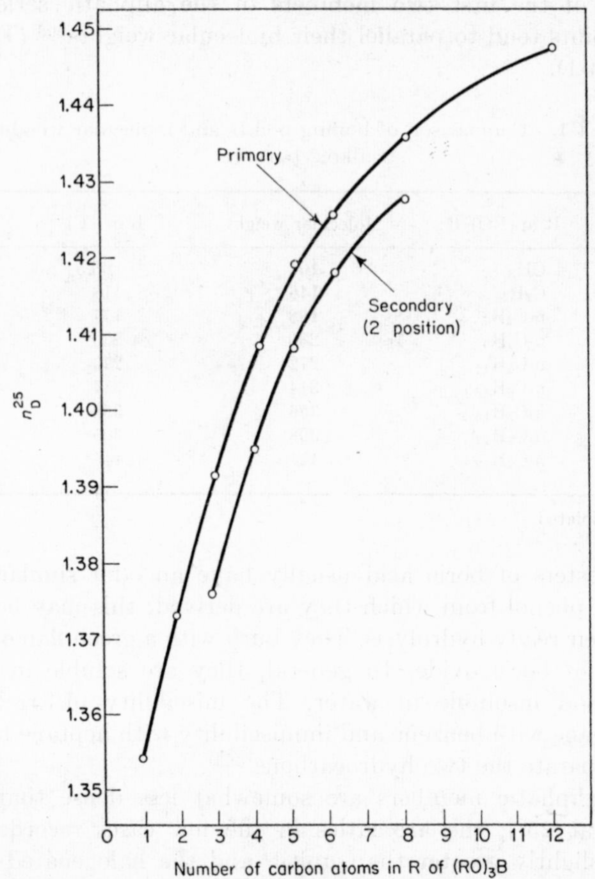

Fig. 4-2. Index of refraction versus number of carbon atoms in alkyl group of $(RO)_3B$.

Table 4-2. Octet refractivities of trialkoxy- and triaryloxyboranes

Structure	Number of compounds	Refractivity	Reference
$B:\ddot{\underset{..}{O}}:C_{Alkyl}$	52	3.10 ± 0.14	493
$B:\ddot{\underset{..}{O}}:C_{Alkyl}$	21	3.14 ± 0.14	107
$B:\ddot{\underset{..}{O}}:C_{Aryl}$	4	2.68 ± 0.30	493

The ^{11}B nuclear magnetic resonance chemical shifts relative to boron trifluoride etherate are given in Table 4-3.[358] It appears that

Table 4-3. ^{11}B nuclear magnetic resonance chemical shifts

Compound	$\delta = \frac{H_s - H_r}{H_r} \times 10^6$ [a]
$(o\text{-Cl—}C_6H_4O)_3B$ (ether soln.)	-13.7 ± 2.0
$(o\text{-}CH_3\text{—}C_6H_4O)_3B$ (ether soln.)	-15.0 ± 1.0
$(CH_2{=}CHCH_2O)_3B$	-17.5
$(CH_3O)_3B$	-18.1 [b]
$(C_2H_5O)_3B$	-18.1

[a] Relative to boron trifluoride etherate.
[b] $-18.$[134]

three oxygen atoms bonded to trivalent boron have chemical shift values which occur approximately in the region -14 to -19.*

Proton magnetic resonance chemical shifts for triisobutoxyborane and tri-*t*-butoxyborane have been recorded.[129] Raman spectra are available for a variety of lower trialkoxyboranes[10,38,225,230,231,257,343,346] and triphenoxyborane.[225] X-ray diffraction patterns of trimethoxy, triethoxy and triisobutoxyborane have been determined.[237]

On occasion, boric acid esters have been referred to as ethers. This analogy is logical if boron is equivalent to carbon in its role. However, the reactivity of the trialkoxyboranes towards hydrolysis, alcoholysis, reaction with organometals, etc., is orders of magnitude greater than the reactivity of ethers. The boric acid esters indeed act like true esters, and consequently the boron atom can be considered to be equivalent to a carbonyl group (V) in its influence on the molecule.

$$\rangle BOR \approx -\overset{\overset{\displaystyle O}{\|}}{C}OR$$

(V)

The electrophilic nature of the boron atom by virtue of its electron deficiency and vacant *p* orbital permits acceptance of nucleophiles in a manner similar to the carbonyl group. In the case of the carbonyl group, the mobile electrons of the double bond are

* Triethanolamine borate (Chapter 5) and oxybis(diacetoxyborane) (Chapter 8) are exceptions.

shifted to the carbonyl oxygen on entry of a nucleophile (equation 4-2). Boron is capable of tetracovalency and thus accepts a nucleophile by rehybridization from sp^2 to sp^3 with the boron atom assuming a formal negative charge (equation 4-3).

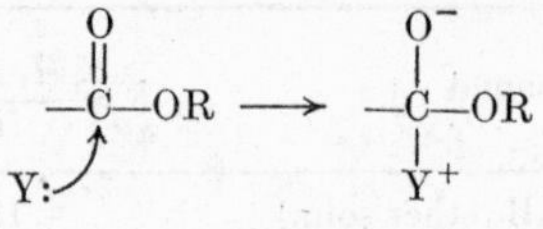

$$\mathrm{Y{:}} + \mathrm{-C(=O)-OR} \longrightarrow \mathrm{-C(O^-)(Y^+)-OR} \quad (4\text{-}2)$$

$$\mathrm{Y{:}} + \mathrm{RO-B(OR)-OR} \longrightarrow \mathrm{RO-B^-(OR)(Y^+)-OR} \quad (4\text{-}3)$$

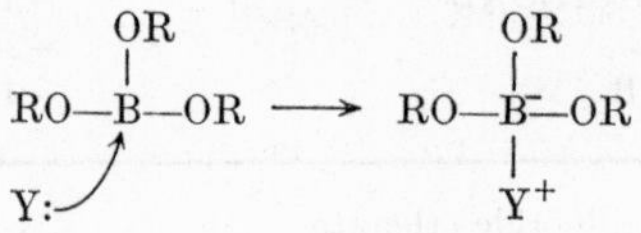

B. Structure

All data[431a] including molecular weight determinations[106,163,234,352,471] and Trouton constants[505] support a monomeric structure for the orthoborates. No evidence to the contrary has been presented. Apparently, the tendency for boron to coordinate intermolecularly with an available pair of electrons (VI)* is offset by an overpowering intramolecular coordination of which structure (VII)[517] represents

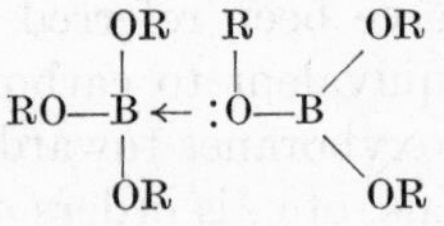

$$\mathrm{RO-B(OR)_2 \leftarrow :O(R)-B(OR)_2} \quad \text{(VI)} \qquad \mathrm{(RO)_2\overset{-}{B}=\overset{+}{O}R} \quad \text{(VII)}$$

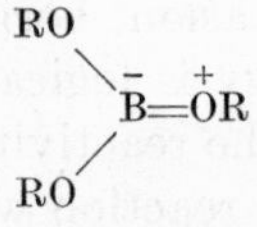

one of three equivalent canonical forms. The resonance energy of the borates has been estimated to be 8 to 9 kcal[300] and in excess of 17 kcal/mole.[73]

The relatively low solubility of hydrogen chloride in tributoxyborane has been attributed to the decreased availability of the free electron pairs on the oxygen atoms for coordination with the hydrogen atom of the hydrogen chloride due to p_π–p_π overlap with the boron atom.[189] However, the coordination of the unbonded electron pairs on the oxygen atoms with the vacant p orbital of the boron atom does not rule out the behavior of trialkoxyboranes as typical Lewis acids. Indeed, it has been demonstrated that boric acid esters

* Infrared absorption of several lower trialkoxyboranes at 8.00 and 8.40 μ has been attributed to this interaction.[491]

display the first two of Lewis' phenomenological criteria for acid behavior: they exhibit acid colors with indicators (benzonitrile and methanol solution), and they undergo neutralization with a base (sodium methoxide in methanol solution).[527]

The planarity of the BO_3 group demanded by the electron shifts of structure (VII) is consistent with the conclusions of planarity based on parachor measurements.[17,151,229,282] Dipole moment data for a variety of trialkoxyboranes also have been interpreted to be consistent with a planar structure with the O–B–O angle equal to 120°.[13,18,122,201,291,300,359,457] It was further concluded that steric effects would tend to twist the carbon atoms attached to the oxygen atoms out of the BO_3 plane and that conformations of high moment in which all the alkyl groups were simultaneously above or below the BO_3 plane were improbable due to steric requirements.[291] Dispersal of the alkyl groups above and below the BO_3 plane is consistent with viscosity and parachor data for a series of long chain alkyl borates which indicate that the esters in dilute solution are in the extended form (VIII) with two chains disposed in parallel fashion on one side of the BO_3 plane.[15] This conformation would eliminate the possibility of p_π–p_π overlap.

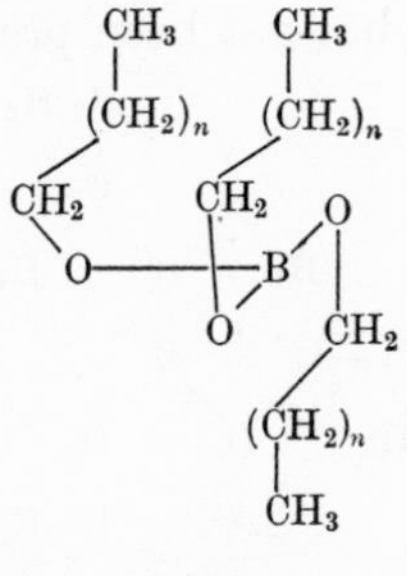

```
 CH3       CH3
  |         |
 (CH2)n    (CH2)n
 /         /
CH2       CH2   O
  \        |   /|
   O-------|-B  |
           |/   |
           O   CH2
               /
            (CH2)n
              |
             CH3
```

(VIII)

Electron diffraction studies of trimethoxyborane led to the conclusions that it has a planar BO_3 group with the boron valence angles equal to 120°, but that there is considerable motion of the methyl groups away from the planar configuration. The internal rotations about the B–O bonds are synchronized so that the most probable conformation is somewhat like that shown in Figure 4-3.[29] Dipole moment and refractivity studies in carbon tetrachloride solution indicated the deviation of the C–O bonds from the BO_3 plane to be approximately 74°.[18] Other dipole studies indicated a mean amplitude of 40°.[300] However, a consideration of Raman and

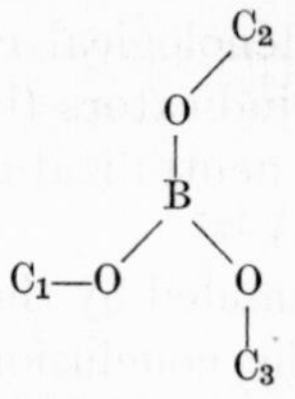

$$
\begin{array}{c}
C_2 \\
/ \\
O \\
| \\
B \\
/ \quad \backslash \\
C_1—O \qquad O \\
\qquad | \\
\qquad C_3
\end{array}
$$

B–O = 1.38 ± 0.02 Å
C–O = 1.43 ± 0.03 Å
B–O–C = 113 ± 3°

Fig. 4-3. Trimethoxyborane conformation of high probability. C_1–O bond slightly below BO_3 plane, C_2–O bond well below BO_3 plane, C_3–O bond above BO_3 plane.

infrared spectral data led to a conformation in which the carbon atoms and BO_3 group were coplanar (Fig. 4-4).[38,257]

The short B–O bond length in trimethoxyborane, 1.38 Å versus 1.54 Å for the sum of the boron and oxygen covalent radii,[360] is consistent with the shift of the infrared B–O stretching vibration from an average of 7.49 μ for trialkoxyboranes in general to 7.40 μ for trimethoxyborane. The shortening also is consistent with the relatively high density of trimethoxyborane.[491] The B–O bonds were not attributed any double bond character.[38]

Although sterically hindered esters have been prepared,[444] and the possibility of the existence of isomeric forms due to restricted rotation about the B–O bond has been stated,[112] no evidence for the isolation of diastereomers has yet been presented.

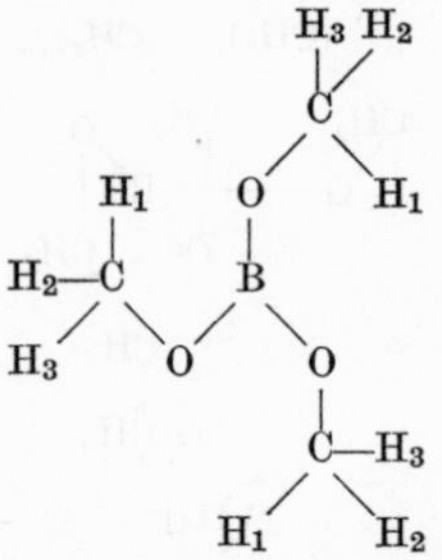

$$
\begin{array}{c}
H_3\ H_2 \\
|\ / \\
C \\
/ \quad \backslash \\
H_1 \qquad O \qquad H_1 \\
| \qquad\quad | \\
H_2—C \qquad B \\
/ \quad \backslash \quad / \quad \backslash \\
H_3 \qquad O \qquad O \\
| \\
C—H_3 \\
/ \quad \backslash \\
H_1 \qquad H_2
\end{array}
$$

Fig. 4-4. Planar conformation of trimethoxyborane. Hydrogen atoms H_1 are in the $B(OC)_3$ plane, hydrogen atons H_2 and H_3 are situated symmetrically above and below the $B(OC)_3$ plane.

IV. METHODS OF PREPARATION

A. From Boric Acid

1. METHODS OF WATER REMOVAL

The most efficient and common method of preparation involves the esterification of boric acid with three moles of an alcohol or a phenol.

$$B(OH)_3 + 3\,ROH \rightleftarrows B(OR)_3 + 3\,H_2O \tag{4-4}$$

Since the reaction is reversible with the equilibrium point lying far to the left* (see Chapter 21), the ease of the reaction depends upon the facility with which the water of the reaction or the ester itself can be removed from the reaction zone. With the exception of triethanolamine[298] and triisopropanolamine borate[445] (discussed in Chapter 5), the esterification does not proceed at a measurable rate unless the equilibrium is shifted by the removal of either the water or the product ester. The boiling point of the ester and the facility with which the ester or alcohol forms azeotropes thus play an important role, at least in the production of the lower members of the series.

The first use of boric acid for the preparation of esters was in 1907.[463] Terpene alcohols were involved. In 1911, boric acid was used for the preparation of the methyl, ethyl and isobutyl esters.[108] Hydrogen chloride and concentrated sulfuric acid were used as catalysts. The subsequent literature contains sporadic references to the use of mineral acid catalysts for the esterification of boric acid.[13,103] However, the reaction appears to proceed equally well in the absence of acids,[269] and it is probable that there is no appreciable acceleration in rate when acid is present. In some cases the acid can be harmful by catalyzing dehydration of the alcohol or promoting ether formation.[414]

The esterification technique has been simplified by employing excess alcohol and removing the water of the reaction at atmospheric pressure as an azeotrope with the excess alcohol.[24] This method was originally applied to tributoxyborane, was subsequently verified[37] and developed,[226] and also was shown to be applicable to tripropoxyborane[208] and a wide variety of higher borates derived from primary and secondary alcohols[48,352,397,443] as well as from phenol.[111] Obviously, this method cannot be employed for alcohols that do not form azeotropes with water or for methanol or ethanol which form lower boiling azeotropes with their respective esters than they do with water (see Sections IV-A-4 and IV-A-6). It also failed for allyl

* An equilibrium constant of 0.0907 has been reported for the system

$$B(OH)_3 + CH_3OH \rightleftarrows B(OCH_3)_3 + 3\ H_2O$$

at 20° with a CH_3OH to $B(OH)_3$ mole ratio of 10.[60] However, the value was determined by removing the volatile constituents and weighing the residual boric acid, and thus it can hardly be called an equilibrium constant since the removal of the trimethoxyboranes provides a driving force to shift the equilibrium.

Ref. 57 records a 27% ester yield at equilibrium for the reaction

$$H_3BO_3 + 3\ CH_3OH \rightarrow (CH_3O)_3B + 3\ H_2O.$$

alcohol[208] and tertiary alcohols.[56,397] The direct esterification of tertiary alcohols is not generally practiced because of the slowness of the reaction and the tendency of the alcohol to dehydrate to the corresponding olefin under the conditions of the esterification.[294]

The need for an excess of an alcohol capable of forming an azeotrope with water was obviated by adding an azeotroping solvent, such as toluene, and by percolating the reflux liquor through anhydrous copper sulfate.[138] This method, with anhydrous magnesium sulfate as the desiccant, was applied with partial success to the preparation of esters from tertiary alcohols.[11] However, attempts to isolate the esters led to decomposition. The facile decomposition of esters derived from tertiary alcohols is discussed in Section V-A.

The innovation of removing the water of the reaction as a ternary azeotrope with the reactant alcohol and added benzene was introduced in the preparation of tri-n-propoxyborane.[516] Subsequent workers[169,294] have prepared and isolated a variety of esters derived from tertiary alcohols by using both the binary and ternary azeotrope methods with benzene, toluene, carbon tetrachloride and petroleum naphtha as the azeotroping agents by separating and removing the water layer from the condensed azeotrope and recycling the organic layer. The driving force in these reactions is supplied by the use of an efficient distillation column which allows the small concentration of water in the vapor phase to be effectively removed without depletion of the alcohol or added solvent.

The binary azeotrope process with either benzene, toluene or xylene as the azeotroping agent is probably the most common method of preparation in use today. It has been applied to a large variety of monohydric compounds including unsaturated,[41,147,185,220,223,260,518] alicyclic,[218,269,352,430,444] aromatic,[213,214,260,444,521] unsubstituted saturated[214,260,269,352,444] and chloro,[172,229,269,444] carboxy,[213] alkoxy,[213,521] and cyano[384] substituted saturated alcohols. Other azeotroping agents which have been used include ethylbenzene,[372,373,375,376,520,522] isopropylbenzene[372] and *o*-dichlorobenzene.[374,375,376] Triphenylcarbinol failed to react with boric acid in boiling ethylbenzene.[521]

2. RATE OF ESTERIFICATION

The rate of esterification of a given alcohol is a function of the azeotroping agent employed (Table 4-4).[490] For a given azeotroping agent, the rate of esterification of boric acid is dependent upon the steric requirements of the alcohol. Primary alcohols react more rapidly than secondary alcohols which in turn esterify more rapidly

Table 4-4. Relative rate of esterification of boric acid with a given alcohol and various azeotroping agents

Azeotroping agent	Relative rate
None	1
Benzene	2
1-Octene	2.01
Diisobutylene	2.16

than tertiary alcohols.[11] This rate order was utilized to separate the three general classes of trialkoxyboranes.[416,525] Esterifications with phenols are laboriously slow. No quantitative data have been recorded other than for triisopropanolamine borate (see Chapter 5).

It has been reported that *trans*-α-decalol (m.p. 63°) reacts with boric acid to give the borate but that *cis*-α-decalol (m.p. 93°), *cis*-β-decalol (m.p. 105°) and *trans*-β-decalol (m.p. 75°) do not.[217] The negative results with *cis*-β-decalol (m.p. 105°) are surprising in view of the *cis–cis* configuration[128] of the alcohol and the apparent lack of strain in the Fisher–Taylor–Hirschfelder model of the borate. Since the configuration of the other alcohols is not known, it is difficult to ascribe any stereochemical significance to the reported unreactivities.

3. MECHANISM

The actual mechanism of the esterification has not been investigated. One can write a straightforward concerted displacement of hydroxyl by alkoxyl proceeding through a tetrahedral transition state with subsequent collapse to an intermediate alkoxyhydroxyborane. This species then reacts with a second and third mole of alcohol in a similar manner.

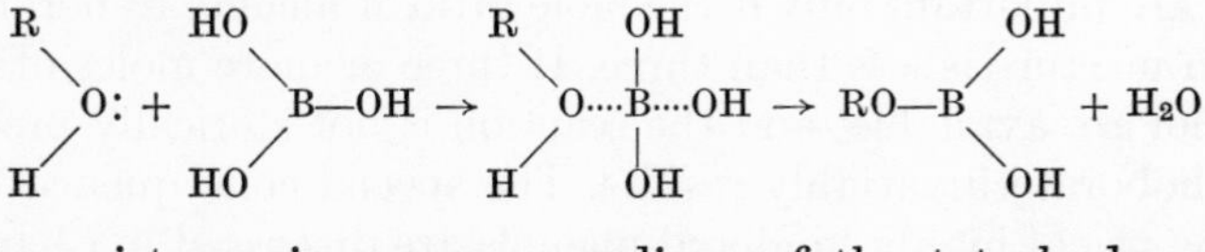

$$\mathrm{R(H)\ddot{O}} + \mathrm{(HO)_2B{-}OH} \rightarrow \mathrm{R(H)O \cdots B(OH)_2 \cdots OH} \rightarrow \mathrm{RO{-}B(OH)_2} + \mathrm{H_2O} \qquad (4\text{-}5)$$

The existence in aqueous medium of the tetrahydroxyborate anion (IX)[146] coupled with the well known and isolable tetra-

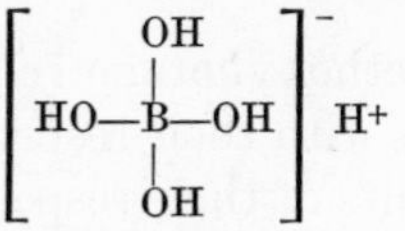

$$\left[\mathrm{HO{-}B(OH)_2{-}OH}\right]^- \mathrm{H^+} \qquad \left[\mathrm{RO{-}B(OR)_2{-}OR}\right]^- \mathrm{Na^+} \qquad \left[\mathrm{RO{-}B(OH)_2{-}OH}\right]^- \mathrm{H^+}$$

(IX) 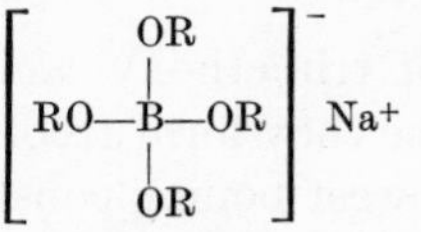 (X) 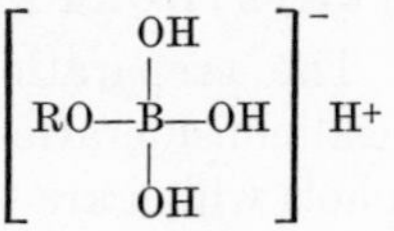 (XI)

alkoxyborates (X) (see Chapter 14) lends credibility to the possibility of a short-lived intermediate acid (XI).

Since boric acid loses water at about 100° to give metaboric acid, and since orthoborates can indeed be prepared from metaboric acid (see Section IV-B), it is possible that the reaction, at least in the second step of the esterification, involves the rupture of a B–O–B bond. Cleavage of the B–O–B bond takes place of necessity when an ester is prepared from boric oxide (see Section IV-C).

$$\left[\begin{matrix}-B-O-B-O-\\ \ \ |\qquad\ \ |\\ OH\quad OH\end{matrix}\right]_n \xrightarrow[-2n\,H_2O]{+2n\,ROH} \left[\begin{matrix}-B-O-B-O-\\ \ \ |\qquad\ \ |\\ OR\quad OR\end{matrix}\right]_n$$

$$\xrightarrow{+n\,ROH} \left[\begin{matrix}-B-OH\quad RO-B-O-\\ \ \ |\qquad\qquad\qquad |\\ OR\qquad\qquad\quad OR\end{matrix}\right]_n \tag{4-6}$$

A final complication in any mechanistic considerations is the possible intermolecular dehydration of the intermediate alkoxyhydroxyboranes. Thus, it is possible that the synthesis of an orthoborate proceeds through the metaborate (XII).

$$2\,ROB(OH)_2 \rightarrow \underset{OH}{ROB}-O-\underset{OH}{BOR} + H_2O \tag{4-7}$$

$$\underset{OH}{ROB}-O-\underset{OH}{BOR} + ROB(OH)_2 \longrightarrow RO-B\begin{matrix}\diagup O \diagdown\\ \\ O \quad\ O\\ \diagdown B \diagup\\ |\\ OR\end{matrix}B-OR + 2\,H_2O \tag{4-8}$$

(XII)

Equations (4-5) through (4-8) and all the various possible ramifications are important only if the mole ratio of alcohol to boron in the reaction mixture is less than three. If three or more moles of alcohol or phenol are available, and the reaction is not sterically precluded, the orthoborate invariably results. The special consequences arising from the use of highly hindered phenols are discussed in Chapter 6.

4. TRIMETHOXYBORANE

The preparations of trimethoxy- and triethoxyborane require special consideration since they form azeotropes with their respective alcohols which are the lowest boiling constituents of their respective borate–alcohol systems (Table 4-5).

Table 4-5. Boiling points in the trimethoxyborane and triethoxyborane systems[a]

Trimethoxyborane system		Triethoxyborane system	
	B.p. (°C)		B.p. (°C)
$(CH_3O)_3B$–CH_3OH	54.6	$(C_2H_5O)_3B$–C_2H_5OH	76.6[b]
CH_3OH–H_2O	Nonazeotrope	C_2H_5OH–H_2O	78.2
CH_3OH	64.7	C_2H_5OH	78.3
$(CH_3O)_3B$	68.7	H_2O	100
H_2O	100	$(C_2H_5O)_3B$	118.6

[a] Abstracted from L. H. Horsley, *Azeotropic Data, Advances in Chemistry Series 6*, American Chemical Society, Washington, 1952.

[b] Ref. 485.

The trimethoxyborane–methanol azeotrope, discovered by Lecat,[284] is reported to contain 75.5,[414] 75.7[13] and 75.8%[471] by weight trimethoxyborane. These compositions correspond to molar ratios of ester to methanol of 0.949, 0.958 and 0.967. A molar ratio of 1.0 corresponds to 76.4% ester by weight. An erroneous value of 30%[151] trimethoxyborane may have been the result of non-equilibrium conditions during attempted distillation of the azeotrope.

For all practical purposes, the azeotrope is equimolar in ester and methanol and, therefore, the stoichiometry of equation (4-4) is altered as follows:

$$B(OH)_3 + 4\,CH_3OH \rightarrow [B(OCH_3)_3 + CH_3OH] + 3\,H_2O \qquad (4\text{-}9)$$

In practice, the use of stoichiometric amounts of methanol leads to some trimethoxyboroxine production[414] and an excess of methanol is employed* to insure complete reaction and accelerate the rate of azeotrope removal.[13,414] Azeotrope removal also has been accelerated by removal of the water of reaction with sulfuric acid,[348] sulfonated cationic ion exchange resins,[104] or calcium chloride.[60,220,309] The original use of calcium chloride probably stems from analytical procedures[297,495] in which the boron compound is placed in methanol, calcium chloride is added, and trimethoxyborane–methanol azeotrope is distilled into water which is then titrated for boric acid (see Section VI).

Non-equilibrium conditions during the preparation expedite the removal of a methanol enriched distillate which can be concentrated to the azeotrope composition in a subsequent distillation.[13]

* An early patent[95] used this reaction for the isolation of boric acid from Chilean saltpeter by heating a mixture of methanol and saltpeter and hydrolyzing the distillate.

Azeotrope preparation has been performed on a continuous basis by taking advantage of the solubility of boric acid in methanol (Table 4-6)[317] and feeding such a solution into an intermediate

Table 4-6. Solubility of boric acid in methanol–water solution

	Grams boric acid/100 grams solution				
Weight percent CH_3OH/H_2O	25°	30°	35°	40°	45°
100/0	21.5	22.6	23.7	24.9	26.1
80/20	11.7	12.9	14.3	15.8	17.3
70/30	9.1	10.4	11.8	13.1	14.5
50/50	7.1	8.2	9.3	10.2	11.1
30/70	5.8	7.0	8.0	8.9	9.8
10/90	5.2	6.3	7.2	8.1	9.0
0/100	5.5	6.3	7.0	8.0	9.1

position of a distillation column and removing azeotrope at the head of the column.[61]

The possibility that the almost equimolar composition of the azeotrope may be due to the formation of the acid (XIII)* has been

$$(CH_3O)_3B + CH_3OH \rightarrow \underset{\text{(XIII)}}{[(CH_3O)_4B]H} \quad (4\text{-}10)$$

explored.[471] A molecular weight determination of the azeotrope by the Dumas vapor density method was 69.7, which is essentially the average molecular weight of trimethoxyborane and methanol, 67.98. Attempts to "purify" the azeotrope by repeated freezing, rejection of the liquid phase, melting and refreezing resulted in an increase in the boron content of the solid phase in each successive cycle to a value in excess of 76.4% required by compound (XIII). The molar refractivity of the azeotrope, 16.320, was almost identical to the value, 16.408, calculated from methanol (8.206) and trimethoxyborane (24.610) on the basis of equation (4-11) with x = mole fraction = 0.5.[471]

$$R_{1,2} = x_1R_1 + x_2R_2 \quad (4\text{-}11)$$

In addition, the complete additivity of the infrared spectra of methanol and trimethoxyborane as compared to the spectrum of the azeotropic composition and the molecular weights of the azeotrope in nitrobenzene and in dioxane are characteristic of a true solution mixture.[106]

On the basis of molecular weight, freezing, refractivity, and

* Acids of tetraalkoxyborate anions have not been isolated although their salts are well known[75,97,116,328] (see Chapter 14).

infrared data it was concluded that the trimethoxyborane–methanol azeotrope is a simple mixture and that there is no evidence for compound formation.*[57,106,471]

5. SEPARATION OF THE TRIMETHOXYBORANE–METHANOL AZEOTROPE

A variety of physical and chemical methods have been employed to effect separation of the trimethoxyborane–methanol azeotrope. Schiff[402] separated a mixture of trimethoxyborane and methanol by shaking it with either concentrated sulfuric acid or calcium chloride. In each case two liquid layers are formed. The upper layer, which is greatly enriched in methyl borate, is withdrawn and either recycled with fresh acid or salt or distilled to give a forerun of azeotrope followed by the pure ester. In practice, several extractions with sulfuric acid are necessary to effect an 80 to 85% recovery of pure trimethoxyborane. This method has been employed by subsequent workers.[13,422,492] Recoveries in excess of 90% were obtained by first diluting the azeotrope with an equal volume of ligroin.[414] Surprisingly, comparable or improved recoveries have been obtained by a single extraction with twenty weight percent concentrated sulfuric acid.[447]

A continuous countercurrent extraction procedure which involves passage of azeotrope in the vapor state through Raschig rings coated with sulfuric acid was reported to result in 99.8% pure trimethoxyborane in 96.5% yield.[424]

Calcium chloride has been used by later workers,[38,151,231,441] but it was discarded in favor of lithium chloride[94,414] which resulted in a 96% yield of 99.6% pure trimethoxyborane. Further advantages of lithium chloride are that it is negligibly soluble in trimethoxyborane and is easily recovered from methanol, which allows its repeated re-use. A disadvantage of the lithium chloride method, from a commercial process viewpoint, is that the cost of the salt necessitates quantitative recovery. In addition, tight control of the methanol recovery step is necessary since the residual lithium chloride solidifies to a hard solid mass as the last four or five percent of the methanol is distilled. Lastly, lithium chloride systems present

* In view of these data it is difficult to rationalize the corrosive nature of the azeotrope in metal containers as compared to the mild behavior of trimethoxyborane itself. It is logical to assume that the corrosion is due to the acidic species, $(CH_3O)_4BH$. Apparently, the methanol enhances the acidity of the trimethoxyborane without the formation of a discrete compound; possibly an induced dipole association.

a corrosion problem. However, use of a methanol solution saturated with lithium chloride instead of solid lithium chloride, and adaptation of the extraction process to a countercurrent liquid–liquid system[125] tends to eliminate all the objections to the use of lithium chloride except its corrosive nature.

The concept of separating the azeotrope by washing with a hydrocarbon was suggested by Schlesinger[404] during the early forties but was never published in an open journal. Subsequently, two patents were issued which employed the same principle. It was claimed that mineral oils preferentially dissolved the trimethoxyborane. This allowed for recovery of the pure ester by flash distillation of the oil layer and fractionation of the resulting distillate.[465] Enrichment of the azeotrope by the same process also was claimed.[470] Kerosene was found to be unsuitable.[60]

In actual practice the mineral oil extraction method is practical only in a continuous cyclic process. It is capable of about a 50% conversion to pure ester per pass.[448] Modification to a countercurrent extraction system requires dilution of the azeotrope with methanol to about a 44% trimethoxyborane content so that its density is less than that of the mineral oil. This avoids the self-defeating situation wherein the methanol phase rich in trimethoxyborane is heavier than the oil phase and the methanol phase poor in trimethoxyborane is less dense than the oil phase.[385]

Distillation methods of separating the azeotrope are attractive in that they do not contribute to corrosion problems and they are readily amenable to continuous processes. One such process involves the enrichment of a trimethoxyborane–methanol solution from 26 to 40 weight percent methanol by distillation at seven atmospheres.[150] Thus, the still residue is essentially pure trimethoxyborane.

Another distillation method of freeing the ester is to remove the methanol as a lower boiling azeotrope with a third component. The third component necessarily must be sufficiently different in boiling point from its methanol azeotrope and from trimethoxyborane, be inert to trimethoxyborane, and should be immiscible with methanol so it can be recycled. Some third component candidates require the addition of a trace of water in order to meet this latter requirement. Miscibility, of course, necessitates the use of large amounts of the third component. Table 4-7 records a number of possible third components. The use of 2-methylpentane, 3-methylpentane, 2,3-dimethylbutane, 2,2-dimethylbutane, and 3-methyl-1-pentene as the third component has been patented.[91]

Carbon disulfide was considered to have the most desirable

Table 4-7. Possible third components for separating trimethoxyborane–methanol azeotrope by azeotropic removal of methanol[a]

Third component	B.p. (°C)	B.p. of azeotrope with methanol (°C)	Wt.% methanol in azeotrope
3-Methyl-1-butene	22.5	19.8	3
2-Methylbutane	27.95	24.5	~4
1,1-Dichloroethylene	31	27.5–28	6 (by vol.)
Isoprene	34.8	~29.5	—
n-Pentane	36.1	30.6	15 (by vol.)
2-Pentene	35.8	31.5	12 (by vol.)
2-Methyl-2-butene	37.15	31.75	7
2-Chloropropane	36.25	33.4	6
Methyl sulfide	37.3	<34.5	<13
Ethyl bromide	38	35	5
3-Methyl-1,2-butadiene	40.8	~35	~10
Cyclopentene	43	37	20 (by vol.)
cis-Piperylene	42	37.5	16.7 (by vol.)
Carbon disulfide	46.25	37.65	14
Methylene chloride	40.0	37.8	7.3
Methyl iodide	64.7	37.8	4.5
Cyclopentane	49.4	38.8	14
Neohexane	49.7	39	~17
3-Chloropropene	45.15	39.85	10
1-Chloropropane	46.4	40.6	10
2-Bromopropene	48.35	42.7	11
2-Chloro-2-methylpropane	51.6	43.75	10
2-Methylpentane	60.2	44.7	17[b]
2,3-Dimethylbutane	58.0	45.0	20
Ethylene sulfide	55.7	<47.0	<21
Biallyl	60.2	47.05	22.5
cis-1-Bromopropene	57.8	48	12
2-Bromopropane	59.4	49.0	14.5
trans-1-Bromopropene	63.25	50.8	15
Methylcyclopentane	72.0	51.3	32
cis-1,2-Dichloroethylene	60.25	51.5	~13
Methyl *t*-butyl ether	55	51.6	15
2,3-Dimethyl-1,3-butadiene	68.9	52	25
Methyl nitrate	64.8	52.5	27
Methylcyclopentene	75.85	53.0	35

[a] Abstracted from L. H. Horsley, *Azeotropic Data, Advances in Chemistry Series 6*, American Chemical Society, Washington, 1952.

[b] Ethyl Corporation report to U.S. Army Signal Corp., LTD. 44-14, March 15, 1944, in collaboration with H. I. Schlesinger, Univ. of Chicago.

third-component properties. In batch operation it effected a 92.3% recovery of pure trimethoxyborane. A highly efficient fractionation column is necessary for recycle of the carbon disulfide since as little as 1.5% of trimethoxyborane produces miscibility with methanol.[414]

The extremely low flash point of carbon disulfide precludes its use on a commercial scale.

The azeotrope has also been separated or enriched by chemical means. Batch[313] and continuous[312,314] processes for enriching the azeotrope by the addition of boric oxide to consume the methanol have been devised.

$$3\,[(CH_3O)_3B + CH_3OH] + B_2O_3 \rightarrow 4\,(CH_3O)_3B + H_3BO_3 \quad (4\text{-}12)$$

Using a different approach, the ester is consumed by forming the tetramethoxyborate salt with sodium methoxide.[124] It is recovered by distilling the adhering methanol at reduced pressure and finally thermally decomposing the tetraalkoxy salt to regenerate the original sodium methoxide and pure trimethoxyborane.

$$[(CH_3O)_3B + CH_3OH] + NaOCH_3 \rightarrow [(CH_3O)_4B]Na + CH_3OH \quad (4\text{-}13)$$

$$[(CH_3O)_4B]Na \xrightarrow{\text{Heat}} CH_3ONa + (CH_3O)_3B \quad (4\text{-}14)$$

6. TRIETHOXYBORANE

The triethoxyborane–ethanol azeotrope is reported to contain 31–32%[484] and 29%[69] by weight triethoxyborane. These compositions correspond to mole ratios of ethanol to ester of 6.90 and 7.75. Thus, direct synthesis from boric acid and ethanol is not practical in that a large excess of ethanol must be employed to give a product which is only 30% pure. However, pure triethoxyborane can be prepared from boric acid by the ternary azeotrope method with benzene,[294] since the boiling point of the ethanol–water–benzene azeotrope, 64.9°,[216] is well below that of the triethoxyborane–ethanol azeotrope, 76.6° (see Table 4-5). After complete dehydration, the benzene is distilled as the ethanol azeotrope (b.p. 68.2°),[216] which allows recovery of pure triethoxyborane in good yield.

A more expedient ternary azeotrope process involves continuous production of pure triethoxyborane by feeding a solution of boric acid in ethanol to an intermediate tray of a fractionating column with simultaneous addition of ethyl alcohol to a lower tray and addition of benzene to a higher tray. The ternary azeotrope of benzene–ethanol–water is removed at the top of the column and pure triethoxyborane is collected at the bottom of the column.[49]

Use was made of calcium chloride[155] to separate the triethoxyborane–ethanol azeotrope five years prior to its use by Schiff[402] for separation of the trimethoxyborane–methanol azeotrope. Schiff[402,403] also used concentrated sulfuric acid to separate the triethoxyborane–ethanol azeotrope, as did other workers.[484,492] Enrichment of the azeotrope by reaction with boric oxide also has been recorded.[312]

Other means of separating the ethyl borate azeotrope, as have been employed for the methyl borate azeotrope, undoubtedly are applicable but as yet have not been reported.

7. TRIPROPOXYBORANE AND TRI-*t*-BUTOXYBORANE

Direct preparation of triisopropoxy or tri-*t*-butoxyborane from boric acid requires the use of a ternary azeotrope,[294,444] as evidenced by the boiling points of the respective ester–alcohol azeotropes (Table 4-8). Removal of water as the isopropyl or *t*-butyl alcohol azeotropes

Table 4-8. Boiling points in the tripropoxy- and tri-*t*-butoxyborane systems[a]

	B.p. (°C)		
	n-C_3H_7OH	i-C_3H_7OH	*t*-C_4H_9OH
ROH–H_2O–C_6H_6	67/740	66.5	67.3
H_2O–C_6H_6	69.3	69.3	69.3
ROH–C_6H_6	71.1	71.9	73.95
C_6H_6	80.2	80.2	80.2
ROH–H_2O	87	80.3	79.9
ROH	97.3	82–82.3	82.9
$(RO)_3B$	176–179[b]	139–140[b]	63–67/18[b]

[a] Abstracted from L. H. Horsley, *Azeotropic Data, Advances in Chemistry Series 6*, American Chemical Society, Washington, 1952.
[b] Ref. 444.

would require the fractionation of azeotropes boiling at 80.3° and 79.9° from isopropyl alcohol and *t*-butyl alcohol, which boil only 2 to 3° higher. The use of benzene allows temperature differentials of 16°.

In addition, even if the boiling point differentials of 2–3° for the isopropyl and *t*-butyl systems and 10.3° for the n-propyl system were considered sufficient, benzene would be necessary to cause phase separation in the condensed azeotrope and allow for return of the alcohol to the reaction mixture. The miscibility of the alcohols and water would preclude return of the alcohol in the absence of benzene and very large excesses of alcohol would have to be used over the extended reaction periods.

8. REACTION WITH ESTERS OF INORGANIC ACIDS

Boric acid has been converted to borates by reaction with esters of various inorganic acids. Friedel and Crafts[164] first reported the preparation of triethoxyborane from ethyl silicate and boric acid. Later, a series of silicates similarly were converted to the borates (4-15);[256] however, the transformation could not be confirmed for

$$3\,Si(OR)_4 + 4\,B(OH)_3 \rightarrow 4\,B(OR)_3 + 3\,SiO_2 + 6\,H_2O \quad (4\text{-}15)$$

$$3\,Si(OC_2H_5)_4 + 4\,B(OH)_3 \rightarrow 12\,C_2H_5OH + 3\,SiO_2 \cdot 2\,B_2O_3 \quad (4\text{-}16)$$

the ethyl derivative (4-16).[487] Methyltriethoxysilane also does not react with boric acid to produce an ester.[487] However, dialkoxysilanes have been a source of borates in their conversion to silicone polymers in the presence of boric acid.[98,292,487]

$$3n\,R_2Si(OR)_2 + n\,H_3BO_3 \rightarrow n\,(RO)_3B + 3\left[\begin{array}{c} R \\ | \\ -SiO- \\ | \\ R \end{array}\right]_n + 3n\,ROH \quad (4\text{-}17)$$

Monoalkoxysilanes behave similarly.[487]

$$(CH_3)_3SiOC_2H_5 + B(OH)_3 \rightarrow (C_2H_5O)_3B + ((CH_3)_3Si)_2O + C_2H_5OH \quad (4\text{-}18)$$

Transformations to the borate with ethyl sulfate, ethyl phosphate, and ethyl benzenesulfonate have also been claimed.[441] The reaction given in equation (4-19) could not be confirmed.[69]

$$3\,(C_2H_5O)_2SO_2 + 2\,B(OH)_3 \rightarrow 2\,B(OC_2H_5)_3 + 3\,H_2SO_4 \quad (4\text{-}19)$$

$$(C_2H_5O)_3PO + B(OH)_3 \rightarrow B(OC_2H_5)_3 + H_3PO_4 \quad (4\text{-}20)$$

$$3\,C_6H_5SO_3C_2H_5 + B(OH)_3 \rightarrow B(OC_2H_5)_3 + 3\,C_6H_5SO_3H \quad (4\text{-}21)$$

9. REACTION WITH ENOLS

The diketones (XIV) and (XV) are capable of forming enols. Possible products of their reaction with boric acid are (XVI) and (XVII).[11]

$$CH_3\overset{O}{\overset{\|}{C}}CH_2\overset{O}{\overset{\|}{C}}CH_3 \quad \text{(XIV)} \qquad CH_3\overset{O}{\overset{\|}{C}}CH_2\overset{O}{\overset{\|}{C}}OC_2H_5 \quad \text{(XV)}$$

$$\left(CH_3\overset{O}{\overset{\|}{C}}CH{=}\underset{CH_3}{\underset{|}{C}}O-\right)_3B \quad \text{(XVI)} \qquad \left(C_2H_5O\overset{O}{\overset{\|}{C}}CH{=}\underset{CH_3}{\underset{|}{C}}O-\right)_3B \quad \text{(XVII)}$$

10. CONDENSATION WITH FORMALDEHYDE AND CARBON MONOXIDE

The known condensation of formaldehyde, carbon monoxide, and hydrogen chloride (4-22) was used to predict the reaction of equation (4-23).[295]

$$\overset{\displaystyle O}{\overset{\|}{HCH}} + CO + HCl \xrightarrow[900\ atm.]{180°} ClCH_2CO_2H \tag{4-22}$$

$$3\ \overset{\displaystyle O}{\overset{\|}{HCH}} + 3\ CO + B(OH)_3 \rightarrow B(OCH_2CO_2H)_3 \tag{4-23}$$

B. From Metaboric Acid

A common misconception[138] still prevalent in present patent literature is that if one wishes to prepare an orthoborate boric acid is used, and if one wishes to prepare a metaborate metaboric acid is used. Such reasoning, however, is not based on fact. Although the literature contains few actual references to the preparation of orthoborates from metaboric acid, such as the conversion of methyl cellosolve to tri-β-methoxyethoxyborane by reaction with either metaboric or orthoboric acid (equations 4-24 and 4-25),[386] many

$$3\ CH_3OCH_2CH_2OH + HBO_2 \rightarrow (CH_3OCH_2CH_2O)_3B + 2\ H_2O \tag{4-24}$$

$$3\ CH_3OCH_2CH_2OH + H_3BO_3 \rightarrow (CH_3OCH_2CH_2O)_3B + 3\ H_2O \tag{4-25}$$

similar preparations have been performed in the laboratories of the U.S. Borax Research Corporation, and presumably the reaction has been observed in many other laboratories. Conversely, many metaborates have been prepared from orthoboric acid (see Chapter 9).

Indeed, if boric acid with three esterifiable hydroxyl groups leads to an orthoborate (4-26), and metaboric acid with one esterifiable hydroxyl groups leads to a metaborate (4-27), then boric oxide, which has no esterifiable hydroxyl groups, should be inert to alcohols (equation 4-28).

$$B(OH)_3 + 3\ ROH \rightarrow B(OR)_3 + 3\ H_2O \tag{4-26}$$

$$O{=}BOH + ROH \rightarrow O{=}B{-}OR + H_2O \tag{4-27}$$

$$B_2O_3 + ROH \rightarrow \text{no reaction} \tag{4-28}$$

Obviously, all three boron sources, as far as esterification is concerned, are chemically equivalent and differ only in the amount of water which they release per boron atom upon complete reaction with an alcohol. The differentiating factor in the production of an orthoborate versus a metaborate is the stoichiometry employed. Complete dehydration of a mixture containing a three to one mole ratio of alcohol to boron usually leads to an orthoborate regardless of the boron source. On the other hand, complete dehydration of a

$$B(OH)_3 + 3\,ROH \rightarrow B(OR)_3 + 3\,H_2O \tag{4-29}$$

$$HBO_2 + 3\,ROH \rightarrow B(OR)_3 + 2\,H_2O \tag{4-30}$$

$$B_2O_3 + 6\,ROH \rightarrow 2\,B(OR)_3 + 3\,H_2O \tag{4-31}$$

mixture containing one mole of alcohol for every boron atom usually leads to a metaborate regardless of the boron source (see Chapter 9).

It is possible that esterifications which employ boric acid at a temperature near or in excess of 100° proceed at least in part through metaboric acid, since boric acid readily loses one mole of water at about 100° to give metaboric acid.

Metaboric acid is a convenient source of boron in the laboratory (it is not commercially available) if one wishes to decrease the amount of water to be removed from the system and cannot more advantageously use boric oxide due to its insolubility in the media involved. In general, the order of solubility in organic media decreases from boric acid to metaboric acid and is at a minimum with boric oxide.

C. From Boric Oxide

1. NO WATER REMOVAL

The use of boric oxide in 100% excess obviates the need for the removal of water or separation of the product from water since the water of reaction is consumed by the oxide. Consequently, yields based upon boron are limited to 50%.

$$\tfrac{1}{2}\,B_2O_3 + 3\,ROH \rightarrow B(OR)_3 + \tfrac{3}{2}\,H_2O \tag{4-32}$$

$$\tfrac{1}{2}\,B_2O_3 + \tfrac{3}{2}\,H_2O \rightarrow H_3BO_3 \tag{4-33}$$

$$B_2O_3 + 3\,ROH \rightarrow B(OR)_3 + H_3BO_3 \tag{4-34}$$

The ester, however, must be separated from the boric acid before it is distilled to avoid further reaction with production of meta- and polyborates (see Chapter 9). This fact was not appreciated by the early workers and resulted in many impure products and frequent decomposition upon attempted distillation.

Thus, the use of boric oxide offers a convenient method for preparing borates of the lower alcohols by simply heating the admixture, removing the boric acid by filtration, and distilling the filtrate. If the economics of the loss of one-half of the boron as boric acid are not important, the method obviates the need for the more time-consuming ternary azeotrope method.

Although boric oxide is prepared from boric acid, the preparation of esters from boric oxide preceded the use of boric acid[108] by sixty-one years. Ebelmen first used boric oxide* for the preparation of the methyl, ethyl and amyl esters. Equal weights of the alcohol and oxide were heated to give the impure esters.[139] In 1867, Schiff[402] published a masterly work which described a variety of preparative methods, reactions, and interconversions. He introduced two different types of esters, mixed orthoborates (see Chapter 6) and metaborates (see Chapter 9), as well. He prepared a series of aliphatic esters (methyl, ethyl, amyl, and cetyl) and the first aromatic member (triphenoxyborane) by heating the alcohol or phenol with boric oxide under pressure in a copper digestor for twenty-four hours. The method subsequently was extended to the synthesis of esters derived from secondary alcohols and unsaturated alcohols by heating the alcohol and oxide in a sealed tube.[118,129,121] Pure triethoxyborane was prepared in this manner at 120° and two atmospheres.[116] Attempts to prepare pure tri-2-octoxyborane were unsuccessful due to decomposition of the ester on distillation. A rotating autoclave also has been used for the preparation of the ethyl and isopropyl esters.[113]

A pressure bottle method at 120° subsequently was extended to the preparation of trimethoxyborane.[151] A less involved method performed at atmospheric pressure resulted in a 77% yield (based on methanol) of enriched azeotrope (92% trimethoxyborane) by digesting and distilling a reaction mixture with a mole ratio of methanol to oxide of 1.5:1.[400]

Trimethoxyborane was also obtained directly without con-

$$B_2O_3 + 3\ C_6H_{10}(OCH_3)_2 \longrightarrow 2\ (CH_3O)_3B + 3\ C_6H_{10}{=}O \quad (4\text{-}35)$$

tamination with methanol from the reaction of boric oxide and 1,1-dimethoxycyclohexane (4-35),[54] 2,2-dimethoxypropane (4-36),[55]

* The exact nature of the boron species is unknown. Ebelmen called it melted boric acid. A melt of boric acid results in a glass containing 86% B_2O_3. Metaboric acid, HBO_2, is 79.5% B_2O_3.

or methyl orthoformate (4-37).[52] Reaction (4-36) with diethoxypropane[55] or reaction (4-37) with ethyl orthoformate[52] resulted in triethoxyborane.

$$B_2O_3 + 3\,CH_3C(OCH_3)_2CH_3 \rightarrow 2\,(CH_3O)_3B + 3\,CH_3C(=O)CH_3 \quad (4\text{-}36)$$

$$B_2O_3 + 3\,HC(OCH_3)_3 \rightarrow 2\,(CH_3O)_3B + 3\,HC(=O)OCH_3 \quad (4\text{-}37)$$

A recent convenient method of obtaining the lower alkyl borates involves a liquid–liquid extraction procedure. A solution of boric oxide in the appropriate alcohol is passed countercurrently to a hydrocarbon solvent such as kerosene or mineral oil. The equilibrium concentration of trialkoxyborane present in the alcohol phase is preferentially soluble in the hydrocarbon phase which is drawn off at the top of the extraction column. The ester is removed from the hydrocarbon liquors by distillation.[350,476]

2. WATER REMOVAL

As stated in the previous section, the esterification of boric oxide does not require the removal of water, but if high yields based on boron are desired, six or more moles of alcohol must be employed and water separation must again be considered.

$$B_2O_3 + 6\,ROH \rightarrow 2\,B(OR)_3 + 3\,H_2O \quad (4\text{-}38)$$

One method of water removal involves the formation of a binary azeotrope with benzene or toluene and percolation of the condensed distillate through anhydrous copper sulfate in a Soxhlet extractor,[518] as had been performed earlier with boric acid.[138] A number of aromatic as well as aliphatic borates were prepared in this manner; *t*-alkyl borates or the borates from ethanolamine or *o*-chlorophenol could not be prepared by this method. Other workers were also able to prepare aliphatic members but could not prepare tri-*t*-butoxyborane.[230,231]

Water from a preparation of trimethoxyborane was removed with anhydrous copper or zinc sulfate.[293] Drying agents are not absolutely necessary and, as in the preparations from boric acid, the trimethoxyborane–methanol azeotrope can be distilled leaving the water of reaction as such in the reaction mixture. Yields of azeotrope in excess of 90% (based on boron) have been realized with mole ratios of methanol to boric oxide of 4:1 to 12:1.[414] More recently, a continuous process for preparing trimethoxyborane utilizing a mole ratio of 8:1 has been patented.[61]

3. EFFECT OF AZEOTROPING AGENT

The rate of water removal (*i.e.* the rate of ester production) by the binary azeotrope method is dependent upon the azeotroping agent. For aliphatic borates, olefins (Table 4-9)[491] appear to be more

Table 4-9. Effect of azeotropic medium on rate of ester formation

Azeotropic medium	Weight percent H_2O in binary azeotrope	Rate, moles/hr. $(n\text{-}C_4H_9O)_3B$	Rate, moles/hr. $(n\text{-}C_{12}H_{25}O)_3B$
1-Butanol	42.5	1.12	—
1-Dodecanol	—	—	1.56
Benzene	8.83	2.21	1.45
Xylene	35.8	—	1.47
Diisobutylene	13.0	2.56	2.16
1-Octene	34.7	2.78	2.01
Tripropylene	28.6	2.58	1.74
Tetrapropylene	66.0	2.48	1.74

effective than an excess of alcohol or the more commonly used aromatic media. Olefinic azeotropic agents also are more effective for producing aromatic borates. With a given azeotroping agent, the rate of ester production is greater with boric oxide than with boric acid (Table 4-10).[491]

Table 4-10. Comparison of rate of ester formation from boric oxide and boric acid

Alcohol	Moles of alcohol	Moles of boron compound	Rates, moles/hr. Boric oxide	Rates, moles/hr. Boric acid
1-Butanol	5.83	0.971	2.56	—
	5.27	1.76	—	1.45
2-Ethylhexanol	3.52	0.586	2.57	—
	3.31	1.10	—	1.75
2-Methyl-2-pentanol	4.39	0.731	2.03	—
	4.07	1.36	—	1.50
2-Methyl-7-ethyl-4-undecanol	2.20	0.367	1.88	—
	2.12	0.708	—	1.18
1-Dodecanol	2.52	0.420	2.16	—
	2.41	0.804	—	1.30

4. REACTION WITH ESTERS OF INORGANIC ACIDS

Silicates,[442,487] and alkoxytrialkylsilanes[5] reacted with boric oxide with the net result of transferring the alkoxy group to boron.

$$3\ Si(OR)_4 + 2\ B_2O_3 \rightarrow 4\ B(OR)_3 + 3\ SiO_2 \quad (4\text{-}39)$$

$$3\ C_2H_5OSi(CH_3)_3 + B_2O_3 \rightarrow (C_2H_5O)_3B + [(CH_3)_3SiO]_3B \quad (4\text{-}40)$$

Reaction (4-39) offers a means of preparing the methyl and ethyl esters directly without the production and separation of azeotropes. Scheme (4-40) is analogous to the cleavage of ethers by boron trichloride (see Chapter 12).

The mixed anhydride of sulfuric acid and boric acid has been alcoholyzed to the methyl, ethyl and amyl esters.[367]

$$(SO_3)_2B_2O_3 + 6\ ROH \rightarrow 2\ B(OR)_3 + 2\ H_2SO_4 + H_2O \quad (4\text{-}41)$$

D. From Borax and Related Compounds

Direct conversions of borate salts to esters have been limited in number. In the nineteenth century investigators obtained triethoxyborane by the dry distillation of anhydrous borax and potassium ethyl sulfate.[155,389] Esters of other inorganic acids also have served as the alkoxyl source. Tetraalkoxysilanes heated with borax or sodium metaborate have been reported to give volatile products, presumably esters, which burn with a green flame.[256]

Direct alcoholysis of borax has been reported to result in a 28% yield of ester (4-42).[512] Methanolysis of borax was claimed to result in a mixture of trimethoxyborane and sodium tetramethoxyborate (4-43).[286] The ester would be recovered as the methanol azeotrope. Methanolysis of sodium pentaborate led to 72% conversion of the available boron to the azeotrope (4-44).[440,512] Reaction with metha-

$$Na_2B_4O_7 + 6\ ROH \rightarrow 2\ (RO)_3B + Na_2B_2O_4 + 3\ H_2O \quad (4\text{-}42)$$

$$Na_2B_4O_7 + 14\ CH_3OH \rightarrow 2\ (CH_3O)_3B + 2\ NaB(OCH_3)_4 + 7\ H_2O \quad (4\text{-}43)$$

$$Na_2B_{10}O_{16} + 32\ CH_3OH \rightarrow 8\ [(CH_3O)_3B + CH_3OH] + Na_2B_2O_4 + 12\ H_2O \quad (4\text{-}44)$$

nol followed by hydrolysis of the azeotrope has been patented as a method of recovering boric acid from borax without the use of a strong mineral acid.[317]

$$Na_2B_4O_7 + 8\ CH_3OH \rightarrow 2\ [(CH_3O)_3B + CH_3OH] + 2\ NaBO_2 + 3\ H_2O \quad (4\text{-}45)$$

$$\xrightarrow{6\ H_2O} 2\ H_3BO_3 + 8\ CH_3OH$$

A variety of lower trialkoxyboranes, excluding trimethoxyborane, have been prepared from the alcoholysis of ammonium pentaborate octahydrate (4-46). The water is removed as an azeotrope with either excess alcohol or an added reagent such as diisobutylene.[316]

$$(NH_4)_2B_{10}O_{16} \cdot 8H_2O + 30\ ROH \rightarrow 10\ (RO)_3B + 2\ NH_3 + 24\ H_2O \qquad (4\text{-}46)$$

The conversion of borax to lower alkyl borates via treatment with ammonium chloride and ethylene glycol (4-47) followed by transesterification of the glycol borate (4-48) has been patented.[513]

$$Na_2B_4O_7 \cdot 10H_2O + 2\ NH_4Cl + 12\ HOCH_2CH_2OH \rightarrow \underset{(XVIII)}{4\ B(OCH_2CH_2OH)_3} + 2\ NaCl + 17\ H_2O + 2\ NH_3 \qquad (4\text{-}47)$$

$$\underset{(XVIII)}{4\ B(OCH_2CH_2OH)_3} + 16\ CH_3OH \rightarrow 4\ [(CH_3O)_3B + CH_3OH] + 12\ HOCH_2CH_2OH \qquad (4\text{-}48)$$

The β-hydroxyethyl borate (XVIII) formulated in equation (4-47) may be a mixture of the stoichiometric equivalent biborate (XIX) and ethylene glycol.

```
CH2—O                    O—CH2
|     \                 /    |
|      BOCH2CH2OB           |
|     /                 \    |
CH2—O                    O—CH2
              (XIX)
```

A novel "synthesis" of trimethoxyborane has been reported from the reaction of Pyrex glass and methanol. Methanol stored for several months in a Pyrex bottle was shown by means of mass spectrometric analysis to contain 0.04 mole percent trimethoxyborane.[371]

An attempt to react silver borate and ethyl iodide metathetically was unsuccessful.[349]

In situ conversions of borax to boric acid with a mineral acid and simultaneous esterification have been employed in a number of cases.[96,243]

$$Na_2B_4O_7 \cdot 10H_2O + H_2SO_4 + 16\ CH_3OH \rightarrow 4\ [(CH_3O)_3B + CH_3OH] + Na_2SO_4 + 17\ H_2O \qquad (4\text{-}49)$$

$$3\ Na_2B_4O_7 + 6\ HCl + 15\ C_2H_5OH \rightarrow 6\ NaCl + 5\ B(OC_2H_5)_3 + 7\ H_3BO_3 \qquad (4\text{-}50)$$

In the preparation of trimethoxyborane, the mole ratio of sulfuric acid to anhydrous borax influences the yield.[198] One mole of sulfuric acid is sufficient to liberate boric acid (4-51), but better

$$Na_2B_4O_7 + H_2SO_4 + 16\ CH_3OH \rightarrow 4\ [(CH_3O)_3B + CH_3OH] + Na_2SO_4 + 7\ H_2O \qquad (4\text{-}51)$$

yields are realized with two moles of acid (4-52). A 93% yield of methyl borate was obtained with two moles of sulfuric acid and

$$Na_2B_4O_7 + 2\ H_2SO_4 + 16\ CH_3OH \rightarrow 4\ [(CH_3O)_3B + CH_3OH] + 2\ NaHSO_4 + 7\ H_2O \quad (4\text{-}52)$$

100% excess of methanol.[414] It was concluded that identical ultimate yields could be obtained with one mole of sulfuric acid but that longer reaction times were necessary.[414,447]

In situ conversions of borax (4-53),[361,398,474] sodium metaborate (4-54),[361] and colemanite (4-55)[398] to trimethoxyborane–methanol azeotrope have been performed with carbon dioxide in methanol.

$$Na_2B_4O_7 + CO_2 + 16\ CH_3OH \rightarrow 4\ [(CH_3O)_3B + CH_3OH] + Na_2CO_3 + 6\ H_2O \quad (4\text{-}53)$$

$$NaBO_2 + CO_2 + 4\ CH_3OH \rightarrow [(CH_3O)_3B + CH_3OH] + NaHCO_3 + H_2O \quad (4\text{-}54)$$

$$Ca_2B_6O_{11} \cdot 5H_2O + 2\ CO_2 + 24\ CH_3OH \rightarrow 6\ [(CH_3O)_3B + CH_3OH] + 2\ CaCO_3 + 14\ H_2O \quad (4\text{-}55)$$

E. Transesterification

A convenient method of preparation which requires no special considerations for water removal or filtration of by-products is realized by simple displacement of the alkoxy substituents on boron by reaction with an alcohol or phenol.

$$B(OR)_3 + 3\ R'OH \rightarrow B(OR')_3 + 3\ ROH \quad (4\text{-}56)$$

In practice, an ester of lower molecular weight is converted to one of higher molecular weight by treatment with a higher boiling alcohol. The only requirement is that the liberated alcohol must be lower boiling than any other species present so that it may be distilled at a convenient rate.

An ester of higher molecular weight can be converted to one of lower molecular weight by treatment with a large excess of a lower boiling alcohol under non-equilibrium conditions and removal of the higher boiling alcohol by entrainment. The procedure is not efficient and has been used infrequently.

If either trimethoxyborane or methanol is employed, trimethoxyborane–methanol azeotrope distills leaving the higher boiling ester or alcohol.

$$4\ (CH_3O)_3B + 3\ ROH \rightarrow (RO)_3B + 3\ [(CH_3O)_3B + CH_3OH] \quad (4\text{-}57)$$

$$(RO)_3B + 4\ CH_3OH \rightarrow 3\ ROH + [(CH_3O)_3B + CH_3OH] \quad (4\text{-}58)$$

1. EXAMPLES

Schiff[402] generally is considered to have originated the transesterification method in 1867 with the preparation of triethoxyborane from the reaction of glyceryl borate and ethanol. The method then lay dormant for forty-four years until applicability to the preparation of aromatic esters was shown by the preparation of a series of carboxy- and carboxamidophenyl and naphthyl esters.[108] Shortly thereafter, in a study of new azeotropic systems, it was discovered that the system triethoxyborane–isobutanol resulted in the formation of triisobutoxyborane.[283]

The general usefulness of transesterification as a preparative method was shown by the displacement of propanol from a slight excess of tri-n-propoxyborane with a variety of primary, secondary, tertiary, and alicyclic alcohols as well as a variety of phenols and sugars.[516] Tertiary alkyl borate preparation from tripropoxyborane could not be confirmed.[461] Similarly, tri-*t*-butoxyborane could not be prepared from the reaction of triethoxyborane and *t*-butyl alcohol[333] or from the reaction of triphenoxyborane and *t*-butyl alcohol; isobutene and diisobutene resulted instead.[111] In contrast to these failures, triethoxyborane has been converted to tri-*t*-butoxyborane in 45% yield by treatment with *t*-butyl alcohol and a catalytic amount of sodium.[169] Preparations without sodium behaved capriciously. Sodium had been used earlier in the transesterification of the n-butyl ester with furfuryl alcohol.[392] Further applicability of the transesterification method to tertiary ester preparation was shown in a Russian patent[234] which described the preparation of the borate of diacetone alcohol in quantitative yield from tri-n-butoxyborane.

$$(C_4H_9O)_3B + CH_3\overset{\overset{O}{\|}}{C}CH_2\underset{\underset{CH_3}{|}}{\overset{\overset{CH_3}{|}}{C}}OH \rightarrow (CH_3\overset{\overset{O}{\|}}{C}CH_2\underset{\underset{CH_3}{|}}{\overset{\overset{CH_3}{|}}{C}}O)_3B + 3\,C_4H_9OH \qquad (4\text{-}59)$$

Trimethoxyborane also has been converted to a tertiary alkyl ester by reaction with *t*-butyl alcohol.[7] In this case the removal of the trimethoxyborane–methanol azeotrope provides the driving force (see equation 4-57). The low yield (54.5%) was attributed to the formation of mixed esters (see Chapter 6). The tertiary ester (XX) was formed from the reaction of trimethoxyborane and methyl

$$(CH_3O\overset{\overset{O}{\|}}{C}-\underset{\underset{CH_3}{|}}{\overset{\overset{CH_3}{|}}{C}}O-)_3B$$

(XX)

α-hydroxyisobutyrate in pentane solution.[167] In this case the driving force is the removal of the pentane–methanol azeotrope (b.p. 30.6°).

Aminoalcohol borates have been prepared by transesterification of the methyl and propyl esters with ethanolamine,[461] β-dimethylaminoethanol, and γ-dimethylaminopropanol.[342] Complex products derived from transesterification of the lower trialkoxyboranes with various bis(hydroxyphenyl)alkanes also have been described.[224]

The transesterification of trimethoxyborane with ethanol, propanol, and the butanols has been accomplished on a continuous basis by feeding the ester and alcohol in the required stoichiometry (see equation 4-57) to an intermediate plate of a fractional distillation column and removing trimethoxyborane–methanol azeotrope at the top of the column and pure ester at the bottom of the column.[319,477]

The preparation of methyl and ethyl borate as their alcoholic azeotropes has been accomplished by the methanolysis and ethanolysis of both alkyl[471,484] and phenyl[111] borates. In these cases the azeotropes are the lowest boiling species (see equation 4-58). The sugar derivatives, (XXI)[482] and (XXII),[483] also were converted to trimethoxyborane on treatment with methanol.

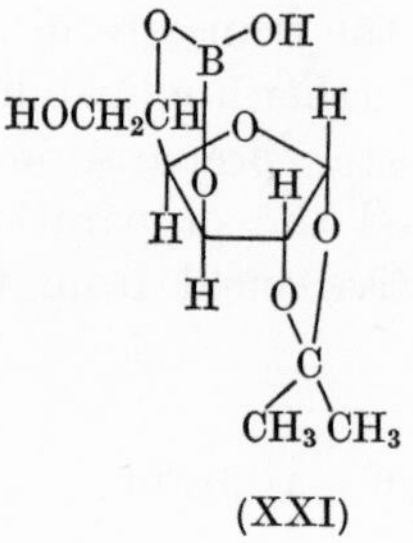

(XXI)

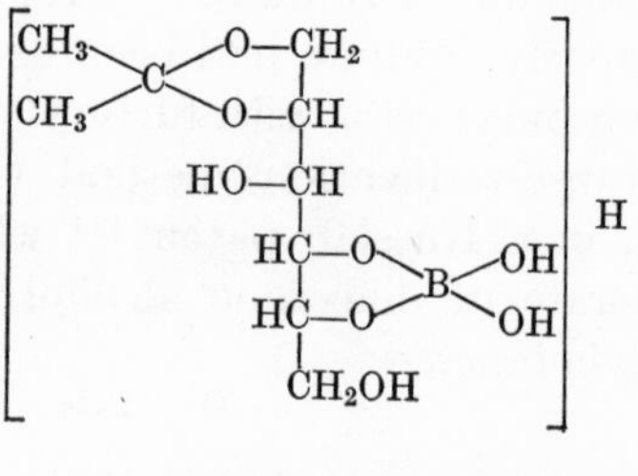

(XXII)

An interesting higher molecular weight borate (XXIII) has been reported from the reaction of tri-n-butoxyborane with the Diels–Alder adduct of allyl alcohol and hexachlorocyclopentadiene.[152]

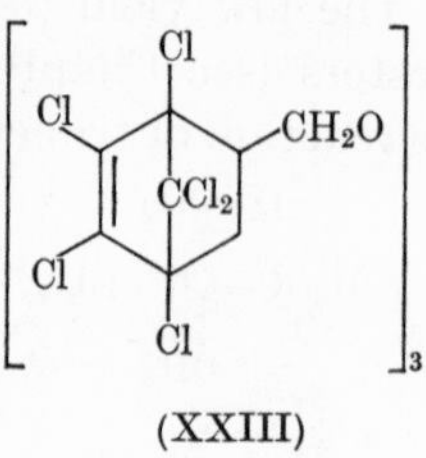

(XXIII)

The transesterification of 1.25 moles of tri-n-propoxyborane with three moles of salicylaldehyde was found to yield propanol and

$$o\text{-}HOC_6H_4CHO + (C_3H_7O)_3B \longrightarrow C_3H_7OH + o\text{-}(C_3H_7O)_2BOC_6H_4CHO$$

$$\longrightarrow o\text{-}(C_3H_7O)_2BOC_6H_4CH(OH)OC_3H_7 \qquad (4\text{-}60)$$

propionaldehyde.[516] A sequence involving hemiacetal formation (4-60), followed by a peculiar decomposition of the hemiacetal (4-61),

$$o\text{-}(C_3H_7O)_2BOC_6H_4CH(OH)OC_3H_7 \longrightarrow o\text{-}(C_3H_7O)_2BOC_6H_4CH_2OH + CH_3CH_2CHO \qquad (4\text{-}61)$$

and then an intramolecular transesterification (4-62) was offered to explain the origin of the propanol and propionaldehyde.

$$o\text{-}(C_3H_7O)_2BOC_6H_4CH_2OH \longrightarrow C_6H_4(CH_2O)(O)B{-}OC_3H_7 + C_3H_7OH \qquad (4\text{-}62)$$

The identical products can be envisaged arising via an intermolecular or intramolecular oxidation-reduction path (4-63) which was shown to be operative in intermolecular reactions of alkyl borates and aldehydes or ketones[260] (see Section V-H).

The conversion of (XXIV) to (XXV) involves an exchange of alkoxy groups between two boron atoms, a reaction which has been recorded for triethoxyborane and tri-*o*-nitrophenoxyborane[112] (see Section V-G-1).

Transesterification has been applied to the isolation and purification of alcohols from close boiling impurities. A recent patent describes the separation of C_7 to C_{30} alcohols from hydrocarbons by transesterification with trimethoxyborane. The C_7–C_{30} alkyl borates boil at temperatures sufficiently high to allow the distillation of the

o-$HOC_6H_4CHO + (C_3H_7O)_3B \longrightarrow$

$\longrightarrow C_3H_7OH + o$-$OHCC_6H_4OB(OC_3H_7)_2$

$\qquad \longrightarrow C_6H_4\langle CH_2O\text{—}, O\text{—}\rangle BOC_3H_7 + C_3H_7OH$

$\qquad \xrightarrow{o\text{-}HOC_6H_4CHO} [o\text{-}OHCC_6H_4O\text{—}]_3B + C_3H_7OH$

$\longrightarrow [o\text{-}HOC_6H_4CH_2O\text{—}]_3B + CH_3CH_2CHO$

$\longrightarrow [o\text{-}(C_3H_7O)_2BOC_6H_4CH_2O\text{—}]_3B + C_3H_7OH + CH_3CH_2CHO$

(XXIV) $\longrightarrow C_6H_4\langle CH_2O\text{—}, O\text{—}\rangle B\text{—}OC_3H_7$ (XXV)

(4-63)

hydrocarbons. The alcohols are then regenerated from their esters by a second transesterification with methanol.[150]

2. MECHANISM

In the nucleophilic attack of an alcohol or phenol upon a relatively unhindered ester, the steric requirements of the alcohol or phenol determine how far along the energy-bonding distance surface the alcohol or phenol can approach. If the activation energy required to bring the alcohol–oxygen and boron atoms within bonding distance is very large, the reaction does not proceed at measurable rates. Thus, qualitatively, propyl salicylate failed[516] to react with tripropoxyborane whereas salicyclic acid displaced ethanol from triethoxyborane.[108] Quantitative data also are available which indicate the steric requirements of the borate and alcohol to be rate controlling. The uncatalyzed methanolysis and ethanolysis of a series of alkyl borates were followed dilatometrically and found to be pseudo first order. Methanolysis of tri-*s*-butoxyborane proceeded more rapidly than ethanolysis and had a lower apparent activation energy (7.1 kcal/mole versus 10.1 kcal/mole).[363] In general, primary alkyl borates reacted at a rate too fast to measure while secondary borates proceeded at measurable rates. Tri-*t*-butoxyborane solvolyzed very slowly. Table 4-11 summarizes the rate data.[363]

Table 4-11. Rates of solvolysis of trialkoxyboranes

$(RO)_3B$	Solvent	Temp. (°C)	k (min.$^{-1}$)
$(CH_3O)_3B$	Ethanol	0	Large
$(n\text{-}C_4H_9O)_3B$	Ethanol	0	Large
$(i\text{-}C_4H_9O)_3B$	Ethanol	0	Large
$(i\text{-}C_3H_7O)_3B$	Ethanol	25	0.28
$(s\text{-}C_4H_9O)_3B$	Methanol	25	0.173
$(s\text{-}C_4H_9O)_3B$	Ethanol	25	0.0226
$(t\text{-}C_4H_9O)_3B$	Ethanol	25	1.02×10^{-5}

A series of transesterifications with various carbohydrates tends further to support the importance of steric factors. Glucose (XXVI), with five hydroxyl groups available for esterification, displaced four moles of propanol per mole of glucose from a given quantity of tripropoxyborane by heating at 190° and five moles by heating at 210°. Sucrose (XXVII), with eight available hydroxyl groups, but more hindered due to its dimeric form, displaced 2.7 moles of propanol per mole of sucrose at 180° and 3.6 moles at 215°. Cellulose, with highly hindered hydroxyl groups due to its polymeric structure, did not react at all.[516] Solubility factors, of course, could be responsible for the results as well as the steric factors.

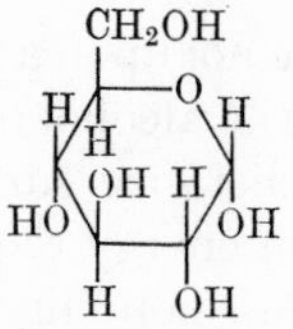

(XXVI) 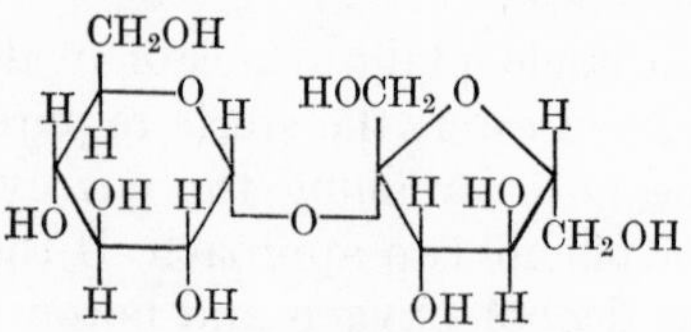 (XXVII)

The 2,6-disubstituted phenols offer an excellent opportunity to observe steric phenomena.[220] 2,6-Di-*t*-butylphenol readily forms a series of unsymmetrical esters by displacement of an alkoxy group from a lower molecular weight borate (4-64) (see Chapter 6). On the

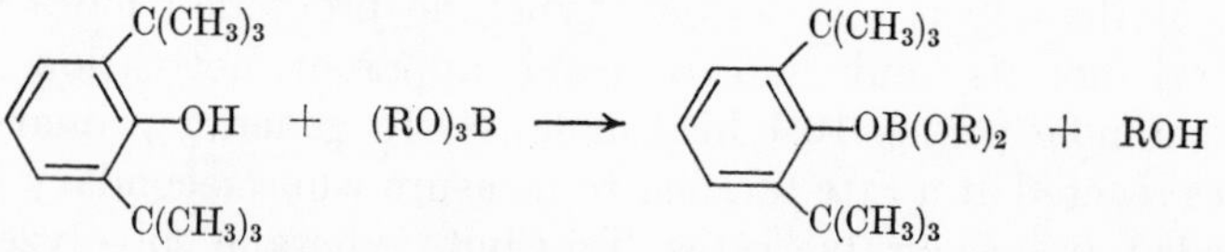

$$2,6\text{-}[C(CH_3)_3]_2C_6H_3OH + (RO)_3B \longrightarrow 2,6\text{-}[C(CH_3)_3]_2C_6H_3OB(OR)_2 + ROH \quad (4\text{-}64)$$

other hand, the sterically less demanding 2,6-diisopropyl- and 2-*t*-butylphenol completely displace butanol from tributoxyborane to give the triaryl esters. The difference in the relative rates* of displacement of alkoxyl groups from an alkyl borate by a 2,6-di-*t*-alkylphenol and a 2-*t*-alkylphenol was made the basis of a means of separation of these physically similar materials by subsequently distilling the unreacted 2,6-di-*t*-alkylphenol from the higher boiling tri-2-alkylphenoxyborane.[469]

The alcoholysis of trialkoxyboranes has been claimed to be catalyzed by mineral acids such as sulfuric acid and hydrochloric acid, and subsequent kinetic data[363] confirmed the original qualitative observations.[485] Water and base also were claimed to catalyze the solvolysis; however, the rate of the acid catalyzed reaction was decreased by small amounts of water.[363] It is difficult to envisage the continued existence of water in a medium containing an alkyl borate such as tri-*s*-butoxyborane, since the rate of hydrolysis of tri-*s*-butoxyborane in aqueous dioxane is equivalent to a half-life of 3.5 sec.[444] Thus, adding water is tantamount to adding boric acid.

* It was incorrectly assumed that 2,6-di-*t*-alkylphenols would not undergo transesterification with trialkoxyboranes.[469]

Since boric acid in ethanol solution may be in equilibrium with the acid (XXVIII), the catalysis by water may be no different in kind than the catalysis by an acid.

$$\left[\begin{array}{c} OH \\ | \\ HO{-}B{-}OC_2H_5 \\ | \\ OH \end{array}\right]H$$

(XXVIII)

The solvolysis was postulated to proceed through a tetrahedral transition state with the first displacement the rate controlling step.[363] Proton transfer from R′O to RO with the concerted or

$$R'OH + (RO)_3B \rightarrow \begin{array}{c} R' \quad\; OR \\ \diagdown \quad | \\ O\cdots B\cdots OR \\ \diagup \quad | \\ H \quad\; OR \end{array} \rightarrow R'O{-}B\begin{array}{l} \diagup OR \\ \diagdown OR \end{array} + ROH \qquad (4\text{-}65)$$

subsequent leaving of ROH would be assisted by acid to account for the catalysis.

The mechanism, however, cannot be exclusively a straightforward S_N2 reaction involving only B–O and O–H fission as pictured in equation 4-65, since the alcoholysis of tri-3-methylallyloxyborane with n-octanol gave a mixture of alcohols consisting of 91.3% of the expected 3-methylallyl alcohol and 8.7% of the rearranged alcohol, 1-methylallyl alcohol. Carbon–oxygen fission which would allow

$$(CH_3CH{=}CHCH_2O)_3B + 3\ C_8H_{17}OH$$
$$\rightarrow (C_8H_{17}O)_3B + CH_3CH{=}CHCH_2OH + CH_2{=}CH\underset{\displaystyle CH_3}{\underset{|}{C}}HOH \qquad (4\text{-}66)$$

rearrangement of the resulting carbonium ion (4-67) may have occurred.[185]

$$CH_3CH{=}CHCH_2{-}OB\begin{array}{l} \diagup O{-} \\ \diagdown O{-} \end{array} \rightarrow CH_3CH{=}CHCH_2^+ + RCH_2OB\begin{array}{l} \diagup O{-} \\ \diagdown O{-} \end{array} + OH^- \rightarrow$$
$$HO{-}CH_2R \qquad\qquad \updownarrow \; CH_3\overset{+}{C}HCH{=}CH_2 \qquad (4\text{-}67)$$

$$RCH_2OB\begin{array}{l} \diagup O{-} \\ \diagdown O{-} \end{array} + CH_3CH{=}CHCH_2OH + CH_2{=}CH\underset{\displaystyle CH_3}{\underset{|}{C}}HOH$$

A second possibility involves the ion pair (XXIX). Internal return from the ion pair could give the species (XXX) which upon transesterification would account for the rearranged alcohol observed.

$$(CH_3CH{=}CHCH_2O)_2BOR + CH_3CH{=}CHCH_2OH$$

$$\uparrow ROH$$

$$(CH_3CH{=}CHCH_2O)_3B \rightleftarrows (CH_3CH{=}CHCH_2O)_2B\bar{O}\ CH_2{\cdots}CH{\cdots}\overset{+}{C}HCH_3 \quad (4\text{-}68)$$

(XXIX)

$$\downarrow$$

$$(CH_3CH{=}CHCH_2O)_2BOCHCH{=}CH_2 \text{ (with } CH_3 \text{ on the OCH carbon)}$$

(XXX)

$$\downarrow ROH$$

$$(CH_3CH{=}CHCH_2O)_2BOR + CH_2{=}CHCHOH \text{ (with } CH_3 \text{ on the CHOH carbon)}$$

Alternatively, a concerted reaction involving C–O fission (4-69) may be envisaged but in which the double bond shift in the ester itself offers the driving force.

$$(-O)_2B{-}O{-}CH_2{-}CH{=}CH{-}CH_3 + R{-}O{-}H \rightarrow (-O)_2B{-}OR + CH_2{=}CHCH(OH)CH_3 \quad (4\text{-}69)$$

The ethanolysis of tri-*s*-butoxyborane also was found to be subject to general catalysis by amines and phenols[132] with the rate constant, k, of the solvolysis governed by the relation (4-70), where k_c is the catalytic constant of the phenol or amine at a concentration

$$k = 0.0226 + k_c[C] \quad (4\text{-}70)$$

$[C]$. Table 4-12 records relative rates for the ethanolysis of tri-*s*-butoxyborane in the presence of various catalysts.[132] It is seen that the rate constants in general decrease with decreasing basicity of the amines or decreasing acidity of the phenols.

If the mechanism postulated[132] for the basic catalysis involves the formation of an intermediate complex of amine and borate (XXXI), it is not clear why amines should catalyze the solvolysis at

$$RNH_2{:}B(OC_4H_9)_3$$

(XXXI)

all. The electrophilicity of the boron in (XXXI) is much lower than that in uncomplexed tri-*s*-butoxyborane, and ethanol would be

Table 4-12. Relative rates of ethanolysis of tri-*s*-butoxyborane at 25°

Catalyst (0.02 mole/l.)	$-\log K$ Water	$-\log K$ Ethanol	Relative rate
n-Butylamine	3.39	7.8	457
t-Butylamine	3.55		161
Triethylamine	3.35	7.3	10.0
Acetate ion	9.25	9.3	9.85
p-Toluidine	8.90	13.3	2.66
Aniline	9.36	13.8	2.09
Pyridine	8.75	14.6	1.91
2,6-Dimethylpyridine	7.36		1.71
p-Chloroaniline	10.00	14.9	1.27
p-Nitrophenol			1.07
Phenol	9.89		1.04
Water		18.4	1.03
p-Nitroaniline	13.0	18.0	1.03
Ethanol		20.8	1

expected to attack it more slowly. Further, if the postulated mechanism of the basic catalysis involves the actual displacement of a *s*-butoxy radical by the amine to form an aminodialkoxyborane (XXXII),[132] it is not clear why the tertiary amines, triethylamine,

$$RNHB(OC_4H_9)_2$$
(XXXII)

pyridine and dimethylpyridine, which cannot form a structure such as (XXXII), do indeed catalyze the solvolysis. The authors point out that the tertiary amines show a negative rate deviation which is indicative of steric control; however, they also state that *t*-butylamine and 2,6-lutidine, which are relatively unreactive in displacement and association reactions in general, are reactive catalysts in this case. Therefore, their choice of a mechanism should reflect these facts and their postulate that the function of the amine is to remove the proton after addition of the ethanol is probably nearer the truth.

3. ALKOXY SOURCES OTHER THAN ALCOHOLS

The displacing alkoxy group does not necessarily have to come from an alcohol. Esters of both inorganic (4-71) and organic acids (4-72

$$4\ (C_4H_9O)_3B + 3\ (CH_3O)_4Si \rightleftarrows 4\ (CH_3O)_3B + 3\ (C_4H_9O)_4Si \qquad (4\text{-}71)$$

$$(CH_3O)_3B + 3\ CH_3\overset{\overset{\displaystyle O}{\|}}{C}OC_4H_9 \rightleftarrows (C_4H_9O)_3B + CH_3\overset{\overset{\displaystyle O}{\|}}{C}OCH_3 \qquad (4\text{-}72)$$

and 4-73) as well as antimony triethoxide (4-75) have served as carriers.[362] 2,2-Dimethoxypropane serves the same purpose (4-76).[53]

$$(C_4H_9O)_3B + 3\ C_4H_9\overset{\overset{O}{\|}}{C}OCH_3 \rightleftarrows (CH_3O)_3B + 3\ C_4H_9\overset{\overset{O}{\|}}{C}OC_4H_9 \quad (4\text{-}73)$$

$$(CH_3O)_3B + CH_3\overset{\overset{O}{\|}}{C}OCH{=}CH_2 \rightarrow \text{No reaction} \quad (4\text{-}74)$$

$$(C_4H_9O)_3B + Sb(OC_2H_5)_3 \rightleftarrows (C_2H_5O)_3B + Sb(OC_4H_9)_3 \quad (4\text{-}75)$$

$$2\ (C_4H_9O)_3B + 3\ CH_3\underset{\underset{OCH_3}{|}}{\overset{\overset{OCH_3}{|}}{C}}CH_3 \rightarrow 2\ (CH_3O)_3B + 3\ CH_3\underset{\underset{OC_4H_9}{|}}{\overset{\overset{OC_4H_9}{|}}{C}}CH_3 \quad (4\text{-}76)$$

The redistribution of alkoxyl groups in reactions (4-71), (4-72) and (4-73) does not take place in the absence of catalysts. The yields reported in these reactions were obtained by the use of catalytic amounts of $Mg[Al(OC_2H_5)_4]_2$. Antimony triethoxide (4-75) acted as its own catalyst. Reactions (4-71), (4-75) and (4-76) are convenient methods for the direct preparation of trimethoxy and triethoxyborane without the complications of azeotrope formation.

The redistribution can be formulated as taking place via alkoxyl groups bridged between the electrophilic centers (XXXIII). The

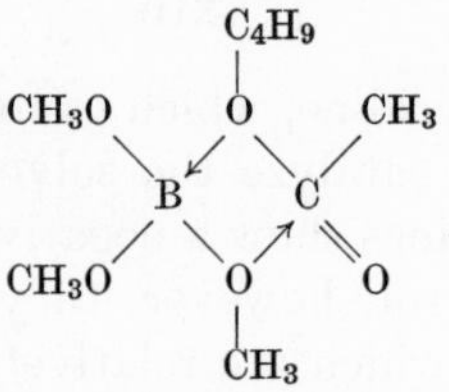

C_4H_9 / CH_3O O CH_3 / B C / CH_3O O O / CH_3

(XXXIII)

inertness of vinyl acetate towards trimethoxyborane (4-74) may be explained by the decrease in the availability of electrons on the vinyloxy oxygen atom. Conjugation with the double bond (XXXIV)

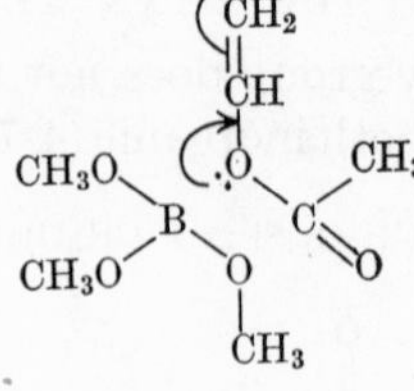

CH_2 / CH / CH_3O O CH_3 / B C / CH_3O O O / CH_3

(XXXIV)

contributes to a loss of nucleophilic power in addition to that due to conjugation with the carbonyl group.

An interesting ramification of the transesterification reaction has been performed with borates of hydroxy esters to give macro ring lactones.[123] This procedure (4-77) possibly could compete with the earlier lactone preparative method involving peracid oxidation of many-membered cyclic ketones.[395]

$$\left[\overset{O}{\overset{\|}{ROC}}(CH_2)_nCH_2O\right]_3B \xrightarrow[\substack{3\text{ mm.}\\ \text{RONa}\\ \text{catalyst}}]{230\text{–}240^\circ} (RO)_3B + 3\ \underbrace{CH_2(CH_2)_n\overset{O}{\overset{\|}{C}}}_{O} \quad n = 10, 12, 14 \qquad (4\text{-}77)$$

F. *From Triacetoxyborane*

Triacetoxyborane, the mixed anhydride of boric acid and acetic acid (see Chapter 8), can be solvolyzed with alcohols or phenols to produce esters and acetic acid.[366,463] The displacement, which can be considered identical with the alcoholysis of an ester (see Section

$$B(O\overset{O}{\overset{\|}{C}}CH_3)_3 + 3\,ROH \rightarrow B(OR)_3 + 3\,CH_3\overset{O}{\overset{\|}{C}}OH \qquad (4\text{-}78)$$

IV-E), should proceed more rapidly than transesterification. The withdrawal of the electron pair on oxygen by the carbonyl group (XXXV) facilitates the attack of a nucleophile on the boron atom; whereas the alkoxyl group deters the attack of a nucleophile by mesomerically supplying electrons (XXXVI).

$$\underset{H}{\overset{R}{>}}\ddot{O}{:}\!\rightarrow\!B\!-\!\ddot{O}\!-\!\overset{O}{\overset{\|}{C}}CH_3 \qquad\qquad \underset{H}{\overset{R}{>}}\ddot{O}{:}\!\rightarrow\!B\!\leftarrow\!\ddot{O}\!-\!R$$

(XXXV) (XXXVI)

The reaction is not reversible, but special precautions are still necessary since acetic acid reacts with boric acid esters to produce boric acid and acetic acid esters.[214]

$$3\,CH_3\overset{O}{\overset{\|}{C}}OH + (RO)_3B \rightarrow 3\,CH_3\overset{O}{\overset{\|}{C}}OR + B(OH)_3 \qquad (4\text{-}79)$$

Trialkoxyboranes were prepared from a series of primary alcohols, isopropyl alcohol, ethylene glycol, and glycerol, and triaryloxyboranes were prepared from phenol and naphthols by warming the alcohols or phenols with the acetate and separating the product from the acetic acid by distillation.[366] Repetition of this procedure for trimethoxy- and triethoxyborane revealed the distilled products to be, in the case of methanol, a ternary mixture of methyl alcohol, trimethoxyborane and methyl acetate, and in the case of ethanol, a mixture of triethoxyborane and acetic acid.[151,208] The presence of methyl acetate would tend to confirm equation (4-79).

It was believed the distillation of the acetic acid from the aromatic borates at atmospheric pressure caused some thermal decomposition of the products. Distillation at reduced pressure was advised, but this procedure also failed to give pure products. Pure products were obtained, however, by performing the solvolysis in benzene solution, which allowed the removal of the acetic acid as a benzene azeotrope at a lower boiling point. This was taken as proof of the thermal instability of aryl borates.[8] If impure aryl borates were indeed obtained, it is more likely that reaction of the products with acetic acid (4-79) was the cause of the contamination rather than thermal decomposition since aromatic borates have been recommended as high temperature heat transfer media.[458]

The synthesis of tri-*s*-butoxyborane and tri-*t*-butoxyborane from the butyl alcohols and boron acetate has been reported.[231] A detailed description was not given, but the boiling point and melting point data were consistent with other literature values for the products. The reaction recorded for the *t*-butyl ester could not be repeated[113,169] and during another attempted repetition yielded only *t*-butyl acetate,[11] again confirming equation (4-79). Neither could the preparation of triisopropoxyborane be repeated.[366] However, tricyclohexoxyborane, which is also derived from a secondary alcohol, could be prepared.[113] Thus, it appears that tertiary alkyl borates cannot be prepared by this method and that secondary alkyl borates can be made only when the alkyl groups are tied back in a ring such as in cyclohexanol. The steric requirements for displacement of acetoxy from triacetoxyborane, therefore, are greater than those for the displacement of alkoxyl from trialkoxyborane, since transesterification proceeds smoothly in the latter case to yield a variety of secondary trialkoxyboranes and tri-*t*-butoxyborane.

G. From Boron Trihalides

The boron trihalides react with a variety of oxygenated organic compounds including alcohols, alkoxides, phenols, ethers, cyclic ethers, aldehydes, carboxylic acid esters, and various other materials to produce boric acid esters.

1. BORON TRICHLORIDE AND ALCOHOLS OR PHENOLS

In 1824, Berzelius[44] observed that boron trichloride reacted with ethanol to produce a volatile product possessing an ether-like odor. Later, it was learned that boron trichloride and the lower primary alcohols could be warmed to produce the lower alkyl borates.[93,140] The reaction, however, does not require heating, and trimethoxy- and triethoxyborane have been prepared at $-60°$ or less.[505]

Thus, the classical preparation of carboxylic acid esters from acid chlorides and alcohols has its counterpart in boron chemistry. Boron halides and particularly boron trichloride in many instances can be considered to behave as the acid halide of boric acid with the electron deficient boron atom assuming a role parallel to the carbonyl group.

$$RC(=O)Cl + R'OH \rightarrow RC(=O)OR' + HCl \tag{4-80}$$

$$BCl_3 + 3\,ROH \rightarrow B(OR)_3 + 3\,HCl \tag{4-81}$$

The advantages of the method are that many esters can be prepared at room temperature by simply admixing the halide and alcohol. The reaction is essentially irreversible.* Therefore, it is not subject to the quantitative removal of products for driving force and complications of azeotrope formation are obviated.

The course of the reaction was shown to proceed via the mono-alkoxy and dialkoxyhaloboranes with the end product depending upon the stoichiometry employed.[505]

$$BCl_3 + ROH \rightarrow ROBCl_2 + HCl \tag{4-82}$$

$$\downarrow {+ROH \atop -HCl}$$

$$BCl_3 + 2\,ROH \rightarrow (RO)_2BCl + 2\,HCl \quad {+2\,ROH \atop -2\,HCl} \tag{4-83}$$

$$\downarrow {+ROH \atop -HCl}$$

$$BCl_3 + 3\,ROH \rightarrow (RO)_3B + 3\,HCl \tag{4-84}$$

Other primary alcohols (2-chloroethanol,[143,308] 2-bromoethanol,[521] ethyl glycolate,[156] and ethyl β-hydroxypropionate[156]) and secondary alcohols (ethyl malate,[156] ethyl lactate,[156] and 1-methylallyl

* Some exceptions have been recorded. The reverse reactions for both triethoxy and tributoxyborane have been reported.[102] In addition, the reaction

$$(RO)_3B + 3\,HCl \rightarrow 3\,RCl + H_3BO_3$$

has been reported for tri-3-methylallyloxyborane.[185]

alcohol[185]) were converted to the borate at $-80°$ employing the 3:1 stoichiometry of equation (4-84).

Unsaturation in the alcohol is not detrimental to the reaction; thus, allyl,[118,183] 2-methylallyl[183] and propynyl borate[183] could be prepared in this manner. Benzyl alcohol could not be converted to benzyl borate; dibenzyl[119,121] or benzyl chloride[174] were formed instead. The former conversion is reminiscent of the formation of a hydrocarbon resembling dibenzyl or stilbene from the reaction of boron trifluoride or boric oxide with benzyl alcohol.[99]

Polyfluoroalcohols were readily converted to the borates (XXXVII–XXXIX) in 60–66% yield by reaction with boron tri-

$(CF_3CH_2O)_3B$	$(CF_3CF_2CH_2O)_3B$	$(CF_3CF_2CF_2CH_2O)_3B$
(XXXVII)	(XXXVIII)	(XXXIX)

chloride in cold petroleum ether solution.[418,419] The trihydro species (XL) similarly was prepared in benzene solution.[25]

$$(CHF_2CF_2CH_2O)_3B$$

(XL)

Aromatic borates were prepared along with chlorinated by-products at 100–160° in a sealed tube.[337] The necessity of heating the reaction is doubtful since a variety of aromatic borates were obtained in 96–100% yield by the addition of three moles of the phenol to one mole of boron trichloride in methylene chloride solution at -60 to $-80°$.[111,112] In addition, an 84% yield of tri-2,6-dimethylphenoxyborane was obtained in toluene solution at 20 to 26°,[27] and a 44% yield of triphenoxyborane was obtained in benzene solution below 45° using urea to neutralize the hydrogen chloride.[438]

Attempts to convert the highly hindered phenol (XLI) to the borate by reaction with boron trichloride in toluene solution up to 250° led to dealkylation of the *t*-butyl groups and the formation of (XLII).[27] 2-6-Di-*t*-butylphenol failed to react with boron trichloride

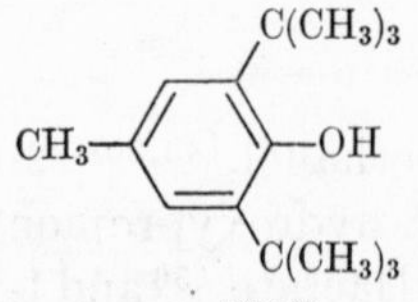

C(CH₃)₃ / CH₃–C₆H₂(–OH) / C(CH₃)₃

(XLI)

$[CH_3–C_6H_3(C(CH_3)_3)–O–]_3B$

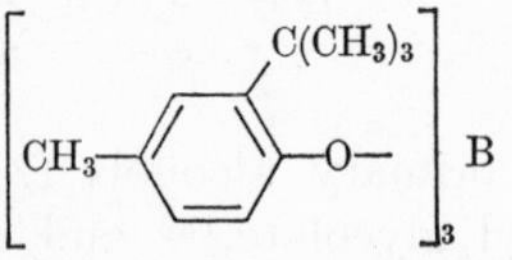

(XLII)

in boiling hexachlorobutadiene.[521] The steric limitations of the 2,6-dialkylphenoxyboranes lie, therefore, somewhere between methyl and *t*-butyl. The reaction of triphenylcarbinol and boron trichloride in methylene chloride solution resulted in trityl chloride instead of the borate.[521]

Advantages of the boron trichloride–phenol method over alternative procedures for preparing aryl borates include the nearly quantitative yields obtained in relatively short reaction times and the easy removal of by-products. In addition, functional groups may be present on the ring.[174] Thus, tri-*p*-hydroxyphenoxyborane was obtained from the reaction of hydroquinone and boron trichloride in chloroform solution.[351]

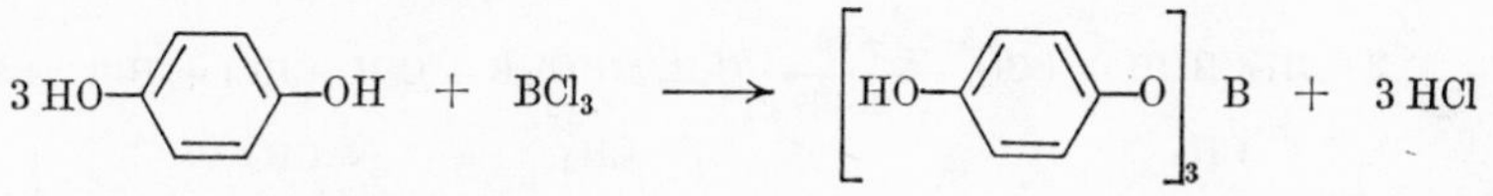

$$3\,HO{-}C_6H_4{-}OH + BCl_3 \longrightarrow [HO{-}C_6H_4{-}O]_3B + 3\,HCl \qquad (4\text{-}85)$$

a. *Solvents.* Pentane was found to be a useful solvent for conversion of a variety of primary,[143,176,178,185] secondary,[176,178] and chloroalcohols[2] to their borates at -10 to $-80°$ employing the 3:1 stoichiometry of equation (4-84).

Chloroform also has been used at $-10°$ for the preparation of tri-α-carbethoxyethoxyborane.[156] A highly hindered secondary alcohol, hexachloro-2-propanol, required refluxing hexane to effect the reaction.[172]

b. *Mechanism.* Speculations concerning the mechanism of the boron trichloride–alcohol reaction favored a four-centered transition state (XLIII) as compared to the displacement (XLIV).[170,175,176] The process is then repeated in the intermediate alkoxy- (XLV) and dialkoxyhaloboranes (XLVI).

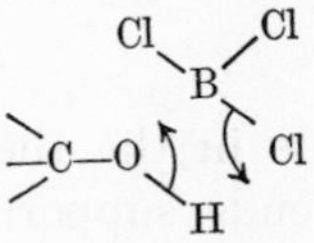

Cl, Cl, B, C—O, Cl, H

(XLIII)

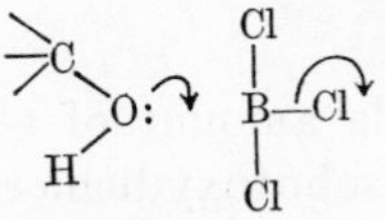

C, O:, H, Cl, B—Cl, Cl

(XLIV)

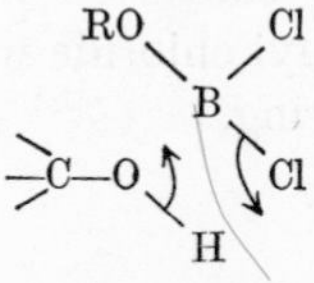

RO, Cl, B, C—O, Cl, H

(XLV)

RO, OR, B, C—O, Cl, H

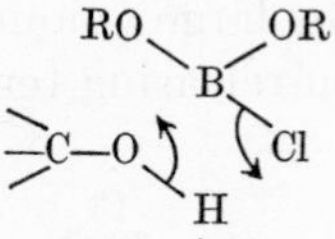

(XLVI)

Although postulated,[507] there is no evidence for the formation of an isolable complex, ROH:BCl_3, prior to the displacement of halogen, as is the case with boron fluoride.[203,212] The presence of strong electron-withdrawing groups in the alcohol, as in the case of ethers, does not prevent reaction, since β,β,β-trifluoroethanol afforded a 70% yield of the borate on treatment with boron trichloride.[4]

The conversions of (+)-2-octanol and (+)-1-phenylethanol to their respective (+)-borates were accompanied by the formation of almost completely racemized (−)-2-chlorooctane and partially racemized (+)-α-chloroethylbenzene.[127] The formation of the racemized octyl halide was attributed to the collapse of the inter-

$$3\,C_6H_{13}CH(CH_3)OH + BCl_3 \xrightarrow[\text{2. distill}]{\text{1. }-10^\circ} \underset{83.5\%\text{ yield}}{(C_6H_{13}CH(CH_3)O)_3B} + \underset{9\%\text{ yield}}{C_6H_{13}CH(CH_3)Cl} + HCl \quad (4\text{-}86)$$

(Hydrolyze: borate → $C_6H_{13}CH(CH_3)OH$)

$$3\,C_6H_5CH(CH_3)OH + BCl_3 \xrightarrow[\text{2. distill}]{\text{1. }10^\circ}$$

$$\underset{24\%\text{ yield}}{(C_6H_5CH(CH_3)O)_3B} + \underset{51\%\text{ yield}}{C_6H_5CH(CH_3)Cl} + \underset{12\%\text{ yield}}{C_6H_5CH(CH_3)\text{—O—}CH(CH_3)C_6H_5} + HCl \quad (4\text{-}87)$$

mediate alkoxydihaloborane to a carbonium ion. The formation of

$$\text{—}\overset{|}{\underset{|}{C}}\text{—O—}B(Cl)\text{—Cl} \rightarrow \text{—}\overset{|}{\underset{|}{C}}{}^{+} + Cl^- + \{O{=}B\text{—}Cl\} \rightarrow \text{—}\overset{|}{\underset{|}{C}}\text{—Cl} + \tfrac{1}{3}B_2O_3 + \tfrac{1}{3}BCl_3 \quad (4\text{-}88)$$

a considerable amount of *t*-butyl chloride in the thermal decomposition of isobutoxydichloroborane[176] lends support to the S_N1 mechanism of equation (4-88). Retention of activity in the phenylethyl halide was attributed to an S_Ni[117] concerted front side displacement. The large amount of phenylethyl chloride was attributed to the electron-releasing tendency of the ring.

$$\text{—}C{<}(O,Cl){>}B\text{—Cl} \rightarrow \text{—}\overset{|}{\underset{|}{C}}\text{—Cl} + \{O{=}B\text{—}Cl\} \quad (4\text{-}89)$$

Phenylethyl chloride, in contrast to 2-chlorooctane, was readily racemized by boron trichloride. This was attributed to the increased tendency of the phenyl substituted halide to form a tetrachloroborate.[175]

$$RCl + BCl_3 \rightleftarrows \overset{\delta+}{R}—Cl—\overset{\delta-}{B}Cl_3 \rightleftarrows R[BCl_4] \quad (4\text{-}90)$$

The authors point out that the yield of phenylethyl chloride increased as the ratio of alcohol to boron trichloride decreased.[127] Thus, for one mole of boron trichloride, three moles of alcohol gave a 51% yield of halide; whereas 1.2 moles of alcohol led to an 87% yield of halide. Indeed, if the halide arises via the alkoxydihaloborane, the theoretical yields of the alkoxydihaloboranes dictate the yields of halide; 33% for the reaction with three moles of alcohol and 83% for the reaction with 1.2 moles of alcohol. Further, if the by-product BOCl continues to exhaustively regenerate additional alkoxydihaloborane via path (4-91) or (4-92), the theoretical yields increase to 50% (path 4-91) or 66.7% (path 4-92) for the case of three moles of starting alcohol, and 100% by either path (4-91) or (4-92) for the case of one mole of starting alcohol. The actual yields

$$BOCl \rightarrow \begin{cases} \frac{1}{3}\,BCl_3 \xrightarrow{\frac{1}{3}\,ROH} \frac{1}{3}\,ROBCl_2 + \frac{1}{3}\,HCl & (4\text{-}91) \\ \quad + \\ \frac{1}{3}\,B_2O_3 \xrightarrow{ROH} \frac{1}{3}\,H_3BO_3 + \frac{1}{3}\,(RO)_3B \xrightarrow{\frac{1}{3}\,BCl_3} \frac{1}{6}\,(RO)_3B + \frac{1}{2}\,ROBCl_2{}^{*} & (4\text{-}92) \end{cases}$$

are, therefore, in good agreement with the theoretical yields, lending some weight to the proposed mechanism for halide formation and tending to discount a possible alternative path (4-93), which would

$$(RO)_3B + 3\,HCl \rightarrow 3\,RCl + B(OH)_3 \quad (4\text{-}93)$$

allow 100% yields for both the stoichiometries employed. Equation 4-93 was shown to be operative for tri-α-phenylethoxyborane in an independent experiment.[175]

t-Butyl alcohol could not be converted to the borate by a 3:1 molar reaction with boron trichloride; a 90% yield of *t*-butyl chloride was obtained instead.[176] Two paths were proposed for the halide production. The intermediate alkoxydihaloborane could collapse as in equation (4-89) or the tri-*t*-butoxyborane, once formed, could react with the hydrogen chloride by-product to produce halide and boric acid (4-93). The latter possibility was independently shown to take place with authentic tri-*t*-butoxyborane.

Since the reaction via alkoxydihaloborane at the 3:1 stoichiometry employed only allows a 67% conversion to halide, the 90% yield of *t*-butyl chloride would require at least some halide formation

* Conversions of borates to alkoxyhaloboranes by treatment with boron halides are discussed in Chapter 12.

via the path of equation (4-93), and in all probability the reaction proceeded exclusively via path (4-93).

It is instructive to review the yields of halide in the attempted borate preparations with the alcohols listed in Table 4-13. Emphasis

Table 4-13. Yield of halide from reaction of three moles of alcohol and one mole of boron trichloride

Alcohol	% Yield of halide	Reference
$C_6H_5CH_2OH$	?	174
$CH_3(CH_2)_5CH(CH_3)OH$	9	175
$C_6H_5CH(CH_3)OH$	50.1	175
$CH_3CH{=}CHCH_2OH$	70	185
$(CH_3)_3COH$	90	176

has been placed upon "the degree of reactivity of the alcoholic carbon atom."[175,176] If the inductive effect, *i.e.* the ability of the alkyl group to donate electrons, were the controlling factor in the production of halide, the yields should decrease from *t*-butyl to 2-octyl to phenylethyl. This, however, is not the case. If the facility with which the alkyl group could form a carbonium ion controlled the yield of halide, the order would be *t*-butyl > phenylethyl > 2-octyl, as is observed. This order is consistent with equations (4-88) and (4-89).

c. *Effect of Amines.* The yield of tri-α-phenylethoxyborane was found to increase from 24% to 69% when the boron trichloride–phenylethanol reaction was performed in the presence of three equivalents of pyridine (4-94).[175] Change of solvent from pentane to

$$3\,ROH + BCl_3 + 3\,C_5H_5N \rightarrow B(OR)_3 + 3\,C_5H_5N{\cdot}HCl \qquad (4\text{-}94)$$

chloroform eliminated the precipitation of the pyridine–boron trichloride complex and resulted in further increase in yield to 86%. The function of the pyridine is believed to be assistance in the removal of the proton from the alcohol, which would tend to promote the continued alcoholysis of boron at the expense of the halide producing reactions (4-88 and 4-89).

Tertiary alkyl borates and a variety of other alkyl borates were prepared in excellent yield by refluxing three moles of the appropriate alcohol with one mole of the pyridine–boron trichloride com-

$$3\,ROH + C_5H_5N\cdot BCl_3 + 2\,C_5H_5N \rightarrow B(OR)_3 + 3\,C_5H_5N\cdot HCl \qquad (4\text{-}95)$$

plex and two moles of pyridine in chloroform solution for ten hours.[173] The pyridine–boron trichloride complex (XLVII), however, could

$C_5H_5N{:}BCl_3$

(XLVII)

not be used to advantage even though it is a convenient form of boron trichloride, since it was found to be less reactive towards alcohols than boron trichloride itself.[175,275]* Indeed, the rate of ester production via reaction (4-94) was shown to be much faster than that produced by reaction (4-95).[275] Thus, alcohols, even those of large steric requirement, successfully compete with pyridine for boron trichloride. If they did not, and the pyridine–boron trichloride complex formed first, the subsequent alcoholysis would involve, in both cases, displacement of halide from a partially negatively charged sp^3 boron atom (4-96) and the rate of borate production for equations (4-94) and (4-95) would be identical.

$$ROH + Cl{-}\overset{\overset{\delta+}{NC_5H_5}\downarrow\delta-}{\underset{Cl}{B}}{-}Cl \rightarrow \underset{H}{\overset{R}{O}}\cdots\overset{\overset{\delta+}{NC_5H_5}\downarrow\delta-}{\underset{Cl}{B}}\cdots Cl \rightarrow RO{-}\overset{\overset{\delta+}{NC_5H_5}\downarrow\delta-}{\underset{Cl}{B}}{-}Cl + HCl \qquad (4\text{-}96)$$

Pyridine offered no advantage for the preparation of aromatic borates by either equation (4-94) or (4-95) and in fact lowered the yield of isolable ester.[174] This was attributed to the formation of an aryl borate–pyridine complex (XLVIII). The complex had previously been prepared independently.[112] The presence of pyridine also

$(ArO)_3B{:}NC_5H_5$

(XLVIII)

lowered the yield of tri(heptafluorobutoxy)borane from the reaction of the polyfluoro alcohol and boron trichloride.[418]

Other basic materials have been used as acid acceptors. Tri-*t*-butoxyborane was reportedly prepared (undisclosed yield) from the reaction of *t*-butyl alcohol and boron trichloride in the presence of

* $(CH_3)_3N{:}BCl_3$ can be recrystallized from hot ethanol.[221]

urea.[438] Trimethoxy- and triisopropoxyborane were prepared similarly.* Ammonia has been stated to be useful for the removal of hydrogen chloride from methyl and ethyl borate preparations.[485]

d. *Boron Trichloride Complexes and Alcohols.* Boron trichloride in the form of an ether complex has been converted to the borate in quantitative yield (4-97). This conversion was offered as evidence

$$ClCH_2CH_2OCH_3{:}BCl_3 + 3\ n\text{-}C_4H_9OH \rightarrow (n\text{-}C_4H_9O)_3B + 3\ HCl + ClCH_2CH_2OCH_3 \quad (4\text{-}97)$$

that the ether complex has the structure (XLIX) and not (L).[145] There is little justification on this basis alone for this conclusion

$$R'R\,O{:}BCl_3 \qquad [ROBCl_3]^-R'^+$$

(XLIX) (L)

since a tetracovalent boron anion with halogen ligands has been converted to a trivalent ester by treatment with an alkoxide.[417] In addition, on the basis of conductivity and other physical measure-

$$[BF_4]K + Al(OC_2H_5)_3 \rightarrow B(OC_2H_5)_3 + AlF_3 + KF \quad (4\text{-}98)$$

ments, it was concluded that the boron trifluoride–ethyl ether complex had structure (LI).[204]

$$[C_2H_5OBF_3]C_2H_5$$

(LI)

Other evidence for structure (XLIX), however, does exist; reaction of the complex with pyridine yielded ether and the pyridine–boron trichloride complex.[145] Equilibration of (XLIX) with structure (L) was viewed as a possibility.[174]

The tetrahydrofuran and dioxane complexes of boron trichloride[143,158] as well as the di-n-butyl sulfide,[276] benzamide,[187] acetonitrile[188] and triphenyl phosphate[161] complexes also have been converted to borates by treatment with butanol, as has the ethyl acetate–boron trichloride complex by treatment with n-octanol.[156]

* With boron trifluoride in place of the boron trichloride, esters of carbamic and carbonic acid are produced in place of the borates.[436]

$$ROH + NH_2\overset{O}{\overset{\|}{C}}NH_2 + BF_3 \rightarrow RO\overset{O}{\overset{\|}{C}}NH_2 + NH_3{:}BF_3$$

$$RO\overset{O}{\overset{\|}{C}}NH_2 + ROH + BF_3 \rightarrow RO\overset{O}{\overset{\|}{C}}OR + NH_3{:}BF_3$$

2. BORON TRIBROMIDE AND TRIFLUORIDE AND ALCOHOLS

Boron tribromide reacted with tribromoethanol to produce β,β,β-tribromoethoxyborane.[304] It was subsequently shown to be similar to boron trichloride in that it readily afforded tri-n-butoxy and triisobutoxyborane but converted *t*-butyl alcohol to *t*-butyl bromide.[84] *s*-Butyl alcohol represented a departure from boron trichloride since boron tribromide led to 2-bromobutane as well as tri-*s*-butoxyborane.[84] Reaction of boron tribromide with n-butyl alcohol in the presence of urea to take up the hydrogen bromide was reported to give an 80% yield of tri-n-butoxyborane.[438]

The reaction of alcohols with boron trifluoride does not, in general, afford alkyl borates. In many cases a complex results,[203,212] in some cases dehydration occurs,[325,439] and the resulting olefin may polymerize under the catalytic activity of the boron trifluoride.

$$RCH_2CH_2OH + BF_3 \rightarrow RCH_2CH_2OH{:}BF_3$$
$$RCH_2CH_2OH + BF_3 \xrightarrow{-H_2O} RCH{=}CH_2 \xrightarrow{BF_3} \left[-\underset{\displaystyle R}{\underset{|}{C}}HCH_2-\right]_n \qquad (4\text{-}99)$$

The fluorinated alcohols CF_3CH_2OH, $CF_3CF_2CH_2OH$, and $CF_3CF_2CF_2CH_2OH$ do not react with boron trifluoride etherate under reflux.[418]

An isolated example of the production of an alkyl borate from a mixture of boron trifluoride, propanol and urea has been reported.[437]

$$6.5\,BF_3 + 16\,C_3H_7OH + 4\,NH_2\overset{\displaystyle O}{\overset{\|}{C}}NH_2 \rightarrow 0.32\,(C_3H_7O)_3B + 2.35\,NH_2\overset{\displaystyle O}{\overset{\|}{C}}OC_3H_7$$
$$+ 1.25\,C_3H_7O\overset{\displaystyle O}{\overset{\|}{C}}OC_3H_7 + 6\,NH_3{:}BF_3 \qquad (4\text{-}100)$$

If the basic catalysis of the urea or the ammonia *in situ* is in this case sufficient to effect the condensation, then esters should be produced readily from alcoholysis of a variety of amine–boron trifluoride complexes or from treatment of alcohol–boron trifluoride complexes with amines. One such example has been recorded.[277]

$$4\,BF_3{:}2C_4H_9OH + 3\,C_5H_5N \rightarrow (C_4H_9O)_3B + 5\,C_4H_9OH + 3\,[C_5H_5NH]BF_4 \qquad (4\text{-}101)$$

No alcoholyses of boron iodide to yield trialkoxyboranes have been reported.

3. REACTION WITH ALKOXIDES

In contrast to the difficulty of producing esters from boron trifluoride and alcohols, sodium[142,168] and aluminum[417] alkoxides have acted as ready donors of alkoxyl groups to both boron trifluoride and trichloride. These reactions are capable of yielding both methyl and

$$3\ NaOCH_3 + BF_3 \text{ or } BCl_3 \rightarrow (CH_3O)_3B + 3\ NaF \text{ or } 3\ NaCl \quad (4\text{-}102)$$

$$Al(OR)_3 + BF_3 \rightarrow (RO)_3B + AlF_3 \quad (4\text{-}103)$$

ethyl borate without recourse to azeotrope separation if they are run in inert solvents such as the polyethylene glycol ethers.

Use of boron trifluoride etherate and methanol solvent led to production of the trimethoxyborane–methanol azeotrope and was suggested as a convenient means of converting the readily available $^{10}BF_3$ etherate to ^{10}B esters.[26] Substitution of an inert solvent such

$$BF_3{:}(C_2H_5)_2O + 3\ NaOCH_3 + CH_3OH \rightarrow [B(OCH_3)_3 + CH_3OH] + (C_2H_5)_2O + 3\ NaF \quad (4\text{-}104)$$

as toluene or xylene for the methanol resulted in the direct production of pure trimethoxyborane.[321]

Sodium methoxide may be employed in the form of its salt with trimethoxyborane, sodium tetramethoxyborate (4-105),[142] and boron trifluoride may be employed in the form of its salt with potassium fluoride, potassium fluoborate (4-106).[417]

$$3\ NaB(OCH_3)_4 + BCl_3 \rightarrow 4\ B(OCH_3)_3 + 3\ NaCl \quad (4\text{-}105)$$

$$KBF_4 + Al(OR)_3 \rightarrow B(OR)_3 + AlF_3 + KF \quad (4\text{-}106)$$

4. REACTION WITH ETHERS

In 1891 Moissan reported the cleavage of ethyl ether with boron iodide (4-107).[347] Once again, analogous reactions with acyl halides (4-108 to 4-110) are apparent.[207,301,331]

$$3\ C_2H_5OC_2H_5 + BI_3 \rightarrow (C_2H_5O)_3B + 3\ C_2H_5I \quad (4\text{-}107)$$

$$ROR + CH_3\overset{O}{\overset{\|}{C}}Cl \rightarrow CH_3\overset{O}{\overset{\|}{C}}OR + RCl \quad (4\text{-}108)$$

$$ROR + CH_3\overset{O}{\overset{\|}{C}}Br \rightarrow CH_3\overset{O}{\overset{\|}{C}}OR + RBr \quad (4\text{-}109)$$

$$ROR + CH_3\overset{O}{\overset{\|}{C}}I \rightarrow CH_3\overset{O}{\overset{\|}{C}}OR + RI \quad (4\text{-}110)$$

a. *Boron Trichloride.* The cleavage of dimethyl and diethyl ether with boron trichloride was shown to proceed through a series

$$BCl_3 + R_2O \xrightarrow{-80^\circ} R_2O{:}BCl_3 \xrightarrow{50^\circ} RCl + ROBCl_2 \xrightarrow[-80^\circ]{R_2O} R_2O{:}(ROBCl_2)_2 \xrightarrow{0^\circ} R_2O{:}BCl_3 + (RO)_2BCl \quad (4\text{-}111)$$

of intermediate ether complexes and alkoxyhaloboranes.[381,506] The resulting dialkoxyhaloboranes did not react further[505,506] with ether and the origin of the ester was attributed to disproportionation (4-112) or reaction with the monoalkoxydihaloborane (4-113).[381]

$$2\ (RO)_2BCl \rightarrow ROBCl_2 + B(OR)_3 \quad (4\text{-}112)$$

$$(RO)_2BCl + ROBCl_2 \rightarrow BCl_3 + (RO)_3B \quad (4\text{-}113)$$

The facility with which boron trichloride and the monoalkoxy derivative react with ethers as compared to the dialkoxyhaloboranes and esters themselves testifies to the diminishing of the Lewis acid, strength of boron trichloride as the halogen is replaced by alkoxyl groups. Undoubtedly, this is a function of the greater availability of the free electron pair on oxygen as compared to chlorine.

Ethers of insufficient nucleophilic character, diphenyl ether[111] and bischloromethyl ether,[145] do not react with boron trichloride. The unreactivity of the chloroether points out once again the similarity of the boron halides to acyl halides since bischloromethyl ether was also found to be unreactive towards chloroacetyl iodide, a reagent which cleaved all ordinary ethers.[207]

Prior complexing of the boron trichloride does not appear to preclude the ether cleavage reaction, as evidenced by the almost quantitative yield of triethoxyborane from the room temperature reaction of diethyl ether and the di-n-butyl sulfide–boron trichloride complex.[276] Only a minor portion of the triethoxyborane and ethyl

$$3\ (C_2H_5)_2O + 2\ (C_4H_9)_2S\!:\!BCl_3 \rightarrow (C_2H_5O)_3B + 2\ C_2H_5Cl + (C_4H_9)_2SC_2H_5^+BCl_4^- + (C_4H_9)_2S \quad (4\text{-}114)$$

chloride could have arisen from the direct reaction of ether and free boron trichloride, formed by dissociation of the complex, since the complex alone underwent only a very slow rate of decomposition at 215°.

Table 4-14. Cleavage reactions with boron tribromide

Ether	ROH after hydrolysis of $(RO)_3B$	RBr
$(C_2H_5)_2O$	C_2H_5OH	C_2H_5Br
$(i\text{-}C_3H_7O)_2O$	$i\text{-}C_3H_7OH$	$i\text{-}C_3H_7Br$
$(n\text{-}C_4H_9O)_2O$	$n\text{-}C_4H_9OH$	$n\text{-}C_4H_9Br$
$i\text{-}C_3H_7OC_6H_5$	C_6H_5OH	$i\text{-}C_3H_7Br$
$n\text{-}C_4H_9OC_6H_5$	C_6H_5OH	$n\text{-}C_4H_9Br$
$2\text{-}BrC_6H_5OCH_3$	$2\text{-}BrC_6H_5OH$	—
$2,4,6\text{-}(CH_3)_3C_6H_2OCH_3$	$2,4,6\text{-}(CH_3)_3C_6H_2OH$	—
$n\text{-}C_3H_7OCH_2C_6H_5$	$n\text{-}C_3H_7OH$	$C_6H_5CH_2Br$

b. *Boron Tribromide.* The cleavage reaction subsequently was extended to boron bromide. Alkyl bromide and ester in good yield were the only products from a 3:1 molar reaction of ether and bromide at water bath temperature. Table 4-14 records the available data.[42]

c. *Boron Trifluoride.* The cleavage of ethers with boron fluoride to produce boric acid esters has not been reported as a synthetic method. However, in the search for routes to boron trifluoride complexes of polyamines, the reaction of boron trifluoride etherate with various amine hydrochlorides resulted in the formation of triethoxyborane.[335] The sequence was formulated as in equation (4-115), which

$$3\,RNH_3Cl + 3\,(C_2H_5)_2O{:}BF_3 \xrightarrow{60\text{–}100^\circ} 3\,C_2H_5Cl + 3\,RNH_3[C_2H_5OBF_3] \quad (4\text{-}115)$$

$$\downarrow$$

$$(C_2H_5O)_3B + 2\,RNH_3[BF_4] + RNH_3F$$

involves essentially the disproportionation of ethoxydifluoroborane to triethoxyborane.

$$4\,BF_3{:}(CH_3)_2O + 3\,(CH_3)_4NCl \rightarrow (CH_3O)_3B + (CH_3)_2O + CH_3Cl + (CH_3)_4NBF_4 \quad (4\text{-}116)$$

The attempted metathesis of boron trifluoride methyl etherate and tetramethyl ammonium chloride yielded trimethoxyborane.[494] Since the same reaction course was followed with longer chain alkylammonium halides, ether cleavage must have taken place.

Thus, it appears that the distribution of electrons in the B–F bond is a deterrent to the nucleophilic attack of ether as compared to the electronic distribution in the B–Cl bond which allows facile attack. Apparently, fluorine enriches boron with electrons via its large $+M$ effect more than chlorine does,[222] and the relatively weak reference base, ether in this case, may be capable of attacking only the most electron-deficient boron atom. However, a preliminary displacement by the relatively strong base, chloride,* available from the ammonium chloride of reactions 4-115 and 4-116, would lessen the activation energy of the subsequent ether attack on boron trifluoride.

d. *Mechanism.* The mechanism of the ether fission, at least for the first step, was postulated to proceed via a carbonium ion

* The equilibrium $3\,Cl^- + BF_3 \rightleftarrows BCl_3 + 3\,F^-$ would be expected to lie far to the left. However, the reaction of the fluoride ion with excess BF_3 to give BF_4^- may well provide a driving force for the displacement, as is the case in the reaction $AlCl_3 + BF_3 \rightarrow AlF_3 + BCl_3$ in which the formation of non-volatile and polymeric aluminium fluoride serves to promote the transfer of chloride to boron.[166]

formed from the electron-releasing group of the ether; R′ in equation (4-117).[174,177] A more accurate restatement of the postulate is that

$$ROR' + BCl_3 \rightarrow \begin{matrix} R' & & Cl \\ & O \rightarrow & B\text{—}Cl \\ R & & Cl \end{matrix} \rightarrow R'^{+} + ROBCl_2 + Cl^{-} \rightarrow R'Cl + ROBCl_2 \quad (4\text{-}117)$$

the moiety of the ether which can best form a stable carbonium ion does so, and is incorporated in the halide product. Thus, phenyl alkyl ethers (Table 4-14) give alkyl halide, since phenyl has little tendency to form a carbonium ion, and benzyl n-alkyl ether leads to benzyl halide due to the relative stability of the benzyl carbonium ion versus the alkyl carbonium ion.

The postulated mechanism is consistent with the data of Tables 4-14 and 4-15, the loss of optical activity in the cleavage of ethyl 1-phenylethyl ether (4-118) and ethyl 2-octyl ether (4-119),[175] and the isolation of a mixture of butenyl chlorides from the fission of 3-methylallyl ether (4-120).[174,185] The rearranged butenyl chloride of equation (4-120) could be formed without recourse to a carbonium

$$\underset{\alpha_D^{20}\ +58.5^\circ}{C_2H_5O\underset{CH_3}{\underset{|}{C}}HC_6H_5} + BCl_3 \rightarrow C_2H_5OBCl_2 + \underset{\alpha_D^{20}\ 0^\circ}{C_6H_5\underset{CH_3}{\underset{|}{C}}HCl} \quad (4\text{-}118)$$

$$\underset{\alpha_D^{20}\ +5.3^\circ}{C_2H_5O\underset{CH_3}{\underset{|}{C}}HC_6H_{13}} + BCl_3 \rightarrow C_2H_5OBCl_2 + \underset{\alpha_D^{20}\ -3.1^\circ}{C_6H_{13}\underset{CH_3}{\underset{|}{C}}HCl} \quad (4\text{-}119)$$

$$[CH_3CH{=}CHCH_2]_2O + BCl_3 \rightarrow [CH_3CH{=}CHCH_2 \rightleftarrows CH_3CHCH{=}CH_2]^+ + Cl^-$$
$$+ CH_3CH{=}CHCH_2OBCl_2 \rightarrow CH_3CH{=}CHCH_2Cl + CH_2{=}CH\underset{CH_3}{\underset{|}{C}}HCl$$
$$+ CH_3CH{=}CHCH_2OBCl_2 \quad (4\text{-}120)$$

ion by a concerted mechanism (4-121) in which the shift of the double bond in the ether itself supplies the driving force.

$$\begin{matrix} & CH\text{—}CH_2 & \\ CH_3CH\!\!=\!\! & & O\text{—}CH_2CH{=}CHCH_3 \\ & Cl\text{—}B\text{—}Cl & \\ & Cl & \end{matrix}$$

$$\rightarrow CH_3\underset{Cl}{\underset{|}{C}}HCH{=}CH_2 + Cl_2BOCH_2CH{=}CHCH_3 \quad (4\text{-}121)$$

The ready cleavage of anisole and the lack of rearranged halides

Table 4-15. Cleavage reactions with boron trichloride

Ether	Products: $ROBCl_2$	$(RO)_2BCl$	$(RO)_3B$	RCl	Reference
n-C_4H_9—O—i-C_4H_9	n-$C_4H_9OBCl_2$			i-C_4H_9Cl + *t*-C_4H_9Cl	177
n-C_4H_9—O—*s*-C_4H_9	n-$C_4H_9OBCl_2$			*s*-C_4H_9Cl	177
i-C_4H_9—O—*s*-C_4H_9	i-$C_4H_9OBCl_2$			*s*-C_4H_9Cl	177
n-C_4H_9—O—*t*-C_4H_9	n-$C_4H_9OBCl_2$			*t*-C_4H_9Cl	177
i-C_4H_9—O—*t*-C_4H_9	i-$C_4H_9OBCl_2$			*t*-C_4H_9Cl	177
s-C_4H_9—O—*t*-C_4H_9			(*s*-$C_4H_9O)_3B$	*t*-C_4H_9Cl	177
n-$C_8H_{17}OC_2H_5$	$C_2H_5OBCl_2$			n-$C_8H_{17}Cl$	177
s-$C_8H_{17}OC_2H_5$	$C_2H_5OBCl_2$			*s*-$C_8H_{17}Cl$	177
$C_6H_5CH_2CH_2OC_2H_5$	$C_2H_5OBCl_2$			$C_6H_5CH_2CH_2Cl$	177
$C_6H_5OCH_3$	$C_6H_5OBCl_2$				177
$C_6H_5OC_2H_5$	$C_6H_5OBCl_2$				177
$CH_2{=}CHCH_2OCH(CH_3)C{=}CH_2$			$(CH_2{=}CHCH_2O)_3B$		183
$CH_2{=}CHCH_2O$—n-C_4H_9	n-$C_4H_9OBCl_2$				184
$CH_2{=}CHCH_2O$—*s*-C_4H_9			$(CH_2{=}CHCH_2O)_3B$		184
$CH_2{=}CHCH_2O$—*t*-C_4H_9			$(CH_2{=}CHCH_2O)_3B$		184
$CH_2{=}CHCH_2O$—n-C_3H_7		(n-$C_3H_7O)_2BCl$			184
$CH_2{=}CHCH_2O$—i-C_3H_7			$(CH_2{=}CHCH_2O)_3B$		184

from primary alkyl ethers led to the conclusion that the fission reaction was S_N2 in nature, at least for ethers of this type.[90]

An interesting application of the boron trichloride–ether reaction has been found in the Claisen rearrangement. The rearrangement of allyl phenyl ether, which normally requires temperatures of about 200°,[459] was effected at −80° in the presence of boron trichloride.[186] The phenol subsequently was obtained by hydrolysis or methanolysis of the allylphenyl borate.

$$3\ C_6H_5OCH_2CH{=}CH_2 + BCl_3 \longrightarrow [o\text{-}(CH_2{=}CHCH_2)C_6H_4O]_3B + 3\,HCl \qquad (4\text{-}122)$$

The path of reaction (4-122) was not discussed in the preliminary publication, but it can be speculated that departures from the normal mechanism of the Claisen rearrangement (4-123) would include the

$$C_6H_5OCH_2CH{=}CH_2 \longrightarrow \text{(cyclohexadienone with H and } CH_2CH{=}CH_2) \qquad (4\text{-}123)$$

$$\longrightarrow o\text{-}(CH_2CH{=}CH_2)C_6H_4OH$$

formation of a B—O bond in preference to a C═O bond and subsequent loss of the *ortho* hydrogen by chloride attack instead of by enolization (4-124).

$$C_6H_5O(BCl_3)CH_2CH{=}CH_2 \longrightarrow [\text{cyclohexadienyl cation with } OBCl_2,\ H,\ CH_2CH{=}CH_2] + Cl^- \qquad (4\text{-}124)$$

$$\longrightarrow o\text{-}(CH_2CH{=}CH_2)C_6H_4OBCl_2 + HCl$$

5. REACTION WITH CYCLIC ETHERS

The cleavage of a cyclic ether, if similar in mechanism to the cleavage of an alicyclic ether, should result in the formation of an ω-haloalkyl borate (4-125). However, it has been shown that the reaction is complicated by the simultaneous formation of higher

$$3\ \overline{(CH_2)_n\quad O} + BCl_3 \rightarrow [Cl(CH_2)_nO]_3B \qquad (4\text{-}125)$$

molecular weight haloalkyl borates (LII). The actual haloalkyl borates produced from the reaction of boron trichloride and a series

$$[Cl(CH_2)_n(O[CH_2]_n)_mO]_3B$$
(LII)

of cyclic ethers were identified by treatment of the reaction mixtures with methanol and removal of the trimethoxyborane–methanol azeotrope from the haloalcohols (Table 4-16).[144]

In general, the three-membered ring oxides gave predominantly the monomeric borate and the five- and six-membered oxides favored the dimeric borate. Boron trichloride–ether complexes could be isolated only from tetrahydrofuran and tetrahydropyran.[144] Although 1:1 complexes were reported for both ethylene oxide and propylene oxide,[205] it was felt that immediate fission to the chloroalkoxydichloroborane had actually taken place in these systems.[143]

It was pointed out[144] that the relative stability of the tetrahydrofuran and tetrahydropyran–boron trichloride complexes, and the lack of stability of complexes of ethylene oxide and trimethylene oxide could be interpreted in terms of *I*-strain, as had been proposed to explain somewhat analogous results for the trend in stabilities of the trimethylborane complexes of cyclic amines.[74] If this analogy is valid, then the steric requirements of the reference acid, boron trichloride, are less than those of trimethylborane. This would allow the subordination of the *F*-strain of the cycles as compared to the *I*-strain and result in the shift of the ring size of maximum stability to five or six from the four observed with trimethylborane. However, since a methyl substituent has essentially the same steric requirements as a chloro substituent,[8] an alternative explanation for the relative stabilities of the cyclic ether complexes must be found.

The mechanism of the cleavage must be consistent with two observations: in all cases dimeric and higher molecular weight materials are formed and unsymmetrical oxides, at least in the case

Table 4-16. Alcohols and esters derived from boron trichloride cleavage reactions of cyclic ethers

Ether	Mole ratio ether to BCl_3	Yield, %		
		Ester	Monomeric alcohol	Dimeric alcohol
$\overset{O}{\overbrace{CH_2CH_2}}$	6		$ClCH_2CH_2OH$, 76.5	$Cl(CH_2)_2O(CH_2)_2OH$, 3.0
$CH_3\overset{O}{\overbrace{CHCH_2}}$	1		$ClCH_2\underset{CH_3}{\underset{\vert}{C}}HOH$, 21–32 $CH_3\underset{Cl}{\underset{\vert}{C}}HCH_2OH$, 39–50	Trace
$CH_3\overset{O}{\overbrace{CHCH_2}}$	3	$(ClC_3H_6O)_3B$, 98		
$ClCH_2\overset{O}{\overbrace{CHCH_2}}$	1		$(ClCH_2)_2CHOH$, 60	$(ClCH_2)_2CHOCH_2\overset{OH}{\overset{\vert}{C}}HCH_2Cl$, 22.8
$ClCH_2\overset{O}{\overbrace{CHCH_2}}$	6	$[(ClCH_2)_2CHO]_3B$, 57.8	$(ClCH_2)_2CHOH$, 17.4	Some
CH_2—CH_2—CH_2—O (ring)	1		$Cl(CH_2)_3OH$, 17	Some
CH_2—CH_2—O—CH_2—CH_2 (ring)	6		$Cl(CH_2)_4OH$, 13.5	$Cl(CH_2)_4O(CH_2)_4OH$, 44.5
CH_2—CH_2—CH_2—O—CH_2—CH_2 (ring)	6		$Cl(CH_2)_5OH$, 22.2	$Cl(CH_2)_5O(CH_2)_5OH$, 21.4

of epichlorohydrin, exhibit a prejudicial opening. For the three- and four-membered rings, represented by ethylene oxide in equation (4-126), a path avoiding the complex has been proposed.[144] For the

$$\begin{array}{l} CH_2{-}CH_2{>}\ddot{O} \curvearrowright BCl_3 \rightarrow \{^{+}CH_2CH_2O\bar{B}Cl_3\} \rightarrow ClCH_2CH_2OBCl_2 \\ \quad \downarrow \overset{O}{CH_2{-}CH_2} \\ \{^{+}CH_2CH_2OCH_2CH_2O\bar{B}Cl_3\} \rightarrow ClCH_2CH_2OCH_2CH_2OBCl_2 \\ \quad \downarrow \overset{O}{CH_2{-}CH_2} \\ \text{etc.} \end{array} \qquad (4\text{-}126)$$

five- and six-membered rings, the complex has been proposed as the starting material.[144]

$$\begin{array}{l} (CH_2)_m{-}CH_2,\ CH_2,\ CH_2{-}\overset{+}{O}{-}\bar{B}Cl_3 \ \leftarrow\ O\,(CH_2)_{m+3} \longrightarrow (CH_2)_m{-}CH_2,\ CH_2{-}O{-}{}^{-}BCl_3,\ CH_2{-}O^{+}(CH_2)_{m+3} \rightarrow \\ (CH_2)_m{-}CH_2,\ CH_2{-}O{-}{}^{-}\ddot{B}Cl_3,\ CH_2O(CH_2)_{m+2}\overset{+}{C}H_2 \\ \downarrow \\ \text{continues as in equation (4-126)} \end{array} \qquad (4\text{-}127)$$

However, some doubt can be cast upon the validity of formulating the tetrahydrofuran reaction as passing through the boron trichloride complex, since a reaction in which the boron trichloride complex was actually employed as a starting material ultimately yielded a much higher percentage of the monomeric alcohol at the expense of the dimeric alcohol (Table 4-17).[144]

With epichlorohydrin, the initial opening would be expected to involve nucleophilic attack of chloride on the unsubstituted carbon

Table 4-17. Comparison of alcohol yields obtained from boron trichloride-cleavage of cyclic ethers followed by hydrolysis

Reactants	% Yield	
	$Cl(CH_2)_nOH$	$Cl(CH_2)_nO(CH_2)_nOH$
$6\,\overline{(CH_2)_4}O + BCl_3$ 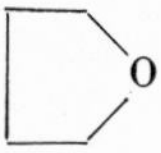	13.5	44.5
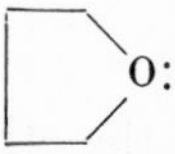 $\overline{(CH_2)_4}O:BCl_3 + 5\,\overline{(CH_2)_4}O$ 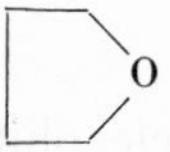	38.8	25.2
$6\,\overline{(CH_2)_5}O + BCl_3$ 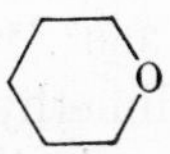	22.2	21.4
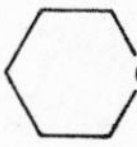 $\overline{(CH_2)_5}O:BCl_3 + 5\,\overline{(CH_2)_5}O$ 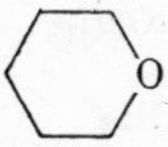	25.5	18.2

atom[514] accounting for the formation of 1,3-dichloro-2-propanol after hydrolysis (4-128) and the absence of 2,3-dichloropropanol.

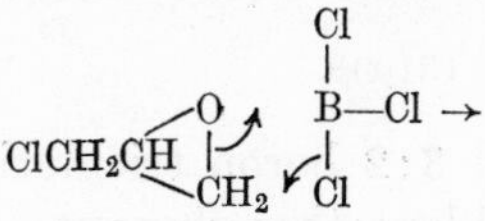

$$ClCH_2CH\overline{\langle O \rangle CH_2} + BCl_3 \rightarrow (ClCH_2)_2CHOBCl_2 \xrightarrow{3H_2O} (ClCH_2)_2CHOH + H_3BO_3 + 2\,HCl \qquad (4\text{-}128)$$

With propylene oxide, 1-chloro-2-propanol would be the predicted product by reaction (4-129). The fact that the isomeric alcohol,

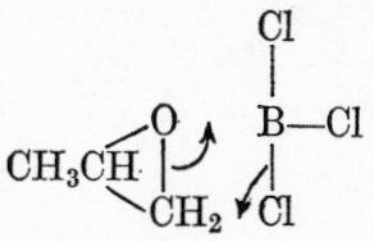

$$CH_3CH\overline{\langle O \rangle CH_2} + BCl_3 \rightarrow ClCH_2\underset{\displaystyle CH_3}{\underset{|}{C}}HOBCl_2 \xrightarrow{3H_2O} ClCH_2\underset{\displaystyle CH_3}{\underset{|}{C}}HOH + H_3BO_3 + 2\,HCl \qquad (4\text{-}129)$$

2-chloropropanol, is obtained in even greater yield[174] might indicate the importance of reaction (4-130) in which the more stable secondary carbonium ion (LIII), as compared to the alternative primary carbonium ion (LIV), gives rise to the 2-chloropropanol.

$$\underset{\substack{|\\ CH_3}}{CH_2\overset{O}{—}CH}\cdot BCl_3 \rightarrow \underset{\text{(LIII)}}{CH_3\overset{+}{C}HCH_2OBCl_2} + Cl^- \rightarrow CH_3\overset{Cl}{\overset{|}{C}}HCH_2OBCl_2 \qquad (4\text{-}130)$$

$$\underset{\text{(LIV)}}{\overset{+}{C}H_2\underset{\substack{|\\ CH_3}}{CH}OBCl_2}$$

The necessity for a certain minimal nucleophilicity of the ether oxygen is indicated by the unreactivity of perfluoro-2-butyltetrahydrofuran with boron trichloride up to temperatures of 350°.[480]

Cleavage of epichlorohydrin with boron trifluoride dimethyl[330] and diethyl[327,330] etherate was reported to give esters and ethers with an alkoxy group in place of the fluorine.

$$4\ ClCH_2\overset{O}{CH—CH_2} + 2\ R_2O{:}BF_3 + 3\ R_2O \rightarrow \left[\begin{matrix} ClCH_2 \\ \quad\diagdown \\ \quad\quad CHO \\ \quad\diagup \\ ROCH_2 \end{matrix}\right]_3 B + 2\ RF$$

$$+ ClCH_2CH\begin{matrix} OR \\ \\ CH_2OR \end{matrix} + [R_3O]BF_4 \qquad (4\text{-}131)$$

Thermal decomposition of the 1:1 and 3:2 boron trichloride–dioxane complexes afforded chlorobis-2-chloroethoxyborane and tri-2-chloroethoxyborane.[114]

$$4\ C_4H_8O_2{:}BCl_3 \rightarrow (ClCH_2CH_2O)_2BCl + 2\ (ClCH_2CH_2O)_3B + BCl_3 \qquad (4\text{-}132)$$

1,3-Dioxolane did not form an isolable complex with boron trichloride, but immediately underwent fission to give the chloromethoxyethoxy derivatives (LV).[114]

$$(ClCH_2OCH_2CH_2O)_xBCl_{3-x}$$
(LV)

6. REACTION WITH ALKOXYSILANES

Boron trichloride and several butoxysilanes undergo stepwise replacement of alkoxyl by chlorine, with a noticeable fall in rate for each successive step. Tetra-*s*-butoxysilane (4-133) and both n- and *s*-butoxytrimethylsilane (4-134) have been used.[162]

$$(C_4H_9O)_4Si + BCl_3 \rightarrow C_4H_9OSiCl_3 + (C_4H_9O)_3B \quad (4\text{-}133)$$

$$3\,(CH_3)_3SiOC_4H_9 + BCl_3 \rightarrow 3\,(CH_3)_3SiCl + (C_4H_9O)_3B \quad (4\text{-}134)$$

7. REACTION WITH ALDEHYDES

The chloroacetaldehydes and β-phenylpropionaldehyde have been condensed with boron trichloride to yield tri-α-chloroalkoxy-

$$3\,R\overset{\displaystyle O}{\overset{\|}{C}}H + BCl_3 \rightarrow (R\overset{\displaystyle Cl}{\overset{|}{C}}HO)_3B \quad (4\text{-}135)$$

boranes.[157] Since α-chloroalcohols are unknown, the condensation affords the only direct path to the α-chloro esters.

The reaction was formulated as proceeding via a four-centered transition state with subsequent disproportionation of the resulting alkoxyhaloborane.

$$\underset{\displaystyle H}{\overset{\displaystyle O}{\overset{\|}{RC}}}\;\;\; \overset{\displaystyle Cl}{\overset{|}{B}}\text{—}Cl \ (Cl) \rightarrow R\overset{\displaystyle Cl}{\overset{|}{C}}HOBCl_2 \rightarrow (R\overset{\displaystyle Cl}{\overset{|}{C}}HO)_2BCl + BCl_3 \quad (4\text{-}136)$$

$$\downarrow$$

$$(R\overset{\displaystyle Cl}{\overset{|}{C}}HO)_3B + R\overset{\displaystyle Cl}{\overset{|}{C}}HOBCl_2$$

The possibility of an initial complex (LVI) was ruled out on the

$$\begin{matrix} R \\ \diagdown \\ & C{=}O{:}BCl_3 \\ \diagup \\ H \end{matrix}$$

(LVI)

basis of the unreactivity of tribromoacetaldehyde, which could meet the requirements of (LVI) sterically but not of the four-centered mechanism (4-136).

Acetaldehyde, n-butyraldehyde, and isobutyraldehyde were believed to have yielded the corresponding chloroalkyl borates, which then decomposed by an internal displacement reaction to yield a bis-α-chloroalkyl ether and a metaborate.

$$3\,CH_3\overset{\displaystyle O}{\overset{\|}{C}}H + BCl_3 \rightarrow \left[\begin{matrix} CH_3 \quad Cl \\ CH \\ | \\ O \end{matrix}\;\; \begin{matrix} CH_3 \\ CH \\ Cl \end{matrix}\;\; O \right] B\text{—}O\overset{\displaystyle Cl}{C}H\underset{\displaystyle CH_3}{} \rightarrow \left[\begin{matrix} CH_3CH \\ | \\ Cl \end{matrix}\right]_2 O + \left\{\begin{matrix} CH_3CHOB{=}O \\ | \\ Cl \end{matrix}\right\} \quad (4\text{-}137)$$

The attack of oxygen on the chlorine-bearing carbon was believed to be precluded in the di- and trichloroacetaldehyde cases due to the increased pull of electrons by the added halogens which decreased the availability of the electron pair on oxygen. The phenyl group in β-phenylpropionaldehyde would serve the same function.

The validity of the influence of electronic factors as compared to steric factors is evident in the conversion of dichloroacetaldehyde to the borate whereas the homomorph,[72] isobutyraldehyde, yields the ether.[157]

8. REACTION WITH ESTERS

Silicates (4-138),[499] phosphates (4-139),[171] and phosphites (4-140)[159,160] have been cleaved with boron halides to effect an exchange of the alkoxy groups and halogens.

$$Si(OR)_4 + BBr_3 \rightarrow ROSiBr_3 + B(OR)_3 \qquad (4\text{-}138)$$

$$(Cl_3CCH_2O)_3PO + BCl_3 \rightarrow (Cl_3CCH_2O)_3PO{:}BCl_3 \xrightarrow{150\text{–}160°} (Cl_3CCH_2O)_3B$$
$$+ (Cl_3CCH_2O)_3PO + Cl_3CCH_2OPOCl_2 + POCl_3 \text{ (not balanced)} \qquad (4\text{-}139)$$

$$(C_6H_5O)_3P + BX_3 \rightarrow PX_3 + (C_6H_5O)_3B \qquad (4\text{-}140)$$

A four-centered transition state was used to explain the phosphite transformation (4-141) although no actual mechanistic evidence exists.[159]

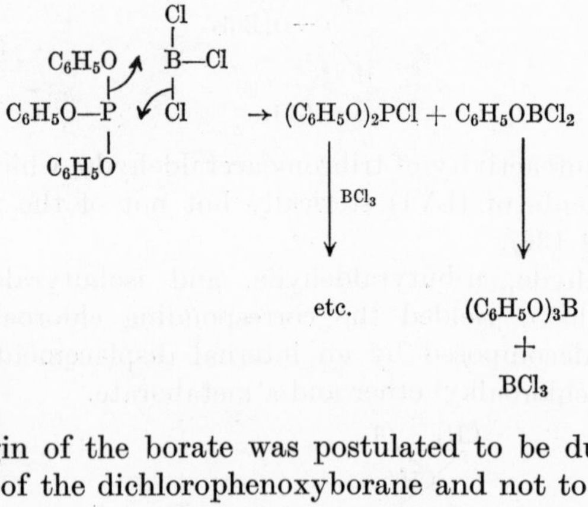

$$(C_6H_5O)_3P + BCl_3 \text{ [four-centered transition state: } C_6H_5O\text{—P, B—Cl]} \rightarrow (C_6H_5O)_2PCl + C_6H_5OBCl_2$$
$$(C_6H_5O)_2PCl \xrightarrow{BCl_3} \text{etc.} \qquad C_6H_5OBCl_2 \rightarrow (C_6H_5O)_3B + BCl_3 \qquad (4\text{-}141)$$

The origin of the borate was postulated to be due to disproportionation of the dichlorophenoxyborane and not to the reaction of the latter with a $C_6H_5OP\langle$ compound. In addition, it was thought that the reverse of reaction (4-140) did not take place due to the low electron density on the triphenoxyborane oxygen atoms as a result of the removal of electrons by the phenyl groups (LVII).[159] However, there must be a more compelling explanation since alkyl borates also do not react with phosphorus trichloride even on boiling.[262]

$$C_6H_5\ddot{O}-B(OC_6H_5)_2$$

(LVII)

Exchange of the phenol moiety of a carboxylic acid ester with the chlorines of boron trichloride (4-142) also has been reported.[156]

$$CH_3COOC_6H_5 + BCl_3 \xrightarrow{\text{Heat}} CH_3COCl + \text{residue} \xrightarrow{180°} (C_6H_5O)_3B \quad (4\text{-}142)$$

A four-centered reaction followed by disproportionation (4-143) can be envisaged.

$$CH_3C(=O)OC_6H_5 + ClBCl_2 \rightarrow CH_3COCl + C_6H_5OBCl_2 \rightarrow \tfrac{1}{3}(C_6H_5O)_3B + \tfrac{2}{3}BCl_3 \quad (4\text{-}143)$$

9. REACTION WITH SODIUM TRIMETHOXYHYDROBORATE

Reductions of boron trifluoride[79] and its etherate[412] with sodium trimethoxyhydroborate have yielded trimethoxyborane as a by-product.

$$NaBH(OCH_3)_3 + BF_3 \rightarrow B(OCH_3)_3 + NaBHF_3 \quad (4\text{-}144)$$

$$6\ NaBH(OCH_3)_3 + 8\ (C_2H_5)_2O{:}BF_3 \rightarrow 6\ B(OCH_3)_3 + 6\ NaBF_4 + B_2H_6 + 8\ (C_2H_5)_2O \quad (4\text{-}145)$$

10. REACTION WITH SILVER ISOCYANATE

Boron tricyanate (LVIII) reportedly was prepared from the

$$BCl_3 + 3\ AgNCO \rightarrow \underset{\text{(LVIII)}}{B(OCN)_3} + 3\ AgCl \quad (4\text{-}146)$$

metathetical reaction of boron trichloride and silver isocyanate.[154]

The cyanate linkage was indicated by the evolution of carbon dioxide on hydrolysis (4-147). Since boron triisocyanate would also be ex-

$$B(OCN)_3 + 3\,H_2O \rightarrow H_3BO_3 + 3\,\{HOCN\} \xrightarrow{3H_2O} 3\,CO_2 + 3\,NH_3 \quad (4\text{-}147)$$

pected to give carbon dioxide on hydrolysis (4-148), the true structure of (LVIII) remains in doubt, a belief shared by subsequent investigators.[281]

$$B(NCO)_3 + 3\,H_2O \rightarrow H_3BO_3 + 3\,\{HNCO\} \xrightarrow{3H_2O} 3\left[H_2N\overset{O}{\overset{\|}{C}}OH\right] \rightarrow 3\,CO_2 + 3\,NH_3 \quad (4\text{-}148)$$

H. From Alkoxyhaloboranes

1. DISPROPORTIONATION

A variety of unsymmetrical trigonal coplanar boron compounds, $ROBY_2$ and $(RO)_2BY$, are thermodynamically unstable with regard to their symmetrical counterparts, $(RO)_3B$ and BY_3, and are, therefore, converted to the symmetrical esters on heating.

$$2\,ROBY_2 \rightleftarrows (RO)_2BY + BY_3 \quad (4\text{-}149)$$

$$3\,ROBY_2 \rightleftarrows (RO)_3B + 2\,BY_3 \quad (4\text{-}150)$$

$$2\,(RO)_2BY \rightleftarrows (RO)_3B + ROBY_2 \quad (4\text{-}151)$$

$$3\,(RO)_2BY \rightleftarrows 2\,(RO)_3B + BY_3 \quad (4\text{-}152)$$

a. *Alkoxychloroboranes.* Alkoxychloroboranes have been the most common starting material for the preparation of esters by disproportionation reactions. The first recorded case involved the heating of chlorodimethoxyborane at 100° with trimethylamine.[508]

$$2\,(CH_3O)_2BCl + 2\,(CH_3)_3N \rightarrow 2\,(CH_3)_3N{:}BCl(OCH_3)_2 \xrightarrow[4\text{ hr.}]{100^\circ} (CH_3)_3N{:}BCl_2(OCH_3) + (CH_3)_3N + B(OCH_3)_3 \quad (4\text{-}153)$$

In the absence of amines this particular compound was stable for fifty hours at 78°[505] and for several hours at 200°.[508] The pyridine complex of chlorodi-(2-chloroethoxy)borane behaved somewhat similarly to give tri-2-chloroethoxyborane.[143] Dichloromethoxyborane, which decomposed to chloroform and boric oxide at 70°,[505] was converted to the borate in the presence of trimethylamine

(4-154);[508] butoxydichloroborane in the form of its pyridine complex behaved similarly (4-155).[275]

$$3\,CH_3OBCl_2 + 3\,(CH_3)_3N \rightarrow 3\,(CH_3)_3N\!:\!BCl_2(OCH_3) \xrightarrow[4\text{ hr.}]{180^\circ} B(OCH_3)_3 + 2\,(CH_3)_3N\!:\!BCl_3 + (CH_3)_3N \quad (4\text{-}154)$$

$$3\,C_5H_5N\!:\!BCl_2(OC_4H_9) \xrightarrow[1\text{ hr.}]{100^\circ} B(OC_4H_9)_3 + 2\,C_5H_5N\!:\!BCl_3 + C_5H_5N \quad (4\text{-}155)$$

It was proposed that the borate promoting role of the base in the disproportionation reaction was due to the negative charge that it created on the boron atom which would deter the shift of electrons from the alkyl group (LIX) and thus prevent carbonium ion formation and decomposition (4-156).[275] An intermolecular nucleophilic attack

$$R\text{—}O\text{—}\overset{-}{B}(Cl)_2 \longleftarrow :\overset{+}{N}C_5H_5$$

(LIX)

$$R\text{—}O\text{—}BCl_2 \rightarrow R^+ + \{O{=}B\text{—}Cl\} + Cl^- \rightarrow RCl + \tfrac{1}{3}\,B_2O_3 + \tfrac{1}{3}\,BCl_3 \quad (4\text{-}156)$$

on anionic boron (LX or LXI) was considered plausible and it was postulated as the probable mechanism of the first step of the disproportionation.[275]

$$C_5H_5N\!:\!BCl_2\text{—}\underset{R}{O}\!: \rightarrow \underset{OR}{B}Cl_2\!:\!NC_5H_5 \quad \text{or} \quad C_5H_5N\!:\!BCl_2(\!:\!OR)_2BCl_2\!:\!NC_5H_5$$

(LX) (LXI)

It is proposed that the reaction does not proceed through nucleophilic attack of a negatively charged boron atom, but rather that the

$$C_5H_5N\!:\!BCl_2\text{—}\underset{R}{O}\;\; (OR)BCl\text{—}Cl \rightarrow C_5H_5N\!:\!\overset{+}{B}Cl_2 + (RO)_2BCl + Cl^-$$

$$\rightarrow C_5H_5N\!:\!BCl_3 + (RO)_2BCl \quad (4\text{-}157)$$

pyridine complex attacks an uncomplexed molecule of alkoxyhaloborane. The negatively charged boron atom of the complex would increase its ability to donate an alkoxy group. The presence of an appreciable concentration of uncomplexed alkoxyhaloborane molecules in the reaction mixture, which presumably contains an equimolar amount of amine and borane, would depend upon dissociation of the complex under the conditions of the reaction. It is further proposed that the 3:2 stoichiometry of reaction (4-158), which has been employed with alkoxyfluoroboranes,[277] would be more conducive to borate formation with the alkoxychloroboranes than the 1:1 stoichiometry which has been used.

$$3\,ROBCl_2 + 2\,R'_3N \rightarrow (RO)_3B + 2\,R'_3N{:}BCl_3 \tag{4-158}$$

In the final analysis, since boron trichloride is more electrophilic than its alkoxy derivative, the ability of pyridine or other tertiary amines to displace the equilibrium (4-159) to the right cannot

$$3\,ROBCl_2 \rightleftarrows (RO)_3B + 2\,BCl_3 \xrightarrow{2\,C_5H_5N} 2\,C_5H_5N{:}BCl_3 \tag{4-159}$$

be overlooked, and all considerations involving pyridine complexes of the starting alkoxyhaloborane may be of secondary importance.

With the higher molecular weight homologs, the borate promoting effects of the amine can be replaced by other artifacts. Thus, a better yield of tri-2-chloroethoxyborane was obtained by heating chlorodi-(2-chloroethoxy)borane at 100–120° and one millimeter in the absence of base (82%) than with pyridine (26%).[143]

The necessity for performing the disproportionation at reduced pressure and temperature to minimize simultaneous decomposition to boric oxide and alkyl halide (see Section IV-H-2) subsequently has been demonstrated for the propyl, n-butyl and isobutyl dialkoxychloroboranes,[278] and for dichloro(octoxy)borane.[178] Thus, in certain cases mild reaction conditions are sufficient to effect the removal of boron trichloride and shift the equilibrium towards the production of ester without causing decomposition.[174]

b. *Aryloxyhaloboranes.* Aryloxydihaloboranes are generally more prone to undergo disproportionation than the alkoxy derivatives.[174] Dichlorophenoxyborane readily disproportionated to chlorodiphenoxyborane at 15° (4-160); however, the monochloroborane

$$2\,C_6H_5OBCl_2 \xrightarrow{15^\circ} (C_6H_5O)_2BCl + BCl_3 \tag{4-160}$$

had to be heated to 100° to yield ester (4-161).[111] Bromodiphenoxyborane yielded triphenoxyborane on heating at 200° at reduced pressure.[160]

$$3\,(C_6H_5O)_2BCl \xrightarrow{100^\circ} 2\,(C_6H_5O)_3B + BCl_3 \qquad (4\text{-}161)$$

The *o*-chloro, *o*-methyl and *p*-nitro derivatives of dichlorophenoxyborane were also easily disproportionated at room temperature to give the corresponding diaryl derivatives. As in the case of the parent diphenoxy compound, the diaryl derivatives required heating at 120–130° for conversion to the esters.[112]

Dichloro-*o*-nitrophenoxyborane, in contrast to the *para* derivative, exhibited a marked level of stability and could not be disproportionated even by prolonged heating. The stability was attributed to intramolecular coordination of the nitro oxygen and boron atom (LXII).[112] A similar interaction has been proposed to

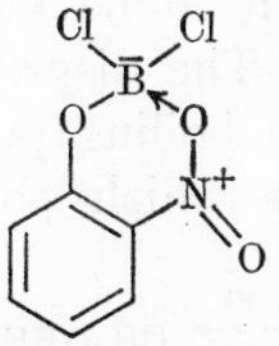

(LXII)

explain the abnormally low acidity of *o*-nitrobenzeneboronic acid.[45]

It is of interest that the disproportionation of the lower alkoxy and dialkoxyhaloboranes appears to be promoted by amines; whereas the normally facile disproportionation of dichloro(phenoxy)-borane is prevented by complex formation with pyridine.[111] Possibly the increased electrophilic character of the boron atom in the aromatic derivatives, as compared to the aliphatic derivatives, allows for the formation of a stronger complex with the amine. This complex does not dissociate on heating to give both complexed and uncomplexed molecules, which as stated earlier (4-157) may be the source of the apparent amine catalysis of the disproportionation reaction.

The relative order for ease of disproportionation, $C_6H_5OBCl_2 > ROBCl_2 > (C_6H_5O)_2BCl > (RO)_2BCl$, can be rationalized on the basis of the electrophilic character of the boron atom which either promotes or deters schemes (LXIII) and (LXIV). Since alkoxy or phenoxy groups contribute more electrons to boron than does chloro, the monochloro derivatives are more stable than their dichloro counterparts, and since an alkoxy group contributes more electrons to boron than the phenoxy group due to the $-M$ effect of the ring (LXV), the alkoxy compounds are more stable than the aryloxy compounds.

(LXIII) (LXIV)

(LXV)

c. *Alkoxyfluoroboranes.* Fluorodimethoxyborane, unlike chlorodimethoxyborane, was shown to be unstable with respect to its disproportionation products. The disproportionation, however, did not occur on heating to the boiling point (52.7°) but instead on cooling to $-30°$ (4-162), at which point difluoromethoxyborane

$$2\,(CH_3O)_2BF \underset{52.7°}{\overset{-30°}{\rightleftharpoons}} CH_3OBF_2 + B(OCH_3)_3 \qquad (4\text{-}162)$$
$$\updownarrow$$
$$\tfrac{1}{2}\,[CH_3OBF_2]_2$$

crystallized as a dimer (see Chapter 12).[196] Thus, the mobile equilibrium could be shifted by volatilizing the monofluoro derivative, or crystallizing the dimeric difluoro derivative.

The instability of di-n-butoxyfluoroborane on successive distillations was attributed to disproportionation to butoxydifluoroborane and tri-n-butoxyborane. Subsequent workers were unable to prepare the monofluoro compound by a variety of means, the difluoro derivative always resulting. They attributed this to the ready disproportionation of the monofluoro derivative. On the other hand, n-butoxydifluoroborane, which exists as the dimer, was inordinately stable and required heating at 120° for thirty hours to effect a 72% conversion to the borate.[277] The addition of pyridine allowed the

$$3\,[C_4H_9OBF_2]_2 \rightarrow 2\,(C_4H_9O)_3B + 4\,BF_3 \qquad (4\text{-}163)$$

reaction to proceed smoothly to 86% conversion at room temperature.[277]

$$3\,[C_4H_9OBF_2]_2 + 4\,C_5H_5N \rightarrow 2\,(C_4H_9O)_3B + 4\,C_5H_5N{:}BF_3 \qquad (4\text{-}164)$$

Dibutoxybutylborane has been reported to undergo redistribution with butoxydifluoroborane.[63] The ease of the reaction (23°) and yield (97%) preclude the possibility that the boronate was the

$$2\ C_4H_9B(OC_4H_9)_2 + C_4H_9OBF_2 \rightarrow B(OC_4H_9)_3 + C_4H_9BF(OC_4H_9) \qquad (4\text{-}165)$$

source of the tributoxyborane, since this transformation has been shown to be difficult.[323]

2. DECOMPOSITION

The disproportionation reactions of both the mono- and dialkoxyhaloboranes (see Section IV-H-1) afford borates with attendant conservation of both the number and kind of bonds in the starting materials. By contrast, decomposition reactions of the dialkoxyhaloboranes yield borates with attendant alkyl–oxygen cleavage and the production of bond types not present in the starting material.[2,176,184,278] In general decomposition takes place when the

$$3\ (RO)_2BCl \rightarrow (RO)_3B + B_2O_3 + 3\ RCl \qquad (4\text{-}166)$$

$$3\ (RO)_2BCl \rightarrow (RO)_3B + B_2O_3 + 3\ \text{olefin} + 3\ HCl \qquad (4\text{-}167)$$

dialkoxyhaloboranes are heated under reflux or in a sealed tube at greater than atmospheric pressure.[278]

a. *Factors Influencing Stability.* The stability of the dialkoxychloroboranes is a function of both the steric and electronic nature of the alkyl groups present as well as environmental factors such as the presence of Lewis acids (see Table 4-18). In the uncatalyzed decompositions, primary alkyl derivatives are generally more stable than secondary derivatives, which in turn are more stable than tertiary derivatives. Thus, at 20° the borane derived from *t*-butyl alcohol was 88% decomposed in one-third of an hour; whereas the *s*-butyl derivative required 72 hours for 37% decomposition, and the n-butyl derivative was completely intact after three weeks at that temperature. Similarly, the n-octyl derivative did not decompose at 20° for 504 hours; whereas the 2-octyl derivative was 26% decomposed after 42 hours at that temperature.[278] Within each group increased chain length is also a stabilizing factor. Thus, the order of stability for primary alkyls is n-octyl > n-butyl > n-propyl, and for straight chain secondary alkyls, 2-octyl > *s*-butyl.

Chain branching is also a stabilizing influence; neopentyl > i-butyl > n-butyl and methyl-*t*-butylcarbinyl > 2-octyl. Thus, within the primary and secondary series, steric factors are rate determining, whereas electronic factors control the relative reactivity of primary versus secondary versus tertiary alkyl derivatives.

Table 4-18. Decomposition of dialkoxychloroboranes

R in $(RO)_2BCl$	Temp. (°C)	Time (hr.)	Catalyst	% Decomposition	Reference
C_2H_5	150	1		1	2
	150	3		2	2
	150	5		6	2
$ClCH_2CH_2$	150	3		7	2
	150	5		8	2
	150	7		10	2
n-C_3H_7	20	504		0	278
	150	1		90	278
	150	2		95	278
$ClCH_2CH_2CH_2$	150	0.5		2	2
	150	1.5		2	2
	150	5		9	2
$CH_2{=}CHCH_2$	20	0.5		20	183
	100	4		77	183
n-C_4H_9	20	504		0	278
	20	1	HCl (saturated)	<2	278
	100	1		5	278
	100	3		23	278
	20	48	$FeCl_3$ (0.05%), $(C_2H_5)_2O$ (1 Mole)	34	278
	100	5		38	278
	150	1		62.5	278
	150	2		88	278
	20	48	$FeCl_3$ (0.05%), C_5H_{12} (1 mole)	93	278
	20	48	$FeCl_3$ (0.05%), n-C_4H_9Cl (1 mole)	94	278
	20	48	$FeCl_3$ (0.05%), (n-$C_4H_9O)_3B$ (1 mole)	98	278
	20	1 min.	$FeCl_3$ (0.05%)	98	278
$Cl(CH_2)_3CH_2$	100	0.25		5	2
	100	1		5	2
	100	5		9	2
	100	7.5		14	2
	100	12.5		22	2
	20	5 min.	$AlCl_3$ (2%)	99	278
$CH_2{=}CHCH_2CH_2$	20	22		<1	185
$CH_3CH{=}CHCH_2$	20	20		74–100	185
i-C_4H_9	20	504		0	278
	100	1		0	278
	100	3		1	278
	100	5		1.5	278
	150	1		3	278
	150	2		56	278
	0	0.43	<0.1% Lewis acid	58	176
	0	18	<0.1% Lewis acid	80	278

(Table continued)

Table 4-18—*continued*

R in $(RO)_2BCl$	Temp. (°C)	Time (hr.)	Catalyst	% Decomposition	Reference
$CH_2{=}C(CH_3)CH_2$	20	3		11	183
$s\text{-}C_4H_9$	20	0.33		0.5	278
	20	2.5		2	278
	20	22		13	278
	20	72		37	278
	20	2.5	BCl_3 (4%)	45	278
	20	23	BCl_3 (4%)	95	278
$CH_2{=}CHCH(CH_3)$	135	1		62	185
$t\text{-}C_4H_9$	20	0.33		88	278
$n\text{-}C_5H_{11}$	150	1		3	2
	150	2		6	2
	150	4		7	2
	150	6		20	2
$Cl(CH_2)_4CH_2$	100	7		6	2
	100	10		9	2
	150	1		14	2
	150	2		27	2
	150	4		64	2
	150	8		83	2
$(CH_3)_3CCH_2$	20	504		0	278
	150	5		0	278
	200	28		92	278
	20	1	$FeCl_3$ (2%)	96	278
$(CH_3)_3CCH(CH_3)$	20	144		0	278
	150	1		2	278
	150	2		35	278
	150	5		68	278
$n\text{-}C_8H_{17}$	20	504		0	278
	150	5		0	278
$n\text{-}C_6H_{13}CH(CH_3)$	20	72		1	278
	20	2.5	BCl_3 (4%)	25	278
	20	42		26	278
$(CH_3)_3CCH(CH_2)_5CH_3$	20	552	BCl_3 (4%)	55	278
	20	288	BCl_3 (4%)	95	278

The further influence of electronic factors was made evident by the isolation of rearranged alkyl halides in the isobutyl, neopentyl and methyl-*t*-butylcarbinyl systems. In two of the three cases

Table 4-19. Composition of alkyl halides from decomposition of β-branched dialkoxychloroboranes

R in $(RO)_2BCl$	% Halide	
	Unrearranged	Rearranged
$(CH_3)_2CHCH_2$	$(CH_3)_2CHCH_2Cl$, ~9	$(CH_3)_3CCl$, ~91
$(CH_3)_3CCH_2$	$(CH_3)_3CCH_2Cl$, 85	$(CH_3)_2C(Cl)CH_2CH_3$, 15
$(CH_3)_3C\overset{\vert}{C}HCH_3$	$(CH_3)_3CCH(Cl)CH_3$, 2	$(CH_3)_2C(Cl)CH(CH_3)_2$, 98

(Table 4-19) the tertiary halide resulting from a Wagner–Meerwin rearrangement (4-168 to 4-170) predominated.

$$CH_3\text{—}C(H)(CH_3)\text{—}CH_2^+ \rightleftarrows CH_3\text{—}\overset{+}{C}(CH_3)\text{—}CH_3 \qquad (4\text{-}168)$$

$$CH_3\text{—}C(CH_3)_2\text{—}CH_2^+ \rightleftarrows CH_3\overset{+}{C}(CH_3)CH_2CH_3 \qquad (4\text{-}169)$$

$$CH_3C(CH_3)_2\text{—}\overset{+}{C}H\text{—}CH_3 \rightleftarrows CH_3\text{—}\overset{+}{C}(CH_3)\text{—}CH(CH_3)CH_3 \qquad (4\text{-}170)$$

It is of further significance that the unrearranged borates were obtained in every case and that *d*-(+)-chlorodi-(2-octoxy)borane gave *l*-(−)-2-octyl chloride. Thus, at least two paths must be available to the alkyl groups, and the halide producing path must accommodate rearrangement and inversion of configuration.

b. *Mechanism.* The proposed mechanism[278] of the decomposition involves an initial rate determining heterolytic cleavage of the B–Cl bond (4-171). Such a reaction would be facilitated by the presence of Lewis acids (A in equations 4-171 and 4-172) which could

$$(\overrightarrow{R}\text{—}O)_2B\text{—}Cl\ A \rightleftarrows (RO)_2B^+ + ACl^- \qquad (4\text{-}171)$$

$$ACl^- \rightleftarrows A + Cl^- \qquad (4\text{-}172)$$

accept chloride and would be deterred by the presence of Lewis bases. This explains the marked catalytic activity of ferric chloride (Table 4-18). The cleavage would also be facilitated by electron repulsion of the alkyl groups, which would explain the observed tertiary, secondary, primary rate order,[278] the observations (Table 4-18) that the allyl derivative decomposed more easily than the n-propyl derivative and the 2-methallyl derivative more rapidly than the isobutyl derivative,[183] and the rate order $CH_3CH{=}CHCH_2 >$ $CH_2{=}CHCH_2CH_3 >$ n-C_4H_9.[185] The stabilizing influence of increased chain length and branching was thought to be due to steric repulsion of the catalyst (A).[278]

Introduction of ω-chloro substituents in the alkyl groups (Table 4-18) reversed the sterically controlled order of stability to that predicted by electronic control. Withdrawal of electrons due to the $-I$ effect of the halogen inhibited reaction (4-173), and the shorter the chain the more effective the withdrawal. Thus, the order of stability was $Cl(CH_2)_2 > Cl(CH_2)_3 > Cl(CH_2)_4 \approx Cl(CH_2)_5$.[2]

In further speculation on the mechanism,[278] the dialkoxyboronium ion of equation (4-171) could either collapse to metaborate and carbonium ion (4-173), which would account for the formation of rearranged alkyl halides (4-174), or undergo S_N2 attack by chloride to give inversion of configuration with retention of optical activity (4-175).

$$(R{-}O)_2B^+ \rightarrow \{R{-}O{-}B{=}O\} + R^+ \qquad (4\text{-}173)$$

$$R^+ + Cl^- \rightarrow RCl \qquad (4\text{-}174)$$

$$Cl^- \; \overset{|}{\underset{/\,\backslash}{C}}{-}O{-}\overset{+}{B}{-}OR \rightarrow Cl{-}\overset{|}{\underset{|}{C}}{-} + \{R{-}O{-}B{=}O\} \qquad (4\text{-}175)$$

Elimination of a proton from the carbonium ion or dehydrohalogenation of the alkyl chloride would account for the olefin and hydrogen chloride of reaction 4-167. A 35% yield of octene was found in the decomposition of chlorodi-(2-octoxy)borane.

The metaborates produced in reactions (4-173) and (4-175) could disproportionate (see Section IV-I-1) to yield the trialkoxyboranes (4-176), and since the alkyl groups of the metaborates did not at any time undergo alkyl–oxygen cleavage, the unrearranged esters would be produced.

$$3\{R{-}O{-}B{=}O\} \rightarrow (RO)_3B + B_2O_3 \qquad (4\text{-}176)$$

c. *2-Chloro-1,3,2-Dioxaborolanes and Borinanes.* The decomposition of 2-chloro-1,3,2-dioxaborolanes and borinanes affords a method of synthesis of tri-ω-chloroalkoxyboranes since cleavage of one of the carbon–oxygen bonds does not completely sever the alkylene moiety from the boron residue.[48]

$$3\ \begin{matrix} CH_2\text{—}O \\ | \\ CH_2\text{—}O \end{matrix}\!\!>\!B\text{—}Cl \xrightarrow[30\,\text{hr.}]{300^\circ} 3\,\{\overset{+}{C}H_2CH_2OB{=}O + Cl^-\} \rightarrow 3\,\{ClCH_2CH_2OB{=}O\} \rightarrow (ClCH_2CH_2O)_3B + B_2O_3 \qquad (4\text{-}177)$$

Thermal decomposition of (LXVI) at 100° led to the fully oxygenated products, (LXVII) and (LXVIII).[153] The reaction was

$$\underset{\text{(LXVI)}}{CH_2\!\!<\!\!\begin{matrix} CH_2\text{—}O \\ CH_2\text{—}O \end{matrix}\!\!>\!\!BCl} \qquad \underset{\text{(LXVII)}}{CH_2\!\!<\!\!\begin{matrix} CH_2\text{—}O \\ CH_2\text{—}O \end{matrix}\!\!>\!\!BO(CH_2)_3Cl} \qquad \underset{\text{(LXVIII)}}{[Cl(CH_2)_3O]_3B}$$

formulated, as previously proposed for the alicyclic case,[278] as involving an initial heterolytic carbon–oxygen cleavage and loss of chloride from boron (4-178). Subsequent reaction of the product metaborate with (LXVI) results in (LXVII) and boron oxychloride (4-179).

$$CH_2\!\!<\!\!\begin{matrix} CH_2\text{—}O \\ CH_2\text{—}O \end{matrix}\!\!>\!\!B\text{—}Cl \rightarrow \{ClCH_2CH_2CH_2OB{=}O\} \qquad (4\text{-}178)$$

$$\{ClCH_2CH_2CH_2OB{=}O\} + \underset{\text{(LXVI)}}{CH_2\!\!<\!\!\begin{matrix} CH_2\text{—}O \\ CH_2\text{—}O \end{matrix}\!\!>\!\!BCl} \rightarrow \underset{\text{(LXVII)}}{CH_2\!\!<\!\!\begin{matrix} CH_2\text{—}O \\ CH_2\text{—}O \end{matrix}\!\!>\!\!BO(CH_2)_3Cl} + \{O{=}BCl\} \qquad (4\text{-}179)$$

Decomposition of the O=B—Cl produces boron trichloride (4-180), which cleaves the ring in (LXVII) to yield (LXIX) and more

$$3\,\{O{=}B\text{—}Cl\} \rightarrow BCl_3 + B_2O_3 \qquad (4\text{-}180)$$

$$BCl_3 + \underset{\text{(LXVII)}}{CH_2\!\!<\!\!\begin{matrix} CH_2\text{—}O \\ CH_2\text{—}O \end{matrix}\!\!>\!\!BO(CH_2)_3Cl} \rightarrow \underset{\text{(LXIX)}}{[Cl(CH_2)_3O]_2BCl} + \{O{=}B\text{—}Cl\} \qquad (4\text{-}181)$$

O=B—Cl (4-181). Final reaction of (LXIX) with (LXVI) produces (LXVIII) and a third mole of O=B—Cl.

If (LXVII) indeed is formed by reaction (4-179) or by some other path, then there seems to be no need for speculating as to the feasibility of reaction (4-181) since (LXVIII) could form simply from the disproportionation of (LXVII).

d. *Aryloxyhaloboranes.* Diaryloxychloroboranes do not undergo decomposition to yield triaryloxyboranes. This has been attributed to the difficulty of nucleophilic aromatic substitution (4-175).[174]

3. ALCOHOLYSIS

The alcoholysis of the alkoxyhaloboranes proceeds in a manner exactly analogous to the complete alcoholysis of boron trichloride itself[505] (see Section IV-G-1).

$$ROBCl_2 + ROH \rightarrow (RO)_3B + 2\ HCl \qquad (4\text{-}182)$$

$$(RO)_2BCl + ROH \rightarrow (RO)_3B + HCl \qquad (4\text{-}183)$$

Sodium methoxide (4-184 and 4-185)[142,168] and sodium tetramethoxyborate in ether solvents (4-186)[142] have also served as the source of alkoxide.

$$CH_3OBF_2 + 2\ NaOCH_3 \rightarrow B(OCH_3)_3 + 2\ NaF \qquad (4\text{-}184)$$

$$(CH_3O)_2BCl + NaOCH_3 \rightarrow B(OCH_3)_3 + NaCl \qquad (4\text{-}185)$$

$$(CH_3O)_2BCl + NaB(OCH_3)_4 \rightarrow 2\ B(OCH_3)_3 + NaCl \qquad (4\text{-}186)$$

4. REDUCTION

Chlorodimethoxyborane reacts with sodium borohydride in diglyme solution to give diborane and trimethoxyborane (4-187). The products are suggestive of the reduction of boron trichloride (4-188) and indicate that the initial reaction may be a disproportionation (4-189).[80]

$$3\ (CH_3O)_2BCl + 3\ NaBH_4 \rightarrow 2\ B_2H_6 + 2\ (CH_3O)_3B + 3\ NaCl \qquad (4\text{-}187)$$

$$BCl_3 + 3\ NaBH_4 \rightarrow 2\ B_2H_6 + 3\ NaCl \qquad (4\text{-}188)$$

$$3\ (CH_3O)_2BCl \rightarrow 2\ (CH_3O)_3B + BCl_3 \qquad (4\text{-}189)$$

5. REACTION WITH CARBOXYLIC ACIDS

Tributoxyborane was isolated in 80 to 90% yields from treatment of the n-butoxychloroboranes with acetic acid in pentane solution.[182]

The reactions were formulated as preceding via unstable intermediate acetoxybutoxyboranes.

$$6\,(C_4H_9O)_2BCl + 6\,CH_3\overset{O}{\overset{\|}{C}}OH \xrightarrow{-6\,HCl} 6\left\{CH_3\overset{O}{\overset{\|}{C}}OB(OC_4H_9)_2\right\}$$

$$\rightarrow 4\,B(OC_4H_9)_3 + \left[(CH_3\overset{O}{\overset{\|}{C}}O)_2B\right]_2O \quad (4\text{-}190)$$

$$3\,C_4H_9OBCl_2 + 6\,CH_3\overset{O}{\overset{\|}{C}}OH \xrightarrow{-6\,HCl} 3\left\{(CH_3\overset{O}{\overset{\|}{C}}O)_2BOC_4H_9\right\}$$

$$\rightarrow B(OC_4H_9)_3 + \left[(CH_3\overset{O}{\overset{\|}{C}}O)_2B\right]_2O + (CH_3\overset{O}{\overset{\|}{C}})_2O \quad (4\text{-}191)$$

I. From Trialkoxyboroxines

1. DISPROPORTIONATION

Trialkoxyboroxines, which can be prepared by the reaction of trialkoxyboranes and boric oxide, are reconverted to their starting materials when heated at about 100° above the boiling point of the orthoborate. The reaction (4-192), first used for the preparation of triethoxyborane,[403] subsequently was applied to trimethoxyborane,[191,194] tributoxyborane[355] and a series of primary and secondary trialkoxyboranes and triphenoxyborane.[279]

$$(ROBO)_3 \text{ [boroxine ring: } RO{-}B\langle O{-}B(OR){-}O\rangle B{-}OR] \rightarrow (RO)_3B + B_2O_3 \quad (4\text{-}192)$$

The orthoborate must be removed from the system as it is formed in order to effect any overall change, as evidenced by the fact that tributoxyboroxine was unchanged after refluxing at 290° for six hours.[279]

Attempts to cause trimethoxyboroxine to react with aluminum chloride or phosphorus pentachloride by heating under reduced pressure evidently resulted in disproportionation since trimethoxyborane was the major product.[241]

Schiff[402] formulated the reaction of triethoxyboroxine with aniline to give triethoxyborane and an aniline–boric oxide complex

(4-193). Subsequent work with pyridine and other amines indicated the by-product complex (LXX) retained some alkoxy residues.[280]

$$(C_2H_5OBO)_3 + C_6H_5NH_2 \rightarrow B(OC_2H_5)_3 + C_6H_5NH_2{:}B_2O_3 \qquad (4\text{-}193)$$

$$\tfrac{4}{3}\,(C_4H_9OBO)_3 + C_5H_5N \xrightarrow{20^\circ} B(OC_4H_9)_3 + \underset{\text{(LXX)}}{[C_4H_9O(NC_5H_5)B_3O_4]} \text{ or equivalent polymer} \qquad (4\text{-}194)$$

The amine complexes are not surprising since the thermal disproportionation of metaborates to give orthoborates and boric oxide must necessarily pass through intermediates containing an increasing ratio of boron atoms to alkoxy residues. Any amine present would be expected to complex at some stage. However, the temperature at which the reaction proceeds (20°) is difficult to rationalize in view of the elevated temperatures ordinarily necessary for thermal decomposition. The sequence (4-194) is thus undoubtedly catalyzed by amines and can be formulated in a manner similar to that proposed for the basic catalysis of the disproportionation of alkoxyhaloboranes (see Section IV-H-1).

$$C_5H_5N\cdot(ROBO)_3 + (ROBO)_3 \longrightarrow C_5H_5N\rightarrow \overset{+}{B}(RO)_2B_2O_3 + (RO)_2B\text{–}\bar{O}\text{–}B_2O_2(OR)_2$$

$$\longrightarrow C_5H_5N \rightarrow B[(ROBO)_2](OB)_2O(OR)_2 \qquad (4\text{-}195)$$

2. ALCOHOLYSIS

Schiff first reported the conversion of triethoxyboroxine to triethoxy borane by reaction with alcohol[402,403] or potassium

$$(C_2H_5OBO)_3 + 3\,C_2H_5OH \rightarrow 2\,B(OC_2H_5)_3 + H_3BO_3 \qquad (4\text{-}196)$$

$$2\,(C_2H_5OBO)_3 + 3\,C_2H_5OK \rightarrow 3\,(BOC_2H_5)_3 + 3\,KBO_2 \qquad (4\text{-}197)$$

ethoxide.[402] The amyl derivative behaved similarly with amyl alcohol as did tributoxyboroxine and butanol.[280] Reaction of triethoxy-

$$(C_2H_5OBO)_3 + 3\,C_5H_{11}OH \rightarrow (C_2H_5O)_3B + (C_5H_{11}O)_3B + H_3BO_3 \qquad (4\text{-}198)$$

boroxine and amyl alcohol produced both orthoborates.[402]

3. PARTIAL HYDROLYSIS

Partial hydrolysis of tributoxyboroxine in ether solution has resulted in tributoxyborane.[280]

$$(C_4H_9OBO)_3 + 3\,H_2O \rightarrow B(OC_4H_9)_3 + 2\,H_3BO_3 \qquad (4\text{-}199)$$

4. REACTION WITH SODIUM HYDRIDE

Treatment of trimethoxyboroxine with sodium hydride is a convenient preparative method for diborane.[473] Trimethoxyborane is the co-product. Presumably the reaction proceeds via a dimethoxyborane intermediate which disproportionates to give the observed

$$(CH_3OBO)_3 + NaH \rightarrow \{(CH_3O)_2BH\} + CH_3ONa + B_2O_3 \qquad (4\text{-}200)$$
$$\{(CH_3O)_2BH\} \downarrow \tfrac{2}{3}\,(CH_3O)_3B + \tfrac{1}{6}\,B_2H_6$$

products. The reaction has also been formulated as in equation (4-201).[92]

$$10\,(CH_3OBO)_3 + 6\,NaH \rightarrow 6\,(CH_3O)_3B + 6\,(CH_3O)_2BH + 3\,Na_2B_6O_{10} \qquad (4\text{-}201)$$

5. REACTION WITH SODIUM BOROHYDRIDE

The reactions of trimethoxyboroxine with varying amounts of sodium borohydride have been formulated as in equations (4-202) to (4-204).[92]

$$2\,(CH_3OBO)_3 + 3\,NaBH_4 \rightarrow 6\,(CH_3O)_3B + 12\,(CH_3O)_2BH + 3\,NaBO_2 \qquad (4\text{-}202)$$

$$7\,(CH_3OBO)_3 + 6\,NaBH_4 \rightarrow 9\,(CH_3O)_3B + 24\,(CH_3O)_2BH + 3\,Na_2B_4O_7 \qquad (4\text{-}203)$$

$$10\,(CH_3OBO)_3 + 6\,NaBH_4 \rightarrow 6\,(CH_3O)_3B + 24\,(CH_3O)_2BH + 3\,Na_2B_6O_{10} \qquad (4\text{-}204)$$

6. REACTION WITH SODIUM TRIMETHOXYHYDROBORATE

Di- and trimethoxyborane have been recorded as the products of the reaction of trimethoxyboroxine and sodium trimethoxyhydroborate.[92]

$$10\,(CH_3OBO)_3 + 6\,NaBH(OCH_3)_3 \rightarrow 6\,(CH_3O)_2BH + 12\,(CH_3O)_3B + 3\,Na_2B_6O_{10} \qquad (4\text{-}205)$$

J. From Hydridic Compounds

1. ALKOXYBORANES

a. *Disproportionation.* Dialkoxyboranes disproportionate reversibly above 0° to give diborane and the corresponding trialkoxy-

$$6\,(RO)_2BH \rightleftarrows B_2H_6 + 4\,(RO)_3B \tag{4-206}$$

boranes.[78,88,285,454,515] Intermediate monoalkoxyboranes or alkoxydiboranes could not be isolated.[88]

The rate of decomposition of dimethoxyborane in the gas phase is comparatively low; however, the decomposition is very rapid in the liquid state at temperatures above 0°.[88,284] The heat of disproportionation of dimethoxyborane is -16.8 kcal/mole for the liquid phase reaction and -20.5 kcal/mole for the vapor phase reaction.[115]

The rate of disproportionation in the gas phase was found to be surface dependent,[475] and in contrast to earlier statements of pressure independence,[88] was shown to be proportional to the square of the partial pressure of dimethoxyborane.

A proposed mechanism of disproportionation involved adsorption of the alkoxyborane on a surface followed by formation of a four-centered transition state and exchange of methoxyl for hydrogen.[475]

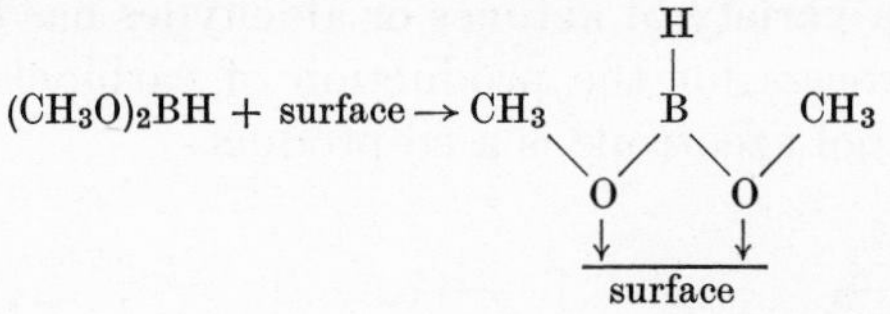

$(CH_3O)_2BH$ + surface → [H–B bonded to two O atoms, each O bearing CH_3 and coordinated (↓) to the surface] (4-207)

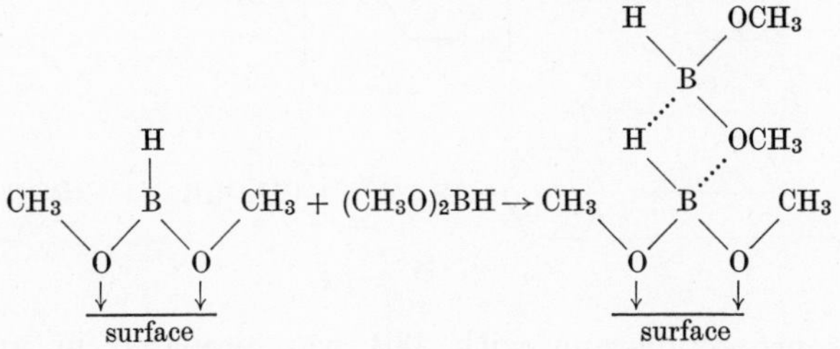

[CH_3–O and O–CH_3 groups on B–H, both O ↓ surface] + $(CH_3O)_2BH$ → [surface-bound CH_3O–B(H)–OCH_3 with the H····B(H)(OCH_3) and OCH_3····B four-centered interaction: H, OCH_3 on upper B; H, OCH_3 bridging; CH_3, B, CH_3; O, O ↓ surface] (4-208)

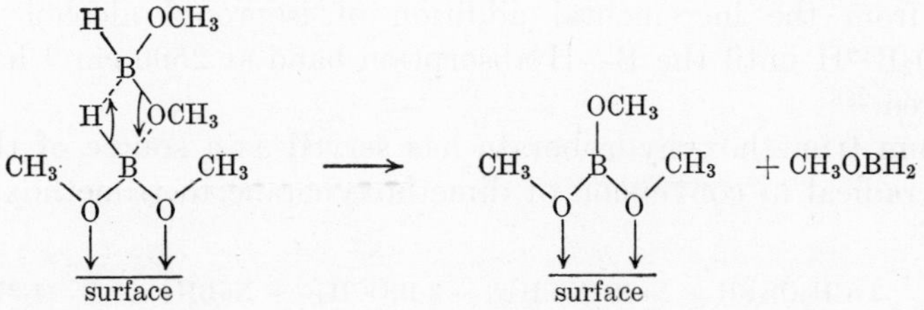

[four-centered transition state: H, OCH_3 on upper B; H↑ ↓OCH_3 exchanging; CH_3–O–B–O–CH_3, O ↓ surface] ⟶ [OCH_3 on B; CH_3–O–B–O–CH_3, O ↓ surface] + CH_3OBH_2 (4-209)

$$CH_3OBH_2 + CH_3 \overset{H}{\underset{|}{}} B \; CH_3 \rightarrow \text{etc.} \quad \text{(O, O} \downarrow \text{surface)} \qquad (4\text{-}210)$$

Polymeric monomethoxyborane decomposes on standing at room temperature to give diborane, dimethoxyborane, and trimethoxyborane.[88]

$$7\,(CH_3OBH_2)_n \rightarrow 2n\,B_2H_6 + 2n\,(CH_3O)_2BH + n\,(CH_3O)_3B \qquad (4\text{-}211)$$

b. *Alcoholysis.* The dialkoxyboranes derived from the lower primary and secondary alcohols are readily converted to trialkoxyboranes on treatment with a third mole of alcohol.[78,287,288,427,475,526]

$$(RO)_2BH + ROH \rightarrow (RO)_3B + H_2 \qquad (4\text{-}212)$$

With dialkoxyboranes derived from tertiary alcohols, extended heating under reflux is required to replace the hydrogen with a third mole of alcohol.[76]

Methanolysis of the alkoxyboranes derived from the reaction of diborane and a variety of ketones or aldehydes has been patented as a synthetic process for the production of carbinols.[71] Trimethoxyborane–methanol azeotrope is a co-product.

$$B_2H_6 + C_6H_{10}{=}O \longrightarrow [C_6H_{11}{-}O]_2BH \xrightarrow{CH_3OH} C_6H_{11}{-}OH + [(CH_3O)_3B + CH_3OH] + H_2 \qquad (4\text{-}213)$$

Triisopropoxyborane with ^{10}B was prepared in an infrared gas cell from the incremental addition of isopropyl alcohol to $(i\text{-}C_3H_7O)_2B^{10}H$ until the B—H absorption band at 2500 cm^{-1} had disappeared.[288]

Sodium trimethoxyhydroborate has served as a source of the methoxy radical in conversion of dimethoxyborane to trimethoxyborane.[413]

$$3\,(CH_3O)_2BH + NaBH(OCH_3)_3 \rightarrow 3\,B(OCH_3)_3 + NaBH_4 \qquad (4\text{-}214)$$

2. ALCOHOLYSIS OF BORON HYDRIDES

a. *Diborane and Borane Complexes.* The methanolysis of a large excess of diborane has yielded some trimethoxyborane in addition to the desired dimethoxyborane.[88]

$$\text{(excess) } B_2H_6 + CH_3OH \rightarrow B(OCH_3)_3 + (CH_3O)_2BH + \text{white solid} \quad (4\text{-}215)$$

The gas phase ethanolysis of diborane has been followed in an infrared cell. No absorption bands appeared that could not be ascribed to either diethoxyborane or triethoxyborane. The absence of detectable amounts of monoethoxyborane was ascribed to its formation being the rate determining step.[287,427] Of further significance is the fact that triethoxyborane was not formed in any appreciable quantity until all the diborane had been converted to diethoxyborane, and thus the transfer of ethoxy through the bridge, as shown in (LXXI), is a slow process.

$$\begin{array}{ccccc} H & & H & & OC_2H_5 \\ & B & \rightleftarrows & B & \\ C_2H_5O & & OC_2H_5 & & OC_2H_5 \end{array}$$

(LXXI)

The reaction of β-dimethylaminoethanol with excess diborane led to both ester formation and complexing of the amino groups with borane radicals.[342]

$$3\,(CH_3)_2NCH_2CH_2OH + 2\,B_2H_6 \rightarrow \left[\begin{array}{c} BH_3 \\ (CH_3)_2\ddot{N}CH_2CH_2O \end{array}\right]_3 B + 3\,H_2 \quad (4\text{-}216)$$

Metal alkoxides also have served as the source of the alkoxyl group. The preparation of sodium,[407,435] lithium (4-217),[435] alkaline earth (4-218),[498] and rare earth[524] borohydrides (4-219) from the appropriate metal alkoxide and diborane has given a variety of esters as by-products. Similarly amine–borane complexes have been

$$3\,MOR + 2\,B_2H_6 \rightarrow B(OR)_3 + 3\,MBH_4 \quad (4\text{-}217)$$

$$3\,M(OR)_2 + 4\,B_2H_6 \rightarrow 2\,B(OR)_3 + 3\,M(BH_4)_2 \quad (4\text{-}218)$$

$$M(OR)_3 + 2\,B_2H_6 \rightarrow B(OR)_3 + M(BH_4)_3 \quad (4\text{-}219)$$

converted to the corresponding borohydride and ester (4-220 and 4-221).[250] The reaction with aluminum isopropoxide is reported to

$$3\,MOR + 4\,R_3N{:}BH_3 \rightarrow B(OR)_3 + 3\,MBH_4 + 4\,R_3N \quad (4\text{-}220)$$

$$M(OR)_2 + 8\,R_3N{:}BH_3 \rightarrow 2\,B(OR)_3 + 3\,M(BH_4)_2 + 8\,R_3N \quad (4\text{-}221)$$

yield a complex aluminum borohydride as well as triisopropoxyborane (4-222).[247]

$$4\,(i\text{-}C_3H_7O)_3Al + 2\,B_2H_6 \rightarrow (i\text{-}C_3H_7O)_3B + AlH_3\cdot(BH_3)_3\cdot 3(i\text{-}C_3H_7O)_3Al \quad (4\text{-}222)$$

b. *Higher Boron Hydrides.* The higher boron hydrides have also been alcoholyzed to yield esters. Tetraborane with a deficient proportion of ethanol at $-78°$ gave triethoxyborane (4-223).[89] Pentaborane with a stoichiometric amount of methanol at $-30°$ was essentially completely converted to trimethoxyborane,[415] and with ethanol or butanol at 10° gave 85 to 95% yields of the corresponding trialkoxyboranes (4-225).[526] Decaborane was similarly converted in good yield to a variety of primary, secondary and tertiary alkyl borates (4-226).[35] Methanolysis of a substituted decaborane (4-227) and a nonaborane derivative (4-228) have also been recorded.[202]

$$B_4H_{10} + 4.3\ C_2H_5OH \rightarrow 0.88\ (C_2H_5O)_3B + 0.61\ (C_2H_5O)_2BH + 2.45\ B_2H_6 + 4.1\ H_2 + 2.4\ (BH)_x \quad (4\text{-}223)$$

$$B_4H_{10} + 12\ C_2H_5OH \rightarrow 4\ B(OC_2H_5)_3 + 11\ H_2 \quad (4\text{-}224)$$

$$B_5H_9 + 15\ ROH \rightarrow 5\ B(OR)_3 + 12\ H_2 \quad (4\text{-}225)$$

$$B_{10}H_{14} + 30\ ROH \rightarrow 10\ B(OR)_3 + 22\ H_2 \quad (4\text{-}226)$$

$$[(C_2H_5)_2S]_2B_{10}H_{12} + 3\ CH_3OH \rightarrow (CH_3O)_3B + (C_2H_5)_2SB_9H_{13} + H_2 + (C_2H_5)_2S \quad (4\text{-}227)$$

$$(CH_3)_4NB_9H_{12} + 18\ CH_3OH \rightarrow 6\ (CH_3O)_3B + (CH_3)_4NB_3H_8 + 11\ H_2 \quad (4\text{-}228)$$

The ethanolysis of tetraborane or pentaborane with an amount of alcohol considerably less than that called for in equations (4-224) and (4-225) still led to an appreciable amount of triethoxyborane. The observed formation of triethoxyborane in addition to diethoxyborane under conditions of excess tetraborane or pentaborane is significant, since reactions involving diborane, which does not have a B–B bond, do not yield triethoxyborane until all of the diborane has been converted to diethoxyborane. Thus, the triethoxyborane can be accounted for as a direct consequence of the rupture of the B–B bonds in tetraborane and pentaborane, and the addition of one molecule of ethanol to a compound such as diboron tetraethoxide would result in formation of one molecule of triethoxyborane and one molecule of diethoxyborane.[427]

$$B_4H_{10} + 8\ ROH \rightarrow 2\ (RO)_2BH + (RO)_2B\text{—}B(OR)_2 + 8\ H_2 \quad (4\text{-}229)$$

$$(RO)_2B\text{—}B(OR)_2 + ROH \rightarrow (RO)_3B + (RO)_2BH \quad (4\text{-}230)$$

A twofold difference in the rate of alcoholysis of tetraborane with ROH and ROD indicated the cleavage of the oxygen–hydrogen bond to be rate determining (4-231). In general, the reaction was

$$\underset{|}{\overset{|}{B}}\!-\!\underset{\underset{H}{|}}{\overset{|}{B}} + ROH \xrightarrow{\text{Fast}} \underset{|}{\overset{|}{B}}\!-\!\underset{\underset{H}{|}}{\overset{|}{B}}\!:\!\underset{\underset{H}{|}}{O}\!-\!R \xrightarrow{\text{Slow}} \underset{|}{\overset{|}{B}}\!-\!\overset{|}{B}\!-\!OR + H_2 \qquad (4\text{-}231)$$

inhibited by electron withdrawal of the alkyl group except in the case of the β-haloethanols which had the order F > Cl > Br > I.[36]

The mechanism of the alcoholysis of pentaborane has been postulated to involve an initial stepwise extraction of two borane groups with the residual fragment losing its remaining hydrides, followed by breaking of the boron–boron bonds. In this last step, hydrides are created from the alcoholic protons. Concurrently, approximately one-third of the trialkoxyborane is formed without passing through the dialkoxyborane intermediate.[426]

c. *Metal Borohydrides.* Alcoholysis of sodium borohydride with a large excess of alcohol in the presence of an equivalent of acetic acid has been shown to be a convenient general procedure for the synthesis of primary, secondary and tertiary alkyl borates.[76] The reaction is formulated as proceeding through the liberation of borane (4-232), since isopropyl and *t*-butyl alcohol do not react with sodium borohydride in the absence of acetic acid even upon prolonged reflux.[77]

$$NaBH_4 + H^+ \rightarrow Na^+ + H_2 + \{BH_3\} \qquad (4\text{-}232)$$

$$2\,ROH + \{BH_3\} \rightarrow (RO)_2BH + 2\,H_2 \qquad (4\text{-}233)$$

$$ROH + (RO)_2BH \rightarrow (RO)_3B + H_2 \qquad (4\text{-}234)$$

In the case of the *t*-butyl and *t*-amyl alcohols, the reaction stopped at the di-*t*-alkoxyborane stage (4-233), with the last hydrogen atom undergoing replacement (4-234) only at higher temperature.[76]

Indium borohydride evidently undergoes an analogous reaction in methanolic hydrochloric acid.[500]

$$In[BH_4]_3 + 12\,CH_3OH \xrightarrow{H^+} In(OCH_3)_3 + 3\,B(OCH_3)_3 + 12\,H_2 \qquad (4\text{-}235)$$

3. Reaction of Diborane and Tetrahydrofurans

The sealed tube reaction of diborane and tetrahydrofuran at 60° for sixty-four hours led to a 61% yield of tri-n-butoxyborane. 1-Methyltetrahydrofuran reacted similarly. Reactions performed at room temperature required about sixteen weeks for completion.[246]

The relative unreactivity at room temperature would account for the fairly general use of tetrahydrofuran as a solvent for diborane reactions.

$$6\ \begin{matrix} CH_2\text{—}CH_2 \\ |\quad\quad | \\ CH_2\quad CH_2 \\ \diagdown\ \diagup \\ O \end{matrix} + B_2H_6 \rightarrow 2\ (n\text{-}C_4H_9O)_3B \qquad (4\text{-}236)$$

4. REACTION OF DIBORANE AND SODIUM TRIMETHOXYHYDROBORATE OR SODIUM TETRAMETHOXYBORATE

The reaction of diborane with sodium trimethoxyhydroborate involves the net exchange of hydride and methoxy groups.[410]

$$B_2H_6 + 2\ NaBH(OCH_3)_3 \rightarrow 2\ B(OCH_3)_3 + 2\ NaBH_4 \qquad (4\text{-}237)$$

Sodium,[408,410,413] lithium[408,413] and potassium[408,413] tetramethoxyborate reacted similarly (4-238), as did the alkaline earth salts (4-239).[501]

$$2\ B_2H_6 + 3\ MB(OCH_3)_4 \rightarrow 4\ B(OCH_3)_3 + 3\ MBH_4 \qquad (4\text{-}238)$$

$$4\ B_2H_6 + 3\ M[B(OR)_4]_2 \rightarrow 8\ B(OR)_3 + 3\ M(BH_4)_2 \qquad (4\text{-}239)$$

5. REACTIONS OF BORON HYDRIDES AND KETONES

The reduction of *p*-benzoquinone with ethylamine–borane in ether solution resulted in the amine complex of tri-*p*-hydroxy-

$$3\ O{=}C_6H_4{=}O + CH_3CH_2NH_2{:}BH_3 \rightarrow \left[HO\text{—}C_6H_4\text{—}O\right]_3 B{:}NH_2CH_2CH_3 \qquad (4\text{-}240)$$

phenoxyborane.[351] Similarly, triisopropoxyborane has been produced from the reaction of pentaborane-9 and acetone.[288,526]

6. SODIUM TRIALKOXYHYDROBORATES

The thermal decompositions of sodium trimethoxyhydroborate[406,410,411,413] and sodium triethoxyhydroborate[411] have led to the corresponding trialkoxyboranes. Reaction (4-241) does not go to com-

$$4\ NaBH(OCH_3)_3 \xrightarrow{230^\circ} 3\ B(OCH_3)_3 + NaBH_4 + 3\ NaOCH_3 \qquad (4\text{-}241)$$

pletion unless the trimethoxyborane is removed, and even then some dimethoxyborane is obtained.[411]

Treatment of sodium trimethoxyhydroborate with carbon dioxide has served to liberate trimethoxyborane.[79]

$$NaBH(OCH_3)_3 + CO_2 \rightarrow HCO_2Na + B(OCH_3)_3 \qquad (4\text{-}242)$$

7. HYDROXYLAMINE–BORANE COMPLEXES

Pyrolytic decomposition of the borane complexes of *O,N*-dimethyl(LXXII) and *O,N,N*-trimethylhydroxylamine (LXXIII) have yielded trimethoxyborane.[46]

$$\underset{\text{(LXXII)}}{CH_3ONHCH_3{:}BH_3} \qquad \underset{\text{(LXXIII)}}{CH_3ON(CH_3)_2{:}BH_3}$$

The proposed mechanism for the decomposition of *O,N*-dimethylhydroxylamine involved the initial intermolecular splitting out of hydrogen from nitrogen and boron followed by rapid shift of methoxy from nitrogen to boron.

$$CH_3ONHCH_3{:}BH_3 + CH_3O{-}N(H)(CH_3){:}BH_3 \rightarrow CH_3ONHCH_3{:}BH_2(OCH_3) + H_2 + \{CH_3\ddot{N}{:}BH_3\} \rightarrow CH_3NHBH_2 \qquad (4\text{-}243)$$

The decomposition of *O,N,N*-trimethylhydroxylamine was considered to involve an initial borane–oxygen complex which decomposed to amine and methoxyborane. Disproportionation of the methoxyborane gave the observed products.

$$(CH_3)_2N{-}O(CH_3){:}BH_3 \rightarrow (CH_3)_2NH + \{CH_3OBH_2\} \rightarrow \tfrac{1}{3}\,(CH_3O)_3B + \tfrac{1}{3}\,B_2H_6 \qquad (4\text{-}244)$$

K. From Tetraalkoxyborates

The pyrolysis of tetraalkoxyborate salts results in the reverse of the reaction of their preparation (4-245) (see Chapter 14). Thus, tri-

$$[(RO)_4B]M \rightleftarrows B(OR)_3 + MOR \qquad (4\text{-}245)$$

methoxyborane was obtained by heating lithium[405] or sodium[124] tetramethoxyborate in excess of 250° at reduced pressure. The lithium salt was recommended due to the higher vapor pressure of trimethoxyborane in equilibrium with it (Table 4-20).[124]

The alkaline earth tetramethoxyborates[496] and tetraethoxyborates[497] were found to be even less stable and gave 45–90% yields

Table 4-20. Vapor pressure of trimethoxyborane over lithium and sodium tetramethoxyborate

	Vapor pressure (mm.)	
Temp. (°C)	$[(CH_3O)_4B]Li$	$[(CH_3O)_4B]Na$
230	25.5	
250	63.5	3
260	96.5	
280		13
290		19
300		27

of decomposition products (4-246) on heating at 145 to 265° under high vacuum for ten to twenty minutes.[496]

$$[(RO)_4B]_2M \rightarrow 2\ B(OR)_3 + M(OR)_2 \tag{4-246}$$

Lower trialkoxyboranes have been prepared by carbonating an alcoholic solution of an alkali or alkaline earth tetraalkoxyborate.[7,126,127]

$$[(RO)_4B]M + CO_2 \rightarrow B(OR)_3 + MRCO_3 \tag{4-247}$$

L. From Boron–Carbon Compounds

1. DISPROPORTIONATION

In general, the esters of boronic acids are thermally stable. However, a few cases of disproportionation to trialkoxyboranes and trialkylboranes on heating to greater than 150° have been reported.[322,323]

$$3\ RB(OR)_2 \rightarrow 2\ (RO)_3B + R_3B \tag{4-248}$$

In addition, dimethoxy(phenyl)borane has given rise to trimethoxyborane on heating at 200° for one hundred hours.[3]

$$2\ C_6H_5B(OCH_3)_2 \rightarrow (CH_3O)_3B + (C_6H_5)_2BOCH_3 \tag{4-249}$$

The disproportionation is greatly facilitated by the introduction of boron trifluoride, thereby allowing substitution of the more facile halide–alkoxy transfers for the difficult alkyl–alkoxy transfer.[63]

$$3\ C_4H_9B(OC_4H_9)_2 + BF_3 \xrightarrow[2\ \text{hr.}]{20°} B(OC_4H_9)_3 + 3\ C_4H_9BF(OC_4H_9) \tag{4-250}$$

Borinates disproportionate with equal difficulty and only one case has been recorded. The ethyl ester of diphenylborinic acid underwent both disproportionation and decomposition on heating to 200° for a prolonged period.[3]

$$(C_6H_5)_2BOC_2H_5 \xrightarrow[100\ \text{hr.}]{200°} (C_2H_5O)_3B + C_6H_5B(OC_2H_5)_2 + C_6H_6 + (C_6H_5)_3B \qquad (4\text{-}251)$$

2. REACTION WITH DIBORANE

Alkoxy(diaryl)boranes (4-252) and dialkoxy(aryl)boranes (4-253) react with diborane in ether solution at room temperature to produce symmetrical diaryldiboranes and trialkoxyboranes.[339]

$$3\ Ar_2BOR + 2\ B_2H_6 \rightarrow 3\ (ArBH_2)_2 + (RO)_3B \qquad (4\text{-}252)$$

$$6\ ArB(OR)_2 + 2\ B_2H_6 \rightarrow 3\ (ArBH_2)_2 + 4\ (RO)_3B \qquad (4\text{-}253)$$

Reaction (4-252) was believed to proceed via an initial alkoxy–hydrogen exchange (4-254) followed by reaction of the diarylborane with diborane (4-255) and disproportionation of the alkoxyborane (4-256).

$$Ar_2BOR + \{BH_3\} \rightarrow Ar_2BH + ROBH_2 \qquad (4\text{-}254)$$

$$Ar_2BH + \{BH_3\} \rightarrow [ArBH_2]_2 \qquad (4\text{-}255)$$

$$3\ ROBH_2 \rightarrow (RO)_3B + B_2H_6 \qquad (4\text{-}256)$$

The sequence (4-257) to (4-260) was proposed for the path of reaction (4-253).

$$ArB(OR)_2 + \{BH_3\} \rightarrow ArBH(OR) + ROBH_2 \qquad (4\text{-}257)$$

$$2\ ArBH(OR) \rightarrow ArBH_2 + ArB(OR)_2 \qquad (4\text{-}258)$$

$$2\ ArBH_2 \rightarrow [ArBH_2]_2 \qquad (4\text{-}259)$$

$$3\ ROBH_2 \rightarrow (RO)_3B + B_2H_6 \qquad (4\text{-}260)$$

3. ALCOHOLYSIS

Aromatic boron–carbon compounds are particularly susceptible to electrophilic displacement of the boron residue (4-261). With tri-α-

$$C_6H_5\text{–}B{<}\ \cdots\ H\text{–}A \longrightarrow C_6H_5\text{–}H + A\text{–}B{<} \qquad (4\text{-}261)$$

naphthylborane and methanol, the reaction proceeds all the way to trimethoxyborane.[388]

$$(\alpha\text{-}C_{10}H_7)_3B + 4\ CH_3OH \xrightarrow{\text{Heat}} [(CH_3O)_3B + CH_3OH] + 3\ C_{10}H_8 \qquad (4\text{-}262)$$

A series of alkyl esters of diphenylborinic acid were similarly converted (4-263). A mixture of borates was obtained when the alkyl

$$(C_6H_5)_2BOR + 2\,ROH \xrightarrow{200^\circ} (RO)_3B + 2\,C_6H_6 \qquad (4\text{-}263)$$

group of the ester and alcohol were different (4-264).[3]

$$(C_6H_5)_2BOR + 2\,R'OH \xrightarrow{200^\circ} \tfrac{1}{3}\,(RO)_3B + \tfrac{2}{3}\,(R'O)_3B + 2\,C_6H_6 \qquad (4\text{-}264)$$

The conversion of optically active 2-octyl diphenylborinate with optically active 2-octanol into (+)-2-octyl borate indicated that the reaction proceeded through B–O and C–O cleavage.[3]

4. OXIDATION

Aliphatic boron–carbon compounds are oxidized in a stepwise fashion to the borinic acid ester, boronic acid ester, and finally the borate (4-265). The first boron–carbon bond oxidizes faster than the

$$R_3B \xrightarrow{[O]} R_2BOR \xrightarrow{[O]} RB(OR)_2 \xrightarrow{[O]} B(OR)_3 \qquad (4\text{-}265)$$

second and the second much faster than the third.[344,345] The presence of water prevents the oxidation of the third bond.[345]

Much of the work of this nature is concerned with the intermediate products;[23] however, examples of borate production are available. Triethoxyborane was obtained from treatment of triethylborane with dry air,[155,332] and tributoxyborane was produced by treatment of tributylborane with either benzoyl peroxide or perbenzoic acid.[227] Treatment of various trialkylboranes with oxygen or air resulted in products containing three gram atoms of oxygen per atom of boron.[305]

Mechanisms have been proposed for the first two steps of the oxidation.[227] An oxygen complex of the borane (4-266) was considered to react with the borane to produce the borinate (4-267). The boronate would arise by a similar sequence (4-268 and 4-269).

$$R_3B + O_2 \rightarrow R_3B{:}O_2 \qquad (4\text{-}266)$$

$$R_3B{:}O_2 + R_3B \rightarrow 2\,R_2BOR \qquad (4\text{-}267)$$

$$R_2BOR + O_2 \rightarrow R_2BOR{:}O_2 \qquad (4\text{-}268)$$

$$R_2BOR{:}O_2 + R_2BOR \rightarrow 2\,RB(OR)_2 \qquad (4\text{-}269)$$

Further complexing of the boronate with oxygen was not pictured due to the decreased electrophilicity of the boron atom as a result of the availability of the free electron pairs on the two alkoxy–oxygen atoms.

The coordination of molecular oxygen with the trialkylborane in equation (4-266) has been pictured to involve a subsequent 1–3 shift of the alkyl group from boron to oxygen (4-270).[6]

$$\begin{array}{c} R \\ | \\ -B \curvearrowleft O_2 \\ | \end{array} \longrightarrow \begin{array}{c} R \uparrow \ddot{O}:^{+} \\ | \\ \bar{-B}-\ddot{O}: \\ | \end{array} \longrightarrow \begin{array}{c} R-O \\ | \\ -B-O \\ | \end{array} \qquad (4\text{-}270)$$

Homolytic decomposition of the intermediate alkylperoxyboron compound was thought to produce alkyl and alkoxyl radicals which initiated reactions leading to the formation of aldehydes, ketones, ethers, esters, acids, olefins, and paraffins as by-products.[344,345]

A radical mechanism involving wall participation also has been proposed.[23]

5. THERMAL DECOMPOSITION

Decomposition of lithium triisobutoxy-(2-pyridylmethyl)borate at 250–390° under reduced pressure resulted in the formation of α-picoline and a 65% recovery of triisobutoxyborane.[340]

6. REACTION WITH HYDROGEN CHLORIDE

Treatment of lithium triisobutoxy-(2-pyridylmethyl)borate with hydrogen chloride in ether solution resulted in a precipitate of lithium chloride and α-picoline hydrochloride and an 85% yield of triisobutoxyborane.[340]

M. From Boron–Nitrogen Compounds

The alcoholysis of a tris(alkylamino)borane to produce a trialkoxyborane and free amine (4-271) should proceed rapidly, since, unlike the analogous transesterification reaction, reversibility is precluded by the slow rate of displacement of alkoxyl by alkylamino.[320]

$$(RNH)_3B + 3\,ROH \rightarrow (RO)_3B + 3\,RNH_2 \qquad (4\text{-}271)$$

The lack of recorded examples of reaction (4-271) testifies only to the relative difficulty of obtaining aminoboranes as compared to alkoxyboranes. However, some examples of alcoholysis of alkoxyaminoboranes and borazines have been reported. Butoxybis(diethylamino)borane[181] and dibutoxy(diethylamino)borane[180] were converted to tributoxyborane on reaction with butanol (4-272 and 4-273), and *B*-trichloro-*N*-trimethylborazine reacted with aliphatic alcohols

$$C_4H_9OB[N(C_2H_5)_2]_2 + 2\,C_4H_9OH \rightarrow B(OC_4H_9)_3 + 2\,(C_2H_5)_2NH \qquad (4\text{-}272)$$

$$(C_4H_9O)_2BN(C_2H_5)_2 + C_4H_9OH \rightarrow B(OC_4H_9)_3 + (C_2H_5)_2NH \qquad (4\text{-}273)$$

or phenol in benzene solution at room temperature to produce the corresponding trialkoxy- or triphenoxyborane.[58,59]

$$\text{(ClBNCH}_3)_3 + 9\,\text{ROH} \rightarrow 3\,(\text{RO})_3\text{B} + 3\,\text{CH}_3\text{NH}_2\cdot\text{HCl} \qquad (4\text{-}274)$$

N. *From Boron–Sulfur Compounds*

It was stated, without experimental details, that treatment of trimethylthioborane with alcohol resulted in a brisk reaction and formation of an ester and mercaptan.[197]

$$(\text{CH}_3\text{S})_3\text{B} + 3\,\text{C}_2\text{H}_5\text{OH} \rightarrow (\text{C}_2\text{H}_5\text{O})_3\text{B} + 3\,\text{CH}_3\text{SH} \qquad (4\text{-}275)$$

Trimethoxyborthiin disproportionates on heating to give trimethoxyborane and boron sulfide[504] in a manner completely analogous to the disproportionation of the trialkoxyboroxines.

$$(\text{CH}_3\text{OBS})_3 \rightarrow \text{B(OCH}_3)_3 + \text{B}_2\text{S}_3 \qquad (4\text{-}276)$$

O. *From B–O–P Compounds*

Reaction (4-277) resulted in a 51% conversion of the boron to triphenoxyborane.[39]

$$3\,(\text{C}_6\text{H}_5\text{O})_2\text{P(=O)H} + 3\,\text{BCl}_3 \xrightarrow{20^\circ} 3\,\text{HCl} + 3\,(\text{C}_6\text{H}_5\text{O})_2\text{POBCl}_2 \xrightarrow[\text{0.1–0.5 mm.}]{\text{Heat}} \text{B}_2\text{O}_3 + (\text{C}_6\text{H}_5\text{O})_3\text{B} + \text{C}_6\text{H}_5\text{OPCl}_2 \qquad (4\text{-}277)$$

P. *From Diboron Compounds*

The disproportionation of tetramethoxydiboron to trimethoxyborane and boron (4-278) by standing under vacuum at room temperature has been reported,[502] but could not be verified.[67] Trimethoxy- and triethoxyborane were obtained from the corresponding tetraalkoxy-

$$3\,(\text{CH}_3\text{O})_2\text{BB(OCH}_3)_2 \rightarrow 4\,\text{B(OCH}_3)_3 + 2\,\text{B} \qquad (4\text{-}278)$$

diboron compounds on heating above 110°, but elemental boron was not a co-product.[67]

The decomposition of tetra-(2-chloroethoxy)diboron at 135° has been formulated as follows:[310]

$$n\ B_2(OCH_2CH_2Cl)_4 \rightarrow n\ (ClCH_2CH_2O)_3B + (ClCH_2CH_2OB)_n \qquad (4\text{-}279)$$

Oxidation of this compound also produced tri-(2-chloroethoxy)-borane.[310]

$$6\ B_2(OCH_2CH_2Cl)_4 + 3\ O_2 \rightarrow 8\ (ClCH_2CH_2O)_3B + 2\ B_2O_3 \qquad (4\text{-}280)$$

Q. From Tri(alkylperoxy)boranes

Treatment of tri-*t*-butylperoxyborane with three moles of ethanol immediately resulted in a reaction mixture from which ethanol could not be recovered by reduced pressure distillation. Reaction (4-281) was presumed although pure triethoxyborane could not be

$$(t\text{-}C_4H_9OO)_3B + 3\ C_2H_5OH \rightarrow (C_2H_5O)_3B + 3\ t\text{-}C_4H_9OOH \qquad (4\text{-}281)$$

obtained due to the similarity of its boiling point and that of *t*-butyl hydroperoxide.[131]

R. From Unsymmetrical Orthoborates

Mixed esters prepared from boric oxide and two different alcohols could not be distilled. The separate symmetrical esters were obtained

$$6\ ROH + 6\ R'OH + 2\ B_2O_3 \xrightarrow[-H_2O]{C_6H_6} \{ROB(OR')_2 + (RO)_2BOR' + (RO)_3B + (R'O)_3B\} \xrightarrow{\text{distill}} 2\ (RO)_3B + 2\ (R'O)_3B \qquad (4\text{-}282)$$

(4-282).[462] The reaction product of butoxydichloroborane and phenol behaved similarly (4-283).[111]

$$C_4H_9OBCl_2 + 2\ C_6H_5OH \rightarrow 2\ HCl + \{C_4H_9OB(OC_6H_5)_2\} \xrightarrow{\text{distill}} \tfrac{1}{3}\ (C_4H_9O)_3B + \tfrac{2}{3}\ (C_6H_5O)_3B \qquad (4\text{-}283)$$

Attempts to prepare amine complexes of (LXXIV) resulted in disproportionation of the unsymmetrical ester.[165]

3 [$C_6H_4O_2$]B—OC_6H_5 (LXXIV) ⟶ [$C_6H_4O_2$]B—O—C_6H_4—O—B[$O_2C_6H_4$] + $(C_6H_5O)_3B$

S. As a Means of Separating and Purifying Alcohols

Alcohols and phenols have been isolated from a variety of naturally occurring products by conversion to the borate with boric acid, boric oxide, boron acetate, and other borates, distillation of the volatile non-hydroxylic constituents, and subsequent hydrolysis and distillation or steam distillation of the residual borate.[11,77,239,240,416,525] Synthetic mixtures of alcohols and non-hydroxylic constituents also have been separated by this method.[81,136,150,190,245,289,336,356,357,393,423,434,453]

V. REACTIONS

A. Thermal Stability

1. ELIMINATION

The conversion of alcohols to olefins has been accomplished by many methods, including the pyrolysis of a variety of different ester types.[21,30,133,353,354] Symmetrical orthoborates subsequently were included in the list when it was shown that an equimolar mixture of n-octanol and boric acid, when heated to 350°, resulted in a 90% yield of octene. This reaction, as well as the dehydration of other primary and secondary alcohols, was formulated (4-285) as pro-

$$3\,RCH_2CH_2OH + H_3BO_3 \xrightarrow{-3\,H_2O} 3\,(RCH_2CH_2O)_3B \rightarrow 3\,RCH{=}CH_2 + H_3BO_3 \qquad (4\text{-}285)$$

ceeding through the orthoborate.[62] However, the equimolar stoichiometry actually employed in the reaction would be expected to result in a metaborate and not an orthoborate (see Chapter 9). Further indication that the orthoborate is not the labile intermediate species is shown by the quantitative distillation of trioctoxyborane and other trialkoxyboranes at temperatures in excess of 350°.[444] Trimethoxyborane has been shown to be stable up to 470°.[303] In addition, the thermal stability of orthoborates derived from secondary alcohols has been shown by the absence of reaction on heating *l*-menthyl orthoborate at 300°* for one hour versus the evolution of menthene (89% yield) from *l*-menthyl metaborate heated at 270°.[355] *l*-Menthyl orthoborate, on heating at 270° with two moles of boric acid, gave a 92% yield of menthene indicating the *in situ* conversion of orthoborate to metaborate (see Chapter 9 for a discussion of the mechanism of the decomposition of metaborates).

* Menthyl orthoborate was reported earlier to decompose at approximately 170°.[11]

In view of the above data and discussion it is difficult to rationalize the reported thermal instabilities of hexyl and octyl borate (Table 4-21).[522] Hexyl borate was reported to decompose at

Table 4-21. Decomposition temperatures of C_6 to C_{10} trialkoxyboranes

R in $(RO)_3B$	Decomposition temperature (°C)	Total alkene yield (%)	Composition of alkene (mole %)		
			1	*cis*[a]	*trans*[a]
n-C_6H_{13}	250–316	73	55	—	45
n-C_8H_{17}	300–350	84	49	13	38
n-C_8H_{17}[b]	294–350	78	49	13	38
n-$C_{10}H_{21}$	320	83	54	24	22

[a] Figures are approximate. Position of double bonds not established.
[b] Pyrolyzed in presence of equimolar quantity of boric oxide.

250–316° although its boiling point has been recorded at 310–311°.[444] Octyl borate was reported to decompose at 300–350° although its boiling point has been recorded at 378–379°.[444] In addition, the decomposition temperature of octyl borate was not significantly altered by the addition of a molar equivalent of boric oxide, even though this procedure would result in the production of octyl metaborate. It is possible that the samples of hexyl and octyl borate used in the decomposition experiments were partially hydrolyzed and, in consequence, already contaminated with boric acid. The decomposition temperatures of 250° and 300° in Table 4-21 then actually would be the metaborate decomposition temperatures, and these values would not be expected to be lowered any further by the addition of boric oxide. The presence of octyl alcohol in the distillate from the decomposition of octyl borate lends support to this possibility.

Thus, the thermal stability of an orthoborate cannot be properly assessed unless it is first freed from boric acid or boric oxide. It can be concluded that the thermal decomposition of 2-octyl borate,[121] the destructive distillation of castor oil,[109] the dehydration of various hydroxy esters in the presence of inorganic boron compounds,[110] the dehydration of various α-aryl-β-haloethanols in the presence of boric acid,[370] and the dehydration of 2-β-oxycholestan[368] and ethyl β-hydroxy-γ,γ,γ-trifluorobutyrate[488] with boric oxide probably proceeded via the metaborate and not the orthoborate. The dehydration of various styrene halohydrins via distillation of the borate esters resulted in the best yields at an approximate one to one mole ratio of halohydrin and boric acid.[211]

Various dienes also have been prepared by elimination reactions (4-286[28] and 4-287[12]), but once again it is debatable whether any orthoborates actually were involved as intermediates.

$$(CH_3)_2C{=}CHCH_2CH_2C(OH)(CH_3)_2 \xrightarrow[180^\circ,\ 3\ hr.]{H_3BO_3} (CH_3)_2C{=}CHCH_2CH_2C(CH_3){=}CH_2 \quad (4\text{-}286)$$

$$R_1R_2C(OH)CH_2CH{=}CHCH_2C(OH)R_3R_4 \xrightarrow[Heat]{H_3BO_3} R_1R_2C(OH)CH_2CH{=}CHCH{=}CR_3R_4 \quad (4\text{-}287)$$

Regardless of the above inconclusive evidence as to the thermal instability of boric acid esters, definitive data indicating an inherent thermal instability in the higher molecular weight esters has been presented.[491] The thermal stability was investigated by heating samples of selected esters (Table 4-22) under reflux at atmospheric

Table 4-22. Stability of trialkoxyboranes to distillation at atmospheric pressure[a]

	% Boron		
Ester	Theoretical	Distillate	Distilland
n-Butyl	4.70	4.63	4.72
2-Methyl-4-pentyl	3.44	3.37	3.43
Tetrahydrofurfuryl	3.44	1.18	4.52
Cyclohexyl	3.50	3.30	3.85
m,p-Cresyl	3.26	1.99	3.43
2-Ethylhexyl	2.72	2.65	2.84
n-Dodecyl	1.91	0.87	4.29
2-Methyl-7-ethyl-4-undecyl	1.66	0.39	2.96

[a] Preceded by one hour of reflux.

pressure for one hour. After the reflux period, approximately fifty percent by volume of the ester was distilled at atmospheric pressure. Analyses of the distillate and distilland indicated that the higher molecular weight esters underwent thermal decomposition, as evidenced by the decreased boron content of the distillate and the increased boron content of the distilland.

The observed decompositions of n-dodecyl borate and tetrahydrofurfuryl borate (Table 4-22) are consistent with the reported production of 1-dodecene on pyrolysis of n-dodecyl borate[19] and the decomposition of tetrahydrofurfuryl borate at 500° to give 2,3-dihydropyran.[31]

Decomposition temperatures determined for a series of esters in an isoteniscope are recorded in Table 4-23.[47] Some conclusions

Table 4-23. Decomposition temperatures of aliphatic and aromatic borates and di-2-ethylhexyl sebacate

Ester	Decomposition point (°C)
Tridodecyl borate	349
Tri-1-methylcyclohexylmethyl borate	367
Tri-*m*-phenoxyphenyl borate	443
Di-2-ethylhexyl sebacate	284

drawn from these data are that alkyl borates are more stable than typical organic esters such as di-2-ethylhexyl sebacate, and aromatic borates are more stable than aliphatic borates. The greater stability of the aromatic members was attributed to the greater inherent stability of the phenyl rings towards free radical decomposition as compared to the alkyl chains and the greater strength of the aromatic C–O bond as compared to the aliphatic C–O bond due to resonance stabilization.

The small increase in thermal stability of 1-methylcyclohexylmethyl borate over dodecyl borate indicated the decomposition path could not be blocked by a simple structural modification such as the absence of β-hydrogen atoms.

Esters of tertiary alcohols (thermal thresholds of 100–150°[11,428] are less stable than those derived from primary and secondary alcohols. Thus, *t*-butyl borate decomposed on attempted distillation at atmospheric pressure;[231] whereas *s*-butyl borate was distilled at 195°,[397] and attempted transesterification of phenyl borate with *t*-butyl alcohol gave isobutylene and diisobutylene.*[111] Advantage has been taken of this fact to effect separation of secondary and tertiary alcohols in pine oil by conversion to a mixture of borates and distillation at elevated temperatures to eliminate the olefins derived from the tertiary alcohols.[428]

Butyl borate, as a boron trifluoride–butanol complex (LXXV),

$$BF_3 \cdot (C_4H_9O)_3B \cdot C_4H_9OH$$

(LXXV)

* The possibility that phenyl borate served as a Lewis acid dehydrating catalyst directly on the *t*-butyl alcohol cannot be ruled out.

gave a 75% yield of n-butene on heating at 180° for fourteen hours.[277] This, however, cannot be considered a straightforward example of the thermal stability of butyl borate since in an uncomplexed form it is quite stable at its boiling point of 230°.

Some insight into the mechanism of the elimination reaction has been gained from the decomposition of tetrahydrofurfuryl borate. The fact that the same product, 2,3-dihydropyran, was obtained by the vapor phase dehydration of tetrahydrofurfuryl alcohol,[31] which presumably proceeds via a carbonium ion intermediate, was offered as evidence for an acid-catalyzed mechanism and not a pyrolytic *cis* elimination mechanism for the borate decomposition.[133] Further evidence for an acid catalyzed mechanism versus a pyrolytic *cis* elimination is shown by the exclusive formation of rearranged products from treatment of *t*-butylmethylcarbinol under conditions of borate pyrolysis.[101]

Questions which have not yet been investigated in the production of olefins from boric acid esters include the possibilities of *exo* versus *endo* products in alicyclic systems, terminal versus internal olefins, the conditions which favor Hofmann or Saytzeff rules, 1,3- versus 1,4-dienes from 1,3-glycols, and the fates of an enol borate, a borate derived from an acyloin, and neopentyl borate.

2. ETHER FORMATION

The tri-α-chloroalkoxyboranes derived from the reaction of boron trichloride with acetaldehyde, n-butyraldehyde, and isobutyraldehyde (LXXVI, LXXVII, LXXVIII)[157] or from the boron tri-

$$(CH_3\overset{Cl}{\overset{|}{C}}HO)_3B \quad (CH_3CH_2CH_2\overset{Cl}{\overset{|}{C}}HO)_3B \quad (CH_3\underset{\underset{CH_3}{|}}{C}H\overset{Cl}{\overset{|}{C}}HO)_3B \quad (ClCH_2O)_3B \quad (ClCH_2\overset{Cl}{\overset{|}{C}}HO)_3B$$

(LXXVI) (LXXVII) (LXXVIII) (LXXIX) (LXXX)

chloride cleavage of chloromethyl methyl ether (LXXIX)[145] undergo decomposition at room temperature to yield α-chloroalkyl ethers.

$$2\,(R\overset{Cl}{\overset{|}{C}}HO)_3B \rightarrow 3\,(R\overset{Cl}{\overset{|}{C}}H)_2O + B_2O_3 \tag{4-288}$$

Elevated temperatures were required to decompose the dichloro derivative (LXXX). The mechanism of the decomposition is discussed in Section IV-G-7.

Tri-2-chloromethoxyethoxyborane underwent decomposition at 56° and 0.3 mm. according to equation (4-289).[114]

$$(ClCH_2OCH_2CH_2O)_3B \rightarrow ClCH_2OCH_2CH_2OCH_2Cl + \begin{array}{l} CH_2{-}O \\ | \qquad\quad \diagdown \\ | \qquad\qquad B{-}OCH_2CH_2OCH_2Cl \\ | \qquad\quad \diagup \\ CH_2{-}O \end{array} \qquad (4\text{-}289)$$

3. REVERSE ALDOL REACTION

Attempts to dehydrate (LXXXI) by pyrolysis with boric acid led to a reverse aldol reaction.[209]

$$\underset{\text{(LXXXI)}}{CH_3CH_2CH(OH){-}C(CH_3)(CH_2C_6H_5){-}C(=O)OCH_2CH_3} \rightarrow CH_3CH_2CH{=}O + C_6H_5CH_2CH(CH_3)C(=O)OCH_2CH_3 \qquad (4\text{-}290)$$

B. *Hydrolysis*

Most boric acid esters are susceptible to hydrolysis, contact with water or atmospheric moisture resulting in complete reversal to boric acid and alcohol or phenol (4-291). However, some sterically hindered

$$(RO)_3B + 3\,H_2O \rightarrow H_3BO_3 + 3\,ROH \qquad (4\text{-}291)$$

or electronically unusual esters possess a remarkable degree of hydrolytic stability. These compounds are discussed in Chapter 21.

C. *Alcoholysis*

The reaction with alcohols and phenols has been discussed as a preparative method in Section IV-E.

An unusual reaction (4-292) involving the alkylation of starch with triisopropoxyborane in aqueous sodium hydroxide medium has been claimed.[242] Other alkylations with boric acid esters in a manner

$$\begin{array}{c} | \\ HC{-}OH \\ | \\ HC{-}OH \\ | \end{array} + (i\text{-}C_3H_7O)_3B \xrightarrow[NaOH]{H_2O} \begin{array}{c} | \\ HC{-}O{-}i\text{-}C_3H_7 \\ | \\ HC{-}O{-}i\text{-}C_3H_7 \\ | \end{array} \qquad (4\text{-}292)$$

analogous to alkylations with methyl sulfate have not been reported, and in view of the aqueous medium and the rapid rate of hydrolysis of triisopropoxyborane (see Chapter 21), it is proposed that the alkylation involves isopropyl alcohol in a sodium borate buffered solution, and not triisopropoxyborane.

D. With Amines

The reactions of boric acid esters with amines fall into two general classes; a complex is formed (4-293) or an alkoxyl group undergoes displacement by an alkylamino group (4-294).

$$(RO)_3B + R'NH_2 \rightarrow (RO)_3B{:}NH_2R' \tag{4-293}$$

$$(RO)_3B + R'NH_2 \rightarrow ROH + (RO)_2BNHR \xrightarrow{R'NH_2} \text{etc.} \tag{4-294}$$

1. COMPLEX FORMATION

Trigonal coplanar boron compounds in many instances form solid 1:1 complexes with a variety of nucleophilic reagents. The boron atom thus assumes sp^3 hybridization (LXXXII). The statement

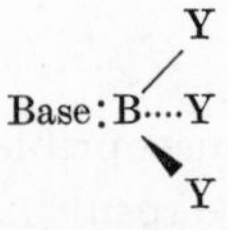

Base:B(Y)(Y)(Y)

(LXXXII)

that borates do not combine at all with amines[431] is incorrect, although boric acid esters do not generally share the affinity for amines possessed by the boron halides[203,306,307] and borane.[86,87] The electrophilic character of the boron atom in an ester is reduced by virtue of the $+M$ effect of the neighboring oxygen atoms (LXXXIII) to a greater extent than it is in the halides; however,

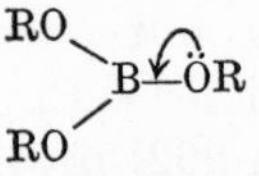

(RO)₂B←ÖR

(LXXXIII)

other factors such as steric requirements[478] and crystal lattice energies[517] must be considered and may well be the predominating factors.

a. *Trimethoxyborane.* Trimethoxyborane, which has the minimum steric requirements of any boric acid ester and at the same time the minimum contribution of electrons from the alkyl groups, appears to be the only non-halogenated aliphatic ester which routinely forms complexes with amines. The 1:1 addition compound with ammonia (LXXXIV)[192,399,432] sublimes at 45°, is stable to at least 375° and, in contrast to trimethoxyborane itself, does not react with sodium hydroxide. Trimethoxyborane also forms isolable

$$(CH_3O)_3B{:}NH_3$$
(LXXXIV)

1:1 complexes with hydrazine,[272] the methyl amines,[195,478] ethylamine,[272] *t*-butylamine,[478] ethylenediamine,[272,478] pyrolidine[272] and piperidine.[272,478]

The addition reactions with trimethoxyborane were found to be strongly catalyzed by the lower alcohols.[215,478] Since methanol would tend to cause the formation of (LXXXV), there appears to be no

$$[(CH_3O)_4B]H$$
(LXXXV)

reason for this effect. Indeed a mixture of trimethoxyborane and *t*-butyl amine did not result in a solid product until methanol was added, but the solid product was the salt (LXXXVI) and not the complex (LXXXVII).[318]

$$[(CH_3O)_4B]^- \, t\text{-}C_4H_9NH_3^+ \qquad (CH_3O)_3B{:}NH_2\text{–}t\text{-}C_4H_9$$
(LXXXVI) (LXXXVII)

Other amines, diethyl, di-n-propyl, di-n-butyl, di-n-amyl and tri-n-butyl, form solid addition compounds with trimethoxyborane, but they are not stable enough to isolate by sublimation.[478] Vapor pressure studies indicate piperazine and triethanolamine also form complexes with trimethoxyborane.[215] No evidence of reaction was obtained for triethylamine, diisopropylamine, pyridine, or quinoline.[215,478]

Examination of Table 4-24 reveals that, in general, unhindered strongly basic amines form isolable complexes with trimethoxyborane which are capable of purification, slightly hindered strongly basic amines result in complexes which cannot withstand sublimation or which have not been isolated, and weakly basic amines or highly hindered amines do not interact at all.

b. *Higher Trialkoxyboranes.* For some period of time it was thought that triethoxyborane and the higher alkyl borates were incapable of forming solid complexes with amines due to the greater steric requirements of the alkyl groups as compared to the methyl ester. However, considerable heat is evolved when triethoxyborane and a variety of amines are mixed, which indicates some chemical interaction.[478] Indeed, crystalline complexes of triethoxyborane

Table 4-24. Stability of trimethoxyborane–amine complexes as a function of base strength and steric requirements of the amine

Amine	Ionization constant of amine	$(CH_3O)_3B$:Amine
$C_5H_{10}NH$	1.6×10^{-3}	Isolable complex
$C_2H_5NH_2$	5.6×10^{-4}	
$(CH_3)_2NH$	5.12×10^{-4}	
CH_3NH_2	4.38×10^{-4}	
$t\text{-}C_4H_9NH_2$	2.8×10^{-4}	
$NH_2CH_2CH_2NH_2$	8.5×10^{-5}	
$(CH_3)_3N$	5.27×10^{-5}	
NH_3	1.8×10^{-5}	
N_2H_4	3×10^{-6}	
$(C_2H_5)_2NH$	1.26×10^{-3}	Indications of complex formation
$(n\text{-}C_3H_7)_2NH$	8.2×10^{-4}	
HN NH (ring)	6.4×10^{-5}	
$(n\text{-}C_4H_9)_2NH$		
$(n\text{-}C_5H_{11})_2NH$		
$(n\text{-}C_4H_9)_3N$		
$(HOCH_2CH_2)_3N$		
$(C_2H_5)_3N$	5.65×10^{-4}	Do not form complexes
C_5H_5N	1.4×10^{-9}	
Quinoline	6.3×10^{-10}	
$(i\text{-}C_3H_7)_2NH$		

with hydrazine, ethylamine and ethylenediamine and of triallyloxyborane with hydrazine, ethylamine, ethylenediamine, piperidine, and pyrrolidine have been prepared.[271,272] Tri-n-propoxyborane gave no evidence of reaction except with hydrazine.[271] Tri-n-butoxy and tri-n-pentoxyborane exhibited no heat of mixing with amines.[478] The absence of heat of reaction on mixing tri-n-butoxyborane and pyridine in conjunction with the reported 17 kcal heat of reaction of gaseous trimethylborane and gaseous pyridine led to the assignment of at least 17 kcal/mole for the resonance energy of tri-n-butoxyborane (4-295).[73]

$$(C_4H_9O)(OC_4H_9)\overset{-}{B}{=}\overset{+}{O}C_4H_9 \longleftrightarrow (C_4H_9\overset{+}{O}{=})\overset{-}{B}(OC_4H_9)(OC_4H_9) \longleftrightarrow (C_4H_9O)(OC_4H_9)\overset{-}{B}{=}\overset{+}{O}C_4H_9 \qquad (4\text{-}295)$$

Tri-(2,2,2-trichloroethoxy)borane did not form a stable complex with pyridine even though the $-I$ effect of the nine chlorine atoms would be expected to greatly enhance the electrophilic character of the boron atom.[64] On the other hand, tri-(2,2,2-trifluoroethoxy)-borane, which has less steric requirements and greater inductive withdrawal of electrons from the boron, did form an isolable solid complex.[4] Reaction of tri-(2-chloroethoxy)borane and trimethyl-amine has been indicated.[310]

The reaction product of tributoxyborane and potassium *N*-methylaniline[135] was formulated as the complex (LXXXVIII).[338]

$$\left[C_6H_5\overset{\overset{\large CH_3}{|}}{N}{:}B(OC_4H_9)_3 \right] K$$

(LXXXVIII)

c. *Triaryloxyboranes.* The decreased electron density on the boron atom in aromatic esters, due to the withdrawal of electrons by the $-M$ effect of the ring, was suggested as an explanation of the ready formation of 1:1 complexes of triphenoxyborane with the weakly basic amines, pyridine and quinoline.[111,165] Ethylamine also resulted in a complex; however, the more sterically hindered diethyl and triethylamine did not.[111] The isolation of the diisobutylamine complex of tri-*m*-cresyloxyborane is not consistent with this rationale.[165] Further evidence of the importance of the steric requirements of the amine is shown by the formation of (LXXXIX)

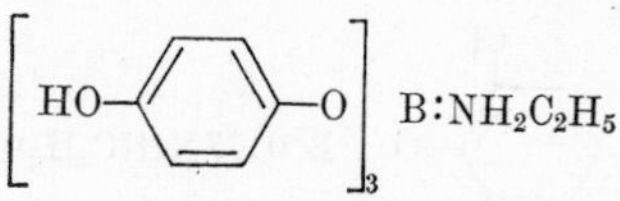

$$\left[HO{-}C_6H_4{-}O \right]_3 B{:}NH_2C_2H_5$$

(LXXXIX)

from the reaction of tri-*p*-hydroxyphenoxyborane and ethylamine, but the inertness of this ester to dimethylamine or *t*-butylamine.[421] In addition, the preferential reaction of tri-*o*-cresyloxyborane and certain other aromatic esters with γ-picoline served as the basis for separation of γ-picoline from β-picoline and 2,6-lutidine.[486]

The steric requirements of the ester can also become the dominating factor, as shown by the formation of stable complexes from pyridine and a series of 2-, 4-, and 2,5-substituted phenyl esters, and the failure of complex formation between pyridine and tri-(2,6-dimethylphenoxy)borane or tri-(2,4,6-trichlorophenoxy)-borane.[112]

Amine complexes of aromatic borates with a stoichiometry

Table 4-25. Triaryloxyborane–amine complexes with stoichiometry different from 1 : 1

Complex
$[C_6H_5O]_3B:2NH_3$
$[2,4,6\text{-}Cl_3C_6H_2O]_3B:3NH_3$
$[2,6\text{-}(OCH_3)_2C_6H_3O]_3B:0.36C_5H_5N$
$[2,5\text{-}Cl_2C_6H_3O]_3B:0.44N(C_2H_5)_3$
$[2,5\text{-}Cl_2C_6H_3O]_3B:0.77NH(C_2H_5)_2$
$[C_6H_5O]_3B:0.45$ (2,4,6-trimethylpyridine)
$[4\text{-}ClC_6H_4O]_3B:0.59N(C_2H_5)_3$

different than 1:1 have been described (Table 4-25). The integral number of ammonia molecules associated with triphenoxyborane and tri-(2,4,6-trichlorophenoxy)borane seems fortuitous in view of the other entries in the Table and the fact that a 1.45 : 1 complex of ammonia and tri-(2,4,6-trichlorophenoxy)borane melting at 138° was described as an intermediate in the preparation of the 3 : 1 compound.[112]

On the basis of conductivity measurements in acetone, the complexes with integral units of ammonia were formulated as (XC) and (XCI).[112]

$$[(C_6H_5O)_2B(NH_3)_2]^+ [C_6H_5O]^- \quad \text{(XC)}$$

$$[Cl_3C_6H_2OB(NH_3)_3]^{2+} [Cl_3C_6H_2O]_2^- \quad \text{(XCI)}$$

2. DISPLACEMENT

The first recorded example of alkoxyl displacement by amine in 1867 indicated that some ethylamine was obtained from the reaction of ammonia and triethoxyborane.[402] The liberation of alcohol, however, is the usual course of the reaction.

Reaction of ammonia or the ammonia–trimethoxyborane complex with an excess of trimethoxyborane was reported to give a series of covalently bonded boron–nitrogen compounds resulting from the elimination of methanol.[192,193] Triisobutoxyborane gave, at most, a trace of reaction with ammonia.[121] The unreactivity of ammonia in this case is not surprising in view of its volatility, since equilibrium (4-296) would be pulled to the left if the amine were the

$$(RO)_3B + 3\,R'NH_2 \rightleftarrows (R'NH)_3B + 3\,ROH \qquad (4\text{-}296)$$

lowest boiling constituent. Passage of ammonia and trimethoxyborane or triethoxyborane into a furnace at 800° circumvented any equilibrium conditions and resulted in products with empirical formulas approximating $10B_2(NH)_3 \cdot 7B_2O_3 \cdot OCH_3$.[315]

Decomposition at 0° of the dimethylamine complex of trimethoxyborane (followed tensimetrically) was formulated according to equations (4-297) and (4-298).[195]

$$(CH_3)_2NH{:}B(OCH_3)_3 \rightarrow (CH_3)_2NH + B(OCH_3)_3 \qquad (4\text{-}297)$$

$$B(OCH_3)_3 + (CH_3)_2NH{:}B(OCH_3)_3 \rightarrow (CH_3O)_3B{:}\overset{\displaystyle CH_3}{\underset{\displaystyle CH_3}{N}}\text{—}\overset{\displaystyle OCH_3}{\underset{\displaystyle OCH_3}{B}}{:}NH(CH_3)_2 \qquad (4\text{-}298)$$

Higher boiling amines such as ethylenediamine (4-299),[199] butylamine (4-300), cyclopentylamine, cyclohexylamine (4-301), diethylenetriamine (4-302), hexamethylenediamine (4-303), 3,3′-

iminobispropylamine (4-304) and *o*-phenylenediamine (4-305)[66] have undergone reactions with various alkyl borates at finite rates.[68,320,449]

$$NH_2CH_2CH_2NH_2 + (C_2H_5O)_3B \xrightarrow{\text{Benzene}} \left[\begin{array}{c} N\text{——}B \\ CH_2 \quad NH \\ CH_2 \end{array} \right]_n + 3\,C_2H_5OH\text{—benzene azeotrope} \quad (4\text{-}299)$$

$$3\,C_4H_9NH_2 + 4\,(CH_3O)_3B \rightarrow (C_4H_9NH)_3B + 3\,[(CH_3O)_3B + CH_3OH] \quad (4\text{-}300)$$

$$3\,C_6H_{11}NH_2 + (i\text{-}C_3H_7O)_3B \rightarrow (C_6H_{11}NH)_3B + 3\,i\text{-}C_3H_7OH \quad (4\text{-}301)$$

$$(NH_2CH_2CH_2)_2NH + (i\text{-}C_3H_7O)_3B \longrightarrow \left[NCH_2CH_2NHCH_2CH_2NHB \right]_n + 3\,i\text{-}C_3H_7OH \quad (4\text{-}302)$$

$$NH_2(CH_2)_6NH_2 + (i\text{-}C_3H_7O)_3B \rightarrow \left[\begin{array}{c} O\text{-}i\text{-}C_3H_7 \\ | \\ BNH(CH_2)_6NH \end{array} \right]_n + 2\,i\text{-}C_3H_7OH \quad (4\text{-}303)$$

$$(NH_2CH_2CH_2CH_2)_2NH + (i\text{-}C_3H_7O)_3B \longrightarrow \begin{array}{c} O\text{-}i\text{-}C_3H_7 \\ NH \quad NH \\ CH_2 \quad B \quad CH_2 \\ CH_2 \quad NH \quad CH_2 \\ CH_2 \quad CH_2 \end{array} + 2\,i\text{-}C_3H_7OH \quad (4\text{-}304)$$

$$3\,C_6H_4(NH_2)_2 + 3\,(i\text{-}C_3H_7O)_3B \longrightarrow [\text{tricyclic product: } B_3N_3 \text{ ring with three } C_6H_4\text{-fused NH–B–N units}] + 9\,i\text{-}C_3H_7OH \quad (4\text{-}305)$$

Aminations with amines boiling as low as butylamine are possible with trimethoxyborane since the most volatile species in the reaction is the trimethoxyborane–methanol azeotrope.[320] An aminoborazine (XCII) was the actual product of the reaction with 2 : 1

stoichiometry of ester to amine. Other borazenes prepared in this manner[448] are described in Volume II of this series.

$$12\,(CH_3O)_3B + 6\,C_4H_9NH_2 \rightarrow 9\,[(CH_3O)_3B + CH_3OH]$$

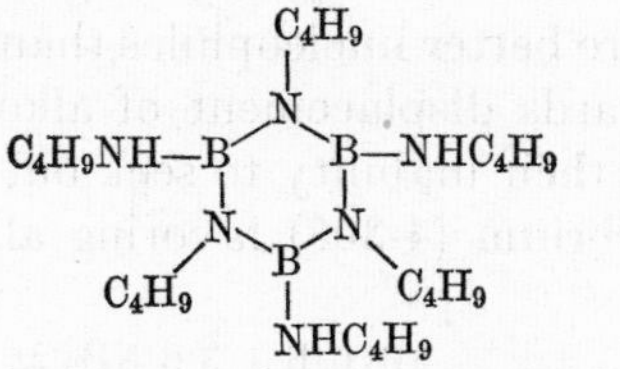

$$+ \quad \text{(XCII): } B_3N_3 \text{ ring with } N\text{-}C_4H_9 \text{ on each N and } NHC_4H_9 \text{ on each B} \qquad (4\text{-}306)$$

(XCII)

Triethoxyborane[228,402] and triisobutoxyborane[121] originally were reported to be unreactive with aniline even at the boiling point. However, it subsequently was shown that triisopropoxyborane was attacked by aniline in refluxing xylene to give a slow evolution of isopropyl alcohol and a small yield of tris(anilino)borane,[68,320] and that triisobutoxyborane also was reactive towards aniline with a rate of displacement similar to the rate of isopropyl alcohol removal from triisopropoxyborane.[338] *p*-Toluidine was found to displace isobutyl alcohol from triisobutoxyborane more rapidly than aniline,[338] which may be due to the greater base strength of the methyl derivative.

Tributoxyborane could not be made to react with either diethylamine or di-n-butylamine[181] and it was concluded that secondary amines would not displace alkoxyl groups from boron.[179] It is evident that the steric requirements of the amine could preclude the formation of a tetrahedral transition state (XCIII), but diethyl

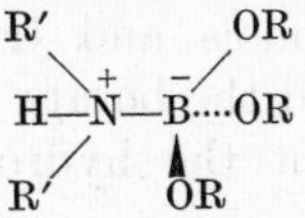

$$\begin{array}{c} R' \qquad OR \\ H-\overset{+}{N}(R')-\overset{-}{B}(OR)\cdots OR \\ R' \qquad OR \end{array}$$

(XCIII)

and dibutylamine do not appear to possess the necessary bulk in view of the fact that diphenylamine can transaminate tris(diethylamino)borane (4-307).[148] It is possible that the procedure employed,

$$3\,(C_6H_5)_2NH + [(C_2H_5)_2N]_3B \rightarrow [(C_6H_5)_2N]_3B + 3\,(C_2H_5)_2NH \qquad (4\text{-}307)$$

admixture of reactants and immediate distillation, did not allow sufficient time for reaction.[338] Even less explicable is the unreactivity of piperidine towards triisopropoxyborane. Piperidine is a fairly strong amine with low steric requirements due to the tying back of the alkyl groups into a ring.[318]

The reactivity of boric acid esters with amines thus seems to be lower than the reactivity with alcohols or water, since trans-esterification and hydrolysis generally proceed with ease. Since amines are better nucleophiles than alcohols, their apparent sluggishness towards displacement of alkoxyl from boron cannot be attributed to their inability to seek out boron but rather must be due to an equilibrium (4-308) favoring alkoxyboranes over aminoboranes.

$$(RO)_3B + 3\,R'NH_2 \rightleftarrows (R'NH)_3B + 3\,ROH \qquad (4\text{-}308)$$

However, this explanation suffers since it is reasonable to believe that resonance contributions of the tris(alkylamino)borane, of which (XCIV) represents one canonical form, are more operative than those of the trialkoxyborane (XCV). This conclusion is based on the

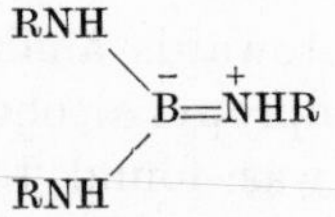

$$(RNH)_2\overset{-}{B}{=}\overset{+}{N}HR \qquad\qquad (RO)_2\overset{-}{B}{=}\overset{+}{O}R$$

(XCIV) 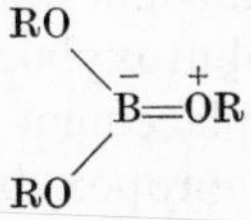 (XCV)

greater $+M$ effect of $-NR_2$ versus $-OR$[222] and the greater hydrolytic stability of boron–nitrogen compounds as compared to boron–oxygen compounds.[450] The equilibrium (4-308) might thus be expected to favor the products on the right.

a. *Amino Alcohols.* Competitive reactions of amines and alcohols with boric acid esters have not been performed. However, reactions with amino alcohols and tripropoxyborane have been recorded. Ethanolamine and the borate were formulated to give the aminoester (4-309) and not the hydroxyaminoborane (XCVI).[461]

$$3\,NH_2CH_2CH_2OH + (C_3H_7O)_3B \rightarrow (NH_2CH_2CH_2O)_3B + 3\,C_3H_7OH \qquad (4\text{-}309)$$

However, unequivocal evidence for this choice was not presented. The presence of free amino groups rests upon the titration with hydrochloric acid, presumably in an aqueous medium, conditions

$$(HOCH_2CH_2N)_3B$$

(XCVI)

which also would lead to rapid hydrolysis of (XCVI) and formation of amino groups. Structure (XCVI) and the mixed species (XCVII) and (XCVIII) cannot, therefore, be precluded.*

$(NH_2CH_2CH_2O)_2BNHCH_2CH_2OH$ (XCVII)

$NH_2CH_2CH_2OB(NHCH_2CH_2OH)_2$ (XCVIII)

In support of the possibility of competitive aminolysis and alcoholysis, the reaction of *p*-aminophenol and tripropoxyborane resulted in the formation of a resin (4-310).[516] Bifunctionality of the aminophenol thus is indicated.

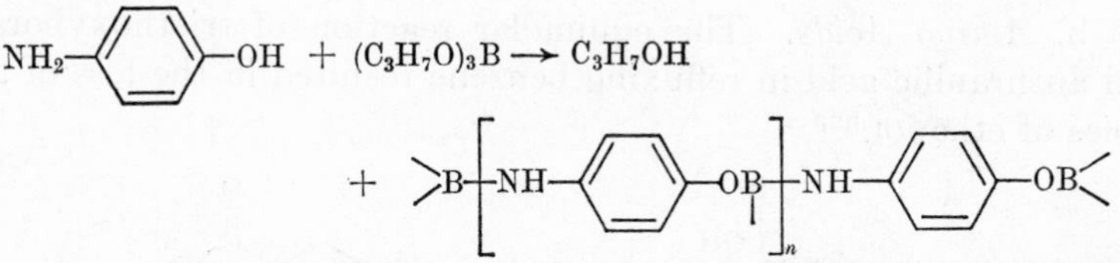

$$NH_2-C_6H_4-OH + (C_3H_7O)_3B \rightarrow C_3H_7OH + \;>B{-}[NH{-}C_6H_4{-}OB(-)]_n{-}NH{-}C_6H_4{-}OB< \quad (4\text{-}310)$$

It is interesting that the reaction of equimolar quantities of ethanolamine and triisopropoxyborane resulted in three moles of isopropyl alcohol. The products can be formulated as (XCIX) or (C).[320]

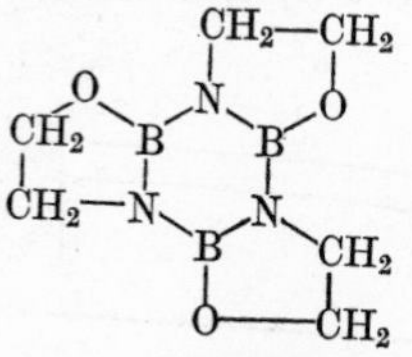

(XCIX)

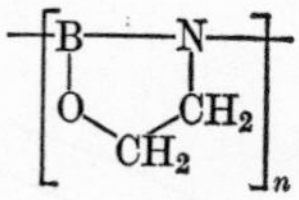

(C)

Two moles of isopropyl alcohol were displaced from the equimolar reactions of triisopropoxyborane with 3-aminopropanol and 4-aminobutanol to give products approximating (CI) and (CII).[320]

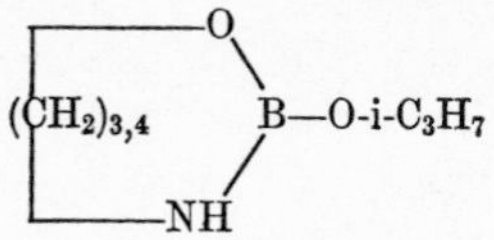

(CI) $(CH_2)_{3,4}$ ring: $-O-B(O\text{-}i\text{-}C_3H_7)-NH-$

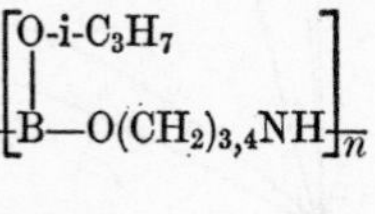

(CII) $[-B(O\text{-}i\text{-}C_3H_7)-O(CH_2)_{3,4}NH-]_n$

* The infrared spectrum of a material prepared by reaction (4-309) showed absorption bands attributable to both amino and hydroxyl groups.[149]

o-Aminophenol reacted with all three valencies of triisopropoxyborane to give the substituted borazine (CIII).[68,320]

(CIII)

b. *Amino Acids.* The equimolar reaction of triethoxyborane and anthranilic acid in refluxing benzene resulted in the loss of two moles of ethanol.[333]

$$(C_2H_5O)_3B + o\text{-}H_2NC_6H_4COOH \longrightarrow 2C_2H_5OH + C_6H_4(C(=O)O)(NH)B{-}OC_2H_5 \quad (4\text{-}311)$$

c. *Mechanism.* A comparison[320] of the initial rate of removal of isopropyl alcohol from the reaction of triisopropoxyborane with a series of amines and amino alcohols (Fig. 4-5) and the base strength[273]

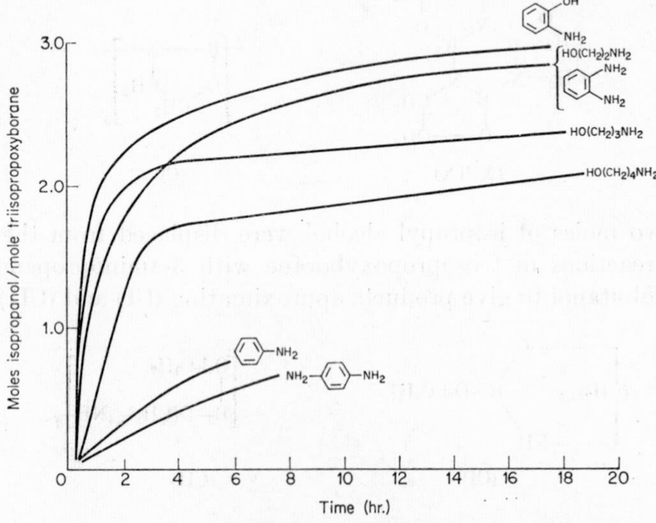

Fig. 4-5. Relative rates of removal of isopropanol from reactions of triisopropoxyborane with various amines and amino alcohols.

of the amines (Table 4-26) reveals that those amines with ionization constants approximating 10^{-5} and which possess a hydroxyl group react more rapidly than those with constants smaller than about 10^{-8} and which do not have an hydroxyl function. *o*-Phenylenediamine is an exception in that it reacts fairly rapidly even though it is the weakest base that was studied. Therefore, it is not possible

Table 4-26. Relative order of reaction rate of amines and amino alcohols with triisopropoxyborane

Amine or aminoalcohol	Ionization constant	Relative order of reaction rate with triisopropoxyborane from Fig. 4-5
o-aminophenol (benzene ring with OH and NH_2)	?	1st
$HO(CH_2)_3NH_2$	ca. 10^{-5}	2nd
$HOCH_2CH_2NH_2$	2.77×10^{-5}	3rd
$HO(CH_2)_4NH_2$	ca. 10^{-5}	4th
$NH_2-C_6H_4-NH_2$ (*p*-)	1.1×10^{-8}	6th
$C_6H_5-NH_2$	3.83×10^{-10}	5th
o-phenylenediamine (benzene ring with NH_2 and NH_2)	3.3×10^{-10}	3rd

to say unequivocally whether the initial attack on boron is by the amine or hydroxyl function. If it were the hydroxyl function, *o*-phenylenediamine might be expected to be the least reactive since it possesses no hydroxyl group and it is the weakest of the bases studied.

It is evident that 1,2- or *ortho*-amino and hydroxyl functions lead to accelerated rates; thus some cyclic mechanism involving favorable entropy relationships might be operative. Sequence (4-312) illustrates this path.

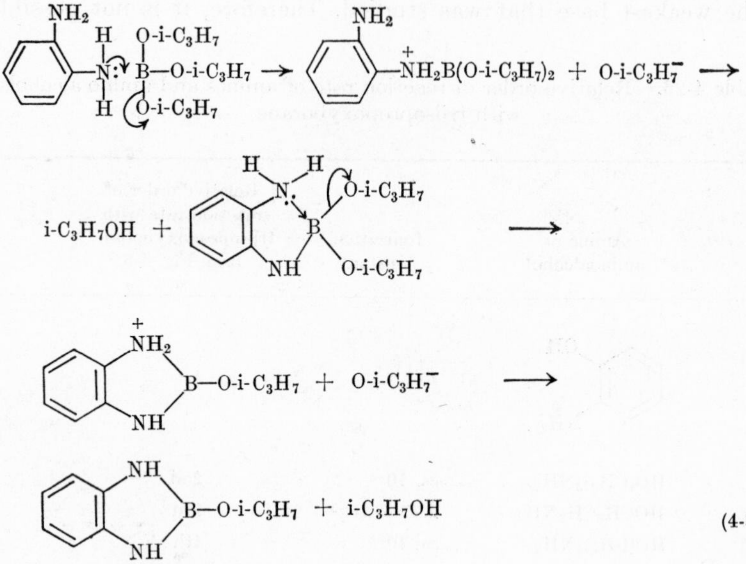

$$o\text{-}H_2NC_6H_4\text{-}\ddot{N}H_2 \cdot B(O\text{-}i\text{-}C_3H_7)_3 \rightarrow o\text{-}H_2NC_6H_4\text{-}\overset{+}{N}H_2B(O\text{-}i\text{-}C_3H_7)_2 + O\text{-}i\text{-}C_3H_7^- \longrightarrow$$

$$i\text{-}C_3H_7OH + C_6H_4(NH_2)(NH)B(O\text{-}i\text{-}C_3H_7)_2 \longrightarrow$$

$$C_6H_4(\overset{+}{N}H_2)(NH)B\text{—}O\text{-}i\text{-}C_3H_7 + O\text{-}i\text{-}C_3H_7^- \longrightarrow$$

$$C_6H_4(NH)_2B\text{—}O\text{-}i\text{-}C_3H_7 + i\text{-}C_3H_7OH \qquad (4\text{-}312)$$

After removal of two moles of isopropyl alcohol, the cyclic intermediate (CIV) has no particular advantage over the energetically less favorable ring system (CV), or linear system (CVI), and

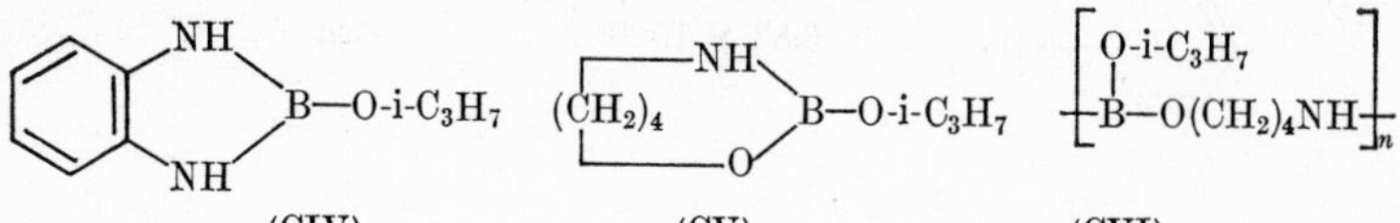

$$C_6H_4(NH)_2B\text{—}O\text{-}i\text{-}C_3H_7 \quad (CIV)$$

$$(CH_2)_4(NH)(O)B\text{—}O\text{-}i\text{-}C_3H_7 \quad (CV)$$

$$\left[\text{—}\underset{|}{\overset{O\text{-}i\text{-}C_3H_7}{B}}\text{—}O(CH_2)_4NH\text{—}\right]_n \quad (CVI)$$

thus the rates of removal of the third mole of alcohol are essentially equivalent. This is seen by the similar slopes of the latter stages of the reaction curves in Fig. 4-5.

3. OTHER REACTIONS

The reaction of aniline with tri-*o*-carboxyphenoxyborane to produce salicylanilide[108] possibly proceeds via path (4-313). Phenylhydrazine produced products of unknown nature.[108]

$$[o\text{-}(CO_2H)C_6H_4O]_3B + 3\,C_6H_5NH_2 \rightarrow [o\text{-}(C_6H_5NHCO)C_6H_4O]_3B + 3H_2O$$

$$\longrightarrow o\text{-}HOC_6H_4\overset{O}{\overset{\|}{C}}NH\text{-}C_6H_5 + H_3BO_3 \qquad (4\text{-}313)$$

E. *With Acids*

1. CARBOXYLIC ACIDS

The general reaction of carboxylic acids with boric acid esters involves esterification of the acid with the alkoxy radical of the ester with the attendant production of boric acid.

$$3\,R\overset{O}{\overset{\|}{C}}OH + (R'O)_3B \rightarrow 3\,R\overset{O}{\overset{\|}{C}}OR' + H_3BO_3 \qquad (4\text{-}314)$$

Triethoxyborane was found to esterify aliphatic, aromatic, and dibasic carboxylic acids on heating with (4-315) or without (4-316) sulfuric acid.[402]

$$(C_2H_5O)_3B + 2\,R\overset{O}{\overset{\|}{C}}OH + H_2SO_4 \rightarrow 2\,R\overset{O}{\overset{\|}{C}}OC_2H_5 + C_2H_5SO_4H + H_3BO_3 \qquad (4\text{-}315)$$

$$2\,(C_2H_5O)_3B + 3\,HO\overset{O}{\overset{\|}{C}}CH_2CH_2\overset{O}{\overset{\|}{C}}OH \rightarrow 3\,C_2H_5O\overset{O}{\overset{\|}{C}}CH_2CH_2\overset{O}{\overset{\|}{C}}OC_2H_5 + 2\,H_3BO_3 \qquad (4\text{-}316)$$

The reaction subsequently was applied as a facile synthesis of formic acid esters (4-317),[435] and as a means for preparing a series

$$(RO)_3B + 3\,H\overset{O}{\overset{\|}{C}}OH \rightarrow 3\,H\overset{O}{\overset{\|}{C}}OR + H_3BO_3 \qquad (4\text{-}317)$$

of acetates, benzoates and cinnamates from the appropriate acid and a variety of boric acid esters derived from primary, secondary, and tertiary alcohols and phenols.[213,214]

The reported[108] esterification of salicylic acid by prolonged reflux with trimethoxyborane could not be repeated.[213] If the original report is correct, the initial reaction of trimethoxyborane and salicylic acid under mild conditions is a transesterification to give (CVII).[108] Esterification of the free carboxyl group of (CVII) with the methanol upon prolonged reflux would liberate three moles of water which could then hydrolyze (CVII) and result in the observed methyl salicylate. *p*-Hydroxybenzoic acid reportedly did not react with trimethoxyborane.[108]

$$(CH_3O)_3B + 3\ \text{[o-}HOC_6H_4CO_2H] \longrightarrow [o\text{-}HO_2CC_6H_4O]_3B + 3\ CH_3OH \quad (4\text{-}318)$$

(CVII)

The reaction of a boric acid ester and a carboxylic acid was formulated as proceeding through a tetrahedral intermediate (4-319),

$$(RO)_3B + R'\overset{O}{\overset{\|}{C}}OH \rightarrow \left[R'\overset{O}{\overset{\|}{C}}OB(OR)_3\right]H \quad (4\text{-}319)$$

which collapsed to a mixed anhydride (CVIII) and free alcohol (4-320), with subsequent esterification of the original acid (4-321).[102] However, no definitive mixed anhydrides were isolated.

$$\left[R'\overset{O}{\overset{\|}{C}}OB(OR)_3\right]H \rightarrow \underset{\text{(CVIII)}}{R'\overset{O}{\overset{\|}{C}}OB(OR)_2} + ROH \quad (4\text{-}320)$$

$$R'\overset{O}{\overset{\|}{C}}OH + ROH \rightarrow R'\overset{O}{\overset{\|}{C}}OR + H_2O \quad (4\text{-}321)$$

2. SULFURIC ACID

In 1867, Schiff formulated the reaction of triethoxyborane and sulfuric acid in a manner indicating both the transfer of ethyl groups and simultaneous decomposition (4-322).[402] Later workers formulated

$$(C_2H_5O)_3B + H_2SO_4 \xrightarrow{\Delta} C_2H_5SO_4H + 2\ CH_2{=}CH_2 + HBO_2 + H_2O \quad (4\text{-}322)$$

an intermediate tetracovalent anion with subsequent mixed anhydride formation followed by esterification of the sulfuric acid (4-323).[102] The stoichiometry of the reaction indicated a mixed

$$(C_2H_5O)_3B + H_2SO_4 \xrightarrow{200^\circ} [HOSO_2OB(OC_2H_5)_3]^- H^+ \rightarrow C_2H_5OH + HOSO_2OB(OC_2H_5)_2$$

$$\xrightarrow{H_2SO_4} C_2H_5OSO_2OH + H_2O \quad (4\text{-}323)$$

anhydride residue of the composition (CIX).

$$\underset{\text{(CIX)}}{(C_2H_5O)_2BOSO_2O\underset{\displaystyle OC_2H_5}{\underset{|}{B}}OSO_2OB(OC_2H_5)_2}$$

3. PHOSPHORIC ACID

Boron phosphate was found to be the product of the reactions of triethoxy- and tributoxyborane with phosphoric acid,[102] thus indicating greater reactivity of the series of alkoxy intermediates such as (CX) than the corresponding sulfates and carboxylates, which did not proceed to complete alcohol removal.

$$(RO)_3B + H_3PO_4 \rightarrow \left[(HO)_2\overset{\overset{O}{\|}}{P}OB(OR)_3\right]H \rightarrow ROH + \underset{(CX)}{(HO)_2\overset{\overset{O}{\|}}{P}OB(OR)_2}$$

$$\xrightarrow{\text{etc.}} BPO_4 + 2\,ROH \qquad (4\text{-}324)$$

4. NITRIC ACID

Triethoxyborane was solvolyzed by nitric acid according to equation (4-325).[402]

$$(C_2H_5O)_3B + 3\,HNO_3 \xrightarrow{\Delta} H_3BO_3 + 3\,C_2H_5ONO_2 \qquad (4\text{-}325)$$

5. HYDROGEN CHLORIDE

A series of esters derived from both primary and secondary alcohols were reported to be unreactive with hydrogen chloride;[175,176,185,244,402] however, the elimination of ethanol and butanol from heated mixtures of hydrogen chloride and triethoxyborane and tributoxyborane was interpreted according to equations (4-326) and (4-327).[102] In addition, tri-3-methylallyloxyborane and hydrogen chloride reacted at 110° according to equation (4-328).[185]

$$(RO)_3B + HCl \rightleftarrows ROH + (RO)_2BCl \qquad (4\text{-}326)$$

$$(RO)_2BCl + HCl \rightleftarrows ROH + ROBCl_2 \qquad (4\text{-}327)$$

$$(RO)_3B + 3\,HCl \rightarrow 3\,RCl + H_3BO_3 \qquad (4\text{-}328)$$

Tri-*t*-butoxyborane[176] and tri-(+)-1-phenylethoxyborane[175] underwent rapid reactions with hydrogen chloride at 15° according to equation (4-328). Retention of configuration in the resultant phenylethyl chloride[175] would tend to rule out the S_N2 (4-329) and S_N1 (4-330) mechanisms proposed for the displacement[274] since

$$(RO)_3B + HCl \rightarrow \underset{\underset{H}{|}}{R\overset{+}{O}}B(OR)_2 + Cl^- \qquad (4\text{-}329)$$

$$Cl^- \; R\overset{+}{\underset{\underset{H}{|}}{O}}B(OR)_2 \longrightarrow RCl + HOB(OR)_2$$

$$\underset{\underset{H}{|}}{R\overset{+}{O}}B(OR)_2 + Cl^- \rightarrow R^+ + HOB(OR)_2 + Cl^- \rightarrow RCl + HOB(OR)_2 \qquad (4\text{-}330)$$

reaction (4-329) would result in inversion of configuration of the alkyl halide and reaction (4-330) would result in racemization of the halide with possibly some inversion if shielding effects are operative.[150] An S_N1[117] mechanism (4-331) would seem to account for the facts.

$$(RO)_3B + HCl \rightarrow (RO)_2B\text{—}O\cdots H\cdots Cl\cdots R \rightarrow (RO)_2BOH + RCl \qquad (4\text{-}331)$$

6. HYDROGEN BROMIDE AND IODIDE

The greater reactivity of hydrogen bromide and iodide as compared to hydrogen chloride towards the lower trialkoxyboranes via path (4-328) is illustrated in Table 4-27.[176] The boiling points of the

Table 4-27. Reactivity of the hydrogen halides with the tributoxyboranes

			% Yield of butyl halide		
HX	Temp. (°C)	Time (hr.)	n-Butyl	Isobutyl	*s*-Butyl
HCl	35	8	0		
HCl	115	13		0	
HCl	120	12			0
HBr	115	7	35		
HBr	115	16		25	
HBr	20	60			85
HI	18	0.75	7		
HI	50	4	96		
HI	20	2			55

halides produced indicate the absence of rearrangement, and, therefore, once again no evidence for the postulated S_N1 mechanism[273] (4-330) is evident.

The conversions[175] of (+)-1-phenylethyl borate to (−)-1-phenylethyl bromide with hydrogen bromide and (+)-2-octyl borate to (−)-2-octyl bromide and (−)-2-octyl iodide with hydrogen bromide and iodide, respectively, indicate overall inversion of configuration[222] for the bromide and iodide reactions. These results are in contrast to overall retention for the chloride reaction,[175] and in these cases appear to be consistent with the proposed S_N2 mechanism (4-329).[273]

7. HYDROGEN FLUORIDE

The lower trialkoxyboranes react with hydrogen fluoride at 30° to give boron trifluoride dialcoholates in a reaction (4-332)[334,401]

$$(RO)_3B + 3\,HF \rightarrow BF_3\cdot 2ROH + ROH \qquad (4\text{-}332)$$

reminiscent of that postulated for hydrogen chloride (4-326). Triphenoxyborane behaved similarly.[334]

The hydrogen fluoride can be generated *in situ* from sodium fluoborate and strong acids.[401,489]

$$3\,NaBF_4 + 3\,HCl + (CH_3O)_3B + 5\,CH_3OH \rightarrow 4\,BF_3{\cdot}2CH_3OH + 3\,NaCl \quad (4\text{-}333)$$

The incorporation of anhydrides as alcohol acceptors resulted in diminished yields of the boron trifluoride complexes.[334]

$$(CH_3O)_3B + 3\,HF + 3\,(C_2H_5CO)_2O \rightarrow 3\,C_2H_5CO_2H + 2\,C_2H_5CO_2CH_3 + BF_3{:}C_2H_5CO_2CH_3 \quad (4\text{-}334)$$

$$(CH_3O)_3B + 3\,HF + 3\,(CF_3CO)_2O + (C_2H_5)_2O \rightarrow 3\,CF_3CO_2H + 3\,CF_3CO_2CH_3 + BF_3{:}O(C_2H_5)_2 \quad (4\text{-}335)$$

8. BORIC ACID

The reaction of orthoborates with boric acid or its dehydration products to produce metaborates is discussed in Chapter 9.

Ethanol has been distilled from an essentially equimolar mixture of triethoxyborane and boric acid.[102] Presumably the boric acid dehydrated in the hot mixture and the evolved water hydrolyzed the ester.

F. With Acid Anhydrides

The preparation of oxybis(diacyloxyboranes) from the reactions of various acid anhydrides and trialkoxyboranes is described in Chapter 8.

G. With Esters

1. BORATES

The redistribution of an admixture of esters (4-336) undoubtedly

$$(RO)_3B + (R'O)_3B \rightleftarrows (RO)_2BOR' + (R'O)_2BOR \quad (4\text{-}336)$$

proceeds at a finite rate, but attempts to isolate the unsymmetrical products invariably led to a shift in the equilibrium and recovery of the symmetrical esters (see Chapter 6). Evidence for reaction (4-336), however, has been presented as shown by the isolation of the unsymmetrical ester in equation (4-337).[112]

$$(C_2H_5O)_3B + 2\left[o\text{-}NO_2C_6H_4\text{—}O\right]_3B \rightarrow 3\left[o\text{-}NO_2C_6H_4\text{—}O\right]_2BOC_2H_5 \quad (4\text{-}337$$

The preparation of unsymmetrical esters from the redistribution reaction of trialkoxyboranes and tri-glycol biborates is discussed in Chapter 6.

2. SILICATES

The reaction of tributoxyborane with methyl silicate to give trimethoxyborane and butyl silicate has been discussed in Section IV-E-3.

3. CARBOXYLATES

Reactions of trimethoxy- and tributoxyborane with various carboxylic acid esters can lead to the preparation of new orthoborates. These reactions are discussed in Section IV-E-3.

H. With Aldehydes and Ketones

Early workers[329] were unable to effect reduction of aldehydes and ketones with boric acid esters, but propionaldehyde subsequently was found to be a product of the reaction of tripropoxyborane and salicylaldehyde.[516] See Section IV-E-1.

The first clear-cut reduction was reported for a series of aliphatic and aromatic aldehydes and alicyclic ketones with allyl, isopropyl and isobutyl borate (4-338).[260]

$$\left[\begin{matrix}R\\ \quad\diagdown\\ \quad\quad CHO\\ \quad\diagup\\ R\end{matrix}\right]_3 B + 3\,R'\overset{O}{\overset{\|}{C}}R'' \rightarrow \left[\begin{matrix}R'\\ \quad\diagdown\\ \quad\quad CHO\\ \quad\diagup\\ R''\end{matrix}\right]_3 B + R\overset{O}{\overset{\|}{C}}R \qquad (4\text{-}338)$$

The reaction with benzaldehyde subsequently was extended to the borates of cyclohexanol and ethylene glycol. However, cyclohexanone with either propyl or butyl borate underwent condensation to cyclohexylidenecyclohexanone.[265]

Aromatic aldehydes were reduced more easily than aliphatic aldehydes and aldehydes in general were more easily reduced than

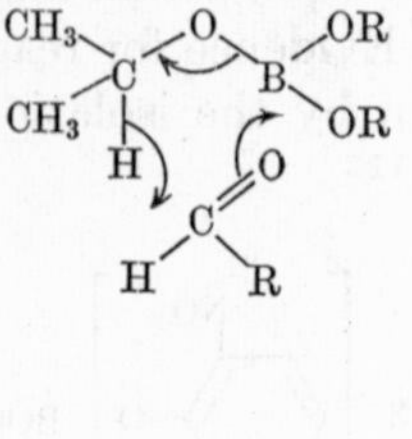

(CXI)

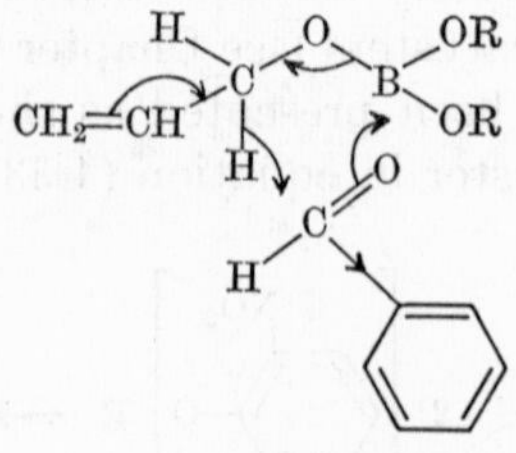

(CXII)

ketones. Allyl borate was more effective than isopropyl borate.[260] These trends are consistent with the cyclic path (CXI) in which the electron shifts shown would be facilitated by vinyl in place of methyl, and phenyl in place of alkyl (CXII).

I. With Acetals

The reaction of tributoxyborane with 2,2-dimethoxypropane is described in Section IV-E-3.

J. With Ethers

In contrast to the boron trihalides, boric acid esters do not cleave ethers. Trimethoxy- and triethoxyborane did not react with methyl and ethyl ether,[505] and triphenoxyborane did not react with ethyl ether, dioxane or tetrahydrofuran.[111] This unreactivity is undoubtedly due to the decreased electrophilic character of the esters.

K. With Hydroperoxides

The attempted preparation of alkylperoxyboranes by treatment of tripropoxyborane with *t*-butyl, 1-methyl-1-phenylethyl and pinane hydroperoxide led to only small displacements of propanol.[130,131] The initial reaction product with 1-methyl-1-phenylethyl hydroperoxide was formulated as undergoing an oxygen–oxygen heterolysis accompanied by migration of the phenyl group from carbon to oxygen (4-339).[130] No boron-containing products were isolated.

$$(CH_3)_2C(C_6H_5)\text{—O—O—B}\langle \longrightarrow (CH_3)_2C(OC_6H_5)\text{—OB}\langle \qquad (4\text{-}339)$$

L. With Alkoxides

The reaction of boric acid esters with metal alkoxides offers a convenient method for the preparation of tetraalkoxyborate salts. Chapter 14 deals with this class of compound.

M. With Hydroxides

Alkoxyhydroxyborate salts resulting from the reaction of boric acid esters and metal hydroxides are discussed in Chapter 14.

N. With Halogen Compounds

1. THE HALOGENS

The reaction of trimethoxyborane with chlorine gas at room temperature proceeds virtually quantitatively in two hours to produce boron trichloride, phosgene, and hydrogen chloride.[324]

$$B(OCH_3)_3 + 9\,Cl_2 \rightarrow BCl_3 + 3\,COCl_2 + 9\,HCl \qquad (4\text{-}340)$$

Definitive halogenations of higher unsubstituted boric acid esters have not yet been reported. Schiff[402] found that triethoxyborane reacted with chlorine gas to give products containing two atoms of chlorine per ester molecule. It was later shown that five atoms of chlorine could be introduced per triethoxyborane unit.[116] Attempted distillation of this product was believed to result in the isolation of (CXIII). No rational explanation is available for the formation of this ether.

$$Cl_2CHCH(Cl)OCH_2CH_3$$

(CXIII)

The 1,1-dihydrofluoroalkyl borates (CXIV) were readily converted to the monochloro derivatives (CXV) by treatment with

$$(R_FCH_2O)_3B \qquad\qquad (R_FCH(Cl)O)_3B$$

$R_F = CF_3, CF_3CF_2, CF_3CF_2CF_2$

(CXIV) (CXV)

gaseous chlorine in the presence of ultraviolet light. The chlorine uptake did not stop after the formation of (CXV) but proceeded to give the cleavage products (CXVI). The perhalogenated derivatives

$$(R_FCH(Cl)O)_2BCl \qquad\qquad (R_FCCl_2O)_3B$$

(CXVI) (CXVII)

(CXVII) were not produced. Bromination of (CXIV) was unsuccessful, as was the attempted fluorination with silver difluoride.[418]

2. GROUP I HALIDES

Lithium chloride did not react with triethoxyborane at 185° or with refluxing tributoxyborane.[102]

3. GROUP II HALIDES

Calcium chloride did not react with refluxing tributoxyborane. Similarly zinc chloride did not react with triethoxyborane, but upon heating with tributoxyborane at about 250°, 1-butene was evolved. At 300°, butanol and butyl chloride were obtained. The reaction was formulated as proceeding through the complex (CXVIII).[102]

$$[(C_4H_9O)_3BCl]^-ZnCl^+$$
(CXVIII)

4. GROUP III HALIDES

The reaction of trialkoxyboranes with boron trihalides offers a convenient method of synthesis of the alkoxyhaloboranes. This chemistry is discussed in Chapter 12.

Tripropoxyborane and aluminum chloride at 75–90° and tributoxyborane and aluminum chloride at 200° gave no evidence of alkyl chloride formation.[267] In direct contradiction, the reaction of tributoxyborane and aluminum chloride was reported to result in a complex mixture of products including n-butyl chloride, isobutyl chloride, *s*-butyl chloride, dibutyl ether, and 2-butene.[302]

5. GROUP IV HALIDES

Stannic chloride and bromide complexes of trimethoxy- and triethoxyborane have been reported.[261]

Silicon tetrachloride did not react with boiling tributoxyborane, but in the presence of ferric chloride, butene and butyl chloride were evolved leaving a boric oxide–silica residue.[100]

6. GROUP V HALIDES

Esters do not react with phosphorus trichloride even on boiling.[100,262] However, in the presence of oxygen the phosphorylation of the alkyl chains proceeds in the cold.

$$(C_4H_9O)_3B + PCl_3 \xrightarrow{O_2} (Cl_2\overset{O}{\overset{\|}{P}}C_4H_8O)_3B + 3\,HCl \qquad (4\text{-}341)$$

The mechanism of reaction (4-341) does not involve prior formation of phosphoryl chloride from oxidation of the trichloride since phosphoryl chloride reacts with trialkoxyboranes to produce alkyl halides[100,262] and olefins.[100] The phosphorylated products could not be distilled without decomposition and were not isolated pure, but were hydrolyzed to the hydroxyphosphonic acids.

In the presence of ferric chloride, tributoxyborane and phosphorus trichloride react under prolonged heating at 95° to give butyl chloride.[100]

Phosphorus pentachloride originally was formulated by Schiff[402] to give products in a stepwise reaction (4-342 and 4-343) similar to those obtained with antimony chloride.

$$2\ B(OC_2H_5)_3 + 2\ PCl_5 \xrightarrow[\text{temperature}]{\text{Room}} 2\ POCl_3 + 4\ C_2H_5Cl + 2\ C_2H_5OBO \quad (4\text{-}342)$$

$$2\ C_2H_5OBO + PCl_5 \xrightarrow{\Delta} POCl_3 + 2\ C_2H_5Cl + B_2O_3 \quad (4\text{-}343)$$

$$2\ B(OC_2H_5)_3 + 3\ PCl_5 \xrightarrow{\Delta} 3\ POCl_3 + 6\ C_2H_5Cl + B_2O_3 \quad (4\text{-}344)$$

It was stated that phosphorus pentachloride did not give chloro(diisopentoxy)borane with triisopentoxyborane.[244]

Phosphoryl chloride readily reacts with trialkoxyboranes at 100° to produce alkyl halides. The boron is left in the form of boron phosphate.[262]

$$(RO)_3B + POCl_3 \rightarrow 3\ RCl + BPO_4 \quad (4\text{-}345)$$

The reaction of triethoxyborane with antimony chloride in a closed tube at 160° has been formulated as follows:[402]

$$2\ (C_2H_5O)_3B + SbCl_3 \rightarrow SbOCl + 2\ C_2H_5Cl + (C_2H_5)_2O + 2\ C_2H_5OBO \quad (4\text{-}346)$$

7. THIONYL CHLORIDE

It has been stated that the reaction of thionyl chloride and triisopentoxyborane does not give chloro(diisopentoxy)borane.[244]

Tributoxyborane and thionyl chloride do not react at 130°; however, if ferric chloride is present, sulfur dioxide and butyl chloride are evolved.[100]

8. ALKYL HALIDES

Reaction (4-347) has been reported to be reversible when R is

$$3\ (RO)_2BCl \rightarrow B_2O_3 + (RO)_3B + 3\ RCl \quad (4\text{-}347)$$

primary and a straight chain.[278] No experimental evidence was given in support of this statement and it is most doubtful that the reaction is indeed reversible.

9. ACYL HALIDES

Acetyl chloride and benzoyl chloride reportedly react with triethoxyborane at room temperature, but the products were not described.[402] Acetyl chloride did not react with tributoxyborane under reflux; however, butyl chloride and butyl acetate were formed at 60° in the presence of ferric chloride.[100]

As in the case of carboxylic acids, benzoyl chloride was esterified by reaction with triphenoxyborane (4-348).[268] Subsequent heating

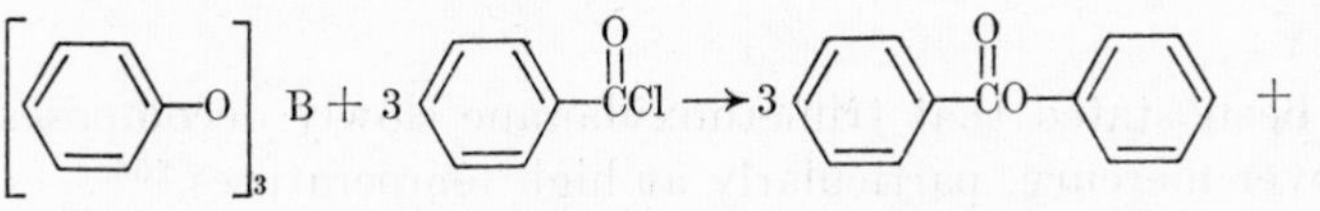

$$[C_6H_5O]_3B + 3\,C_6H_5COCl \rightarrow 3\,C_6H_5COOC_6H_5 + BCl_3 \qquad (4\text{-}348)$$

of the reaction mixture from tri-*p*-cresyloxyborane with aluminum chloride led to rearranged products (4-349).

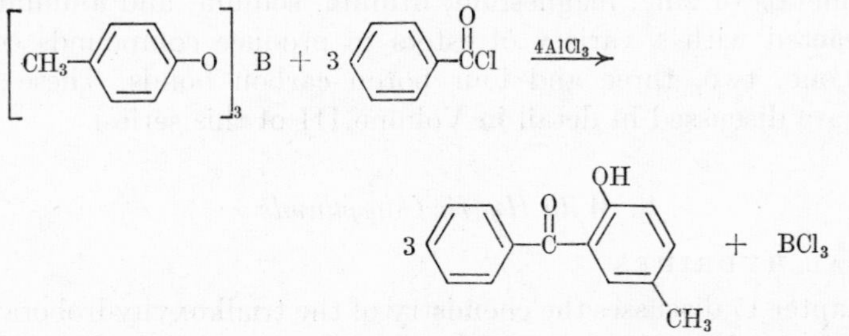

$$[CH_3C_6H_4O]_3B + 3\,C_6H_5COCl \xrightarrow{4AlCl_3} 3\,C_6H_5CO\text{-}C_6H_3(OH)(CH_3) + BCl_3 \qquad (4\text{-}349)$$

10. ALKOXYDIHALOBORANES

The reaction of esters with alkoxydihaloboranes to produce dialkoxyhaloboranes is discussed in Chapter 12.

O. *With Silicon Compounds*

Reactions with silyl halides, silanols and acetoxysilanes to produce siloxyboranes are discussed in Chapter 13. No reaction was observed between silane and trimethoxyborane under a variety of conditions.[141]

P. *With Nitriles*

An increase in the e.m.f. of the system triisopentoxyborane–benzonitrile or triisopropoxyborane–isovaleronitrile–toluene was interpreted as being due to the formation of a nitrile–ester complex.[468]

Q. *With Metals*

1. SODIUM

Tributoxyborane can be refluxed over sodium and recovered quantitatively.[108] Such treatment offers a convenient method for removing certain reactive impurities, such as alcohols. The method has been used to purify trimethoxyborane.[206,303]

2. MERCURY

It has been stated that trimethoxyborane slowly decomposes on storage over mercury, particularly at high temperatures.[206]

R. With Organometallic Reagents

Organometals of zinc, magnesium, lithium, sodium, and aluminum have reacted with a variety of esters to produce compounds containing one, two, three and four boron–carbon bonds. These reactions are discussed in detail in Volume III of this series.

S. With Hydric Compounds

1. METAL HYDRIDES

Chapter 17 discusses the chemistry of the trialkoxyhydroborates derived from the reaction of trialkoxyboranes and metal hydrides. Chapter 14 discusses this reaction when the stoichiometry is such that it produces tetraalkoxyborates, and Chapter 11 describes the reaction when dialkoxyboranes are produced. An excess of the hydride results in complete reduction of the ester to the borohydride.[200,364,409,410,411]

$$(RO)_3B + 4\,MH \rightarrow MBH_4 + 3\,MOCH_3 \qquad (4\text{-}350)$$

Aluminum hydride and aliphatic esters resulted in a complex product (4-351).[247,248] An amine–borane was produced in the presence of triethylamine (4-352). Triphenoxyborane reacted with aluminum hydride to give diborane (4-353).[247]

$$4\,AlH_3 + 3\,(RO)_3B \rightarrow AlH_3(BH_3)_3[Al(OR)_3]_3 \qquad (4\text{-}351)$$

$$AlH_3 + (i\text{-}C_3H_7O)_3B + (C_2H_5)_3N \rightarrow (C_2H_5)_3N\!:\!BH_3 + (i\text{-}C_3H_7O)_3Al \qquad (4\text{-}352)$$

$$2\,AlH_3 + 2\,(C_6H_5O)_3B \rightarrow B_2H_6 + 2\,(C_6H_5O)_3Al \qquad (4\text{-}353)$$

Diisobutylaluminum hydride and triisopropoxyborane reacted to exchange alkyl and alkoxyl groups.

$$3\,(i\text{-}C_4H_9)_2AlH + 3\,(i\text{-}C_3H_7O)_3B + (C_2H_5)_3N \rightarrow 3\,(i\text{-}C_3H_7O)_3Al + 2\,(i\text{-}C_4H_9)_3B + (C_2H_5)_3N\!:\!BH_3 \qquad (4\text{-}354)$$

Lithium aluminum hydride and sodium aluminum hydride are reported to reduce borates to the corresponding borohydride in 70–90% yield.[247]

$$LiAlH_4 + (RO)_3B \rightarrow LiBH_4 + (RO)_3Al \qquad (4\text{-}355)$$

2. BORON HYDRIDES

The lower trialkoxyboranes in the presence of aluminum chloride have been claimed as alkylating agents for pentaborane-9.[511] Thus, methyl, propyl and butylpentaborane-9 have been prepared by reaction of the corresponding trialkoxyboranes with pentaborane-9 and aluminum chloride at 100°.

Tris-(β-dimethylaminoethoxy)borane reacts with diborane to give the amine–borane complex (CXIX),[342] Reaction with tetra-

$$\left[(CH_3)_2\overset{BH_3}{\ddot{N}}CH_2CH_2O\right]_3B$$

(CXIX)

alkyldiboranes results in an exchange of alkyl and alkoxyl groups.[341]

$$R_4B_2H_2 + 2\,(R'O)_3B \rightarrow 3\,RB(OR')_2 + \tfrac{1}{2}\,R_2B_2H_4 \qquad (4\text{-}356)$$

Reactions with diborane to produce alkylboranes are discussed in Volume III of this series.

T. With Diazoalkanes

A variety of trialkoxyboranes have been shown to decompose diazomethane catalytically at below room temperature to give an almost quantitative yield of what was believed to be a crosslinked polymethylene-type polymer.[326] Catalytic activity decreased in the order

$$Cl_3CCH_2O > ClCH_2CH_2O > CH_3O_2CCH_2O > C_6H_5CH_2O > CH_2{=}CHCH_2O > CH_3O > CH_3CH_2O > CH_3CH_2CH_2O > (CH_3)_2CHO$$

which is the order of ability of the esters to complex with metal alkoxides. A reaction mechanism dependent upon the electrophilic character of the boron atom, therefore, is indicated.

Later evidence indicated the polymer to be essentially a straight chain paraffin and the scope was broadened to include mixtures of diazomethane and higher diazolkanes (4-357).[83,382] Sterically hin-

$$CH_2N_2 + RCHN_2 \xrightarrow{(RO)_3B} \left(\overset{R}{\overset{|}{C}}HCH_2\right)_n + N_2 \qquad (4\text{-}357)$$

dered diazo compounds such as diazodiphenylmethane could not be made to enter into a copolymer with diazomethane.[249]

The mechanism of the catalytic decomposition can be formulated to involve an attack of the carbanion form of diazomethane on boron, as has been postulated for the diazomethane–boron trifluoride reaction.[236,425]

$$N{\equiv}\overset{+}{N}{-}\overset{-}{C}H_2 \curvearrowright B(OR)_3 \rightarrow N{\equiv}\overset{+}{N}{-}CH_2\overset{-}{B}(OR)_3 \qquad (4\text{-}358)$$

$$N{\equiv}\overset{+}{N}{-}CH_2\overset{-}{B}(OR)_3 \rightarrow N_2 + \overset{+}{C}H_2\overset{-}{B}(OR)_3 \qquad (4\text{-}359)$$

$$N{\equiv}\overset{+}{N}{-}\overset{-}{C}H_2 \curvearrowright \overset{+}{C}H_2\overset{-}{B}(OR)_3 \rightarrow N{\equiv}\overset{+}{N}CH_2CH_2\overset{-}{B}(OR)_3 \qquad (4\text{-}360)$$

$$N{\equiv}\overset{+}{N}{-}CH_2CH_2\overset{-}{B}(OR)_3 \rightarrow N_2 + \overset{+}{C}H_2CH_2\overset{-}{B}(OR)_3 \qquad (4\text{-}361)$$

Termination* by proton transfer (4-362 and 4-363)[236] was believed

$$\overset{+}{C}H_2CH_2(CH_2)_n\overset{-}{B}(OR)_3 \rightarrow CH_2{=}CH(CH_2)_n\overset{-}{B}(OR)_3 + H^+ \qquad (4\text{-}362)$$

$$CH_2{=}CH_2(CH_2)_n\overset{-}{B}(OR)_3 + H^+ \rightarrow CH_2{=}CH(CH_2)_{n-1}CH_3 + B(OR)_3 \qquad (4\text{-}363)$$

to be unlikely in view of the fact that alcohols do not behave as cocatalysts.[33] Anionic migration from boron to the positive center (4-364) which was thought to be operative, would account for the

$$\overset{+}{C}H_2CH_2(CH_2)_n\overset{-}{B}(OR)_3 \rightarrow ROCH_2CH_2(CH_2)_nB(OR)_2 \qquad (4\text{-}364)$$

presence of end groups in the polymers. Subsequent hydride migration (4-365) would account for the presence of unsaturation.[33]

$$\begin{matrix} H{-}CH(CH_2)_nOR \\ (RO)_2B{-}CH_2 \end{matrix} \rightarrow (RO)_2BH + CH_2{=}CH(CH_2)_nOR \qquad (4\text{-}365)$$

The role of the boric acid ester as portrayed above may not in every case be truly catalytic. It has been known that during the polymerization of diazomethane in the presence of ethyl alcohol and an excess of tributoxyborane, small quantities of methyl butyl ether, ethyl butyl ether, and propyl butyl ether were obtained, indicating actual chemical transformation of the ester.[32]

* Termination by monomer deactivation has been formulated.[34]

$$N{\equiv}\overset{+}{N}{-}\overset{-}{C}H_2 + \overset{+}{C}H_2(CH_2)_nBF_3 \rightarrow \text{dead polymer}$$

U. With Sulfur Compounds

Metathioboric acid (CXX)[503] and tribromoborthiin (CXXI)[504] have been converted to trimethoxyborthiin (CXXII) by treatment with trimethoxyborane.

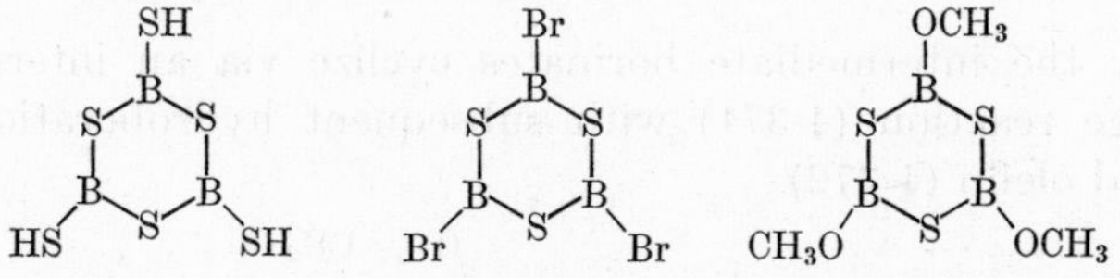

(CXX) (CXXI) (CXXII)

Triisobutoxyborane and phosphorus pentasulfide on slight warming were believed to give triisobutylthioborane; carbon disulfide did not react up to 200°.[121]

V. With Boron–Carbon Compounds

Triethoxyborane and triethylborane were reported[332] not to react, but boronate and borinate products (4-366) were realized at 200° in

$$(RO)_3B + R'_3B \rightarrow ROBR'_2 + (RO)_2BR' \tag{4-366}$$

a pressure vessel with a boron trichloride or butyldichloroborane catalyst.[85] Diborane and alkyldiboranes also catalyze the transformation.[252,341] The necessity for the boron halide catalyst seems doubtful since reaction (4-366) was performed by heating tributoxyborane and triallylborane at 160–170° for sixteen hours in the absence of catalyst,[523] and reactions (4-367)* and (4-368) were performed in closed vessels at 200°, also without catalyst.[251,253]

$$2\,(RO)_3B + R'_3B \rightarrow 3\,R'B(OR)_2 \tag{4-367}$$

$$(RO)_3B + 2\,R'_3B \rightarrow 3\,R'_2BOR \tag{4-368}$$

Tributoxyborane slowly reacts with butoxydiphenylborane at 200° to give dibutoxyphenylborane in good yield, based upon recovered starting materials.[3]

$$(C_4H_9O)_3B + (C_6H_5)_2BOC_4H_9 \xrightarrow[100\text{ hr.}]{200^\circ} 2\,C_6H_5B(OC_4H_9)_2 \tag{4-369}$$

An interesting ramification of the alkyl–alkoxy exchange

* The reverse reaction has been reported to proceed at 150°.[322]

$$3\,R'B(OR)_2 \rightarrow 2\,(RO)_3B + R'_3B$$

reaction takes place with allyl borate in the presence of an amine–borane.[255] Although the path of reaction (4-370) was not recorded,

$$BR_3 + B(OCH_2CH{=}CH_2)_3 + R'_3N{:}BH_3 \rightarrow 3\,RB\begin{matrix} O\text{—}CH_2 \\ | \\ CH_2\text{—}CH_2 \end{matrix} + R'_3N \quad (4\text{-}370)$$

possibly the intermediate borinates cyclize via an internal olefin exchange reaction (4-371) with subsequent hydroboration of the liberated olefin (4-372).

$$R_2BOCH_2CH{=}CH_2 \rightarrow RB\begin{matrix} O\text{—}CH_2 \\ | \\ CH_2\text{—}CH_2 \end{matrix} + \text{Olefin} \quad (4\text{-}371)$$

$$3\ \text{Olefin} + R'_3N{:}BH_3 \rightarrow R_3B + R'_3N \quad (4\text{-}372)$$

Exchange reactions with alkylborolanes appear to leave the ring boron–carbon bonds intact.[254]

$$(CH_3O)_3B + \begin{matrix} CH_2\text{—}CH_2 \\ | \\ CH_2\text{—}CH_2 \end{matrix}B\text{—}i\text{-}C_4H_9 \xrightarrow{200^\circ} (CH_3O)_2B\text{—}i\text{-}C_4H_9 + \begin{matrix} CH_2\text{—}CH_2 \\ | \\ CH_2\text{—}CH_2 \end{matrix}BOCH_3 \quad (4\text{-}373)$$

W. *With Boron–Nitrogen Compounds*

The reaction of tributoxyborane and tris(diethylamino)borane did not result in redistribution to $C_4H_9OB[N(C_2H_5)_2]_2$; starting materials were recovered.[181]

X. *Friedel–Crafts Reaction*

A German patent[238] first revealed that the halides, alcohols or olefins normally used in the Friedel–Crafts alkylation of aromatic compounds[377] could be replaced by boric acid esters using the usual aluminum chloride catalyst. The alkylation also could be effected in

$$(i\text{-}C_4H_9O)_3B + 3\ (\text{1,3-}(CH_3)_2C_6H_4) + AlCl_3 \rightarrow 3\ (\text{1,3-}(CH_3)_2\text{-5-}t\text{-}C_4H_9C_6H_3) + 3\,HCl + \tfrac{1}{2}B_2O_3 + \tfrac{1}{2}Al_2O_3 \quad (4\text{-}374)$$

$$(i\text{-}C_4H_9O)_3B + 3\ C_6H_5\text{—}OCH_3 + AlCl_3 \rightarrow 3\ t\text{-}C_4H_9\text{—}C_6H_4\text{—}OCH_3 + 3\,HCl + \tfrac{1}{2}\,B_2O_3 + \tfrac{1}{2}\,Al_2O_3 \quad (4\text{-}375)$$

$$[C_6H_5\text{—}CH_2O]_3B + 3\ C_6H_6 + AlCl_3 \rightarrow 3\ C_6H_5\text{—}CH_2\text{—}C_6H_5 + 3\,HCl + \tfrac{1}{2}\,B_2O_3 + \tfrac{1}{2}\,Al_2O_3 \quad (4\text{-}376)$$

the presence of concentrated sulfuric acid.[311] Other examples include the preparation of butylbenzene from tributoxyborane and benzene, and dibenzyl from tri-(2-chloroethoxy)borane and benzene in the presence of aluminum chloride.[266,302] In addition to benzene and alkyl and alkoxy substituted benzene, chlorobenzene and phenol also were alkylated.[267] As might be expected, arylation of benzene with triphenoxyborane could not be accomplished.[267,302]

A novel alkylation involves the reaction of triphenoxyborane with triisobutoxyborane at 190–220° in the presence of sulfuric acid to produce *p*-*t*-butylphenol, after hydrolysis of the reaction mixture. The reaction did not proceed with isobutylene or ethylene in place of the triisobutoxyborane.[264] Similar alkylations of triphenoxyborane with triisopropoxyborane, triisobutoxyborane, and tricyclohexyloxyborane in the presence of aluminum chloride have been reported.[429] Alkyl halides also have been used.[263]

Alkylations with boric acid esters proceed under milder conditions and consume less aluminum chloride than alkylations with alcohols. Primary and secondary alkyl alkylating agents[266] result in the usual rearranged products.[377]

$$(n\text{-}C_4H_9O)_3B + C_6H_6 \xrightarrow{AlCl_3} CH_3CH_2CH(CH_3)\text{—}C_6H_5 \quad (4\text{-}377)$$

$$(CH_3CH(CH_3)CH_2O)_3B + C_6H_6 \xrightarrow{AlCl_3} (CH_3)_3C\text{—}C_6H_5 \quad (4\text{-}378)$$

Difficulties normally experienced in the allylation of aromatic compounds[377] were overcome by the use of triallyoxyborane in the presence of ferric chloride. This procedure resulted in a 35% yield of allylbenzene and a 40% yield of p-allylcumene.[421] An aluminum chloride catalyst with this ester, however, resulted in a double alkylation and formation of some rearranged material as a by-product.[266]

$$(CH_2{=}CHCH_2O)_3B + C_6H_6 \xrightarrow{AlCl_3} C_6H_5{-}CH_2CH(CH_3){-}C_6H_5 + (CH_3)_2CH{-}C_6H_5 \qquad (4\text{-}379)$$

The statement[467] that organoboron compounds can result from the reaction of tributoxyborane, benzene, and aluminum chloride could not be substantiated.[266] If, indeed, organoboron compounds are not formed, then in view of the similarity of the borate and alkyl halide alkylations of aromatic hydrocarbons and derivatives, a carbonium ion path (4-380) can be postulated for the borate alkylation reaction as opposed to a boronium ion path (4-381).

$$(RO)_3B + AlCl_3 \rightarrow [(RO)_2BOAlCl_3]^- \; R^+ \rightleftharpoons R^+ + (RO)_2BOAlCl_3^-$$

$$R^+ + C_6H_6 \longrightarrow [C_6H_6R]^+ \text{ (H, R on the ring carbon)} \longrightarrow C_6H_5R + H^+ \qquad (4\text{-}380)$$

$$(RO)_3B + AlCl_3 \rightarrow [ROAlCl_3]^-(RO)_2B^+ \rightleftharpoons (RO)_2B^+ + ROAlCl_3^-$$

$$(RO)_2B^+ + C_6H_6 \longrightarrow C_6H_5B(OR)_2 + H^+ \qquad (4\text{-}381)$$

The alkyl–oxygen cleavage of the carbonium ion path (4-380) is not a common occurrence in boric acid ester chemistry, and it may be that the requisite carbonium ions are formed via decomposition of intermediate alkoxyhaloboranes. Unfortunately, this postulate suffers from the fact that no alkyl halides were produced from aluminum chloride and either tripropoxy or tributoxyborane.[267]

$$(RO)_3B + AlCl_3 \rightarrow ROBCl_2 + (RO)_2AlCl \tag{4-382}$$

$$R\frown O \frown BCl_2 \longrightarrow R^+ + \{O{=}BCl\} + Cl^- ;\quad \{O{=}BCl\} \downarrow \tfrac{1}{3} B_2O_3 + \tfrac{1}{3} BCl_3 \tag{4-383}$$

Y. Oxidation

Attempted distillation of tri-2-octoxyborane resulted in a distillate of methyl hexyl ketone. Reaction (4-384) was formulated to

$$2\left[\begin{array}{c}CH_3(CH_2)_5CHO \\ | \\ CH_3\end{array}\right]_3 B + 3\,O_2 \rightarrow 2\,H_3BO_3 + 6\,CH_3(CH_2)_5\overset{\overset{\displaystyle O}{\|}}{C}CH_3 \tag{4-384}$$

rationalize this product.[121] Since the purity of the tri-2-octoxyborane is questionable, and since 2-octanol itself undergoes air oxidation to methyl hexyl ketone, it is probable that reaction (4-384) did not indeed occur as written.

Z. Reduction

The reduction of trimethoxyborane with hydrogen and aluminum powder at 800 mm. and 170° for five hours in the presence of an aluminum chloride–sodium chloride flux was reported to give a 20% yield of diborane.[232] Passage of trimethoxyborane and hydrogen through a tube of graphite heated to 1400° resulted in a variety of volatile products including diborane.[233]

AA. Of Unsaturated Esters

1. ADDITION

Allyl borate adds bromine in carbon tetrachloride solution to give the dibromopropyl borate (CXXIII)[118,119,121] which presumably gives the corresponding dinitropropyl borate (CXXIV) with silver nitrite.[121]

$$\underset{\text{CXXIII)}}{(BrCH_2\overset{\displaystyle Br}{\overset{|}{C}}HCH_2O)_3B} \qquad \underset{\text{CXXIV)}}{(O_2NCH_2\overset{\displaystyle NO_2}{\overset{|}{C}}HCH_2O)_3B}$$

Addition of hydrogen bromide to the terminal double bond of unsaturated alcohols, even in the presence of peroxides, leads to the formation of secondary bromides.[20] However, anti-Markownikoff addition was realized by hydrobromination of the borate of an unsaturated alcohol in the presence of peroxide.[41]

$$[CH_2{=}CH(CH_2)_nO]_3B + 3\,HBr \xrightarrow{t\text{-}C_4H_9OO/t\text{-}C_4H_9} [BrCH_2CH_2(CH_2)_nO]_3B$$

$$\xrightarrow{3\,H_2O} 3\,BrCH_2CH_2(CH_2)_nOH + H_3BO_3 \qquad (4\text{-}385)$$

It has been claimed that trichloromethanesulfonyl chloride adds to allyl borate to give sulfur dioxide plus (CXXV).[270]

$$\underset{\text{(CXXV)}}{(Cl_3CCH_2\overset{\displaystyle Cl}{\overset{|}{C}}HCH_2O)_3B}$$

Thioacetic acid has been added to propargyl borate with azobisisobutyronitrile as a catalyst.[518]

$$(CH_2{=}CCH_2O)_3B + CH_3\overset{\displaystyle O}{\overset{\|}{C}}SH \xrightarrow[2.\ H_2O]{1.\ \text{catalyst}} CH_3\overset{\displaystyle O}{\overset{\|}{C}}SCH{=}CHCH_2OH \qquad (4\text{-}386)$$

2. POLYMERIZATION

In contrast to the statement that methallyl and furfuryl borate do not form homopolymers,[392] and the failure of allyl borate to polymerize in the presence of benzoyl peroxide,[396] methallyl borate has been polymerized by subjection to a stream of air,[22] and allyl borate

$$(CH_2{=}CHCH_2O)_3B \xrightarrow{O_2} \left[\begin{array}{l} -CHCH_2- \\ \;|\\ CH_2 \\ \;| \\ O \\ \;| \\ BOCH_2CH{=}CH_2 \\ \;| \\ O \\ \;| \\ CH_2 \\ \;| \\ -CHCH_2- \end{array}\right]_m \xrightarrow{H_2O} \left[\begin{array}{l} -CH_2CH- \\ \quad\;\; | \\ \quad CH_2OH \end{array}\right]_m$$

(4-387)

has been polymerized by both this technique[22] and by treatment with stannic chloride.[199] Hydrolysis of the polymer from the air-treated allyl borate gave a 51% yield of polyallyl alcohol.[22]

3. COPOLYMERIZATION

Allyl borate has been claimed to copolymerize with vinylidene chloride to give a copolymer containing 7% of the allyl ester.[65] If, indeed, copolymerization and not parallel homopolymerization has taken place, an idealized structure (CXXVI) may be formulated.

$$\left[-CH_2CH(CH_2CCl_2)_{25}- \atop \quad | \atop CH_2-O-B(OCH_2CH{=}CH_2)_2 \right]_n$$

(CXXVI)

Methallyl borate and furfuryl borate have been copolymerized with methyl acrylate, methyl methacrylate and vinyl acetate with benzoyl peroxide as a catalyst.[392]

Phenol formaldehyde-type resins have been claimed for the reaction of phenyl borate and formaldehyde.[472]

$$(C_6H_5O)_3B + HCHO \longrightarrow \left[-C_6H_4-O-B(-O-C_6H_4-CH_2-)-O-C_6H_4-CH_2- \right]_n \qquad (4\text{-}388)$$

BB. Of *Tri(mercaptoalkoxy)boranes*

Mercapto borates have been condensed with dialkyl and diaryl tin oxides to give unusual heterocyclic derivatives of the diborate type.[379,380] These are represented in equation (4-389) as monomers

$$2\ (HSCH_2CH_2O)_3B + 3\ R_2SnO \rightarrow \left[R_2Sn \begin{matrix} SCH_2CH_2O \\ SCH_2CH_2O \end{matrix} BOCH_2CH_2S \right]_2 SnR_2 + 3\ H_2O \qquad (4\text{-}389)$$

although polymers would probably form in place of ten-membered rings. They also have been condensed with trialkyl and triaryl tin hydroxides to yield esters of type (CXXVII).[380]

$$(R_3SnSRO)_3B$$
(CXXVII)

VI. ANALYTICAL

A. Hydrolytically Unstable "Neutral" Esters

The method used for the determination of boron in a trialkoxy- or triaryloxyborane is dependent upon the hydrolytic stability of the ester in question and the nature of the hydrolysis products.

Hydrolytically unstable species[397] which result in neutral or strongly acidic or basic organic fragments can be dissolved in water and titrated for boric acid in the presence of mannitol[481] in the usual manner. The water solution of the ester is acidified with hydrochloric acid. The slightly acid solution is gently boiled on a hot plate for ten minutes and cooled to room temperature in a cold water bath. Three drops of methylene blue solution are added and the solution and cover rinsings are adjusted to the methyl red end-point with 0.1 *N* sodium hydroxide. (The red-violet to green end-point effected by the methylene blue is more accurately discernible than the normal red to yellow change of methyl red itself.) Phenolphthalein (8 drops) and excess mannitol (30g.; the use of less than seven moles of mannitol per mole of boric acid at the dilutions used results in a hazy end-point and low boron determination) are then added and the boric acid complex is titrated with 0.1 *N* sodium hydroxide to the phenolphthalein end-point (green to red-violet).[219]

The boron analysis of an ester, however, is not always an accurate means of determining the purity of the ester since a small amount of dissolved boric acid will compensate for a relatively large amount of non-boron-containing impurity. Fortunately a simple means of distinguishing the two boron sources is available. The Karl Fischer reagent is active to boric acid and inert to the ester.[456] A discussion of the useful consequences of this fact is given in Chapter 7.

B. Hydrolytically Unstable "Acidic" or "Basic" Esters

In the case of aromatic or alkanolamine esters, the phenols or aminoalcohols liberated in the hydrolysis may, depending upon their ionization constants, interfere with the indicator titration for boric acid. In these cases the "identical pH" method[460,510] may be used to advantage. A dilute solution of the ester is adjusted to a selected pH near neutrality, mannitol is added, and the solution is titrated with alkali to the original pH. The exact pH used has varied with different workers from 6.3 to 7.6. Since boric acid begins to react with alkali at pH 5.5 and since boric acid with mannitol is not completely neutralized until about pH 8.2, such a titration is not intrinsically stoichiometric. Any pH selected will result in either some boric acid neutralized before mannitol addition, or some boric acid remaining unneutralized after titration or both. However, if approximately constant volumes, constant amounts of mannitol, and suitably low boric acid concentrations are employed, the method can be empirically standardized by merely titrating known amounts of boric acid in the same fashion.[460]

Gravimetric methods also may be used to circumvent the interferences of the weakly acidic or basic residues. A weighed quantity of the ester is heated to constant weight with two to three times its weight of freshly ignited magnesia. The increase in weight of the magnesia is due to the residual boric oxide.[8,366] The method is not recommended.[208]

A second gravimetric procedure appears applicable. After the ester is hydrolyzed, the boric acid is converted to tetrafluoboric acid with hydrofluoric acid and precipitated with nitron (1,4-diphenyl-3,5-endanilohydrotriazol, $C_{20}H_{16}N_4$). Fluoride ion and weak acids and bases do not interfere.[299]

A transesterification procedure involves treatment of the ester with methanol and sulfuric acid followed by distillation of trimethoxyborane–methanol azeotrope.[461] The azeotrope is collected in water in which the trimethoxyborane instantly hydrolyzes and the resulting boric acid is titrated in the usual manner. This procedure, adapted from the original method of Chapin,[495] is at best unwieldy and often suffers from incomplete volatilization of the boron as trimethoxyborane. In addition, it is not applicable at all to highly sterically hindered esters such as tri-(2-cyclohexylcyclohexyl) borate and tri-(diisobutylcarbinyl) borate[444] since only a small percentage of these esters are transesterified in a reasonable time.

The degradative methods described in the next section also may be applied to the hydrolytically unstable "acidic" or "basic" esters.

C. Hydrolytically Stable Esters

In the event the ester to be analyzed is grossly insoluble in water or possessed of high hydrolytic stability,[444] it is necessary to maintain prolonged periods of reflux in boron-free glassware to effect hydrolysis. Low results are often obtained and a second and more prolonged hydrolysis must be performed.

A general procedure[219] which has been found to be applicable with slight modification to boric acid esters of this type is the method for determination of boron in acid-insoluble minerals,[420] a procedure which also has been used for the determination of boron in boric acid complexes of hydroxy acids,[390,391] hydroxy ketones,[391] and catechol.[259,390] The ester is fused with sodium carbonate in a platinum crucible. The cooled melt is dissolved in hydrochloric acid, boiled to expel carbon dioxide, and neutralized with dilute base. Excess mannitol is then added and the boric acid titrated to the phenolphthalein end-point.

Other degradative methods include oxidation in a Parr oxygen bomb,[258] oxidation in an Inconel bomb at high temperature and pressure,[9] oxidation of a methanol or acetone solution of the ester in a oxygen–hydrogen flame,[509] oxidation by the Schöniger combustion technique,[519] oxidation in a Parr peroxide bomb[219] as originally applied to the determination of boron in boronic acids[433] and boron fluoride–ester complexes,[365] and oxidation with trifluoroperoxyacetic acid.[455]

VII. PHYSICAL CONSTANTS

A. Trialkoxyboranes

ROH in $(RO)_3B$	M.p. (°C)	B.p. (°C)/mm.	d_4^t	n_D^t	Reference
CH_3OH		67.5–68/750			414
		68.0–68.5	0.920^{20}		444
		68–70		1.350^{25}	52, 54
		68–70			55
		68.5	0.9260^{25}	1.3548^{25}	201
	−29	68.7			505
		69/750		$1.3585^{22.5}$	352
	−29.3 ± 0.1				492
	−34				464
			0.9185^{25}	1.3543^{25}	471
			0.9327^{20}	1.3575^{20}	457
$(CH_3O)_3B$–CH_3OH azeotrope		54.3/760	0.8804^{25}	1.3472^{25}	471
		54.6		1.3488^{20}	414
C_2H_5OH		50–52/8, 117–119	0.859^{26}	1.3723^{25}	444
		117–119		1.374^{25}	52
	−84.8	117.2/740	0.8546^{28}		17
		117.2/740	0.88640^{0}		151
		117.5	0.8577^{25}	1.3718^{25}	201
		118–119/743		1.3798^{20}	76
		118.3–118.4/740.5			492
		119.2/756	0.8635^{20}	1.3741^{20}	122
		120	0.864^{26}	1.3721^{25}	479

(*Table continued*)

A. *Trialkoxyboranes* (continued)

ROH in $(RO)_3B$	M.p. (°C)	B.p. (°C)/mm.	d_4^t	n_D^t	Reference
$(C_2H_5O)_3B$–7.75 C_2H_5OH azeotrope		76.6–76.8			69
$(C_2H_5O)_3B$–6.90 C_2H_5OH azeotrope		76.6			484
$ClCH_2CH_2OH$		64/0.06, 68/0.1		1.4558^{20}	114
		70/0.1			2, 143
		121–123/6			266
		144/15	1.2714^{25}	1.4547^{25}	201
		175/50	1.2780^{20}	1.4556^{20}	229
$CH_3CHClOH$			1.2780^{20}	1.4556^{20}	107
Cl_2CHCH_2OH		118–120/0.5	1.496^{20}	1.4840^{19}	2
$ClCH_2CHClOH$		Not isolated pure			157
Cl_3CCH_2OH	97–98	112/0.05			64
$Cl_2CHCHClOH$		116–118/11	1.647^{20}	1.5052^{20}	157
$Cl_3CCHClOH$		98–105/0.5	1.702^{20}	1.5090^{20}	157
$BrCH_2CH_2OH$		169–170/6			521
Br_2CCH_2OH	179–182				304
FCH_2CH_2OH		173			113
F_3CCH_2OH		43/60		1.297^{20}	4
		77/200		1.2975^{23}	418, 419
$CF_3CHClOH$		100/200		1.3405^{20}	418
$NH_2CH_2CH_2OH$	74				461
	95–98	126–127/8			387

$(CH_3)_2NCH_2CH_2OH$		Nonvolatile			342
$(CH_3)_2NCH_2CH_2OH$ (↓ BH_3)	86–89.5	> 100/0.001			342
$NCCH_2CH_2OH$		High boiling		1.4418^{20}	384
	—	—	—	—	383
$HSCH_2CH_2OH$		> 160/15			379, 380
$HOCH_2CH_2OH$ (structure in doubt)	161				120, 121
$CH_3OCH_2CH_2OH$		130–131/13			386
		134–135/15	1.0096^{28}	1.4059^{20}	397
$ClCH_2OCH_2CH_2OH$			1.297^{20}	1.4632^{20}	114
$CH_3CH(OCH_3)OH$			1.0096^{20}	1.4059^{20}	107
$CH_3OCH_2CH_2OCH_2CH_2OH$			1.0606^{20} (calc.)	1.4350^{20} (calc.)	491
$C_2H_5OCH_2CH_2OCH_2CH_2OH$		222–223/5	0.9955^{20}	1.4247^{25}	520, 521
$C_4H_9OCH_2CH_2OH$		161–163/0.7	1.0399^{20}	1.4327^{25}	520, 521
2,4-$Cl_2C_6H_3$–OCH_2CH_2OH	109–111	295–315/0.16			452
2,4,5-$Cl_3C_6H_2$–OCH_2CH_2OH	120–124				82
$CH_3(CH_2)_8C(=O)OCH_2CH_2OH$	—	—	—	—	210

(Table continued)

A. Trialkoxyboranes (continued)

ROH in $(RO)_3B$	M.p. (°C)	B.p. (°C)/mm.	d_4^t	n_D^t	Reference
$CH_3(CH_2)_{10}\overset{O}{\overset{\|}{C}}OCH_2CH_2OH$	—	—	—	—	210
$CH_3(CH_2)_{12}\overset{O}{\overset{\|}{C}}OCH_2CH_2OH$	—	—	—	—	210
$CH_3(CH_2)_{14}\overset{O}{\overset{\|}{C}}OCH_2CH_2OH$	49–50				210
$CH_3(CH_2)_{16}\overset{O}{\overset{\|}{C}}OCH_2CH_2OH$	—	—	—	—	210
$HO\overset{O}{\overset{\|}{C}}CH_2OH$	—	—	—	—	296
$CH_3O\overset{O}{\overset{\|}{C}}CH_2OH$	—	—	—	—	326
$C_2H_5O\overset{O}{\overset{\|}{C}}CH_2OH$		124/0.01	1.160^{20}	1.4290^{20}	156
n-C_3H_7OH		68.5–69/12	0.8576^{20}	1.3948^{20}	17
		176/760	0.861^{20}	1.3969^{20}	178
		176–177	$0.8554^{28-29.5}$	$1.3935^{28-29.5}$	208
		176–179	0.856^{24}	1.3933^{25}	444
		177	0.8540^{25}	1.3937^{25}	201
		180–183/760		$1.4266^{22.5}$	352

i-C_3H_7OH		75/76, 90/120		1.3762^{20}	76
		137	0.8183^{25}	1.3742^{25}	201
		139–140	0.815^{23}	1.3750^{25}	444
			0.820^{25}	1.3750^{25}	369
$CH_2{=}CHCH_2OH$		42/7		1.4496^{20}	76
		76/15	0.926^{20}	1.4276^{21}	183
		77–80/17			446
		95/36			421
		163–165/630			208
		175–177/741	0.9215^{20}	1.4285^{20}	266
		179	0.9241^{0}	1.4333^{0}	223
			0.928^{25}	1.4230^{25}	369
$CH{\equiv}CCH_2OH$		68–69/2, 79–81/4		1.4564^{15}	518
		99/12	1.040^{10}	1.4540^{20}	183
$ClCH_2CH_2CH_2OH$		96/0.075	1.190^{20}	1.4571^{20}	2, 153
ClC_3H_6OH		102–103/1		1.4437^{21}	144
$ClCH_2CH(Cl)CH_2OH$		143/0.004	1.419^{19}	1.4952^{20}	2
$(ClCH_2)_2CHOH$		126–130/0.004		1.4902^{17}	144
		128/0.004	1.417^{19}	1.4891^{20}	2
		166–179/1–2	$1.396^{25.5}$	1.4858^{25}	444
		240/25	1.4028^{20}	1.4883^{20}	229
$Cl_3CCH_2CH(Cl)CH_2OH$	—	—	—	—	338
$(Cl_3C)_2CHOH$	325				172
			1.396^{25}	1.4858^{25}	369
$BrCH_2CH(Br)CH_2OH$		120 (decomp.)			119, 121

(Table continued)

A. Trialkoxyboranes (continued)

ROH in $(RO)_3B$	M.p. (°C)	B.p. (°C)/mm.	d_4^t	n_D^t	Reference
$CHF_2CF_2CH_2OH$		128/69	1.527^{20}		25
$CF_3CF_2CH_2OH$		110/200		1.2940^{23}	418, 419
$CF_3CF_2CH(Cl)OH$		117/200		1.3262^{25}	418
$(CH_3)_2NCH_2CH_2CH_2OH$		Viscous liquid			342
$O_2NCH_2CH(NO_2)CH_2OH$	—	—	—	—	121
$(CH_3)_2C(CN)OH$	—	—	—	—	70
$(C_6H_{11})_3SnSCH(CH_3)CH_2OH$	—	—	—	—	380
$CH_3OCH_2CH(CH_3)OH$		125–128/15	0.9525^{20}	1.4257^{25}	520, 521
$CH_3OCH_2CH(CH_2Cl)OH$		150–162/2	1.205^{15}		351
$C_2H_5OCH_2CH(CH_2Cl)OH$		145–150/0.05			327
		210–216/12	1.148^{22}		330
$CH_3OCH_2CH(CH_3)OCH_2CH(CH_3)OH$		183–184/2	0.9774^{20}	1.4082^{25}	520, 521

$Cl\text{-}C_6H_4\text{-}OCH_2CH(OH)CH_3$	275–295/0.3			452
$Cl_2C_6H_3\text{-}OCH_2CH(OH)CH_3$	290–305/0.2			220
$Cl_3C_6H_2\text{-}OCH(CH_3)CH_2OH$			1.5740^{25}	82
$C_2H_5OC(=O)CH_2CH_2OH$	134/0.01	1.108^{20}	1.4331^{20}	156
$C_2H_5OC(=O)CH(OH)CH_3$	110/0.01	1.070^{20}	1.4215^{20}	156
$C_3H_7OC(=O)CH(OH)CH_3$	169–175/5			461

(*Table continued*)

A. *Trialkoxyboranes* (continued)

ROH in $(RO)_3B$	M.p. (°C)	B.p. (°C)/mm.	d_4^t	n_D^t	Reference
n-C_4H_9OH		71–72/2	0.8551^{20}	1.4102^{20}	339
		103–105/8			226
		105–106/8	0.8567^{20}	1.4080^{20}	17
		114–115/15, 234–238/745	$0.856^{27.5}$		37
		116/15			162
		128–130/20	0.847^{28}	1.4078^{25}	444
		136/30		$1.4806^{22.5}$	352
		227	0.8546^{25}	1.4077^{25}	201
		229–230	$0.8527^{28-29.5}$	$1.4062^{28-29.5}$	208
		230–231	0.8470^{28}	1.4089^{28}	397
			0.853^{25}	1.4063^{25}	369
i-C_4H_9OH		59–60/215		1.4041^{20}	339
		96/12		1.4050^{18}	176
		205	0.8404^{25}	1.4014^{25}	201
		207–209	0.843^{23}	1.4014^{25}	444
		211.5–213	0.8391^{25}	1.4029^{25}	397
			0.861^{25}	1.4020^{25}	369
s-C_4H_9OH		83/14		1.3974^{19}	176
		92/10		$1.3950^{22.5}$	352
		92–96/26		1.3983^{21}	162
		114/40		1.3962^{20}	162
		184–192	0.829^{24}	1.3942^{25}	444
		195.4–195.8	0.8264^{25}	1.3960^{25}	397
t-C_4H_9OH		45–50/41			199
		53/9		1.3872^{20}	76
	12	59.5–60.5/12			231

		60/12	0.8113^{25}	1.3855^{25}	201
		60–64/5, 175/760	0.8153^{20}	1.3879^{20}	294
		63–67/18	$0.811^{25.5}$	1.3863^{25}	444
		65–66/11		$1.3860^{22.5}$	352
	18–19	101/74, 88–89/53		1.3879^{20}	169
			0.820^{25}	1.3843^{25}	369
$CH_3CH{=}CHCH_2OH$		108/3–5			392
		112/9	$0.9160^{15.5}$	1.4428^{25}	185
$CH_2{=}CHCH_2CH_2OH$		112/15	0.8925^{22}	1.4332^{20}	185
$CH_2{=}CCH_2OH$ $\vert$ CH_3	30	91–92/3–4			392
	29.5–30	118/19			183
	28–29	220–226			461
	29–30	225–225.2			397
$CH_2{=}CHCHOH$ $\vert$ CH_3		78/10	0.8717^{18}	1.4177^{20}	185
$ClCH_2CH_2CH_2CH_2OH$		136–140/0.1	1.350^{20}	1.4618^{21}	2, 143
CH_3 $\vert$ Cl_3CCHOH $\vert$ CH_3	183–195				444
Cl $\vert$ $Cl_3CCH_2CHCH_2OH$	—	—	—	—	270
$CF_3CF_2CF_2CHOH$ $\vert$ Cl		150/200		1.3250^{25}	418
$CF_3CF_2CF_2CH_2OH$		137/200		1.2596^{23} 1.2965^{23}	418, 419

(Table continued)

A. Trialkoxyboranes (continued)

ROH in $(RO)_3B$	M.p. (°C)	B.p. (°C)/mm.	d_4^t	n_D^t	Reference
$C_{17}H_{33}C(=O)NHC(CH_3)_2CH_2OH$	—	—	—	—	147
$HS(CH_2)_4OH$	—	—	—	—	380
$[Cl\text{-}C_6H_4\text{-}CH_2]_3SnS(CH_2)_4OH$	—	—	—	—	380
4-Cl-2-CH_3-C_6H_3-$OCH_2CH_2CH_2CH_2OH$		Liquid			82
3,4-Cl_2-C_6H_3-$OCH_2CH_2CH_2CH_2OH$			1.305_{25}^{25}	1.5567^{25}	82
4-Br-C_6H_4-$OCH(CH_3)CH_2CH_2OH$		Liquid			82

$CH_3OC(=O)—C(OH)(CH_3)_2$		106–108			167
$C_2H_5OC(=O)CH_2CH(OH)C(=O)OC_2H_5$		180/0.01	1.167^{20}	1.4408^{20}	156
n-$C_5H_{11}OH$		110–114/2, 274.5–276	0.852^{27}	1.4183^{25}	444
		146–148/16			226
		154/16		$1.4205^{22.5}$	352
		156/30	0.8565^{25}	1.4183^{25}	201
		270–271	0.8557^{28-29}	$1.4176^{28-29.5}$	208
		274.5–276.1	0.8522^{27}	1.4197^{27}	397
(n-$C_5H_{11}O)_3B^{10}$		154–9/25			220
i-$C_5H_{11}OH$		131.8–133/12	0.8518^{20}		516
		250/760	0.8473^{25}	1.4142^{25}	201
		256.1/761	0.8514^{20}	1.4156^{20}	122
		258–259	$0.8504^{28-29.5}$	$1.4134^{28-29.5}$	208
			0.8514^{20}	1.4156^{20}	107
t-$C_5H_{11}OH$		77–91/0.3–0.4	0.847^{24}	1.4104^{25}	444
		87/6, 105/13		1.4112^{20}	76
		92/8	0.853^{20}	1.4025^{19}	173
		235/760	0.8482^{20}	1.4124^{20}	294
$CH_3CH_2CH_2CH(CH_3)OH$	236.5–238.0		0.8298^{27}	1.4075^{27}	397
			0.8375^{20}	1.4075^{20}	107
$CH_3CH_2CH(CH_3)CH_2OH$		109.8–114/12	0.8375^{20}		516
		260–261.2	0.8470^{28}	1.4170^{20}	397

(Table continued)

A. *Trialkoxyboranes* (continued)

ROH in $(RO)_3B$	M.p. (°C)	B.p. (°C)/mm.	d_4^t	n_D^t	Reference
$(CH_3)_2CHCHOH$ │ CH_3		59–61/0.4	0.844^{20}	1.4080^{20}	178
		226.0–230.0	0.8340^{28}	1.4079^{20}	397
$(CH_3)_3CCH_2OH$	57–59	229–230			397
	58–58.5	104/12			178
$(CH_3CH_2)_2CHOH$		105/8	0.841^{20}	1.4127^{15}	173
		125–133/23, 238–240	0.839^{25}	1.4090^{25}	444
		235.6–236.6	0.8337^{28}	1.4097^{20}	397
$Cl(CH_2)_5OH$		170/0.5	1.090^{20}	1.4626^{20}	2
$CHF_2(CF_2)_3CH_2OH$		166–167/24			220
[tetrahydrofuryl ring]—CH_2OH		158–164/2			31
			1.1067^{20} (calc.)	1.4608^{20} (calc.)	491
[furyl ring]—CH_2OH		159/2			31
		172/5–6			392
n-$C_6H_{13}OH$		182.2–183.0/15	0.8471^{28}	1.4250^{20}	397
		310–311, 140–146/2	0.847^{28}	1.4248^{25}	444
$CH_3(CH_2)_3CHOH$ │ CH_3		127–128/5	0.7694^{25}	1.4160^{20}	397
$(CH_3)_2CHCH_2CHOH$ │ CH_3		108.5–109.5/5	0.7575^{25}	1.4109^{20}	397
		130–131/17			461
		257–262, 139–143/19	0.823^{25}	1.4096^{25}	444

$(CH_3)_3CCHOH$ │ CH_3		122/9	0.841^{20}	1.4151^{20}	178
$CH_3CH_2CH_2CHCH_2OH$ │ CH_3		139–140/5	0.8520^{27}	1.4261^{20}	397
$(C_2H_5)_2CHCH_2OH$		169.0–169.2/15	0.8572^{28}	1.4283^{20}	397
CH_3 │ $CH_3CH_2CH_2COH$ │ CH_3		74–95/1–2			294
O CH_3 ‖ │ CH_3CCH_2COH │ CH_3		92–96/6	0.8852^{20}		234
	—	—	—	—	235
(S)—OH	59–61	135–140/0.6			144, 208
		137.8–141.2/1.5			516
		153–155/2	0.9567^{40}		15
	54	203/17			113
	56.4	323–326/750			352
$n-C_7H_{15}OH$		185–186/2	0.8398^{20}	1.4280^{20}	17
		192/4–6		$1.4355^{22.5}$	352
$(n-C_3H_7)_2CHOH$	37–39	169–182/24			220
$(i-C_3H_7)_2CHOH$	58.4–61.6	163–167/15			444
	54–55	285–290			397
	60.4–61.4				491

(Table continued)

A. *Trialkoxyboranes* (continued)

ROH in $(RO)_3B$	M.p. (°C)	B.p. (°C)/mm.	d_4^t	n_D^t	Reference
CH_3CH_2 | $CH_3(CH_2)_3CHOH$		176–186/19	0.838^{27}	1.4223^{25}	444
CH_3 | $CH_3(CH_2)_3COH$ | CH_3		102.4–117.2/1			516
$C_6H_5CH_2OH$		180.4–189.8/3			516
		210–215/0.3, 258–260/20	1.095^{26}	1.5546^{25}	220
		212/4			213
		255/17			113
$n\text{-}C_8H_{17}OH$		182–184/0.5	0.855^{20}	1.4377^{20}	178
		200/2	0.8548^{20}	1.4360^{20}	17
		378–379, 192–194/2	0.846^{23}	1.4350^{25}	444
CH_3 | $CH_3(CH_2)_5CHOH$		148/0.5	0.8642^{4}	1.4280^{22}	175
		170/1		$1.4275^{22.5}$	352
		340–349, 210–218/15	$0.837^{24.5}$	1.4270^{25}	444
OH | $CH_3(CH_2)_4CHCH_2CH_3$		150–170/0.5	1.006^{27}	1.4889^{25}	444
		183–185/3	0.8619^{20}	1.4385^{20}	267
		348–352/745		$1.4365^{22.5}$	352
		350–354, 227–228/20	0.857^{24}	1.4359^{25}	444

(S ring)$C(CH_3)CH_2OH$	—	—	—	—	47
$(CH_3)_2CHCH_2CH(OH)CH{=}CHCH_3$		147–150/10			137
(S ring)$C(OH)C{\equiv}CH$		150–170/0.5	1.006^{27}	1.4889^{25}	444
$C_6H_5CH_2CH_2OH$		215/1			245
$C_6H_5CH(CH_3)OH$		170–174/0.4	1.064^{20}	1.5347	175 107
$o\text{-}ClC_6H_4CH(CH_3)OH$			1.2058^{25}	1.5455^{25}	1, 136
$p\text{-}ClC_6H_4CH(CH_3)OH$			1.2048^{25}	1.5457^{25}	1, 136

(Table continued)

A. Trialkoxyboranes (continued)

ROH in $(RO)_3B$	M.p. (°C)	B.p. (°C)/mm.	d_4^t	n_D^t	Reference
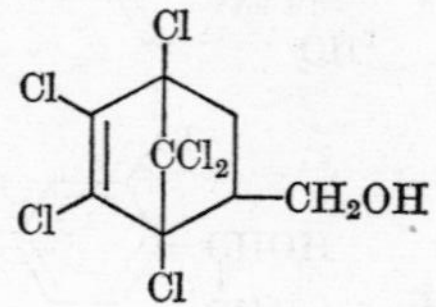 [structure: Cl, Cl, Cl, Cl, CCl_2, $-CH_2OH$]	232–233				152
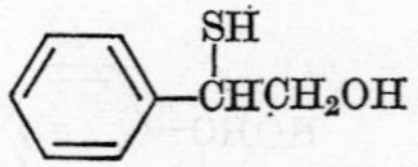 [structure: C_6H_5–$\overset{SH}{CH}CH_2OH$]	—	—	—	—	379, 380
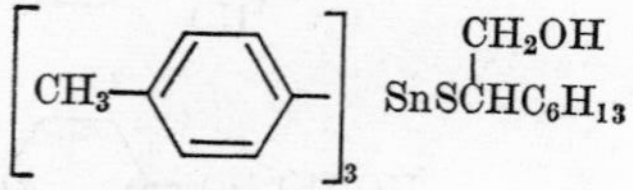 $[CH_3C_6H_4]_3SnS\overset{CH_2OH}{CH}C_6H_{13}$	—	—	—	—	380
$n\text{-}C_9H_{19}OH$		228–230/1.5	0.8575^{20}	1.4405^{20}	15
$(n\text{-}C_4H_9)_2CHOH$	55–56	167/1.5	0.8159^{60}		16
$(i\text{-}C_4H_9)_2CHOH$	97–98				491
	99–100	198–209/22			51, 444
$(CH_3)_3CCH_2\overset{CH_3}{CH}CH_2CH_2OH$	—		—	—	40
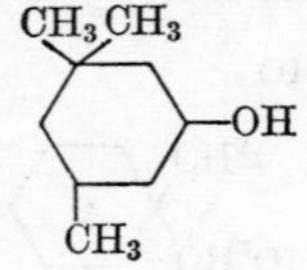 [structure: cyclohexanol ring with CH_3, CH_3 (gem) and CH_3; –OH]			0.9105^{20} (calc.)	1.4588^{20} (calc.)	491

$C_6H_5C(CH_3)_2OH$	42				294
$C_6H_5CH_2CH_2CHClOH$	—	—	—	—	157
n-$C_{10}H_{21}OH$		250/1.5 273–276/0.5	 0.8581^{20}	 1.4440^{20}	522 17
$(CH_3)_2C{=}CH(CH_2)_2C(OH)(CH_3)CH{=}CH_2$		> 80/1–2			294
	—	—	—	—	214
$(CH_3)_2C{=}CH(CH_2)_2C(CH_3){=}CHCH_2OH$	—	—	—	—	516
l-Menthol (4-methyl-2-hydroxy-1-isopropylcyclohexane; CH_3, OH, $CH(CH_3)_2$ on ring)	150 150–152 151–155				463 355 451
dl-Menthol	35–47	184–186/0.7			451

(*Table continued*)

A. *Trialkoxyboranes* (continued)

ROH in $(RO)_3B$	M.p. (°C)	B.p. (°C)/mm.	d_4^t	n_D^t	Reference
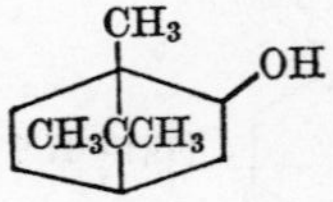 CH_3, OH, CH_3CCH_3	225–226				516
	—	—	—	—	430, 463
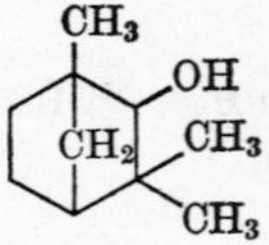 CH_3, OH, CH_2, CH_3, CH_3	147				217
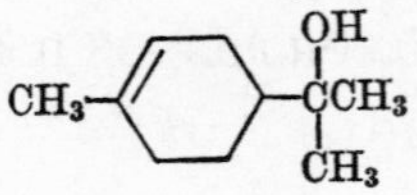 CH_3, OH, CCH_3, CH_3		> 80/1–2			294
	—	—	—	—	214
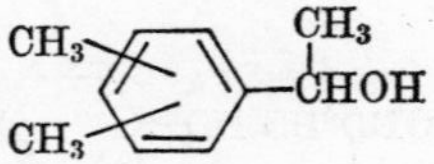 CH_3, CH_3, CH_3, CHOH		> 250/10	1.0127^{25}	1.5286^{25}	1, 136
trans-α-decalol	155				217
$CH_2{=}CH(CH_2)_8CH_2OH$	—	—	—	—	41
$BrCH_2(CH_2)_9CH_2OH$	—	—	—	—	41
n-$C_{12}H_{25}OH$		287–288/3.5	0.845^{27}	1.4472^{25}	444
		313/10			43

$CH_3CH(CH_3)CH_2CH(CH_3)CH_2CH(OH)CH_2CH(CH_3)CH_3$		247–255/19	0.834^{29}	1.4372^{25}	50, 51, 444
cis,trans-2-cyclohexylcyclohexanol	172–198	230–250/0.3			218, 444
cis-2-cyclohexylcyclohexanol	198–199				218
	218–221				444
cis,trans-2-phenylcyclohexanol	96–106.6	284–288/0.4			218, 444
cis-2-phenylcyclohexanol	123–135				444
	Granules, 138–143; Needles, 144–151				218
trans-2-phenylcyclohexanol	108–116				218, 444
4-cyclohexylcyclohexanol		295–302/0.1			151, 416
$2,4\text{-}Cl_2C_6H_3\text{-}O\text{-}C_6H_{10}OH$ (2-(2,4-dichlorophenoxy)cyclohexanol)	—	—	—	—	452
$CH_3OC(=O)(CH_2)_{10}CH_2OH$	—	—	—	—	123
$CH_2{=}CH(CH_2)_{10}CH_2OH$	—	—	—	—	41
$BrCH_2(CH_2)_{11}CH_2OH$	—	—	—	—	41
$(C_6H_{11})_2CHOH$	154.6–157.8				444
$(C_6H_5)_2CHOH$	171–176				521
	175.2–177.4				452
$CH_3(CH_2)_3CH(CH_2CH_3)(CH_2)_2CH(OH)CH_2CH(CH_3)CH_3$		224–226/0.6	0.846^{26}	$1.4473^{20.9}$	290
		250–274/0.5			50, 51
					203, 208

(*Table continued*)

A. *Trialkoxyboranes* (continued)

ROH in $(RO)_3B$	M.p. (°C)	B.p. (°C)/mm.	d_4^t	n_D^t	Reference
$CH_3OC(=O)(CH_2)_{12}CH_2OH$	—	—	—	—	123
$CH_3C(CH_3){=}CH$– ring bearing CH_3, CH_2OH, CH_3, CH_3	—	—	—	—	394
$CH_3C(CH_3){=}CH$– ring (one C=C) bearing CH_3, CH_2OH, CH_3, CH_3	—	—	—	—	394
$CH_2{=}CH(CH_2)_{12}CH_2OH$	—	—	—	—	41
$BrCH_2(CH_2)_{13}CH_2OH$	—	—	—	—	41
$CH_3(CH_2)_{14}CH_2OH$	43–44	328–329/< 0.5			14
$CH_3(CH_2)_3OC(=O)(CH_2)_{14}CH_2OH$	—	—	—	—	123
$(CH_3CH_2)_2CH(CH_2)_2CH(OH)(CH_2)_2CH(CH_2CH_3)(CH_2)_3CH_3$		255–265/1			466
n-$C_{18}H_{37}OH$	41–44	339–343/0.3			444

$CH_3(CH_2)_7CH{=}CH(CH_2)_7CH_2OH$		305–315/0.3	0.860[24]	1.4614[25]	444
$CH_3(CH_2)_5CH(OH)(CH_2)_{10}CO_2H$	111–120				219
CH_3 CH_2OH, CH_3, $CH(CH_3)_2$	—	—	—	—	378

B. Triaryloxyboranes

ArOH in $(ArO)_3B$	M.p. (°C)	B.p. (°C)/mm.	d_4^t	n_D^t	Reference
C_6H_5–OH	38–40	141.6–148/1.5			516
	50	165/1			438
	55–57	150/0.02			156
	71–81	360–370, 224–230/17			444
	83–84	180–186/0.7			156
	89	155/0.05			39
	89–91				491
	92–93	157–158/0.5, 177–178/0.5			111

(Table continued)

B. *Triaryloxyboranes* (continued)

ArOH in $(ArO)_3B$	M.p. (°C)	B.p. (°C)/mm.	d_4^t	n_D^t	Reference
	146				213
		178/0.4			177
		203–206/3			269
		205–215/6			372
$HO-C_6H_4-OH$ (p-)	142				351
$o-CH_3C_6H_4OH$		189–195/2, 385–386	1.079^{22}	1.5546^{25}	444
		198/2.5			372
$m-CH_3C_6H_4OH$	40				337
	54.2	185–195/3			516
			1.0784^{20} (calc.)	1.5555^{20} (calc.)	491
$p-CH_3C_6H_4OH$	58–61	248–250/12			461
	137–140				491
	142	206/3			213
$o-HSCH_2C_6H_4OH$	—	—	—	—	379, 380

$HSCH_2$–C_6H_4–OH (*p*)	—	—	—	—	380
2-($CH_2CH{=}CH_2$)C_6H_4OH		188/0.05		1.5600*	186
2-($C(CH_3)_3$)C_6H_4OH	55–95	200–218/0.5–1			220
$(CH_3)_3C$–C_6H_4–OH (*p*)		275–280/2.5			372
2-(C_6H_{11})C_6H_4OH	106–124	269–275/0.5 280–285/2.5			444 372
C_6H_{11}–C_6H_4–OH (*p*)		370–375/3.7			372

* Temperature not recorded.

(*Table continued*)

B. Triaryloxyboranes (continued)

ArOH in $(ArO)_3B$	M.p. (°C)	B.p. (°C)/mm.	d_4^t	n_D^t	Reference
2-$C_6H_5C_6H_4OH$	119–135	258–297/0.6 320–330/7.5			444 372
n-C_8H_{17}–C_6H_4–OH (para)	82				112
$(CH_2{=}C(CH_3)CH_2)_3SnSCH_2$–$C_6H_4$–OH (para)	—	—	—	—	380
2,6-$(CH_3)_2C_6H_3OH$	110–120 135 156–157	242–245/0.6			27 112 491
2,4-$(CH_3)_2C_6H_3OH$			1.0570^{20} (calc.)	1.5469^{20} (calc.)	491

CH_3, OH, CH_3	147–148				491
CH_3, CH_3, OH	72–73				491
CH_3, OH, CH_3	145–148				491
$CH(CH_3)_2$, OH, CH_3	67–69 —	170–176/0.05 —	 —	 —	521 214
$C(CH_3)_3$, CH_3, OH	163–171				27

(Table continued)

B. Triaryloxyboranes (continued)

ArOH in $(ArO)_3B$	M.p. (°C)	B.p. (°C)/mm.	d_4^t	n_D^t	Reference
$CH(CH_3)_2$, OH, $CH(CH_3)_2$	273–280				521
	286–290				491
	white plates				220
Cl, OH	47–49	242/6			461
	47–49	264–270/14			444
Cl–, –OH	55				112
	60–64	258–260/5			461
		260–270/3.7			372
HO, Cl		242–247/3.7			372
Cl, OH, Cl	106				112

$2,4,6\text{-}Cl_3C_6H_2OH$	173	230–272/12			112 220
$o\text{-}IC_6H_4OH$	90				112
$o\text{-}NO_2C_6H_4OH$	108				112
$o\text{-}HSC_6H_4OH$	—	—	—	—	380
$p\text{-}HSC_6H_4OH$	—	—	—	—	379

(*Table continued*)

B. *Triaryloxyboranes* (continued)

ArOH in $(ArO)_3B$	M.p. (°C)	B.p. (°C)/mm.	d_4^t	n_D^t	Reference
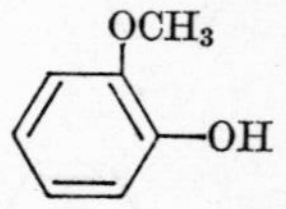 OCH_3, OH	101 101–101.8	 >200/2 230/2.5			213 516 372
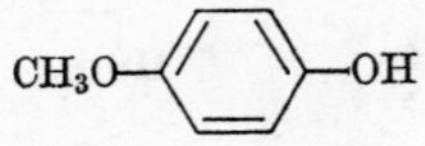 CH_3O–, –OH	43–45	288/7			461
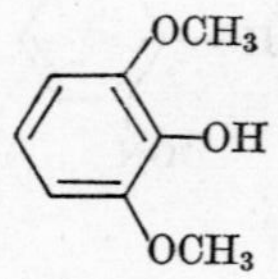 OCH_3, OH, OCH_3	134				112
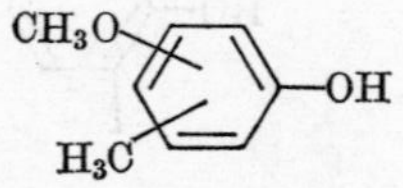 CH_3O, OH, H_3C	—	—	—	—	214
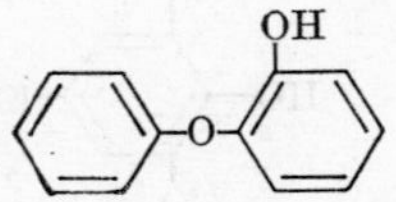 OH, O	—	—	—	—	47

CNH_2 (C=O), OH	265	108
CO_2H, OH	258 (d.) 258–259 260–270 (d.)	213 366 108
HO_2C, CH_3, OH	245–247	108
CH_3, HO_2C, OH	261	108
CH_3, OH, CO_2H	210–212	108

(*Table continued*)

B. *Triaryloxyboranes* (continued)

ArOH in $(ArO)_3B$	M.p. (°C)	B.p. (°C)/mm.	d_4^t	n_D^t	Reference
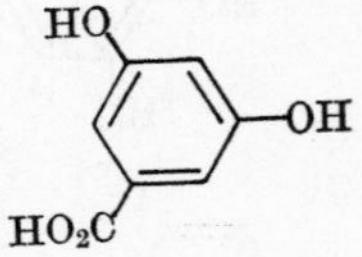 HO, OH, HO_2C	> 260				108
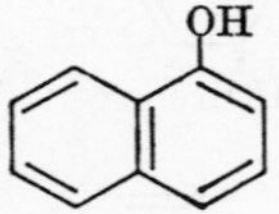 OH	85 108	325–330/5			7 112 372
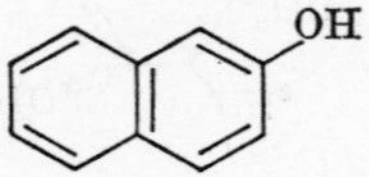 OH	115 115.5 120				337 7 112
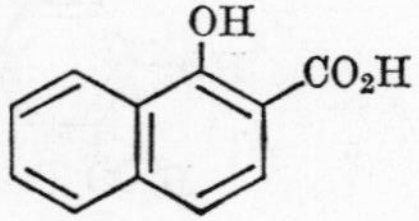 OH, CO_2H	255				108
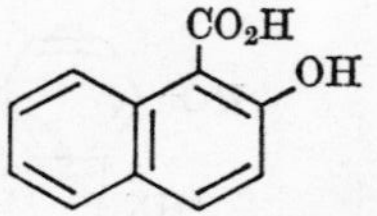 CO_2H, OH	> 263				108

C. Amine Complexes of Trialkoxyboranes

$(RO)_3B:NR_3$	M.p. (°C)	Reference
$(CH_3O)_3B:NH_3$	45	399
	68.6	432
	72	195
	Solid	192
$(CH_3O)_3B:N_2H_4$	79–80	272
$(CH_3O)_3B:NH_2CH_3$	42	195
	67	478
$(CH_3O)_3B:NH(CH_3)_2$	9	195
$(CH_3O)_3B:N(CH_3)_3$	~ -50	195
$(CH_3O)_3B:NH_2CH_2CH_3$	67–69	272
$(CH_3O)_3B:NH_2CH_2CH_2NH_2$	81–82	272, 478
$(CH_3O)_3B:NH_2C(CH_3)_3$	67–70	478
$(CH_3O)_3B:HN$ 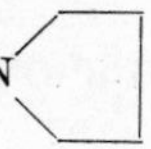	74–75	272
$(CH_3O)_3B:HN$ 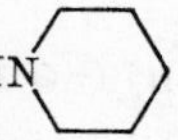	75	272, 478
$(C_2H_5O)_3B:N_2H_4$	Crystalline	272
$(C_2H_5O)_3B:NH_2CH_2CH_3$	Crystalline	272
$(C_2H_5O)_3B:NH_2CH_2CH_2NH_2$	Crystalline	272
$(CF_3CH_2O)_3B:NC_5H_5$	48	4
$(CH_2{=}CHCH_2O)_3B:N_2H_4$	41–42	272

(Table continued)

C. Amine Complexes of Trialkoxyboranes (continued)

$(RO)_3B:NR_3$	M.p. (°C)	Reference
$(CH_2{=}CHCH_2O)_3B:NH_2C_2H_5$	Crystalline	272
$(CH_2{=}CHCH_2O)_3B:NH_2CH_2CH_2NH_2$	31–33	272
$(CH_2{=}CHCH_2O)_3B:HN$ (pyrrolidine ring)	Crystalline	272
$(CH_2{=}CHCH_2O)_3B:HN$ (piperidine ring)	44–45	272

D. Amine Complexes of Triaryloxyboranes

$(ArO)_3B:NR_3$	M.p. (°C)	Reference
$[C_6H_5O]_3B:NH_3$	Colorless crystals	165

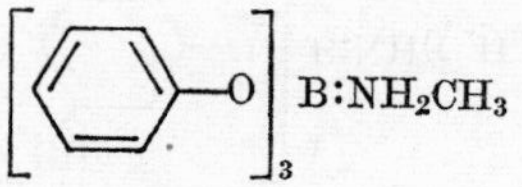 $[C_6H_5O]_3B:NH_2CH_3$	Colorless crystals	165
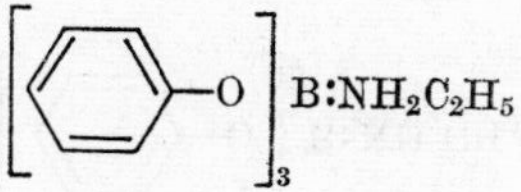 $[C_6H_5O]_3B:NH_2C_2H_5$	White solid	111
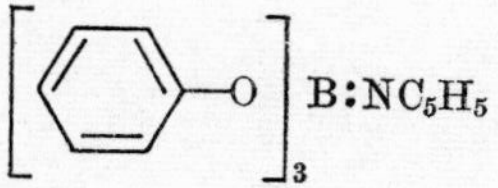 $[C_6H_5O]_3B:NC_5H_5$	148	111
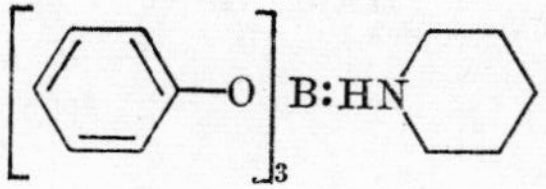 $[C_6H_5O]_3B:HNC_5H_{10}$ (piperidine)	Colorless crystals	165
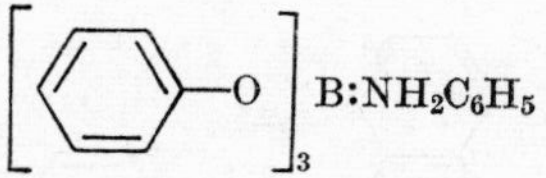 $[C_6H_5O]_3B:NH_2C_6H_5$	Transparent crystals	165
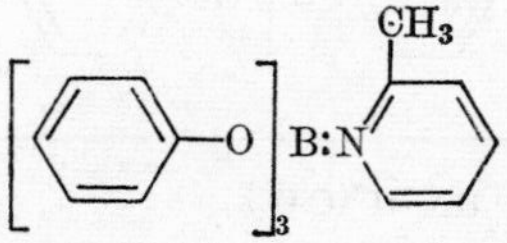 $[C_6H_5O]_3B:NC_5H_4CH_3$ (2-methylpyridine)	104	112

(*Table continued*)

D. Amine Complexes of Triaryloxyboranes (continued)

$(ArO)_3B:NR_3$	M.p. (°C)	Reference
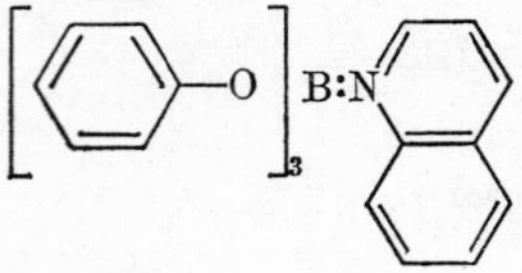 $[C_6H_5O]_3B:NC_9H_7$ (quinoline)	93–94	111
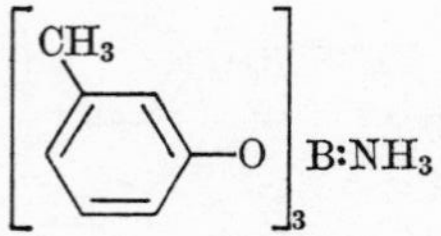 $[m\text{-}CH_3C_6H_4O]_3B:NH_3$	Colorless crystals	165
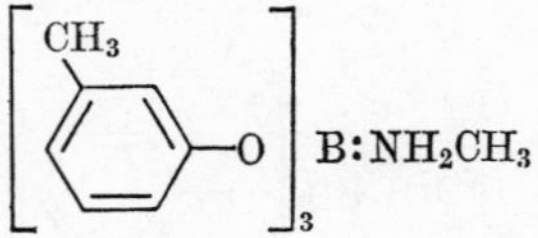 $[m\text{-}CH_3C_6H_4O]_3B:NH_2CH_3$	Solid	165
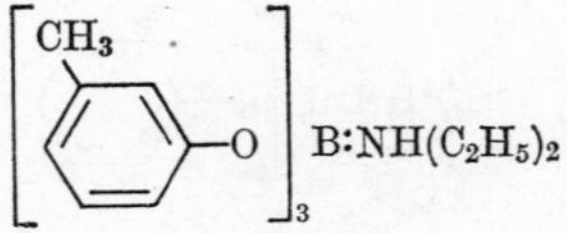 $[m\text{-}CH_3C_6H_4O]_3B:NH(C_2H_5)_2$	Needles	165

$[3\text{-}CH_3C_6H_4O]_3B{:}NC_5H_5$	Colorless crystals	165
$[3\text{-}CH_3C_6H_4O]_3B{:}N(2\text{-}CH_3C_5H_4)$	Colorless crystals	165
$[3\text{-}CH_3C_6H_4O]_3B{:}NH(i\text{-}C_4H_9)_2$	Colorless crystals	165
$[3\text{-}CH_3C_6H_4O]_3B{:}NC_9H_7$ (quinoline)	Colorless crystals	165

(*Table continued*)

D. Amine Complexes of Triaryloxyboranes (continued)

$(ArO)_3B:NR_3$	M.p. (°C)	Reference
$[C_8H_{17}-C_6H_4-O]_3B:NC_5H_5$	112	112
$[HO-C_6H_4-O]_3B:NH_2CH_2CH_3$	> 245	351
$[Cl-C_6H_4-O]_3B:NC_5H_5$	68–70	112
$[2,5\text{-}Cl_2C_6H_3-O]_3B:NC_5H_5$	146–148	112
$[2\text{-}I-C_6H_4-O]_3B:NC_5H_5$	52–55	112

$[o\text{-}IC_6H_4O]_3B:NC_5H_4(2\text{-}CH_3)$	110	112
$[o\text{-}NO_2C_6H_4O]_3B:NC_5H_5$	167	112
$(\alpha\text{-}C_{10}H_7O)_3B:NC_5H_5$	174	112
$(\beta\text{-}C_{10}H_7O)_3B:NC_5H_5$	57–60	112
$(\beta\text{-}C_{10}H_7O)_3B:NC_5H_4(2\text{-}CH_3)$	66–68	112
$(\alpha\text{-}C_{10}H_7O)_3B:NC_5H_2(2,4,6\text{-}(CH_3)_3)$	Semi-liquid	112

(Table continued)

D. Amine Complexes of Triaryloxyboraneo (continued)

$(ArO)_3B{:}NR_3$	M.p. (°C)	Reference
$(\beta\text{-}C_{10}H_7O)_3B{:}N(C_5H_2)(CH_3)_3$ (2,4,6-CH_3)	110	112
$[C_6H_5O]_3B{:}2NH_3$	125	112
$[C_6H_5O]_3B{:}[0.45N(C_5H_2)(CH_3)_3]$ (2,4,6-CH_3)	Semi-liquid	112
$[Cl\text{-}C_6H_4\text{-}O]_3B{:}[0.59N(C_2H_5)_3]$	Semi-liquid	112

$[Cl_2C_6H_3O]_3B:[0.77NH(C_2H_5)_2]$	175	112
$[Cl_2C_6H_3O]_3B:[0.44N(C_2H_5)_3]$	Semi-liquid	112
$[Cl_3C_6H_2O]_3B:3NH_3$	150	112
$[(OCH_3)_2C_6H_3O]_3B:[0.36NC_5H_5]$	108	112

VIII. REFERENCES

1. Abbey, A., Brit. Pat. 668,763 (1952, to Dow Chemical Co.).
2. Abel, E. W., J. D. Edwards, W. Gerrard, and M. F. Lappert, *J. Chem. Soc.*, 501 (1957).
3. Abel, E. W., W. Gerrard, and M. F. Lappert, *J. Chem. Soc.*, 1451 (1958).
4. Abel, E. W., W. Gerrard, M. F. Lappert, and R. Shafferman, *J. Chem. Soc.*, 2895 (1958).
5. Abel, E. W., and A. Singh, *J. Chem. Soc.*, 690 (1959).
6. Abraham, M. H., and A. G. Davies, *J. Chem. Soc.*, 429 (1959).
7. Adams, R. M., and W. H. Schechter, U.S. Pat. 2,937,195 (1960, to Callery Chemical Co.).
8. Ahmad, T., S. Z. Haider, and M. H. Khundkar, *J. Appl. Chem.*, **4**, 543 (1954).
9. Allen, H. Jr., and S. Tannenbaum, *Anal. Chem.*, **31**, 265 (1959).
10. Ananthakrishnan, R., *Proc. Indian Acad. Sci.*, **4A**, 74 (1936); through *Chem. Abstracts*, **31**, 3787 (1937).
11. Anderson, J. R., K. G. O'Brien, and F. H. Reuter, *J. Appl. Chem.*, **2**, 241 (1952).
12. Andier, Dupont, and Dulou, Fr. Pat. 1,163,155 (1958, to Centre National de la Recherche Scientifique).
13. Appel, F. J., U.S. Pat. 2,217,354 (1939, to E. I. duPont de Nemours & Co.).
14. Arbuzov, B. A., and V. S. Vinogradova, *Bull. Acad. Sci. U.S.S.R., Div. Chem. Sci.*, 483 (1952).
15. Arbuzov, B. A., and V. S. Vinogradova, *Bull. Acad. Sci. U.S.S.R., Div. Chem. Sci.*, 773 (1952).
16. Arbuzov, B. A., and V. S. Vinogradova, *Bull. Acad. Sci. U.S.S.R., Div. Chem. Sci.*, 535 (1954).
17. Arbuzov, B. A., and V. S. Vinogradova, *Compt. rend. acad. sci. U.R.S.S.*, **55**, 411 (1947).
18. Aroney, M., R. J. W. Le Fèvre, and P. M. Linthen, *J. Chem. Soc.*, 4140 (1961).
19. Asahara, T., and K. Kanabu, *J. Chem. Soc. Japan, Ind. Chem. Sect.*, **55**, 589 (1952); through *Chem. Abstracts*, **49**, 2297 (1955).
20. Ashton, R., and J. C. Smith, *J. Chem. Soc.*, 1308 (1934).
21. Bailey, W. J., and J. J. Hewitt, *J. Org. Chem.*, **21**, 543 (1956).
22. Ballard, S. A., U.S. Pat. 2,431,224 (1947, to Shell Development Co.).
23. Bamford, C. H., and D. M. Newitt, *J. Chem. Soc.*, 695 (1946).
24. Bannister, W. J., U.S. Pat. 1,668,797 (1928, to Commercial Solvents Corporation).
25. Barna, P., F. O. Groch, E. G. Teach, M. L. Ummel, and M. Weiner, Stauffer Chemical Company ONR Semi-Annual Technical Report, 1-1-58 to 7-1-58, Contract Nonr-2259(00), Project NR 356-387.
26. Barnes, R. F., H. Diamond, and P. R. Fields, U.S. Pat. 2,739,979 (1956, to U.S.A.).
27. Bastin, E. L., *et al.*, Shell Development Company, Chemical Corps Procurement Agency Final Report, April 30, 1954, Contract No. CML-4564, Project No. 4-08-03-001.

28. Bateman, L., J. I. Cunneen, and E. S. Waight, *J. Chem. Soc.*, 1714 (1952).
29. Bauer, S. H., and J. Y. Beach, *J. Am. Chem. Soc.*, **63**, 1394 (1941).
30. Baumgarten, H. E., and R. A. Setterquist, *J. Am. Chem. Soc.*, **79**, 2605 (1957).
31. Baumgartner, G. J., and C. L. Wilson, *J. Am. Chem. Soc.*, **81**, 2440 (1959).
32. Bawn, C. E. H., and A. Ledwith, *Chem. & Ind.* (*London*), 1329 (1958).
33. Bawn, C. E. H., A. Ledwith, and P. Matthies, *J. Polymer Sci.*, **34**, 95 (1959).
34. Bawn, C. E. H., and T. B. Rhodes, *Trans. Faraday Soc.*, **50**, 934 (1954).
35. Beachell, H. C., and T. R. Meeker, *J. Am. Chem. Soc.*, **78**, 1796 (1956).
36. Beachell, H. C., and W. C. Schar, *J. Am. Chem. Soc.*, **80**, 2943 (1958).
37. Bean, F. R., and J. R. Johnson, *J. Am. Chem. Soc.*, **54**, 4415 (1932).
38. Becher, H. J., *Z. Physik. Chem.*, **2**, 276 (1954).
39. Bedell, R., M. J. Frazer, and W. Gerrard, *J. Chem. Soc.*, 4037 (1960).
40. Beears, W. L., U.S. Pat. 2,650,908 (1953, to B. F. Goodrich Co.).
41. Beets, M. G. J., and W. Meerburg, *Perfumery Essent. Oil Record*, **44**, 310 (1953).
42. Benton, F. L., and T. E. Dillon, *J. Am. Chem. Soc.*, **64**, 1128 (1942).
43. Beran, F., V. Prey, and H. Böhm, *Mitt. Chem. Forschungsinst. Wirtsch. Oesterr.*, **6**, 54 (1952).
44. Berzelius, J. J., *Ann. Physik*, **78**, 113 (1824).
45. Bettman, B., G. E. K. Branch, and D. L. Yabroff, *J. Am. Chem. Soc.*, **56**, 1865 (1934).
46. Bissot, T. C., D. H. Campbell, and R. W. Parry, *J. Am. Chem. Soc.*, **80**, 1868 (1958).
47. Blake, E. S., W. C. Hammann, J. W. Edwards, T. E. Reichard, and M. R. Ort, *J. Chem. Eng. Data*, **6**, 87 (1961).
48. Blau, J. A., W. Gerrard, and M. F. Lappert, *J. Chem. Soc.*, 4116 (1957).
49. Bohm, R. E., and H. Steinberg, U.S. Pat. 3,005,011 (1961, to United States Borax and Chemical Corporation).
50. Borax Consolidated Limited, Brit. Pat. 775,418 (1957); Ger. Pat. 1,047,761 (1958).
51. Borax Consolidated Limited, Dutch Pat. 93,161 (1959).
52. Bowman, C. M., U.S. Pat. 2,976,315 (1961, to Dow Chemical Co.).
53. Bowman, C. M., U.S. Pat. 2,976,328 (1961, to Dow Chemical Co.).
54. Bowman, C. M., and E. J. Watson, U.S. Pat. 2,976,313 (1961, to Dow Chemical Co.).
55. Bowman, C. M., and E. J. Watson, U.S. Pat. 2,976,314 (1961, to Dow Chemical Co.).
56. Bradley, J. A., and P. M. Christopher, 129th Meeting American Chemical Society, Dallas, April 1956, Abstracts of Papers, p. 39-N.
57. Bradley, J. A., and R. W. Palizay, 140th Meeting American Chemical Society, Chicago, Sept. 1961, Abstracts of Papers, p. 61-T.
58. Bradley, M. J., G. E. Ryschkewitsch, and H. H. Sisler, 135th Meeting American Chemical Society, Boston, April, 1959, Abstracts of Papers, p. 35-M.
59. Bradley, M. J., G. E. Ryschkewitsch, and H. H. Sisler, *J. Am. Chem. Soc.*, **81**, 2635 (1959).

60. Bradley, J. A., T. J. Tully, J. R. Rolder, and W. Lange, Newark College of Engineering, Technical Research Report, MCC-1023-TR-62, June, 1954.
61. Bragdon, R. W., U.S. Pat. 2,813,115 (1957, to Metal Hydrides, Incorporated).
62. Brandenberg, W., and A. Galat, *J. Am. Chem. Soc.*, **72**, 3275 (1950).
63. Brindley, P. B., W. Gerrard, and M. F. Lappert, *J. Chem. Soc.*, 824 (1956).
64. Brindley, P. B., W. Gerrard, and M. F. Lappert, *J. Chem. Soc.*, 1540 (1956).
65. Britton, E. C., C. W. Davis, and F. L. Taylor, U.S. Pat. 2,160,942 (1939, to The Dow Chemical Co.).
66. Brotherton, R. J., U.S. Pat. 2,948,751 (1960, to United States Borax and Chemical Corporation); see also Can. Pat. 621,059 (1961).
67. Brotherton, R. J., A. L. McCloskey, J. L. Boone, and H. M. Manasevit, *J. Am. Chem. Soc.*, **82**, 6245 (1960).
68. Brotherton, R. J., and H. Steinberg, *J. Org. Chem.*, **26**, 4632 (1961).
69. Brotherton, R. J., and H. Steinberg, Unpublished results.
70. Brothman, A., U.S. Pat. 2,571,194 (1951, to A. Brothman and Associates and Process Plants Division of Industrial Process Engineers).
71. Brown, H. C., U.S. Pat. 2,709,704 (1955).
72. Brown, H. C., *et al.*, *J. Am. Chem. Soc.*, **75**, 1 (1953).
73. Brown, H. C., and E. A. Fletcher, *J. Am. Chem. Soc.*, **73**, 2808 (1951).
74. Brown, H. C., and M. Gerstein, *J. Am. Chem. Soc.*, **72**, 2926 (1950).
75. Brown, H. C., and E. J. Mead, *J. Am. Chem. Soc.*, **78**, 3614 (1956).
76. Brown, H. C., E. J. Mead, and C. J. Shoaf, *J. Am. Chem. Soc.*, **78**, 3613 (1956).
77. Brown, H. C., E. J. Mead and B. C. Subba Rao, *J. Am. Chem. Soc.*, **77**, 6209 (1955).
78. Brown, H. C., H. I. Schlesinger, and A. B. Burg, *J. Am. Chem. Soc.*, **61**, 673 (1939).
79. Brown, H. C., H. I. Schlesinger, I. Sheft, and D. M. Ritter, *J. Am. Chem. Soc.*, **75**, 192 (1953).
80. Brown, H. C., and P. A. Tierney, *J. Am. Chem. Soc.*, **80**, 1552 (1958).
81. Bruson, H. A., U.S. Pat. 2,305,236 (1942, to the Resinous Products and Chemical Co.).
82. Brust, H. F., U.S. Pat. 2,904,578 (1959, to The Dow Chemical Co.).
83. Buckley, G. D., and N. H. Ray, *J. Chem. Soc.*, 3701 (1952).
84. Bujuid, Z. J., W. Gerrard, and M. F. Lappert, *Chem. & Ind.* (*London*), 1386 (1957).
85. Buls, Y. W., and R. I. Thomas, U.S. Pat. 2,835,693 (1958, to Shell Development Co.).
86. Burg, A. B., *J. Chem. Educ.*, **37**, 482 (1960).
87. Burg, A. B., *Record Chem. Progr.*, **15**, 159 (1954).
88. Burg, A. B., and H. I. Schlesinger, *J. Am. Chem. Soc.*, **55**, 4020 (1933).
89. Burg, A. B., and F. G. A. Stone, *J. Am. Chem. Soc.*, **75**, 228 (1953).
90. Burwell, R. L. Jr., *Chem. Rev.*, **54**, 615 (1954).
91. Bush, J. D., U.S. Pat. 2,880,144 (1959, to Callery Chemical Co.); see also Ger. Pat. 1,094,724 (1960); Can. Pat. 623,949 (1961).
92. Bush, J. D., U.S. Pat. 3,014,060 (1961, to Callery Chemical Co.).

93. Cahours, A., *Compt. Rend.*, **76**, 1383 (1873).
94. Callery Chemical Company, Fr. Pat. 1,241,016 (1960).
95. Calvert, R. P., and O. L. Thomas, U.S. Pat. 1,308,576 (1919, to E. I. duPont de Nemours & Co.).
96. Calvert, R. P., and O. L. Thomas, U.S. Pat. 1,308,577 (1919, to E. I. duPont de Nemours & Co.).
97. Cambi, L., *Atti Accad. Nazl. Lincei*, **23**, 244 (1914).
98. Campbell, A. H., Brit. Pat. 609,324 (1948, in part to Revertex Ltd.).
99. Cannizzaro, S., *Ann. Chem. Pharm.*, **92**, 113 (1854).
100. Chainani, G., and W. Gerrard, *J. Chem. Soc.*, 3168 (1960).
101. Chapman, O. L., and G. W. Borden, Private Communication to C. H. DePuy and R. W. King, *Chem. Rev.*, **60**, 431 (1960).
102. Cherbuliez, E., J. P. Leber, and A. M. Ulrich, *Helv. Chim. Acta*, **36**, 910 (1953).
103. Chichibabin, A. E., *Fundamental Principles of Organic Chemistry*, Vol. 1, State Chem. Press, 1953, p. 222; through V. K. Kuskov and V. A. Zhukova, *Bull. Acad. Sci. U.S.S.R., Div. Chem. Sci.*, 743 (1956).
104. Chiras, S. J., U.S. Pat. 2,947,776 (1960, to Olin Mathieson Chemical Corp.); see also Fr. Pat. 1,172,868 (1959).
105. Christopher, P. M., *J. Chem. Eng. Data*, **5**, 568 (1960).
106. Christopher, P. M., *J. Phys. Chem.*, **64**, 1336 (1960).
107. Christopher, P. M., and T. J. Tully, *J. Am. Chem. Soc.*, **80**, 6516 (1958).
108. Cohn, G., *Pharm. Zentralhalle*, **52**, 479 (1911).
109. Colbeth, I. M., U.S. Pats. 2,278,425; 2,278,426; 2,278,427 (1942, to The Baker Castor Oil Co.).
110. Colbeth, I. M., U.S. Pat. 2,469,370 (1949, to The Baker Castor Oil Co.).
111. Colclough, T., W. Gerrard, and M. F. Lappert, *J. Chem. Soc.*, 907 (1955).
112. Colclough, T., W. Gerrard, and M. F. Lappert, *J. Chem. Soc.*, 3006 (1956).
113. Cook, H. G., J. D. Ilett, B. C. Saunders, and G. J. Stacey, *J. Chem. Soc.*, 3129 (1950).
114. Cooper, S., M. J. Frazer, and W. Gerrard, *J. Chem. Soc.*, 5545 (1961).
115. Cooper, W. J., and J. F. Masi, *J. Phys. Chem.*, **64**, 682 (1960).
116. Copaux, H., *Compt. Rend.*, **127**, 719 (1898).
117. Coudrey, W. A., E. D. Hughes, C. K. Ingold, S. Masterman, and A. D. Scott, *J. Chem. Soc.*, 1252 (1937).
118. Councler, C., *Ber.*, **9**, 485 (1876).
119. Councler, C., *Ber.*, **10**, 1655 (1877).
120. Councler, C., *Ber.*, **11**, 1106 (1878).
121. Councler, C., *J. Prakt. Chem.*, **18**, 371 (1878).
122. Cowley, E. G., and J. R. Partington, *Nature*, **136**, 643 (1935).
123. Crabalona, L. L., Brit. Pat. 655,428 (1951).
124. Cunningham, G. L., U.S. Pat. 2,830,070 (1958, to Callery Chemical Co.).
125. Cunningham, G. L., U.S. Pat. 3,004,058 (1961, to Callery Chemical Co.); see also Can. Pat. 631,524 (1961).
126. Cunningham, G. L., and F. Pretka, U.S. Pat. 2,894,975 (1959, to Callery Chemical Co.).
127. Cunningham, G. L., and F. Pretka, U.S. Pat. 2,938,920 (1960, to Callery Chemical Co.).
128. Dauben, W. G., and E. Hoerger, *J. Am. Chem. Soc.*, **73**, 1504 (1951).

129. Davies, A. G., D. G. Hare, and R. F. M. White, *J. Chem. Soc.*, 1040 (1960).
130. Davies, A. G., and R. B. Moodie, *Chem. & Ind.* (*London*), 1622 (1957).
131. Davies, A. G., and R. B. Moodie, *J. Chem. Soc.*, 2372 (1958).
132. Denson, C. L., and T. I. Crowell, *J. Am. Chem. Soc.*, **79**, 5656 (1957).
133. DePuy, C. H., and R. W. King, *Chem. Rev.*, **60**, 431 (1960).
134. Dickinson, W. C., *Phys. Rev.*, **81**, 717 (1951).
135. Dornow, A., and H. H. Gehrt, *Z. Anorg. Allgem. Chem.*, **294**, 81 (1958).
136. Dreisback, R. R., R. A. Martin, and A. J. Erbel, U.S. Pat. 2,507,506 (1950, to The Dow Chemical Co.).
137. Dubois, J. E., R. Luft, and F. Weck, *Ann. Univ. Saraviensis*, **1**, 157 (1952); through *Chem. Abstracts*, **47**, 9920 (1953).
138. Dupire, A., *Compt. Rend.*, **202**, 2086 (1936).
139. Ebelmen, J. J., *Ann.*, **57**, 319 (1846); *Ann. chim. phys.*, **16**, 129 (1846).
140. Ebelmen, J. J., and M. Bouquet, *Ann. chim. phys.*, **17**, 54 (1846); *Ann.*, **60**, 251 (1846).
141. Edwards, L. J., XVIIth International Congress of Pure and Applied Chemistry, Munich, 1959, Inorganic Chemistry Abstracts, p. 50.
142. Edwards, L. J., U.S. Pat. 2,884,439 (1959, to Callery Chemical Co.).
143. Edwards, J. D., W. Gerrard, and M. F. Lappert, *J. Chem. Soc.*, 1470 (1955).
144. Edwards, J. D., W. Gerrard, and M. F. Lappert, *J. Chem. Soc.*, 348 (1957).
145. Edwards, J. D., W. Gerrard, and M. F. Lappert, *J. Chem. Soc.*, 377 (1957).
146. Edwards, J. O., G. C. Morrison, V. F. Ross, and J. W. Schultz, *J. Am. Chem. Soc.*, **77**, 266 (1955).
147. Emrick, D. D., U.S. Pat. 3,009,791 (1961, to The Standard Oil Co., Ohio).
148. English, W. D., A. L. McCloskey, and H. Steinberg, *J. Am. Chem. Soc.*, **83**, 2122 (1961).
149. English, W. D., and W. G. Woods, Unpublished results.
150. Esso Research and Engineering Co., Ger. Pat. 1,005,499 (1957).
151. Etridge, J. J., and S. Sugden, *J. Chem. Soc.*, 989 (1928).
152. Fields, E. K., *J. Am. Chem. Soc.*, **78**, 5821 (1956).
153. Finch, A., J. C. Lockhart, and J. Pearn, *Chem. & Ind.* (*London*), 471 (1960).
154. Forbes, G. S., and H. H. Anderson, *J. Am. Chem. Soc.*, **62**, 761 (1940).
155. Frankland, E., *Ann.*, **124**, 129 (1862).
156. Frazer, M. J., and W. Gerrard, *J. Chem. Soc.*, 2959 (1955).
157. Frazer, M. J., W. Gerrard, and M. F. Lappert, *J. Chem. Soc.*, 739 (1957).
158. Frazer, M. J., W. Gerrard, and S. N. Mistry, *Chem. & Ind.* (*London*), 1263 (1958).
159. Frazer, M. J., W. Gerrard, and J. K. Patel, *Chem. & Ind.* (*London*), 90 (1959).
160. Frazer, M. J., W. Gerrard, and J. K. Patel, *Chem. & Ind.* (*London*), 728 (1959).
161. Frazer, M. J., W. Gerrard, and J. K. Patel, *J. Chem. Soc.*, 726 (1960).
162. Frazer, M. J., W. Gerrard, and J. A. Strickson, *J. Chem. Soc.*, 4701 (1960).

163. French, H. E., and S. D. Fine, *J. Am. Chem. Soc.*, **60**, 352 (1938).
164. Friedel, C., and J. M. Crafts, *Ann. chim. phys.*, **9**, 5 (1866).
165. Funk, H., and H. J. Koch, *Wiss. Z. Univ. Halle*, **8**, 1025 (1959).
166. Gamble, E. L., P. Gilmont, and J. F. Stiff, *J. Am. Chem. Soc.*, **62**, 1257 (1940).
167. Gardner, J. H., U.S. Pat. 2,847,444 (1958, to Escambia Chemical Co.).
168. Gasselin, M. V., *Ann. chim. phys.*, **3**, 5 (1894).
169. George, P. D., and J. R. Ladd, *J. Am. Chem. Soc.*, **77**, 1900 (1955).
170. Gerrard, W., *Chem. & Ind. (London)*, 463 (1951).
171. Gerrard, W., and P. F. Griffey, *J. Chem. Soc.*, 4095 (1961).
172. Gerrard, W., and B. K. Howe, *J. Chem. Soc.*, 505 (1955).
173. Gerrard, W., and M. F. Lappert, *Chem. & Ind. (London)*, 53 (1952).
174. Gerrard, W., and M. F. Lappert, *Chem. Rev.*, **58**, 1081 (1958).
175. Gerrard, W., and M. F. Lappert, *J. Chem. Soc.*, 1020 (1951).
176. Gerrard, W., and M. F. Lappert, *J. Chem. Soc.*, 2545 (1951).
177. Gerrard, W., and M. F. Lappert, *J. Chem. Soc.*, 1486 (1952).
178. Gerrard, W., and M. F. Lappert, *J. Chem. Soc.*, 3084 (1955).
179. Gerrard, W., M. F. Lappert, and B. A. Mountfield, *J. Chem. Soc.*, 1529 (1959).
180. Gerrard, W., M. F. Lappert, and C. A. Pearce, *Chem. & Ind. (London)*, 292 (1958).
181. Gerrard, W., M. F. Lappert, and C. A. Pearce, *J. Chem. Soc.*, 381 (1957).
182. Gerrard, W., M. F. Lappert, and R. Schafferman, *J. Chem. Soc.*, 3648 (1958).
183. Gerrard, W., M. F. Lappert, and H. B. Silver, *J. Chem. Soc.*, 3285 (1956).
184. Gerrard, W., M. F. Lappert, and H. B. Silver, *J. Chem. Soc.*, 4987 (1956).
185. Gerrard, W., M. F. Lappert, and H. B. Silver, *J. Chem. Soc.*, 1647 (1957).
186. Gerrard, W., M. F. Lappert, and H. B. Silver, *Proc. Chem. Soc.*, 19 (1957).
187. Gerrard, W., M. F. Lappert, and J. W. Wallis, *J. Chem. Soc.*, 2141 (1960).
188. Gerrard, W., M. F. Lappert, and J. W. Wallis, *J. Chem. Soc.*, 2178 (1960).
189. Gerrard, W., A. M. A. Mincer, and P. L. Wyvill, *J. Appl. Chem.*, **9**, 89 (1959).
190. Gorin, Y. A., V. S. Ivanov, T. G. Pushnova, and V. V. Zlatogurskaya, *Zh. Obshch. Khim.*, **29**, 1104 (1959).
191. Goubeau, J., H. J. Becker, and F. Griffel, *Z. Anorg. Allgem. Chem.*, **282**, 86 (1955).
192. Goubeau, J., and U. Bohm, *Z. Anorg. Allgem. Chem.*, **266**, 161 (1951).
193. Goubeau, J., and E. Ekhoff, *Z. Anorg. Allgem. Chem.*, **268**, 145 (1952).
194. Goubeau, J., and H. Keller, *Z. Anorg. Allgem. Chem.*, **267**, 1 (1951).
195. Goubeau, J., and R. Link, *Z. Anorg. Allgem. Chem.*, **267**, 27 (1951).
196. Goubeau, J., and K. E. Lucke, *Ann.*, **575**, 37 (1952).
197. Goubeau, J., and H. W. Wittmeier, *Z. Anorg. Allgem. Chem.*, **270**, 16 (1952).
198. Gould, D. R., and H. A. Beatty, Ethyl Corp. Report to Signal Corp., LTD-44-13, March 10, 1944.
199. Gould, E. S., S. V. Urs, C. G. Overberger, F. Martinez, and R. Brill, Boron Polymers Final Report, April 30, 1952, Signal Corps, Project No. 32-2005-34 (C 03642.02).
200. Governale, L. J., A. F. Limper, J. R. Mangham, and F. L. Padgitt, U.S. Pat. 3,002,806 (1961, to Ethyl Corporation).

201. Grau, A., and H. Lumbroso, *Bull. Soc. Chim. France*, 1860 (1961).
202. Graybill, B. M., J. K. Ruff, and M. F. Hawthorne, *J. Am. Chem. Soc.*, **83**, 2669 (1961).
203. Greenwood, N. N., and R. L. Martin, *Quart. Rev.* (*London*), **8**, 1 (1954).
204. Greenwood, N. N., R. L. Martin, and H. J. Emeléus, *J. Chem. Soc.*, 3030 (1950).
205. Grimley, J., and A. K. Holliday, *J. Chem. Soc.*, 1212 (1954).
206. Grisby, R. G., W. E. Gorgas, and L. N. Canjar, *Am. Inst. Chem. Engrs, J.*, **6**, 128 (1960).
207. Gustus, E. L., and P. G. Stevens, *J. Am. Chem. Soc.*, **55**, 378 (1933).
208. Haider, S. Z., M. H. Khundkar, and Md. Siddiqullah, *J. Appl. Chem.*, **4**, 93 (1954).
209. Hanley, J. R. Jr., H. S. Killam, R. D. Lanyon, and S. MacKenzie, 132nd Meeting American Chemical Society, New York, 1957, Abstracts of Papers, p. 16-P.
210. Hartman, L., *J. Chem. Soc.*, 1918 (1957).
211. Heeringa, L. G., and M. G. J. Beets, U.S. Pat. 2,944,077 (1960, to Polak and Schwarz International).
212. Hennion, G. F., H. D. Hinton, and J. A. Nieuwland, *J. Am. Chem. Soc.*, **55**, 2857 (1933).
213. Hirao, N., and T. Yabuuchi, *J. Pharm. Soc. Japan*, **74**, 1073 (1954).
214. Hirao, N., and S. Yagi, *J. Chem. Soc. Japan, Ind. Chem. Sect.*, **56**, 371 (1953).
215. Horn, H., and E. S. Gould, *J. Am. Chem. Soc.*, **78**, 5772 (1956).
216. Horsley, L. A., *Azeotropic Data, Advances in Chemistry Series No. 6*, American Chemical Society, Washington, 1952, p. 254; 216a, p. 62.
217. Hückel, W., O. Neunhoeffer, A. Gercke, and E. Frank, *Ann.*, **477**, 99 (1929).
218. Hunter, D. L., and E. W. Fajans, U.S. Pat. 2,878,256 (1959, to United States Borax and Chemical Corporation); see also Ger. Pat. 962,431 (1957).
219. Hunter, D. L., L. L. Petterson, and H. Steinberg, *Anal. Chim. Acta*, **21**, 523 (1959).
220. Hunter, D. L., and H. Steinberg, Unpublished results.
221. Hurd, D. T., and R. C. Osthoff, "Boron Halide–Amine Coordination Compounds," in T. Moeller, *Inorganic Syntheses*, Vol. 5, McGraw-Hill Book Company, Inc., New York, 1957, p. 26.
222. Ingold, C. K., *Structure and Mechanism in Organic Chemistry*, Cornell Univ. Press, Ithaca, 1953, p. 77.
223. Irany, E. P., U.S. Pat. 2,523,433 (1950).
224. Irish, G. E., J. B. Hinkamp, and J. D. Bartleson, U.S. Pat. 3,014,061 (1961, to Ethyl Corporation).
225. Joglekar, M. S., and V. N. Thatte, *Z. Physik.*, **98**, 692 (1936).
226. Johnson, J. R., and S. W. Tompkins, *Organic Syntheses*, Coll. Vol. 2, Wiley, New York, 1955, p. 106.
227. Johnson, J. R., and M. G. Van Campen Jr., *J. Am. Chem. Soc.*, **60**, 121 (1938).
228. Jones, R. G., and C. R. Kinney, *J. Am. Chem. Soc.*, **61**, 1378 (1939).
229. Jones, W. J., L. H. Thomas, E. H. Pritchard, and S. T. Bowden, *J. Chem. Soc.*, 824 (1946).

230. Kahovec, L., *Z. Physik. Chem.*, **40**, 135 (1938).
231. Kahovec, L., *Z. Physik. Chem.*, **43**, 109 (1939).
232. Kalb, G. A., Ger. Pat. 1,054,080 (1959, to E. I. duPont de Nemours & Co.); see also Brit. Pat. 832,134 (1960); U.S. Pat. 2,985,510 (1961).
233. Kalb, G. H., and E. L. Muetterties, Can. Pat. 623,367 (1961, to E. I. duPont de Nemours & Co.).
234. Kamenskii, I. V., V. I. Itinskii, and G. D. Krylova, Russ. Pat. 119,340 (1959).
235. Kamenskii, I. V., I. K. Sanin, V. I. Itinskii, and G. D. Krylova, *Plasticheskie Massy*, 15 (1960); through *Chem. Abstracts*, **55**, 1051 (1961).
236. Kantor, S. W., and R. C. Osthoff, *J. Am. Chem. Soc.*, **75**, 931 (1953).
237. Katz, J. R., and J. Selman, *Z. Physik.*, **46**, 392 (1928).
238. Kaufmann, A., Ger. Pat. 555,403 (1930); Brit. Pat. 367,292 (1931).
239. Kaufmann, A., Ger. Pat. 582,917 (1933).
240. Kaufmann, A. A., U.S. Pat. 1,886,885 (1932).
241. Keller, R. N., and E. M. Vander Wall, 133rd Meeting American Chemical Society, San Francisco, April, 1958, Abstracts of Papers, p. 31-L.
242. Kerr, R. W., U.S. Pat. 2,858,305 (1958, to Corn Products Refining Co.).
243. Khotinskii, E. S., and S. L. Pupko, *Ukr. Khim. Zh.*, **4**, Sci. Pt., 13 (1929), through *Chem. Abstracts*, **23**, 4441 (1929).
244. Kinney, C. R., H. T. Thompson, and L. C. Cheney, *J. Am. Chem. Soc.*, **57**, 2396 (1935).
245. Klipstein, K. H., U.S. Pat. 2,068,415 (1937, to The Calco Chemical Co.).
246. Kollonitsch, J., *J. Am. Chem. Soc.*, **83**, 1515 (1961).
247. Kollonitsch, J., *Nature*, **189**, 1005 (1961).
248. Kollonitsch, J., U.S. Pat. 2,903,470 (1959, to Metal Hydrides Incorporated).
249. Korshak, V. V., and V. A. Sergeyev, *Doklady Akad. Nauk. S.S.S.R.*, **115**, 308 (1957).
250. Köster, R., *Angew. Chem.*, **69**, 94 (1957).
251. Köster, R., *Angew. Chem.*, **71**, 31 (1959).
252. Köster, R., *Angew. Chem.*, **73**, 66 (1961).
253. Köster, R., Ger. Pat. 1,061,781 (1959, to Studiengesellschaft Kohle, m.b.H.); see also Brit. Pat. 848,519 (1961); U.S. Pat. 2,992,267 (1961).
254. Köster, R., XVIIth International Congress of Pure and Applied Chemistry, Munich, 1959, p. 8 of Abstracts; *Angew. Chem.*, **71**, 520 (1959).
255. Köster, R., and G. Schomburg, *Angew. Chem.*, **72**, 567 (1960).
256. Kreshkov, A. P., *J. Appl. Chem. U.S.S.R.*, **23**, 545 (1960).
257. Krishnan, K., *Proc. Indian Chem. Soc.*, **54**, 89 (1961).
258. Kuck, J. A., and E. C. Grim, *Microchem. J.*, **3**, 35 (1959).
259. Kuemmel, D. F., and M. G. Mellon, *J. Am. Chem. Soc.*, **78**, 4572 (1956).
260. Kuivila, H. J., S. C. Slack, and P. K. Siiteri, *J. Am. Chem. Soc.*, **73**, 123 (1951).
261. Kurnakov, N. S., and N. K. Voskresenskaya, *Bull. acad. sci. U.R.S.S., Classe sci. math. nat., Ser. chim.*, 797 (1937); through *Chem. Abstracts*, **32**, 2511 (1938).
262. Kuskov, V. K., G. F. Bebikh, and A. D. Iaroshenko, *Proc. Acad. Sci. U.S.S.R., Chem. Sect.*, **120**, 409 (1958).
263. Kuskov, V. K., and T. A. Burtseva, *Doklady Akad. Nauk S.S.S.R.*, **125**, 811 (1959).

264. Kuskov, V. K., and G. F. Filippova, *Zh. Obshch. Khim.*, **29**, 4063 (1959).
265. Kuskov, V. K., and A. N. Neverov, *Zh. Obshch. Khim.*, **29**, 1127 (1959).
266. Kuskov, V. K., and B. M. Sheiman, *Proc. Acad. Sci. U.S.S.R., Chem. Sect.*, **106**, 83 (1956).
267. Kuskov, V. K., B. M. Sheiman, and Z. I. Maksimova, *Zh. Obshch. Khim.*, **27**, 1454 (1957).
268. Kuskov, V. K., and L. P. Yuryeva, *Proc. Acad. Sci. U.S.S.R., Chem. Sect.*, **109**, 389 (1956).
269. Kuskov, V. K., and Va. A. Zhukova, *Bull. Acad. Sci. U.S.S.R., Div. Chem. Sci.*, 743 (1956).
270. Ladd, E. C., and L. Y. Kiley, U.S. Pat. 2,568,859 (1951, to United States Rubber Co.).
271. Landesman, H., and R. E. Williams, 138th Meeting American Chemical Society, New York, Sept., 1960, Abstracts of Papers, p. 39-N.
272. Landesman, H., and R. E. Williams, *J. Am. Chem. Soc.*, **83**, 2663 (1961).
273. Lange, N. A., *Handbook of Chemistry*, 8th Ed., Handbook Publishers, Inc., Sandusky, 1952, p. 1229.
274. Lappert, M. F., *Chem. Rev.*, **56**, 959 (1956).
275. Lappert, M. F., *J. Chem. Soc.*, 667 (1953).
276. Lappert, M. F., *J. Chem. Soc.*, 2784 (1953).
277. Lappert, M. F., *J. Chem. Soc.*, 784 (1955).
278. Lappert, M. F., *J. Chem. Soc.*, 1768 (1956).
279. Lappert, M. F., *J. Chem. Soc.*, 2790 (1958).
280. Lappert, M. F., *J. Chem. Soc.*, 3256 (1958).
281. Lappert, M. F., and H. Pyszora, *Proc. Chem. Soc.*, 350 (1960).
282. Laubengayer, A. W., R. P. Ferguson, and A. E. Newkirk, *J. Am. Chem. Soc.*, **63**, 559 (1941).
283. Lecat, M., *Ann. Soc. Sci. Bruxelles*, **47B**, I, 21 (1927).
284. Lecat, M., *Ann. Soc. Sci. Bruxelles*, **47B**, I, 63 (1927).
285. Lehmann, W. J., T. P. Onak, and I. Shapiro, *J. Chem. Phys.*, **30**, 1215 (1959).
286. Lehmann, H. A., and D. Tiess, *Z. Anorg. Allgem. Chem.*, **304**, 89 (1960); see also *Wiss. Z. Tech. Hochsch. Chem. Leuna-Merseburg*, **2**, 285 (1959/1960); through *Chem. Abstracts*, **55**, 1257 (1961).
287. Lehmann, W. J., H. G. Weiss, and I. Shapiro, *J. Chem. Phys.*, **30**, 1222 (1959).
288. Lehmann, W. J., H. G. Weiss, and I. Shapiro, *J. Chem. Phys.*, **30**, 1226 (1959).
289. Lemon, R. C., and W. F. Goldsmith, Brit. Pat. 812,498 (1959, to Union Carbide Corporation).
290. Levens, E., and R. M. Washburn, U.S. Pat. 2,875,236 (1959, to American Potash and Chemical Corp.).
291. Lewis, G. L., and C. P. Smyth, *J. Am. Chem. Soc.*, **62**, 1529 (1940).
292. Leznov, N. S., L. A. Sabun, and K. A. Andrianov, *J. Gen. Chem. U.S.S.R.*, **29**, 1247 (1959).
293. Ligot, A. J. L., Belg. Pat. 580,815 (1960).
294. Lippincott, S. B., U.S. Pat. 2,642,453 (1953, to Standard Oil Development Co.).
295. Loder, D. J., U.S. Pat. 2,298,138 (1942, to E. I. duPont de Nemours & Co.).

296. Loder, D. J., U.S. Pat. 2,298,139 (1942, to E. I. duPont de Nemours & Co.).
297. Low, W. H., *J. Am. Chem. Soc.*, **28**, 807 (1906).
298. Lucchesi, C. A., Ph.D. Thesis, Northwestern University, 1955.
299. Lucchesi, C. A., and D. D. Deford, *Anal. Chem.*, **29**, 1169 (1957).
300. Lumbroso, H., and A. Grau, *Bull. Soc. Chim. France*, 1866 (1961).
301. Lyden, R., *Chem. Zentr.*, **I**, 1813 (1927); **II**, 2133 (1928); **I**, 2379 (1930).
302. Makarov-Zemlyanskii, Y. Y., *Nauchn. Trudy Mosk., Tekhnol. Inst. Legkoi Prom., Sb.*, **13**, 205 (1958); through *Chem. Abstracts*, **54**, 14100 (1960).
303. Makishima, S., Y. Yoneda, and T. Tajima, *J. Phys. Chem.*, **61**, 1618 (1957).
304. Mangini, A., *Riv. biol.*, **22**, 457 (1937); through *Chem. Abstracts*, **32**, 3900 (1938).
305. Marshall, D., and P. Smith, Brit. Pat. 879,242 (1961, to Imperial Chemical Industries Ltd.).
306. Martin, D. R., *Chem. Rev.*, **34**, 461 (1944).
307. Martin, D. R., *Chem. Rev.*, **42**, 581 (1948).
308. Martin, D. R., and L. S. Mako, *J. Am. Chem. Soc.*, **73**, 2674 (1951).
309. Mason, R. G., Brit. Pat. 818,062 (1959, to A. Boake Roberts & Co. Ltd. and Borax Consolidated Ltd.).
310. Massey, A. G., and A. K. Holliday, *J. Chem. Soc.*, 1893 (1961).
311. Mauersberger, E. A., U.S. Pat. 2,036,593 (1936).
312. May, F. H., Brit. Pat. 864,226 (1961, to American Potash and Chemical Corporation).
313. May, F. H., U.S. Pat. 2,808,424 (1957, to American Potash and Chemical Corp.).
314. May, F. H., U.S. Pat. 2,855,427 (1958, to American Potash and Chemical Corp.).
315. May, F. H., and V. V. Levasheff, U.S. Pat. 2,824,787 (1958, to American Potash and Chemical Corp.).
316. May, F. H., and V. V. Levasheff, U.S. Pat. 3,011,871 (1961, to American Potash and Chemical Corporation).
317. May, F. H., V. V. Levasheff, and H. N. Hammar, U.S. Pat. 2,833,623 (1958, to Callery Chemical Co.).
318. McCloskey, A. L., Unpublished Results.
319. McCloskey, A. L., and R. J. Brotherton, U.S. Pat. 2,987,537 (1961, to United States Borax and Chemical Corporation); also see Can. Pat. 621,937 (1961).
320. McCloskey, A. L., H. Goldsmith, R. J. Brotherton, H. Steinberg, and G. W. Willcockson, 135th Meeting American Chemical Society, Boston, April, 1959, Abstracts of Papers, p. 34-M.
321. McCloskey, A. L., and L. L. Petterson, U.S. Pat. 3,000,926 (1961, to United States Borax and Chemical Corporation); see also Brit. Pat. 853,098 (1960).
322. McCusker, P. A. *Angew. Chem.*, **69**, 677 (1957).
323. McCusker, P. A., XVIth International Congress of Pure and Applied Chemistry, Paris, 1957, Divisions of Physical Chemistry and Inorganic Chemistry, Resumé of Communications, p. 167.
324. McElroy, A. D., U.S. Pat. 2,943,916 (1960, to Callery Chemical Co.).

325. McKenna, J. F., and F. J. Sowa, *J. Am. Chem. Soc.*, **59**, 470 (1937).
326. Meerwein, H., *Angew. Chem.*, **60**, 78 (1948).
327. Meerwein, H., E. Battenberg, H. Gold, E. Pfeil, and G. Willfang, *J. Prakt. Chem.*, **154**, 83 (1939).
328. Meerwein, H., and T. Bersin, *Ann.*, **476**, 113 (1929).
329. Meerwein, H., B. von Bock, B. Kirschnick, W. Lenz, and A. Miggl, *J. Prakt. Chem.*, **147**, 211 (1936).
330. Meerwein, H., G. Hinz, P. Hofmann, E. Kronig, and E. Pfeil, *J. Prakt. Chem.*, **147**, 257 (1937).
331. Meerwein, H., and H. Maier-Huser, *J. Prakt. Chem.*, **134**, 51 (1932).
332. Meerwein, H., and H. Sönke, *J. Prakt. Chem.*, **147**, 251 (1936).
333. Mehrotra, R. C., and G. Srivastava, *J. Indian Chem. Soc.*, **38**, 1 (1961).
334. Meutterties, E. L., *J. Am. Chem. Soc.*, **80**, 4526 (1958).
335. Meutterties, E. L., *Z. Naturforsch.*, **12B**, 265 (1957).
336. Michael, V. F., U.S. Pat. 2,606,936 (1952, to Wood River Oil and Refining Co.).
337. Michaelis, A., and F. Hillringhaus, *Ann.*, **315**, 19 (1901).
338. Mikhailov, B. M., and P. M. Aronovich, *J. Gen. Chem. U.S.S.R.*, **29**, 3090 (1959).
339. Mikhailov, B. M., and V. A. Dorokhov, *Proc. Acad. Sci. U.S.S.R.*, **130**, 137 (1960).
340. Mikhailov, B. M., and T. K. Kozminskaya, *Izv. Akad. Nauk S.S.S.R. Odtel. Khim. Nauk*, 80 (1959).
341. Mikhailov, B. M., and L. S. Vasil'ev, *Izv. Akad. Nauk S.S.S.R. Otd. Khim. Nauk*, 531 (1961).
342. Miller, H. C., U.S. Pat. 2,990,423 (1961, to E. I. duPont de Nemours & Co.).
343. Milone, M., *Gazz. Chim. Ital.*, **68**, 582 (1938); through *Chem. Abstracts*, **33**, 1596 (1939).
344. Mirviss, S. B., 139th Meeting American Chemical Society, St. Louis, March 1961, Abstracts of Papers, p. 27-O.
345. Mirviss, S. B., *J. Am. Chem. Soc.*, **83**, 3051 (1961).
346. Mitra, S. M., *Indian J. Phys.*, **12**, 9 (1938).
347. Moissan, H., *Compt. Rend.*, **112**, 717 (1891).
348. Montecatini, S.p.A., Belg. Pat. 594,668 (1960).
349. Nason, H. B., *Ann.*, **104**, 126 (1857).
350. Nelson, G. D., and R. E. Bohm, Can. Pat. 629,396 (1961, to United States Borax and Chemical Corporation).
351. Nöth, H., and H. Beyer, *Ber.*, **93**, 1078 (1960).
352. O'Brien, K. G., *Australian J. Chem.*, **10**, 91 (1957).
353. O'Connor, G. L., and H. R. Nace, *J. Am. Chem. Soc.*, **74**, 5454 (1952).
354. O'Connor, G. L., and H. R. Nace, *J. Am. Chem. Soc.*, **75**, 2118 (1953).
355. O'Connor, G. L., and H. R. Nace, *J. Am. Chem. Soc.*, **77**, 1578 (1955).
356. O'Connor, B., and F. G. Pearce, U.S. Pat. 2,587,753 (1952, to Stanolind Oil and Gas Co.).
357. Ohloff, G., *Ber.*, **93**, 2673 (1960).
358. Onak, T. P., H. Landesman, R. E. Williams, and I. Shapiro, *J. Phys. Chem.*, **63**, 1533 (1959).
359. Otto, M. M., *J. Am. Chem. Soc.*, **57**, 1476 (1935).
360. Pauling, L., *The Nature of the Chemical Bond*, 2nd ed., Cornell Univ. Press, Ithaca, 1948, p. 164.

361. Pearson, R. K., J. C. Renforth, L. J. Edwards, Callery Chemical Company, Rept. No. CCC-1024-TR-200, Sept. 1956.
362. Peppard, D. F., W. G. Brown, and W. C. Johnson, *J. Am. Chem. Soc.*, **68**, 77 (1946).
363. Perkins, G. T., and T. I. Crowell, *J. Am. Chem. Soc.*, **78**, 6013 (1956).
364. Peterson, W. D., U.S. Pat. 2,898,184 (1959, to American Potash and Chemical Corporation).
365. Pflaum, D. J., and H. H. Wenzke, *Ind. Eng. Chem.*, **4**, 392 (1932).
366. Pictet, A., and A. Geleznoff, *Ber.*, **36**, 2219 (1903).
367. Pictet, A., and G. Karl, *Bull. Soc. Chim. France*, **3**, 1114 (1908).
368. Plattner, P. A., A. Furst, and H. Els, *Helv. Chim. Acta*, **72**, 1399 (1954).
369. Ploquin, J., *Bull. Soc. Pharm. Bordeaux*, **97**, 145 (1958).
370. Polak, N. V., and Schwarz Essence Fabrieken, Brit. Pat. 809,186 (1959).
371. Porter, R. P., *J. Phys. Chem.*, **61**, 1260 (1957).
372. Prescott, R. F., R. C. Dosser, and J. J. Sculati, U.S. Pat. 2,260,336 (1941, to The Dow Chemical Co.).
373. Prescott, R. F., R. C. Dosser, and J. J. Sculati, U.S. Pat. 2,260,337 (1941, to The Dow Chemical Co.).
374. Prescott, R. F., R. C. Dosser, and J. J. Sculati, U.S. Pat. 2,260,338 (1941, to The Dow Chemical Co.).
375. Prescott, R. F., R. C. Dosser, and J. J. Sculati, U.S. Pat. 2,260,339 (1941, to The Dow Chemical Co.).
376. Prescott, R. F., R. C. Dosser, and J. J. Sculati, U.S. Pat. 2,300,006 (1942, to The Dow Chemical Co.).
377. Price, C. C., "The Alkylation of Aromatic Compounds by the Friedel–Crafts Method," in R. Adams, ed., *Organic Reactions*, Vol. III, John Wiley & Sons, New York, 1946, p. 1.
378. Raczynski, W. A., U.S. Pat. 2,510,904 (1950, to Hercules Powder Co.).
379. Ramsden, H. E., Brit. Pat. 742,975 (1956, to Metal and Thermit Corp.).
380. Ramsden, H. E., U.S. Pat. 2,904,570 (1959, to Metal and Thermit Corp.).
381. Ramser, H., and E. Wiberg, *Ber.*, **63**, 1136 (1930).
382. Ray, N. H., U.S. Pat. 2,670,333 (1954, to Imperial Chemical Industries).
383. Remes, N. L., and T. W. Martinek, U.S. Pat. 2,890,255 (1959, to The Pure Oil Co.).
384. Remes, N. L., and T. W. Martinek, U.S. Pat. 2,927,125 (1960, to The Pure Oil Co.).
385. Rice, C. H., U.S. Pat. 2,944,076 (1960, to Callery Chemical Co.).
386. Rippere, R. E., and V. K. LaMer, *J. Phys. Chem.*, **47**, 204 (1943).
387. Rojahn, C. A., Ger. Pat. 582,149 (1933).
388. Rondestvedt, C. R. Jr., R. M. Scribner, and C. E. Wulfman, *J. Org. Chem.*, **20**, 9 (1955).
389. Rose, H., *Pogg. Ann.*, **98**, 245 (1856).
390. Rosenheim, A., and H. Vermehren, *Ber.*, **57**, 1337 (1924).
391. Roth, H., *Angew. Chem.*, **50**, 593 (1937).
392. Rothrock, H. S., U.S. Pat. 2,276,094 (1942, to E. I. duPont de Nemours & Co.).
393. Rottig, W., U.S. Pat. 2,746,984 (1956, to Ruhrchemie Aktiengesellschaft).
394. Rummelsburg, A. L., U.S. Pat. 2,354,774 (1944, to Hercules Powder Co.).
395. Ruzicka, L., and M. Stole, *Helv. Chim. Acta*, **11**, 1159 (1928).

396. Rytovsky, B. N., and N. S. Leznov, *J. Appl. Chem. U.S.S.R.*, **22**, 887 (1949); through *Chem. Abstracts*, **44**, 1007 (1950).
397. Scattergood, A., W. H. Miller, and J. Gammon Jr., *J. Am. Chem. Soc.*, **67**, 2150 (1945).
398. Schechter, W. H., Can. Pat. 624,125 (1961, to Callery Chemical Co.).
399. Schechter, W. H., U.S. Pat. 2,629,732 (1953, to Callery Chemical Co.).
400. Schechter, W. H., U.S. Pat. 2,689,259 (1954, to Callery Chemical Co.).
401. Schechter, W. H., U.S. Pat. 2,889,370 (1959, to Callery Chemical Co.).
402. Schiff, H., *Ann. Suppl.*, **5**, 154 (1867).
403. Schiff, H., and E. Bechi, *Compt. Rend.*, **61**, 697 (1865).
404. Schlesinger, I., Progress Report on Contract W-3434-SC-174, Aug. 31, 1943.
405. Schlesinger, H. I., and H. C. Brown, *J. Am. Chem. Soc.*, **62**, 3429 (1940).
406. Schlesinger, H. I., and H. C. Brown, U.S. Pat. 2,461,661 (1949, to U.S.A.).
407. Schlesinger, H. I., and H. C. Brown, U.S. Pat. 2,461,662 (1949, to U.S.A.),
408. Schlesinger, H. I., and H. C. Brown, U.S. Pat. 2,461,663 (1949, to U.S.A.).
409. Schlesinger, H. I., and H. C. Brown, U.S. Pat. 2,534,533 (1950).
410. Schlesinger, H. I., H. C. Brown, *et al.*, *J. Am. Chem. Soc.*, **75**, 186 (1953)
411. Schlesinger, H. I., H. C. Brown, and A. E. Finholt, *J. Am. Chem. Soc.* **75,** 205 (1953).
412. Schlesinger, H. I., H. C. Brown, J. R. Gilbreath, and J. J. Katz, *J. Am. Chem. Soc.*, **75**, 195 (1953).
413. Schlesinger, H. I., H. C. Brown, H. R. Hoekstra, and L. R. Rapp, *J. Am. Chem. Soc.*, **75**, 199 (1953).
414. Schlesinger, H. I., H. C. Brown, D. L. Mayfield, and J. R. Gilbreath, *J. Am. Chem. Soc.*, **75**, 213 (1953).
415. Schlesinger, H. I., R. O. Schaeffer, *et al.*, University of Chicago, Hydrides and Borohydrides of Light Weight Elements and Related Compounds, Contract N6ori-20, Final Report, Aug. 1, 1950 to June 30, 1951.
416. Schmidt, H., *Chem.-Ztg.*, **52**, 898 (1928).
417. Schmidt, H. W., M. Schmeisser, and H. Jenkner, Brit. Pat. 738,703 (1953, to Kali-Chemie Aktiengesellschaft).
418. Schroeder, H., *J. Org. Chem.*, **25**, 1682 (1960).
419. Schroeder, H. A., U.S. Pat. 2,951,871 (1960, to Olin Mathieson Chemical Corp.).
420. Scott, W. W., *Standard Methods of Chemical Analysis*, 5th ed., D. Van Nostrand Co., Inc., New York, 1947, p. 164.
421. Scriabine, I., and A. Peyrolade, Ger. Pat. 1,014,984 (1957, to Société des Usines Chimiques); Brit. Pat. 787,615 (1957); Fr. Pat. 1,124,561 (1956).
422. Seaman, W., and J. R. Johnson, *J. Am. Chem. Soc.*, **53**, 711 (1931).
423. Selwitz, C. M., U.S. Pat. 2,897,244 (1959, to Gulf Research and Development Company).
424. Senkaruck, V., and S. Hoffmann, *Magy. Kem. Folyoirat*, **67**, 49 (61).
425. Seyferth, D., *Chem. Rev.*, **55**, 115 (1955).
426. Shapiro, I., and H. G. Weiss, XVIIth International Congress of Pure and Applied Chemistry, Munich, Sept., 1959, p. 46 of Abstracts.
427. Shapiro, I., and H. G. Weiss, *J. Phys. Chem.*, **63**, 1319 (1959).
428. Sheffield, D. H., U.S. Pat. 2,050,671 (1936, to Hercules Powder Co.).

429. Sheiman, B. M., and V. K. Kuskov, *Izv. Vysshikh Uchebn. Zavedenii. Khim. i Khim. Tekhnol.*, **3**, 876 (1960); through *Chem. Abstracts*, **55**, 9320 (1961).
430. Shoruigin, P. P., and Ya. Makarov-Zemlyanskii, *J. Russ. Phys. Chem. Soc.*, **62**, 2047 (1930); through *Chem. Abstracts*, **25**, 4251 (1931).
431. Sidgwick, N. V., *Chemical Elements and Their Compounds*, Vol. 1, University Press, Oxford, 1951, p. 403; 431a, p. 387.
432. Siegel, S., and W. L. Jolly, University of California, Radiation Laboratory, Livermore, California, Contract No-W-7405-eng-48, April 15, 1955 ASTIA Document UCRL-4513.
433. Snyder, H. R., J. A. Kuck, and J. R. Johnson, *J. Am. Chem. Soc.*, **60**, 105 (1938).
434. Société Belge de L'Azote et des Produits Chimiques du Marly, Belg. Pat. 541,333 (1955).
435. Soloveichik, S., U.S. Pat. 2,617,821 (1952).
436. Sowa, F. J., Brit. Pat. 840,866 (1960).
437. Sowa, F. J., U.S. Pat. 2,834,799 (1958).
438. Sowa, F. J., U.S. Pat. 2,953,592 (1960); Brit. Pat. 840,868 (1960).
439. Sowa, F. J., G. F. Hennion, and J. A. Nieuwland, *J. Am. Chem. Soc.*, **57**, 709 (1935).
440. Stange, H., Can. Pat. 611,103 (1960, to Olin Mathieson Chemical Corporation).
441. Stanley, J., U.S. Pat. 2,077,967 (1937, to W. A. Cleary Corp.).
442. Steinberg, H., U.S. Pat. 2,951,864 (1960, to United States Borax and Chemical Corp.); see also Can. Pat. 600,883 (1960).
443. Steinberg, H., and D. L. Hunter, Can. Pat. 574,094 (1959, to United States Borax and Chemical Corporation).
444. Steinberg, H., and D. L. Hunter, *Ind. Eng. Chem.*, **49**, 174 (1957).
445. Steinberg, H., and D. L. Hunter, *J. Am. Chem. Soc.*, **82**, 85 (1960).
446. Steinberg, H., and D. L. Hunter, Unpublished results.
447. Steinberg, H., D. L. Hunter, L. L. Petterson, and A. L. McCloskey, Unpublished results.
448. Steinberg, H., and A. L. McCloskey, Can. Pat. 625,365 (1961, to United States Borax and Chemical Corporation).
449. Steinberg, H., and A. L. McCloskey, Can. Pat. 629,813 (1961, to United States Borax and Chemical Corporation).
450. Steinberg, H., A. L. McCloskey, R. J. Brotherton, and D. L. Hunter, Unpublished results.
451. Steinberg, H., and L. L. Petterson, Unpublished results.
452. Steinberg, H., and G. W. Willcockson, Unpublished results.
453. Stoll, M., and M. Hinder, U.S. Pat. 2,802,880 (1957, to Firmenich et Cie.).
454. Stone, F. G. A., and H. J. Emeléus, *J. Chem. Soc.*, 2755 (1950).
455. Strahm, R. D., and M. F. Hawthorne, *Anal. Chem.*, **32**, 530 (1960).
456. Strizhevskii, I. I., *Zavodsk. Lab.*, **25**, 146 (1959); through *Chem. Abstracts*, **54**, 18179 (1960).
457. Strohmeier, W., and H. Langhäuser, *Z. Physik. Chem.*, **25**, 427 (1960).
458. Sully, B. T. D., Brit. Pat. 759,482 (1956, to A. Boake Roberts & Co. Ltd.); see also U.S. Pat. 2,975,138 (1961).

459. Tarbell, D. S., "The Claisen Rearrangement," in R. Adams, Ed., *Organic Reactions*, Vol. II, John Wiley & Sons, Inc., New York, 1957, p. 1.
460. Taylor, D. S., *J. Assoc. Offic. Agr. Chemists*, **33**, 132 (1950).
461. Thomas, L. H., *J. Chem. Soc.*, 820 (1946).
462. Thomas, L. H., *J. Chem. Soc.*, 823 (1946).
463. Thron, H., U.S. Pat. 841,738 (1907, to Vereinigte Chininfabriken Zimmer & Co., G.M.B.H.).
464. Timmermans, J., and Th. J. F. Mattaar, *Bull. Soc. Chim. Belges*, **30**, 213 (1921).
465. Ton, J. C., U.S. Pat. 2,802,018 (1957, to Callery Chemical Co.); see also Brit. Pat. 863,315 (1961).
466. Trautman, C. E., U.S. Pat. 2,813,830 (1957, to Gulf Research and Development Co.).
467. Tronov, B. V., and A. M. Petrova, *Zh. Obshch. Khim.*, **23**, 1019 (1953).
468. Tronov, B. V., and N. D. Strel'nikova, *Izv. Tomsk. Politekhn. Inst.*, **83**, 98 (1956); through *Chem. Abstracts*, **53**, 12804 (1959).
469. Trubek Laboratories, Brit. Pat. 806,239 (1958).
470. Tully, T. J., U.S. Pat. 2,889,352 (1959, to Olin Mathieson Chemical Corp.); see also Brit. Pat. 851,661 (1960).
471. Tully, T. J., and P. M. Christopher, *J. Phys. Chem.*, **61**, 1578 (1957).
472. Twiss, S. B., H. Woods, and A. P. Sporzynski, U.S. Pat. 2,623,866 (1952, to Chrysler Corporation).
473. Tyson, G. N., Ger. Pat. 1,062,687 (1959, to Olin Mathieson Chemical Corp.).
474. Tyson, G. N., U.S. Pat. 2,884,440 (1959, to Olin Mathieson Chemical Corp.).
475. Uchida, H. S., H. B. Kreider, A. Murchison, and J. F. Masi, *J. Phys. Chem.*, **63**, 1414 (1959).
476. United States Borax and Chemical Corp., Belg. Pat. 580,560 (1959).
477. United States Borax and Chemical Corp., Brit. Pat. 842,534 (1960); see also Ger. Pat. 1,093,785 (1960).
478. Urs, S. V., and E. S. Gould, *J. Am. Chem. Soc.*, **74**, 2948 (1952).
479. Urs, S. V., C. G. Overberger, and E. S. Gould, "Ethyl Orthoborate," in T. Moeller, *Inorganic Syntheses*, Vol. 5, McGraw-Hill Book Company, Inc., New York, 1957, p. 29.
480. Van Dyke Tiers, G., *J. Am. Chem. Soc.*, **77**, 4837 (1955).
481. Van Liempt, J. A. M., *Rec. Trav. Chim.*, **39**, 38 (1920).
482. Vargha, L. V., *Ber.*, **66**, 704 (1933).
483. Vargha, L. V., *Ber.*, **66**, 1394 (1933).
484. Vaughn, T. H., U.S. Pat. 2,088,935 (1937, to Union Carbide and Carbon Chemicals Corporation).
485. Vaughn, T. H., U.S. Pat. 2,114,866 (1938, to Union Carbide and Carbon Chemicals Corporation).
486. Von Dohlen, W. C., and W. F. Tully, U.S. Pat. 2,924,602 (1960, to Union Carbide Corporation).
487. Voronkov, M. G., and V. N. Zgonnik, *J. Gen. Chem. U.S.S.R.*, **27**, 1557 (1957).
488. Walborsky, H. M., and M. Schwarz, *J. Am. Chem. Soc.*, **75**, 3241 (1953).

489. Walters, R. R., F. F. Koblitz, L. Zeldin, and P. R. Girardot, U.S. Pat. 2,855,440 (1958, to Callery Chemical Co.).
490. Washburn, R. M., E. Levens, C. F. Albright, and F. A. Billig, 131st Meeting American Chemical Society, Miami, April, 1957, Abstracts of Papers, p. 12-L.
491. Washburn, R. M., E. Levens, C. F. Albright, and F. A. Billig, "Preparation, Properties, and Uses of Borate Esters," in *Metal–Organic Compounds, Advances in Chemistry Series 23*, American Chemical Society, Washington, 1959, p. 129.
492. Webster, S. H., and L. M. Dennis, *J. Am. Chem. Soc.*, **55**, 3233 (1933).
493. Weidmann, H., and H. K. Zimmerman Jr., *J. Phys. Chem.*, **64**, 182 (1960).
494. Wheeler, C. M. Jr., and R. A. Sandstedt, *J. Am. Chem. Soc.*, **77**, 2024 (1955).
495. Wherry, E. T., and W. H. Chapin, *J. Am. Chem. Soc.*, **30**, 1687 (1908).
496. Wiberg, E., and R. Hartwimmer, *Z. Naturforsch.*, **10b**, 290 (1955).
497. Wiberg, E., and R. Hartwimmer, *Z. Naturforsch.*, **10b**, 291 (1955).
498. Wiberg, E., and R. Hartwimmer, *Z. Naturforsch.*, **10b**, 294 (1955).
499. Wiberg, E., and U. Kruerke, *Z. Naturforsch.*, **8b**, 608 (1953).
500. Wiberg, E., and H. Nöth, *Z. Naturforsch.*, **12b**, 59 (1957).
501. Wiberg, E., H. Nöth, and R. Hartwimmer, *Z. Naturforsch.*, **10b**, 292 (1955).
502. Wiberg, E., and W. Ruschmann, *Ber.*, **70**, 1393 (1937).
503. Wiberg, E., and W. Sturm, *Z. Naturforsch.*, **8b**, 689 (1953).
504. Wiberg, E., and W. Sturm, *Z. Naturforsch.*, **10b**, 108 (1955).
505. Wiberg, E., and W. Sutterlin, *Z. Anorg. Allgem. Chem.*, **202**, 1 (1931).
506. Wiberg, E., and W. Sutterlin, *Z. Anorg. Allgem. Chem.*, **202**, 22 (1931).
507. Wiberg, E., and W. Sutterlin, *Z. Anorg. Allgem. Chem.*, **202**, 31 (1931).
508. Wiberg, E., and W. Sutterlin, *Z. Anorg. Allgem. Chem.*, **222**, 92 (1935).
509. Wickhold, R., and F. Nagel, *Angew. Chem.*, **71**, 405 (1959).
510. Wilcox, L. V., *Ind. Eng. Chem., Anal. Ed.*, **4**, 38 (1932).
511. Williams, R. E., U.S. Pat. 2,917,547 (1959, to Olin Mathieson Chemical Corp.).
512. Wilson, C. O., Mathieson Chemical Corporation, Technical Research Report, Project Zip, MCC-1023-TR-13, Jan. 26, 1954.
513. Wilson, C. O., U.S. Pat. 2,880,227 (1959, to Olin Mathieson Chemical Corp.).
514. Winstein, S., and R. B. Henderson, "Ethylene and Trimethylene Oxides," in R. C. Elderfield, ed., *Heterocyclic Compounds*, Vol. I, Wiley, New York, 1950, p. 1.
515. Wirth, H. E., Syracuse University, for Olin Mathieson Chemical Corporation, Technical Research Report, Project Zip, OMCC-HEF-105, 1958.
516. Wuyts, M. H., and A. Duquesne, *Bull. Soc. Chim. Belges*, **48**, 77 (1939).
517. Yabroff, D. L., G. E. K. Branch, and H. J. Almquist, *J. Am. Chem. Soc.*, **55**, 2935 (1933).
518. Yamagishi, V. K., T. Tanaka, and T. Hoshino, *Bull. Chem. Soc. Japan*, **30**, 455 (1957).
519. Yasuda, S. K., and R. N. Rogers, *Microchem. J.*, **4**, 155 (1960).
520. Young, D. M., Can. Pat. 630,611 (1961, to The Dow Chemical Co.).

521. Young, D. M., and C. D. Anderson, *J. Org. Chem.*, **26**, 1669 (1961).
522. Young, D. M., and C. D. Anderson, *J. Org. Chem.*, **26**, 2158 (1961).
523. Zakharkin, L. I., and V. I. Stanko, *Bull. Acad. Sci. U.S.S.R. Div. Chem. Sci.*, 1774 (1960).
524. Zange, E., *Ber.*, **93**, 652 (1960).
525. Zeitschel, F. O., U.S. Pat. 1,733,440 (1929).
526. Zhigach, A. F., E. B. Kazakova, and R. A. Kigel, *Proc. Acad. Sci. U.S.S.R.*, **106**, 9 (1956).
527. Zuffante, S., R. T. Oliver, and W. F. Luder, *J. Phys. Chem.*, **63**, 1537 (1959).

5

ORTHOBORATES OF POLYHYDRIC ALCOHOLS AND PHENOLS

I. ORTHOBORATES DERIVED FROM DIHYDRIC ALCOHOLS AND PHENOLS

A. Introduction

Orthoborates of dihydric alcohols or phenols are composed of three alkylenedioxy or phenylenedioxy residues and two boron atoms. They are capable of existence in two monomeric forms (I and II) and an infinite number of polymeric forms.* Structure (III) represents one possible polymeric configuration.

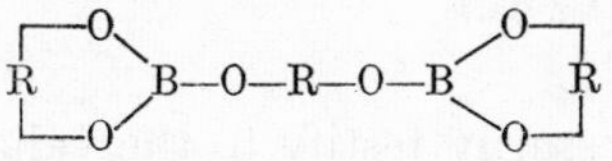

R(O)(O)B—O—R—O—B(O)(O)R

(I)

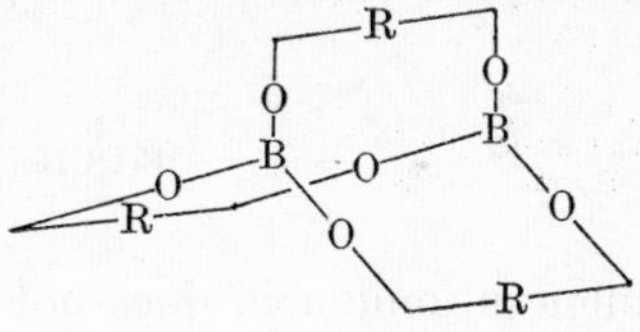

(II)

[—B(O—R—O)(O—R—O)B—O—R—O—]$_n$

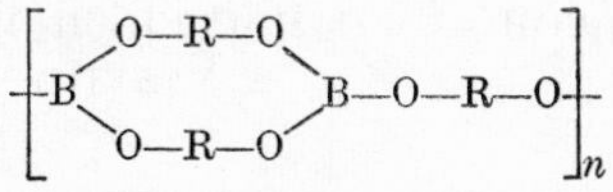

(III)

B. Historical

In 1878 Councler[10] unsuccessfully attempted the preparation of tri(ethylene glycol) biborate by the reaction of ethylene bromide and lead borate. His further attempts from boron trichloride and

* Structures in which a free hydroxyl group exists[2]

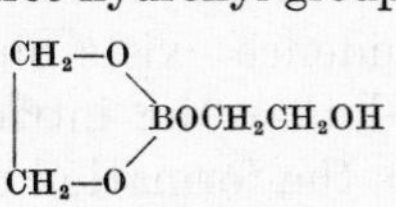

CH_2—O
BOCH$_2$CH$_2$OH
CH_2—O

are treated in Chapter 6.

ethylene glycol were reported to give (IV) instead.[9,10] This particular ester along with the bicyclic ester (V) and free ethylene glycol subsequently were believed to be the products of the reaction of three moles of ethylene glycol with boron trichloride or boric acid.[29]

$$\underset{\text{(IV)}}{B(OCH_2CH_2OH)_3} \qquad \underset{\text{(V)}}{B(OCH_2CH_2O)_3B}$$

The difficulty of isolating hydroxy derivatives of alkyl borates tends to cast doubt on the validity of structure (IV). The stoichiometric equivalent of (IV), the biborate (VI) and three moles of free ethylene glycol, may have been the products of the reactions.

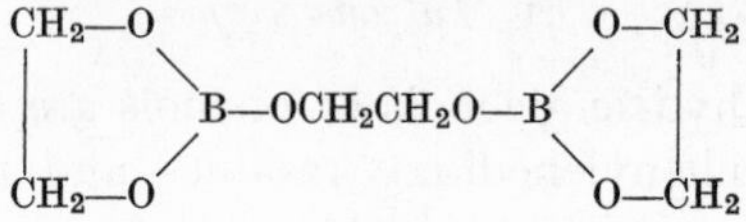

$$\begin{array}{l} CH_2\text{—}O \qquad\qquad\qquad\qquad\quad O\text{—}CH_2 \\ |\qquad\quad \diagdown \qquad\qquad\qquad \diagup \quad | \\ |\qquad\qquad B\text{—}OCH_2CH_2O\text{—}B \qquad | \\ |\qquad\quad \diagup \qquad\qquad\qquad \diagdown \quad | \\ CH_2\text{—}O \qquad\qquad\qquad\qquad\quad O\text{—}CH_2 \end{array}$$

(VI)

The subsequent conversion of the product reported to be (IV) to the mixed ester (VII)[29] by treatment with palmitic acid and

$$B(OCH_2CH_2O\overset{\overset{O}{\|}}{C}C_{15}H_{31})_3$$

(VII)

p-toluenesulfonic acid does not necessarily testify to the validity of structure (IV) since (VII) could arise equally well by transesterification of the biborate (VI) by the monopalmitate (VIII).

$$HOCH_2CH_2OH + C_{15}H_{31}\overset{\overset{O}{\|}}{C}OH \xrightarrow{H^+} \underset{\text{(VIII)}}{C_{15}H_{31}\overset{\overset{O}{\|}}{C}OCH_2CH_2OH} + H_2O \qquad (5\text{-}1)$$

C. Properties

The monomeric nature of the biborates has been shown by cryoscopic molecular weight determinations for the products from propylene glycol,[34,86] trimethylene glycol,[86] 1,3-butanediol,[13] and 2-methyl-2,4-pentanediol,[12] and by the volatility of 2,3-butanediol biborate which can be distilled at atmospheric pressure without decomposition.[58]

The structure of the trialkyl borates is well documented. However, only partial evidence exists on the structure of the diol biborates.[80] It is believed that the intrinsic stability of five- and six-membered rings favors the formation of structure (I) with either 1,2- or 1,3-glycols or with catechol. Thus the partial hydrolysis of tri-(2-methyl-2,4-pentanediol) biborate led to the isolation of the six-membered ring (IX) indicating the biborate structure to be (X). However, complete hydrolysis of the bicyclic structure (II) to diol and boric acid followed by partial esterification to give (IX) cannot be ruled out.

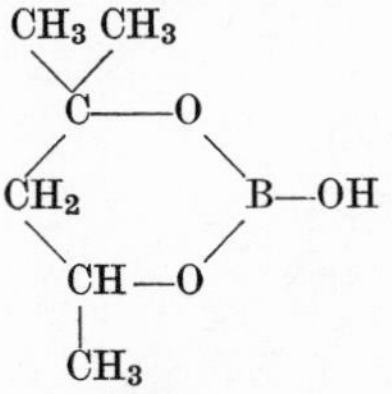

```
CH3 CH3                    CH3 CH3                                 CH3 CH3
  \/                         \/                                      \/
  C——O                       C——O            CH3        O——C
 /    \                     /    \            |        /     \
CH2    B—OH               CH2     B—OCHCH2CO—B              CH2
 \    /                     \    /      |     |        \     /
  CH—O                       CH—O      CH3   CH3        O—CH
  |                          |                            |
  CH3                        CH3                          CH3
   (IX)                                   (X)
```

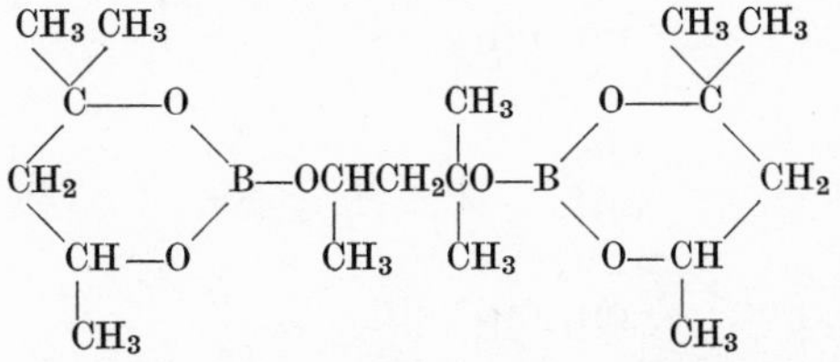

The fact that biborates derived from 1,3-diols remain liquid indefinitely and biborates derived from 1,2-diols, although distillable, become very viscous or even glassy after condensation led to the conclusion that the 1,3-derivatives had the monomeric structure (I) and the 1,2-derivatives, at least in part, the polymeric structure (III). In addition, the extent of the polymeric composition seemed to decrease with increasing substitution of the diol (Table 5-1), presum-

Table 5-1. Effect of diol on molecular weight of biborate

Diol	Nature of biborate
$HOCH_2CH_2OH$	Glass
$HOCH_2\overset{CH_3}{\overset{\vert}{C}}HOH$	Gelatinous liquid
meso-$HO\overset{CH_3}{\overset{\vert}{C}}H—\overset{CH_3}{\overset{\vert}{C}}HOH$	Very viscous liquid
$HOCH_2CH_2CH_2OH$	Liquid

ably due to increased steric difficulties in the network structure. Structure (II) was considered sterically impossible for the biborates from 1,2- and 1,3-diols.[34]

The small amount of evidence available indicates that 1,4-glycols lead to type (II) products when polymeric products are not involved. Thus partial hydrolysis of tri-(2,5-dimethyl-2,5-hexanediol) biborate did not lead to a seven-membered ring (XI)* but gave the

* A mixed ester (see Chapter 6) containing a seven-membered ring has been reported from a 1,4-glycol, *o*-bis(diphenylhydroxymethyl)benzene.[92]

diol and boric acid instead, indicating (XII) to be the structure of the biborate. Of course, it is possible that compound (XI) is not hydrolytically stable, so the structure of tri-(2,5-dimethyl-2,5-hexanediol) biborate still remains in doubt. The conventional structure (I) has been proposed.[34]

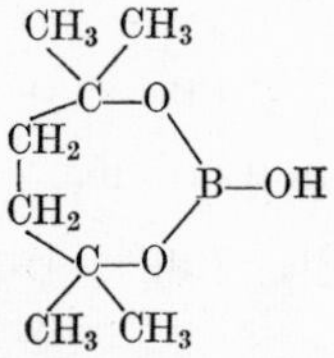

(XI)

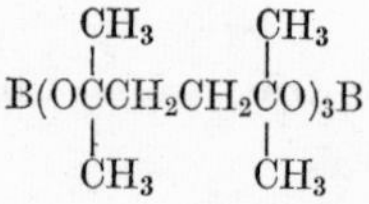

$B(OC(CH_3)_2CH_2CH_2C(CH_3)_2O)_3B$

(XII)

The bicyclic structure (II) was considered sterically improbable for 1,4-diols. Unsuccessful attempts to distill the biborate from 1,4-butanediol indicated a polymeric structure for this derivative.[34]

The bicyclic structure (II) certainly is not a preferred configuration since the biborate of 2,5-dimethyl-3-hexyne-2,5-diol resulted in only polymeric products on esterification with boric acid. This acetylenic diol is incapable of existence as structure (I) due to the linearity of the triple bond which precludes 7-membered ring formation,[90] but it could form the 14-membered rings of structure (II).

The B–O stretching vibration in (XIII) was found to occur at

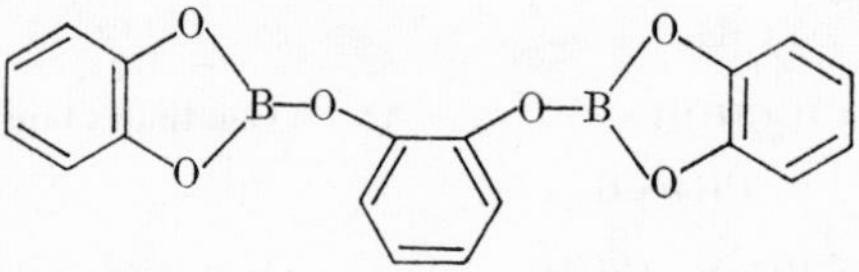

(XIII)

considerably shorter wavelengths (6.91 μ) than that usually recorded for trialkoxyboranes (7.41 to 7.63 μ). These data implied a B–O bond order in (XIII) greater than that in trialkoxyboranes and suggested the importance of canonical forms such as (XIV).[4]

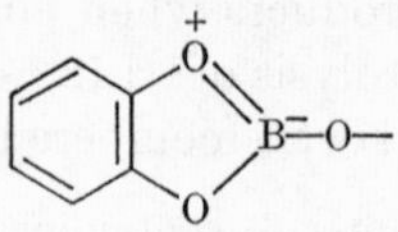

(XIV)

D. Methods of Preparation

1. INTRODUCTION

The indiscriminate reaction of a trivalent boron source with a dihydric alcohol or phenol clearly is capable of producing an infinite variety of chains, rings and three-dimensional polymers with free hydroxyl groups residing either on boron or carbon.[42,43] Fortunately, if one employs a stoichiometry of at least three moles of diol for every two atoms of boron and distills or recrystallizes the final product,

$$3\,R(OH)_2 + 2\,H_3BO_3 \longrightarrow R\!<\!\overset{O}{\underset{O}{}}\!>\!B{-}O{-}R{-}O{-}B\!<\!\overset{O}{\underset{O}{}}\!>\!R + 6\,H_2O \qquad (5\text{-}2)$$

monomeric hydroxyl-free materials of definite structure are obtained. Thus 1,2- and 1,3-glycols (5-2) and catechol (5-3) have

$$3\,C_6H_4(OH)_2 + 2\,H_3BO_3 \rightarrow C_6H_4O_2B{-}O{-}C_6H_4{-}O{-}BO_2C_6H_4 + 6\,H_2O \qquad (5\text{-}3)$$

been converted to the monomeric biborates; whereas 1,4- or higher glycols and resorcinol usually lead to the formation of polymers (5-4).

$$3\,R(OH)_2 + 2\,H_3BO_3 \longrightarrow \left[{-}O{-}R{-}O{-}\underset{\underset{\underset{\underset{-B-}{|}}{O}}{\underset{R}{|}}}{\overset{}{B}}{-}O{-}R{-}O{-}B\!<\right]_n \qquad (5\text{-}4)$$

The large variety of methods of preparation of borates of monohydric alcohols and phenols described in Chapter 4 conceivably also could be employed for the preparation of triglycol biborates. However, the synthetic methods reported to date have included the reaction of dihydric materials with only a limited number of boron sources.

2. FROM BORIC ACID

A German patent in 1933 described the first esterification of boric acid with a diol, diethanolamine.[70] The product probably was polymeric in nature. The azeotropic removal of water with toluene, benzene, or chloroform with a 3:2 mole ratio of glycol to boric acid subsequently was used to prepare the biborates of ethylene glycol,[34] propylene glycol,[13,34,86] trimethylene glycol,[34,86] 1-chloro-2,3-propanediol,[13] 1,3-butanediol,[13,78] 2,3-butanediol,[34,58] diisopropanolamine[81] and 2,2-diethyl- and 2-ethyl-2-butyl-1,3-propanediol.[12] The bicyclic structure (XV) was recorded for the biborate prepared from

$$B(OCH_2CH_2O)_3B$$

(XV)

ethylene glycol by this method.[13] Biborates of a variety of tertiary diols have been prepared with benzene or toluene as the azeotroping agent.[12,49,80]

Monomeric aromatic biborates thus far have been limited to the catechol derivative prepared by the benzene or toluene azeotrope method with [65,91] and without[56] the aid of anhydrous cupric sulfate.

A strong protest against the existence of any biborates was made on the basis of the conversion of a variety of glycols to products consistent with structure (XVI)[69] (see Chapter 7). However, a 1:1 diol

$$R\begin{cases}-O\\ \\ -O\end{cases}\!\!>B-OH$$

(XVI)

to boric acid stoichiometry was employed (5-5) and biborates would

$$R\begin{cases}-OH\\ \\ -OH\end{cases} + B(OH)_3 \rightarrow R\begin{cases}-O\\ \\ -O\end{cases}\!\!>B-OH + 2\,H_2O \qquad (5\text{-}5)$$

not be expected to be formed. The alternate explanation that the absence of an azeotroping agent may have precluded uniform reaction[58] does not have to be called upon.

Use of a stoichiometry of 1–2.4 moles ethylene glycol to one mole of boric acid led to polymers containing six to seven glycol residues per molecule.[36]

The esterification of boric acid with a diol and hydrolysis of the resulting biborate proceeds via B–O cleavage and not C–O cleavage since D-(−)-2,3-butanediol, α_D^{25} − 13.00°, was converted to the biborate (benzene azeotrope) and upon hydrolysis of the ester yielded diol of $\alpha_D{}^5$ −12.96°.[19]

3. FROM BORIC OXIDE

Ethylene glycol biborate has been prepared by heating a 3:1 reaction mixture of the glycol and boric oxide.[77] The sharp melting point, crystallinity and high solubility of the product in ethylene glycol and butanediol are indicative of a monomeric structure.

Tri-(2-methyl-2,4-pentanediol) biborate[14] and tricatechol biborate[84] also have been obtained from boric oxide with the aid of a toluene azeotrope.

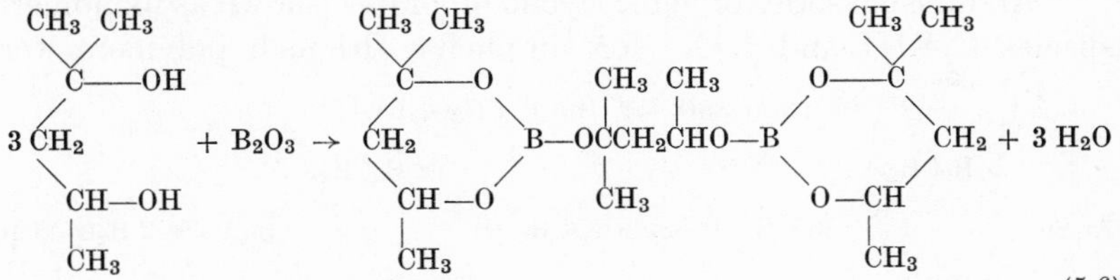

$$3\ (CH_3)_2C(OH)CH_2CH(OH)CH_3 + B_2O_3 \rightarrow \underset{\text{(ring: } (CH_3)_2C{-}O,\ CH_2,\ CH(CH_3){-}O)}{} B{-}OC(CH_3)_2CH_2CH(CH_3)O{-}B \underset{\text{(ring: } O{-}C(CH_3)_2,\ CH_2,\ O{-}CH(CH_3))}{} + 3\ H_2O \qquad (5\text{-}6)$$

$$3\ C_6H_4(OH)_2 + B_2O_3 \longrightarrow C_6H_4O_2B{-}O{-}C_6H_4{-}O{-}BO_2C_6H_4 + 3\ H_2O \qquad (5\text{-}7)$$

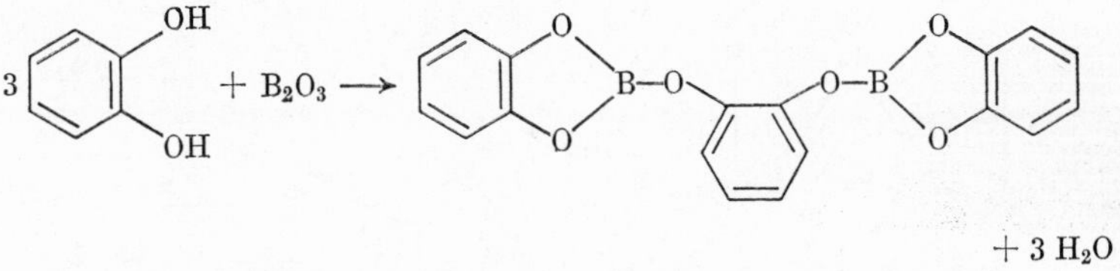

4. FROM BORIC ACID ESTERS

Transesterification of a trialkoxyborane with a diol has been used to only a limited extent to prepare triglycol biborates. Tri(ethylene glycol) biborate and tricatechol biborate were prepared from 2:3 and 1:4 molar reactions of triethoxyborane and ethylene glycol or catechol in refluxing benzene (5-8).[55,56] Treatment of tripropoxy-

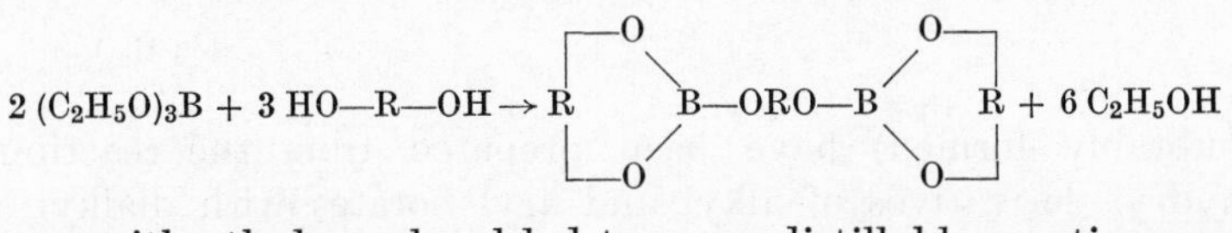

$$2\ (C_2H_5O)_3B + 3\ HO{-}R{-}OH \rightarrow R\!\left<\!\begin{matrix}O\\O\end{matrix}\!\right>\!B{-}ORO{-}B\!\left<\!\begin{matrix}O\\O\end{matrix}\!\right>\!R + 6\ C_2H_5OH \qquad (5\text{-}8)$$

borane with ethylene glycol led to an undistillable reaction product of composition corresponding to ethylene glycol biborate (XVII).[93]

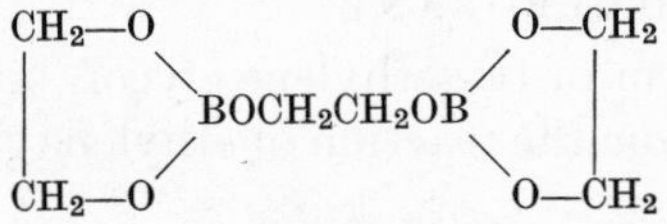

$$\begin{matrix}CH_2{-}O\\ |\\ CH_2{-}O\end{matrix}\!\!>\!BOCH_2CH_2OB\!<\!\!\begin{matrix}O{-}CH_2\\ |\\ O{-}CH_2\end{matrix}$$

(XVII)

The reaction of a borate and a carboxylate has been shown to result in the exchange of alcohol and acid moieties (Chapter 4). Use of a glycol diester in this reaction resulted in the formation of a polymeric methylene glycol borate.[31]

$$2\,(C_2H_5O)_3B + 3\,CH_3\overset{O}{\overset{\|}{C}}OCH_2O\overset{O}{\overset{\|}{C}}CH_3 \rightarrow \left[B\begin{matrix} OCH_2O \\ \\ OCH_2O \end{matrix}BOCH_2O \right]_n + 6\,CH_3\overset{O}{\overset{\|}{C}}OC_2H_5 \quad (5\text{-}9)$$

An unusual series of heterocyclic biborates (shown as monomeric species (XVIII and XIX) for simplicity although polymers were

$$3\,Ar_2SnO + 2\,(HSCH_2CH_2O)_3B \rightarrow$$

$$Ar_2Sn\begin{matrix} SCH_2CH_2O \\ \\ SCH_2CH_2O \end{matrix}BOCH_2CH_2S\overset{Ar}{\underset{Ar}{Sn}}SCH_2CH_2OB\begin{matrix} OCH_2CH_2S \\ \\ OCH_2CH_2S \end{matrix}SnAr_2 + 3\,H_2O \quad (5\text{-}10)$$

(XVIII)

$$3\,R_2SnO + 2\left[HS\!-\!C_6H_4\!-\!O\right]_3B \longrightarrow$$

$$R_2Sn\begin{matrix} S\!-\!C_6H_4\!-\!O \\ \\ S\!-\!C_6H_4\!-\!O \end{matrix}BO\!-\!C_6H_4\!-\!S\overset{R}{\underset{R}{Sn}}S\!-\!C_6H_4\!-\!OB\begin{matrix} O\!-\!C_6H_4\!-\!S \\ \\ O\!-\!C_6H_4\!-\!S \end{matrix}SnR_2 + 3\,H_2O \quad (5\text{-}11)$$

(XIX)

undoubtably formed) have been prepared from the reaction of sulfhydryl derivatives of alkyl and aryl borates with dialkyl and diaryl tin oxides.[66,67,68]

5. FROM TRIACETOXYBORANE

The bicyclic form of tri-(ethylene glycol) biborate has been formulated as arising from the reaction of ethylene glycol and triacetoxyborane.[64]

$$3\,HOCH_2CH_2OH + 2\,B(O\overset{O}{\overset{\|}{C}}CH_3)_3 \xrightarrow{\Delta} B(OCH_2CH_2O)_3B + 6\,CH_3\overset{O}{\overset{\|}{C}}OH \quad (5\text{-}12)$$

6. FROM BORON TRICHLORIDE AND ITS DERIVATIVES

Treatment of boron trichloride with ethylene glycol[2] or catechol[20,21] has resulted in almost quantitative yields of the biborates.

$$3\,HOCH_2CH_2OH + 2\,BCl_3 \rightarrow \begin{matrix} CH_2{-}O \\ | \\ CH_2{-}O \end{matrix} \!\!>\! BOCH_2CH_2OB \!<\!\! \begin{matrix} O{-}CH_2 \\ | \\ O{-}CH_2 \end{matrix} + 6\,HCl \quad (5\text{-}13)$$

3 [catechol: $C_6H_4(OH)_2$] + 2 BCl_3 → [$C_6H_4O_2B{-}O{-}C_6H_4{-}O{-}BO_2C_6H_4$]

+ 6 HCl (5-14)

The intermediate ethylenedioxybis(dichloroborane) (XX)[3] and 2-chloro-1,3,2-benzodioxaborole (XXI)[21] reacted similarly to yield

$$\underset{(XX)}{Cl_2BOCH_2CH_2OBCl_2} + 2\,HOCH_2CH_2OH \rightarrow$$

$$\begin{matrix} CH_2{-}O \\ | \\ CH_2{-}O \end{matrix} \!\!>\! BOCH_2CH_2OB \!<\!\! \begin{matrix} O{-}CH_2 \\ | \\ O{-}CH_2 \end{matrix} + 4\,HCl \quad (5\text{-}15)$$

2 [$C_6H_4O_2B{-}Cl$] (XXI) + [catechol: $C_6H_4(OH)_2$]

→ [$C_6H_4O_2B{-}O{-}C_6H_4{-}O{-}BO_2C_6H_4$] + 2 HCl (5-16)

the same biborates. The thermal disproportionation of (XXI) also was reported to yield tricatechol biborate.[21]

A 1,3-glycol, trimethyleneglycol, reacted with boron trichloride to produce a biborate with dioxaborinane rings.[17]

$$3\,HO(CH_2)_3OH + 2\,BCl_3 \rightarrow CH_2 \!<\!\! \begin{matrix} CH_2{-}O \\ CH_2{-}O \end{matrix} \!\!>\! BO(CH_2)_3OB \!<\!\! \begin{matrix} O{-}CH_2 \\ O{-}CH_2 \end{matrix} \!\!>\! CH_2 + 6\,HCl \quad (5\text{-}17)$$

7. FROM 1,3,2-DIOXABOROLANE AND BORINANE DERIVATIVES

Biborates have been prepared via the esterification and alcoholysis reactions (5-18)[11,63] and (5-19).[63] Tricatechol biborate was prepared via the alcoholysis reaction (5-20).[55]

$$2\,R\begin{matrix}O\\ \\O\end{matrix}BOH + R\begin{matrix}OH\\ \\OH\end{matrix} \rightarrow R\begin{matrix}O\\ \\O\end{matrix}B{-}ORO{-}B\begin{matrix}O\\ \\O\end{matrix}R + 2\,H_2O \qquad (5\text{-}18)$$

$$R\begin{matrix}O\\ \\O\end{matrix}B{-}O{-}B\begin{matrix}O\\ \\O\end{matrix}R + R\begin{matrix}OH\\ \\OH\end{matrix} \rightarrow R\begin{matrix}O\\ \\O\end{matrix}B{-}ORO{-}B\begin{matrix}O\\ \\O\end{matrix}R + H_2O \qquad (5\text{-}19)$$

$$2\;C_6H_4\begin{matrix}O\\ \\O\end{matrix}B{-}OC_2H_5 + C_6H_4\begin{matrix}OH\\ \\OH\end{matrix} \longrightarrow C_6H_4\begin{matrix}O\\ \\O\end{matrix}B{-}O{-}C_6H_4{-}O{-}B\begin{matrix}O\\ \\O\end{matrix}C_6H_4 + 2\,C_2H_5OH \qquad (5\text{-}20)$$

The biborate of catechol also was obtained by the thermal disproportionation of (XXII).[21]

$$3\;C_6H_4\begin{matrix}O\\ \\O\end{matrix}B{-}OCH_3 \longrightarrow$$

(XXII)

$$C_6H_4\begin{matrix}O\\ \\O\end{matrix}B{-}O{-}C_6H_4{-}O{-}B\begin{matrix}O\\ \\O\end{matrix}C_6H_4 + (CH_3O)_3B \qquad (5\text{-}21)$$

8. FROM SODIUM BOROHYDRIDE REDUCTION OF DIKETONES

The sodium borohydride reduction of 1,2- or 1,3-diketones present in excess followed by acidification and distillation has been reported to result in the biborate.[11]

E. Reactions

1. THERMAL STABILITY

The thermal stability of diol biborates has not been explored to any extent. Tricatechol biborate was recovered in 82% yield after heating at 290° for twelve hours.[21]

2. HYDROLYSIS

Most glycol biborates are easily hydrolyzed to their original components (5-22). Partial hydrolysis to a stable 2-hydroxy-1,3,2-dioxaborinane configuration (5-23) has been reported. This chemistry is discussed in Chapter 21.

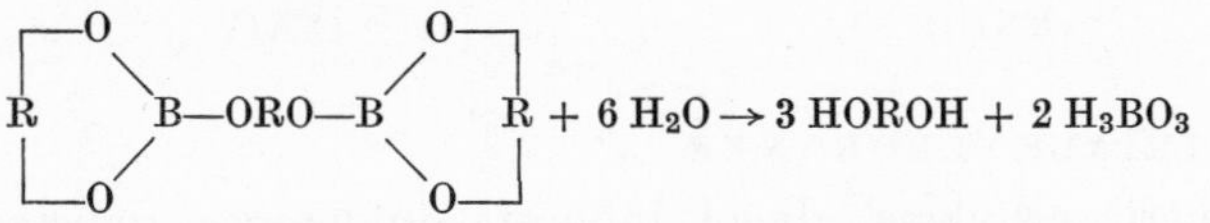

$$R\begin{matrix}O\\O\end{matrix}B{-}ORO{-}B\begin{matrix}O\\O\end{matrix}R + 6\,H_2O \rightarrow 3\,HOROH + 2\,H_3BO_3 \qquad (5\text{-}22)$$

$$R\begin{matrix}O\\O\end{matrix}B{-}ORO{-}B\begin{matrix}O\\O\end{matrix}R + 2\,H_2O \rightarrow 2\,R\begin{matrix}O\\O\end{matrix}BOH + HOROH \qquad (5\text{-}23)$$

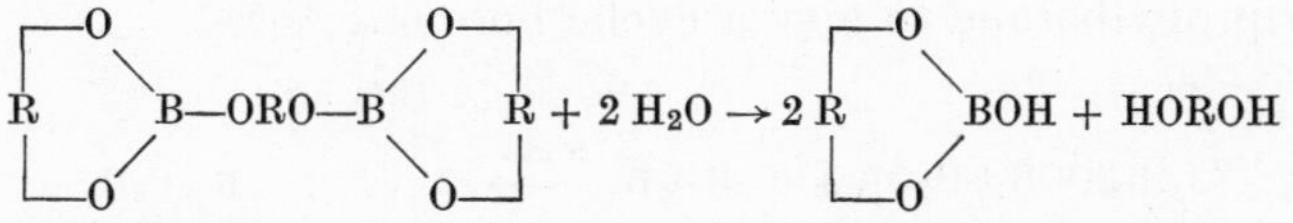

3. ALCOHOLYSIS

An analytical procedure for the determination of boron in catechol biborate involves the quantitative distillation of trimethoxyborane–methanol azeotrope from a methanol solution of the biborate.[84]

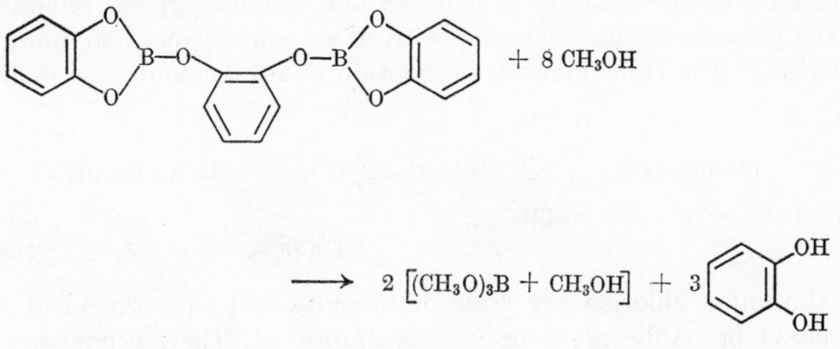

$$C_6H_4O_2B{-}O{-}C_6H_4{-}O{-}BO_2C_6H_4 + 8\,CH_3OH \longrightarrow 2\,[(CH_3O)_3B + CH_3OH] + 3\,C_6H_4(OH)_2 \qquad (5\text{-}24)$$

4. WITH AMINES

The biborate derived from *meso*-2,3-butanediol forms a 1 : 1 precipitate with benzylamine in pentane solution. The complex was too unstable to recrystallize without decomposition.[34]

5. WITH TRIALKOXYBORANES

The redistribution reaction of triglycol biborates and trialkoxyboranes to produce unsymmetrical esters is discussed in Chapter 6.

6. WITH HYDROGEN BROMIDE

Attempts to prepare (XXIII) from (XXIV) by treatment with liquid hydrogen bromide resulted in the formation of ethylene bromide and boric acid.[3]

$$(HO)_2BOCH_2CH_2OB(OH)_2 \qquad \text{(XXIII)}$$

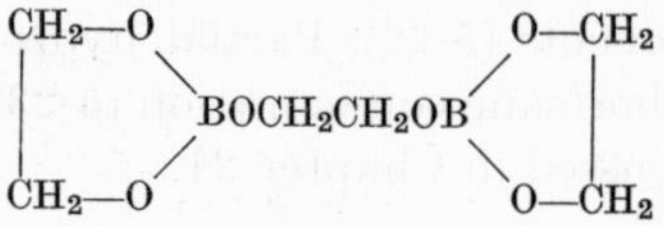

$$\begin{matrix} CH_2{-}O & & O{-}CH_2 \\ | \quad\; \diagdown & & \diagup \quad\; | \\ | & BOCH_2CH_2OB & | \\ | \quad\; \diagup & & \diagdown \quad\; | \\ CH_2{-}O & & O{-}CH_2 \end{matrix} \qquad \text{(XXIV)}$$

7. WITH TRIALKYLBORANES

Polymeric ethylene glycol biborate undergoes redistribution with tripropylborane to give a cyclic boronate.[37,38]

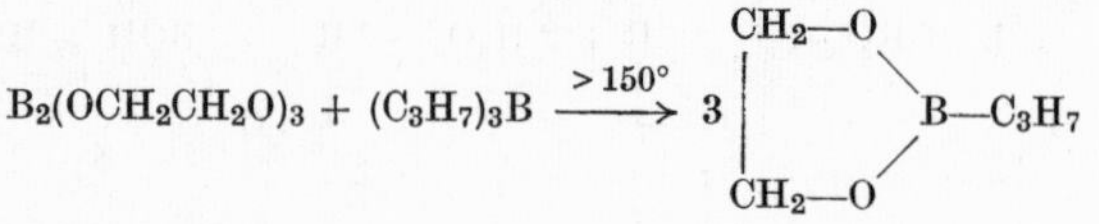

$$B_2(OCH_2CH_2O)_3 + (C_3H_7)_3B \xrightarrow{>150^\circ} 3 \begin{matrix} CH_2{-}O & \\ | \quad\; \diagdown & \\ | & B{-}C_3H_7 \\ | \quad\; \diagup & \\ CH_2{-}O & \end{matrix} \qquad (5\text{-}25)$$

8. FRIEDEL–CRAFTS ALKYLATION

Ethylene glycol biborate (in addition to the variety of alkyl borates discussed in Chapter 4) can serve as an alkylating agent in a Friedel–Crafts type reaction. Thus, a 25% yield of dibenzyl was realized from the reaction of benzene and ethylene glycol biborate in the presence of less than one-third of an equivalent of aluminum chloride.[39] The stoichiometry of reaction (5-26) demands two moles

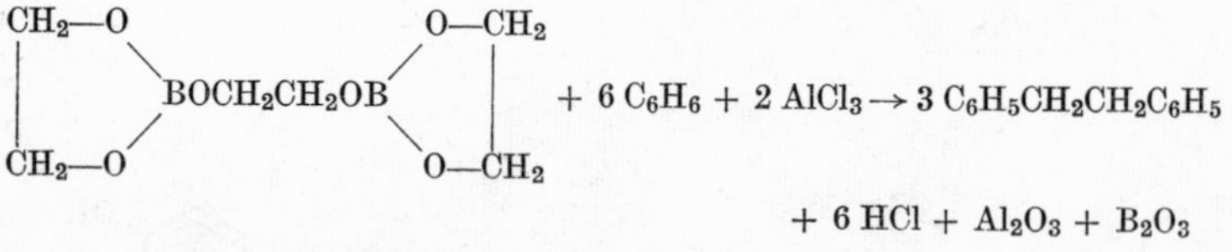

$$\begin{matrix} CH_2{-}O & & O{-}CH_2 \\ | \quad\; \diagdown & & \diagup \quad\; | \\ | & BOCH_2CH_2OB & | \\ | \quad\; \diagup & & \diagdown \quad\; | \\ CH_2{-}O & & O{-}CH_2 \end{matrix} + 6\,C_6H_6 + 2\,AlCl_3 \rightarrow 3\,C_6H_5CH_2CH_2C_6H_5$$

$$+ 6\,HCl + Al_2O_3 + B_2O_3 \qquad (5\text{-}26)$$

of aluminum chloride per mole of biborate and thus the yield of dibenzyl probably could be greatly improved. The mechanism of this reaction is discussed in Chapter 4.

9. MISCELLANEOUS

Biborates of acetylenic glycols have been found to be more convenient than the glycol itself for oxidative cleavage to hydroxy acids.[7]

The biborates, which are prepared from pyroboric acid, are not isolated in the process.

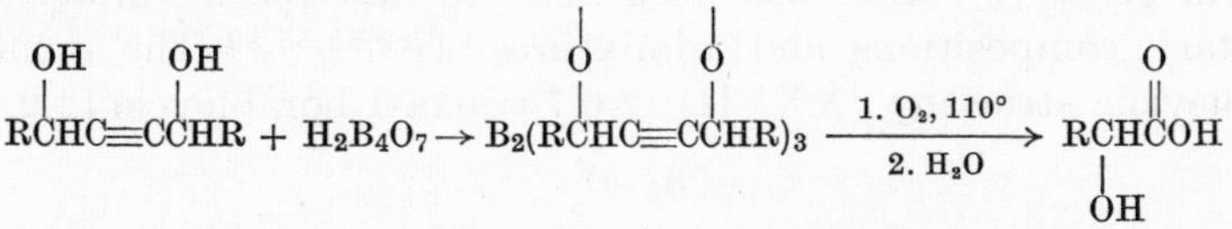

$$\underset{}{\overset{\text{OH}}{\overset{|}{\text{RCH}}}}\text{C}{\equiv}\overset{\text{OH}}{\overset{|}{\text{C}\text{CHR}}} + H_2B_4O_7 \rightarrow B_2(\text{R}\overset{|}{\overset{\text{O}}{\overset{|}{\text{CH}}}}\text{C}{\equiv}\text{C}\overset{|}{\overset{\text{O}}{\overset{|}{\text{CH}}}}\text{R})_3 \xrightarrow[\text{2. } H_2O]{\text{1. } O_2\text{, } 110^\circ} \text{RCH}\underset{\text{OH}}{\underset{|}{}}\overset{\text{O}}{\overset{\|}{\text{C}}}\text{OH} \qquad (5\text{-}27)$$

The biborate derived from *meso*-2,3-butanediol was found to be essentially unreactive to sodium and formed a gelatinous complex when treated with ammonia in acetone solution.[58]

II. ORTHOBORATES DERIVED FROM TRIHYDRIC ALCOHOLS

A. Introduction

Monomeric triol borates exist as the bicyclic structure (XXV) in

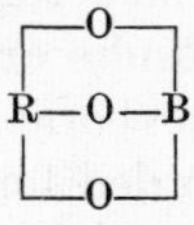

R—O—B, with R and B also bridged by two further —O— links

(XXV)

which boron is at the bridgehead. Their existence is clearly a function of the stability of the bicyclic ring system versus the stability of the stoichiometrically equivalent polymer of which (XXVI) represents one of the almost infinite possibilities.

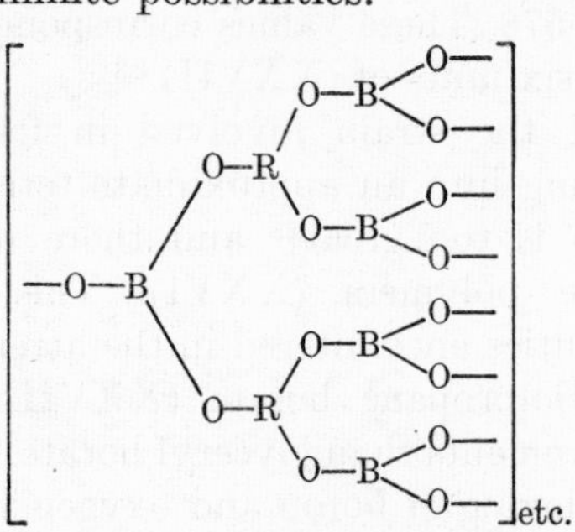

[—O—B(O—R(O—B(O—)₂)₂)₂] etc.

(XXVI)

B. Historical

In 1867 Schiff[75] reported the preparation of glyceryl borate from the reaction of glycerol and boric oxide.

$$2\ \text{HOCH}_2\overset{\text{OH}}{\overset{|}{\text{C}}}\text{HCH}_2\text{OH} + B_2O_3 \xrightarrow{\text{Heat}} 2\ B(C_3H_5O_3) + 3\ H_2O \qquad (5\text{-}28)$$

C. Glyceryl Borate

The term glyceryl borate has been used to describe a variety of proprietary compositions and admixtures.[5,6,32,50,57,83] The monomeric bicyclic structure (XXVII) (2,6,7-trioxa-1-borabicyclo [2.2.1]

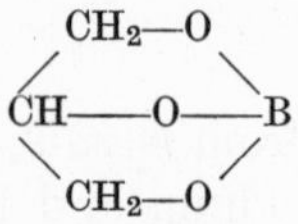

```
     CH2—O
    /     \
CH——O——B
    \     /
     CH2—O
```

(XXVII)

heptane) for reasons discussed below clearly is incapable of existence, yet this particular formulation has been recorded no less than four times. Thus, (XXVII) has been reported from the reaction of glycerol with boric oxide,[75] boric acid in the presence of toluene,[13] and boron acetate.[1,64]

Molecular weight determinations (boiling point elevation of ethyl acetate) agreed well with structure (XXVII): calc. 99.9; found 98.5, 100.0.[1] However, these results are shadowed by the fact that ethyl acetate reacts with some boric acid esters,[82] probably in a manner analogous to that recorded for the reaction of trimethoxyborane and butyl acetate [62] (see Chapter 4). Preparations from equimolar amounts of glycerol and boric acid, boric acid plus toluene in triglyme, boric acid plus benzene in diglyme, boric oxide, oxybis-(diacetoxyborane), and tributoxyborane gave glassy solids with molecular weights (cryoscopic in dioxane, ebullioscopic in acetone) ranging from 368 to 578. These values correspond to polymers containing from four to six units of (XXVII).[63]

It appears that the strain involved in forcing the trigonal coplanar BO_3 grouping into an approximate tetrahedral conformation as in (XXVII) is too great[23] and there results instead the relatively strain-free polymers (XXVI). This explanation was offered for the difficulties encountered in the attempted synthesis of monomeric trimethylolpropane borate (XXVIII),* a molecule of even less steric requirements than glyceryl borate.[8] It is possible that intermolecular complexing of boron and oxygen would tend to lend tetrahedral character to the boron atom and alleviate the strains

* The energetically identical borate from 1,1,1-trimethylolethane had been reported by the late Dr. G. W. Schaeffer in a private communication to the author in 1955. It was prepared by the slow addition of a dioxane solution of the triol (1 g. in 50 ml.) to a dilute solution of trimethoxyborane followed by distillation of the trimethoxyborane–methanol azeotrope. The product hydrolyzed rapidly, dimerized on standing and polymerized on heating. See Section II-D.

imposed by the bicyclic structure. However, formation of the bicyclic structures (XXVII) and (XXVIII) would result in complete

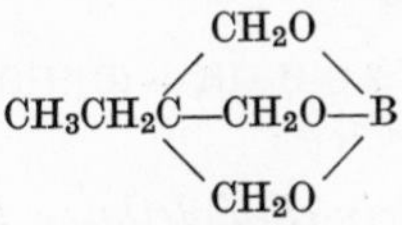

$$\begin{array}{c} CH_2O \\ CH_3CH_2C{-}CH_2O{-}B \\ CH_2O \end{array}$$

(XXVIII)

loss of the resonance energy (5-29) in addition to the imposed strains. The resonance energy of $(RO)_3B$ has been estimated to be greater than 17 kcal/mole.[8]

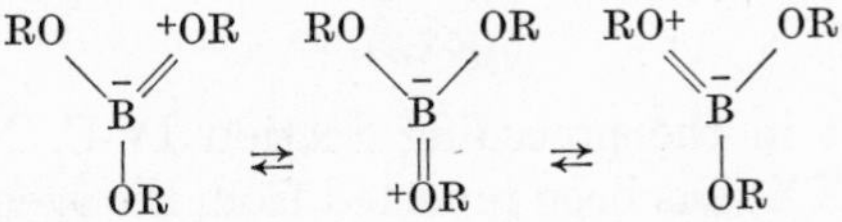

$$\begin{array}{ccc} RO \quad {}^{+}OR & RO \quad OR & RO^{+} \quad OR \\ \bar{B} & \bar{B} & \bar{B} \\ OR & {}^{+}OR & OR \end{array} \quad \rightleftarrows \quad \tag{5-29}$$

Attempts to distill a volatile ester at temperatures up to 225° at high vacuum from an equimolar mixture of glycerol and boric acid were unsuccessful.[69] Complex polymeric borates have been produced by the simultaneous esterification of glycerol with boric acid and malic acid.[72] An alternative monomeric structure (XXIX) obtained from the reaction of glycerol and oxybis(diacetoxyborane) has been proposed.[22]

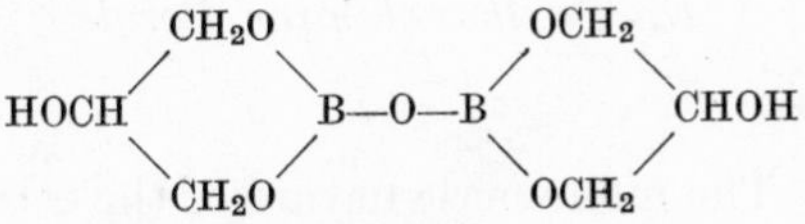

$$\begin{array}{ccccc} & CH_2O & & OCH_2 & \\ HOCH & & B{-}O{-}B & & CHOH \\ & CH_2O & & OCH_2 & \end{array}$$

(XXIX)

Whatever its nature, glyceryl borate hydrolyzes rapidly[1,63,75] to glycerol and boric acid which are in turn in equilibrium with a complex of the two species (see Chapter 15).

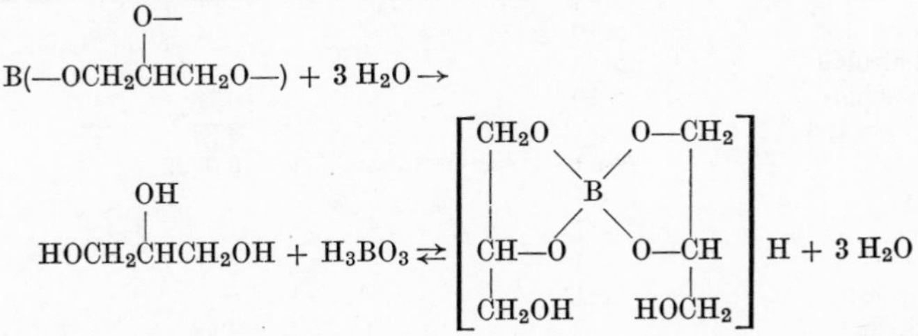

$$B({-}OCH_2\overset{\displaystyle O{-}}{C}HCH_2O{-}) + 3\,H_2O \rightarrow$$

$$HOCH_2\overset{\displaystyle OH}{C}HCH_2OH + H_3BO_3 \rightleftarrows \left[\begin{array}{ccc} CH_2O & & O{-}CH_2 \\ & B & \\ CH{-}O & & O{-}CH \\ CH_2OH & & HOCH_2 \end{array}\right] H + 3\,H_2O \tag{5-30}$$

Treatment of glyceryl borate with ethanol in a sealed tube at

100° resulted in transesterification to triethoxyborane (5-31).[75] Dry ammonia does not react with the ester.[75]

$$\mathrm{B(—OCH_2\overset{\overset{\displaystyle O—}{|}}{C}HCH_2O—) + 3\,C_2H_5OH \rightarrow (C_2H_5O)_3B + HOCH_2\overset{\overset{\displaystyle OH}{|}}{C}HCH_2OH} \quad (5\text{-}31)$$

D. Trimethylolethane Borate

The steric improbability of trimethylolethane borate (XXX) has

$$\mathrm{CH_3C\begin{cases} CH_2O \\ CH_2O \\ CH_2O \end{cases}B}$$

(XXX)

been pointed out in the preceding Section IV-C. Nevertheless the bicyclic ester (XXX) has been reported from the azeotropic dehydration of an equimolar mixture of 1,1,1-trimethylolethane and boric acid followed by sublimation of the product at reduced pressure. The product is converted to a glassy polymer on heating.[54]

Reaction (5-32) also has been recorded.[16]

$$\mathrm{C_{17}H_{33}\overset{\overset{\displaystyle O}{\|}}{C}NHC(CH_2OH)_3 + H_3BO_3 \rightarrow C_{17}H_{33}\overset{\overset{\displaystyle O}{\|}}{C}NHC(CH_2O)_3B + 3\,H_2O} \quad (5\text{-}32)$$

E. Triethanolamine Borate

1. PROPERTIES

a. *General.* The monomeric nature of the ester indicated by its volatility[80] has been established ebulliometrically in acetonitrile and pyridine (calc. 157; found 150, 152)[8] and nitrobenzene (144 to

Table 5-2. Solubility of triethanolamine borate

Solvent	g./100 ml. of solvent[87]	g./100 ml. solution at 25°[51]
Water	>10	
Methyl alcohol	>25	
Ethyl alcohol	>10	6.18
n-Butyl alcohol		3.93
Ether	<1	0.0992
Dioxane	<1	
Benzene	<1	
Acetone	<1	
Ethyl acetate	<1	
Acetonitrile	2–5	2.82
Formamide	>10	

164).[30] The dipole moment in dioxane solution was reported to be 8.8 ± 0.12 D.[18] Magnetic susceptibility data have been recorded.[26]

Triethanolamine borate is soluble in water, acetone, acetonitrile, pyridine, nitrobenzene, acetic acid, chloroform and the alcohols; slightly soluble in petroleum ether and cold benzene, and insoluble in carbon tetrachloride and tetrahydrofuran.[8,82] Quantitative solubilities are given in Table 5-2.

b. *Structure*. Two possible structures (XXXI and XXXII) were proposed for triethanolamine borate.[8] In the first (XXXI), the

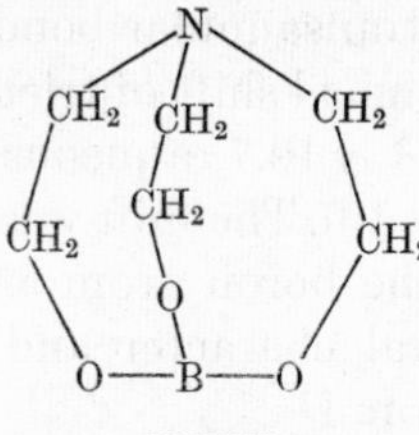

(XXXI) 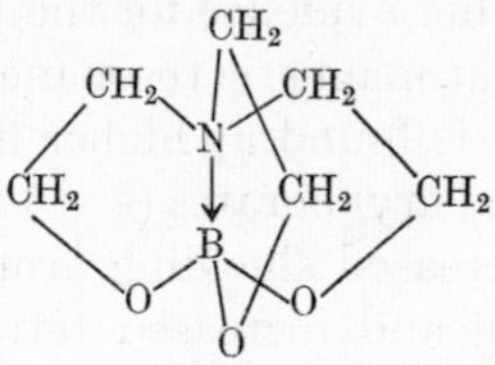 (XXXII)

boron atom maintains trigonal coplanar hybridization and the nucleophilicity of the nitrogen atom would be expected to be comparable to that in quinuclidine (XXXIII). In the second structure

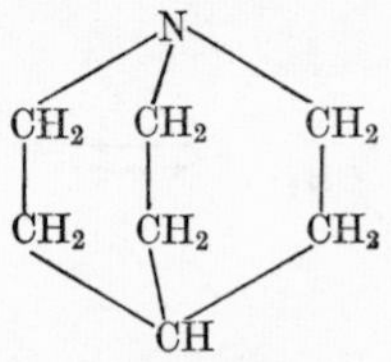

(XXXIII)

(XXXII), a transannular boron–nitrogen interaction is postulated, the boron has assumed sp^3 hybridization, and the availability of the electron pair on nitrogen has been vastly decreased. Triethanolamine borate was concluded to have structure XXXII on the basis of its unreactivity with methyl iodide (Menshchutkin reaction) as compared to quinuclidine (XXXIII) and triethanolamine (Table 5-3).[8] A

Table 5-3. Rate of reaction of methyl iodide with triethanolamine borate and similar compounds at 25°C

Compound	Rate constant (l. mole^{-1} sec.$^{-1}$)	Relative rate
Triethanolamine borate	8.57×10^{-8}	1
Triethanolamine	1.51×10^{-4}	1.76×10^{3}
Quinuclidine	1.88	2.19×10^{7}

variety of boronates,[46,59,73,87] borinates,[45,46,47,48,71,87] and triisopropanolamine borate[80,81] subsequently have been postulated to possess transannular boron–nitrogen bonds.*

The presence of the transannular bond was further supported by the slow measurable rate of reaction of triethanolamine borate with strong acids in both aqueous and non-aqueous media as compared to the rapid titration of triethanolamine itself.[8] The rate-determining step in the neutralization was considered to be hydrolysis of the ester (see Chapter 21).

Still further evidence for the B–N transannular bond is found in the ^{11}B nuclear magnetic resonance chemical shift of triethanolamine borate which is found at higher field (δ −10.7, aqueous soln.) than most alkyl and aryl borates (δ −14 to −19). The shift was interpreted as due to increased shielding around the boron atom as a result of B–N bonding and increased tetrahedral character and number of bonding electrons around the boron atom.[61]

One possible mechanism for the reaction of triethanolamine borate with methyl iodide in acetonitrile involves an equilibrium of the tetrahedral and planar structures (5-33).[8] It subsequently was

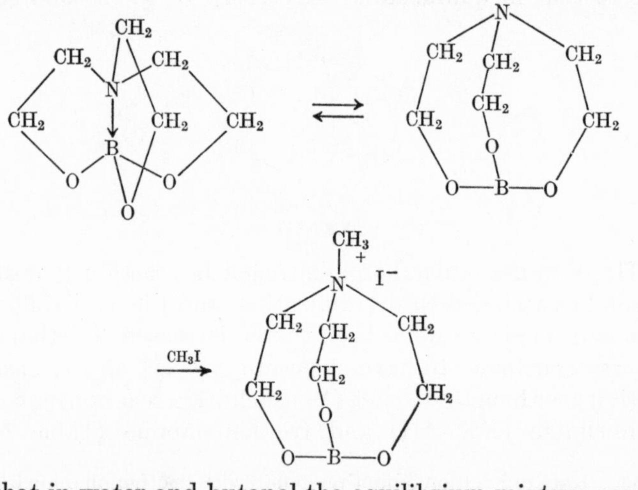

(5-33)

shown that in water and butanol the equilibrium mixture contained about 20% of the tetrahedral species and that in aprotic solvents about 95% was in the tetrahedral form.[51,52] Of further significance is the fact that triethanolamine borate also is formed at room

* Intermolecular hydrogen bonding rather than transannular B–N interaction was suggested to explain the stability of the diethanolamine esters of a series of aliphatic boronic acids.[44]

temperature from a water or butanol solution of equimolar quantities of triethanolamine and boric acid. After about one hour the solution has approximately 80% of the original amine titer available for immediate titration.[51,52] Thus, the equilibrium (5-34) is indicated, but the magnitude of x is unknown since both the starting amine and the planar form of the ester would give an immediate titer.

$$(0.8\text{-}x)\ N(CH_2CH_2OH)_3 + (0.8\text{-}x)\ H_3BO_3 \rightleftharpoons x\ N(CH_2CH_2O)_3B + 3x H_2O \rightleftharpoons 0.2\ N(CH_2CH_2O)_3B\ (N\rightarrow B) + 0.6\,H_2O \qquad (5\text{-}34)$$

The data of Table 5-4 indicates that equilibrium (5-34) shifts to the left with increasing temperature.[95]

Table 5-4. Effect of temperature on the system triethanolamine–boric acid–triethanolamine borate

Temp. (°C)	Initial concentration (mole/l.) Triethanolamine	Initial concentration (mole/l.) Boric acid	Equilibrium conc. (mole/l.) of triethanolamine borate (tetrahedral form)	% esterified
10	0.049	0.049	0.0097	19.8
20	0.049	0.049	0.0089	18.2
25	0.049	0.049	0.0081	16.5
30	0.049	0.049	0.0078	15.9

2. METHODS OF PREPARATION

Triethanolamine borate was first prepared from triethanolamine and boric acid in chloroform solution in accordance with equation (5-35.)[70] It subsequently has been prepared from dehydration of

$$N(CH_2CH_2OH)_3 + H_3BO_3 \rightarrow N(CH_2CH_2O)_3B + 3\ H_2O \qquad (5\text{-}35)$$

triethanolamine and boric acid by the same method,[30] by heating in dimethylformamide solution,[76] by heating without a solvent,[8,24,33,40,87,89] by means of a toluene azeotrope,[80] by the use of an alcohol–hydrocarbon solvent[15] and by removal of a butanol–water azeotrope.[51]

Kinetic studies of the esterification of boric acid with triethanolamine and the hydrolysis of triethanolamine borate indicated the esterification reaction to be second order and to proceed to the transannular-bonded structure via formation of the cage structure.[95]

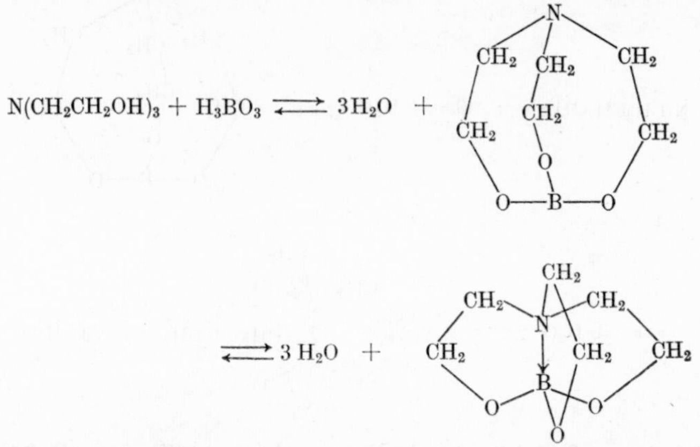

$$N(CH_2CH_2OH)_3 + H_3BO_3 \rightleftharpoons 3H_2O + \text{[cage structure: N(CH}_2\text{CH}_2\text{O)}_3\text{B]}$$

$$\rightleftharpoons 3\,H_2O + \text{[transannular structure: N}\rightarrow\text{B, N(CH}_2\text{CH}_2\text{O)}_3\text{B]} \quad (5\text{-}36)$$

Transesterification of tributoxyborane with triethanolamine gave an immediate precipitate of the cyclic ester (5-37). Triacetyltriethanolamine on heating with tributoxyborane in the presence of a trace of sodium butoxide reacted in a similar manner (5-38).[40]

$$(C_4H_9O)_3B + N(CH_2CH_2OH)_3 \rightarrow N(CH_2CH_2O)_3B + 3\,C_4H_9OH \quad (5\text{-}37)$$

$$(C_4H_9O)_3B + N(CH_2CH_2OC(=O)CH_3)_3 \rightarrow N(CH_2CH_2O)_3B + CH_3C(=O)OC_4H_9 \quad (5\text{-}38)$$

The boric acid complex of triethanolamine borate, $B(OCH_2CH_2)_3N\cdot B(OH)_3$, was prepared from the reaction of triethanolamine and boric oxide.[30]

3. REACTIONS

Attempts to determine the molecular weight of triethanolamine borate cryoscopically in water and in aniline indicated reaction with these solvents as evidenced by a slow measurable decrease with time in the apparent molecular weight.[30] The hydrolysis,[8,30,51,80,81,95] which can be formulated as an equilibrium reaction (5-39), is dis-

$$B(OCH_2CH_2)_3N + 3\,H_2O \rightleftharpoons N(CH_2CH_2OH)_3 + H_3BO_3 \quad (5\text{-}39)$$

cussed in Chapter 21. The aminolysis with aniline at 20°, which is recorded to lead to trisanilinoborane (5-40), can be contrasted to the slow reaction of triisobutoxyborane and triisopropoxyborane with aniline in refluxing xylene (see Chapter 4).

$$B(OCH_2CH_2)_3N + 3\,C_6H_5NH_2 \rightarrow N(CH_2CH_2OH)_3 + (C_6H_5NH)_3B \qquad (5\text{-}40)$$

Triethanolamine borate forms salts with hydrogen chloride (XXXIV) and $H[Cr(NH_3)_2(SCN)_4]$ (XXXV) which retain their respective solvents used in the reaction.[30] It also forms molecular complexes with mercuric chloride (XXXVI), antimony chloride (XXXVII), and stannic chloride (XXXVIII). Salts of fatty acids also have been claimed.[24] The quaternary salt XXXIX was obtained by reaction with chloramine.[60]

$$B(OCH_2CH_2)_3N \cdot HCl \cdot \tfrac{1}{3}CHCl_3 \quad \text{(XXXIV)}$$

$$B(OCH_2CH_2)_3N \cdot H[Cr(NH_3)_2(SCN)_4] \cdot CH_3\overset{\overset{O}{\|}}{C}CH_3 \quad \text{(XXXV)}$$

$$4B(OCH_2CH_2)_3N \cdot 5HgCl_2 \quad \text{(XXXVI)}$$

$$2B(OCH_2CH_2)_3N \cdot 3SbCl_3 \quad \text{(XXXVII)}$$

$$B(OCH_2CH_2)_3N \cdot SnCl_4 \quad \text{(XXXVIII)}$$

$$[B(OCH_2CH_2)_3NNH_2]Cl \quad \text{(XXXIX)}$$

Reaction with benzoyl chloride in pyridine was found to give (XL).[33] This reaction is analogous to the esterification of carboxylic

$$N(CH_2CH_2O\overset{\overset{O}{\|}}{C}C_6H_5)_3 \quad \text{(XL)}$$

acids with the alkoxy moiety of trialkoxyboranes (see Chapter 4).

Treatment with picric acid in anhydrous chloroform or ether was reported to yield triethanolamine picrate.[87]

The planar form of triethanolamine borate (XXXI) was considered to be an effective epoxy resin catalyst by virtue of a push–pull attack on the oxide ring.[41]

$$N(CH_2CH_2O)_3B \curvearrowleft O\!<\!\begin{matrix} CH \\ | \\ CH \end{matrix} \curvearrowleft :N(CH_2CH_2O)_3B$$

F. *Triethanolamine Borate Derivatives*

Syntheses directed towards boron-containing amino acids for cancer chemotherapy have led to the preparation of a series of substituted triethanolamine borates (XLI).[76] The derivatives were prepared by

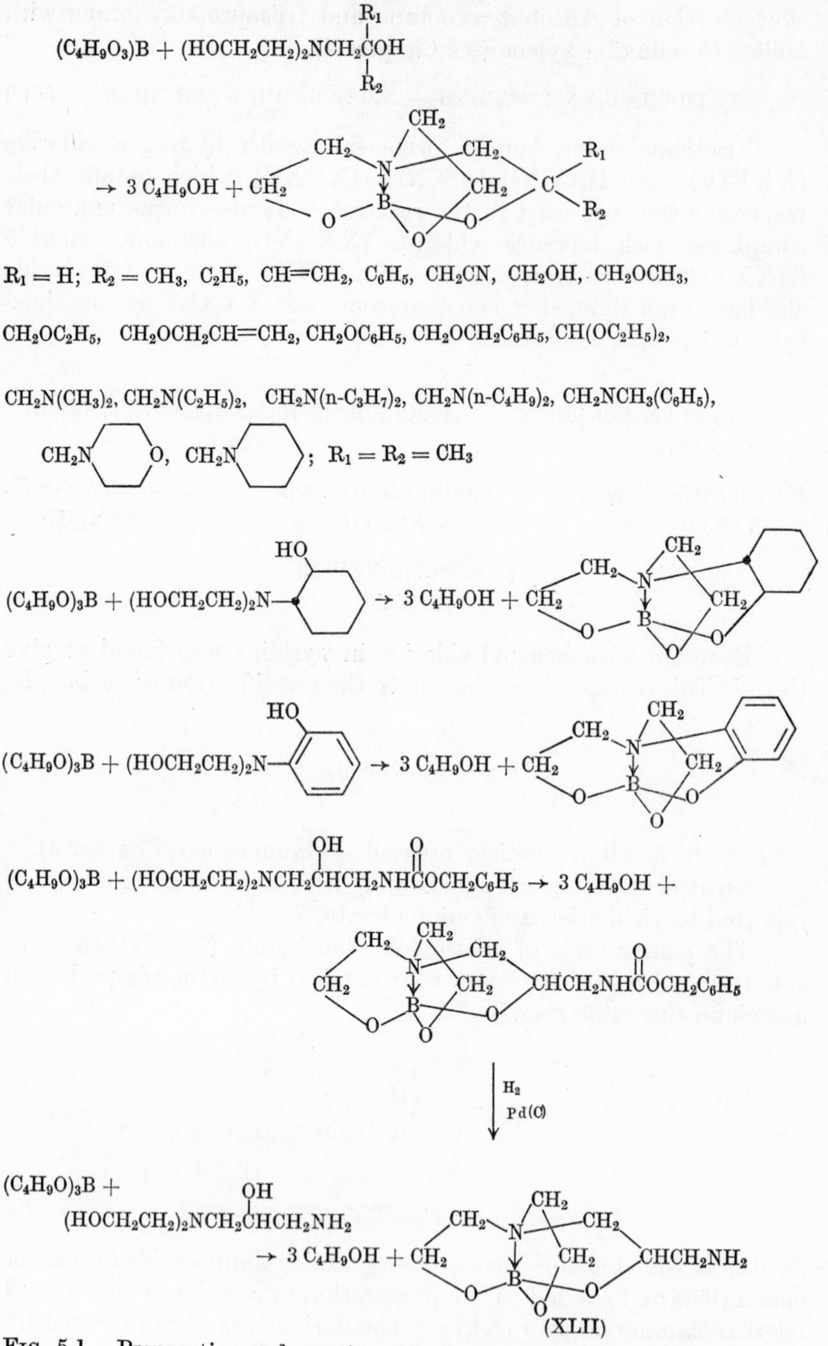

$$(C_4H_9O_3)B + (HOCH_2CH_2)_2NCH_2C(R_1)(R_2)OH$$

$$\rightarrow 3\ C_4H_9OH + \text{[bicyclic borate: } CH_2, CH_2, N \rightarrow B, CH_2, C(R_1)(R_2), O, O, O]$$

$R_1 = H$; $R_2 = CH_3$, C_2H_5, $CH{=}CH_2$, C_6H_5, CH_2CN, CH_2OH, CH_2OCH_3,

$CH_2OC_2H_5$, $CH_2OCH_2CH{=}CH_2$, $CH_2OC_6H_5$, $CH_2OCH_2C_6H_5$, $CH(OC_2H_5)_2$,

$CH_2N(CH_3)_2$, $CH_2N(C_2H_5)_2$, $CH_2N(n\text{-}C_3H_7)_2$, $CH_2N(n\text{-}C_4H_9)_2$, $CH_2NCH_3(C_6H_5)$,

CH_2N(morpholino)O, CH_2N(piperidino); $R_1 = R_2 = CH_3$

$$(C_4H_9O)_3B + (HOCH_2CH_2)_2N\text{-(2-hydroxycyclohexyl)} \rightarrow 3\ C_4H_9OH + \text{[cyclohexane-fused borate: } CH_2, CH_2, N \rightarrow B, CH_2, O, O, O]$$

$$(C_4H_9O)_3B + (HOCH_2CH_2)_2N\text{-(2-hydroxyphenyl)} \rightarrow 3\ C_4H_9OH + \text{[benzo-fused borate: } CH_2, CH_2, N \rightarrow B, CH_2, O, O, O]$$

$$(C_4H_9O)_3B + (HOCH_2CH_2)_2NCH_2CH(OH)CH_2NHC(O)OCH_2C_6H_5 \rightarrow 3\ C_4H_9OH +$$

$$\text{[borate: } CH_2, CH_2, N \rightarrow B, CH_2, CH_2, CH_2, CHCH_2NHC(O)OCH_2C_6H_5, O, O, O]$$

$$\downarrow H_2,\ Pd(C)$$

$$(C_4H_9O)_3B + (HOCH_2CH_2)_2NCH_2CH(OH)CH_2NH_2$$

$$\rightarrow 3\ C_4H_9OH + \text{[borate: } CH_2, CH_2, N \rightarrow B, CH_2, CH_2, CH_2, CHCH_2NH_2, O, O, O]\ \text{(XLII)}$$

FIG. 5.1. Preparation and reactions of substituted triethanolamine borates

transesterification of a lower trialkoxyborane with the appropriately substituted triethanolamine (Fig. 5-1). The aminomethyl derivative

CH_2 / CH_2 — N — CH_2 / R_1 / CH_2 ↓ CH_2 C / B / R_2 / O O / O

(XLI)

(XLII) was further substituted on the primary amino nitrogen atom with a variety of reagents (Fig. 5-2 and 5-3); however the chloromethyl derivative (XLIII) was not as reactive. Thus, sodium methoxide or magnesium methoxide in boiling xylene, potassium cyanide in dimethylformamide, cuprous cyanide in pyridine, sodio diethyl malonate, secondary amines in dimethylformamide, and hydrogen in the presence of palladium-charcoal all failed to react. Reactions did take place with potassium phthalimide, sodium acetate and sodium hydride (Fig. 5-3). Sodium methoxide in methanol or sodium ethoxide in ethanol reacted with (XLIII) to yield the decomposition product (XLIV) when a 1 : 1 mole ratio of alkoxide to (XLIII) was employed, or the alkoxy derivatives (XLV) when a 4 : 1 mole ratio was used. The origin of (XLIV) was attributed to a

(XLIII) $\xrightarrow{3ROH}$ $N(CH_2CH_2OH)_2(CH_2CH(OH)CH_2Cl)$

$\xrightarrow{-HCl}$ $N(CH_2CH_2OH)_2(CH_2CH{-}CH_2$ with O bridge$)$ ⟶ $HOCH_2CH_2N$ (morpholine ring, O) CH_2OH

(XLIV)

base catalyzed alcoholysis of (XLIII) to the parent amino alcohol followed by elimination of hydrogen chloride and an intramolecular alcoholysis of the resulting oxide ring.

In general, the alkyl derivatives are high melting crystalline solids, soluble in acetonitrile and dimethylformamide, less soluble in chloroform, and insoluble in ether, petroleum ether, dioxane and tetrahydrofuran. The alkoxy derivatives are lower melting and are soluble in benzene. The dialkylamino derivatives are moderately

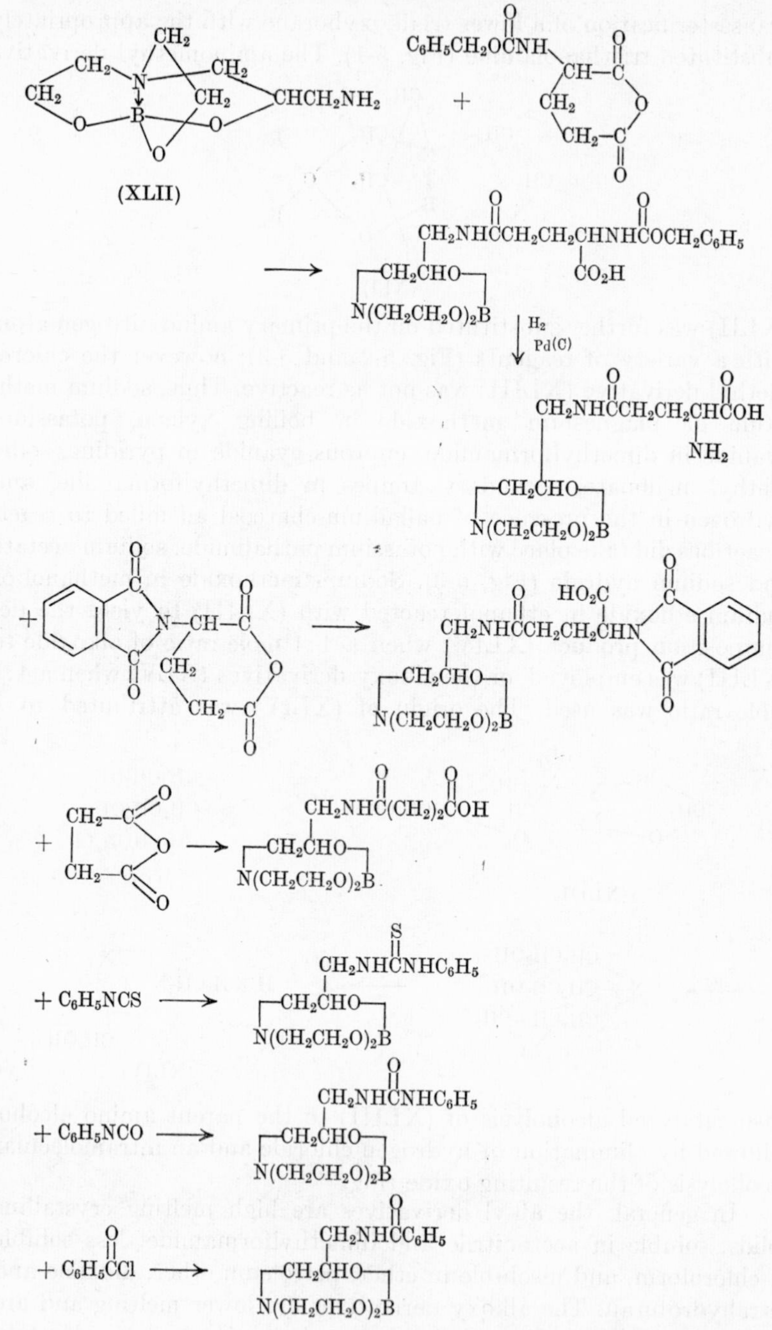

(XLII)

$\xrightarrow{H_2,\ Pd(C)}$

$+ C_6H_5NCS \longrightarrow$

$+ C_6H_5NCO \longrightarrow$

$+ C_6H_5COCl \longrightarrow$

FIG. 5.2. Reactions of aminomethyl derivative of triethanolamine borate

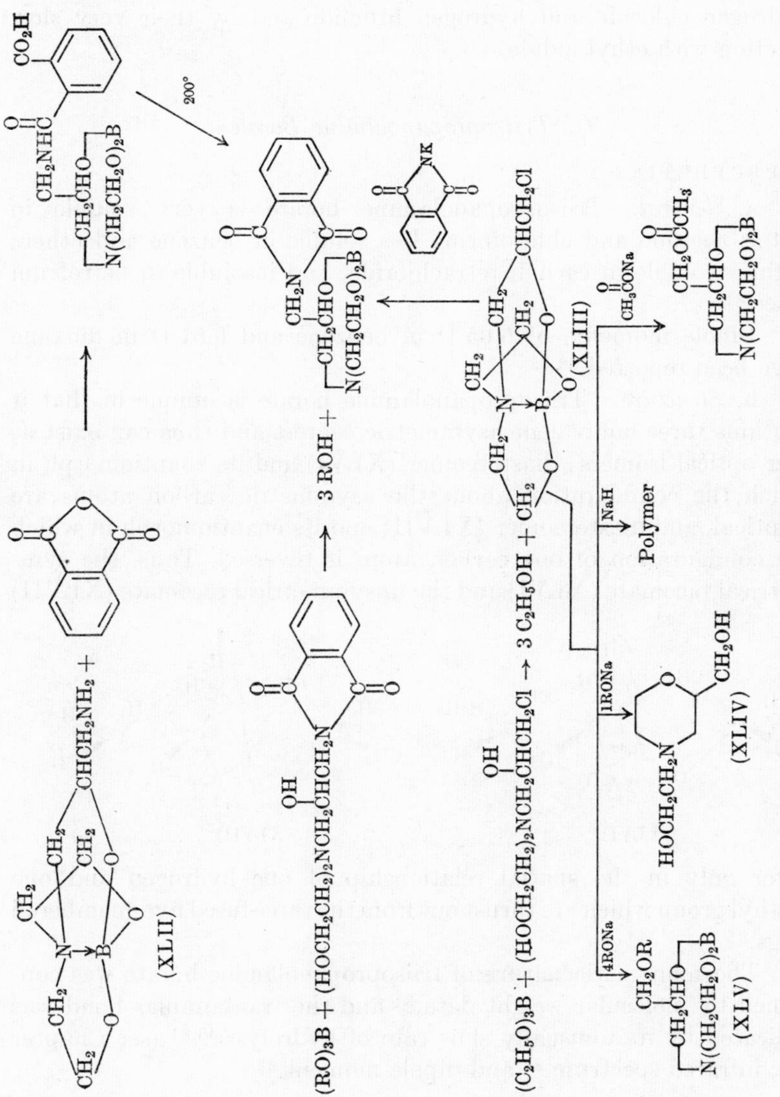

Fig. 5.3. Preparation and reactions of aminomethyl and chloromethyl derivatives of triethanolamine borate

high melting, crystalline solids, soluble in benzene and acetonitrile. They are distillable in high vacuum without decomposition and are only weakly basic as indicated by their failure to form salts with hydrogen chloride and hydrogen bromide and by their very slow reaction with ethyl iodide.

G. Triisopropanolamine Borate

1. PROPERTIES

a. *General.* Triisopropanolamine borate is very soluble in water, acetone and chloroform; less soluble in benzene and ether; slightly soluble in carbon tetrachloride, and insoluble in petroleum ether.[81]

Dipole moments of 6.05 D in benzene and 6.51 D in dioxane have been reported.[26,53]

b. *Structure.* Triisopropanolamine borate is unique in that it contains three equivalent asymmetric centers and thus can exist as four optical isomers: diastereomer (XLVI) and its enantiomorph in which the configuration about the asymmetric carbon atoms are identical, and diastereomer (XLVII) and its enantiomorph in which the configuration of one carbon atom is reversed. Thus, the symmetrical racemate (XLVI) and the unsymmetrical racemate (XLVII)

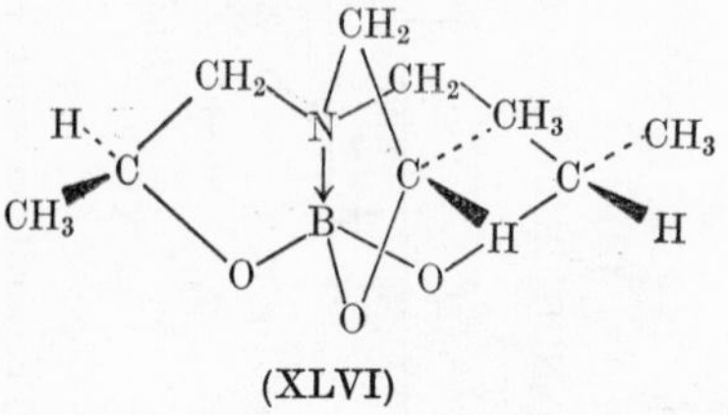

(XLVI)

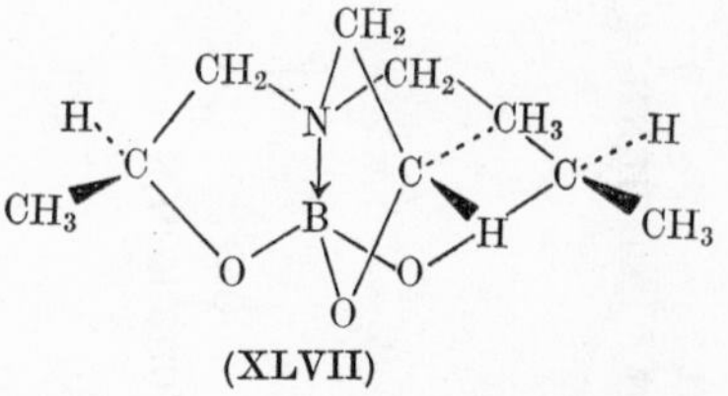

(XLVII)

differ only in the spatial relationship of one hydrogen and one methyl group which are thrust out from the three fused five-membered rings.[81]

The monomeric nature of triisopropanolamine borate was confirmed by molecular weight data,[81] and the transannular bond was indicated by its unusually slow rate of hydrolysis[80,81] (see Chapter 21), infrared spectrum,[88] and dipole moment.[53]

2. METHODS OF PREPARATION

Triisopropanolamine borate has been prepared from the dehydration of equimolar quantities of triisopropanolamine and boric acid with[80,81] and without[40] the aid of toluene. An earlier attempt to use butanol as the azeotroping agent was unsuccessful.[51] It also can be prepared by dissolution of equimolar quantities of triisopropanolamine and boric acid in water.[81]

The kinetics of the esterification of one racemate of triisopropanolamine were followed by periodic removal of aliquots from an equimolar aqueous solution of boric acid and amine and titration of the free amine as a function of time.[81] The rate constant obtained by employing the equilibrium expression (5-42)[25] for a second

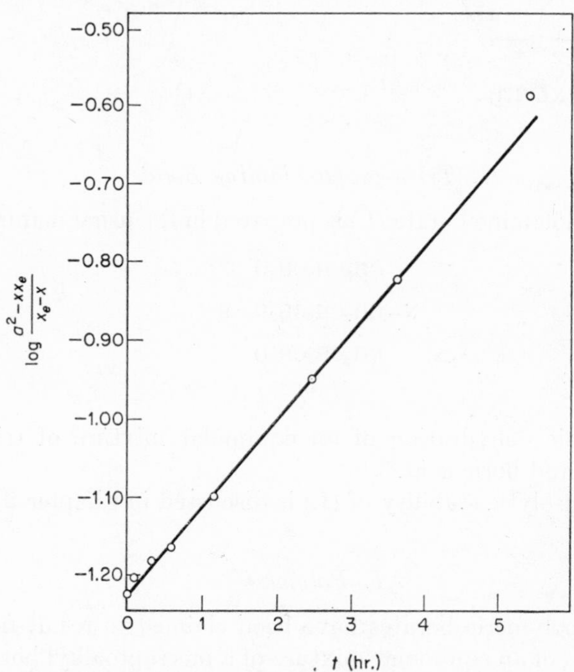

Fig. 5-4. Rate of esterification of one racemate of triisopropanolamine in water at 25°

order reaction opposed by one of the first order and plotting $\log [(a^2 - xx_e)/(x_e - x)]$ versus t (Fig. 5-4) gave a second order rate constant of 10.3 l. mole^{-1} hr.$^{-1}$ for the esterification.

$$\log \frac{a^2 - xx_e}{x_e - x} = \frac{a^2 - x_e^2}{2.303x_e} k_2T - \log \frac{x_e}{a^2} \qquad (5\text{-}42)$$

The equilibrium constant for the esterification of triisopropanolamine (278)[81] as compared to that for triethanolamine (6.25)[51] might indicate a stronger transannular bond in the ester derived from the secondary alcohol. This could serve as the driving force for the esterification. However, as in the case of triethanolamine borate, the extent of the planar form (XLVIII) in solution is unknown and the rate-determining step of the 'esterification' could be the conversion of (XLVIII) to (XLIX).

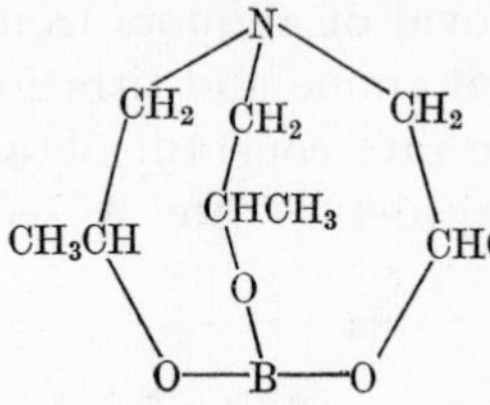

(XLVIII) 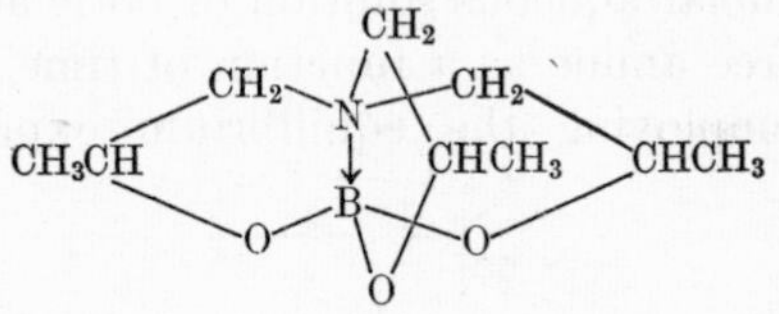 (XLIX)

H. Tri-n-propanolamine Borate

Tri-n-propanolamine borate (L) is prepared in the usual manner from

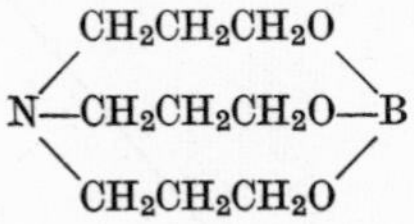

$$N(CH_2CH_2CH_2O)_3B$$

(L)

the azeotropic dehydration of an equimolar mixture of tri-n-propanolamine and boric acid.[27]

The hydrolytic stability of (L) is discussed in Chapter 21.

I. Polymers

A series of polymeric borates have been claimed to result from the condensation of an equimolar mixture of a mercaptoalkyl borate and an alkyl stannoic acid.[68] The monomeric species (LI) is shown for simplicity.

$$RSnOOH + (HSCH_2CH_2O)_3B \rightarrow RSn(SCH_2CH_2O)_3B + 2\,H_2O \qquad (5\text{-}43)$$

(LI)

Pyrogallol reacted with boron trichloride to give the polymer (LII).[21]

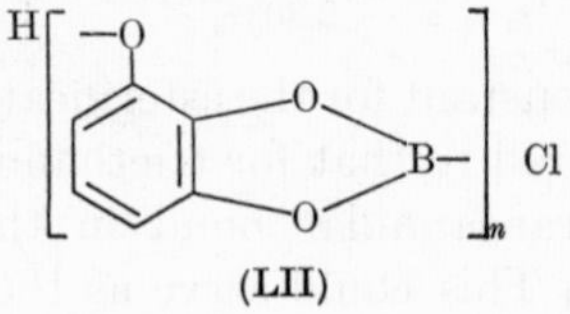

(LII)

A series of ill-defined polymeric borates have been reported from the azeotropic dehydration of high molecular weight triols and boric acid or boric oxide in solvents such as benzene and xylene.[28]

Tris(hydroxymethyl)aminomethane and tris(hydroxymethyl)-dimethylaminomethane appear to form polymeric esters with boric acid.[94]

III. ORTHOBORATES DERIVED FROM TETRAHYDRIC ALCOHOLS

The dehydration of a 4 : 3 molar mixture of boric acid and pentaerythritol resulted in a solid product with an analysis consistent with the formula $[C(CH_2O)_4]_3B_4$. The product was soluble in water with hydrolysis and insoluble in organic solvents.[79] Structure (LIII) represents a portion of one of the many possible matrices that may be drawn for the product.

```
    OCH2     CH2O     OCH2     CH2O     OCH2     CH2O
 \ /     \  /    \   /    \   /    \   /    \   /    \ /
  B       C       B        C        B        C        B
 / \     /  \    /   \    /   \    /   \    /   \    / \
    OCH2     CH2O     OCH2     CH2O     OCH2     CH2O
    |                 |                 |
```

(LIII)

IV. SUGAR BORATES

Clear cut cases of sugar borates of structure similar to (LIV), (LV) or (LVI) have not been reported although many sugars possess the necessary stereochemical relationship of hydroxy groups to allow structures such as (LIV) and (LV).

```
CHO                         CHO
|                           |
CHOH                        CHOH
|                           |
CHO                         OCH
|   \                     / |
|    B—O          O—B       |
|   /                 \     |
CHO       CH——CH        OCH
|         |     |       |
CHOH      CHOH  CHOH    CHOH
|         |     |       |
CH2OH     CHO   CH2OH   CH2OH
```

(LIV)

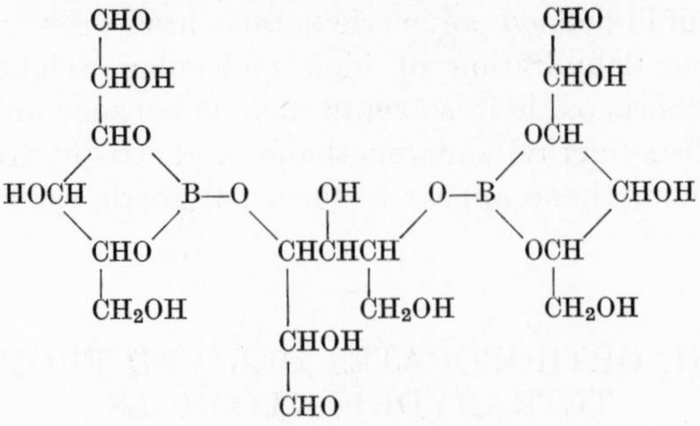

```
          CHO                                         CHO
           |                                           |
          CHOH                                        CHOH
           |                                           |
          CHO                                         OCH
         /   \                                       /   \
    HOCH       B—O       OH          O—B                  CHOH
         \   /      \    |          /    \               /
          CHO        CHCHCH                  OCH
           |          |    |                  |
          CH2OH       |   CH2OH              CH2OH
                     CHOH
                      |
                     CHO
                    (LV)
```

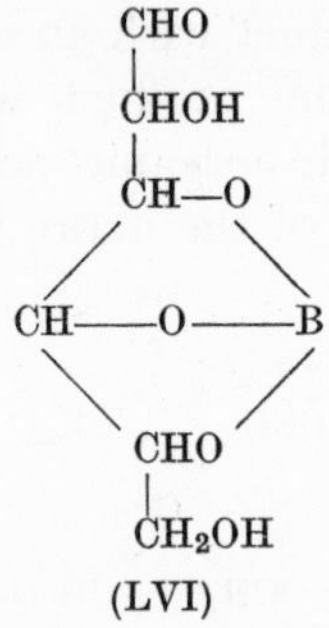

```
            CHO
             |
            CHOH
             |
            CH—O
           /     \
     CH——O——B
           \     /
            CHO
             |
            CH2OH
           (LVI)
```

V. ANALYTICAL

Orthoborates of polyhydric alcohols and phenols can be analyzed for boron by the methods described in Chapter 4 for the esters derived from monohydric alcohols and phenols.

The standard carbonate fusion method led to low values for triethanolamine and triisopropanolamine borate,[80,81] presumably due to loss of some of the sample by sublimation from the hot platinum crucible. However, good values were obtained by the expediency of allowing the esters to stand overnight in concentrated hydrochloric acid before fusion in the carbonate.[35]

The alkanolamine borates[13,80,81] also were analyzed by the Parr bomb method, "identical pH" method, and methanol distillation method as described in Chapter 4. Derivatives of triethanolamine borate were analyzed by the methanol distillation method.[76]

Catechol biborate was analyzed by conversion to trimethoxyborane–methanol azeotrope by distillation of a methanol solution of the ester.[84]

VI. PHYSICAL CONSTANTS

A. *Orthoborates Derived from Dihydric Alcohols and Phenols*

HO—R—OH in R(O)₂BOB(O)₂R	M.p. (°C)	B.p. (°C)	d_4^t	n_D^t	Reference
1,2-Diols					
$HOCH_2CH_2OH$	160				3
	160–162				56
	162–164				2
	163				77
	Glass				34
	—	—	—	—	93
$HOCHCHOH$ (with CH_3 on the first CH; as printed: HOCHCHOH | CH₃)		178/35	1.027^{27}	1.4340^{27}	13
		202–205/1.0		1.4350^{25}	86
		Gelatinous liquid			34
$ClCH_2CH(OH)CH_2OH$		263/20	1.410^{31}	1.4920^{31}	13
meso-$CH_3CH(OH)$—$CH(OH)CH_3$		290–292			58
		Viscous liquid			34
$CH_3CH(OH)$—$CH(OH)CH_3$		184–186/17			82

(*Table continued*)

A. Orthoborates Derived from Dihydric Alcohols and Phenols (continued)

HO—R—OH in R(O)(O)BOROB(O)(O)R	M.p. (°C)	B.p. (°C)	d_4^t	n_D^t	Reference
D-(−)—CH₃CH(OH)—CH(OH)CH₃		138–138.5/6	1.0383[25]	1.4252[25]	19
HOC(CH₃)₂CH₂OH		Slightly viscous liquid			49
HOC(CH₃)₂—C(CH₃)₂OH	193–196				49
1,3-Diols					
$HOCH_2CH_2CH_2OH$		125/0.05		1.4520[25]	17
		165–169/0.6			86
		Liquid			34
$CH_3CH(OH)CH_2CH_2(OH)$		207–213/17	1.071[25]		82
		212/17	1.092[27]	1.4464[17]	13
		Colorless liquid			78
$CH_3CH(OH)CH_2CH(OH)CH_3$		190/13, 300–310/760		1.4355[24]	11

OH OH $CH_3CCH_2CH_2$ CH_3		Liquid			49
CH_3 $HOCH_2CCH_2OH$ CH_3	123–124				85
	—	—	—	—	42
OH OH $CH_3CCH_2CHCH_3$ CH_3		154–162/1 200–205/20	 0.982^{21}	1.4388^{25} 1.4381^{25}	12 80
OH OH $(CH_3)_2CCHCH_2$ CH_3		Viscous liquid			49
C_2H_5 $HOCH_2CCH_2OH$ C_2H_5		Viscous liquid			12
OH OH $CH_3CH_2CH_2CHCHCH_2$ C_2H_5		185–189/2	0.985^{23}	1.4562^{25}	82
C_4H_9 $HOCH_2CCH_2OH$ C_2H_5		Viscous liquid			12

(*Table continued*)

A. Orthoborates Derived from Dihydric Alcohols and Phenals (continued)

HO—Ar—OH in Ar(O)₂BOArOB(O)₂Ar	M.p. (°C)	B.p. (°C)	d_4^t	n_D^t	Reference
o-$C_6H_4(OH)_2$	71–73.5	230–250/8–10			65
	72–74				91
	99–104	240–242/7			84
	104	170–175/0.03			21
	104	214–216/4			55
		214–218/4			56

HO—R—OH in $B_2(ORO)_3$	M.p. (°C)	B.p. (°C)	d_4^t	n_D^t	Reference
$HOCH_2CH_2OH$	100				64
	Solid				13, 29
$CH_3C(OH)(CH_3)CH_2CH_2C(OH)(CH_3)CH_3$	69–104	154–173/0.4			80

HO—R—OH in polymeric $(—ORO—)_3B_2$	M.p. (°C)	B.p. (°C)	d_4^t	n_D^t	Reference
$NH(CH_2CH_2OH)_2$		Oil			70
$NH(CH_2CH(CH_3)OH)_2$	Clear hard glass				81

$CH_3(HO)C_6H_{10}\text{-}C(CH_3)_2OH$ (1-CH_3, 1-OH cyclohexane ring, 4-$C(CH_3)_2OH$)	Brittle glass				49
$HOCH_2CH_2S\text{—}Sn(C_4H_9)_2\text{—}SCH_2CH_2OH$	—	—	—	—	66, 67, 68
$HOCH_2CH_2S\text{—}Sn(C_6H_5)_2\text{—}SCH_2CH_2OH$	—	—	—	—	66, 67, 68
$HOCH_2CH(C_6H_5)S\text{—}Sn(CH_2CH_2C_6H_5)_2\text{—}SCH(C_6H_5)CH_2OH$	—	—	—	—	66, 67, 68

(Table continued)

A. Orthoborates Derived from Dihydric Alcohols and Phenols (continued)

HO—Ar—OH in Polymeric (—OArO—)$_3$B$_2$	M.p. (°C)	B.p. (°C)	d_4^t	n_D^t	Reference
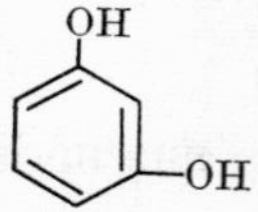 m-$C_6H_4(OH)_2$	—	—	—	—	20
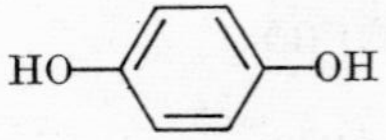 $HO-C_6H_4-OH$ (p)	—	—	—	—	20
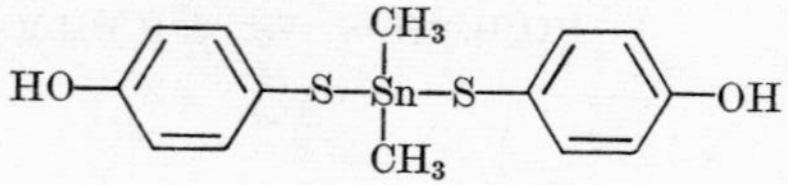 $HO-C_6H_4-S-Sn(CH_3)_2-S-C_6H_4-OH$	—	—	—	—	66, 67, 68
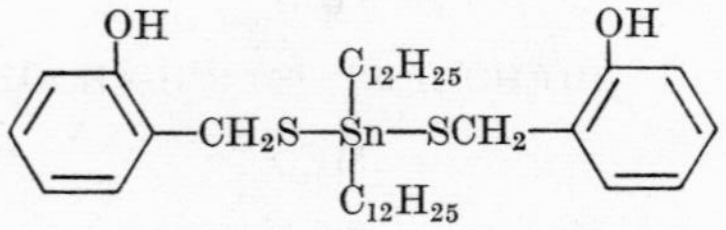 o-$HOC_6H_4-CH_2S-Sn(C_{12}H_{25})_2-SCH_2-C_6H_4OH$-$o$	—	—	—	—	66, 67, 68

B. *Orthoborates Derived from Trihydric Alcohols and Phenols*

	M.p. (°C)	B.p. (°C)	d_4^t	n_D^t	Reference
Alcohols					
$(\text{—OCH}_2\text{CH(O—)CH}_2\text{O—})_3B_2$	100				63
	150–151				1
	Glass				64, 75
$CH_3C(CH_2O)_3B$ (bicyclic: CH_3C linked through three CH_2O groups to B)	215–217	230–275/0.4 (sub.)			54
	—	—	—	—	74
$C_{17}H_{33}C(=O)NHC(CH_2O)_3B$	—	—	—	—	16
Aminoalcohols					
$N(CH_2CH_2O)_3B$	230 (d.)				70
	231				30
	232–234				33
	234–236				15
	235–236, 238–239				76
	235–237	175/0.19 (sub.)			80
	236				26
	236.5–237.5				8, 87
$(HO)_3B\cdot N(CH_2CH_2O)_3B$	105 (d.)				30
$B(OCH_2CH_2)_3N\cdot HCl\cdot \frac{1}{3}CHCl_3$	145 (d.)				30

(Table continued)

B. Orthoborates Derived from Trihydric Alcohols and Phenols (continued)

	M.p. (°C)	B.p. (°C)	d_4^t	n_D^t	Reference
$B(OCH_2CH_2)_3N \cdot H[Cr(NH_3)_2(SCN)_4] \cdot CH_3C(=O)CH_3$	156				30
$4B(OCH_2CH_2)_3N \cdot 5HgCl_2$	140 (d.)				30
$2B(OCH_2CH_2)_3N \cdot 3SbCl_3$	200 (d.)				30
$B(OCH_2CH_2)_3N \cdot SnCl_4$	200 (d.)				30
$[B(OCH_2CH_2)_3NNH_2]Cl$	Semi-solid				60
$N(CH_2CH_2CH_2O)_3B$	248				27
$N(CH_2CH(CH_3)O)_3B$ (mixture of racemates)	142–148	200 (sub.)			40
	153–156	135/0.19 (sub.)			80
	154				26
	155.6–157.6				81
$N(CH_2CH(CH_3)O)_3B$ (one racemate)	144–147				81

R_1 and R_2 in N(–CH₂C(R₁)(R₂)–O–)(–CH₂CH₂O–)(–CH₂CH₂O–)B, i.e. $N\{CH_2C(R_1)(R_2)O\}(CH_2CH_2O)_2B$

R_1	R_2	M.p. (°C)	B.p. (°C)	d_4^t	n_D^t	Reference
H	CH_3	197–198				76
H	C_2H_5	144–145				76

H	$CH{=}CH_2$	155–156	76
H	C_6H_5	228–229	76
H	CH_2CN	155–156	76
H	CH_2OH	Sintered over a wide range	76
H	CH_2OCH_3	89–90	76
H	$CH_2OC_2H_5$	119–120	76
H	$CH_2OCH_2CH{=}CH_2$	73–74.5	76
H	$CH_2OC_6H_5$	184–186	76
H	$CH_2OCH_2C_6H_5$	108–110	76
H	$CH_2OC(=O)CH_3$	128–130	76
H	$CH(OC_2H_5)_2$	—	76
H	CH_2NH_2	60–66, 115–116	76
H	$CH_2NHC(=O)OCH_2C_6H_5$	143–144	76
H	$CH_2NHC(=O)C_6H_5$	145–146	76
H	$CH_2NHC(=O)NHC_6H_5$	205	76
H	$CH_2NHC(=S)NHC_6H_5$	195–196	76
H	$CH_2NHC(=O)CH_2CH_2C(=O)OH$	156–158	76
H	$CH_2NHC(=O)C_6H_4CO_2H$ (o-)	146–148	76

(Table continued)

B. Orthoborates Derived from Trihydric Alcohols and Phenols (continued)

R_1 and R_2 in $N(CH_2CH_2O)_2(CH_2CR_1R_2O)B$		M.p. (°C)	B.p. (°C)	d_4^t	n_D	Reference
H	$CH_2N(CO)_2C_6H_4$	263–264				76
H	$CH_2NHC(=O)CH_2CH_2CH(CO_2H)N(CO)_2C_6H_4$	48–50				76
H	$CH_2NHC(=O)CH_2CH_2CH(CO_2H)NHC(=O)OCH_2C_6H_5$	84–94				76
H	$CH_2NHC(=O)CH_2CH_2CH(NH_2)C(=O)OH$	48–50				76

H	$CH_2N(CH_3)_2$	152–153	76
H	$CH_2N(C_2H_5)_2$	136–137	76
H	$CH_2N(n\text{-}C_3H_7)_2$	126–127	76
H	$CH_2N(n\text{-}C_4H_9)_2$	133–134	76
H	$CH_2NCH_3(C_6H_5)$	174–175	76
H	CH_2N (morpholine ring, O)	189–190	76
H	CH_2N (piperidine ring)	188–189	76
H	CH_2Cl	153–155	76
H	$CHBrCH_2Br$	No definite m.p.	76
CH_3	CH_3	178–180	76
N—CH_2CH_2O—B, CH_2CH_2O, O (cyclohexane ring)		138–139	76
N—CH_2CH_2O—B, CH_2CH_2O, O (benzene ring)		155–156	76

(Table continued)

B. Orthoborates Derived from Trihydric Alcohols and Phenols (continued)

	M.p. (°C)	B.p. (°C)	d_4^t	n_D^t	Reference
Alkyltinmercaptoalcohols					
$CH_2{=}CHSn(SCH_2CH_2O)_3B$	Polymeric				68
$C_6H_5Sn(SCH_2CH_2O)_3B$	Polymeric				68
Phenols					
$[1,3,5\text{-}(\text{—O})_3C_6H_3]_3B_2$	Polymeric				20
Alkyltinmercaptophenols					
$n\text{-}C_8H_{17}Sn[o\text{-}SC_6H_4O]_3B$	Polymeric				68
$C_6H_5CH_2Sn[p\text{-}SC_6H_4O]_3B$	Polymeric				68

VII. REFERENCES

1. Ahmad, T., and M. H. Khundkar, *Chem. & Ind.* (*London*) 248 (1954).
2. Blau, J. A., W. Gerrard, and M. F. Lappert, *J. Chem. Soc.*, 4116 (1957).
3. Blau, J. A., W. Gerrard, and M. F. Lappert, *J. Chem. Soc.*, 667 (1960).
4. Blau, J. A., W. Gerrard, M. F. Lappert, B. A. Mountfield, and H. Pyszora, *J. Chem. Soc.*, 380 (1960).
5. Boughton, W. A., and W. R. Mansfield, U.S. Pat. 2,084,261 (1937, to New England Mica Co.).
6. Bowles, A. F., *Rayon Textile Monthly*, **19**, 177 (1938).
7. Brothman, A., U.S. Pat. 2,663,715 (1953).
8. Brown, H. C., and E. A. Fletcher, *J. Am. Chem. Soc.*, **73**, 2808 (1951).
9. Councler, C., *Ber.*, **11**, 1106 (1878).
10. Councler, C., *J. Prakt. Chem.*, **18**, 371 (1878).
11. Dale, J., *J. Chem. Soc.*, 910 (1961).
12. Darling, S. M., P. S. Fay, and L. S. Szabo, U.S. Pat. 2,741,548 (1956, to Standard Oil Co., Ohio).
13. Dupire, A., *Compt. Rend.*, **202**, 2086 (1936).
14. Dykstra, F. J., U.S. Pat. 3,009,799 (1961, to Ethyl Corporation).
15. Elbling, I. N., and S. H. Langer, U.S. Pat. 2,785,192 (1957, to Westinghouse Electric Corp.).
16. Emrick, D. D., U.S. Pat. 3,009,791 (1961, to The Standard Oil Co., Ohio).
17. Finch, A., J. C. Lockhart, and J. Pearn, *J. Org. Chem.*, **26**, 3250 (1961).
18. Fu, H. C., T. Psarras, H. Weidmann, and H. K. Zimmerman, Jr., *Ann.*, **641**, 116 (1961).
19. Garner, H. K., and H. J. Lucas, *J. Am. Chem. Soc.*, **72**, 5497 (1950).
20. Gerrard, W., and M. F. Lappert, *Chem. Rev.*, **58**, 1081 (1958).
21. Gerrard, W., M. F. Lappert, and B. A. Mountfield, *J. Chem. Soc.*, 1529 (1959).
22. Gerrard, W., and E. F. Mooney, *Chem. & Ind.*, 227 (1958).
23. Gerrard, W., and M. A. Wheelans, *Chem. & Ind.*, 758 (1954).
24. Gilman, H. H., U.S. Pat. 2,441,063 (1948, to Quaker Chemical Products Corp.).
25. Glasstone, S., *Textbook of Physical Chemistry*, D. Van Nostrand Co., New York, 1948, 2nd ed., p. 1071.
26. Grau, A., and H. Lumbroso, *Bull. Soc. Chim. France*, 1860 (1961).
27. Groszos, S. J., and N. E. Day, U.S. Pat. 2,942,021 (1960, to American Cyanamid Company); Can. Pat. 846,374 (1960, to American Cyanamid Company).
28. Hartley, J., and J. D. Downer, U.S. Pat. 2,945,014 (1960, to Shell Oil Co.).
29. Hartman, L., *J. Chem. Soc.*, 1918 (1957).
30. Hein, F., and R. Burkhardt, *Z. Anorg. Allgem. Chem.*, **268**, 159 (1952).
31. Henglein, F. A., R. Lang, and K. Scheinost, *Makromol. Chem.*, **15**, 177 (1955).
32. Henricks, J. A., U.S. Pat. 2,868,671 (1959, to Devex Corp.).
33. Hirata, Y., K. Inukai, and T. Tsujiuchi, *J. Chem. Soc. Japan, Pure Chem. Sect.*, **69**, 58 (1948); through *Chem. Abstracts*, **47**, 3234 (1953).
34. Hubert, A. J., B. Hargitay, and J. Dale, *J. Chem. Soc.*, 931 (1961).
35. Hunter, D. L., L. L. Petterson, and H. Steinberg, *Anal. Chim. Acta*, **21**, 523 (1959).

36. Kobayashi, H., and S. Tsuruta, *J. Chem. Soc. Japan, Pure Chem. Sect.*, **70**, 183 (1949); through *Chem. Abstracts*, **45**, 4089 (1951).
37. Köster, R., *Angew. Chem.*, **71**, 31 (1959).
38. Köster, R., U.S. Pat. 2,992,267 (1961, to Studiengesellschaft Kohle m.b.H.).
39. Kuskov, V. K., B. M. Sheiman, and Z. I. Maksimova, *Zh. Obshch. Khim.*, **27**, 1454 (1957).
40. Langer, S. H., U.S. Pat. 2,871,454 (1959, to Westinghouse Electric Corporation).
41. Langer, S. H., and I. N. Elbling, *Ind. Eng. Chem.*, **49**, 1113 (1957).
42. Laubengayer, A. W., and R. G. Hayter, 132nd Meeting of the American Chemical Society, New York, Sept., 1957, Abstracts of Papers, p. 10-N.
43. Laubengayer, A. W., B. Smith, R. G. Hayter, and W. J. Watt, 134th Meeting of the American Chemical Society, Chicago, Sept., 1958, Abstracts of Papers, p. 16-T.
44. Lawesson, S. O., *Arkiv. Kemi*, **10**, 171 (1956).
45. Letsinger, R. L., and N. Remes, *J. Am. Chem. Soc.*, **77**, 2489 (1955).
46. Letsinger, R. L., and I. Skoog, *J. Am. Chem. Soc.*, **77**, 2491 (1955).
47. Letsinger, R. L., and I. H. Skoog, *J. Am. Chem. Soc.*, **77**, 5176 (1955).
48. Letsinger, R. L., I. Skoog, and N. Remes, *J. Am. Chem. Soc.*, **76**, 4047 (1954).
49. Lippincott, S. B., U.S. Pat. 2,642,453 (1953, to Standard Oil Development Co.).
50. Lothian, J., *Pharm. J.*, **128**, 265, 271 (1932); *Chemist and Druggist*, **116**, 430 (1932); through *Chem. Abstracts*, **26**, 4415 (1932).
51. Lucchesi, C. A., Univ. Microfilms Publ. No. 13,109; *Dissertation Abstr.*, **15**, 2007 (1955); Ph.D. Thesis, Northwestern Univ., D. D. DeFord, 1955.
52. Lucchesi, C. A., and D. D. DeFord, *J. Inorg. & Nucl. Chem.*, **14**, 290 (1960).
53. Lumbroso, H., and A. Grau, *Bull. Soc. Chim. France*, 1866 (1961).
54. McManimie, R. J., U.S. Pat. 2,909,560 (1959, to Monsanto Chemical Co.).
55. Mehrotra, R. C., and G. Srivastava, *J. Chem. Soc.*, 4045 (1961).
56. Mehrotra, R. C., and G. Srivastava, *J. Indian Chem. Soc.*, **38**, 1 (1961).
57. Milne, G. R., and R. M. Todd, *Pharm. J.*, **128**, 195 (1932), through *Chem. Abstracts*, **26**, 4415 (1932).
58. Morell, S. A., and E. C. Lathrop, *J. Am. Chem. Soc.*, **67**, 879 (1945).
59. Musgrave, O. C., and T. O. Park, *Chem. & Ind.* (*London*) 1552 (1955).
60. Omietanski, G. M., U.S. Pat. 2,988,567 (1961, to Ohio State University Research Foundation).
61. Onak, T. P., H. Landesman, R. E. Williams, and I. Shapiro, *J. Phys. Chem.*, **63**, 1533 (1959).
62. Peppard, D. F., W. G. Brown, and W. C. Johnson, *J. Am. Chem. Soc.*, **68**, **77** (1946).
63. Petterson, L. L., and H. Steinberg, Unpublished results.
64. Pictet, A., and A. Geleznoff, *Ber.*, **36**, 2219 (1903).
65. Prochazka, J., Czech. Pat. 84,283 (1955); through *Chem. Abstracts*, **50**, 7858 (1956).
66. Ramsden, H. E., Brit. Pat. 742,975 (1956, to Metal and Thermit Corp.).
67. Ramsden, H. E., Can. Pat. 600,558 (1960, to Metal and Thermit Corp.).
68. Ramsden, H. E., U.S. Pat. 2,904,570 (1959, to Metal and Thermit Corp.).

69. Rippere, R. E., and V. K. LaMer, *J. Phys. Chem.*, **47**, 204 (1943).
70. Rojahn, C. A., Ger. Pat. 582,149 (1933).
71. Rondestvedt, C. S., R. M. Scribner, and C. E. Wulfman, *J. Org. Chem.*, **20**, 9 (1955).
72. Rosenblum, I., U.S. Pat. 2,189,883 (1940).
73. Ruigh, W. L., C. E. Erickson, F. Gunderloy, and M. Sedlak, WADC Technical Report 55–26, Part II, May 1955.
74. Schaeffer, G. W., Unpublished results.
75. Schiff, H., *Ann. Suppl.*, **5**, 154 (1867).
76. Schleppnik, A. A., and C. D. Gutsche, *J. Org. Chem.*, **25**, 1378 (1960).
77. Schouteden, F. L., Brit. Pat. 805,534 (1958, to Gevaert Photo-Production N.V.).
78. Standard Oil Company, Ohio, Belg. Pat. 577,735 (1959).
79. Steinberg, H., Unpublished results.
80. Steinberg, H., and D. L. Hunter, *Ind. Eng. Chem.*, **49**, 174 (1957).
81. Steinberg, H., and D. L. Hunter, *J. Am. Chem. Soc.*, **82**, 853 (1960).
82. Steinberg, H., and D. L. Hunter, Unpublished results.
83. Sun, K. H., P. R. Malmberg, and F. A. Pecjak, *Nucleonics*, **14**, 46 (1956).
84. Thomas, L. H., *J. Chem. Soc.*, 820 (1946).
85. Washburn, R. M., E. Levens, C. F. Albright, and F. A. Bilig, "Preparation, Properties, and Uses of Borate Esters," in *Metal-Organic Compounds, Advances in Chemistry Series No. 23*, American Chemical Society, Washington, 1959, p. 129.
86. Watt, W. J., Ph.D. Thesis, Cornell Univ. (A. W. Laubengayer), 1956.
87. Weidmann, H., and H. K. Zimmerman, Jr., *Ann.*, **619**, 28 (1958).
88. Weidmann, H., and H. K. Zimmerman, Jr., *Ann.*, **620**, 4 (1959).
89. Westinghouse Electric International Co., Brit. Pat. 776,213 (1957).
90. Wheland, G. W., *Advanced Organic Chemistry*, 2nd ed., John Wiley and Sons, New York, p. 76.
91. Willems, J. F., and A. E. Van Hoof, Brit. Pat. 812,673 (1959, to Gevaert Photo-Production N.V.).
92. Wittig, G., and M. Leo, *Ber.*, **64**, 2395 (1931).
93. Wuyts, M. H., and A. Duquesne, *Bull. Soc. Chim. Belges*, **48**, 77 (1939).
94. Zimmerman, H. K. Jr., and H. Weidmann, 137th Meeting American Chemical Society, Cleveland, April, 1960, Abstracts of Papers, p. 7-0.
95. Zimmerman, H. K., Jr., and H. Weidmann, *Ann.*, **628**, 37 (1959).

6

UNSYMMETRICAL ORTHOBORATES

I. INTRODUCTION

Chapters 4 and 5 dealt with orthoborates derived from a single alcohol, phenol or diol. This chapter is concerned with esters which contain two or more different alcohols, phenols, or diols, or combinations thereof. Nine types of mixed esters (I–IX) have been reported.

$(RO)_2BOR'$ (I)

$ROB(OR')(OR'')$ (II)

$R\langle O_2\rangle BOR'OB\langle O_2\rangle R$ (III)

$R\langle O_2\rangle B{-}OR'OB\langle O_2\rangle R''$ (IV)

$R\langle O_2\rangle BOR'OH$ (V)

$R\langle O_2\rangle BOR'$ (VI)

$(RO)_2BOR'OB(OR)_2$ (VII)

$(RO)_2BOR'OH$* (VIII)

$R[{-}OB(OR')_2]_3$† (IX)

II. ESTERS DERIVED FROM MONOHYDRIC ALCOHOLS AND MONOHYDRIC PHENOLS

A. Historical

In the period 1865 to 1867 Schiff[64,65] claimed the preparation of amyl diethyl, diamyl ethyl and diethyl methyl borate by the

* Octet and bond refractivity data have been recorded for this type of mixed ester derived from mono- and dihydric alcohols, $(n\text{-}C_4H_9O)_2BOCH_2CH_2OH$.[12] The method of preparation or origin was not described. Since it appears doubtful that dibutoxyethoxyborane can be isolated, and since hydroxy derivatives of trialkoxyboranes inherently are difficult to isolate, the existence of the unsymmetrical hydroxyethyl derivative is extremely doubtful.

† The properties of these compounds were not recorded.[57] Their existence as monomers is questionable.

reactions (6-1) through (6-4). He reported boiling points and analyses for the two amyl esters.

$$(C_2H_5OBO)_3 + 3\,C_5H_{11}OH \rightarrow (C_2H_5O)_2BOC_5H_{11} + (C_5H_{11}O)_2BOC_2H_5 + H_3BO_3 \quad (6\text{-}1)$$

$$(C_2H_5O)_3B + (C_5H_{11}O)_3B \rightarrow (C_2H_5O)_2BOC_5H_{11} + (C_5H_{11}O)_2BOC_2H_5 \quad (6\text{-}2)$$

$$(CH_3O)_3B + 2\,C_2H_5OH \xrightarrow{100^\circ} (C_2H_5O)_2BOCH_3 + 2\,CH_3OH \quad (6\text{-}3)$$

$$(ROBO)_3 + 3\,R'OH \rightarrow (RO)_2BOR' + (R'O)_2BOR + H_3BO_3 \quad (6\text{-}4)$$

The facility with which mixed esters of the lower alcohols disproportionate to their symmetrical counterparts on attempted distillation (6-5) indicates almost certainly that Schiff's mixed esters

$$3\,(RO)_2BOR' \rightarrow 2\,(RO)_3B + (R'O)_3B \quad (6\text{-}5)$$

after distillation were mainly mixtures of the symmetrical esters.

B. Methods of Preparation

There is no *a priori* reason to preclude the existence of mixed esters derived by the esterification of boric acid with two different alcohols or by the partial transesterification of a symmetrical ester with a second and different alcohol. Indeed, the inherent energy of (X) must be almost identical with that of (XI) or (XII). However, essentially

$$\underset{(X)}{[CH_3(CH_2)_3O]_2BO(CH_2)_4CH_3} \qquad \underset{(XI)}{[CH_3(CH_2)_3O]_3B} \qquad \underset{(XII)}{[CH_3(CH_2)_4O]_3B}$$

all attempts to isolate the mixed species by distillation have resulted in at least partial if not complete disproportionation of the unsymmetrical species to the symmetrical counterparts. Thus, attempts to prepare pure mixed propyl amyl and propyl phenyl esters by esterifying boric oxide with a mixture of the alcohols or alcohol and phenol resulted in the isolation of the symmetrical esters upon reduced pressure distillation of the reaction mixture.[74] The esterification of boric acid with a mixture of isobutyl alcohol and phenol and subsequent distillation resulted in fractions boiling intermediate to triisobutoxyborane and triphenoxyborane. Subsequent redistillations of these "mixed ester" fractions resulted in disproportionation.[39] Attempted partial transesterifications of triethoxyborane with n-butyl alcohol and *t*-butyl alcohol* resulted in the removal of the requisite amount of ethanol for the formation of $C_2H_5OB(OC_4H_9)_2$; however, attempted distillation of the mixed

* The formation of mixed methyl *t*-butyl esters was believed to be responsible, in part, for the low yields of *t*-butyl borate in the transesterification of methyl borate with *t*-butyl alcohol.[9]

ester resulted in the symmetrical disproportionation products.[48] An attempt to distill the product of reaction (6-6) resulted in the isolation

$$C_4H_9OBCl_2 + 2\ C_6H_5OH \rightarrow C_4H_9OB(OC_6H_5)_2 + 2\ HCl \quad (6\text{-}6)$$

of tributyl and triphenyl borate.[13] Claims to the existence of diamyl phenyl,[45] diphenyl propyl,[67] mixed butyl ethyl[67] and mixed aryl substituted-aryl[53,54] borates, therefore, must be considered doubtful in light of the above unsuccessful preparative attempts.

The infrared spectra of diethyl hexyl, dicyclohexyl 2-octyl, cyclohexyl di-2-octyl, cyclohexyl diphenyl, and 2-octyl diphenyl borate have been reported,[77] but the preparative experimental details were not included and proof of their existence will have to await further publication.

The mixed ester (XIII) was claimed as the product of the

CH_3 CH_2O- ... CH_3 ... $CH(CH_3)_2$]$_2$ $BOCH_2CH_2SH$

(XIII)

reaction of dihydroabietyl alcohol, β-mercaptoethanol and boric acid.[56,57] Treatment of (XIII) with trivinyltin hydroxide was claimed to give the tin derivative (XIV).[57]

CH_3 CH_2O- ... CH_3 ... $CH(CH_3)_2$]$_2$ $BOCH_2CH_2SSn(CH{=}CH_2)_3$

(XIV)

Evidence for the existence of mixed alkyl borates at 0° has been presented.[52] Half the ethanol of ethyl borate was displaced by *s*-butyl alcohol in a transesterification reaction. The rate of solvolysis of the resulting solution was followed dilatometrically. Ethanolysis proceeded rapidly and after fifty minutes leveled to a rate identical with that for the solvolysis of pure *s*-butyl borate. It was concluded the original solution contained the four species (XV–XVIII) and that the original rapid reaction involved the conversion of (XV) and (XVI) to (XVIII) and the subsequent steady reaction represented the conversion of (XVII) to (XVIII).

$$(C_2H_5O)_2BO\text{—}s\text{-}C_4H_9 \quad C_2H_5OB(O\text{—}s\text{-}C_4H_9)_2 \quad (s\text{-}C_4H_9O)_3B \quad (C_2H_5O)_3B$$

(XV) (XVI) (XVII) (XVIII)

The first substantiated mixed ester (XIX) was prepared by the alcoholysis of (XX).[14] The existence of (XIX), in favor of the

$$[o\text{-}NO_2C_6H_4O]_2BOC_2H_5 \qquad [o\text{-}NO_2C_6H_4O]_2BCl$$

(XIX) (XX)

mixture of triethoxyborane and tri-*o*-nitrophenoxyborane, and its resistance to disproportionation to these symmetrical esters, was shown by the fact that no triethoxyborane was evolved by evacuation to 0.1 mm. at 25°, nor could it be extracted by pentane. Further indication of the existence of (XIX) was the immediate removal at reduced pressure of all the triethoxyborane from a fresh admixture of one mole of triethoxyborane and two moles of tri-*o*-nitrophenoxyborane; whereas only five percent of the added triethoxyborane could be removed after fifteen hours. The equilibrium (6-7) thus lies far to the right.

$$(C_2H_5O)_3B + 2[o\text{-}NO_2C_6H_4O]_3B \rightleftarrows 3[o\text{-}NO_2C_6H_4O]_2BOC_2H_5 \qquad (6\text{-}7)$$

A novel unsymmetrical ester (XXI) was obtained from the reaction of (XXII) and diborane.[49] Since enough diborane was used to complex all three nitrogen atoms of (XXII), and only two nitrogen

$$CH_2(CH_2O)(CH_2N(CH_3)_2)B[OCH_2CH_2CH_2N(CH_3)_2 \rightarrow BH_3]_2 \qquad [(CH_3)_2NCH_2CH_2CH_2O]_3B$$

(XXI) (XXII)

atoms indeed were complexed, it can be concluded that the intramolecular nitrogen–boron bond shown in (XXI) also is present in (XXII).

C. Reactions

The ready disproportionation of mixed borates derived from monohydric alcohols to their symmetrical counterparts (6-5)[13,74] precludes any systematic study of their reactions. Thus, disproportionation remains the only recorded reaction.

No explanation was offered for the inordinate stability of (XIX). Since disproportionation may involve the bridged transition state (XXIII), an intramolecular complex (XXIV), similar to that believed

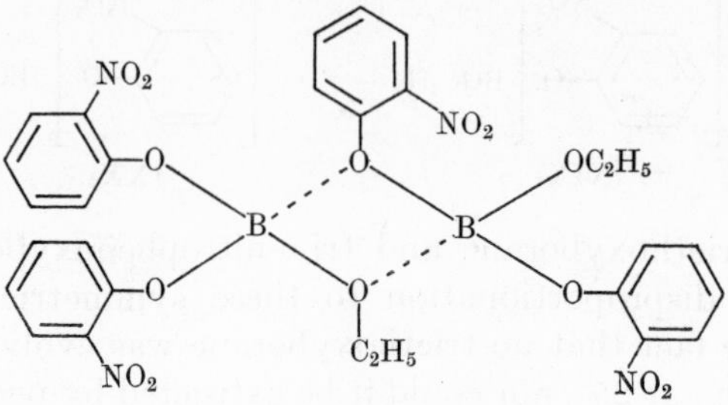

(XXIII)

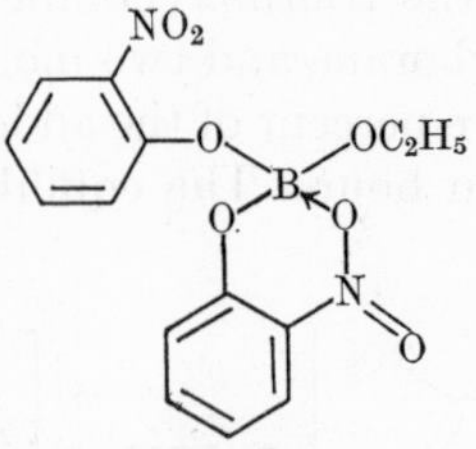

(XXIV)

to be instrumental in stabilizing dichloro(*o*-nitrophenoxy)borane,[14] may be a deterrent to disproportionation. A second possible explanation may be that the steric requirements of the two *o*-nitrophenyl groups prevent the necessary approach of the two halves of the transition state (XXIII). The stability or instability of (XXV),

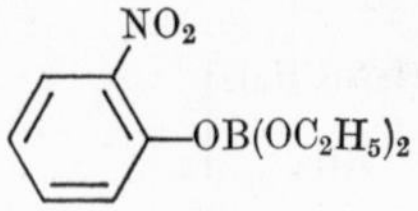

NO_2 — $OB(OC_2H_5)_2$

(XXV)

were it available, could shed light on the factors influencing the stability of (XIX), since (XXV) is capable of forming the intramolecular complex as in structure (XXIV), but is not so sterically hindered as to preclude a bridged transition state similar to (XXIII).

The addition of an equimolar amount of pyridine to (XIX) resulted in its disproportionation (6-8).[14] If the function of the

$$3\,(o\text{-}NO_2\text{—}C_6H_4O)_2BOC_2H_5 + 3\,C_5H_5N \rightarrow B(OC_2H_5)_3 + C_5H_5N + 2\,C_5H_5N{:}B(OC_6H_4\text{-}o\text{-}NO_2)_3 \quad (6\text{-}8)$$

pyridine were the simple removal of tri-*o*-nitrophenoxyborane as a pyridine complex, and thus the displacement of equation (6-7) to the left, it is possible that evacuation might serve the same purpose by the removal of triethoxyborane. Since it did not,[14] the pyridine may serve the purpose of catalyzing the initial attack of the ethoxy group upon an uncomplexed neighbor (6-9), if such can exist in the presence of an equimolar quantity of pyridine.

$$(o\text{-}NO_2\text{—}C_6H_4O)_2B(OC_2H_5)\cdots B(OC_2H_5)(OC_6H_4\text{-}o\text{-}NO_2)_2 + C_6H_5N{:} \rightarrow C_5H_5N{:}\overset{+}{B}(OC_6H_4\text{-}o\text{-}NO_2)_2 + o\text{-}NO_2\text{—}C_6H_4O^- + (C_2H_5O)_2BOC_6H_4\text{-}o\text{-}NO_2 \quad (6\text{-}9)$$

$$C_5H_5N{:}B(OC_6H_4\text{-}o\text{-}NO_2)_2^+ + o\text{-}NO_2\text{—}C_6H_4O^- \rightarrow C_5H_5N{:}B(OC_6H_4\text{-}o\text{-}NO_2)_3 \quad (6\text{-}10)$$

D. Hindered Phenolic Borates

A series of mixed borates (XXVI) derived from 2,6-di-*t*-alkylphenols and alcohols has been reported.[37,55,71,75,76]

$$R''\text{—}C_6H_2(R')_2\text{—}OB(OR)_2$$

(XXVI)

$R = CH_3$ to C_8H_{17}

$R' = t\text{-}C_4H_9,\ t\text{-}C_5H_{11}$

$R'' = H,\ CH_3,\ t\text{-}C_4H_9,\ t\text{-}C_5H_{11}$

The esters range from crystalline solids to high boiling liquids. Their unusual nature is indicated by their inordinate thermal stability since they can be distilled (reduced pressure) without disproportionation.[37,55,71] Furthermore they are the most hydrolytically stable esters known,[37,71] including the symmetrical species of Chapter 4 (see Chapter 21).

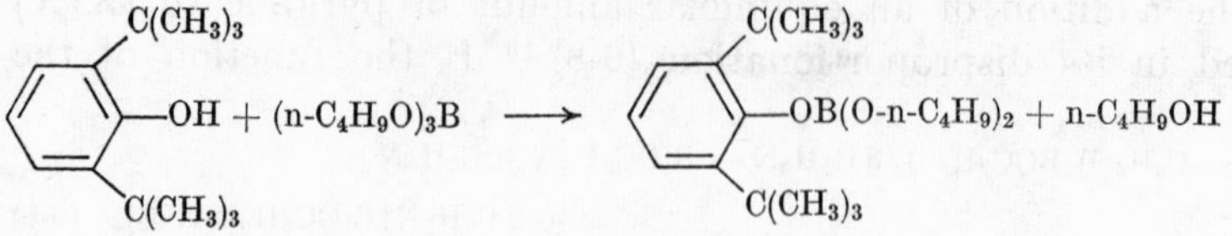

$$2,6\text{-}(C(CH_3)_3)_2C_6H_3\text{-}OH + (n\text{-}C_4H_9O)_3B \longrightarrow 2,6\text{-}(C(CH_3)_3)_2C_6H_3\text{-}OB(O\text{-}n\text{-}C_4H_9)_2 + n\text{-}C_4H_9OH \quad (6\text{-}11)$$

They have been prepared by transesterification of a trialkoxyborane with a hindered phenol (6-11),[37,55,71,75,76]* alcoholysis of a

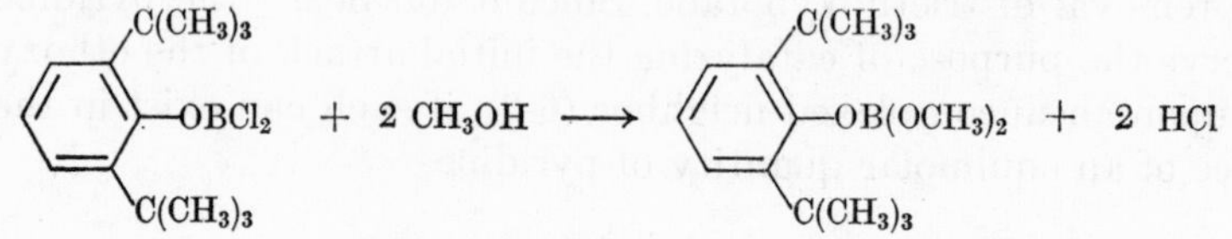

$$2,6\text{-}(C(CH_3)_3)_2C_6H_3\text{-}OBCl_2 + 2\ CH_3OH \longrightarrow 2,6\text{-}(C(CH_3)_3)_2C_6H_3\text{-}OB(OCH_3)_2 + 2\ HCl \quad (6\text{-}12)$$

hindered phenolic dichloroborane (6-12),[71] alcoholysis of a hindered phenolic borate itself (6-13 and 6-14),[37,71] and esterification of a hydroxydioxaborinane with a hindered phenol (6-15).[77]

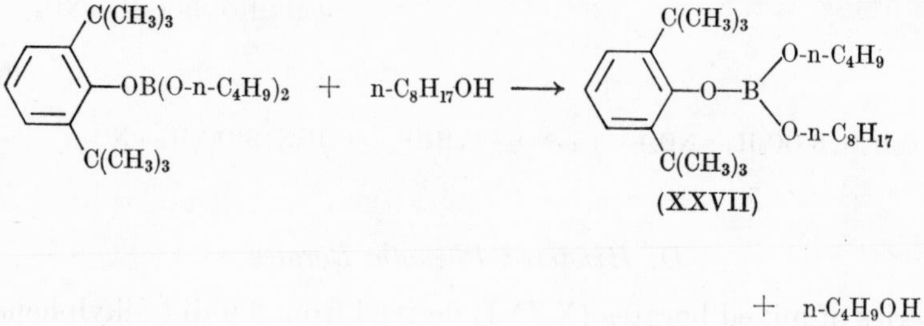

$$2,6\text{-}(C(CH_3)_3)_2C_6H_3\text{-}OB(O\text{-}n\text{-}C_4H_9)_2 + n\text{-}C_8H_{17}OH \longrightarrow 2,6\text{-}(C(CH_3)_3)_2C_6H_3\text{-}O\text{-}B(O\text{-}n\text{-}C_4H_9)(O\text{-}n\text{-}C_8H_{17}) + n\text{-}C_4H_9OH \quad (6\text{-}13)$$

(XXVII)

* Evidence of disubstitution has been obtained.[37]

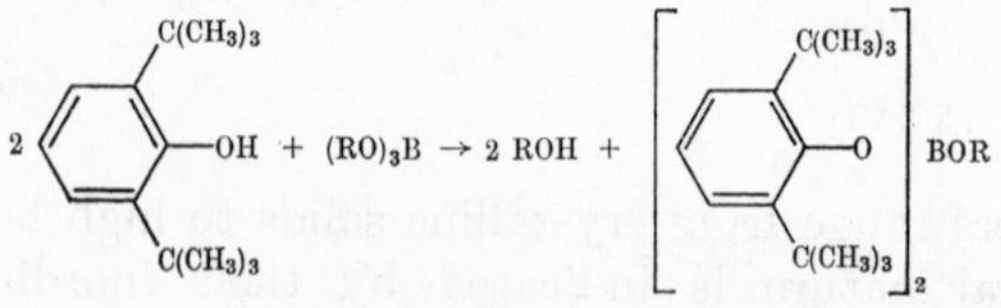

$$2\ [2,6\text{-}(C(CH_3)_3)_2C_6H_3\text{-}OH] + (RO)_3B \rightarrow 2\ ROH + [2,6\text{-}(C(CH_3)_3)_2C_6H_3\text{-}O]_2BOR$$

Attempts to prepare tris-(2,6-di-*t*-butyl-4-methylphenoxy)borane from boron trichloride and the phenol up to 250° resulted in dealkylation and the isolation of tris-(2-*t*-butyl-4-methylphenoxy)borane.[2]

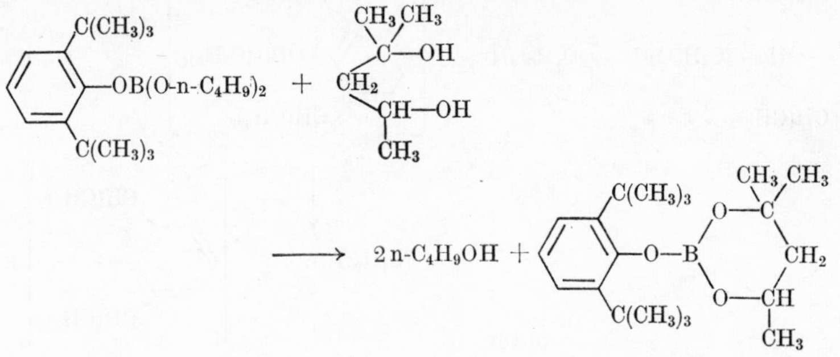

$$2,6\text{-}(t\text{-}C_4H_9)_2C_6H_3OB(O\text{-}n\text{-}C_4H_9)_2 + (CH_3)_2C(OH)CH_2CH(OH)CH_3 \longrightarrow 2\,n\text{-}C_4H_9OH + 2,6\text{-}(t\text{-}C_4H_9)_2C_6H_3O\text{-}B\begin{matrix}O\text{-}C(CH_3)_2\\ \quad\quad CH_2\\ O\text{-}CH(CH_3)\end{matrix} \quad (6\text{-}14)$$

$$2,6\text{-}(t\text{-}C_4H_9)_2C_6H_3OH + (CH_3)_2C\begin{matrix}\text{-}O\\ CH_2\quad BOH\\ CH(CH_3)\text{-}O\end{matrix} \longrightarrow H_2O + 2,6\text{-}(t\text{-}C_4H_9)_2C_6H_3O\text{-}B\begin{matrix}O\text{-}C(CH_3)_2\\ \quad\quad CH_2\\ O\text{-}CH(CH_3)\end{matrix} \quad (6\text{-}15)$$

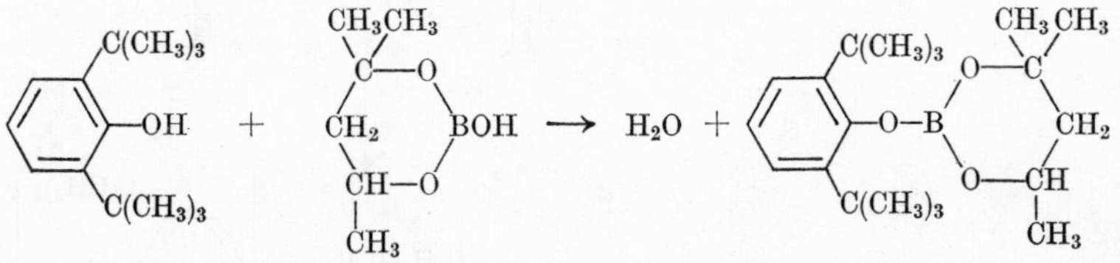

The ester (XXVII) is the only known example of a borate with three different alcohol or phenol residues.[37]

The remarkable stability of the hindered phenolic borates to thermal disproportionation can be attributed to the bulk of the flanking *t*-butyl groups which possibly precludes the approach of a neighbor to within the necessary bonding distance for bridging the alkoxy and phenoxy groups. However, a second possible stabilizing factor cannot be overlooked. The bulky *t*-butyl groups impose a preferred position on the alkoxy groups. Examination of molecular models indicates that the preferred conformation allows for overlap of the π-electrons of the benzene ring and the vacant *p*-orbital of boron. The internal π-complex thus may render boron insensitive to attack by nucleophiles and thereby prevent bridging and disproportionation.

The minimum steric requirements necessary for thermal stability are two *t*-butyl groups in the 2- and 6-positions. Thus, treatment of tributoxyborane with either 2,6-diisopropylphenol or 2-*t*-butylphenol gave the symmetrical borates on distillation.[38]

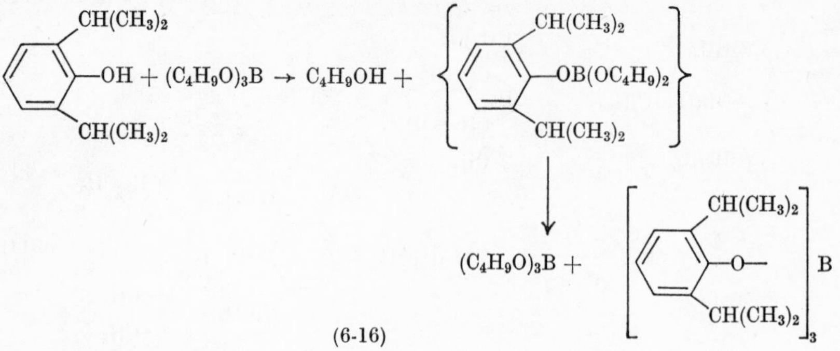

$$\text{2,6-}(CH(CH_3)_2)_2C_6H_3OH + (C_4H_9O)_3B \rightarrow C_4H_9OH + \{\text{2,6-}(CH(CH_3)_2)_2C_6H_3OB(OC_4H_9)_2\} \rightarrow (C_4H_9O)_3B + [\text{2,6-}(CH(CH_3)_2)_2C_6H_3O-]_3B$$

(6-16)

$$\text{2-}C(CH_3)_3C_6H_4OH + (C_4H_9O)_3B \rightarrow C_4H_9OH + \{\text{2-}C(CH_3)_3C_6H_4OB(OC_4H_9)_2\} \rightarrow (C_4H_9O)_3B + [\text{2-}C(CH_3)_3C_6H_4O-]_3B$$

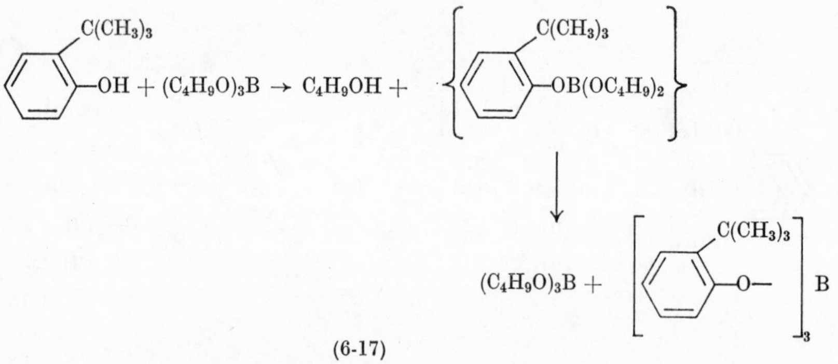

(6-17)

III. ESTERS DERIVED FROM DIHYDRIC ALCOHOLS AND DIHYDRIC PHENOLS

A. Unsymmetrical Biborates

Structures (XXVIII) and (XXIX), derived from three different glycols, have been recorded without experimental details.[17] The

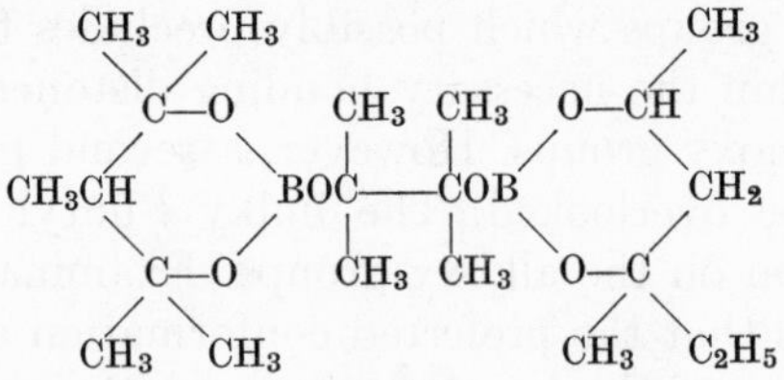

(XXVIII)

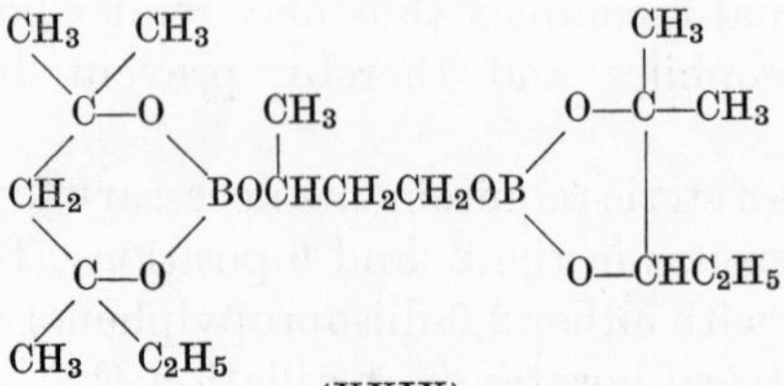

(XXIX)

dehydration of a mixture of three different glycols and two moles of boric acid undoubtedly would give a statistical distribution of products. If the diols were symmetrical, eighteen products might result. Three unsymmetrical diols could lead to fifty-four different products, not counting optical isomers. The isolation of a given ester thus would be an arduous task indeed.

The use of a mixture of 1,3- and 1,4-glycols led to the facile synthesis of a series of type (III) esters due to the difficulty of ring formation with the 1,4-glycol.[46]

$$2\ \mathrm{C(C{-}OH)_2} + \mathrm{HOC{-}C_n{-}COH} + 2\,\mathrm{H_3BO_3} \xrightarrow[-6\,\mathrm{H_2O}\ (n \geq 2)]{\mathrm{C_6H_6}} \mathrm{C(C{-}O)_2B{-}OC{-}C_n{-}C{-}OB(O{-}C)_2C} \qquad (6\text{-}18)$$

The same principle is involved in the synthesis of (XXX) from ethylene glycol, β-mercaptoethanol, boric acid and dibutyl tin

$$\mathrm{(CH_2O)_2BOCH_2CH_2SSn(C_4H_9)_2SCH_2CH_2OB(OCH_2)_2}$$

(XXX)

oxide.[56,57] In this case a 1,7-glycol is produced by the condensation of the sulfhydryl groups with the tin oxide. No experimental evidence was presented for structure (XXX).

Esterification of 2-hydroxy-4,4,6-trimethyl-1,3,2-dioxaborinane (XXXI) or cleavage of its anhydride (XXXII) with the diol (XXXIII) has led to the mixed biborate (XXXIV).[3]

$$\mathrm{(CH_3)_2C{-}O{-}B(OH){-}O{-}CH(CH_3){-}CH_2} \quad \text{(XXXI)}$$

$$\mathrm{[(CH_3)_2C{-}O{-}B{-}O{-}CH(CH_3){-}CH_2]_2O} \quad \text{(XXXII)}$$

$$\mathrm{C_{17}H_{33}C{=}N{-}C(CH_2OH)_2{-}CH_2{-}O} \quad \text{(XXXIII)}$$

$$\text{(XXXIV): } [\text{2,2-dimethyl-4-methyl-1,3,2-dioxaborinan-2-yl}]\text{-OCH}_2\text{C(CH}_2\text{)(CH}_2\text{O-B[dioxaborinane]}) \text{ with oxazoline ring N=C(C}_{17}\text{H}_{33}\text{)-O}$$

(XXXIV)

The room temperature reaction of 2-chloro-1,3,2-dioxaborinane with ethylene glycol has resulted in a 72% yield of the mixed ester.[25]

$$2\ CH_2\begin{matrix} CH_2-O \\ \\ CH_2-O \end{matrix}BCl + HOCH_2CH_2OH \rightarrow CH_2\begin{matrix} CH_2-O \\ \\ CH_2-O \end{matrix}BOCH_2CH_2OB\begin{matrix} O-CH_2 \\ \\ O-CH_2 \end{matrix}CH_2 + 2\ HCl \qquad (6\text{-}19)$$

B. Hydroxy Derivatives

A product with a free hydroxyl group (XXXV) might be expected from a reaction with a stoichiometry of two moles of a glycol to one

$$2\ R\begin{matrix} -OH \\ \\ -OH \end{matrix} + H_3BO_3 \rightarrow 3\ H_2O + R\begin{matrix} -O \\ \\ -O \end{matrix}BO-R-OH \qquad (6\text{-}20)$$

(XXXV)

of boric acid. In most cases, however, the stoichiometric equivalent of (XXXV), a 50–50 mixture of the biborate (XXXVI) and free glycol, is obtained on distillation.

$$2\ R\begin{matrix} -OH \\ \\ -OH \end{matrix} + H_3BO_3 \rightarrow 3\ H_2O + \tfrac{1}{2}\ R\begin{matrix} -O \\ \\ -O \end{matrix}B-O-R-O-B\begin{matrix} O- \\ \\ O- \end{matrix}R + \tfrac{1}{2}\ R\begin{matrix} -OH \\ \\ -OH \end{matrix}$$

(XXXVI) (6-21)

The existence of the hydroxyalkoxy derivative in the reaction mixture before distillation appears to be valid at least in the case of ethylene glycol. The transesterification of (XXXVII) with ethylene glycol resulted in a definite solid compound melting at 128° with elemental analyses consistent with (XXXVIII).[4]

```
CH2—O                      CH2—O
|     \                    |     \
|      BOC4H9              |      BOCH2CH2OH
|     /                    |     /
CH2—O                      CH2—O
(XXXVII)                   (XXXVIII)
```

Similar compounds have been claimed for 1,3-butanediol (XXXIX),[44] 3,4-dimethyl-3,4-hexanediol (XL), 3,4-diethyl-3,4-hexanediol (XLI), 2,4,4-trimethyl-2,3-pentanediol (XLII),[18] and a series of mixed glycols (XLIII).[19,20,21]

```
CH3                                     C2H5
 \                                       |
  CH—O          CH3                 CH3C—O      CH3  CH3
 /     \         |                   |     \     |    |
CH2     BOCH2CH2CHOH                 |      BOC——COH
 \     /                             |     /     |    |
  CH2—O                             CH3C—O      C2H5 C2H5
                                         |
                                        C2H5
      (XXXIX)                            (XL)
```

```
    C2H5                    (CH3)3CCH—O      CH3  OH
     |                          |      \     |    |
C2H5C—O     C2H5 C2H5           |       BOC——CHC(CH3)3
     |  \    |    |             |      /     |
     |   BOC——COH            CH3C————O       CH3
     |  /    |    |             |
C2H5C—O     C2H5 C2H5          CH3
     |
    C2H5
    (XLI)                           (XLII)
```

```
  ┌—O
  |   \
  R    B—OR′OH
  |   /
  └—O
  (XLIII)
```

The resistance to hydrolysis of compounds (XXXIX) to (XLIII) was attributed to intramolecular coordination of the type (XLIV).[20,21]

```
   O     O
  / \   / \
 R   B     R′
  \ /  ↖  /
   O     O
         |
         H
   (XLIV)
```

Competitive esterification reactions with an equimolar mixture of a 1,2-diol, 1,3-diol, and boric acid indicated preferential formation of the six-membered ring.[34]

$$H_3BO_3 + HOCH_2CH_2OH + HOCH_2CH_2CH_2OH$$

$$\rightarrow 3\,H_2O + \begin{array}{l} CH_2{-}O \\ CH_2 \qquad\qquad BOCH_2CH_2OH \\ CH_2{-}O \end{array} \qquad (6\text{-}22)$$

Attempts to convert the hydroxyborolane (XLV) to (XLVI) by

$$\begin{array}{l} CH_2{-}O \\ \qquad\qquad BOH \\ CH_3CH{-}O \end{array} \qquad\qquad \begin{array}{l} CH_2{-}O \qquad\quad CH_3 \\ \qquad\qquad BOCH_2CHOH \\ CH_3CH{-}O \end{array}$$

(XLV) (XLVI)

treatment with propylene glycol or sodium propylene glycolate were unsuccessful.[58] The similar transformation (6-23), however, was claimed.[2]

$$\begin{array}{l} CH_3 \quad CH_3 \\ \quad C{-}O \\ CH_2 \qquad\quad BOH \\ \quad CH{-}O \\ \quad CH_3 \end{array} + \begin{array}{l} \qquad\qquad\quad CH_2OH \\ \qquad\quad N{-}C \\ C_{17}H_{33}C \qquad\quad CH_2OH \\ \qquad\quad O{-}CH_2 \end{array}$$

$$\rightarrow H_2O + \begin{array}{l} CH_3 \quad CH_3 \\ \quad C{-}O \\ CH_2 \qquad\quad BOCH_2C{-}N \\ \quad CH{-}O \\ \quad CH_3 \end{array} \begin{array}{l} CH_2OH \\ \\ \qquad\qquad CC_{17}H_{33} \\ CH_2{-}O \end{array} \qquad (6\text{-}23)$$

A series of phosphorylated derivatives (XLVIII–L) were pre-

$$\begin{array}{l} CH_3 \\ CH{-}O \qquad\qquad\qquad CH_3 \\ CH_2 \qquad\quad BOCH_2CH_2CHONa \\ CH_2{-}O \end{array} \qquad \begin{array}{l} CH_3 \\ CH{-}O \qquad\qquad\qquad CH_3\ O \\ CH_2 \qquad\quad BOCH_2CH_2CHOP(OC_2H_5)_2 \\ CH_2{-}O \end{array}$$

(XLVII) (XLVIII)

$$\left[\begin{array}{l} CH_3 \\ CH{-}O \qquad\qquad\qquad CH_3 \\ CH_2 \qquad\quad BOCH_2CH_2CHO \\ CH_2{-}O \end{array}\right]_2 \begin{array}{l} O \\ \| \\ POCH_3 \end{array} \qquad \left[\begin{array}{l} CH_3 \\ CH{-}O \qquad\qquad\qquad CH_3 \\ CH_2 \qquad\quad BOCH_2CH_2CHO \\ CH_2{-}O \end{array}\right]_3 \begin{array}{l} O \\ \| \\ P \end{array}$$

(XLIX) (L)

pared from reaction of the sodium salt (XLVII) with the appropriate chlorophosphate.[22]

The equimolar reaction of boric acid and the bisphenol A derivative (LI) was reported to give polymers of the type (LII).[30]

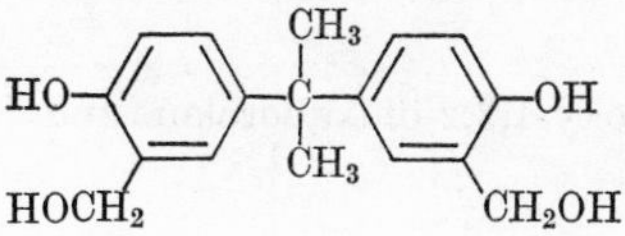

(LI)

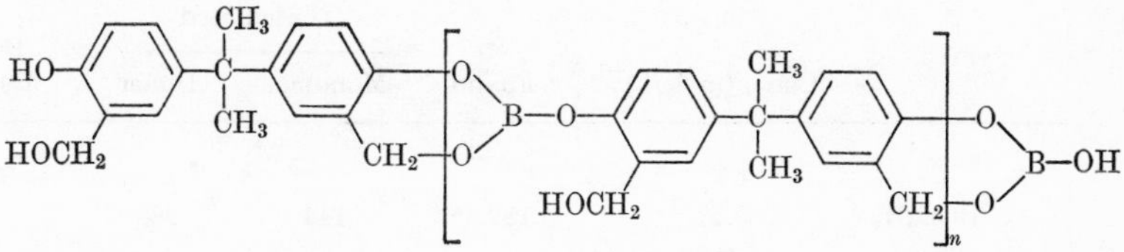

(LII)

The sodium borohydride reduction of bipivaloyl was reported to give in addition to *meso*-2,2,5,5-tetramethyl-3,4-hexanediol a boron-containing fraction which survived dissolution in 2*N* sulfuric acid. The analysis of the product was consistent with structure (LIII). Examination of the products of partial hydrolysis of (LIII),

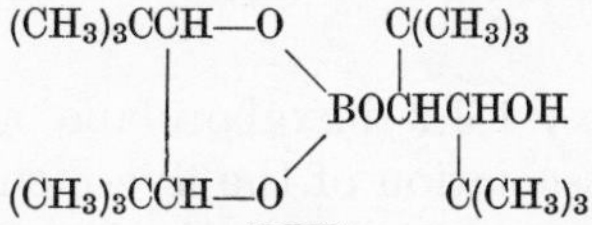

$(CH_3)_3CCH—O \quad C(CH_3)_3$
BOCHCHOH
$(CH_3)_3CCH—O \quad C(CH_3)_3$

(LIII)

diol plus hydroxyborolane, indicated the ring diol to be the racemic modification, and the side chain diol to be the *meso* form.[16]

IV. ESTERS DERIVED FROM MONO- AND DIHYDRIC ALCOHOLS AND PHENOLS

A. 2-*Alkoxy*-1,3,2-*dioxaborolanes and Borinanes*

1. INTRODUCTION

This class of mixed esters contain a five- or six-membered ring with a single alkoxy group on the boron (LIV and LV).

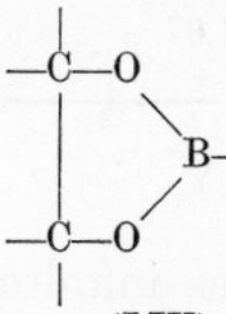

(LIV) 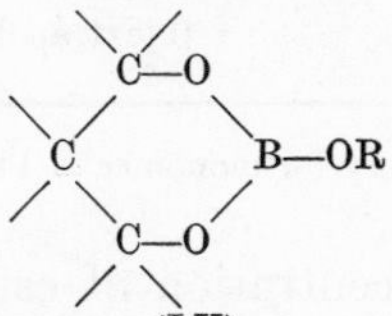 (LV)

A seven-membered ring has been reported.[83]

2. PROPERTIES

The alkyl *o*-phenylene esters are colorless unimolecular liquids.[47] However, some type (VI) esters apparently are not monomeric, at least in benzene solution, since cryoscopic molecular weight deter-

Table 6-1. Cryoscopic molecular weight of 2-butoxy-1,3,2-dioxaborolane and borinane in benzene

	Conc. (mole/l.)	Mol. wt. Found	Calculated Monomer	Calculated Dimer	Degree of association
BOC_4H_9	0.17	182.4[a]	144	288	1.26
O, O, BOC_4H_9	0.14	162.7	158	316	1.03

[a] Ref. 4 reported a value of 143 in cycohexane solution.

minations of 2-butoxy-1,3,2-dioxaborolane and borinane in that solvent indicate an association of the five-membered ring derivative (Table 6-1).[7] The degree of association decreases towards unity as

Table 6-2. Degree of association of 2-butoxy-1,3,2-dioxaborolane in benzene

Conc. (mole/l.)	Molecular weight[a]	Degree of association
0.290	208	1.45
0.192	198	1.38
0.144	188	1.31
0.0965	176	1.22
0.0721	171	1.19
0 (extrapolated)	154	1.07

[a] Theory for monomer = 144.

the concentration of ester in benzene approaches infinite dilution (Table 6-2).[34]

If dimerization indeed occurs, it would be the first recorded case for a borate;* although (LVI) has been found to be dimeric in benzene solution[7] and dimeric aminodihaloboranes are well known.[8,10,23,33,50,68,78,79,80,81,82]

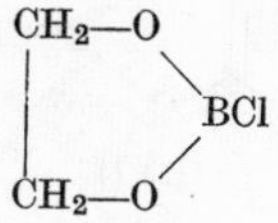

$$\begin{array}{l} CH_2—O \\ \quad\quad\quad\quad BCl \\ CH_2—O \end{array}$$

(LVI)

It is possible that the tying back of two of the alkoxy groups in a five-membered ring reduces the steric requirements (*F*-strain) to the point where intermolecular donation of electrons to boron (LVII) can compete with the more common donation of electrons by adjacent oxygen atoms (LVIII). Further, the nonplanarity of the

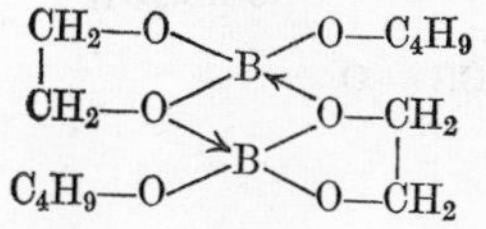

$$\begin{array}{l} CH_2—O \quad\quad O—C_4H_9 \\ \quad\quad\quad\quad B \\ CH_2—O \quad\quad O—CH_2 \\ \quad\quad\quad\quad B \\ C_4H_9—O \quad\quad O—CH_2 \end{array}$$

(LVII)

$$\begin{array}{l} CH_2—\ddot{O} \\ \quad\quad\quad\quad BOC_4H_9 \\ CH_2—O \end{array}$$

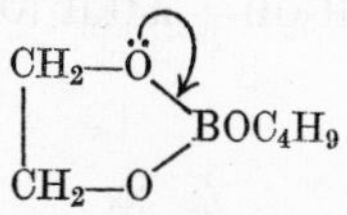

(LVIII)

five-membered ring of (LVIII) would be expected to inhibit the electron shift as shown and thus more readily allow for intermolecular coordination. The possibility of the slow formation of (LIX) to account for the high molecular weight of 2-butoxy-1,3,2-dioxaborolane cannot yet be ruled out.

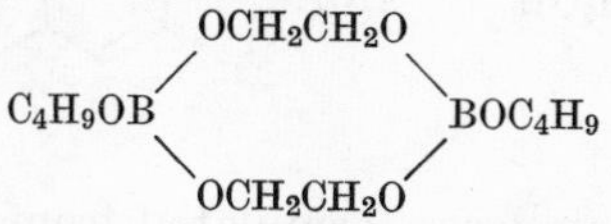

$$\begin{array}{c} OCH_2CH_2O \\ C_4H_9OB \quad\quad\quad\quad BOC_4H_9 \\ OCH_2CH_2O \end{array}$$

(LIX)

Equations for the molar refractions and molar volumes of a series of catechol alkyl borates (LX) have been recorded.[11] Magneto-optic data for a series of type (VI) esters also have been recorded.[41]

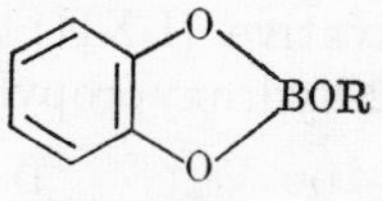

$$C_6H_4O_2BOR$$

(LX)

* Ref. 7 points out that the high reported boiling point for 2-ethoxy-1,3,2-dioxaborolane[4] indicates dimerization or association.

Compound (LXI) was reported to attack the skin and react explosively with concentrated nitric acid.[1]

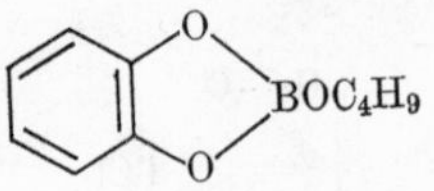

$$C_6H_4O_2BOC_4H_9$$

(LXI)

3. METHODS OF PREPARATION

a. *From Boric Acid or Equivalent.* The most expedient method of preparation of the 2-alkoxy-1,3,2-dioxaborolanes and borinanes is the azeotropic removal of water from a mixture of boric acid[31] or boric oxide,[26,74] a glycol or catechol, and an alcohol or phenol.

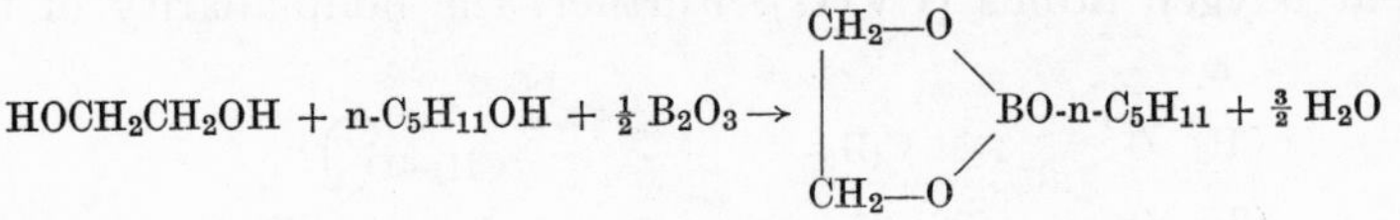

$$HOCH_2CH_2OH + n\text{-}C_5H_{11}OH + \tfrac{1}{2} B_2O_3 \rightarrow (CH_2O)_2BO\text{-}n\text{-}C_5H_{11} + \tfrac{3}{2} H_2O \quad (6\text{-}24)$$

$$C_6H_4(OH)_2 + C_6H_5OH + \tfrac{1}{2}B_2O_3 \longrightarrow C_6H_4O_2B\text{—}O\text{—}C_6H_5 + \tfrac{3}{2}H_2O \quad (6\text{-}25)$$

$$C_6H_4(OH)_2 + C_4H_9OH + H_3BO_3 \rightarrow C_6H_4O_2BOC_4H_9 + 3\,H_2O \quad (6\text{-}26)$$

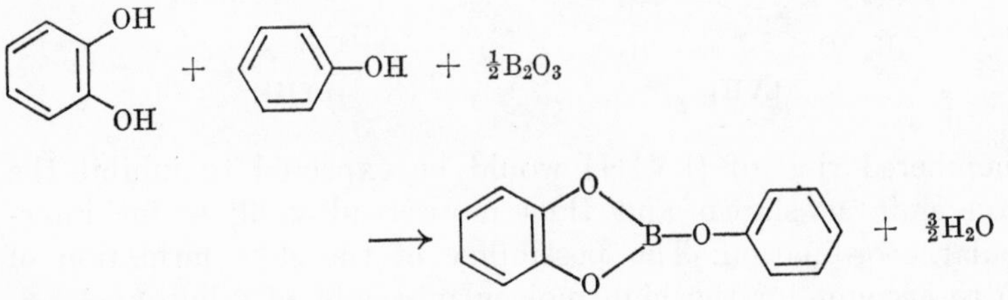

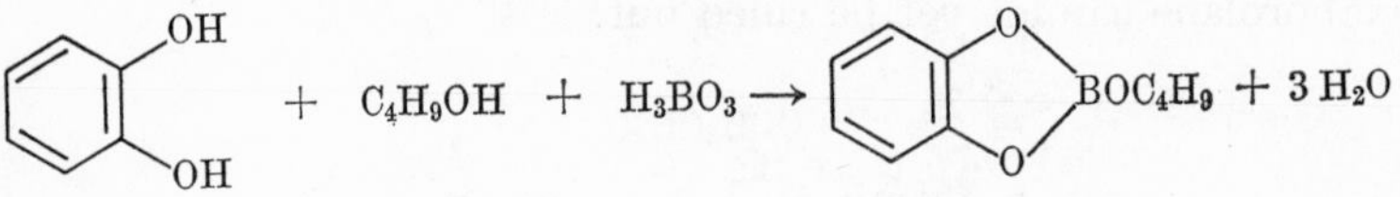

Polymeric products were formulated from the reaction of boric acid, ethylene glycol and phenol.[76]

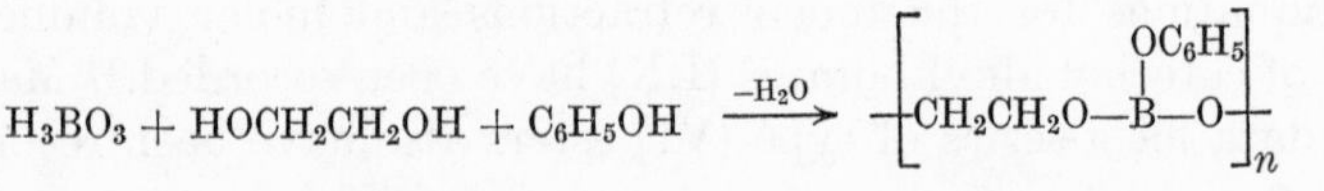

$$H_3BO_3 + HOCH_2CH_2OH + C_6H_5OH \xrightarrow{-H_2O} \left[\text{—}CH_2CH_2O\text{—}\underset{}{\overset{OC_6H_5}{\overset{|}{B}}}\text{—}O\text{—}\right]_n \quad (6\text{-}27)$$

The unsaturated derivative (LXII) was obtained from boric acid, 2,3-butanediol, and 2-hydroxypropyl methacrylate.[40]

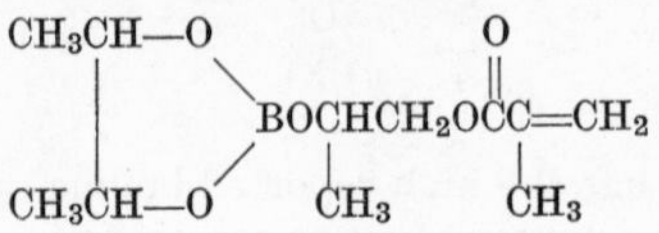

$$(CH_3CH\text{—}O)_2BOCH(CH_3)CH_2OC(=O)C(CH_3)=CH_2$$

(LXII)

The ease of removal from the reaction mixture of a mixed ester derived from an alcohol and diol as contrasted to the difficulty experienced with the mixed esters derived from monohydric alcohols (see Section I-B), was attributed to the relative boiling points of the species involved in the two types of reactions.[74] With monohydric alcohols, the mixed ester has a boiling point intermediate to the two symmetrical species in equilibrium with it, and thus the lowest boiling member, one of the symmetrical species, is removed on distillation. However, when a glycol or catechol is involved, the mixed species may be lower boiling than either symmetrical species and it is removed on distillation.

This simple explanation for the apparent stability of type (VI) esters predicated on a facile equilibrium (6-28) breaks down when one

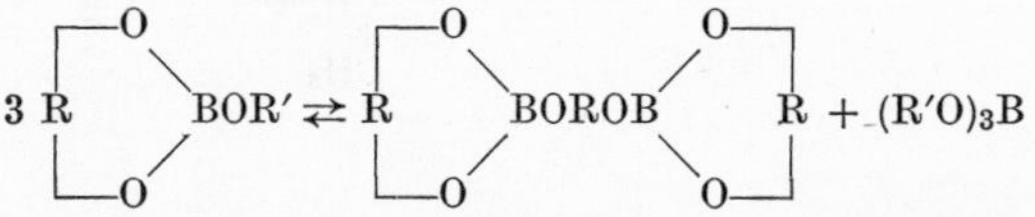

$$3\,R\!\begin{smallmatrix}O\\O\end{smallmatrix}\!\!>BOR' \rightleftharpoons R\!\begin{smallmatrix}O\\O\end{smallmatrix}\!\!>BOB\!<\!\!\begin{smallmatrix}O\\O\end{smallmatrix}\!R + (R'O)_3B \qquad (6\text{-}28)$$

considers the boiling points listed in Table 6-3 or the fact that butyl

Table 6-3. Boiling points of esters derived from ethanol and catechol

Species	B.p. (°C)/mm.
$(C_2H_5O)_3B$	10/10
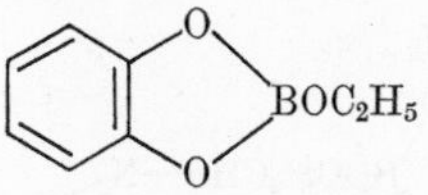 $C_6H_4\begin{smallmatrix}O\\O\end{smallmatrix}\!\!>BOC_2H_5$	91/10
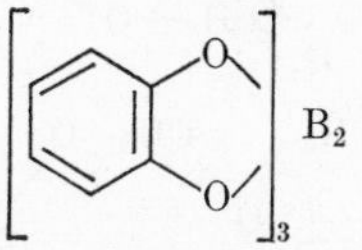 $\left[C_6H_4\begin{smallmatrix}O\\O\end{smallmatrix}\right]_3B_2$	240–242/7

catechol borate was recovered in 96% yield after being heated at 280° for twenty-four hours.[31] Tributyl borate boils at 230° and should have been formed and removed were the reaction of equation (6-28) operative. An inherent stability occasioned by the five-membered ring thus is indicated.

b. *From 2-Hydroxy-1,3,2-dioxaborolanes and Borinanes.* Esterification of the remaining hydroxyl group in a hydroxydioxaborolane or borinane affords a stepwise synthesis of the mixed species.[3,27,38]

Structures (LXIII) and (LXIV) were prepared similarly from 2-hydroxyethyl methacrylate.[40]

$$(CH_3)_2C(OH)CH_2CH(OH)CH_3 + H_3BO_3 \xrightarrow[-2\,H_2O]{\text{Benzene}}$$

$$\text{[cyclic } (CH_3)_2C\text{–}O\text{–}B(OH)\text{–}O\text{–}CH(CH_3)\text{–}CH_2\text{]} \xrightarrow[\text{Toluene},\ -H_2O]{[(CH_3)_2CH]_2CHOH} \text{[cyclic]}BOCH[CH(CH_3)_2]_2 \quad (6\text{-}29)$$

$$\xrightarrow[\text{Xylene},\ -H_2O]{2,6\text{-di-}C(CH_3)_3\text{-}4\text{-}CH_3C_6H_2OH} \text{[cyclic]}BO\text{–}C_6H_2(C(CH_3)_3)_2CH_3 \quad (6\text{-}30)$$

$$\xrightarrow[-H_2O]{C_{17}H_{33}C(=N\text{–}CHCH_2OH)(O\text{–}CH_2)} \text{[cyclic]}BOCH_2CH\text{–}N{=}CC_{17}H_{33}\ (CH_2\text{–}O) \quad (6\text{-}31)$$

$$\text{[cyclic } CH_3CHO\text{–}B\text{–}OCHCH_3\text{]}BOCH_2CH_2OC(=O)C(CH_3){=}CH_2 \quad \text{(LXIII)}$$

$$(CH_3)_2C(CH_2\text{–}O)_2BOCH_2CH_2OC(=O)C(CH_3){=}CH_2 \quad \text{(LXIV)}$$

Dimethoxypropane has served as one of the reactants (6-32).[36]

$$\text{[cyclic } (CH_3)_2C\text{–}O\text{–}B\text{–}O\text{–}CH(CH_3)\text{–}CH_2\text{]}BOH + CH_3C(OCH_3)_2CH_3 \rightarrow \text{[cyclic]}BOCH_3 + CH_3OH + CH_3C(=O)CH_3 \quad (6\text{-}32)$$

The sodium salt of a steroidal dioxaborolane has been converted to (LXV) by treatment with methyl iodide.[73]

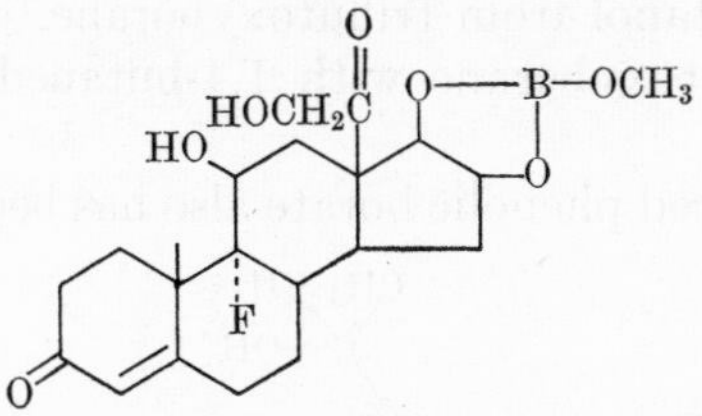

(LXV)

c. *By Transesterification of Trialkoxyboranes.* Treatment of a symmetrical orthoborate with a glycol may result in the displacement of two alkoxy groups and the formation of a mixed ester.

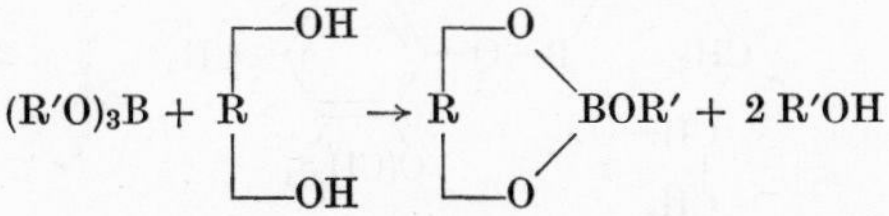

$$(R'O)_3B + R(OH)_2 \rightarrow R(O)_2BOR' + 2\,R'OH \qquad (6\text{-}33)$$

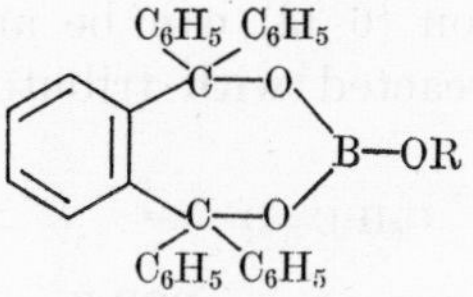

(LXVI, R = C_2H_5, C_4H_9)

The method was first applied to the preparation of (LXVI) from the reaction of *o*-bis(diphenylhydroxymethyl)benzene and either triethoxy- or tributoxyborane.[83] Compound (LXVI) is the only recorded case of a seven-membered ring mixed borate.

Eight-membered rings (LXVII) have been reported in 60–85% yields from the reactions of various trialkoxyboranes and *N,N,N',N'*-tetrakis-(2-hydroxyalkyl)ethylenediamine (6-34).[62]

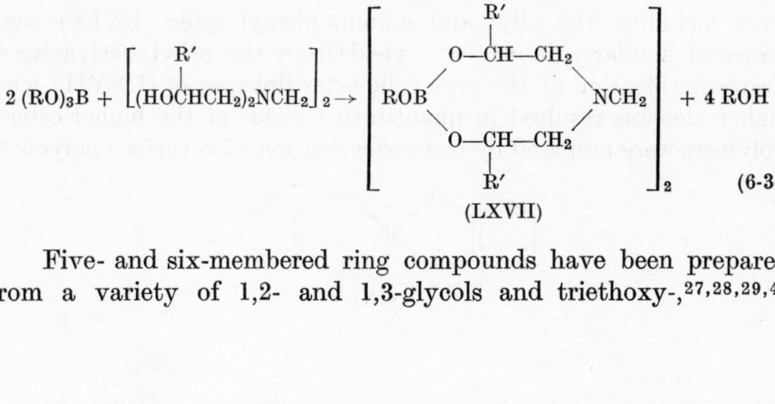

$$2\,(RO)_3B + \left[(HO\overset{R'}{C}HCH_2)_2NCH_2\right]_2 \rightarrow \left[ROB\begin{matrix} O\text{—}\overset{R'}{C}H\text{—}CH_2 \\ O\text{—}\underset{R'}{C}H\text{—}CH_2 \end{matrix}NCH_2\right]_2 + 4\,ROH \qquad (6\text{-}34)$$

(LXVII)

Five- and six-membered ring compounds have been prepared from a variety of 1,2- and 1,3-glycols and triethoxy-,[27,28,29,48] tripropoxy-,[41] tributoxy-,[7,34,41,42] tripentoxy-[41,42] and trihexoxyborane.[41] Catechol has also displaced ethanol from triethoxyborane[47,48] and butanol from tributoxyborane.[1,31] Displacement of butanol from tributoxyborane with 1,4-butanediol led to polymer formation.[34]

A mixed hindered phenolic borate also has been transesterified.[38]

$$2,6\text{-}[C(CH_3)_3]_2\text{-}4\text{-}CH_3C_6H_2OB(OC_4H_9)_2 + (CH_3)_2C(OH)CH_2CH(OH)CH_3 \longrightarrow$$

$$\text{(cyclic } (CH_3)_2C\text{—O—B(—O—}C_6H_2[C(CH_3)_3]_2CH_3\text{)—O—}CH(CH_3)\text{—}CH_2\text{)} + 2\ C_4H_9OH \qquad (6\text{-}35)$$

The diol of equation (6-33) can be an enolizable α-hydroxyketone. Thus benzoin reacted with tributoxyborane to give the dioxaborole (LXVIII).[1]

$$C_6H_5C\text{—O}\diagdown \;\; \Vert \;\; BOC_4H_9 \;\; C_6H_5C\text{—O}\diagup$$

(LXVIII)

d. *By Transesterification of 2-Alkoxy-1,3,2-dioxaborolanes.* Reaction (6-36) was performed in 90% yield.[48] A series of alkyl deriva-

$$C_6H_4O_2BOC_2H_5 + t\text{-}C_4H_9OH \longrightarrow C_6H_4O_2BO\text{-}t\text{-}C_4H_9 + C_2H_5OH \qquad (6\text{-}36)$$

tives including the allyl and *o*-aminophenyl ester (LXIX) were prepared similarly in 67–98% yield from the ethyl derivative.[47] Transesterification of the *exo*-cyclic ester linkages of (LXVII) with higher alcohols resulted in quantitative yields of the higher esters. Polymers were prepared by transesterification with various polyols.[62]

$$C_6H_4O_2B\text{—O—}C_6H_4NH_2$$

(LXIX)

Transesterification of (LXX) with 2-hydroxyethyl methacrylate resulted in a 56% yield of (LXXI). Structure (LXXIII) similarly was prepared in quantitative yield from the reaction of (LXXII) and 2-hydroxyethyl acrylate.[40] The reaction of 2-phenoxy-1,3,2-benzodioxaborole with catechol to give the biborate is discussed in Chapter 5.

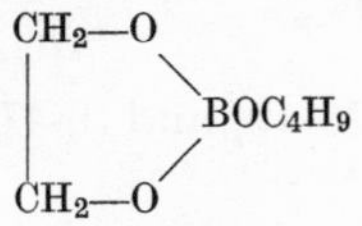

CH_2—O / CH_2—O > BOC_4H_9
(LXX)

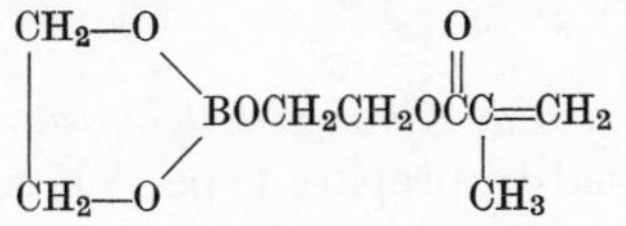

CH_2—O / CH_2—O > $BOCH_2CH_2OC(=O)C(CH_3){=}CH_2$
(LXXI)

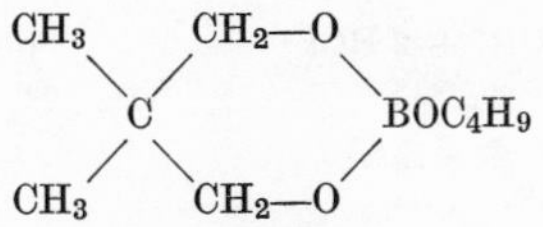

$(CH_3)_2C(CH_2O)_2BOC_4H_9$
(LXXII)

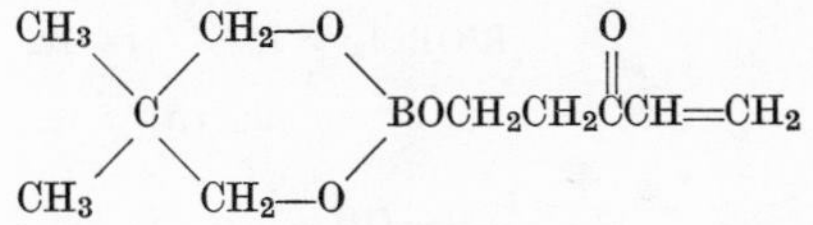

$(CH_3)_2C(CH_2O)_2BOCH_2CH_2C(=O)CH{=}CH_2$
(LXXIII)

1,3-Diketones capable of enolization have been used as the alcohol source.[26]

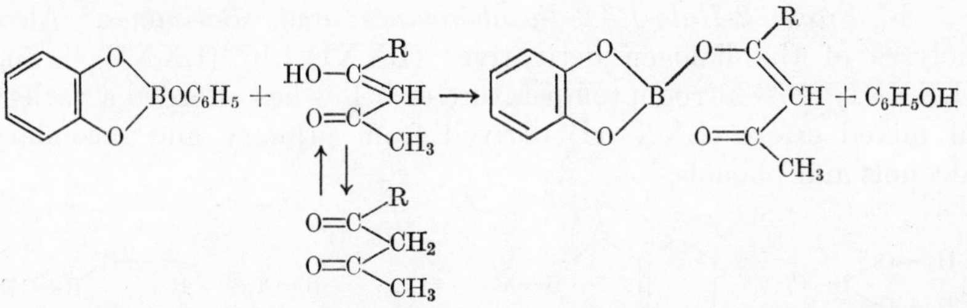

$C_6H_4O_2BOC_6H_5 + HO{-}C(R){=}CH{-}C(=O)CH_3 \;(\rightleftarrows\; O{=}C(R){-}CH_2{-}C(=O)CH_3) \longrightarrow C_6H_4O_2B{-}O{-}C(R){=}CH{-}C(=O)CH_3 + C_6H_5OH$ (6-37)

e. *From Trialkoxyboranes and Glycol Biborates.* The redistribution reaction of triethoxyborane and tricatechol biborate afforded the mixed ester in quantitative yield.[47]

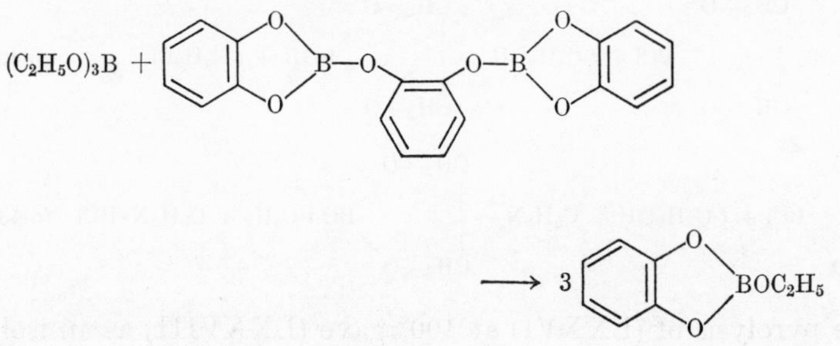

$(C_2H_5O)_3B + C_6H_4O_2B{-}O{-}C_6H_4{-}O{-}BO_2C_6H_4 \longrightarrow 3\; C_6H_4O_2BOC_2H_5$ (6-38)

f. *Thermal Decomposition of Tris-(β-chloromethoxyethoxy)borane.* An unusual decomposition of tris-(β-chloromethoxyethoxy)borane occurred on heating the chloroester to 56° at reduced pressure.[15]

$$(ClCH_2OCH_2CH_2O)_3B \rightarrow ClCH_2OCH_2CH_2OCH_2Cl + \begin{matrix} CH_2\text{—}O \\ | \\ CH_2\text{—}O \end{matrix}\!\!>\!BOCH_2CH_2OCH_2Cl \qquad (6\text{-}39)$$

g. *From Alkoxydihaloboranes.* Reactions (6-40) and (6-41) have been used to prepare type (VI) mixed borates.[4]

$$R'OBCl_2 + R\begin{matrix} \text{—}OH \\ \text{—}OH \end{matrix} \rightarrow R\begin{matrix} \text{—}O \\ \text{—}O \end{matrix}\!\!>\!BOR' + 2\,HCl \qquad (6\text{-}40)$$

$$R'OBCl_2 + R\begin{matrix} \text{—}OH \\ \text{—}OH \end{matrix} + 2\,C_5H_5N \rightarrow R\begin{matrix} \text{—}O \\ \text{—}O \end{matrix}\!\!>\!BOR' + 2\,C_5H_5N\cdot HCl \qquad (6\text{-}41)$$

h. *From 2-Halo-1,3,2-dioxaborolanes and Borinanes.* Alcoholyses of the halogen derivatives (LXXIV),[4,7] (LXXV),[31] and (LXXVI)[7,24,25] at room temperature or below has afforded a variety of mixed esters (LXXVII) derived from primary and secondary alcohols and phenols.

$$\begin{matrix} CH_2\text{—}O \\ | \\ CH_2\text{—}O \end{matrix}\!\!>\!B\text{—}Cl \qquad C_6H_4\begin{matrix} O \\ O \end{matrix}\!\!>\!B\text{—}X \qquad CH_2\begin{matrix} CH_2\text{—}O \\ CH_2\text{—}O \end{matrix}\!\!>\!B\text{—}Cl \qquad R\begin{matrix} \text{—}O \\ \text{—}O \end{matrix}\!\!>\!B\text{—}OR'$$

(LXXIV) (LXXV, X = Cl, Br) (LXXVI) (LXXVII)

t-Butyl alcohol underwent alkyl-oxygen cleavage (6-42) unless pyridine was present (6-43).[4]

$$\begin{matrix} CH_2\text{—}O \\ | \\ CH_2\text{—}O \end{matrix}\!\!>\!BCl + t\text{-}C_4H_9OH \rightarrow \begin{matrix} CH_2\text{—}O \\ | \\ CH_2\text{—}O \end{matrix}\!\!>\!BOH + t\text{-}C_4H_9Cl \qquad (6\text{-}42)$$

$$\begin{matrix} CH_2\text{—}O \\ | \\ CH_2\text{—}O \end{matrix}\!\!>\!BCl + t\text{-}C_4H_9OH + C_5H_5N \rightarrow \begin{matrix} CH_2\text{—}O \\ | \\ CH_2\text{—}O \end{matrix}\!\!>\!BO\text{-}t\text{-}C_4H_9 + C_5H_5N\cdot HCl \qquad (6\text{-}43)$$

The pyrolysis of (LXXVI) at 100° gave (LXXVIII) as an isolable product.[24,25] See Chapter 4 for a discussion of the mechanism of the pyrolysis.

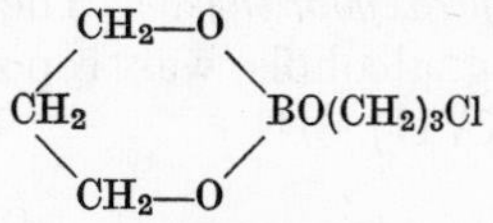

CH_2—O / CH_2 $BO(CH_2)_3Cl$ / CH_2—O

(LXXVIII)

i. *From 2,2′-Oxybis-(1,3,2-dioxaborolanes).* Alcoholysis of (LXXIX) with β-hydroxyquinoline[63] or *s*-butyl alcohol[31] has afforded (LXXX) and (LXXXI). Similarly (LXXXII) and 2,4-dimethyl-3-pentanol resulted in (LXXXIII).[69]

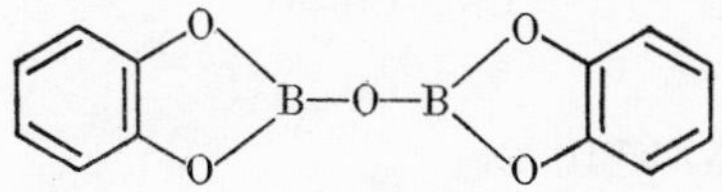

(LXXIX) 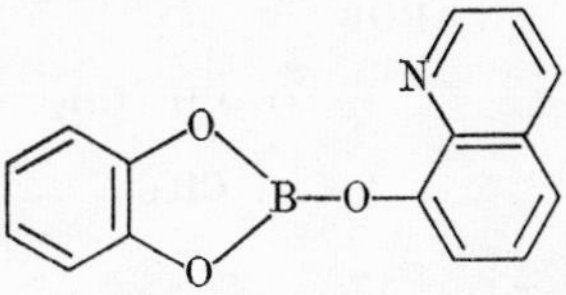 (LXXX)

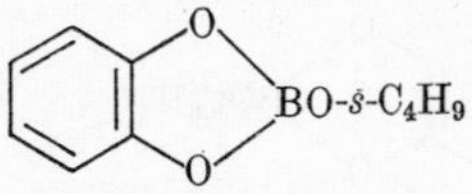

BO-*s*-C_4H_9

(LXXXI)

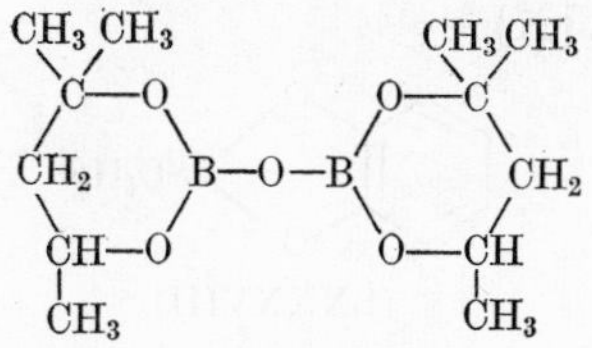

(LXXXII)

$BOCH[CH(CH_3)_2]_2$

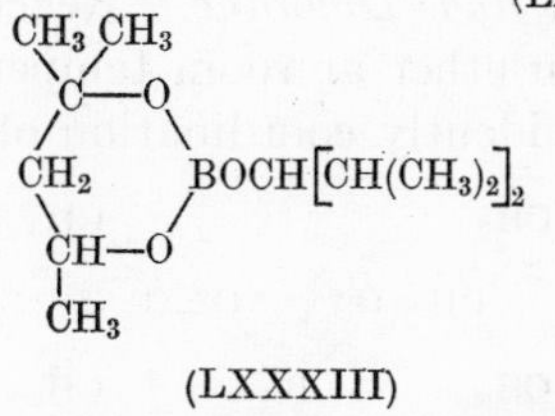

(LXXXIII)

Treatment of (LXXIX) and (LXXXII) with acetylacetone yielded the enol borates (LXXXIV)[63] and (LXXXV).[69]

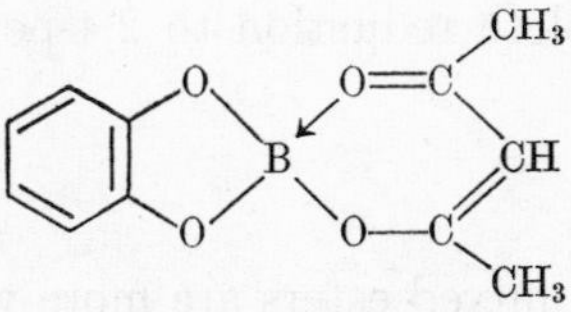

(LXXXIV) 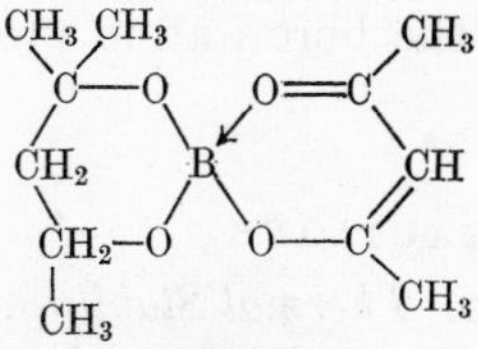 (LXXXV)

Symmetrical borates derived from enols have been described in Chapter 4.

j. *From Alkoxyhydroxyboranes.* The alkoxyhydroxyborane (LXXXVI) in refluxing alcohols was reported to give the corresponding esters (LXXXVII).[61,62]

$$\left[(HO)_2BO\overset{\overset{\displaystyle CH_3}{|}}{C}HCH_2\right]_2NCH_2CH_2N\left[CH_2\overset{\overset{\displaystyle CH_3}{|}}{C}HOB(OH)_2\right]_2$$

(LXXXVI)

```
          CH3                              CH3
          |                                |
       O—CH—CH2                       CH2—CH—O
      /        \                     /         \
  ROB           NCH2CH2N                        BOR
      \        /                     \         /
       O—CH—CH2                       CH2—CH—O
          |                                |
          CH3                              CH3
```

(LXXXVII)

k. *From 2-Alkylthio-1,3,2-dioxaborolanes.* Treatment of (LXXXVIII) with octanol readily produced the mixed ester (LXXXIX).[31]

$C_6H_4O_2BSC_4H_9$ (LXXXVIII) $\quad$ $C_6H_4O_2BOC_8H_{17}$ (LXXXIX)

l. *From Diketones and Diborane.* Reaction of acetylacetone with excess diborane in ether at room temperature resulted in the keto borate (XC).[51] Evidently coordination of the carbonyl oxygen

```
   CH3              CH3
     \              /
      CH—O     O=C
     /     \  ↙    \
  CH2        B       CH2
     \     /   \    /
      CH—O      O—CH
     /              \
   CH3              CH3
```

(XC)

with the boron atom precludes complete reduction to 2,4-pentanediol.

4. REACTIONS

a. *Thermal Stability.* Type (VI) mixed esters are more vulnerable to reaction upon heating than are the symmetrical orthoborates since they can undergo both decomposition (6-44) and disproportionation (6-45).

$$\left(R\begin{smallmatrix}O\\O\end{smallmatrix}\right)BOCH_2CH_2R' \rightarrow \left[R\begin{smallmatrix}O\\O\end{smallmatrix}BOH\right] + CH_2{=}CHR' \qquad (6\text{-}44)$$

$$\downarrow$$

$$\tfrac{1}{2}\, R\begin{smallmatrix}O\\O\end{smallmatrix}B{-}O{-}B\begin{smallmatrix}O\\O\end{smallmatrix}R + H_2O$$

$$3\, R\begin{smallmatrix}O\\O\end{smallmatrix}BOR' \rightarrow (R'O)_3B + R\begin{smallmatrix}O\\O\end{smallmatrix}BOROB\begin{smallmatrix}O\\O\end{smallmatrix}R \qquad (6\text{-}45)$$

Presumably the intact ring structure in equation (6-44) also could be degraded to give a diene (6-46), but a specific example has not yet been reported.*

$$CH_2\begin{smallmatrix}CH(CH_3){-}O\\CH(CH_3){-}O\end{smallmatrix}BOCH_2CH_2R \rightarrow CH_2{=}CHCH{=}CHCH_3 \text{ or}$$

$$CH_2{=}CHCH_2CH{=}CH_2 + CH_2{=}CHR + \{H_3BO_3\} \qquad (6\text{-}46)$$

$$\{H_3BO_3\} \rightarrow \tfrac{3}{2}\, H_2O + \tfrac{1}{2}\, B_2O_3$$

The mixed esters derived from 1,2-diols are distillable as monomeric cyclic esters; however they rearrange to some extent to open-chain polymers on condensation. In contrast, the 1,3-diol borates remain in the monomeric cyclic form on distillation. This behavior was attributed to strain in the five-membered ring due to the trigonal coplanar BO_3 group which is approximately offset by the energy gain in ring formation as compared to a relatively unstrained condition in the six-membered ring.[34]

The stability of the catechol derivatives (XCI) was found to be a function of the alkyl group present.[31] The butyl and octyl derivatives were recovered in 96 and 92% yield, respectively, on heating

* Dienes have been generated during the distillation of tri-(2-methyl-2,4-pentanediol) biborate.[72]

to 280° for twenty-four hours (butyl) and 350° for twelve hours (octyl). The methyl derivative, however, quantitatively dispro-

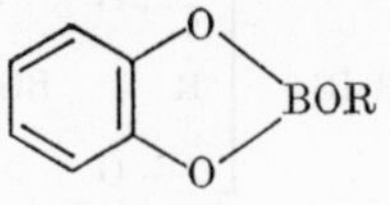

(XCI)

portionated to trimethyl borate and tricatechol biborate on heating to 240° for sixteen hours. The *s*-butyl ester decomposed by reaction (6-47).

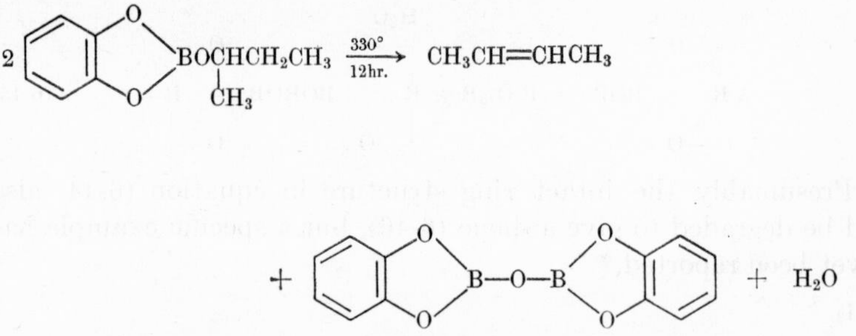

$$2\ C_6H_4O_2BOCH(CH_3)CH_2CH_3 \xrightarrow[12\text{hr.}]{330°} CH_3CH{=}CHCH_3 + C_6H_4O_2B{-}O{-}BO_2C_6H_4 + H_2O \quad (6\text{-}47)$$

The stability of the alkyl catechol borates (XCI) was believed to be due to the aromaticity of the 1,3,2-benzodioxaborole[31] ring system (XCII) which possesses $(4n + 2)$ π-electrons.[35,59] This ex-

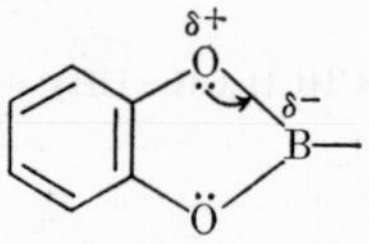

(XCII)

planation, of course, would not be valid for 2-butoxy-1,3,2-dioxaborolane which also is reported to be thermally stable.[4] In addition, the shift of electrons in the canonical structure (XCII) is in the opposite direction to that believed to be operative in aromatic borates.

Unless the basis for comparison is the mixed ester of the type $(RO)_2BOR'$, the alkyl diol and alkyl catechol borates really do not possess any enhanced stability over symmetrical borates in general. Consequently the stability they do possess need not be justified since trioctyl borate itself can be quantitatively distilled at 379° and tri-*o*-cresyl borate is not decomposed at 386°.[70]

b. *Hydrolysis.* The hydrolytic stability of type (VI) mixed esters is discussed in Chapter 21. Their conversion to alkoxyhydroxyboranes is discussed in Chapter 7.

c. *Alcoholysis and Thioalcoholysis.* Transesterification is discussed in Section IV-A-3d. In contrast to the ready reaction with alcohols, no reaction was observed when a mixture of (XCIII) and octanethiol was heated at 200° for one hour.[31]

BOC_4H_9

(XCIII)

d. *With Amines.* In contrast to the symmetrical alkyl borates which do not as a rule form complexes with amines, and like the aryl borates which do complex with amines (see Chapter 4), the alkyl and phenyl catechol borates form stable 1:1 complexes with pyridine,[31,47] aniline,[47] and a variety of other amines (XCIV).[26] Unstable 1:1 complexes were reported for a few aliphatic derivatives (XCV–XCVII).[34]

$OR\ (OC_6H_5)$, B, NH_2R

(XCIV)

CH_2—O, CH_2—O, B, OC_4H_9, NH_3

(XCV)

CH_2—O, CH_2—O, B, OC_4H_9, $NH_2CH_2C_6H_5$

(XCVI)

CH_3CH—O, CH_3CH—O, B, OC_4H_9, $NH_2CH_2C_6H_5$

(XCVII)

It is believed the withdrawal of electrons by the $-T$ effect of the aromatic ring (XCVIII) as contrasted to the $+I$ effect of the alkyl groups (XCIX) results in sufficient electrophilic character in the boron atom in the aromatic derivatives to promote complexing with amines.[31]

Ö—B and B— RO—B

(XCVIII) (XCIX)

The shift of electrons away from the boron atom in the aromatic esters is born out in the solubility relationships of hydrogen chloride in tributyl borate (0.489 moles hydrogen chloride per mole ester at

0°) versus butyl catechol borate (0.242 moles hydrogen chloride per mole ester at 0°).[32]

The amino derivatives (C) and (CI) did not give adducts with pyridine or aniline, presumably due to the internal B–N coordination as shown.[47]

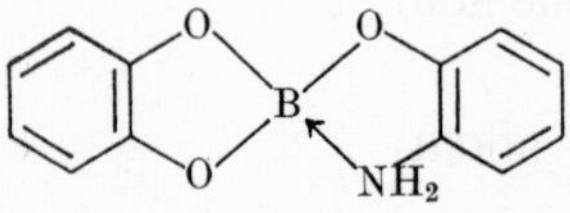

(C) 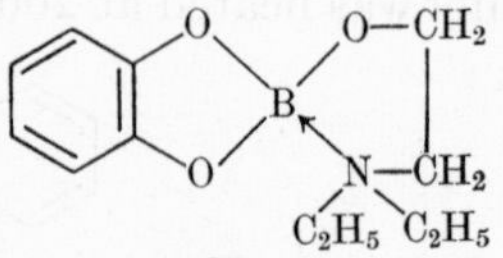 (CI)

A comparison of the heat of reaction of benzylamine and pyrrolidine with mixed esters (Table 6-4) revealed that the borates derived

Table 6-4. Heat of reaction of type (VI) esters and amines[a]

Ester	ΔH^b (kcal/mole) Benzylamine	Pyrrolidine
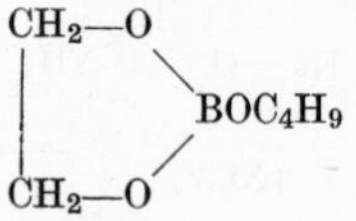 CH_2—O, CH_2—O > BOC_4H_9	−9.63	−8.35
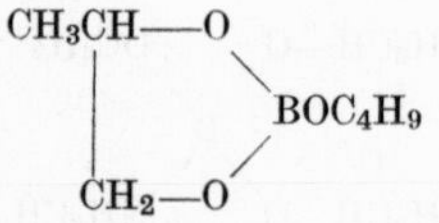 CH_3CH—O, CH_2—O > BOC_4H_9	−4.68	−10.55
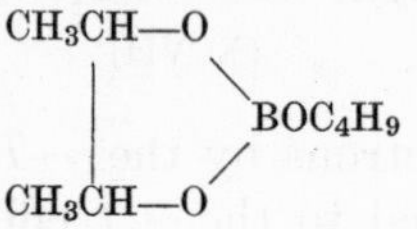 CH_3CH—O, CH_3CH—O > BOC_4H_9	−3.46	−8.35
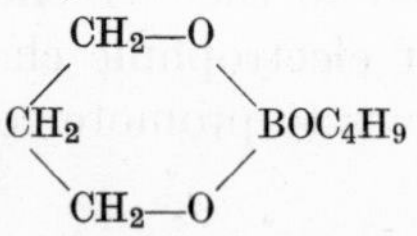 CH_2—O, CH_2, CH_2—O > BOC_4H_9	−0.48	−1.90
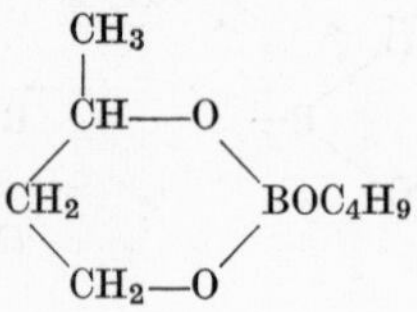 CH_3–CH—O, CH_2, CH_2—O > BOC_4H_9	−0.60	−0.48

[a] 12.5 mmoles of ester + 12.5 mmoles of amine in 96 ml. of octane.
[b] Corrected for heat of dilution.

from 1,2-diols have a much greater heat of reaction than those derived from 1,3-diols. This was attributed to the alleviation of the strain in the five-membered ring by conversion of the trigonal coplanar boron to tetrahedral boron as compared to a relatively unstrained condition in both the sp^2 and sp^3 six-membered rings.[34]

e. *With Boron Trihalides.* Boron trichloride and the type (VI) esters undergo a redistribution reaction to give alkoxychloroboranes and 2-chloro-1,3,2-dioxaborolanes (6-48).[3,23] (See Chapter 12.) Boron

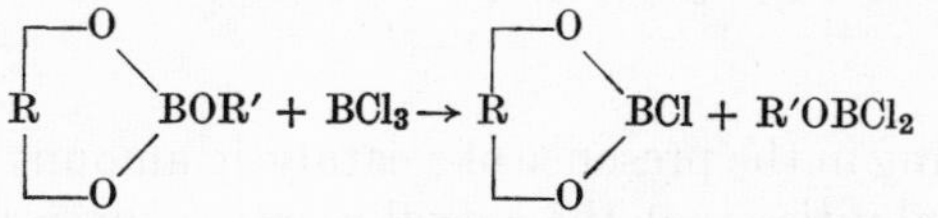

$$R\langle O_2 \rangle BOR' + BCl_3 \rightarrow R\langle O_2 \rangle BCl + R'OBCl_2 \quad (6\text{-}48)$$

tribromide promotes both redistribution and decomposition (6-49).[31]

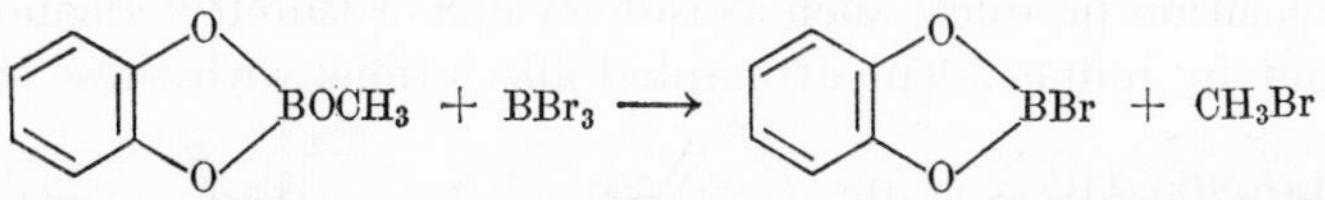

$$C_6H_4O_2BOCH_3 + BBr_3 \longrightarrow C_6H_4O_2BBr + CH_3Br \quad (6\text{-}49)$$

f. *With Alkoxychloroboranes.* The reaction of type (VI) esters with alkoxydichloro- and dialkoxychloroboranes is treated in Chapter 12.

g. *With Alkali Metals.* In contrast to the symmetrical alkyl borates, which do not react with sodium, (CII) was cleaved by treatment with sodium–potassium alloy in dioxane to give (CIII) and (CIV).[83]

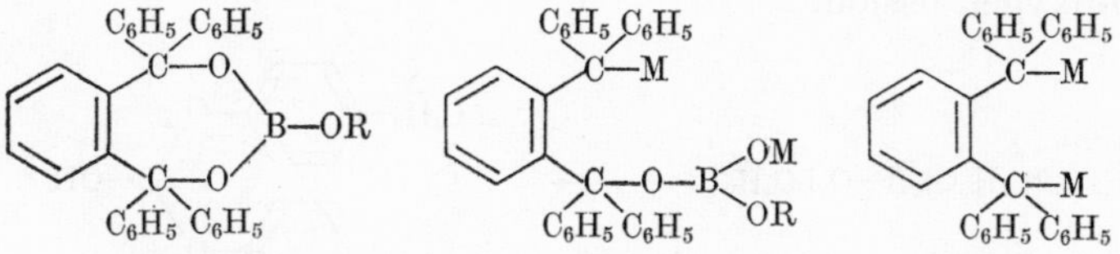

(CII): $C_6H_4[C(C_6H_5)_2O]_2B{-}OR$ (CIII): $C_6H_4[C(C_6H_5)_2M][C(C_6H_5)_2{-}O{-}B(OM)(OR)]$ (CIV): $C_6H_4[C(C_6H_5)_2M]_2$

h. *With Grignard Reagent.* The mixed esters react with Grignard reagents in a manner analogous to that of the symmetrical esters.[42,43] Volume III of this series discusses this chemistry.

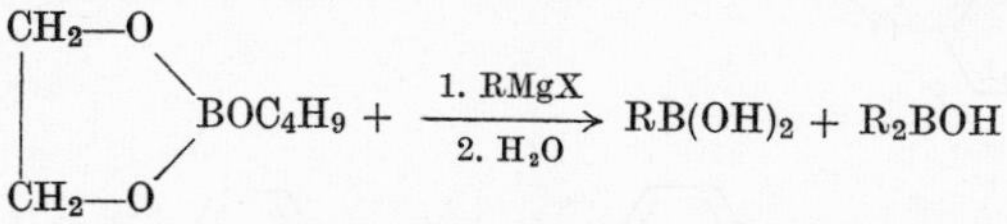

$$\begin{matrix} CH_2{-}O \\ | \\ CH_2{-}O \end{matrix}\!\!>BOC_4H_9 + \xrightarrow[2.\ H_2O]{1.\ RMgX} RB(OH)_2 + R_2BOH \quad (6\text{-}50)$$

i. *Friedel–Crafts Alkylation.* Reaction mixtures derived from the esterification of boric acid with a mixture of various alcohols and phenol or by partial transesterification of a trialkoxyborane with phenol have been found to be effective reactants for Friedel–Crafts type alkylations.[39,66] Thus the reaction mixtures corresponding to the compositions (CV) and (CVI), prepared by the dehydration of

$$\underset{\text{(CV)}}{C_6H_5OB(O\text{-}i\text{-}C_4H_9)_2} \qquad \underset{\text{(CVI)}}{(C_6H_5O)_2BO\text{-}i\text{-}C_4H_9}$$

mixtures of boric acid and the appropriate mole ratios of isobutyl alcohol and phenol, underwent the reactions of equations (6-51) and

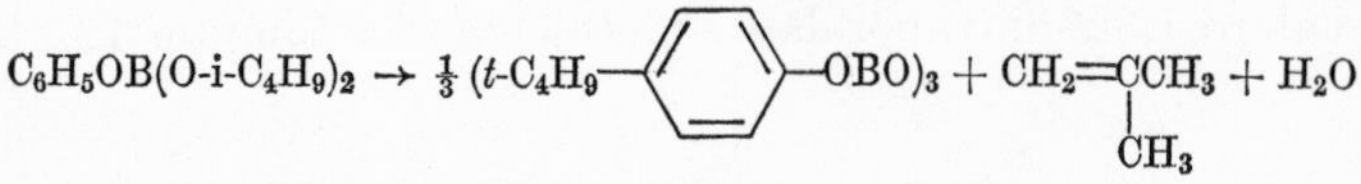

$$C_6H_5OB(O\text{-}i\text{-}C_4H_9)_2 \rightarrow \tfrac{1}{3}\,(t\text{-}C_4H_9\text{—}C_6H_4\text{—}OBO)_3 + CH_2{=}C(CH_3)CCH_3 + H_2O \quad (6\text{-}51)$$

(6-52) on heating in the presence of a catalytic amount of 92% sulfuric acid. The possibilities that the actual reactive species were the symmetrical esters, triisobutoxyborane and triphenoxyborane, or decomposition products such as isobutylene or isobutyl alcohol were ruled out by independent attempted alkylations with these species.

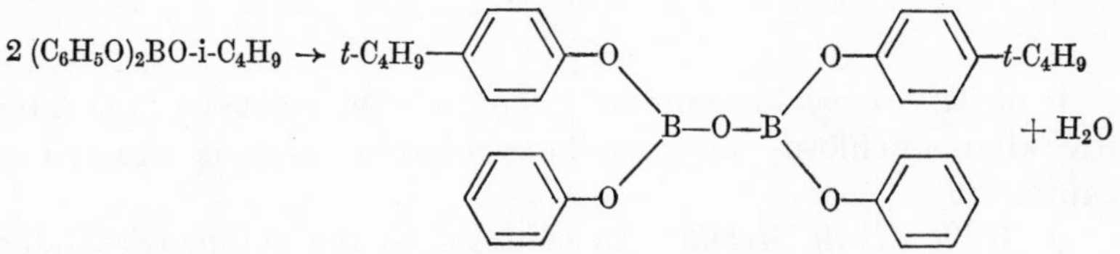

$$2\,(C_6H_5O)_2BO\text{-}i\text{-}C_4H_9 \rightarrow (t\text{-}C_4H_9\text{—}C_6H_4\text{—}O)(C_6H_5O)B\text{—}O\text{—}B(O\text{—}C_6H_4\text{—}t\text{-}C_4H_9)(OC_6H_5) + H_2O \quad (6\text{-}52)$$

Reaction (6-52) was depicted as proceeding via a path involving alkyl-oxygen fission.

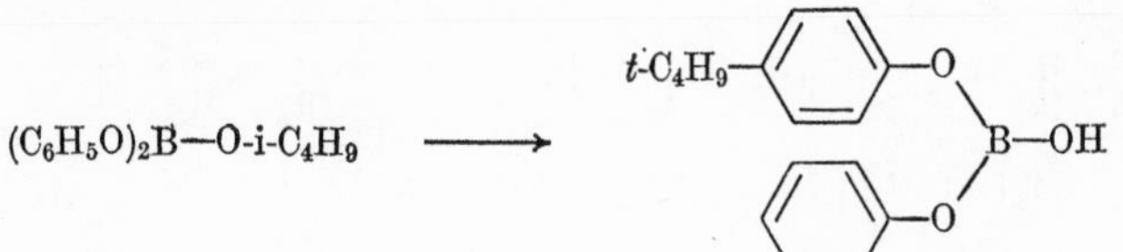

$$(C_6H_5O)_2B\text{—}O\text{-}i\text{-}C_4H_9 \longrightarrow (t\text{-}C_4H_9\text{—}C_6H_4\text{—}O)(C_6H_5O)B\text{—}OH \quad (6\text{-}53)$$

$$2\,(t\text{-}C_4H_9\text{—}C_6H_4\text{—}O)(C_6H_5O)B\text{—}OH \longrightarrow (t\text{-}C_4H_9\text{—}C_6H_4\text{—}O)(C_6H_5O)B(O\text{—}C_6H_4\text{—}t\text{-}C_4H_9)(OC_6H_5) + H_2O \quad (6\text{-}54)$$

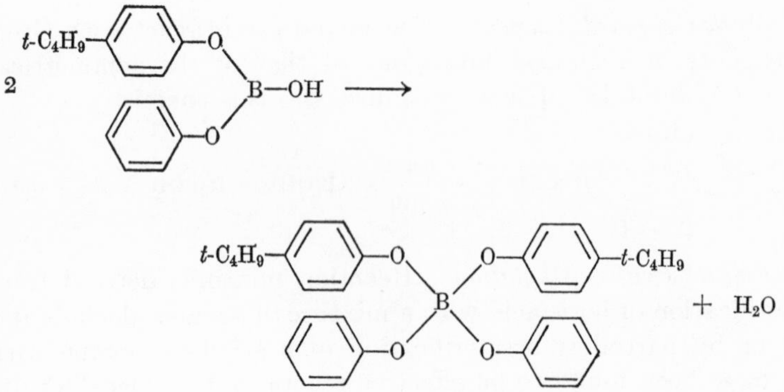

j. *With Tropolones.* The reaction with tropolones to produce structures of type (CVII) is discussed in Chapter 15.

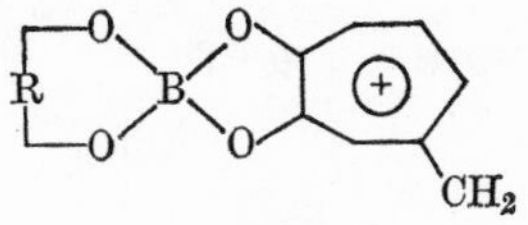

(CVII)

k. *Miscellaneous.* The keto ester (CVIII) is cleaved by phenylhydrazine to give the phenylhydrazone of 2-hydroxy-4-pentanone.[51] The phenyl derivative (CIX) is converted to (CX) by reaction with dimethylglyoxime.[26]

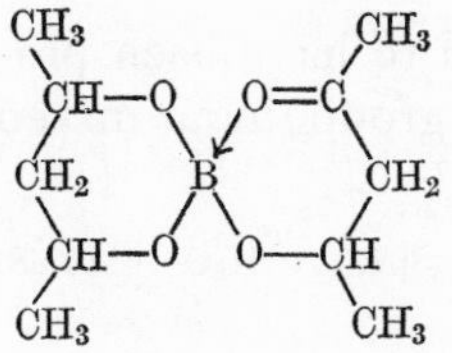

(CVIII) 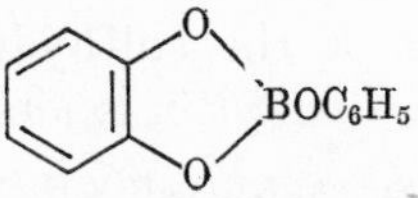 (CIX) 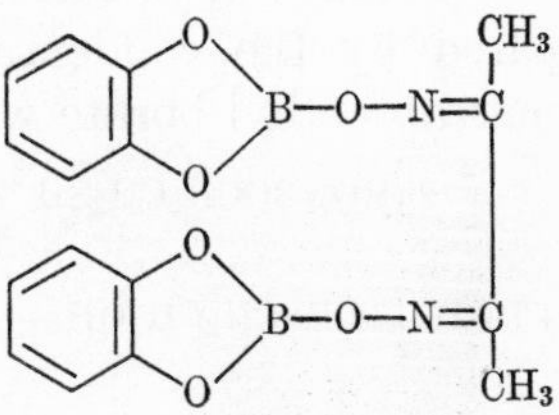 (CX)

B. *Alkylenedioxybis(dialkoxyboranes)*

1. INTRODUCTION

A second type of mixed ester derived from mono and dihydric alcohols and phenols (CXI) bears formal analogy to the unsymmetrical species derived from monohydric alcohols (CXII), but

$$(RO)_2BOR'OB(OR)_2 \quad \text{(CXI)} \qquad (RO)_2BOR' \quad \text{(CXII)}$$

evidently differs markedly in its resistance to disproportionation since a variety of examples have been reported.

2. METHODS OF PREPARATION

Alcoholysis of dialkoxyhaloboranes with ethylene glycol (6-55)

$$2\,(RO)_2BCl + HOCH_2CH_2OH \rightarrow (RO)_2BOCH_2CH_2OB(OR)_2 + 2\,HCl \qquad (6\text{-}55)$$

has afforded a series of type (CXI) esters. The alkyl groups subsequently were replaced by phenoxy groups (6-56).[4]

$$(C_4H_9O)_2BOCH_2CH_2OB(OC_4H_9)_2 + 4\,C_6H_5OH \rightarrow 4\,C_4H_9OH + (C_6H_5O)_2BOCH_2CH_2OB(OC_6H_5)_2 \qquad (6\text{-}56)$$

Reaction (6-57) was used to prepare the tetrabutyl derivative (CXIII).[5]

$$\begin{matrix} Cl & & Cl \\ & \diagdown\;\;\diagup & \\ & BOCH_2CH_2OB & \\ & \diagup\;\;\diagdown & \\ Cl & & Cl \end{matrix} + 4\,C_4H_9OH \rightarrow 4\,HCl + \begin{matrix} C_4H_9O & & OC_4H_9 \\ & \diagdown\;\;\diagup & \\ & BOCH_2CH_2OB & \\ & \diagup\;\;\diagdown & \\ C_4H_9O & & OC_4H_9 \end{matrix} \quad (6\text{-}57)$$

(CXIII)

Attempts to convert (CXIII) to the diacid (CXIV) by treatment

$$(HO)_2BOCH_2CH_2OB(OH)_2$$

(CXIV)

with hydrogen bromide resulted in butyl bromide, ethylene bromide and boric acid.[5]

A series of tinmercapto borates was claimed to have been prepared by the condensation of the sulfhydryl group in a mixed mercaptoethyl borate with a dialkyltin oxide.[56,57]

$$2\,(RO)_2BOCH_2CH_2SH + R'_2SnO \rightarrow [(RO)_2BOCH_2CH_2S]_2SnR'_2 + H_2O \quad (6\text{-}58)$$

$$4\,ROH + 2\,HSCH_2CH_2OH + 2\,H_3BO_3 \xrightarrow[2.\ R'_2SnO,\ -H_2O]{1.\ toluene,\ -6\,H_2O} [(RO)_2BOCH_2CH_2S]_2SnR'_2 \quad (6\text{-}59)$$

V. ESTERS DERIVED FROM MONO- AND TRIHYDRIC ALCOHOLS

Dehydration of a mixture of a monohydric alcohol, a mercaptoalcohol, boric acid, and a stannoic acid in the proper proportions was claimed to give mixed esters which in effect are derived from a monohydric alcohol and a tinmercapto triol.[57]

$$6\,ROH + 3\,HSR'OH + 3\,H_3BO_3 + R''SnOOH \rightarrow 11\,H_2O + R''Sn[SR'OB(OR)_2]_3 \quad (6\text{-}60)$$

VI. ANALYTICAL

No unique methods or techniques for the analysis of mixed borates have been reported. The methods described in Chapter 4 for symmetrical borates pertain.

VII. PHYSICAL CONSTANTS

Type I, $(RO)_2BOR'$	M.p. (°C)	B.p. (°C)	d_4^t	n_D^t	Reference
$(C_2H_5O)_2BOC_6H_{13}$	Proof of structure not yet available.				77
$(C_6H_{11}O)_2BOCH(CH_3)(CH_2)_5CH_3$	Proof of structure not yet available.				77
$(C_6H_{11}O)_2BOCH_2C_6H_4SSn(C_6H_5)_3$	—	—	—	—	57
$[CH_3(CH_2)_5CH(CH_3)O]_2BOC_6H_{11}$	Proof of structure not yet available.				77
$[(CH_3)_2N(\rightarrow BH_3)CH_2CH_2CH_2O]_2BOCH_2CH_2CH_2N(CH_3)_2$	Viscous liquid				49
$[-OB(OCH_2CH_2SSn(C_2H_5)_3)O(CH_2)_5-]_n$	Viscous liquid				57
$[-OB(OCH_2CH_2SSn(C_2H_5)_3)OCH_2CH_2OCH_2CH_2-]_n$	—	—	—	—	57
$(C_6H_5O)_2BOC_6H_{11}$	Proof of structure not yet available.				77
$(C_6H_5O)_2BOCH(CH_3)(CH_2)_5CH_3$	Proof of structure not yet available.				77

(Table continued)

Type I, $(RO)_2BOR'$	M.p. (°C)	B.p. (°C)	d_4^t	n_D^t	Reference
$[o\text{-}NO_2C_6H_4O]_2BOC_2H_5$	Red liquid				14
$[p\text{-}CH_3C_6H_4O]_2BOC_6H_4SSn(CH_2C_6H_5)_3$	—	—	—	—	57
$[CH_3, CH_2O—, CH_3, CH(CH_3)_2]_2$ $BOCH_2CH_2SH$	—	> 183/15			38, 74
$[CH_3, CH_2O—, CH_3, CH(CH_3)_2]_2$ $BOCH_2CH_2SSn(CH{=}CH_2)_3$	—	—	—	—	57

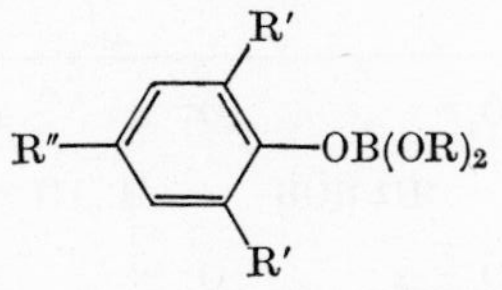

R″	R′	R	M.p. (°C)	B.p. (°C)	d_4^t	n_D^t	Reference
H	t-C_4H_9	CH_3	72.4–74.0				71
H	t-C_4H_9	C_2H_5		114–115/1			71
H	t-C_4H_9	$ClCH_2CH_2$	—	—	—	—	38
H	t-C_4H_9	n-C_3H_7		183–184/18			37, 71
H	t-C_4H_9	i-C_3H_7		80/0.5			76
				155–161/18			37, 71
H	t-C_4H_9	$CH_2{=}CHCH_2$		104–110/0.2			38
H	t-C_4H_9	n-C_4H_9		128/0.75			55
				135–140/0.3			71
				150–154/1			37
H	t-C_4H_9	n-C_8H_{17}		170–176/0.25			71
CH_3	t-C_4H_9	n-C_3H_7		193–195/18			37, 71
CH_3	t-C_4H_9	i-C_3H_7	88–89				76
			Crystalline	173–175/18			37, 71, 75
CH_3	t-C_4H_9	$CH_2{=}CHCH_2$		121/0.6			55
				130–131/0.4	0.957^{20}	1.4928^{20}	76
CH_3	t-C_4H_9	n-C_4H_9		124/0.07			55
				139–146/1			71
				140/0.6			76
				167–171/1			37
CH_3	t-C_4H_9	$(CH_3)_2CHCH_2CHCH_3$		153/0.5	0.909^{20}	1.4753^{20}	76
CH_3	t-C_4H_9	$CH_3(CH_2)_3CHCH_2$ (with C_2H_5 on CH)		161/0.2			55
t-C_4H_9	t-C_4H_9	i-C_3H_7	209–215				76
t-C_5H_{11}	t-C_5H_{11}	n-C_4H_9		160–164/1			37

(Table continued)

$[R''C_6H_2(R')_2O]_2BOR$			M.p. (°C)	B.p. (°C)	d_4^t	n_D^t	Reference
R″	R′	R					
H	t-C_4H_9	i-C_3H_7	Crystalline				37
H	t-C_4H_9	n-C_4H_9	Crystalline	176–191/1			37
CH_3	t-C_4H_9	n-C_3H_7	152–172	220–235/1			37
CH_3	t-C_4H_9	i-C_3H_7	161–177.5	217–235/1			37

Type II, ROB(OR′)(OR″)	M.p. (°C)	B.p. (°C)	d_4^t	n_D^t	Reference
2,6-$[C(CH_3)_3]_2C_6H_3$—O—B(O-n-C_4H_9)(O-n-C_8H_{17})		169–175/0.75			37

Type III, $R(O)_2$BOR′OB$(O)_2R$	M.p. (°C)	B.p. (°C)	d_4^t	n_D^t	Reference

$CH_2(O)_2BOCH_2CH_2OB(O)_2CH_2$ (two 4-membered rings, each CH₂ bonded to two O, both O bonded to B)	—	—	—	—	6
$[CH_2O-CH_2O>BOCH_2CH_2S]_2Sn(C_4H_9)_2$ (five-membered ring: CH₂—O, CH₂—O bonded to B)		Viscous liquid			56, 57
$CH_2(CH_2O)_2BOCH_2CH_2OB(OCH_2)_2CH_2$ (two six-membered rings)		122/0.01		1.4540^{25}	25
$(CH_3)_2C$—O, CH_2, CH—O(CH_3) ring >BOCH₂C(CH₂)₂OB< ring O—C(CH_3)₂, CH_2, O—CH(CH_3); on the central C, N= and CH₂ form a ring: N=C($C_{17}H_{33}$)—O—CH₂		Viscous liquid			3
HOR′OH in $C_2H_5CH(CH_2O)(CH(C_3H_7)O)BOR'OB(OCH_2)(OCH(C_3H_7))CHC_2H_5$ (two six-membered rings)					
$HOCH_2CH{=}CHCH_2OH$		196–200/0.33		1.4630^{25}	46
$HOCH_2C{\equiv}CCH_2OH$		210–214/0.36		1.4646^{25}	46
$HOCH_2CH_2SCH_2CH_2OH$		221–224/0.5		1.4704^{25}	46

(Table continued)

Type III, $R\langle{}^{O}_{O}\rangle BOR'OB\langle{}^{O}_{O}\rangle R$	M.p. (°C)	B.p. (°C)	d_4^t	n_D^t	Reference
$HOCH(CH_3)CH_2CH_2CH(CH_3)OH$		201–202/7		1.4527^{25}	46
$HOCH(CH_3)CH_2OCH_2CH(CH_3)OH$		210–214/0.9		1.4521^{25}	46
HO—⟨S⟩—C(CH_3)(CH_3)—⟨S⟩—OH	—	—	—	—	46

Type IV, $R\langle{}^{O}_{O}\rangle BOR'OB\langle{}^{O}_{O}\rangle R''$	M.p. (°C)	B.p. (°C)	d_4^t	n_D^t	Reference
CH_3 CH_3 CH_3 C—O CH_3 CH_3 O—CH CH_3CH BOC——COB CH_2 C—O CH_3 CH_3 O—C CH_3 CH_3 CH_3 C_2H_5	—	—	—	—	17

Type V, $R\langle(O)(O)\rangle BOR'OH$	M.p. (°C)	B.p. (°C)	d_4^t	n_D^t	Reference
$\overline{CH_3C(CH_3)-O-CH(C_2H_5)-O}\!>\!BOCH_2CH_2CH(CH_3)OB\!<\!\overline{O-C(CH_3)_2-CH_2-C(CH_3)(C_2H_5)-O}$	—	—	—	—	17
1,2-Diols					
$\overline{CH_2-O-CH_2-O}\!>\!BOCH_2CH_2OH$	128				4
$\overline{(CH_3)_2C-O-C(CH_3)_2-O}\!>\!BOCH(CH_3)CH_2C(CH_3)_2OH$		Viscous liquid			19

(*Table continued*)

Type V, $R\begin{matrix}\text{—O}\\ \text{—O}\end{matrix}\!\!>\!BOR'OH$	M.p. (°C)	B.p. (°C)	d_4^t	n_D^t	Reference
$C_2H_5(CH_3)C$—O $\quad|\qquad\quad$ >$BOCH(CH_3)CH_2C(CH_3)_2OH$ $C_2H_5(CH_3)C$—O		Viscous liquid			19
$C_2H_5(CH_3)C$—O $\quad|\qquad\quad$ >$BOC(CH_3)(C_2H_5)$—$C(CH_3)(C_2H_5)OH$ $C_2H_5(CH_3)C$—O		Viscous liquid			18
$C_2H_5(C_2H_5)C$—O $\quad|\qquad\quad$ >$BOCH(CH_3)CH_2C(CH_3)_2OH$ $C_2H_5(C_2H_5)C$—O		Viscous liquid			19

$(C_2H_5)_2C(-O-)C(C_2H_5)_2(-O-)$ (ring) $BOC(C_2H_5)_2C(C_2H_5)_2OH$		Viscous liquid	18
$(CH_3)_3CCH(-O-)C(CH_3)_2(-O-)$ (ring) $BOC(CH_3)_2CH(OH)C(CH_3)_3$		Viscous liquid	18
$(CH_3)_3CCH(-O-)CH(-O-)C(CH_3)_3$ (ring) $BOCH(C(CH_3)_3)CHOHC(CH_3)_3$	152		16
1,3-Diols			
$CH_3CH(-O-)CH_2CH_2(-O-)$ ... CH_3 (ring) $BOCH_2CH_2CH(CH_3)OH$		Mobile liquid	44

(*Table continued*)

Type V, $R\langle O_2 \rangle BOR'OH$	M.p. (°C)	B.p. (°C)	d^t	n_D^t	Reference
CH_3 CH_3 C—O CH_3 CH_3 CH_2 BOC—COH CH—O CH_3 CH_3 CH_3		Viscous liquid			19
CH_3 CH_3 C—O C_2H_5 C_2H_5 CH_2 BOC—COH CH—O CH_3 CH_3 CH_3		Viscous liquid			19
CH_3 CH_3 C—O C_2H_5 C_2H_5 CH_2 B—OC—COH CH—O C_2H_5 C_2H_5 CH_3		Viscous liquid			19

```
CH3   CH3
   \ /
    C——O        CH2OH
   /    \         |
CH2      BOCH2C———N
   \    /         |  \\
    CH—O          |    CC17H33
    |             |   /
    CH3           CH2—O
```

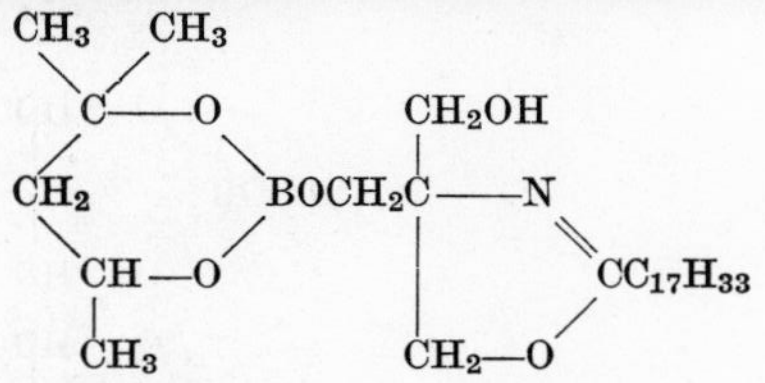 (structure above)	Viscous liquid	3

```
       CH3
       |
       CH—O      CH3  CH3
      /     \     |    |
CH3CH        BOCHCHCHOH
      \     /        |
       CH—O          CH3
       |
       CH3
```

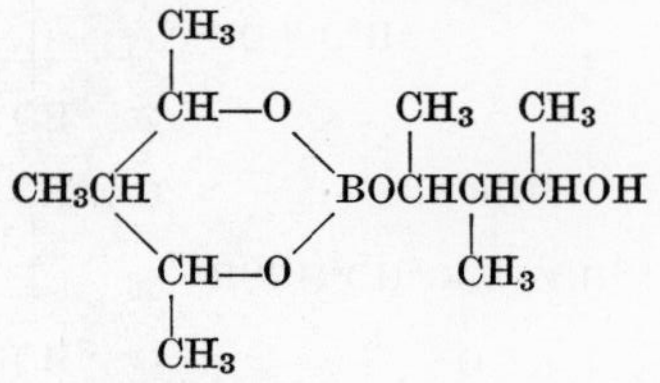 (structure above)	Viscous liquid	20

```
       CH3
       |
       CH—O      CH3  CH3  CH3
      /     \     |    |    |
CH3CH        BOCH—CH—COH
      \     /              |
       C—O                 CH3
      / \
   CH3   CH3
```

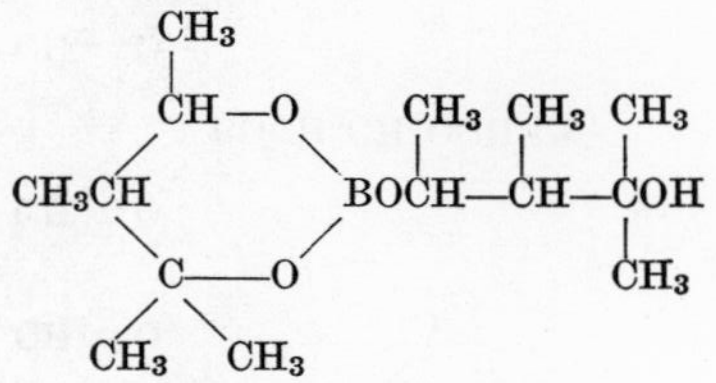 (structure above)	Viscous liquid	20

```
       CH3
       |
       CH—O      CH3  CH3
      /     \     |    |
CH3CH        BOCH—CH—CHOH
      \     /             |
       CH—O               CH
       |                 /  \
       CH             CH3    CH3
      /  \
   CH3    CH3
```

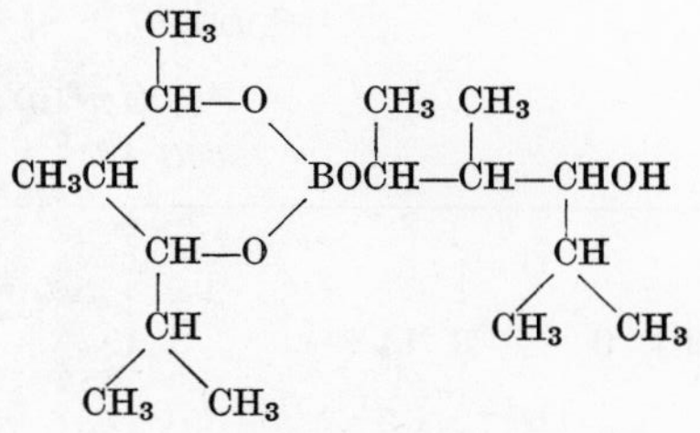 (structure above)	Slightly viscous liquid	20

(*Table continued*)

Type VI, R(O)(O)B—OR′	M.p. (°C)	B.p. (°C)	d_4^t	n_D^t	Reference
1,2-Diols					
CH_2—O, CH_2—O $\rangle BOC_2H_5$		38/0.1		1.4190[20]	4
	Semi-solid				48
CH_2—O, CH_2—O $\rangle BOCH_2CH_2OCH_2Cl$		96–98/0.3			15
CH_2—O, CH_2—O $\rangle BOCH_2CH_2OC(=O)C(CH_3)=CH_2$		90–100/0.01			40
CH_2—O, CH_2—O $\rangle$BO-n-C_3H_7		75/16	0.9518[20]	1.4022[20]	41
		85/16		1.4280[20]	4
CH_2—O, CH_2—O $\rangle$BO-i-C_3H_7	—	—	—	—	6

CH_2—O BO-n-C_4H_9 CH_2—O	84/0.7, 98/18 97/11 105/13, 190 108/30	1.006^{20} 1.0056^{20} 0.9976^{25}	1.4300^{20} 1.4285^{20} 1.4280^{25}	4 34 41 42
CH_2—O BO-i-C_4H_9 CH_2—O	56/0.8		1.4230^{20}	4
CH_2—O BO-*s*-C_4H_9 CH_2—O	45–50/0.8		1.4227^{20}	4
CH_2—O BO-*t*-C_4H_9 CH_2—O	32–33/1	1.022^{20}	$1.4189^{20.5}$	4
CH_2—O BO-n-C_5H_{11} CH_2—O	106/12 110/17 115/17	 0.9971^{20} 	 1.4348^{20} 1.4343^{27}	74 41 42
CH_2—O BO-i-C_5H_{11} CH_2—O	106/15	0.9796^{20}	1.4331^{20}	41

(Table continued)

Type VI, $R\langle O_2 \rangle B{-}OR'$ (cyclic $R(O)_2B{-}OR'$)	M.p. (°C)	B.p. (°C)	d_4^t	n_D^t	Reference
$CH_2{-}O{-}$, $CH_2{-}O{-}$ ring; $BO\text{-}n\text{-}C_6H_{13}$		125/13	0.980^{40}	1.4360^{40}	41
$CH_2{-}O{-}$, $CH_2{-}O{-}$ ring; BO–(S) (cyclohexyl)		119/10 120/10	 1.0602^{70}		74 41
$CH_2{-}O{-}$, $CH_2{-}O{-}$ ring; BOC_6H_5		112–114/0.5 123–127/5		1.5200^{20}	4 74
$CH_3CH{-}O{-}$, $CH_2{-}O{-}$ ring; $BO\text{-}n\text{-}C_4H_9$		98/11			34
$CH_3CH{-}O{-}$, $CH_3CH{-}O{-}$ ring; $BO\text{-}n\text{-}C_4H_9$		92/13			34

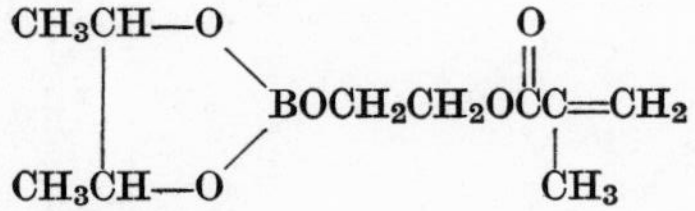 $CH_3CH—O$, $CH_3CH—O$ $\backslash$ $BOCH_2CH_2OC(=O)C(CH_3)=CH_2$		88–94/0.02		1.4451^{25}	40
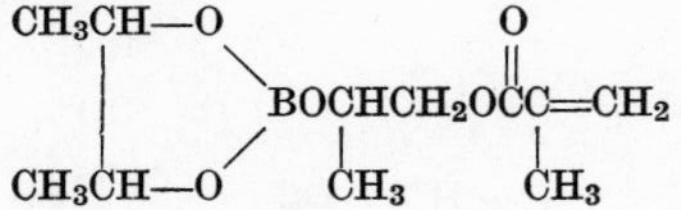 $CH_3CH—O$, $CH_3CH—O$ $\backslash$ $BOCH(CH_3)CH_2OC(=O)C(CH_3)=CH_2$		95–102/0.15			40
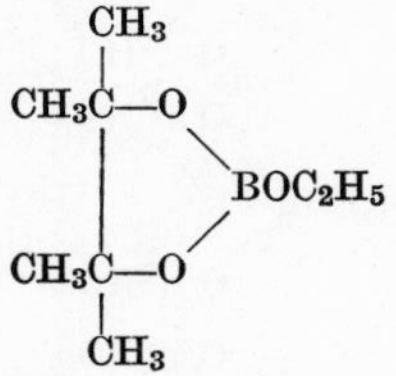 $(CH_3)_2C—O$, $(CH_3)_2C—O$ $\backslash$ BOC_2H_5		171–173			27
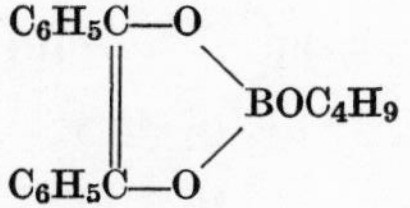 $C_6H_5C—O$, $C_6H_5C—O$ (double bond between the two C atoms) $\backslash$ BOC_4H_9	—	—	—	—	1
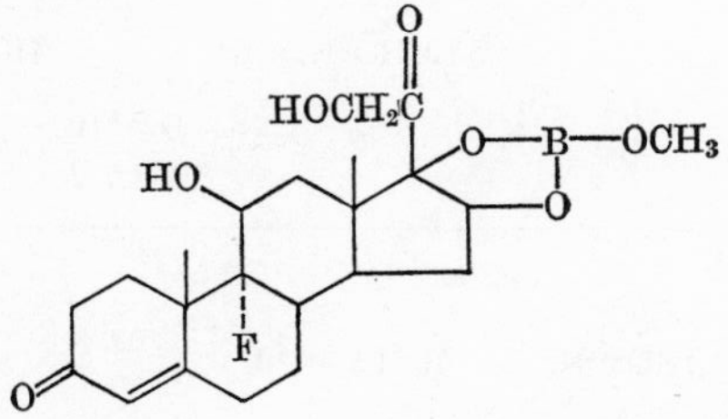 $HOCH_2C(=O)$, HO, O—B—OCH_3, O, F, O (steroid)	Solid				73

(*Table continued*)

Type VI, R(–O–)(–O–)B—OR′	M.p. (°C)	B.p. (°C)	d_4^t	n_D^t	Reference
1,3-Diols					
$CH_2(CH_2O)_2BOCH_2CH_2Cl$		48/0.01		1.4510^{25}	25
	—	—	—	—	24
$CH_2(CH_2O)_2BO\text{-n-}C_3H_7$		29–30/0.08		1.4205^{25}	25
	—	—	—	—	24
$CH_2(CH_2O)_2BO(CH_2)_3Cl$		66–67/0.15, 67–68/0.4	1.4470^{25}	1.4505^{25}	25
	-	—	—	—	24
$CH_2(CH_2O)_2BO\text{-n-}C_4H_9$		37–38/0.05		1.4305^{25}	25
		75–80/1–2		$1.4270^{21.5}$	7
		98/12			34
$CH_3CH(O)CH_2CH_2(O)B\text{—O-n-}C_4H_9$		101/13			34

$CH_2\langle CH(CH_3)\text{—}O,\ CH_2\text{—}O\rangle BOCH_2CH_2CH(CH_3)OP(=O)(OC_2H_5)_2$	—	—	—	—	22
$[CH_2\langle CH(CH_3)\text{—}O,\ CH_2\text{—}O\rangle BOCH_2CH_2CH(CH_3)O]_2P(=O)OCH_3$	—	—	—	—	22
$[CH_2\langle CH(CH_3)\text{—}O,\ CH_2\text{—}O\rangle BOCH_2CH_2CH(CH_3)O]_3P{=}O$	—	—	—	—	22
$CH_2\langle CH(CH_3)\text{—}O,\ CH(CH_3)\text{—}O\rangle BOC_2H_5$		181–184			27, 28, 29

(Table continued)

Type VI, $R\langle O_2 \rangle B\text{—}OR'$	M.p. (°C)	B.p. (°C)	d_4^t	n_D^t	Reference
$CH_2[CH(CH_3)O]_2BOCH(CH_3)CH_2CH(CH_3)OP(O)(OC_2H_5)_2$	—	—	—	—	22
$CH_2[CH(CH_3)O]_2B \leftarrow O{=}C(CH_3)CH_2CH(CH_3)O$ (spiro)		96–97/1	1.0142^{20}	1.4342^{20}	51
$(CH_3)_2C(CH_2O)_2BOCH_2CH_2OC(O)CH{=}CH_2$	—	—	—	—	40
$(CH_3)_2C(CH_2O)_2BOCH_2CH_2OC(O)C(CH_3){=}CH_2$		100–110/0.02		1.4495^{25}	40

CH_3 CH_3 C—O CH_2 $BOCH_3$ CH—O CH_3	Liquid	36
CH_3 CH_3 C—O CH_2 BOC_2H_5 CH—O CH_3	182–185	27, 28, 29
CH_3 CH_3 CH_3 C—O O=C CH_2 B CH CH—O O—C CH_3 CH_3	99–103/1	69
CH_3 CH_3 C—O CH_2 $BOCH[CH(CH_3)_2]_2$ CH—O CH_3	85–87/2 127–132/10	27 69

(Table continued)

Type VI, $R\langle O_2 \rangle B{-}OR'$ (ring: R—O—B(—OR′)—O—R)	M.p. (°C)	B.p. (°C)	d_4^t	n_D^t	Reference
CH_3, CH_3 on C—O; CH_2; CH—O with CH_3; ring B: $BOCH_2CH$—N=$CC_{17}H_{33}$, CH_2—O (ring)		Viscous liquid			3
CH_3, CH_3 on C—O; CH_2; CH—O with CH_3; ring B—O—C_6H_2(2,6-$C(CH_3)_3$)$_2$-4-CH_3	100.5–102	195–197/18			38
CH_3, CH_3 on C—O; CH_2; C—O with CH_3, CH_3; ring BOC_2H_5		186–189			27, 28, 29

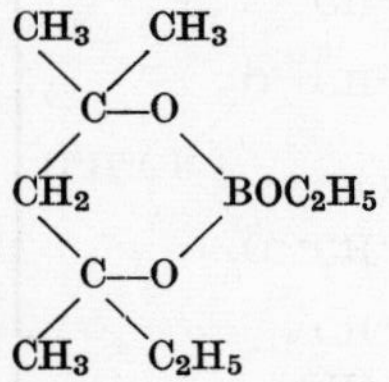 CH_3 CH_3 / C—O / CH_2 BOC_2H_5 / C—O / CH_3 C_2H_5		92.5–94.5/12	27, 28, 29
1,-4 *Diols*			
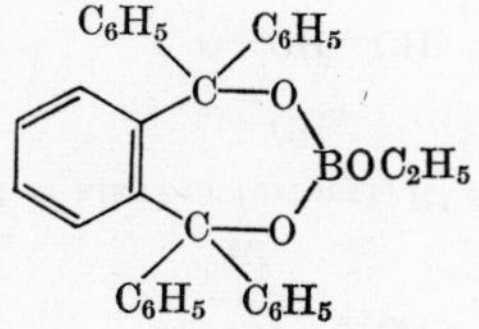 C_6H_5 C_6H_5 / C—O / (o-phenylene) BOC_2H_5 / C—O / C_6H_5 C_6H_5	201–202.5		83
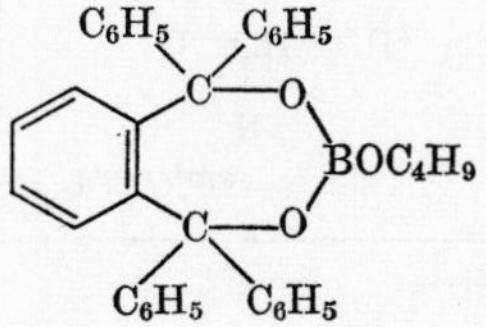 C_6H_5 C_6H_5 / C—O / (o-phenylene) BOC_4H_9 / C—O / C_6H_5 C_6H_5	161–162		83

(*Table continued*)

Type VI, $R\langle(O)_2\rangle B{-}OR'$ 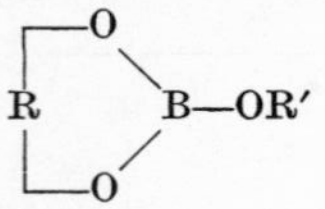	M.p. (°C)	B.p. (°C)	d_4^t	n_D^t	Reference
1,5-Diols					
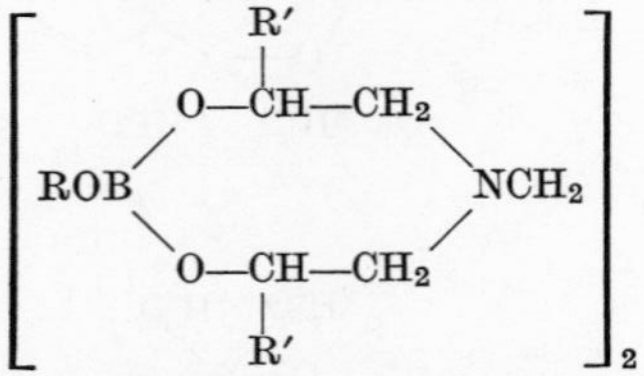 $[ROB(O{-}CH(R'){-}CH_2)_2NCH_2]_2$ R = alkyl or furfuryl, R′ = H or CH_3	—	—	—	—	60, 62
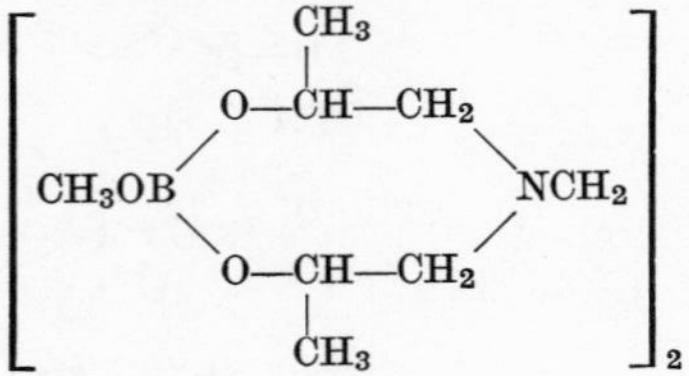 $[CH_3OB(O{-}CH(CH_3){-}CH_2)_2NCH_2]_2$	—	—	—	—	61
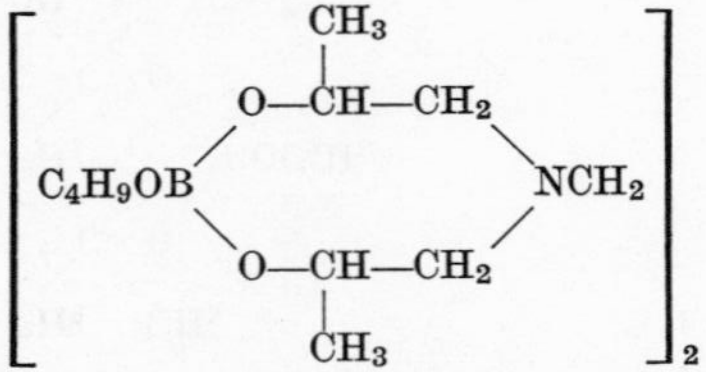 $[C_4H_9OB(O{-}CH(CH_3){-}CH_2)_2NCH_2]_2$	Solid				61

Alicyclic Diols					
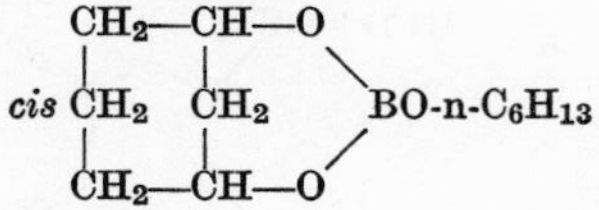 *cis* CH_2—CH—O, CH_2 CH_2, CH_2—CH—O, BO-n-C_6H_{13}		107–120/0.8		1.4390^{21}	16A
Aromatic					
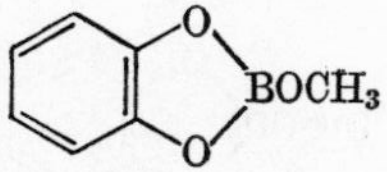 O, O, $BOCH_3$		81/10	1.1890^{20}	1.5059^{20}	31
		86/8			47, 48
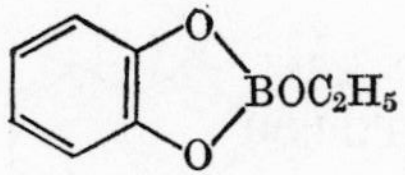 O, O, BOC_2H_5		91/10	1.1316^{20}	1.4960^{20}	31
		92/10.5			47
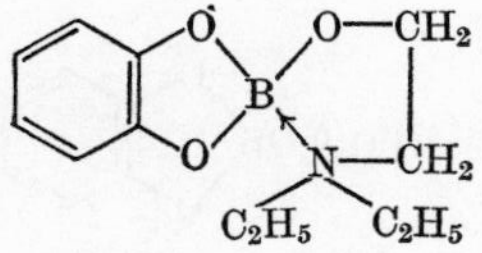 O, O, B, O—CH_2, N—CH_2, C_2H_5 C_2H_5	115				47
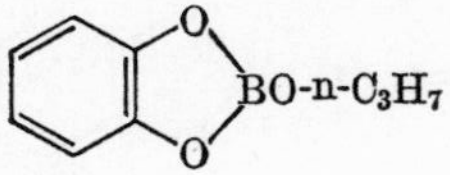 O, O, BO-n-C_3H_7		105/10	1.0937^{20}	1.4900^{20}	31
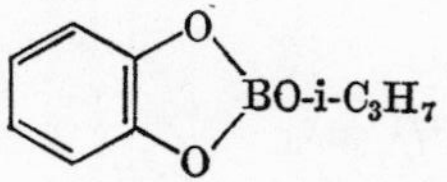 O, O, BO-i-C_3H_7		62/1.5			47

(Table continued)

Type VI, R(O)(O)B—OR′	M.p. (°C)	B.p. (°C)	d_4^t	n_D^t	Reference
$C_6H_4O_2BOCH_2CH{=}CH_2$		93/4.5			47
$C_6H_4O_2BO$-n-C_4H_9		104/5	1.0707^{20}	1.4891^{20}	31
		110/2, 247/760			1
$C_6H_4O_2BO$-i-C_4H_9		100/5	1.0558^{20}	1.4846^{20}	31
$C_6H_4O_2BO$-*s*-C_4H_9		97/5	1.0704^{20}	1.4853^{20}	31
$C_6H_4O_2BO$-*t*-C_4H_9		85/3			47
		85–87/3			48
$C_6H_4O_2BO$-n-C_5H_{11}		116/5	1.0578^{20}	1.4891^{20}	31

$C_6H_4O_2BOCH(CH_3)CH_2CH_2CH_3$		97/2.5	47
$C_6H_4O_2BOC(CH_3)_2CH_2CH_3$		96/4.5	47
$C_6H_4O_2B\leftarrow[O-C(CH_3)=CH-C(CH_3)=O]$	Crystalline Leaflets		26, 63
$C_6H_4O_2B\leftarrow[O-C(CH_2CH_3)=CH-C(CH_3)=O]$	98		26
$C_6H_4O_2BOC_6H_{11}$	55–59	168/20	74

(Table continued)

Type VI, R(O)(O)B—OR′ 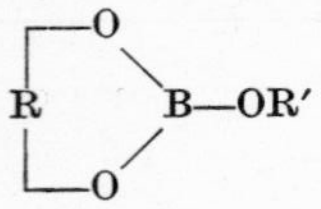	M.p. (°C)	B.p. (°C)	d_4^t	n_D^t	Reference
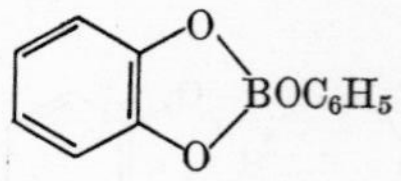 O, O, BOC_6H_5	40–44	166–167/12			74
	44				31
	—	—	—	—	26
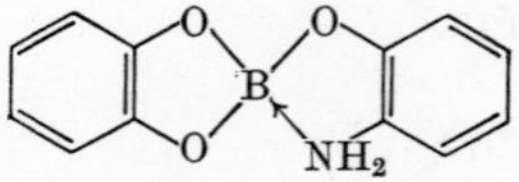 O, O, B, O, NH_2	280	270–290/2 (sub.)			47
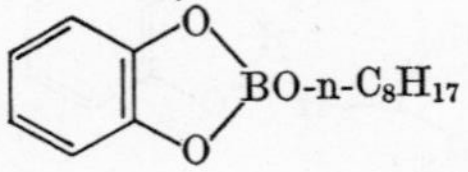 O, O, $BO\text{-}n\text{-}C_8H_{17}$		124/0.05	1.0158[20]	1.4856[20]	31
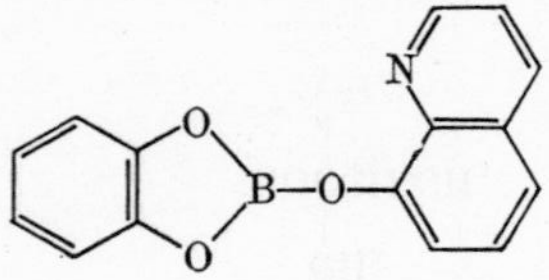 O, O, B—O, N	Crystalline				63
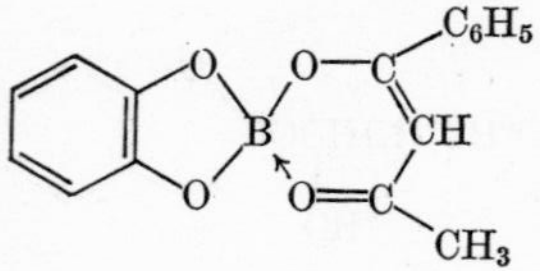 O, O, B, O—C, C_6H_5, CH, O═C, CH_3	218				26

Compound		
(catechol borate)B—O—N=C(CH_3)—C(CH_3)=N—O—B(catechol borate)	156	26
(catechol borate)B(OCH_3)←NC_5H_5	161–163	31
(catechol borate)B(OC_2H_5)←NC_5H_5	130–140	31
(catechol borate)B(OC_2H_5)←$NH_2C_6H_5$	215–217	47
(catechol borate)B(O-n-C_3H_7)←NC_5H_5	148–151	31
(catechol borate)B(O-i-C_3H_7)←$NH_2C_6H_5$	220–221	47

(Table continued)

Type VI, $R{<}(O)(O){>}B—OR'$	M.p. (°C)	B.p. (°C)	d_4^t	n_D^t	Reference
$C_6H_4O_2B(OCH_2CH{=}CH_2) \leftarrow NH_2C_6H_5$	232–233				47
$C_6H_4O_2B(O\text{-}n\text{-}C_4H_9) \leftarrow NC_5H_5$	160–165				31
$C_6H_4O_2B(O\text{-}t\text{-}C_4H_9) \leftarrow NC_5H_5$	143–145				47
$C_6H_4O_2B(O\text{-}t\text{-}C_4H_9) \leftarrow NH_2C_6H_5$	210–212				47
$C_6H_4O_2B(OCH(CH_3)C_3H_7) \leftarrow NH_2C_6H_5$	222–223				47

$C_6H_4O_2B(O\text{-}t\text{-}C_5H_{11}) \leftarrow NH_2C_6H_5$	242–244	47
$C_6H_4O_2B(OC_6H_5) \leftarrow NH_2CH_3$	336	26
$C_6H_4O_2B(OC_6H_5) \leftarrow NH_2C_4H_9$	185	26
$C_6H_4O_2B(OC_6H_5) \leftarrow NH(C_2H_5)_2$	Needles	26
$C_6H_4O_2B(OC_6H_5) \leftarrow NC_5H_{10}$ (piperidine)	248	26
$C_6H_4O_2B(OC_6H_5) \leftarrow N(C_2H_5)_3$	127	26
$C_6H_4O_2B(OC_6H_5) \leftarrow NH_2C_6H_5$	236	26

(Table continued)

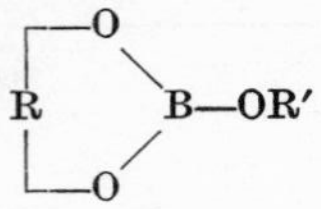 Type VI, $R\langle{}^{O}_{O}\rangle B—OR'$	M.p. (°C)	B.p. (°C)	d_4^t	n_D^t	Reference
$C_6H_4O_2B(OC_6H_5) \leftarrow NH(i\text{-}C_4H_9)_2$	220				26
$C_6H_4O_2B(OC_6H_5) \leftarrow N$(quinoline)	130				26
$C_6H_4O_2B(OC_6H_5) \leftarrow N$(8-hydroxyquinoline, HO—)	220				26
$C_6H_4O_2B(OC_6H_5) \leftarrow NC_5H_5$	135–138				31
	171				26

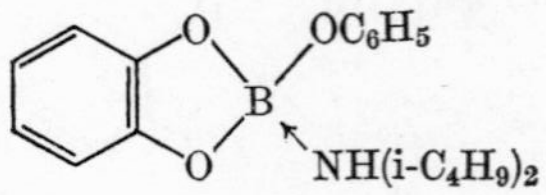

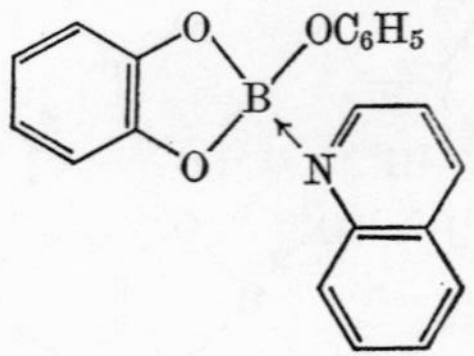

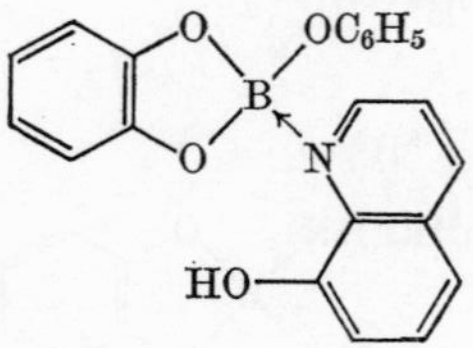

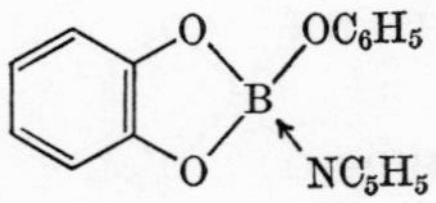

Type VII, $(RO)_2BOR'OB(OR)_2$	M.p. (°C)	B.p. (°C)	d_4^t	n_D^t	Reference
$(n\text{-}C_4H_9O)_2BOCH_2CH_2OB(O\text{-}n\text{-}C_4H_9)_2$		57/0.1		1.4199^{20}	5
		92/0.5	0.9222^{20}	1.4190^{21}	4
$(i\text{-}C_4H_9O)_2BOCH_2CH_2OB(O\text{-}i\text{-}C_4H_9)_2$		56/0.1	0.9231^{20}	1.4158^{20}	4
$(n\text{-}C_5H_{11}O)_2BOCH_2CH_2OB(O\text{-}n\text{-}C_5H_{11})_2$		86–88/1	0.9189^{20}	1.4248^{21}	4
$(C_6H_5O)_2BOCH_2CH_2OB(OC_6H_5)_2$		124/0.05	1.053^{20}	$1.4998^{22.5}$	4
$[—CH_2—C_6H_2(C(CH_3)_3)_2—OB(O\text{-}n\text{-}C_4H_9)_2]_2$		Orange glass			37
$[(C_6H_5O)_2BOCH_2CH_2S]_2Sn(C_6H_5)_2$	—	—	—	—	56, 57
$[(n\text{-}C_4H_9CH(C_2H_5)CH_2O)_2BOCH_2CH_2S]_2Sn(n\text{-}C_4H_9)_2$	—	—	—	—	56, 57
$[(n\text{-}C_6H_{13}CH(C_4H_9)CH_2O)_2BOCH_2CH_2S]_2Sn(n\text{-}C_4H_9)_2$	—	—	—	—	56, 57
$[(\text{Dihydroabietyl}—O)_2BOCH_2CH_2S]_2Sn(n\text{-}C_4H_9)_2$		> 215/3			56, 57

Type VIII, $(RO)_2BOR'OH$	M.p. (°C)	B.p. (°C)	d_4^t	n_D^t	Reference
$(n\text{-}C_4H_9O)_2BOCH_2CH_2OH$			0.9141^{25}	1.4129^{25}	12

(Table continued)

Type IX, $R(OB(OR')_2)_3$	M.p. (°C)	B.p. (°C)	d_4^t	n_D^t	Reference
$n\text{-}C_8H_{17}Sn[S(CH_2)_4OB(OC_4H_9)_2]_3$	—	—	—	—	57
$CH_3Sn[S\text{-}(\text{thiane ring})\text{-}OB(OC_{10}H_{21})_2]_3$ (S and $OB(OC_{10}H_{21})_2$ on adjacent carbons of a six-membered S-containing ring)	—	—	—	—	57
$CH_3\text{-}C_6H_4\text{-}Sn[SCH_2CH_2OB(OCH_2C_6H_5)_2]_3$ (p-tolyl)	—	—	—	—	57
$C_6H_5CH_2Sn[S(CH_2)_{10}OB(CH(C_2H_5)CH_2CH_2CH_3)_2]_3$	—	—	—	—	57

VIII. REFERENCES

1. Balaban, A. T., G. Mihai, R. Antonescu, and P. T. Frangopol, *Tetrahedron*, **16**, 68 (1961).
2. Bastin, E. L., *et al.*, Shell Development Company, Chemical Corps Procurement Agency Final Report, April 30, 1954, Contract No. CML-4564, Project No. 4-08-03-001.
3. Belden, S. H., U.S. Pat. 2,948,597 (1960, to The Standard Oil Company, Ohio).
4. Blau, J. A., W. Gerrard, and M. F. Lappert, *J. Chem. Soc.*, 4116 (1957).
5. Blau, J. A., W. Gerrard, and M. F. Lappert, *J. Chem. Soc.*, 667 (1960).
6. Blau, J. A., W. Gerrard, M. F. Lappert, B. A. Mountfield, and H. Pyszora, *J. Chem. Soc.*, 380 (1960).
7. Brotherton, R. J., and A. L. McCloskey, *J. Org. Chem.*, **26**, 1668 (1961).
8. Brown, J. F., *J. Am. Chem. Soc.*, **74**, 1219 (1952).
9. Brown, H. C., E. J. Mead, and C. J. Shoaf, *J. Am. Chem. Soc.*, **78**, 3613 (1956).
10. Brown, C. A., and R. C. Osthoff, *J. Am. Chem. Soc.*, **74**, 2340 (1952).
11. Christopher, P. M., *J. Chem. Eng. Data*, **5**, 568 (1960).
12. Christopher, P. M., and T. J. Tully, *J. Am. Chem. Soc.*, **80**, 6516 (1958).
13. Colclough, T., W. Gerrard, and M. F. Lappert, *J. Chem. Soc.*, 907 (1955).
14. Colclough, T., W. Gerrard, and M. F. Lappert, *J. Chem. Soc.*, 3006 (1956).
15. Cooper, S., M. J. Frazer, and W. Gerrard, *J. Chem. Soc.*, 5545 (1961).
16. Dale, J., *J. Chem. Soc.*, 910 (1961).

16A. Dale, J., *J. Chem. Soc.*, 922 (1961).

17. Darling, S. M., P. S. Fay, and L. S. Szabo, U.S. Pat. 2,741,548 (1956, to Standard Oil Company, Ohio).
18. Darling, S. M., and Liao, C. W., U.S. Pat. 2,975,135 (1961, to Standard Oil Company, Ohio).
19. Darling, S. M., and Liao, C. W., U.S. Pat. 2,979,459 (1961, to Standard Oil Company, Ohia).
20. Darling, S. M., and Liao, C. W., U.S. Pat. 2,989,469 (1961, to Standard Oil Company, Ohio).
21. Darling, S. M., and Liao, C. W., U.S. Pat. 2,989,470 (1961, to Standard Oil Company, Ohio).
22. Denny, M., and C. W. Liao, U.S. Pat. 3,013,046 (1961, to Standard Oil Company, Ohio).
23. Erickson, C. E., and F. C. Gunderloy Jr., 136th Meeting American Chemical Society, Atlantic City, Sept. 1959, *Abstracts of Papers*, p. 54-N.
24. Finch, A., J. C. Lockhart, and J. Pearn, *Chem. & Ind.* (*London*), 471 (1960).
25. Finch, A., J. C. Lockhart, and J. Pearn, *J. Org. Chem.*, **26**, 3250 (1961).
26. Funk, H., and H. J. Koch, *Wiss. Z. Univ. Halle*, **8**, 1025 (1959).
27. Garner, P. J., Brit. Pat. 722,538 (1955, to Shell Refining and Marketing Company, Ltd.).
28. Garner, P. J., U.S. Pat. 2,839,564 (1958, to Shell Development Co.).
29. Garner, P. J., U.S. Pat. 2,940,839 (1960, to Shell Oil Co.).
30. Garrett, D. E., J. Longoria, and F. J. Weck, Fr. Pat. 1,271,833 (1961, to American Potash and Chemical Corporation).
31. Gerrard, W., M. F. Lappert, and B. A. Mountfield, *J. Chem. Soc.*, 1529 (1959).

32. Gerrard, W., A. M. A. Mincer, and P. L. Wyvill, *J. Appl. Chem.* (*London*), **9**, 89 (1959).
33. Goubeau, J., M. Rahtz, and H. J. Becher, *Z. Anorg. Allgem. Chem.*, **275**, 161 (1954).
34. Hubert, A. J., B. Hargitay, and J. Dale, *J. Chem. Soc.*, 931 (1961).
35. Hückel, E., *Z. Physik.*, **70**, 204 (1931).
36. Hughes, E. C., Can. Pat. 630,708 (1961, to Standard Oil Company, Ohio).
37. Hunter, D. L., and H. Steinberg, Fr. Pat. 1,203,698 (1960, to United States Borax and Chemical Corporation).
38. Hunter, D. L., and H. Steinberg, Unpublished results.
39. Kuskov, V. K., and G. F. Filippova, *Zh. Obshch. Khim.*, **29**, 4063 (1959).
40. Lane, C. A., U.S. Pat. 2,994,713 (1961, to Rohm and Haas Company); see also Can. Pat. 631,946 (1961).
41. Laurent, J. P., *Compt. Rend.*, **252**, 3785 (1961).
42. Letsinger, R. L., and I. Skoog, *J. Am. Chem. Soc.*, **76**, 4174 (1954).
43. Letsinger, R. L., and I. Skoog, *J. Am. Chem. Soc.*, **77**, 2491 (1955).
44. Liao, C. W., and N. Visnapuu, Belg. Pat. 577,735 (1959, to Standard Oil Company, Ohio).
45. Lieber, E., and C. E. Hodges, U.S. Pat. 2,383,605 (1945, to Standard Catalytic Co.).
46. McManimie, R. J., U.S. Pat. 2,894,020 (1959, to Monsanto Chemical Co.).
47. Mehrotra, R. C., and G. Srivastava, *J. Chem. Soc.*, 4045 (1961).
48. Mehrotra, R. C., and G. Srivastava, *J. Indian Chem. Soc.*, **38**, 1 (1961).
49. Miller, H. C., U.S. Pat. 2,990,423 (1961, to E. I. duPont de Nemours and Company).
50. Musgrave, O. C., *J. Chem. Soc.*, 4305 (1956).
51. Nöth, H., and L. P. Winter, *Angew. Chem.*, **71**, 651 (1959).
52. Perkins, G. T., and T. I. Crowell, *J. Am. Chem. Soc.*, **78**, 6013 (1956).
53. Prescott, R. F., R. C. Dosser, and J. J. Sculati, U.S. Pat. 2,260,337 (1941, to Dow Chemical Co.).
54. Prescott, R. F., R. C. Dosser, and J. J. Sculati, U.S. Pat. 2,260,339 (1941, to Dow Chemical Co.).
55. Pruett, R. L., Can. Pat. 631,434 (1961, to Union Carbide Corporation).
56. Ramsden, H. E., Brit. Pat. 750,106 (1956, to Metal & Thermit Corp.).
57. Ramsden, H. E., U.S. Pat. 2,904,569 (1959, to Metal & Thermit Corp.).
58. Rippere, R. E., and V. K. LaMer, *J. Phys. Chem.*, **47**, 204 (1943).
59. Roberts, J. D., A. Streitwieser, Jr., and C. M. Regan, *J. Am. Chem. Soc.*, **74**, 4579 (1952).
60. Rudner, B., and M. S. Moores, U.S. Pat. 3,000,924 (1961, to Koppers Company, Inc.).
61. Rudner, B., and M. S. Moores, U.S. Pat. 3,000,925 (1961, to Koppers Company, Inc.).
62. Rudner, B., M. S. Moores, and J. J. Harris, 140th Meeting American Chemical Society, Chicago, Sept. 1961, *Abstracts of Papers*, p. 103-Q.
63. Schäfer, H., and O. Braun, *Naturwissenshaften*, **39**, 280 (1952).
64. Schiff, H., *Ann. Suppl.*, **5**, 154 (1867).
65. Schiff, H., and E. Bechi, *Compt. Rend.*, **61**, 697 (1865).
66. Sheiman, B. M., and V. K. Kuskov, *Izv. Vysshykh Uchebn. Zavedenii, Khim. i Khim. Tekhnol.*, **3**, 876 (1960); through *Chem. Abstracts*, **55**, 9320 (1961).

67. Shoemaker, B. H., and C. M. Loane, U.S. Pat. 2,160,917 (1939, to Standard Oil Company, Indiana).
68. Skinner, H. A., and N. B. Smith, *J. Chem. Soc.*, 2324 (1954).
69. Spike, C. G., U.S. Pat. 2,961,459 (1960, to The Standard Oil Company, Ohio).
70. Steinberg, H., and D. L. Hunter, *Ind. Eng. Chem.*, **49**, 174 (1957).
71. Steinberg, H., D. L. Hunter, and A. L. McCloskey, 135th Meeting American Chemical Society, Boston, April, 1959, Abstracts of Papers, p. 41-O.
72. Steinberg, H., and L. L. Petterson, Unpublished results.
73. Thomas, G. H., U.S. Pat. 2,831,003 (1958, to Olin Mathieson Chemical Corp.).
74. Thomas, L. H., *J. Chem. Soc.*, 823 (1946).
75. Washburn, R. M., E. Levens, C. F. Albright, and F. A. Billig, 131st Meeting American Chemical Society, Miami, April, 1957, Abstracts of Papers, p. 12-L.
76. Washburn, R. M., E. Levens, C. F. Albright, and F. A. Billig, "Preparation, Properties, and Uses of Borate Esters," in *Metal-Organic Compounds, Advances in Chemistry Series No. 23,* American Chemical Society, Washington, 1959, p. 129.
77. Werner, R. L., and K. G. O'Brien, *Australian J. Chem.*, **9**, 137 (1956).
78. Wiberg, E., A. Bolz, and P. Buckheit, *Z. Anorg. Allgem. Chem.*, **256**, 285 (1948).
79. Wiberg, E., and K. Hertwig, *Z. Anorg. Allgem. Chem.*, **255**, 141 (1947).
80. Wiberg, E., and K. Schuster, *Z. Anorg. Allgem. Chem.*, **213**, 77, 94 (1933).
81. Wiberg, W., and K. Schuster, *Z. Anorg. Allgem. Chem.*, **213**, 89 (1933).
82. Wiberg, E., and W. Sütterlin, *Z. Anorg. Allgem. Chem.*, **202**, 46 (1931).
83. Wittig, G., and M. Leo, *Ber.*, **64**, 2395 (1931).

7

ALKOXYHYDROXYBORANES, 2-HYDROXY-1,3,2-DIOXABOROLANES AND BORINANES AND THEIR ANHYDRIDES AND SALTS

I. INTRODUCTION

The compounds of this Chapter can be classified as the partial esters of boric acid (I, II and III) and their anhydrides (IV and V) and salts (VI).

$(RO)_2BOH$ (I) $ROB(OH)_2$ (II) $R\lt(O)(O)\gt BOH$ (III) $(RO)_2BOB(OR)_2$ (IV)

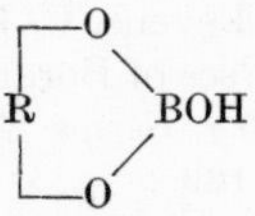

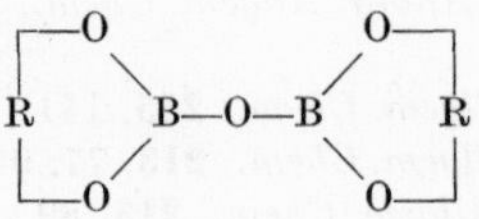

$R\lt(O)(O)\gt B{-}O{-}B\lt(O)(O)\gt R$ (V) $R\lt(O)(O)\gt B{-}O{-}\text{cation}$ (VI)

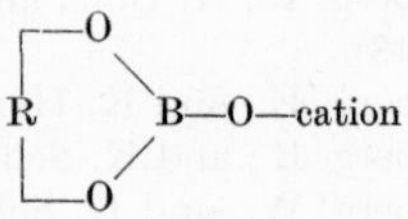

II. DIALKOXYHYDROXYBORANES AND THEIR ANHYDRIDES

Authenticated dialkoxyhydroxyboranes (I) have not yet been isolated. They may be an intermediate in the esterification of boric acid (7-1) or conversely in the hydrolysis[31,66] of an ester (7-2).

$$ROH + H_3BO_3 \xrightarrow{-H_2O} ROB(OH)_2 \xrightarrow[-H_2O]{ROH} (RO)_2BOH \xrightarrow[-H_2O]{ROH} (RO)_3B \quad (7\text{-}1)$$

$$(RO)_3B + H_2O \rightarrow ROH + (RO)_2BOH \xrightarrow{H_2O} \text{etc.} \quad (7\text{-}2)$$

Similarly they are postulated as intermediates in the reaction of esters with hydrogen halides (7-3).[28] However, reaction (7-4) has been

$$(RO)_3B + HX \rightarrow RX + (RO)_2BOH \xrightarrow{RX} \text{etc.} \quad (7\text{-}3)$$

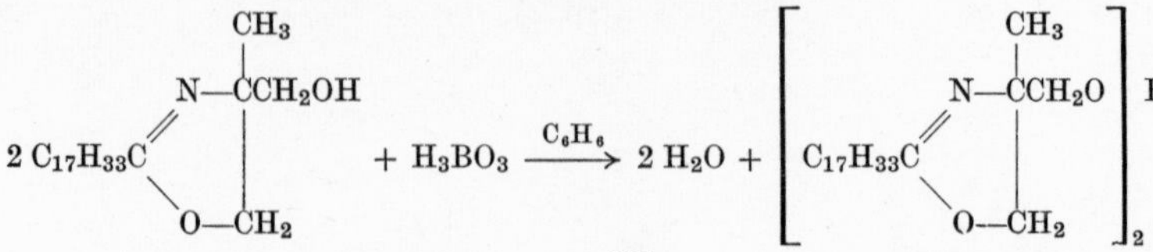

$$2\ C_{17}H_{33}C\lt(=N{-}C(CH_3)(CH_2OH){-}CH_2{-}O{-}) + H_3BO_3 \xrightarrow{C_6H_6} 2\ H_2O + \left[C_{17}H_{33}C\lt(=N{-}C(CH_3)(CH_2O){-}CH_2{-}O{-})\right]_2 BOH \quad (7\text{-}4)$$

claimed.[16] In addition hydroxybis(tetradecyloxy)borane (VII)[60] as well as the anhydrides (VIII)[40] were claimed to have been formed

$$(C_{14}H_{29}O)_2BOH \qquad (RO)_2BOB(OR)_2$$
$$\text{(VII)} \qquad \text{(VIII)}$$

by the air oxidation of paraffinic petroleum fractions in the presence of boric acid or boric oxide.

Schiff believed the pyrolysis of triphenylboroxine, formulated by him as monomeric phenyl metaborate, resulted in the anhydride (IX).[69]

$$5\,C_6H_5OBO \xrightarrow{350^\circ} \underset{\text{(IX)}}{(C_6H_5O)_2BOB(OC_6H_5)_2} + B_3O_5C_6H_5 \tag{7-5}$$

III. ALKOXYDIHYDROXYBORANES

A. From Monohydric Alcohols and Phenols

In contrast to the dialkoxyhydroxyboranes, authenticated examples of alkoxydihydroxyboranes have been reported. When *l*-menthyl metaborate (X) was allowed to stand in the air for several hours, there was a gain in weight and a sharp melting product remained which was completely soluble in organic solvents. Analysis and molecular weight data were consistent with structure (XI).[56] An attempt to prepare (XI) from an equimolar reaction of *l*-menthol and boric acid led only to formation of the metaborate (X).[56]

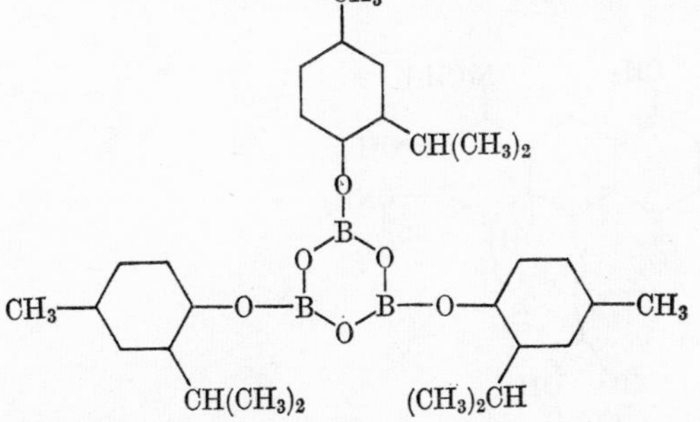

CH₃ | CH(CH₃)₂ | O—B | CH₃—⟨ring⟩—O—B(O)(O)B—O—⟨ring⟩—CH₃ | CH(CH₃)₂ | (CH₃)₂CH

(X)

CH_3—⟨ring⟩—$OB(OH)_2$, $CH(CH_3)_2$

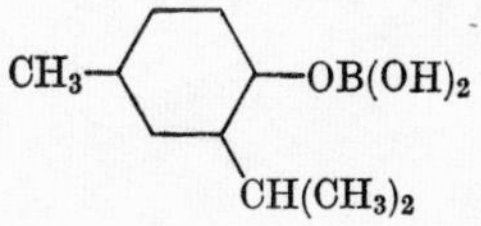

(XI)

The autooxidation of butyldihydroxyborane, which resulted in the formation of butyl alcohol, was formulated as an initial oxidation to butoxydihydroxyborane (7-6) followed by hydrolysis with atmospheric moisture (7-7).[70]

$$2\ C_4H_9B(OH)_2 + O_2 \rightarrow 2\ C_4H_9OB(OH)_2 \quad (7\text{-}6)$$

$$C_4H_9OB(OH)_2 + H_2O \rightarrow C_4H_9OH + H_3BO_3 \quad (7\text{-}7)$$

Trituration of the liquid hindered phenolic dichloro derivative (XII) in water resulted in hydrolysis of the boron–chlorine bonds leaving a white solid whose boron analysis, Karl Fischer analysis (see Section VII), and infrared spectrum were consistent with the dihydroxy derivative (XIII).[34]

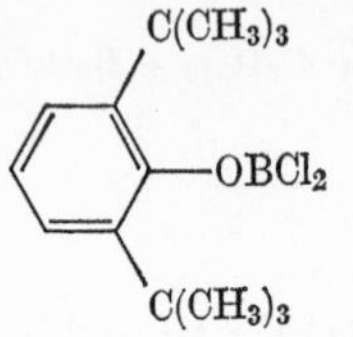

(XII) 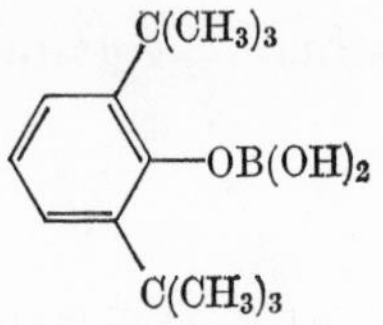 (XIII)

Other authenticated examples have not been recorded, although oxidation products (XIV[40] and XV[60]) from the reaction of a paraffinic petroleum fraction and oxygen in the presence of boric acid have been reported.

$ROB(OH)_2$ (XIV) $C_{18}H_{37}OB(OH)_2$ (XV)

B. From Polyhydric Alcohols and Phenols

Derivatives of polyhydric species have not been well defined. A compound derived from boric acid and aureomycin (XVI) has been postulated.[65]

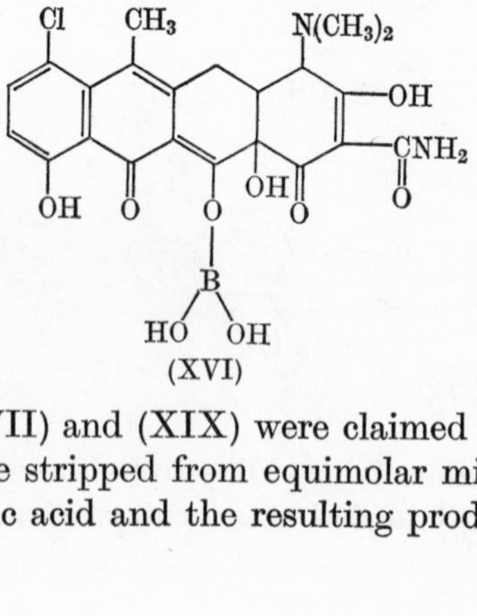

(XVI)

Structures (XVII) and (XIX) were claimed to result when two moles of water were stripped from equimolar mixtures of mannitol or dulcitol and boric acid and the resulting products were partially hydrolyzed by the addition of water.[8] The position of the boron on the secondary carbon atom was determined by the presence of five free hydroxyl groups and two free primary hydroxyl groups. However, there appears to be no evidence for substitution at the 2-position as shown versus the 3-position. In addition there appears

$$\begin{array}{c} CH_2OH \\ | \\ HOCH \\ | \\ HOCH \\ | \\ HCOH \\ | \\ HCOH \\ | \\ CH_2OH \end{array} + H_3BO_3 \xrightarrow{-2\,H_2O} \begin{array}{l} CH_2OH \\ | \\ HOCH \\ | \\ HOCH \\ | \\ HCO \diagdown \\ |\qquad BOH \\ HCO \diagup \\ | \\ CH_2OH \end{array} \xrightarrow{+H_2O} \underset{\text{(XVII)}}{\begin{array}{c} CH_2OH \\ | \\ HOCH \\ | \\ HOCH \\ | \\ HCOH \\ | \\ HCOB(OH)_2 \\ | \\ CH_2OH \end{array}} \qquad (7\text{-}8)$$

to be no evidence for bridging of the 2,3-hydroxy groups in (XVIII) instead of the 3,4-hydroxy groups.

$$\begin{array}{c} CH_2OH \\ | \\ HOCH \\ | \\ HCOH \\ | \\ HCOH \\ | \\ HOCH \\ | \\ CH_2OH \end{array} + H_3BO_3 \xrightarrow{-2\,H_2O} \underset{\text{(XVIII)}}{\begin{array}{l} CH_2OH \\ | \\ HOCH \\ | \\ HCOH \\ | \\ HC{-}O{-}B{-}OH \\ | \\ O{-}CH \\ | \\ CH_2OH \end{array}} \xrightarrow{+H_2O} \underset{\text{(XIX)}}{\begin{array}{c} CH_2OH \\ | \\ HOCH \\ | \\ HCOH \\ | \\ HCOH \\ | \\ (HO)_2BOCH \\ | \\ CH_2OH \end{array}} \qquad (7\text{-}9)$$

Structures (XVII) and (XIX) also were claimed to have been obtained from the partial hydrolysis of (XX) and (XXI).[10]

$$\underset{\text{(XX)}}{\begin{array}{l} CH_2OH \\ | \\ O{-}CH \\ HO{-}B \quad | \\ O{-}CH \\ | \\ HC{-}O \\ |\qquad B{-}OH \\ HC{-}O \\ | \\ CH_2OH \end{array}} \qquad \underset{\text{(XXI)}}{\begin{array}{l} CH_2OH \\ | \\ O{-}CH \\ | \\ HC{-}O{-}B{-}OH \\ | \\ HC{-}O{-}B{-}OH \\ | \\ O{-}CH \\ | \\ CH_2OH \end{array}}$$

Hydrolysis of the mixed esters (XXII) was reported to result in

66–88% yields of (XXIII). Compound (XXIII) was completely hydrolyzed to (XXIV) and boric acid in dilute solution, but was

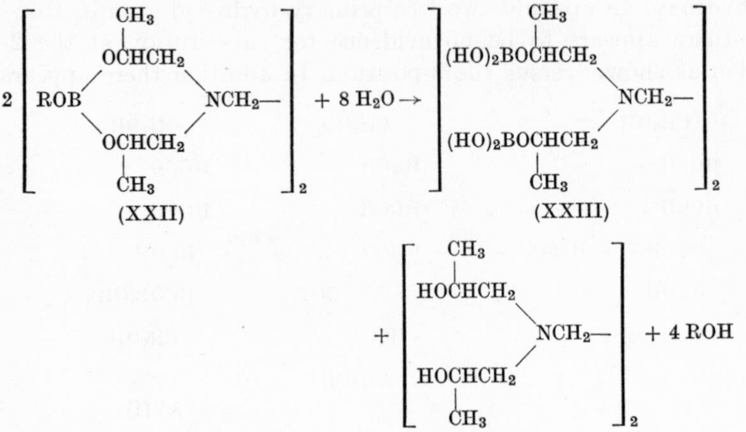

```
    [      CH3                  ]     [        CH3                 ]
    [       |                   ]     [         |                  ]
    [      OCHCH2               ]     [ (HO)2BOCHCH2               ]
    [     /       \             ]     [              \             ]
  2 [ ROB          NCH2—        ] + 8 H2O →  [        NCH2—        ]
    [     \       /             ]     [              /             ]
    [      OCHCH2               ]     [ (HO)2BOCHCH2               ]
    [       |                   ]     [         |                  ]
    [      CH3                  ]2    [        CH3                 ]2
         (XXII)                               (XXIII)

          [      CH3                ]
          [       |                 ]
          [    HOCHCH2              ]
          [           \             ]
        + [            NCH2—        ]  + 4 ROH   (7-10)
          [           /             ]
          [    HOCHCH2              ]
          [       |                 ]
          [      CH3                ]2
               (XXIV)
```

obtained in 75% yield on evaporation of an aqueous solution of boric acid and excess (XXIV). In refluxing alcohols, (XXIII) was converted to the esters (XXII).[52,62,63]

IV. 2-HYDROXY-1,3,2-DIOXABOROLANES AND BORINANES AND RELATED COMPOUNDS

A. Historical

The possibility of forming five-membered rings from glycols and boric acid (XXV) had been stated by Van't Hoff in 1908.[80] Fourteen

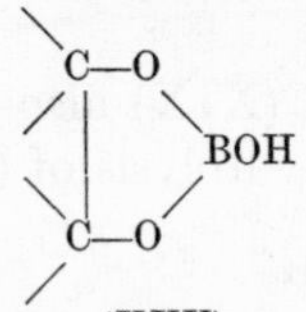

```
   \
    C—O
   /|   \
    |    BOH
   \|   /
    C—O
   /
  (XXV)
```

years later, ether extraction of an equimolar solution of 1,2-cycloheptanediol and boric acid was reported to give (XXVI).[17] However, the possibility that the hydrate indeed was the tetravalent species (XXVII) was stated shortly thereafter.[50]

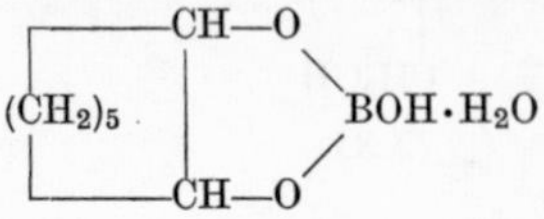

```
  ┌──────CH—O                      ┌──────CH—O     OH
  |       |    \                   |       |    \  /
(CH2)5    |     BOH·H2O          (CH2)5    |     B⁻       H+
  |       |    /                   |       |    /  \
  └──────CH—O                      └──────CH—O     OH
      (XXVI)                           (XXVII)
```

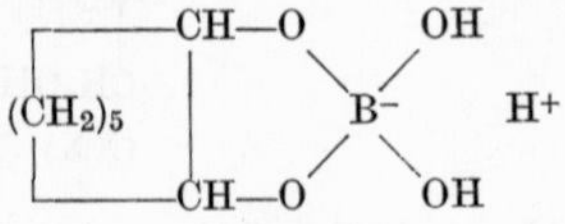

The first authenticated examples (XXVIII–XXX) were prepared by Hermans in the period 1923 to 1925 by dissolving equimolar quantities of the diol and boric acid in hot water and filtering the resulting precipitate after cooling.[31,32]

```
        CH3                      CH3                     CH3   CH3
        |                          \                       \   /
  CH3—C—O                          CH—O                     C—O
        |    \                     /     \                 /     \
        |     BOH               CH2       BOH           CH2       BOH
        |    /                     \     /                 \     /
  CH3—C—O                          CH—O                     C—O
        |                          /                       /   \
        CH3                      CH3                     CH3   CH3
   (XXVIII)                    (XXIX)                     (XXX)
```

B. Properties

The hydroxydioxaborolanes and borinanes range from very viscous liquids or glasses[61] to crystalline solids.[15,32,57,58] The members derived from sugar alcohols are solid at room temperature and melt to viscous liquids.[7,9] The lower alkyl members, up to six or seven carbon atoms, can be distilled at reduced pressure.[32,61] Monomeric structure has been shown by molecular weight determinations on a variety of compounds.[15,17,32,57,83]

The solubility of 2-hydroxy-4,4,6-trimethyl-1,3,2-dioxaborinane in various solvents is recorded in Table 7-1.[24,72] This particular derivative can be recrystallized from water.

Table 7-1. Solubility of 2-hydroxy-4,4,6-trimethyl-1,3,2-dioxaborinane in various solvents

Solvent	g./100 g. solvent (86°)
Water	11
Benzene	58
Isopropyl alcohol	156
Gasoline	2.5–5

In contrast to the tetrahedral derivatives (XXXI, see Chapter 15), the trigonal species (XXXII) are weak acids comparable in

```
  ┌—O     O—┐                  ┌—O
  R    \ /   R-H+              R    \
        B                            BOH
  |    / \   |                 |    /
  └—O     O—┘                  └—O
    (XXXI)                       (XXXII)
```

acidity to boric acid.[32] The equilibria (7-11) and (7-12) thus lie far to the left. Salts of (XXXII) also display a lack of ionic character as evidenced by their inordinate solubility in non-polar solvents.[35]

$$R\langle(O)(O)\rangle BOH \rightleftarrows R\langle(O)(O)\rangle BO^- + H^+ \qquad (7\text{-}11)$$

$$R\langle(O)(O)\rangle BOH + H_2O \rightleftarrows R\langle(O)(O)\rangle B^-(OH)_2 + H^+ \qquad (7\text{-}12)$$

The enhancement of the conductivity of aqueous solutions of boric acid in the presence of various diols and polyols thus is not due to the formation of a single dioxaborolane or borinane ring, as recorded repeatedly in the literature since 1908,[80] but rather to subsequent reaction with a second mole of diol.

$$R\langle(O)(O)\rangle B\text{—}OH + R(OH)_2 \rightleftarrows R\langle(O)(O)\rangle B \leftarrow (O)(OH)\rangle R \rightleftarrows [R\langle(O)(O)\rangle B\langle(O)(O)\rangle R]^- + H^+ \qquad (7\text{-}13)$$

This phenomenon and its application to the stereochemistry and structure of numerous cyclic diols and sugars is discussed in Chapter 15.

Examination of molecular models of the 1,2- and 1,3-diols of cyclopentane, cyclohexane and cycloheptane reveals that dioxaborolane and borinane rings could be formed only in certain cases (Table 7-2). Existing data are consistent with these observations.

Table 7-2. Stereochemical feasibility of hydroxyborylene derivatives of 5- 6-, and 7-membered cyclic diols based on examination of Fischer–Hirschfelder–Taylor atomic models

	1,2-diols		1,3-diols	
	cis	*trans*	*cis*	*trans*
Cyclopentane	Yes[a]	No	Yes	No
Cyclohexane	Yes[a]	No[b]	Yes[a]	No
Cycloheptane	Yes[a]	Maybe[c]	Yes	No

[a] Compounds have been isolated.
[b] Salts could not be isolated.
[c] Ref. 17 states *trans*-1,2-cycloheptanediol enhances the conductivity of boric acid; therefore it appears the *trans* borolane is possible.

C. Methods of Preparation

1. FROM DIOLS AND BORIC ACID OR EQUIVALENT

A variety of 1,2- and 1,3-glycols has been converted to hydroxyborolanes and borinanes by heating with an equimolar amount of boric acid (7-14),[4,22,35,45,54,61,78] or metaboric acid (7-15)[61] and

$$R(OH)_2 + H_3BO_3 \xrightarrow{\Delta} R\langle{}^{O}_{O}\rangle BOH + 2\,H_2O \tag{7-14}$$

$$R(OH)_2 + HBO_2 \xrightarrow{\Delta} R\langle{}^{O}_{O}\rangle BOH + H_2O \tag{7-15}$$

removing the appropriate amount of water. In some cases the product is isolated by extraction of the residue with an organic solvent.[13,32] Addition of gasoline to a mixture of 2-methyl-2,4-pentanediol and boric acid which had been heated to 70° resulted in separation of the water layer.[81] With this particular diol, the product also can be removed from the water of reaction by simple filtration.[15,22,42,72]

Benzene, toluene and xylene have been employed as azeotroping agents for the esterification of 2,3-butanediol,[38,53] 2-methyl-2,4-pentanediol,[26] pinacol,[58] neopentyl glycol,[58] 2-heptadecenyl-4,4-bis(hydroxymethyl)oxazoline[16] and other glycols.[19,20,21,44] The azeotropic method also has been used to prepare the ester from *cis*-1,3-cyclohexanediol (XXXIII).[14]

(XXXIII)

Borates derived from 16,17-dihydroxy steroids (XXXIV) were believed to have been prepared by esterification of the steroidal diol with boric oxide in methanol solution followed by dilution with water to precipitate the ester.[77] Later work, however, indicated

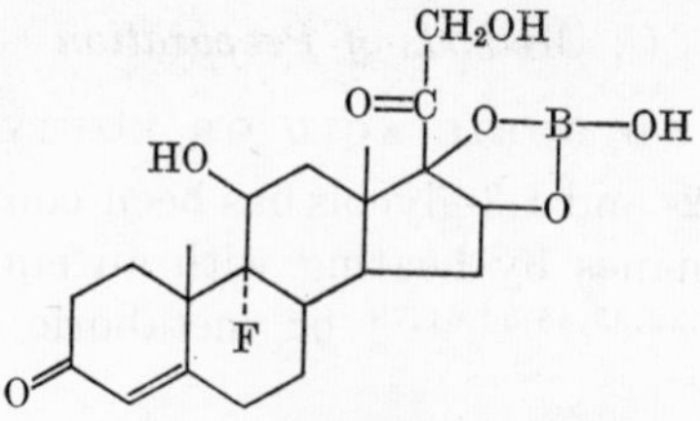

(XXXIV)

that the tetravalent species (XXXV) actually were produced.[46] See Chapter 15.

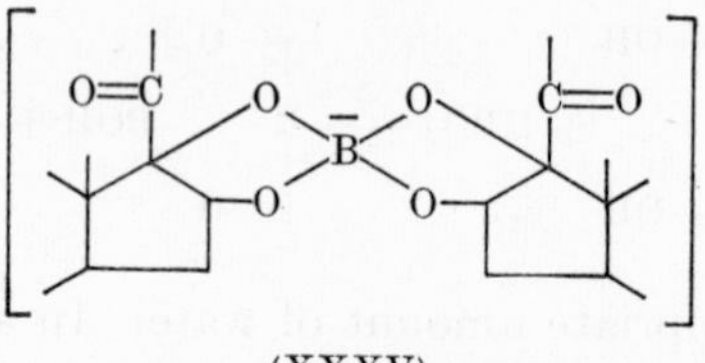

(XXXV)

A novel synthesis of the cyclopentane derivative (XXXVI) was performed by the oxidation of 1,2-dimethylcyclopentene with potassium permanganate in the presence of boric acid.[12]

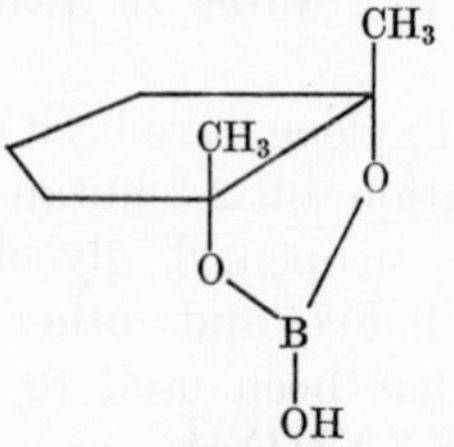

(XXXVI)

The most facile preparation, and one which demonstrates the fundamental difference between the borates of this chapter and the symmetrical esters of Chapter 4, $(RO)_3B$, was performed by Hermans[31,32] by simply dissolving equimolar quantities of a diol and boric acid in hot water and filtering the resulting precipitate after cooling. The rapidity with which this esterification proceeds and the fact that it does so in water solution distinguishes this reaction from ordinary esterifications with monohydric alcohols which proceed at slow measurable rates in non-aqueous media (Chapter 4).* However, not all diols are rapidly esterified. Evidently

* Reluctance to accept the fact of rapid esterification of various diols in aqueous solution without the aid of catalysts or dehydrating agents led to the erroneous conclusion that structures of type (III) did not exist.[2]

certain entropy relationships in the 5- and 6-membered rings coupled with proper insolubility of the product are necessary. The parent diols (XXXVII and XXXVIII) do not result in isolable

$$\begin{array}{c} CH_2OH \\ | \\ CH_2OH \end{array} \qquad \text{(XXXVII)}$$

$$CH_2OH{-}CH_2{-}CH_2OH \qquad \text{(XXXVIII)}$$

borates by this method;[31,32] the substituted diols (XXXIX,[32] XL–XLIII,[57] XLIV[43] and XLV[46]) do.

(XXXIX): $(CH_3)_2C(OH){-}CH_2{-}C(OH)(CH_3)_2$

(XL): $(CH_3)_2C(OH){-}ClCH{-}C(OH)(CH_3)_2$

(XLI): $(CH_3)(CH_2CH_3)C(OH){-}ClCH{-}C(OH)(CH_3)_2$

(XLII): $(CH_3CH_2)_2C(OH){-}ClCH{-}C(OH)(CH_3)_2$

(XLIII): $(CH_3)_2C(OH){-}CH_3CH{-}C(OH)(CH_3)_2$

(XLIV): $(CH_3)_2C(OH){-}CH_2{-}CH(OH){-}CH_3$

(XLV): *cis* cyclopentane-1,2-diol bearing C_6H_5 (OH, OH, C_6H_5)

Other polyols (XLVI[57] and XLVII[32]) required extraction of the borate from water solution with an organic solvent.

(XLVI): $(CH_3)_2C(OH){-}HOCH{-}C(OH)(CH_3)_2$

(XLVII): $(CH_3)(CH_2CH_3)C(OH){-}CH_2{-}C(OH)(CH_3)_2$

Higher glycols have not resulted in discrete products by direct esterification with boric acid. Diethylene glycol resulted in a non-volatile product, which can be formulated as (XLVIII).[61] A series of ill-defined products derived from hydroxystearic acid esters of various glycols[86] and diethanolamine derivatives[87] have been recorded.

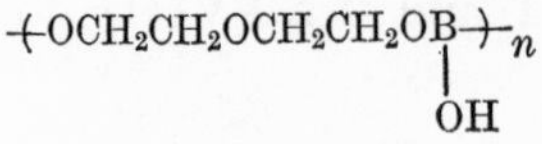

$$-\!\!\left(\!\text{OCH}_2\text{CH}_2\text{OCH}_2\text{CH}_2\text{O}\underset{\underset{\text{OH}}{|}}{\text{B}}\!\right)\!\!-_n$$

(XLVIII)

2. FROM POLYOLS AND BORIC ACID

Addition of an aqueous solution of boric acid to an aqueous solution of polyvinyl alcohol resulted in the precipitation of an uncharacterized white dough-like solid.[47] Possibly some portion of the product structure contained the unit (XLIX). This belief is based

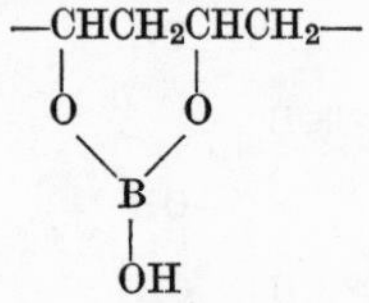

—CHCH₂CHCH₂— with both CH oxygens (O, O) bonded to B, B—OH

(XLIX)

upon the fact that sodium and calcium salts were isolated on addition of sodium hydroxide or calcium chloride to the reaction

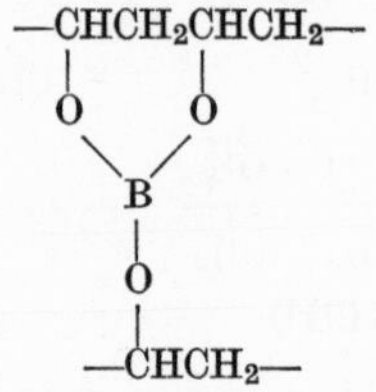

—CHCH₂CHCH₂— with both CH oxygens (O, O) bonded to B, B—O—CHCH₂—

(L)

mixtures. Salt formation would not be expected if all the available sites were esterified (L). In addition, equilibrium dialysis data consistent with structure (XLIX) have been presented.[64]

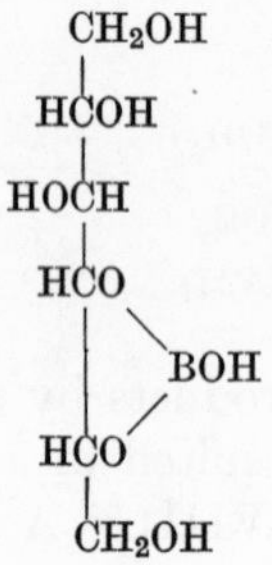

(LI)	(LII)	(LIII)
CH_2OH	CH_2OH	CH_2OH
HCOH	HOCH	HOCH
HOCH	HOCH	HCO (to B—OH)
HCO (to BOH)	HC—O (to BOH)	HCO (to B—OH)
HCO (to BOH)	HC—O (to BOH)	HOCH
CH_2OH	CH_2OH	CH_2OH

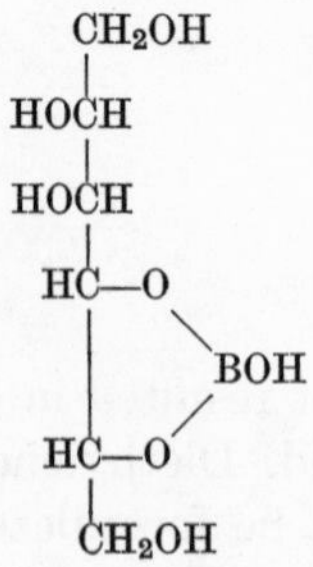

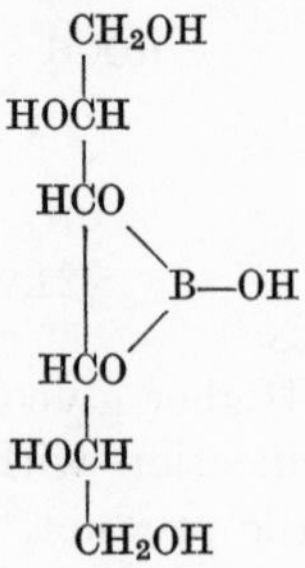

Sugar alcohols such as sorbitol, mannitol and dulcitol have been converted to the borates (LI–LIII) by removing two moles of water from either an equimolar melt of the sugar alcohol and boric acid or an equimolar water solution of the ingredients. A 2:1 mole ratio of boric acid to sugar resulted in the bisborates (LIV–LVI).[7,9,10]

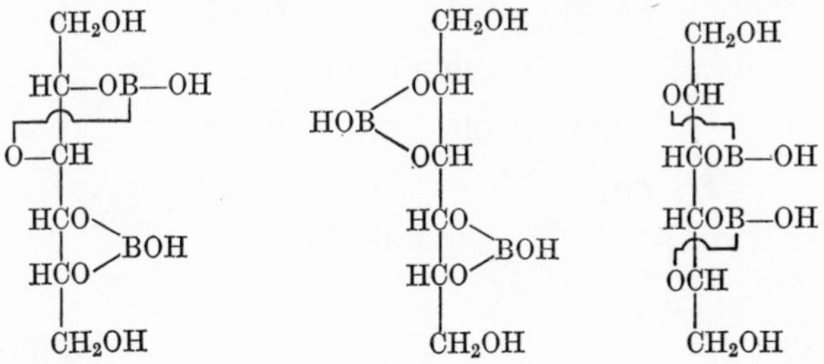

CH₂OH / HC—OB—OH / O—CH / HCO—BOH—OCH / CH₂OH

(LIV)

CH₂OH / HOB(OCH)(OCH) / HCO—BOH—OCH / CH₂OH

(LV)

CH₂OH / OCH / HCOB—OH / HCOB—OH / OCH / CH₂OH

(LVI)

3. BY PARTIAL HYDROLYSIS

In contrast to the partial hydrolysis of a trialkoxyborane, which presumably could yield a dialkoxyhydroxyborane (7-16),[31,66] but

$$(RO)_3B + H_2O \rightarrow (RO)_2BOH + ROH \qquad (7\text{-}16)$$

which has not yet been reported to do so, a variety of alkylenedioxyborane derivatives have been partially hydrolyzed to the hydroxydioxaborolanes and borinanes (7-17).

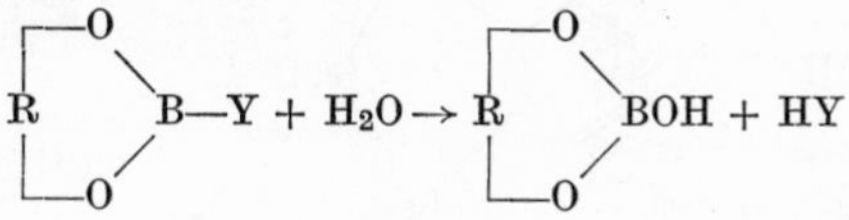

$$R(O)_2B\text{—}Y + H_2O \rightarrow R(O)_2BOH + HY \qquad (7\text{-}17)$$

Y = OR′, Cl, OROB(O)₂R, OB(O)₂R

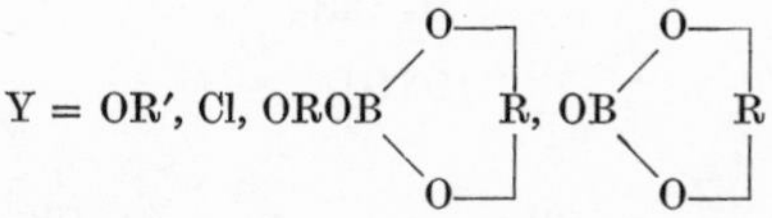

a. *Orthoborates.* The glycol biborates (LVII) and (LVIII) and the mixed borates (LIX) and (LX) were converted to (LXI),[74]

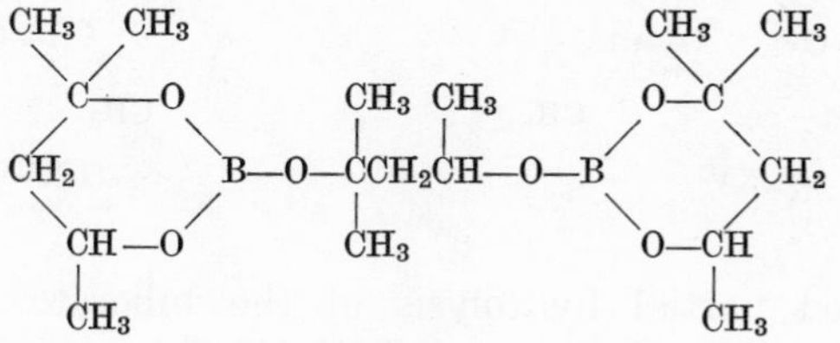

(CH₃)₂C—O—B(—O—CH(CH₃)—CH₂—) —O—C(CH₃)₂CH₂CH(CH₃)—O— B(—O—C(CH₃)₂—CH₂—CH(CH₃)—O—)

(LVII)

(LXII),[13] (LXIII),[85] and (LXIV),[13] respectively, by treatment with water (see Chapter 21). Similarly, (LXV) was converted to (LXVI) on standing in moist air.[55]

```
        CH3                                   CH3
         |                                     |
        CH—O                                 O—CH
       /     \                              /     \
    CH2       BOCHCH2CHOB                          CH2
       \     /    |     |   \              /
        CH—O     CH3   CH3    O—CH
         |                      |
        CH3                    CH3
                 (LVIII)
```

```
   C6H5 C6H5                                                          CH3 CH3
       \ /                                                               \ /
       C—O           (CH3)3CCH—O      C(CH3)3                            C—O
      /    \                |      \    |                               /    \
 [C6H4]     B—OR            |       BOCHCHOH                        CH2       BOH
      \    /                |      /     |                              \    /
       C—O           (CH3)3CCH—O      C(CH3)3                            CH—O
       / \                                                               |
   C6H5 C6H5                                                            CH3
(LIX, R = C2H5, C4H9)              (LX)                                 (LXI)
```

```
    CH3                    C6H5 C6H5
     |                         \ /
    CH—O                       C—O              (CH3)3CCH—O
   /     \                    /    \                  |      \
 CH2      BOH            [C6H4]     BOH               |       BOH
   \     /                    \    /                  |      /
    CH—O                       C—O              (CH3)3CCH—O
     |                         / \
    CH3                    C6H5 C6H5
  (LXII)                    (LXIII)                  (LXIV)
```

```
  CH3              CH3                    CH3
     \             /                         \
      CH—O    O=C                             CH—O
     /     \ ↙    \                          /     \
  CH2       B      CH2                    CH2       BOH
     \     / \    /                          \     /
      CH—O    O—CH                            CH—O
     /            \                          /
  CH3              CH3                    CH3
           (LXV)                            (LXVI)
```

Attempted partial hydrolysis of the biborate of a 1,4-diol (LXVII)[74] and the mixed ester (LXVIII)[58] resulted in complete hydrolysis to the glycol in the case of (LXVII) and the formation of an unidentified glass in the case of (LXVIII).

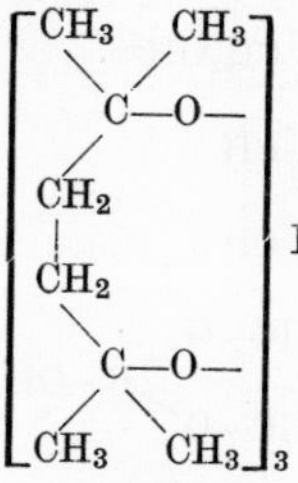

$$\left[\begin{array}{l} (CH_3)_2C{-}O{-} \\ \quad | \\ CH_2 \\ | \\ CH_2 \\ \quad | \\ (CH_3)_2C{-}O{-} \end{array}\right]_3 B_2 \qquad\qquad \begin{array}{l} CH_2{-}O \\ | \qquad\quad \backslash \\ | \qquad\qquad BOC_4H_9 \\ | \qquad\quad / \\ CH_2{-}O \end{array}$$

(LXVII) 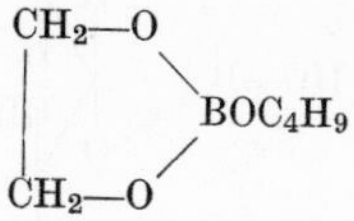 (LXVIII)

b. *Oxybis(dioxaborolanes) and Borinanes.* The anhydrides of hydroxydioxaborolanes and borinanes are sensitive to water or atmospheric moisture and are readily converted to the cyclic hydroxyl derivatives by controlled hydrolysis.[13,15,23,24,73,83]

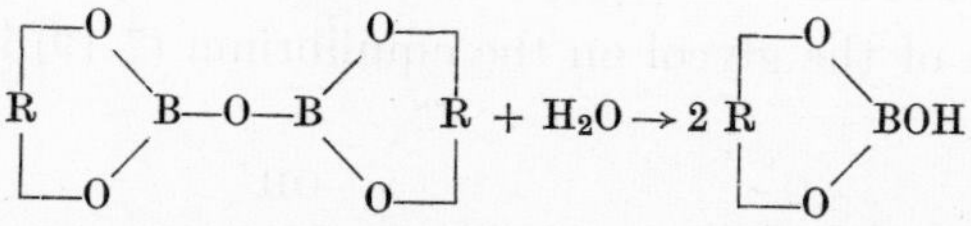

$$R\langle{}^{O}_{O}\rangle B{-}O{-}B\langle{}^{O}_{O}\rangle R + H_2O \rightarrow 2\, R\langle{}^{O}_{O}\rangle BOH \qquad (7\text{-}18)$$

c. *2-Chloro-1,3,2-dioxaborolanes.* The treatment of 2-chloro-1,3,2-dioxaborolane (LXIX)[4] with less than one mole of water in methylene chloride–ether solution reportedly gave (LXX); the treatment of (LXXI) with one mole of water in ether gave (LXXII).[29]

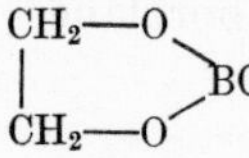

$$\begin{array}{l} CH_2{-}O \\ | \qquad\quad BCl \\ CH_2{-}O \end{array} \qquad \begin{array}{l} CH_2{-}O \\ | \qquad\quad BOH \\ CH_2{-}O \end{array} \qquad C_6H_4\langle{}^{O}_{O}\rangle BCl \qquad C_6H_4\langle{}^{O}_{O}\rangle BOH$$

(LXIX) 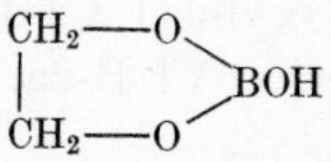 (LXX) 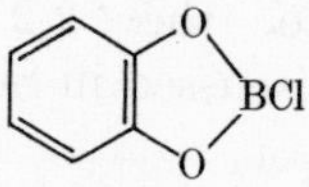 (LXXI) 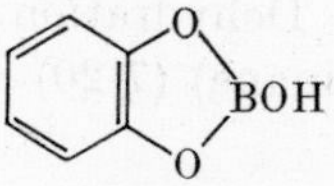 (LXXII)

4. FROM ALKYLENEDIOXYDIHYDROXYBORATES

Treatment of (LXXIII) and (LXXIV) with phosphorus pent-

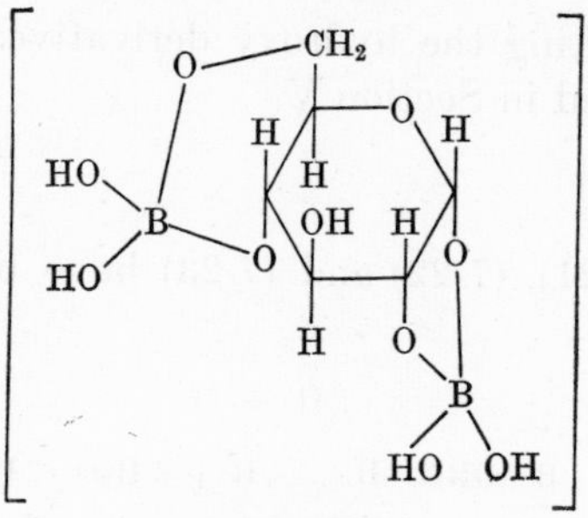

(LXXIII) 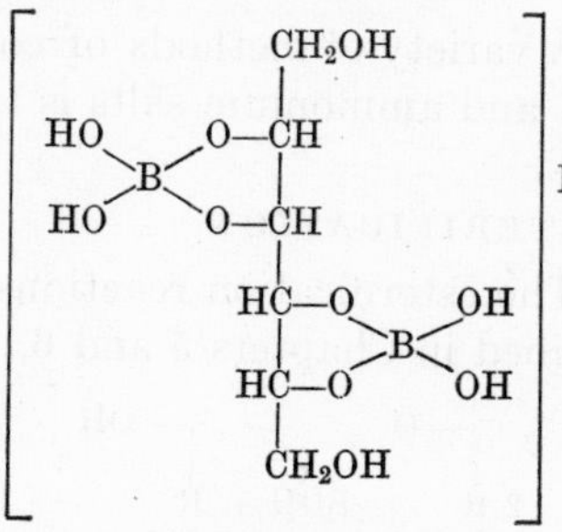 (LXXIV)

oxide under vacuum at 100° resulted in the loss of two moles of water leaving (LXXV) and (LXXVI).[11]

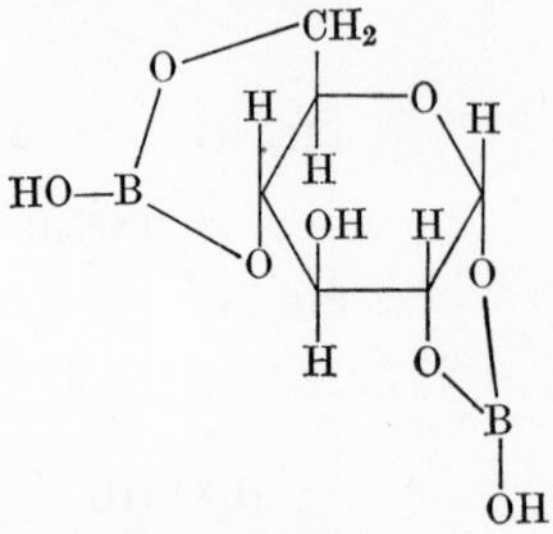

(LXXV) 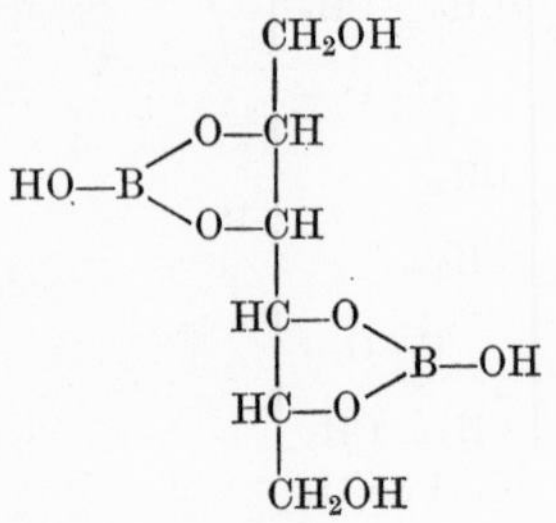 (LXXVI)

D. Reactions

1. HYDROLYSIS

The influence of the glycol on the equilibrium (7-19) is discussed in Chapter 21.

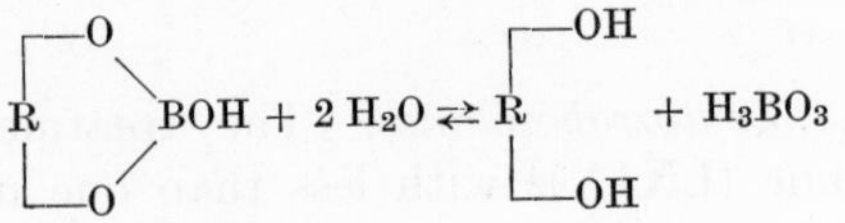

$$R\begin{matrix}-O\\ \\-O\end{matrix}BOH + 2\,H_2O \rightleftarrows R\begin{matrix}-OH\\ \\-OH\end{matrix} + H_3BO_3 \qquad (7\text{-}19)$$

2. DEHYDRATION

Dehydration to the 2,2′-Oxybis(1,3,2-dioxaborolane and borinane) (7-20) is discussed in Section VI-B-2a.

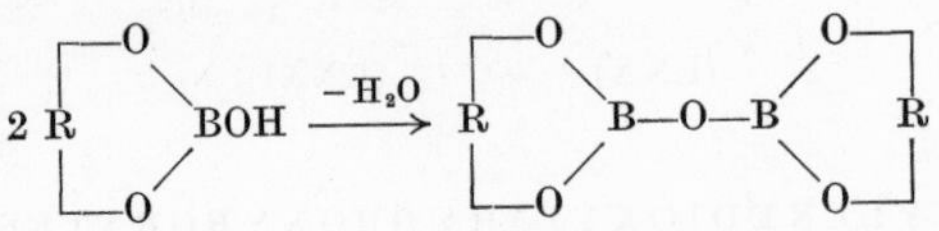

$$2\,R\begin{matrix}-O\\ \\-O\end{matrix}BOH \xrightarrow{-H_2O} R\begin{matrix}-O\\ \\-O\end{matrix}B-O-B\begin{matrix}O-\\ \\O-\end{matrix}R \qquad (7\text{-}20)$$

3. SALT FORMATION

A variety of methods of converting the hydroxy derivatives to metal and ammonium salts is treated in Section V.

4. ESTERIFICATION

The esterification reactions (7-21), (7-22) and (7-23) have been described in Chapters 5 and 6.

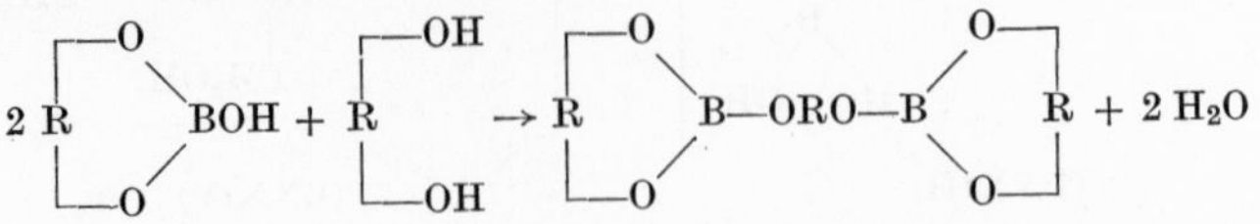

$$2\,R\begin{matrix}-O\\ \\-O\end{matrix}BOH + R\begin{matrix}-OH\\ \\-OH\end{matrix} \rightarrow R\begin{matrix}-O\\ \\-O\end{matrix}B-ORO-B\begin{matrix}O-\\ \\O-\end{matrix}R + 2\,H_2O \qquad (7\text{-}21)$$

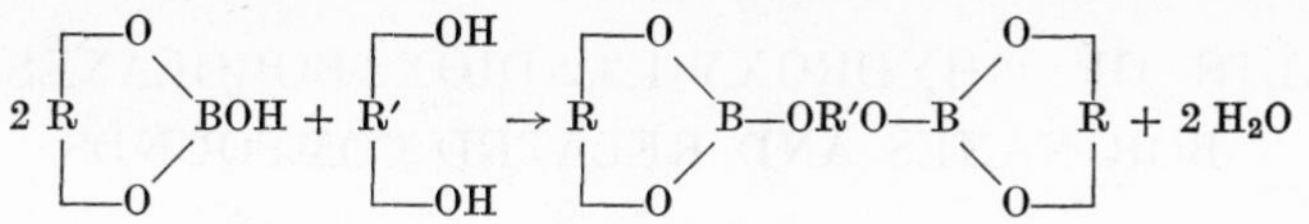

$$2\,R\!\left\langle\begin{matrix}O\\O\end{matrix}\right\rangle\!BOH + R'\left\langle\begin{matrix}OH\\OH\end{matrix}\right. \rightarrow R\!\left\langle\begin{matrix}O\\O\end{matrix}\right\rangle\!B{-}OR'O{-}B\!\left\langle\begin{matrix}O\\O\end{matrix}\right\rangle\!R + 2\,H_2O \qquad (7\text{-}22)$$

$$R\!\left\langle\begin{matrix}O\\O\end{matrix}\right\rangle\!BOH + R'OH \rightarrow R\!\left\langle\begin{matrix}O\\O\end{matrix}\right\rangle\!BOR' + H_2O \qquad (7\text{-}23)$$

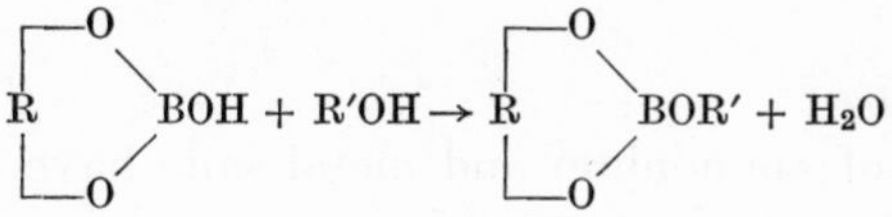

5. ACETYLATION

The steroidal borate (XXXIV) was converted to the acyloxyborane (LXXVII) with concomitant acylation of the 21-hydroxyl

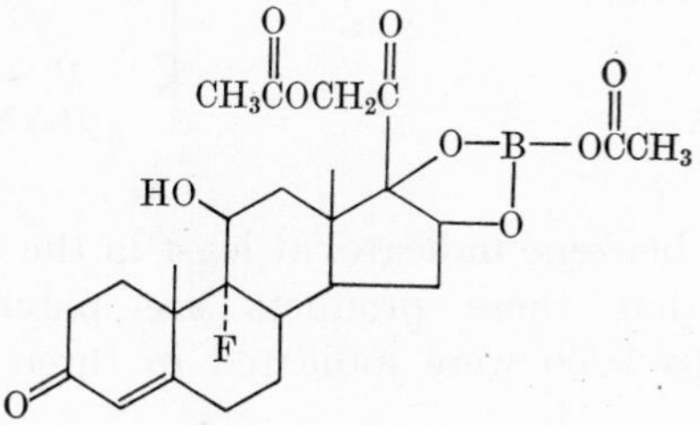

$CH_3\overset{O}{\overset{\|}{C}}OCH_2\overset{O}{\overset{\|}{C}}$, $O{-}B{-}O\overset{O}{\overset{\|}{C}}CH_3$, HO, O, F, O

(LXXVII)

by treatment with acetic anhydride in pyridine.[77] This reaction is consistent with the preparative method for triacetoxyborane involving the treatment of boric acid with acetic anhydride.[59]

Cleavage of the B–O bonds of (LXXVIII) with acetic anhydride

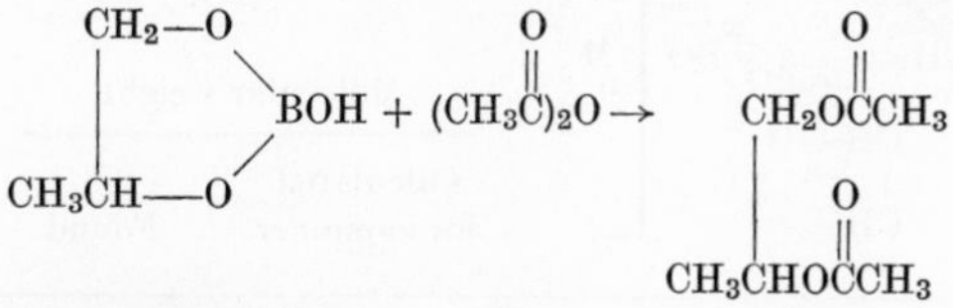

$$\begin{matrix}CH_2{-}O\\ |\\ CH_3CH{-}O\end{matrix}\!\!\!\big\rangle BOH + (CH_3\overset{O}{\overset{\|}{C}})_2O \rightarrow \begin{matrix}CH_2O\overset{O}{\overset{\|}{C}}CH_3\\ |\\ CH_3CHO\overset{O}{\overset{\|}{C}}CH_3\end{matrix} \qquad (7\text{-}24)$$

(LXXVIII)

(7-24) is consistent with the formation of oxybis(diacetoxyborane) (LXXIX) from the reaction of trialkoxyboranes and acetic anhydride.[84]

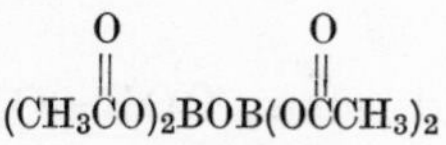

$$(CH_3\overset{O}{\overset{\|}{C}}O)_2BOB(O\overset{O}{\overset{\|}{C}}CH_3)_2$$

(LXXIX)

V. SALTS OF 2-HYDROXY-1,3,2-DIOXABOROLANES AND BORINANES AND RELATED COMPOUNDS

A. Properties

1. STRUCTURE

A variety of ammonium and metal salts have been described, but evidence for their structure or monomeric nature has not been presented. Although their composition corresponds closely to formulas (LXXX) or (LXXXI), cryoscopic molecular weight

$$\text{R}\begin{matrix}\text{—O}\\ \\ \text{—O}\end{matrix}\!\!>\text{B—O—M} \qquad \left[\text{R}\begin{matrix}\text{—O}\\ \\ \text{—O}\end{matrix}\!\!>\text{B=O}\right]^{-}\text{M}^{+}$$

(LXXX) (LXXXI)

determinations in benzene indicate, at least in the case of 2-methyl-2,4-pentanediol, that these products are polymeric. Molecular weights of 1100 to 5000 were indicated in three instances (Table 7-3).[35]

Table 7-3. Cryoscopic molecular weights (benzene) of salts of 2-hydroxy-4,4,6-trimethyl-1,3,2-dioxaborinane

n and M in $\left[(CH_3)_2C(O)CH_2CH(CH_3)O\,BO\right]_n M$		Molecular weight		Number of monomers in aggregate
		Calculated for monomer	Found	
n	M			
1	Na	166.0	4860–5060	29–30
1	Li	149.9	1670–1690	11
2	Ca	326.0	1130–1280	3.5–3.9

Since metaboric acid esters, ROB=O, exist as the trimer (see Chapter 9), (LXXXI) can be reformulated as (LXXXII) or

(LXXXIII) to avoid the boron–oxygen double bond structure, which as yet is an unknown configuration in organoboron chemistry.*

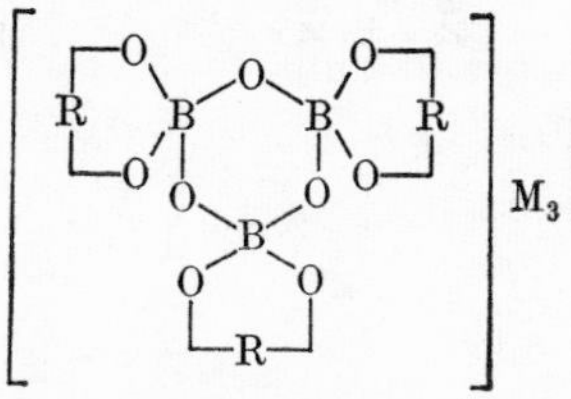

(LXXXII)

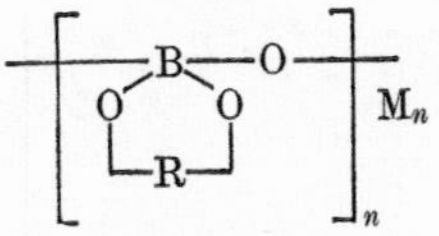

(LXXXIII)

Cross-linking through the glycol units can not as yet be ruled out and structures such as (LXXXIV) may account for the high molecular weights observed.

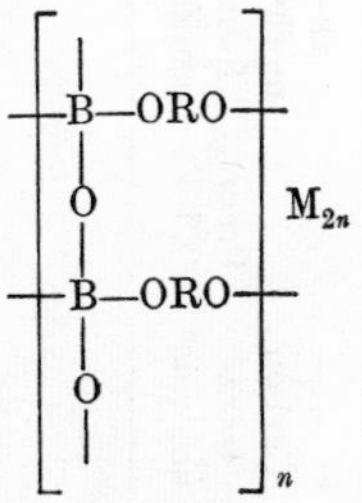

(LXXXIV)

A third possible explanation for the observed molecular weights could be the formation of aggregates of (LXXX) or (LXXXI) held together by secondary valences. It should be possible to verify this hypothesis by comparing cryoscopic molecular weights in solvents of different dielectric properties.

2. SOLUBILITY

The solubility characteristics of the salts in organic solvents vary considerably depending upon the nature of both the glycol and

* Bond distance measurements of the $B_3O_6^{3-}$ anion [L. Pauling, *The Nature of The Chemical Bond*, 2nd ed., Cornell Univ. Press, Ithaca, 1948, p. 212] indicates the importance of double bonded boron oxygen structures in certain inorganic anions.

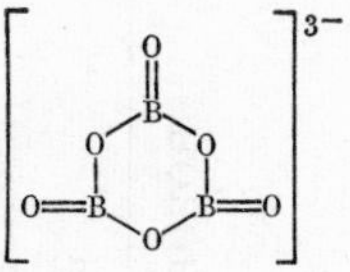

This configuration has not yet been shown for low molecular weight covalent boron compounds.

Table 7-4. Solubility of salts of 2-hydroxy-1,3,2-dioxaborolanes and borinanes in various solvents

HOROH ($R(OH)_2$) and M in $R(O)_2BOM$ — Solubility, 25°, wt. %

HOROH	M	Methanol	Ether	Dioxane	Acetone[a]	Acetonitrile[a]	Chloroform[a]	Carbon tetrachloride[a]	Freon (CCl_3F)	Dimethylformamide[a]	n-Heptane	Gasoline	Lube oil	Benzene	Toluene
$CH_3CH(OH)CH_2OH$	Na														Negligible
$CH_3CH(OH)CH_2CH_2OH$	Na														Negligible
$CH_3C(OH)(CH_3)CH_2CH(OH)CH_3$	Na	40	12	11	0.2–4	1	11–24	25	> 20	9–13	25	34	3–4	43	32
	Li			3				6			3	6			12
	K			1							1	1			3
	Ca			3				26			15	15			28
	Ba							Negligible			Negligible				Negligible

[a] Solvent reacts with salts.

the metal ion (Table 7-4).[35] The solubility in toluene of the sodium salt derived from 2-methyl-2,4-pentanediol is 32 wt. %; whereas the corresponding sodium salts derived from 1,2-propanediol and 1,3-butanediol exhibit a negligible solubility in this solvent. The solubilities of the 2-methyl-2,4-pentanediol derivatives in toluene decrease in the order Na > Ca > Li > K > Ba. The ability of the various solvents to dissolve the salts appeared to decrease in the order benzene > toluene > carbon tetrachloride > n-heptane > freon > diethyl ether > dioxane. Solvents such as carbon tetrachloride, acetone, acetonitrile, chloroform and dimethylformamide, which might be expected to react with basic reagents, reacted to varying extents with the sodium salt derived from 2-methyl-2,4-pentanediol.

B. Methods of Preparation

1. FROM DIOLS AND TRIOLS AND BORATE SALTS

Addition of potassium hydroxide solution to an aqueous solution of boric acid and *cis*-1,2-cyclohexanediol,[6,31,32] *cis*-1,2-tetrahydronaphthalenediol,[32] phenylethylene glycol,[32] *cis*-1,2-cycloheptanediol,[32] and 1-methyl-1,2-dihydroxycyclopentane[41] resulted in precipitates of the salts (LXXXV to LXXXIX). *Trans*-cyclohexanediols and tetrahydronaphthalenediols did not yield salts under the same conditions.[32]

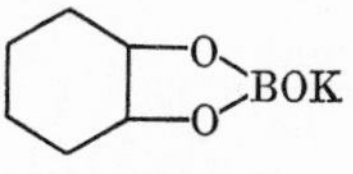

BOK (LXXXV) | O—B—OK (LXXXVI) | C_6H_5CH—O, CH_2—O, BOK (LXXXVII)

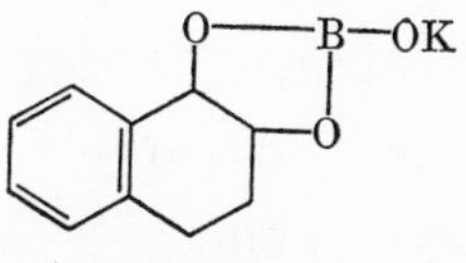

$(CH_2)_5$ CH—O, CH—O, BOK (LXXXVIII) | B—OK, CH_3 (LXXXIX)

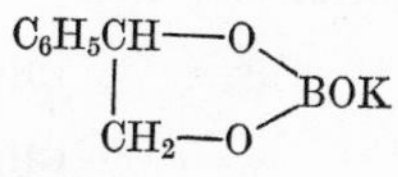

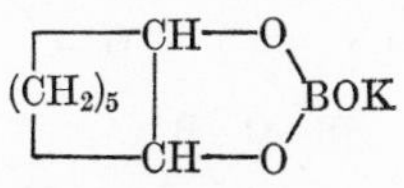

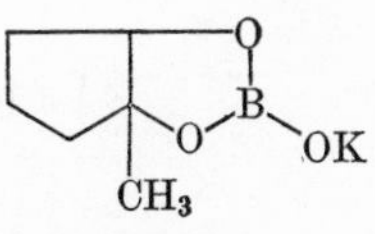

A series of hydrated salts (XC and XCI) were crystallized from water solutions of catechol, boric acid and the appropriate metal carbonate, hydroxide or oxide present in the mole ratio 1:1:0.5.[67] The possibility that the salts were tetravalent species (XCII) cannot be ruled out.

(XC, M = Li, Na) (XCI, M = Sr, Mg)

(XCII)

The reaction of borax with glycerol has been formulated to result in a salt (7-25)[18,79] as has its reactions with 2-methyl-2,4-pentanediol (7-26)[58] and an aqueous solution of catechol and sodium hydroxide (7-27).[82]

$$Na_2B_4O_7 \cdot 10H_2O + 4\,CH_2OH\text{–}CHOH\text{–}CH_2OH \rightarrow 2\,(CH_2\text{–}O)(HOCH_2CH\text{–}O)BONa + 2\,(CH_2\text{–}O)(HOCH_2CH\text{–}O)BOH + 13\,H_2O \quad (7\text{-}25)$$

$$Na_2B_4O_7 \cdot 5H_2O + 4\,(CH_3)_2COH\text{–}CH_2\text{–}CHOH\text{–}CH_3 \rightarrow 2\,(CH_3)_2C(O)\text{–}CH_2\text{–}CH(CH_3)(O)BONa + (CH_3)_2C(O)CH_2CH(CH_3)(O)B\text{–}O\text{–}B(O)(O)C(CH_3)_2CH_2CH(CH_3) + 9\,H_2O \quad (7\text{-}26)$$

$$4\,C_6H_4(OH)_2 + Na_2B_4O_7 \cdot 10H_2O + 2\,NaOH \rightarrow 4\,C_6H_4O_2BONa \cdot H_2O + 14\,H_2O \quad (7\text{-}27)$$

Glycerol, boric acid, and ammonia were formulated to react in an analogous manner (7-28).[27]

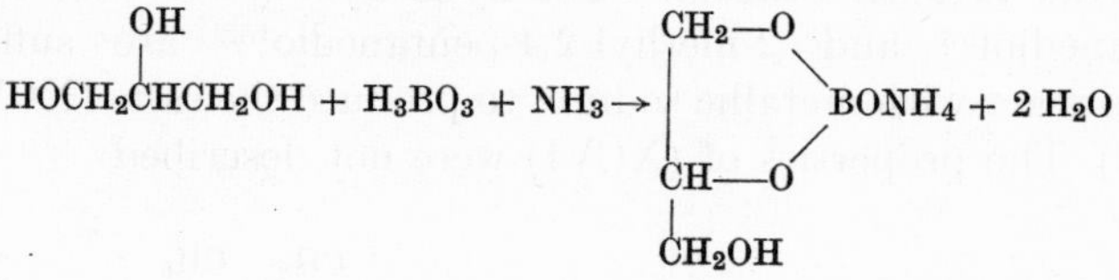

$$HOCH_2CH(OH)CH_2OH + H_3BO_3 + NH_3 \rightarrow \begin{matrix} CH_2\text{—}O \\ | \quad\quad \diagdown \\ \quad\quad\quad BONH_4 \\ | \quad\quad \diagup \\ CH\text{—}O \\ | \\ CH_2OH \end{matrix} + 2\,H_2O \qquad (7\text{-}28)$$

2. FROM POLYOLS

A hot aqueous solution of polyvinyl alcohol, boric acid and sodium hydroxide on cooling yielded a gel. The analysis of the dried product was consistent with structure (XCIII). Addition of a calcium chloride solution to a solution of (XCIII) resulted in a calcium salt approximating (XCIV) in empirical formula.[47]

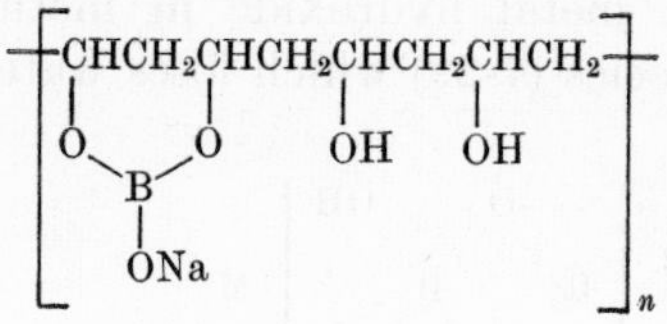

$$\left[\begin{matrix} CHCH_2CHCH_2CHCH_2CHCH_2 \\ | \quad\quad | \quad\quad\quad | \quad\quad\quad | \\ O \quad\; O \quad\quad OH \quad\; OH \\ \diagdown B \diagup \\ | \\ ONa \end{matrix} \right]_n$$

(XCIII)

$$\left[\begin{matrix} CHCH_2CHCH_2CHCH_2CHCH_2 \\ | \quad\quad | \quad\quad\quad | \quad\quad\quad | \\ O \quad\; O \quad\quad OH \quad\; OH \\ \diagdown B \diagup \\ | \\ O \\ | \\ Ca\cdot 6\,H_2O \\ | \\ O \\ | \\ B \\ \diagup \quad \diagdown \\ O \quad\; O \quad\quad OH \quad\; OH \\ | \quad\quad | \quad\quad\quad | \quad\quad\quad | \\ CHCH_2CHCH_2CHCH_2CHCH_2 \end{matrix} \right]_n$$

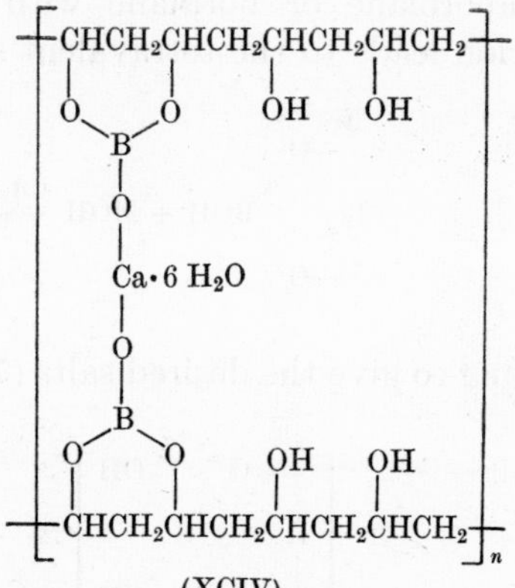

(XCIV)

A series of salts (XCV) were claimed to have been derived from the reaction of boric acid, the appropriate gluconate, and the appropriate metal oxide.[1]

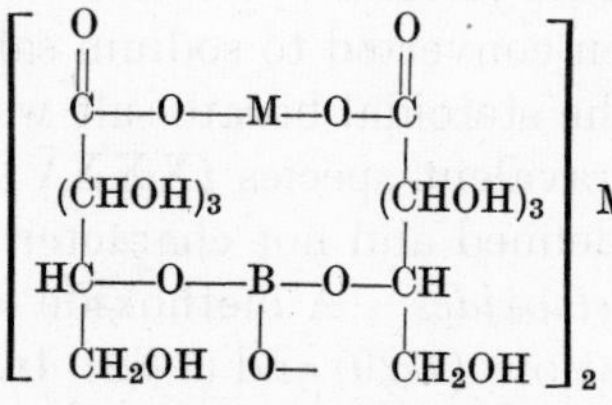

$$\left[\begin{matrix} O \quad\quad\quad\quad\quad\quad O \\ \| \quad\quad\quad\quad\quad\quad \| \\ C\text{—}O\text{—}M\text{—}O\text{—}C \\ | \quad\quad\quad\quad\quad\quad | \\ (CHOH)_3 \quad\quad (CHOH)_3 \\ | \quad\quad\quad\quad\quad\quad | \\ HC\text{—}O\text{—}B\text{—}O\text{—}CH \\ | \quad\quad\quad | \quad\quad\quad | \\ CH_2OH \quad O\text{—} \quad CH_2OH \end{matrix} \right]_2 M'$$

(XCV, M = Ca, Mg, Fe; M′ = Ca, Mg, Fe, Cu)

3. FROM 2-HYDROXY-1,3,2-DIOXABOROLANES AND BORINANES

a. *And Metallic Sodium.* The hydroxyborylene derivatives of 2,3-butanediol[53] and 2-methyl-2,4-pentanediol[58] are sufficiently acidic to react with metallic sodium to produce the salts (XCVI) and (XCVII). The properties of (XCVI) were not described.

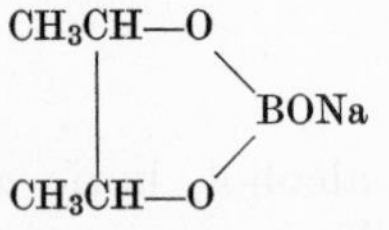

$$\begin{array}{l} CH_3CH{-}O \\ \quad | \qquad\quad \backslash \\ \quad | \qquad\quad BONa \\ \quad | \qquad\quad / \\ CH_3CH{-}O \end{array}$$

(XCVI)

$$\begin{array}{l} \quad CH_3 \quad CH_3 \\ \qquad \backslash \;\; / \\ \qquad C{-}O \\ \quad / \qquad \backslash \\ CH_2 \qquad BONa \\ \quad \backslash \qquad / \\ \quad CH{-}O \\ \quad | \\ \quad CH_3 \end{array}$$

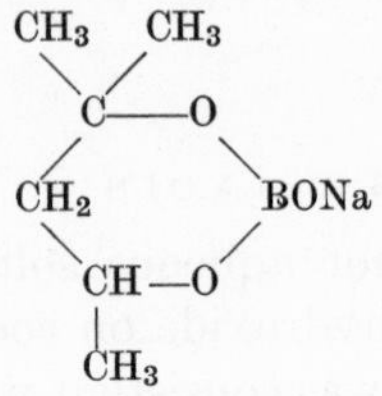

(XCVII)

b. *And Metal Hydroxides.* Treatment of a 2-hydroxy-1,3,2-dioxaborolane or borinane with a metal hydroxide in methanol solution leads to the tetravalent species (7-29) which loses water on

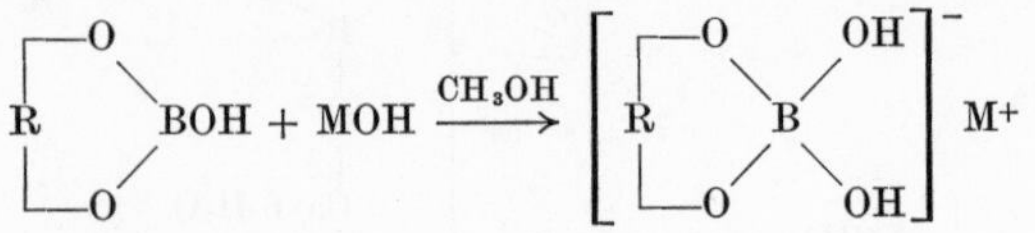

$$R\langle{}^{O}_{O}\rangle BOH + MOH \xrightarrow{CH_3OH} \left[R\langle{}^{O}_{O}\rangle B\langle{}^{OH}_{OH} \right]^- M^+ \qquad (7\text{-}29)$$

heating to give the desired salts (7-30). Glycols which have been used

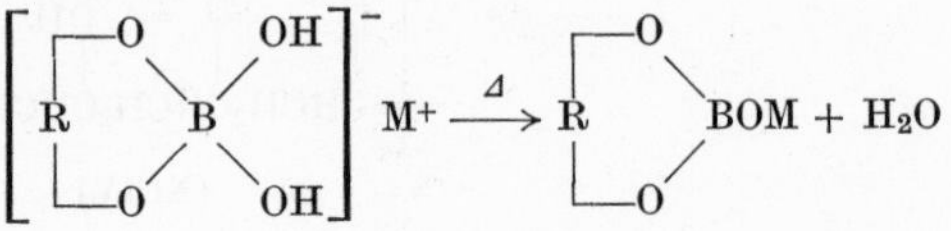

$$\left[R\langle{}^{O}_{O}\rangle B\langle{}^{OH}_{OH} \right]^- M^+ \xrightarrow{\Delta} R\langle{}^{O}_{O}\rangle BOM + H_2O \qquad (7\text{-}30)$$

in these reactions include 1,2-propanediol, 1,3-butanediol, 2-methyl-2,4-pentanediol and 2,2,4-trimethyl-1,3-pentanediol. The sodium, lithium and potassium salts were prepared.[35]

The steroidal borate (XXXIV)[77] and a variety of sugar alcohol borates [7,8,9] have been converted to sodium salts by treatment with sodium hydroxide. The steroidal borate salt was not described. It is believed it is the tetravalent species (XXXV).[46] The sugar alcohol borate salts were ill defined and not characterized.

c. *And Metal Methoxides.* A methoxide can be substituted for the hydroxide of equations (7-29) and (7-30). In these cases (7-31 and 7-32) methanol is finally removed.

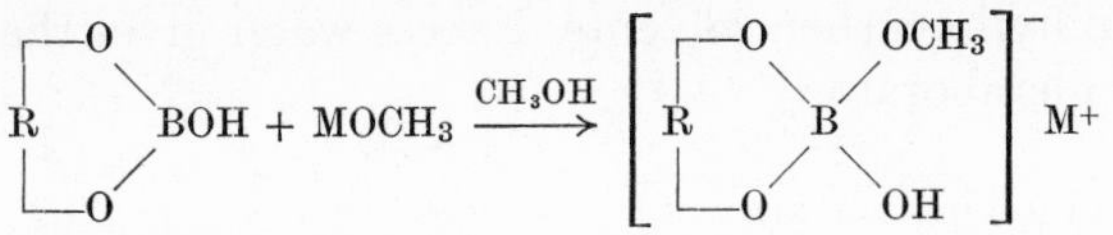

$$\begin{array}{l}\ulcorner O \\ R \quad BOH \\ \llcorner O\end{array} + MOCH_3 \xrightarrow{CH_3OH} \left[\begin{array}{l}\ulcorner O \quad\quad OCH_3 \\ R \quad\quad B \\ \llcorner O \quad\quad OH\end{array}\right]^- M^+ \quad (7\text{-}31)$$

$$\left[\begin{array}{l}\ulcorner O \quad\quad OCH_3 \\ R \quad\quad B \\ \llcorner O \quad\quad OH\end{array}\right]^- M^+ \xrightarrow{\Delta} \begin{array}{l}\ulcorner O \\ R \quad BOM \\ \llcorner O\end{array} + CH_3OH \quad (7\text{-}32)$$

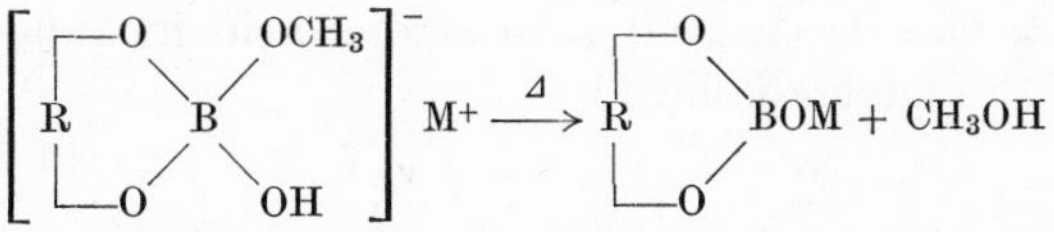

Calcium, barium and benzyltrimethylammonium salts as well as sodium, lithium, and potassium salts were prepared in this manner.[35]

d. *And Alkali Metal Tetraborates.* Ill-defined sodium salts of sorbitol,[7,9] mannitol,[7,8] and dulcitol borate,[8] and uncharacterized lithium and potassium salts of mannitol[8] and dulcitol borate[8] have been postulated to be formed by treatment of the hexahydric alcohol borates with the appropriate metal tetraborate.

e. *And Ammonia.* The hydroxydioxaborolane of *meso*-2,3-butanediol has been described as forming a true salt with ammonia in acetone solution (XCVIII).[53] A gelatinous white precipitate[61] from the reaction of the propylene glycol derivative and dry ammonia in toluene solution may be the salt (XCIX).

$$\begin{array}{l}CH_3CH\text{—}O \\ \quad\quad\quad\quad BONH_4 \\ CH_3CH\text{—}O\end{array} \qquad\qquad \begin{array}{l}CH_3CH\text{—}O \\ \quad\quad\quad\quad BONH_4 \\ CH_2\text{—}O\end{array}$$

(XCVIII) (XCIX)

Ill-defined ammonium salts of the borates of sorbitol,[7,9,33] mannitol[7,9,33] and dulcitol[7,8] were claimed by the dehydration of a solution of ammonium hydroxide and the hydroxydioxaborolane. Ammonium borate also has served as the source of ammonia.[8]

C. Reactions

1. HYDROLYSIS

The salts are readily hydrolyzed (7-33). A limited quantity of water yields products (C) which in contrast to the anhydrous salts are

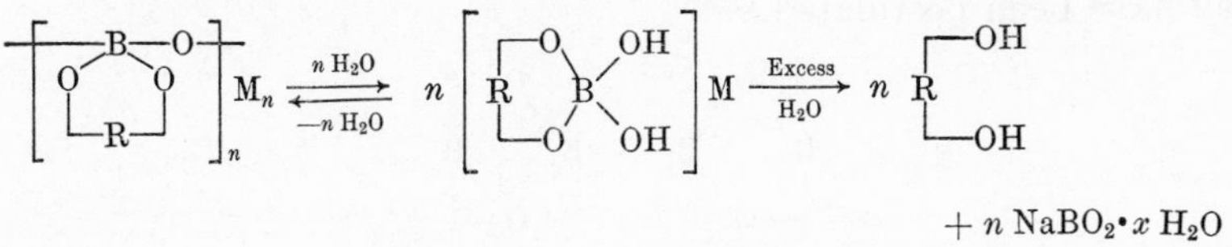

$$\left[\begin{array}{c}\text{—B—O—} \\ O \quad O \\ \llcorner R \lrcorner\end{array}\right]_n M_n \underset{-n\,H_2O}{\overset{n\,H_2O}{\rightleftharpoons}} n\left[\begin{array}{l}\ulcorner O \quad OH \\ R \quad B \\ \llcorner O \quad OH\end{array}\right] M \xrightarrow[H_2O]{\text{Excess}} n\,\begin{array}{l}\ulcorner OH \\ R \\ \llcorner OH\end{array}$$

$$+\, n\, NaBO_2 \cdot x\, H_2O \quad (7\text{-}33)$$

insoluble in hydrocarbon solvents. Excess water gives the free glycol and metal metaborate.[35]

2. WITH STRONG ACID

The salts can be titrated with strong acid in aqueous solution to a methyl orange endpoint.[31,32]

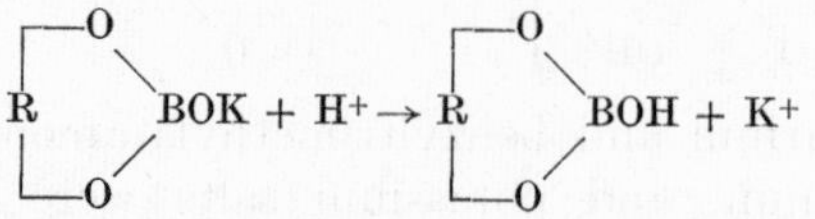

$$R\begin{matrix}O\\O\end{matrix}BOK + H^+ \rightarrow R\begin{matrix}O\\O\end{matrix}BOH + K^+ \qquad (7\text{-}34)$$

3. WITH METHYL IODIDE

The conversion of the sodium salt of the steroidal borate (XXXIV) to the methyl ester by treatment with methyl iodide has been described in Chapter 6.[77]

VI. 2,2′-OXYBIS-(1,3,2-DIOXABOROLANES AND BORINANES)

A. Properties

Examples of 2,2′-oxybis-(1,3,2-dioxaborolanes and borinanes) (V) derived from aliphatic and alicyclic 1,2- and 1,3-diols and aromatic 1,2-diols have been reported. In the main, they are high boiling monomeric liquids[15,24,30,36,71,83] with the exception of the product derived from glycerol which reportedly is a white amorphous powder and the products derived from 2,2,6,6-tetramethyl-3,5-heptanediol, *cis*-1,2-cyclopentanediol and *cis*-1,3-cyclohexanediol which are crystalline solids.[13,14]

Distillation of the derivatives from *meso*-2,3-butanediol and *cis*-1,2-cyclohexanediol resulted in a viscous liquid and glass, respectively, indicating some rearrangement to polymeric structures on condensation.[13]

The derivative of 2-methyl-2,4-pentanediol is miscible in hydrocarbons and the common organic solvents in all proportions. It is very hygroscopic.[24]

Mixed anhydrides (CI) have not yet been described although they have been postulated.[15,23]

$$R\begin{matrix}O\\O\end{matrix}B\text{—}O\text{—}B\begin{matrix}O\\O\end{matrix}R'$$

(CI)

B. Methods of Preparation

1. FROM DIOLS AND BORIC ACID OR EQUIVALENT

The first recorded anhydride was prepared by the fusion of boric oxide and catechol followed by vacuum distillation.[68]

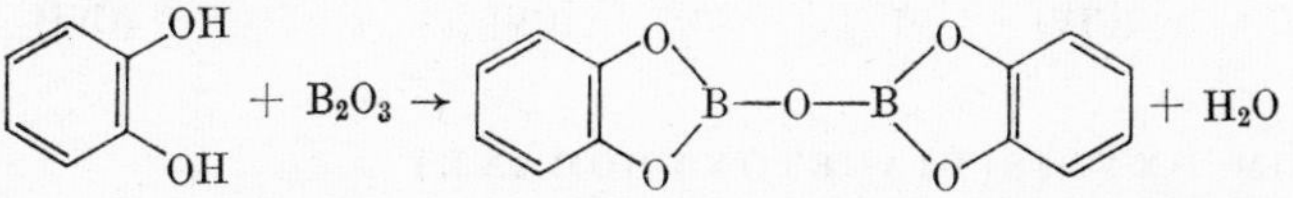

$$o\text{-}C_6H_4(OH)_2 + B_2O_3 \rightarrow C_6H_4O_2B{-}O{-}BO_2C_6H_4 + H_2O \qquad (7\text{-}35)$$

Azeotropic removal of water was subsequently performed for aromatic 1,2-diols[29,78] and both 1,2-[13,83] and 1,3- aliphatic diols[15,16,19,23,24,36,42,43,45,49,71,73] and one mole of boric acid, one mole of metaboric acid[36,71] or one-half mole of boric oxide.[37,71] Cyclization of 1,5-diols (CII and CIII) also has been claimed.[21,44]

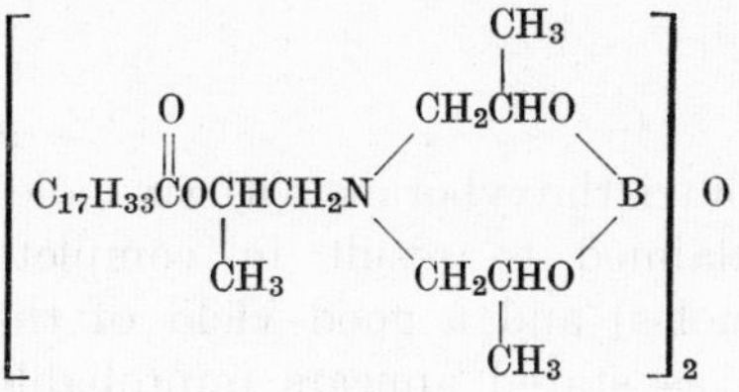

$$\left[C_{17}H_{33}\overset{O}{\overset{\|}{C}}OCH(CH_3)CH_2N\begin{matrix}CH_2CH(CH_3)O \\ CH_2CH(CH_3)O\end{matrix}B\right]_2 O \qquad \left[C_{17}H_{33}\overset{O}{\overset{\|}{C}}{-}N\begin{matrix}CH_2CH_2O \\ CH_2CH_2O\end{matrix}B\right]_2 O$$

(CII) 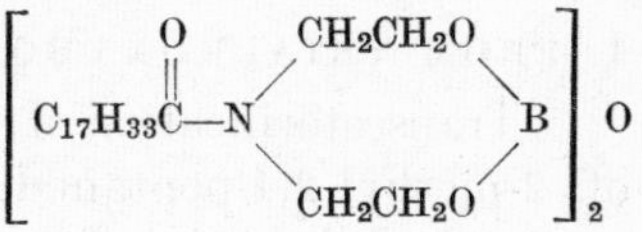 (CIII)

Direct reaction of a diol and boric oxide without the aid of an azeotroping agent also has been claimed.[71]

Evaporation of a methanol solution of 2,2,6,6-tetramethyl-3,5-heptanediol and boric acid followed by extraction of the residue with benzene has been reported to give the anhydride.[13]

2. FROM 2-HYDROXY-1,3,2-DIOXABOROLANES AND BORINANES

a. *Dehydration.* The hydroxy derivatives readily lose water on heating to give the anhydride.[14,15,16,24,29,39,42,43,58,73,83]

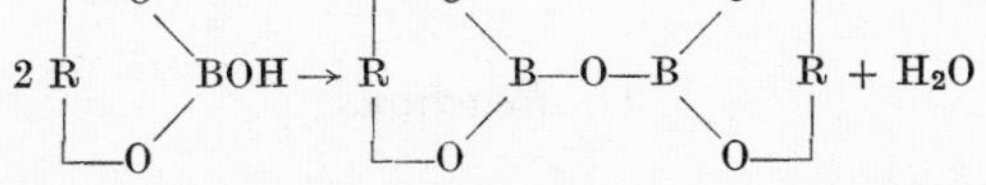

$$2\,R\begin{matrix}O \\ O\end{matrix}BOH \rightarrow R\begin{matrix}O \\ O\end{matrix}B{-}O{-}B\begin{matrix}O \\ O\end{matrix}R + H_2O \qquad (7\text{-}36)$$

b. *And 2-Chloro-1,3,2-dioxaborolanes.* A white gelatinous solid, presumably (CIV), resulted from the removal of hydrogen chloride from an equimolar mixture of (CV) and (CVI) in methylene chloride solution.[5]

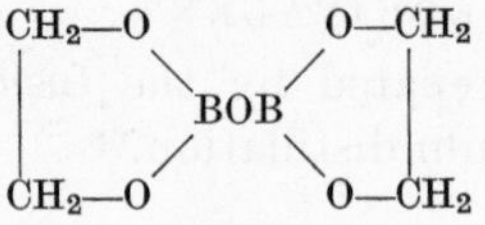

```
CH2—O          O—CH2      CH2—O                 CH2—O
|     \       /     |     |     \               |     \
|      BOB          |     |      BOH            |      BCl
|     /       \     |     |     /               |     /
CH2—O          O—CH2      CH2—O                 CH2—O
        (CIV)                (CV)                  (CVI)
```

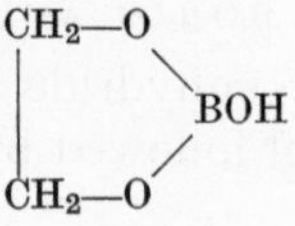

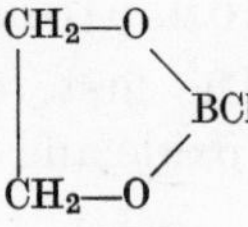

3. FROM OXYBIS(DIACETOXYBORANE)

The reaction of glycerol and oxybis(diacetoxyborane) has been postulated to give (CVII).[30]

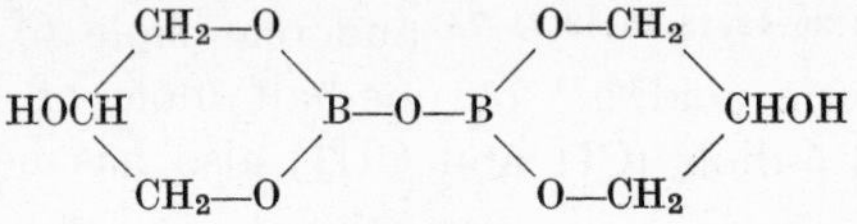

```
         CH2—O           O—CH2
        /     \         /     \
   HOCH        B—O—B           CHOH
        \     /         \     /
         CH2—O           O—CH2
                (CVII)
```

4. FROM TRIALKOXYBORANES

Transesterification of six moles of triethoxyborane with six moles of 2-methyl-2,4-pentanediol was claimed to result in complete removal of the ethanol (eighteen moles) and a good yield of the anhydride (CVIII).[71] The reaction as stated appears improbable

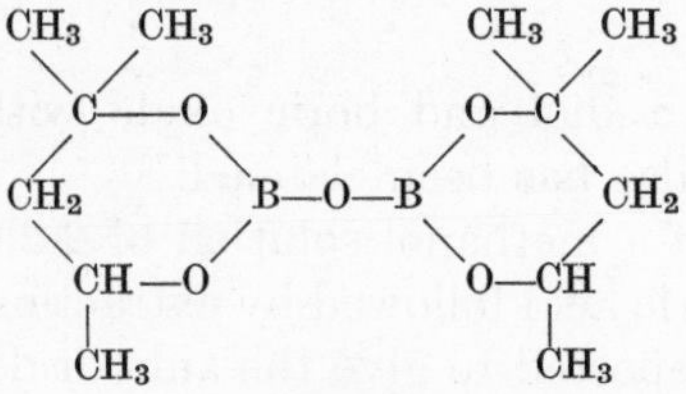

```
       CH3  CH3               CH3  CH3
          \ /                    \ /
           C—O                 O—C
          /    \             /     \
       CH2      B—O—B           CH2
          \    /      \          /
           CH—O         O—CH
           |                 |
           CH3               CH3
                 (CVIII)
```

since only enough hydrogen was available from the diol for production of twelve moles of ethanol and formation of a B–O–B bond would require diethyl ether formation. However, it is possible that some of the glycol dehydrated. The resulting water could lead to the formation of (CVIII) and the evolution of more than twelve moles of ethanol.

C. Reactions

1. HYDROLYSIS

The hydrolytic stability of the anhydrides is discussed in Chapter 21.

2. ALCOHOLYSIS

Partial alcoholysis of the anhydride from catechol[29,68] and 2-methyl- 2,4-pentanediol[71] has provided a variety of mixed esters.

$$(C_6H_4O_2B)_2O + C_4H_9OH \rightarrow 2\ C_6H_4O_2BOC_4H_9 + H_2O \quad (7\text{-}37)$$

$$(C_6H_4O_2B)_2O + \text{8-hydroxyquinoline} \rightarrow 2\ C_6H_4O_2B(OC_9H_6N) + H_2O \quad (7\text{-}38)$$

$$\tfrac{1}{2}\ [(CH_3)_2C(O)CH_2CH(CH_3)O B]_2O + (CH_3)_2CHCH_2CHOHCH_3 \rightarrow (CH_3)_2C(O)CH_2CH(CH_3)O\text{—}B\text{—}OCH(CH_3)CH_2CH(CH_3)_2 + \tfrac{1}{2}\ H_2O \quad (7\text{-}39)$$

Preferential rupture of the B–O–B bonds also has been accomplished with an enol.[68,71]

$$\tfrac{1}{2}\ (C_6H_4O_2B)_2O + CH_3\overset{O}{\overset{\|}{C}}CH_2\overset{O}{\overset{\|}{C}}CH_3 \rightarrow C_6H_4O_2B(OC(CH_3){=}CHC(CH_3){=}O) + \tfrac{1}{2}\ H_2O \quad (7\text{-}40)$$

```
CH3   CH3              CH3   CH3
  \  /                   \  /
   C——O                O—C         O     O
  /    \              /    \       ‖     ‖
½ CH2     B—O—B          CH2 + CH3CCH2CCH3
  \    /              \    /
   CH—O                O—CH
   |                      |
   CH3                    CH3

             CH3   CH3                CH3
               \  /                  /
                C——O          O=C
               /    \       ↙      \
          → CH2       B            CH + ½ H2O   (7-41)
               \    /   \         //
                CH—O      O—C
                |            |
                CH3          CH3
```

A biborate is the end product of alcoholysis with a glycol.[58]

```
CH3   CH3              CH3   CH3
  \  /                   \  /
   C——O                O—C          OH   OH
  /    \              /    \        |    |
CH2       B—O—B          CH2 + CH3CCH2CHCH3
  \    /              \    /        |
   CH—O                O—CH         CH3
   |                      |
   CH3                    CH3

        CH3   CH3                            CH3   CH3
          \  /                                 \  /
           C——O          CH3 CH3              O—C
          /    \          |   |              /    \
     → CH2       B—O—CCH2CHO—B                   CH2 + H2O   (7-42)
          \    /          |                  \    /
           CH—O           CH3                 O—CH
           |                                     |
           CH3                                   CH3
```

Use of a glycol different than that in the anhydride results in a mixed biborate[3] (see Chapter 6).

3. PYROLYSIS

The thermal stability of the anhydride system is evidenced by the 89% recover of (CIX) after heating at 290° for twelve hours.[29]

```
      O              O
     / \            / \
(C6H4)   B—O—B       (C6H4)
     \ /            \ /
      O              O
```

(CIX)

4. WITH AMINES

Addition compounds of (CIX) and two moles of quinoline or piperidine have been reported.[68] The stoichiometry of the complexes can be represented by structures of type (CX).

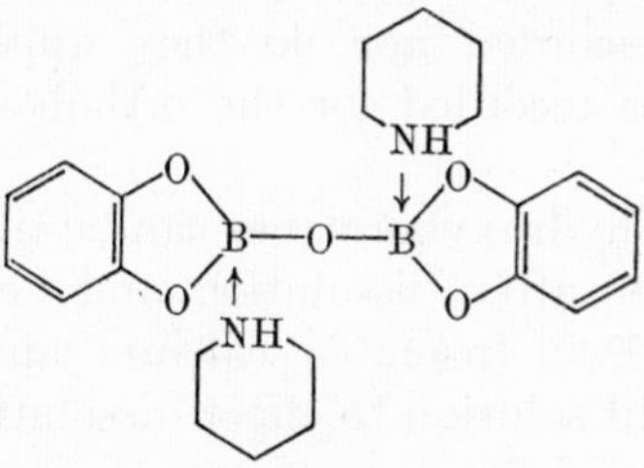

(CX)

5. WITH BORON HALIDES

Boron trifluoride did not react with (CIX).[29] Reactions of (CIX) with boron trichloride and bromide to produce the 2-halo-1,3,2-benzodioxaboroles are described in Chapter 12.

6. MISCELLANEOUS

A polymer of high molecular weight was formed on heating (CXI) to 155° at reduced pressure.[30] The polymerization can be formulated as an alcoholysis (7-43) followed by esterification (7-44).

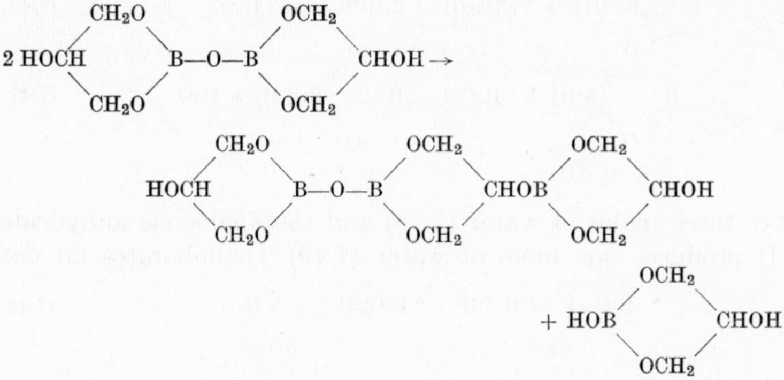

$$2\ HOCH\langle{}^{CH_2O}_{CH_2O}\rangle B{-}O{-}B\langle{}^{OCH_2}_{OCH_2}\rangle CHOH \rightarrow$$

$$HOCH\langle{}^{CH_2O}_{CH_2O}\rangle B{-}O{-}B\langle{}^{OCH_2}_{OCH_2}\rangle CHOB\langle{}^{OCH_2}_{OCH_2}\rangle CHOH + HOB\langle{}^{OCH_2}_{OCH_2}\rangle CHOH \quad (7\text{-}43)$$

$$n\ HOB\langle{}^{OCH_2}_{OCH_2}\rangle CHOH \rightarrow \left[OB\langle{}^{OCH_2}_{OCH_2}\rangle CHO \right]_n + \frac{n}{2} H_2O \quad (7\text{-}44)$$

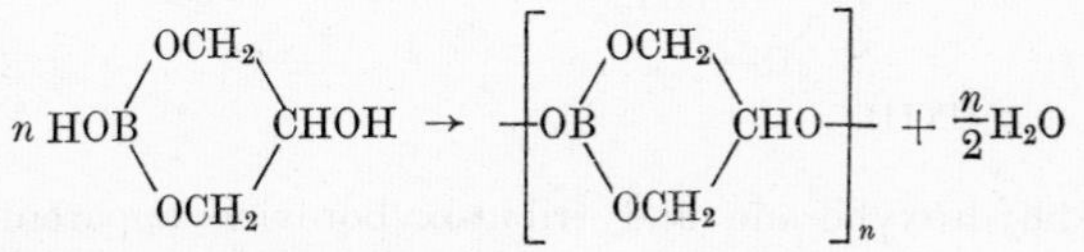

Reactions with phosphorus halides are discussed in Chapter 12.

VII. ANALYTICAL

A. Boron Determination

No special analytical techniques for the determination of boron in the alkoxyhydroxyboranes and hydroxyborolanes and their anhydrides have been recorded nor do they appear necessary. The analytical techniques recorded for the orthoborates in Chapters 4 and 5 are applicable.

The salts of the hydroxyborolanes can be titrated for boric acid in the usual manner after dissolution and neutralization of the resulting alkalinity.[35,67] Insoluble calcium and magnesium salts require boiling in acid solution to effect dissolution.[35]

B. Karl Fischer Determination

The Karl Fischer method for the quantitative determination of water (7-45) offers an extremely valuable procedure for the identi-

$$\underset{\text{deep red color}}{H_2O + I_2} + SO_2 + CH_3OH \rightarrow \underset{\text{bright yellow color}}{2\,HI + HSO_4CH_3} \qquad (7\text{-}45)$$

fication and determination of those boron–oxygen compounds which react with methanol to produce water.* Thus boric acid produces three moles of water (7-46)[51] and the monohydroxy derivative (CXII) similarly evolves one mole of water (7-47); boric oxide

$$B(OH)_3 + 3\,CH_3OH \rightarrow B(OCH_3)_3 + 3\,H_2O \qquad (7\text{-}46)$$

$$\underset{\text{(CXII)}}{R\begin{matrix}\ulcorner O\diagdown\\ \llcorner O\diagup\end{matrix}BOH} + CH_3OH \rightarrow R\begin{matrix}\ulcorner O\diagdown\\ \llcorner O\diagup\end{matrix}BOCH_3 + H_2O \qquad (7\text{-}47)$$

produces three moles of water (7-48) and the analogous anhydride (CXIII) produces one mole of water (7-49). Orthoborates do not

$$B_2O_3 + 6\,CH_3OH \rightarrow 2\,B(OCH_3)_3 + 3\,H_2O \qquad (7\text{-}48)$$

$$\underset{\text{CXIII}}{R\begin{matrix}\ulcorner O\diagdown\\ \llcorner O\diagup\end{matrix}B\text{—}O\text{—}B\begin{matrix}\diagup O\urcorner\\ \diagdown O\lrcorner\end{matrix}R} + 2\,CH_3OH \rightarrow 2\,R\begin{matrix}\ulcorner O\diagdown\\ \llcorner O\diagup\end{matrix}BOCH_3 + H_2O \qquad (7\text{-}49)$$

* Butyldihydroxyborane and tributoxyboroxine apparently were the first organoboron compounds to be "analyzed" by this method.[48] Application to oxybis(diacetoxyborane) is discussed in Chapter 8.

react with methanol to produce water and thus are inert to the reagent. Consequently, mixtures of (CXII) and (CXIII) can be determined by simultaneous solution of equations (7-50) and (7-51), and ternary mixtures of (CXII), (CXIII) and $B(OR)_3$ can be determined by simultaneous solution of equations (7-52), (7-53) and (7-54).

$$Wt_{BOH} + Wt_{BOB} = \text{sample Wt} \qquad (7\text{-}50)$$

$$\frac{Wt_{BOH}}{MW_{BOH}} + \frac{Wt_{BOB}}{MW_{BOB}} = \text{Moles of water determined by Karl Fischer titration} \qquad (7\text{-}51)$$

$$Wt_{BOH} + Wt_{BOB} + Wt_{B(OR)_3} = \text{sample Wt} \qquad (7\text{-}52)$$

$$\frac{Wt_{BOH}}{MW_{BOH}} + \frac{Wt_{BOB}}{MW_{BOB}} = \text{Moles of water determined by Karl Fischer titration} \qquad (7\text{-}53)$$

$$\frac{Wt_{BOH}}{MW_{BOH}} + \frac{2 \cdot Wt_{BOB}}{MW_{BOB}} + \frac{Wt_{B(OR)_3}}{MW_{B(OR)_3}} = \frac{\%\ \text{Boron in sample} \times \text{sample Wt}}{100 \times 10.82} \qquad (7\text{-}54)$$

Since certain metal oxides react with the reagent to produce an apparent mole of water per mole of oxide,[51a] the method has further applicability to the salts (CXIV), which titrate as the equivalent of

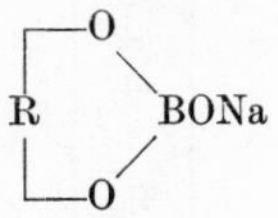

R(O)(O)BONa

(CXIV)

one mole of water. Thus it is apparent that a quaternary mixture of (CXII), (CXIII), (CXIV) and $B(OR)_3$ could be determined by use of equations (7-52) through (7-54) plus a determination of the Na_2O content.

VIII. PHYSICAL CONSTANTS

$(RO)_2BOH$	M.p. (°C)	B.p. (°C)	d_4^t	n_D^t	Reference
$(C_{14}H_{29}O)_2BOH$	—	—	—	—	60
$[C_{17}H_{33}C{=}N{-}C(CH_3)(CH_2O{-})CH_2{-}O]_2BOH$ (2-heptadecenyl-4-methyl-oxazoline ring, 4-CH_2O)		Liquid			16

$(RO)_2BOB(OR)_2$	M.p. (°C)	B.p. (°C)	d_4^t	n_D^t	Reference
$(C_6H_5O)_2BOB(OC_6H_5)_2$	—	—	—	—	69

$ROB(OH)_2$	M.p. (°C)	B.p. (°C)	d_4^t	n_D^t	Reference
$C_{18}H_{37}OB(OH)_2$	—	—	—	—	60
$[{-}CH_2N(CH_2CH(CH_3)OB(OH)_2)_2]_2$	170–174 (d.)				2, 62, 63

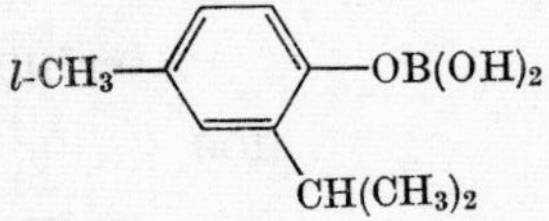 l-CH_3, $OB(OH)_2$, $CH(CH_3)_2$	132–135				56
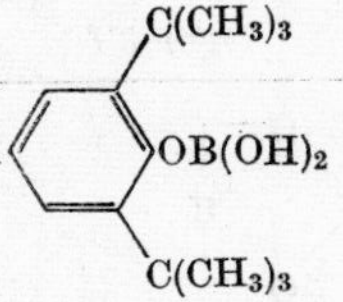 $C(CH_3)_3$, $OB(OH)_2$, $C(CH_3)_3$	105–170 (d.)				34
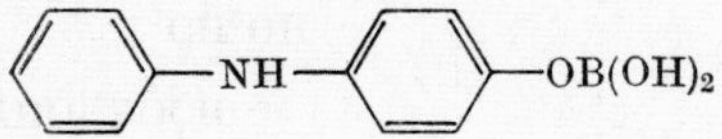 NH, $OB(OH)_2$	—	—	—	—	76
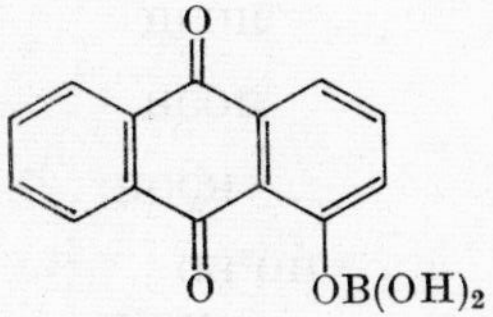 O, O, $OB(OH)_2$	—	—	—	—	79
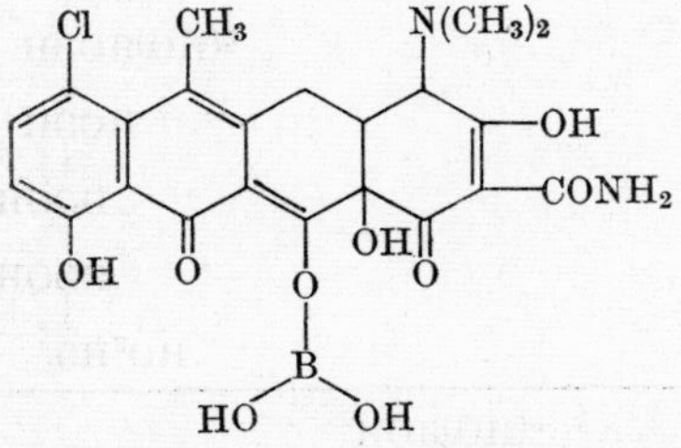 Cl, CH_3, $N(CH_3)_2$, OH, $CONH_2$, OH, O, OH, O, O, B, HO, OH	—	—	—	—	65

(Table continued)

$ROB(OH)_2$	M.p. (°C)	B.p. (°C)	d_4^t	n_D^t	Reference
CH_2OH–HOCH–HOCH–HCOH–$HCOB(OH)_2$–CH_2OH	79–80				8
CH_2OH–HOCH–HCOH–HCOH–$(HO)_2BOCH$–CH_2OH	104–108				8

R(O)(O)BOH and R(O)(O)BOM	M.p. (°C)	B.p. (°C)	d_4^t	n_D^t	Reference
1,2-diols					
CH_2—O, CH_2—O (ring) BOH	114–118				4
	Glass	176–187/1			61

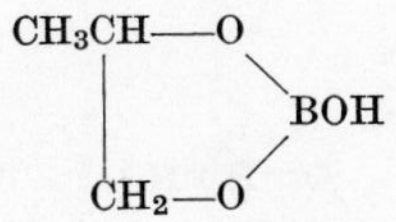 CH_3CH—O BOH CH_2—O		110–114/1,			61
		155–158/15			61
	Semi-solid at room temp.				35
	—	—	—	—	83
Na	>480				35
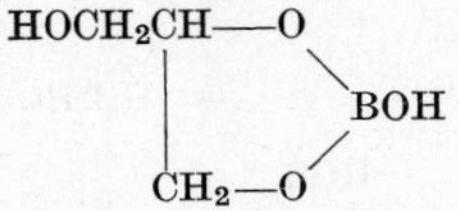 $HOCH_2CH$—O BOH CH_2—O	—	—	—	—	18
Na	—	—	—	—	18
NH_4	—	—	—	—	27
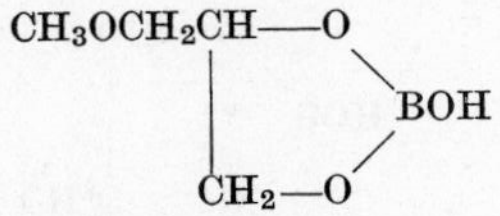 CH_3OCH_2CH—O BOH CH_2—O		145–150/<1			61
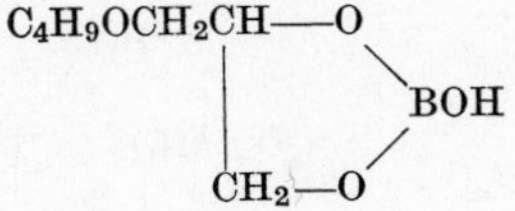 $C_4H_9OCH_2CH$—O BOH CH_2—O		162–165/<1			61
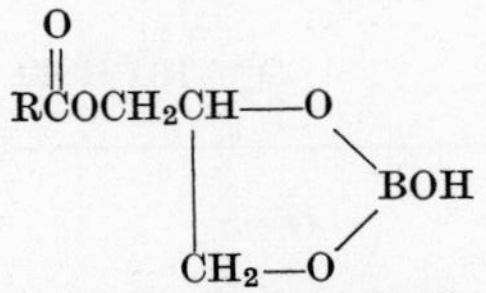 O ‖ $RCOCH_2CH$—O BOH CH_2—O R = long chain alkyl	—	—	—	—	54

(Table continued)

R(O)(O)BOH and R(O)(O)BOM (cyclic)	M.p. (°C)	B.p. (°C)	d_4^t	n	Reference
$ClCH_2CH$—O, CH_2—O (cyclic) >BOH		160–165/< 1			61
$(CH_3)_2C$—O, CH_2—O (cyclic) >BOH		76–79/< 1			61
CH_3CH—O, CH_3CH—O (cyclic) >BOH		110–119/0.6 112–117/< 1			38 61
meso CH_3CH—O, CH_3CH—O (cyclic) >BOH		129–134/4, 266–269			53 53
Na	—	—	—	—	53
NH_4	—	—	—	—	53

CH_3 / CH_3C—O / BOH / CH_3C—O / CH_3	65.2–65.8				58
	70				78
	—	—	—	—	32
C_6H_5CH—O / BOK / CH_2—O	—	—	—	—	32
$(CH_3)_3CCH$—O / BOH / $(CH_3)_3CCH$—O	98–100				13
1,3-diols					
CH_2—O / CH_2 BOH / CH_2—O	Crystalline solid				83
		147–151/3			61
CH_3 / CH—O / CH_2 BOH / CH_2—O	32–33				45
	Semi-solid at room temp.				35
		107–109/< 1			61
Na	> 480				35

(*Table continued*)

$R(O)_2BOH$ and $R(O)_2BOM$ (cyclic)	M.p. (°C)	B.p. (°C)	d_4^t	n_D^t	Reference
$C_{17}H_{33}C(=O)NH-C(CH_3)(CH_2-O)_2BOH$	—	—	—	—	19
$CH_3CH(O)-CH_2-CH(O)CH_3$ BOH (cyclic)	68				32
	69–73				13
	76				15, 23, 24, 72, 73
meso $CH_3CH(O)-CH_2-CH(O)CH_3$ BOH (cyclic)	82–83				13
racemic $CH_3CH(O)-CH_2-CH(O)CH_3$ BOH (cyclic)	40				13

$(CH_3)_2C(CH_2O)_2BOH$ (ring: CH_3, CH_3 on C; CH_2—O, CH_2—O; BOH)		137–142/1			58
Na		—	—	—	58
CH_3 CH_3 C—O, CH_2 BOH, CH—O, CH_3 (ring)	74–76				15, 22, 35, 42, 43, 72
	76–77				55
		109–110/0.7			26
Na	Sinters at 426–429				35
Li	315				35
K	Sinters at 265–275				35
Ca	175–190				35
Ba	>315				35
$C_6H_5CH_2N(CH_3)_3$	Glassy solid				35
CH_3 CH_3 C—O, CH_2 BOH, C—O, CH_3 CH_3 (ring)	100–102				31
	102				32
	120	228			78

(*Table continued*)

R(O)(O)BOH and R(O)(O)BOM	M.p. (°C)	B.p. (°C)	d_4^t	n_D^t	Reference
$(CH_3)_2C$–O–B(OH)–O–$C(CH_3)_2$–CH(OH)– (ring: HOCH bridging both C)	118				57
$(CH_3)_2C$–O–B(OH)–O–$C(CH_3)_2$–CHCl– (ring: ClCH bridging both C)	132				57
$(CH_3)_2C$–O–B(OH)–O–$C(CH_3)_2$–CH(CH_3)– (ring: CH_3CH bridging both C)	72				57

C_2H_5 CH_3 C—O CH_2 BOH C—O CH_3 CH_3	43–45	32, 78
C_2H_5 CH_3 C—O ClCH BOH C—O CH_3 CH_3	58	57
$CH(CH_3)_2$ CH_3 CH—O C BOH CH_3 CH_2—O	29–32	35
Na	314 (softens)	35
C_2H_5 C_2H_5 C—O ClCH BOH C—O CH_3 CH_3	55	57

(*Table continued*)

$R(O)_2BOH$ and $R(O)_2BOM$	M.p. (°C)	B.p. (°C)	d_4^t	n_D^t	Reference
$C_{17}H_{33}C$(=N–C(CH$_2$–O)$_2$BOH)–O–CH$_2$ (oxazoline ring with CH_2–O–B(OH)–O–CH_2 ring)		Liquid			16
1,4-diols					
$C_6H_4[C(C_6H_5)_2O]_2BOH$	145 and 248 (d.) depending upon rate of heating				85
1,5-diols					
$C_{17}H_{33}C(=O)$–N(CH_2CH_2O)$_2$BOH	—	—	—	—	44

$C_{17}H_{33}C(=O)$—N(—$CH_2CH(CH_3)O$—)$_2$BOH	—	—	—	—	44
$C_{17}H_{33}C(=O)OCH(CH_3)CH_2N$(—$CH_2CH(CH_3)O$—)$_2$BOH	—	—	—	—	21
Alicyclic diols					
cis cyclopentane-fused dioxaborolane, B—OK, CH_3	—	—	—	—	41
cis cyclopentane-fused dioxaborolane, B—OH, two CH_3	91–92				12

(Table continued)

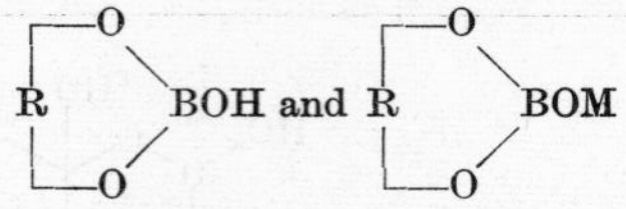 $R(O)_2BOH$ and $R(O)_2BOM$	M.p. (°C)	B.p. (°C)	d_4^{t}	n_D^t	Reference
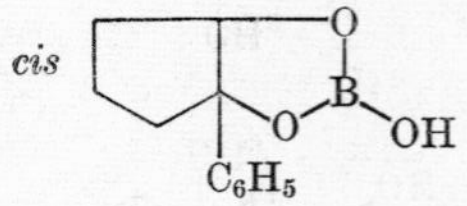 *cis* O, B, OH, C_6H_5	107–110				41
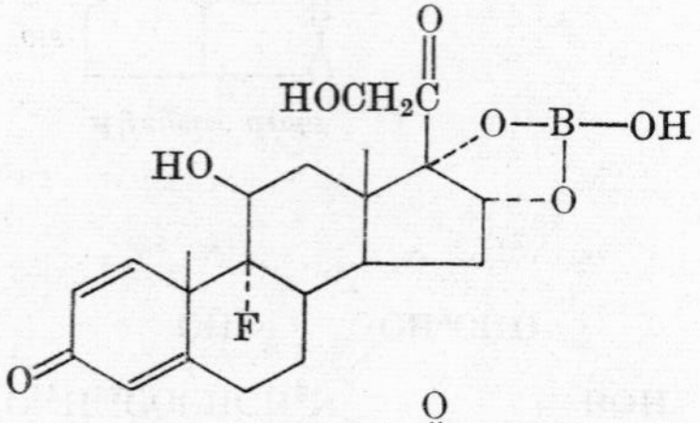 $HOCH_2C(=O)$, O—B—OH, O, HO, F, O	> 300 (structure in doubt)				77
	Na (structure in doubt)	—	—	—	77
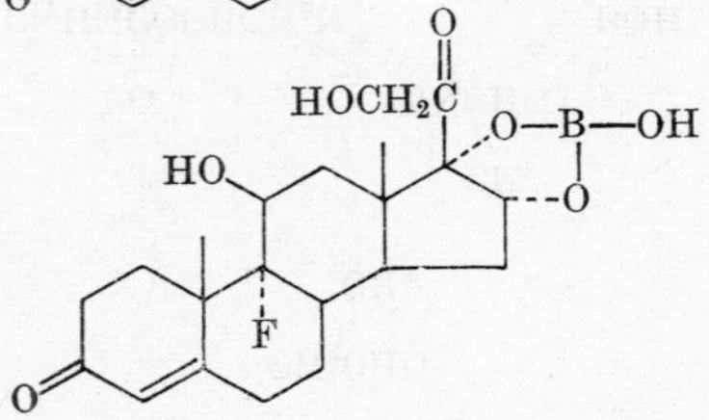 $HOCH_2C(=O)$, O—B—OH, O, HO, F, O	Crystalline (structure in doubt)				77
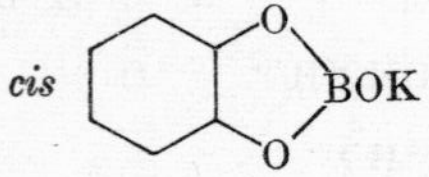 *cis* O, BOK, O	—	—	—	—	6, 31, 32

cis CH_2—CH—O, CH_2 CH_2 BOH, CH_2—CH—O 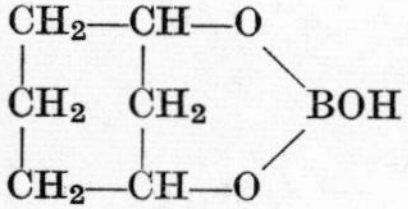	105–110				14
cis 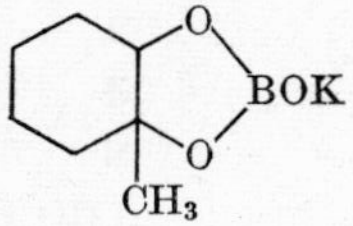 (cyclohexane ring fused O, O) BOK, CH_3	—	—	-	—	41
cis (tetrahydronaphthalene ring) O—BOK, O 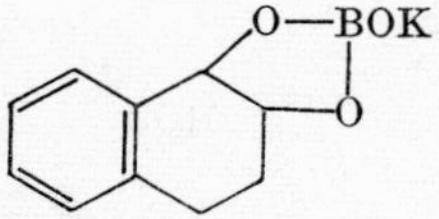	—	—	—	—	32
cis CH_2 (CH_2CH_2CH—O, CH_2CH_2CH—O) $BOH\cdot H_2O$ 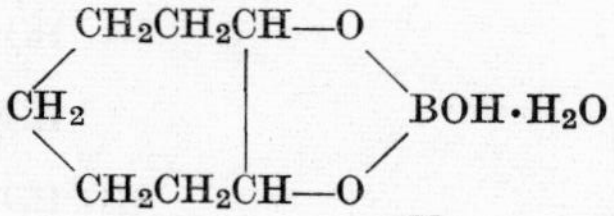	63				17
K	—	—	—	—	32
Aromatic diols					
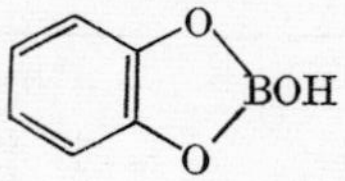 (benzene ring, O, O) BOH	70–75				29
$Li\cdot 3\ H_2O$	—	—	—	—	67
$Na\cdot 4\ H_2O$	—	—	—	—	67
$Sr\cdot 8\ H_2O$	—	—	—	—	67
$Mg\cdot 8\ H_2O$	—	—	—	—	67

(*Table continued*)

R(O)(O)BOH and R(O)(O)BOM	M.p. (°C)	B.p. (°C)	d_4^t	n_D^t	Reference
Sugar alcohols					
2,3-Mannitol					
CH_2OH–HOCH–HOCH–HC(–O)–HC(–O)–CH_2OH, with the two O atoms closing a ring through BOH	Solid				7, 8, 10, 33
Na	—	—	—	—	8
Li	—	—	—	—	8
K	—	—	—	—	8
NH_4	—	—	—	—	7, 8

2,3;4,5-Mannitol CH_2OH OCH HOB OCH HC—O BOH HC—O CH_2OH	Solid				7, 8, 10, 11
Na	—	—	—	—	7, 8
Li	—	—	—	—	8
K	—	—	—	—	8
NH_4	—	—	—	—	7, 8
2,3-Sorbitol CH_2OH HCOH HOCH HC—O BOH HC—O CH_2OH	Solid				7, 9, 33
Na	—	—	—	—	7, 9
NH_4	—	—	—	—	7, 9

(Table continued)

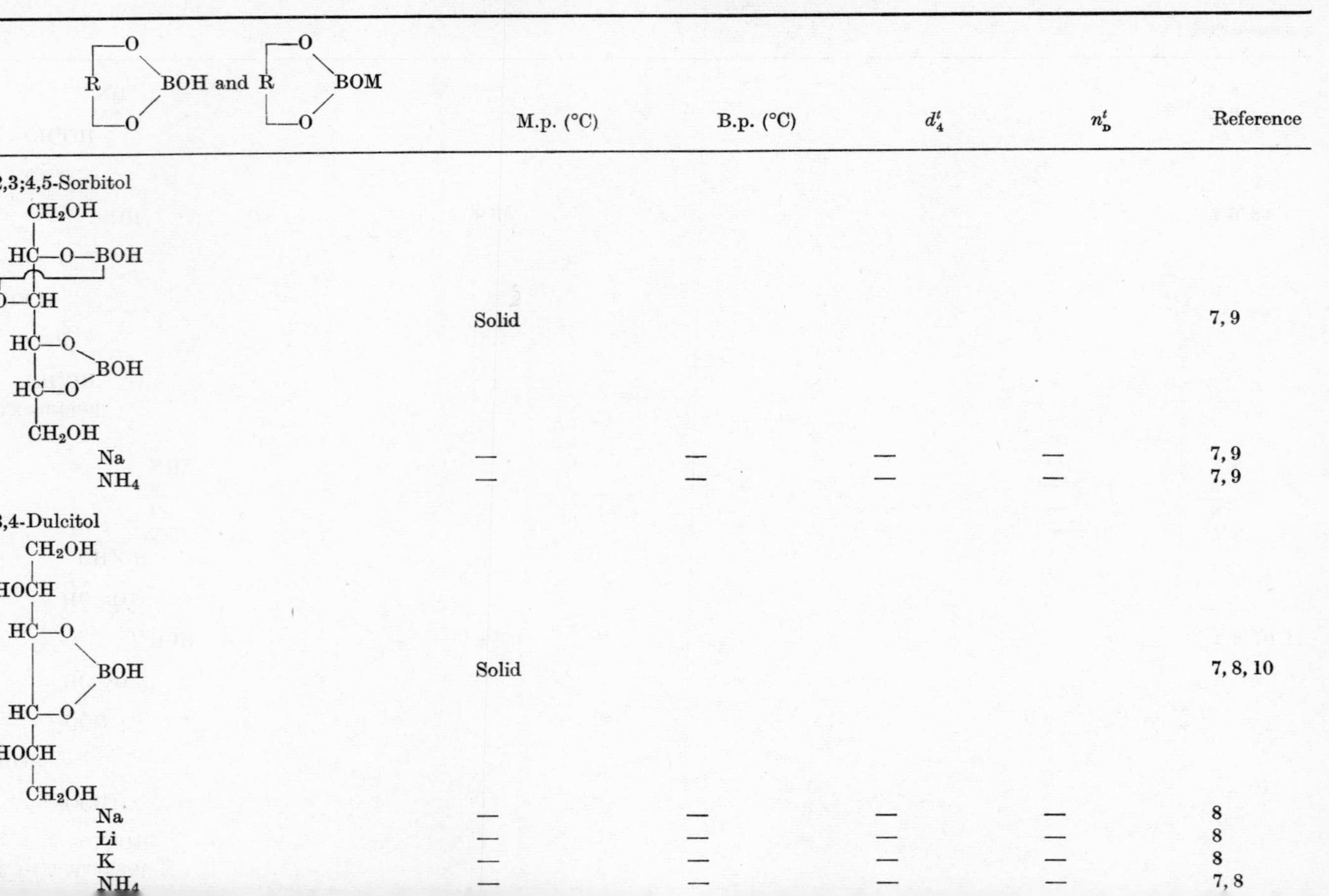

R(O)(O)BOH and R(O)(O)BOM	M.p. (°C)	B.p. (°C)	d_4^t	n_D^t	Reference
2,3;4,5-Sorbitol	Solid				7, 9
Na	—	—	—	—	7, 9
NH_4	—	—	—	—	7, 9
3,4-Dulcitol	Solid				7, 8, 10
Na	—	—	—	—	8
Li	—	—	—	—	8
K	—	—	—	—	8
NH_4	—	—	—	—	7, 8

2,3;4,5-Dulcitol	Solid				7, 8, 10
CH_2OH–CH(O–)–HC(–O–B–OH)–HC(–O–B–OH)–CH(O–)–CH_2OH					
Na	—	—	—	—	8
Li	—	—	—	—	8
K	—	—	—	—	8
NH_4	—	—	—	—	7, 8
Sugars					
1,2;4,6-Glucose					
(pyranose ring with O–CH_2, HO–B bridging 4,6-O; 1,2-O–B–OH)	—	—	—	—	11

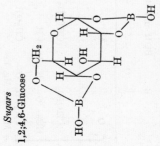

(*Table continued*)

(R(O)(O)BOH and R(O)(O)BOM)	M.p. (°C)	B.p. (°C)	d_4^t	n_D^t	Reference
$[(O{=}C{-}O{-}M{-}O{-}C{=}O)((CHOH)_3)_2(HC{-}O{-}B(O{-}){-}O{-}CH)(CH_2OH)_2]_2M'$ M = Ca, Mg, Fe M′ = Ca, Mg, Fe, Cu	—	—	—	—	1

(R(O)(O)BOB(O)(O)R)	M.p. (°C)	B.p. (°C)	d_4^t	n_D^t	Reference
1,2-diols					
$(CH_2{-}O)_2BOB(O{-}CH_2)_2$	White gelatinous solid				5
$(CH_3CH{-}O)(CH_2{-}O)BOB(O{-}CHCH_3)(O{-}CH_2)$		110–112/0.2			83

meso $\begin{matrix} CH_3CH{-}O & & O{-}CHCH_3 \\ \vert & BOB & \vert \\ CH_3CH{-}O & & O{-}CHCH_3 \end{matrix}$		160–180/11		1.4360^{22}	13
racemic $\begin{matrix} CH_3CH{-}O & & O{-}CHCH_3 \\ \vert & BOB & \vert \\ CH_3CH{-}O & & O{-}CHCH_3 \end{matrix}$		82–89/0.7		1.4233^{27}	13
1,3-diols					
$\begin{matrix} & CH_2{-}O & & O{-}CH_2 & \\ CH_2 & & BOB & & CH_2 \\ & CH_2{-}O & & O{-}CH_2 & \end{matrix}$		115–117/0.01		1.4528^{25}	25
		130–133/0.6		1.4372^{25}	83
$\begin{matrix} & CH_2{-}O & & O{-}CH_2 & \\ HOCH & & BOB & & CHOH \\ & CH_2{-}O & & O{-}CH_2 & \end{matrix}$	White amorphous powder				30
$\begin{matrix} CH_3 & & & & CH_3 \\ & CH{-}O & & O{-}CH & \\ CH_2 & & BOB & & CH_2 \\ & CH_2{-}O & & O{-}CH_2 & \end{matrix}$		181–184/17			34
		Slightly viscous liquid			45
$\begin{matrix} & CH_3 & CH_2{-}O & & O{-}CH_2 & CH_3 & \\ & & C & BOB & C & & \\ C_{17}H_{33}C(=O)NH & & CH_2{-}O & & O{-}CH_2 & & NHC(=O)C_{17}H_{33} \end{matrix}$		—	—	—	19

(Table continued)

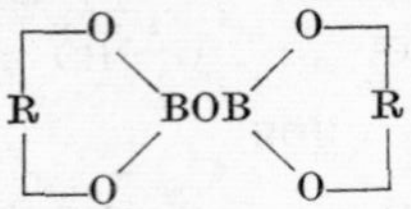 R(O)₂B–O–B(O)₂R	M.p. (°C)	B.p. (°C)	d_4^t	n_D^t	Reference
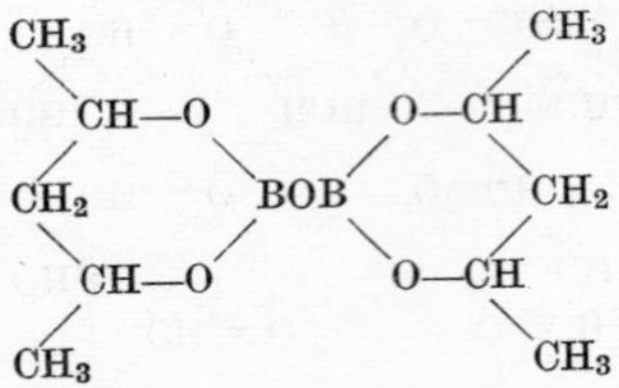 $CH_3CH(O)CH_2CH(CH_3)O$>BOB<$OCH(CH_3)CH_2CH(CH_3)O$		102–104/?		1.4336^{21}	13
		114/1			15, 23, 24, 43, 72, 73
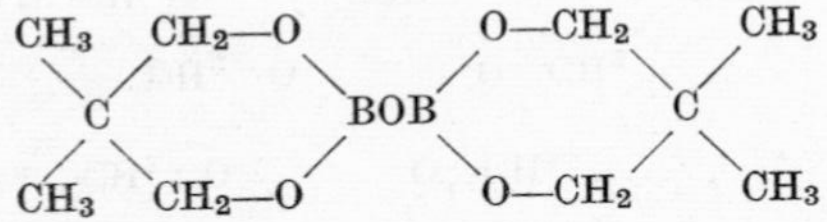 $(CH_3)_2C(CH_2O)_2$>BOB<$(OCH_2)_2C(CH_3)_2$		134–140/0.5			49
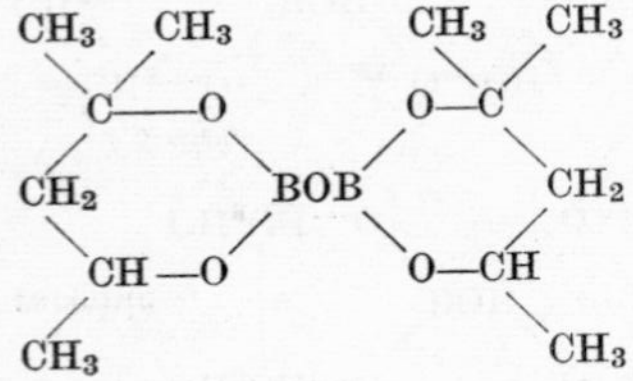 $(CH_3)_2C(O)CH_2CH(CH_3)O$>BOB<$OC(CH_3)_2CH_2CH(CH_3)O$	< −26				42
		84.9/0.1–0.7,			71
		110–127/1–2			71
		114–115/2		1.4318^{20}	36
		140–142/1, 275		1.4310^{25}	15, 23, 24, 42, 43, 73
		170–172/20			75
		274–276	1.013^{24}	1.4308^{25}	75

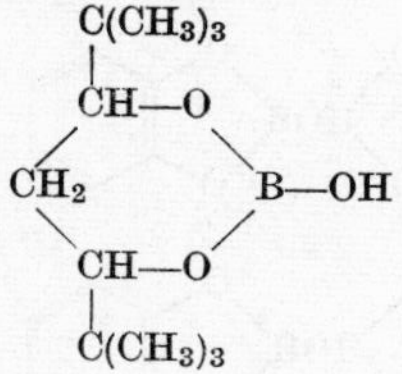 $C(CH_3)_3$–CH–O, CH_2, CH–O–$C(CH_3)_3$ ring with B—OH (cyclic: $CH_2[CH(C(CH_3)_3)O]_2B$—OH)	130–131	100/0.3 (sub.)		13
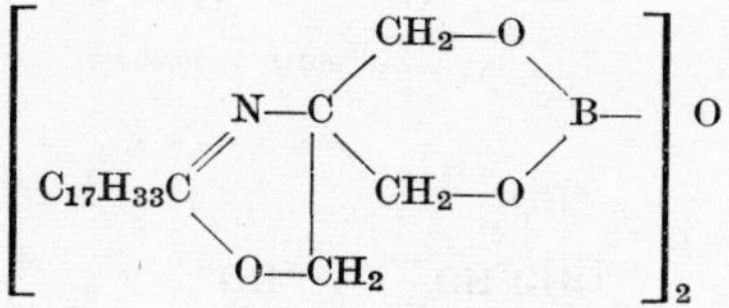 [$C_{17}H_{33}C$=N–C(CH_2–O)(CH_2–O)B—, with O–CH_2 ring]$_2$O		Liquid		16
Alicyclic diols				
cis 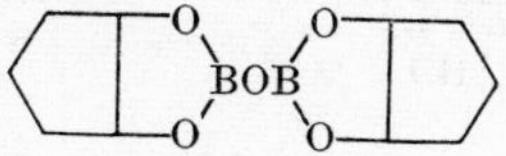 (cyclopentanediol–O)$_2$BOB(O–cyclopentanediol)	32–43	117–119/0.5	1.4710^{15}	13
cis 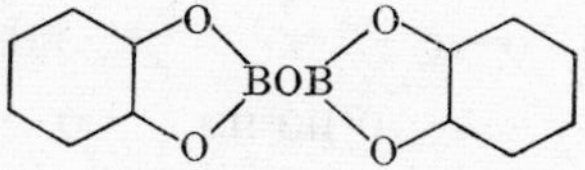 (cyclohexanediol–O)$_2$BOB(O–cyclohexanediol)		190/10^{-3}		13
cis 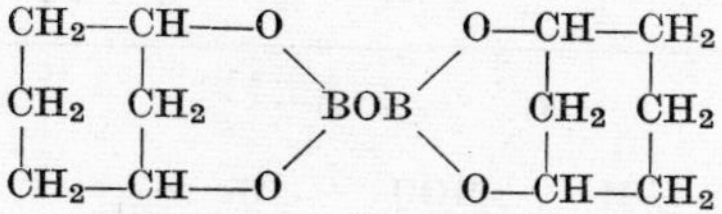 (CH_2–CH–O / CH_2 CH_2 / CH_2–CH–O)BOB(O–CH–CH_2 / CH_2 CH_2 / O–CH–CH_2)	180			14

(Table continued)

$R{<}(O)_2{>}BOB{<}(O)_2{>}R$	M.p. (°C)	B.p. (°C)	d_4^t	n_D^t	Reference
1,5-diols					
$C_{17}H_{33}C(=O)-N(CH_2CH_2O)_2B-O-B(OCH_2CH_2)_2N-C(=O)C_{17}H_{33}$		—	—	—	44
$[C_{17}H_{33}C(=O)OCH(CH_3)CH_2N(CH_2CH(CH_3)O)_2B-]_2O$	—	—	—	—	21
Aromatic diols					
$(C_6H_4O_2)BOB(O_2C_6H_4)$		160/0.1			29
	—	—	—	—	68
$(C_6H_4O_2)BOB(O_2C_6H_4)\cdot 2\,C_9H_7N$	—	—	—	—	68

O, O, BOB, O, O · 2 NH	—	—	—	—	68
$(CH_3)_3C$, O, O, BOB, O, O, $C(CH_3)_3$	—	—	—	—	78

IX. REFERENCES

1. Austin, J. A., and C. J. W. Wiegand, U.S. Pat. 2,937,973 (1960, to Jensen-Salsbery Laboratories, Inc.).
2. Bancroft, W. D., and H. L. Davis, *J. Phys. Chem.*, **34**, 2479 (1930).
3. Belden, S. H., U.S. Pat. 2,948,597 (1960, to The Standard Oil Company, Ohio).
4. Blau, J. A., W. Gerrard, and M. F. Lappert, *J. Chem. Soc.*, 4116 (1957).
5. Blau, J. A., W. Gerrard, and M. F. Lappert, *J. Chem. Soc.*, 667 (1960).
6. Böeseken, J., and J. van Giffen, *Rec. Trav. Chim.*, **39**, 183 (1920).
7. Bremer, C., U.S. Pat. 2,223,349 (1940, to Atlas Powder Co.).
8. Bremer, C., U.S. Pat. 2,223,948 (1940, to Atlas Powder Co.).
9. Bremer, C., U.S. Pat. 2,223,949 (1940, to Atlas Powder Co.).
10. Bremer, C., U.S. Pat. 2,224,011 (1940, to Atlas Powder Co.).
11. Brigl, P., and H. Gruner, *Ann.*, **495**, 60 (1932).
12. Criegee, R., *et al.*, *Ann.*, **599**, 81 (1956).
13. Dale, J., *J. Chem. Soc.*, 910 (1961).
14. Dale, J., *J. Chem. Soc.*, 922 (1961).
15. Darling, S. M., P. S. Fay, and S. Szabo, U.S. Pat. 2,741,548 (1956, to The Standard Oil Company, Ohio).
16. DeGray, R. J., and S. H. Belden, U.S. Pat. 2,965,459 (1960, to The Standard Oil Company, Ohio).
17. Derx, H. G., *Rec. Trav. Chim.*, **41**, 312 (1922).
18. Edenburg, L., U.S. Pat. Re. 19,604 (1935, to Nova Electric Corp.).
19. Emrick, D. D., U.S. Pat. 3,009,791 (1961, to The Standard Oil Company, Ohio).
20. Emrick, D. D., and S. M. Darling, U.S. Pat. 3,012,907 and 3,012,968 (1961, to The Standard Oil Company, Ohio).
21. Emrick, D. D., C. W. Liao, and E. O. Hook, U.S. Pat. 3,011,881 (1961, to The Standard Oil Company, Ohio).
22. Fay, P. S., and L. S. Szabo, Can. Pat. 572,203 (1959, to Standard Oil Company, Ohio).
23. Fay, P. S., and L. S. Szabo, U.S. Pat. 2,767,069 (1956, to The Standard Oil Company, Ohio).
24. Fay, P. S., and L. S. Szabo, U.S. Pat. 2,961,380 (1960, to The Standard Oil Company, Ohio).
25. Finch, A., J. C. Lockhart, and J. Pearn, *J. Org. Chem.*, **26**, 3250 (1961).
26. Garner, P. J., Brit. Pat. 722,538 (1955, to Shell Refining and Marketing Co., Ltd.).
27. Georgiev, A., U.S. Pat. 1,815,768 (1931, to Aerovox Wireless Corporation).
28. Gerrard, W., and M. F. Lappert, *J. Chem. Soc.*, 2545 (1951).
29. Gerrard, W., M. F. Lappert, and B. A. Mountfield, *J. Chem. Soc.*, 1529 (1959).
30. Gerrard, W., and E. F. Mooney, *Chem. & Ind.* (*London*), 227 (1958).
31. Hermans, P. H., *Proc. Acad. Sci. Amsterdam*, **26**, 32 (1923).
32. Hermans, P. H., *Z. Anorg. Allgem. Chem.*, **142**, 83 (1925).
33. Holst, W. H., U.S. Pat. 2,149,961 (1939, to Atlas Powder Co.).
34. Hunter, D. L., and H. Steinberg, Unpublished results.
35. Hunter, D. L., G. W. Willcockson, and H. Steinberg, Unpublished results.

36. Irish, G. E., U.S. Pat. 2,931,774 (1960, to Ethyl Corporation).
37. Irish, G. E., U.S. Pat. 3,009,798 (1961, to Ethyl Corporation).
38. Lane, C. A., U.S. Pat. 2,994,713 (1961, to Rohm and Haas Company).
39. Laubengayer, A. W., and R. G. Hayter, 132nd Meeting American Chemical Society, New York, 1957, Abstracts of Papers, p. 10-N.
40. Lawrence, F. I. L., R. K. Smith, and M. J. Pohorilla, U.S. Pats. 2,721,121; 2,721,180; 2,721,181 (1955, to Kendall Refining Co.).
41. Leeson, L. J., J. A. Lowery, G. M. Sieger, and S. Muller, *J. Pharm. Sci.*, **50**, 193 (1961).
42. Liao, C. W., Can. Pat. 609,257 (1960, to The Standard Oil Company, Ohio).
43. Liao, C. W., U.S. Pat. 2,848,312 (1958, to Standard Oil Company, Ohio).
44. Liao, C. W., D. D. Emrick, and E. O. Hook, U.S. Pat. 3,011,880 (1961, to The Standard Oil Company, Ohio).
45. Liao, C. W., and N. Visnapuu, Belg. Pat. 577,735 (1959, to Standard Oil Company, Ohio).
46. Maan, C. J., *Rec. Trav. Chim.*, **48**, 332 (1929).
47. Marvel, C. S., and C. E. Denoon, Jr., *J. Am. Chem. Soc.*, **60**, 1045 (1938).
48. Mattraw, H. C., C. E. Erickson, and A. W. Laubengayer, *J. Am. Chem. Soc.*, **78**, 4901 (1956).
49. McCloskey, A. L., Unpublished results.
50. Meulenhoff, J., *Rec. Trav. Chim.*, **44**, 150 (1925).
51. Mitchell, J. Jr., and D. M. Smith, *Aquametry*, *Chemical Analysis*, Vol. V, Interscience Publishers, Inc., New York, 1948, p. 256; 51a, p. 249.
52. Moores, M. S., U.S. Pat. 3,000,923 (1961, to Koppers Company, Inc.).
53. Morell, S. A., and E. C. Lathrop, *J. Am. Chem. Soc.*, **67**, 879 (1945).
54. Muncie, F. W., U.S. Pat. 2,209,634 (1940, to Colgate-Palmolive-Peet Co.).
55. Nöth, H., and L. P. Winter, *Angew. Chem.*, **71**, 651 (1959).
56. O'Connor, G. L., and H. R. Nace, *J. Am. Chem. Soc.*, **77**, 1578 (1955).
57. Pastureau, P., and M. Veiler, *Compt. Rend.*, **202**, 1683 (1936).
58. Petterson, L. L., and H. Steinberg, Unpublished results.
59. Pictet, A., and A. Geleznoff, *Ber.*, **36**, 2219 (1903).
60. Pohorilla, M. J., and R. K. Smith, U.S. Pat. 2,815,325 (1957, to Kendall Refining Co.).
61. Rippere, R. E., and V. K. LaMer, *J. Phys. Chem.*, **47**, 204 (1943).
62. Rudner, B., and M. S. Moores, U.S. Pat. 3,000,924 and 3,000,925 (1961, to Koppers Company, Inc.).
63. Rudner, B., M. S. Moores, and J. J. Harris, 140th Meeting American Chemical Society, Chicago, Sept. 1961, Abstracts of Papers, p. 103-Q.
64. Saito, S., O. Haruhiko, J. Kishimoto, and Y. Fujiyama, *Kolloid-Z.*, **144**, 41 (1955); *Chem. Abstracts*, **50**, 7544 (1956).
65. Sakaguchi, T., *Pharm. Bull.* (*Tokyo*), **3**, 170 (1955).
66. Scattergood, A., W. H. Miller, and J. Gammon, Jr., *J. Am. Chem. Soc.*, **67**, 2150 (1945).
67. Schäfer, H., *Z. Anorg. Allgem. Chem.*, **250**, 127 (1942).
68. Schäfer, H., and O. Braun, *Naturwissenschaften*, **39**, 280 (1952).
69. Schiff, H., *Ann. Suppl.*, **5**, 154 (1867).
70. Snyder, H. R., J. A. Kuck, and J. R. Johnson, *J. Am. Chem. Soc.*, **60**, 105 (1938).
71. Spike, C. G., U.S. Pat. 2,961,459 (1960, to The Standard Oil Company, Ohio).

72. Standard Oil Company, Ohio, Brit. Pat. 822,278 (1959).
73. Standard Oil Company, Ohio, Brit. Pat. 822,279 (1959).
74. Steinberg, H., and D. L. Hunter, *Ind. Eng. Chem.*, **49**, 174 (1957).
75. Steinberg, H., and L. L. Petterson, Unpublished results.
76. ter Horst, W. P., U.S. Pat. 2,220,981 (1940, to United States Rubber Company).
77. Thomas, G. A., U.S. Pat. 2,831,003 (1958, to Olin Mathieson Chemical Corp.).
78. Thomas, J. R., and O. L. Harle, U.S. Pat. 2,795,548 (1957, to Calif. Research Corp.).
79. Van der Wielen, P., *Pharm. Weekblad*, **72**, 875 (1935).
80. van't Hoff, J. H., *Die Lagerung der Atome in Raume*, 3rd ed., F. Vieweg and Son, Braunschweig, 1908, p. 90.
81. Visnapuu, N., U.S. Pat. 2,965,582 (1960, to The Standard Oil Company, Ohio).
82. Washburn, R. M., E. Levens, C. F. Albright, and F. A. Billig, "Preparation, Properties, and Uses of Borate Esters," in *Metal-Organic Compounds, Advances in Chemistry Series No. 23*, American Chemical Society, Washington, 1959, p. 129.
83. Watt, W. J., Ph.D. Thesis, Cornell Univ. (A. W. Laubengayer), 1956.
84. Willcockson, G. W., and W. G. Woods, Unpublished results.
85. Wittig, G., and M. Leo, *Ber.*, **64**, 2395 (1931).
86. Worth, H. J., U.S. Pat. 2,943,054 (1960, to Union Oil Company).
87. Worth, H. J., U.S. Pat. 2,943,055 (1960, to Union Oil Company).

8

ACYLOXY DERIVATIVES

I. INTRODUCTION

Acyloxy derivatives of boron are the mixed anhydrides of boric acid and a carboxylic acid (I). The most common types are derived from a monobasic acid (II and III); although biborate type structures from dibasic acids (IV) also have been reported.[64]

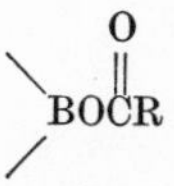

$$>\!BOC(=O)R \quad (RC(=O)O)_3B \quad (RC(=O)O)_2BOB(OC(=O)R)_2 \quad R\!<\!\begin{matrix}C(=O)-O\\C(=O)-O\end{matrix}\!>\!B-OC(=O)RC(=O)O-B\!<\!\begin{matrix}O-C(=O)\\O-C(=O)\end{matrix}\!>\!R$$

(I) 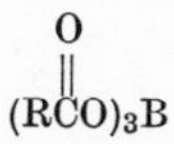 (II) 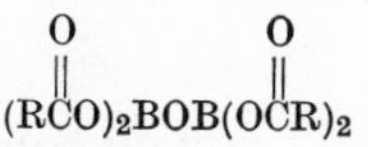 (III) 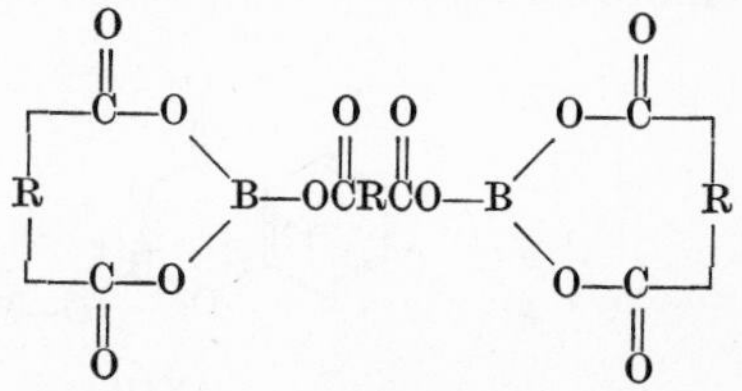 (IV)

Mixed anhydrides derived from two or more different organic acids (V and VI), which would be comparable to the mixed esters of Chapter 6, have not yet been reported; but some evidence is available for the existence of (VII).[24] Authentic examples of mixed

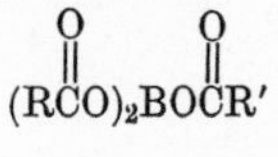

$$(RC(=O)O)_2BOC(=O)R' \quad R\!<\!\begin{matrix}C(=O)-O\\C(=O)-O\end{matrix}\!>\!B-O-C(=O)R'C(=O)O-B\!<\!\begin{matrix}O-C(=O)\\O-C(=O)\end{matrix}\!>\!R \quad C_6H_4\!<\!\begin{matrix}C(=O)-O\\O\end{matrix}\!>\!B-OC(=O)CH_3$$

(V) 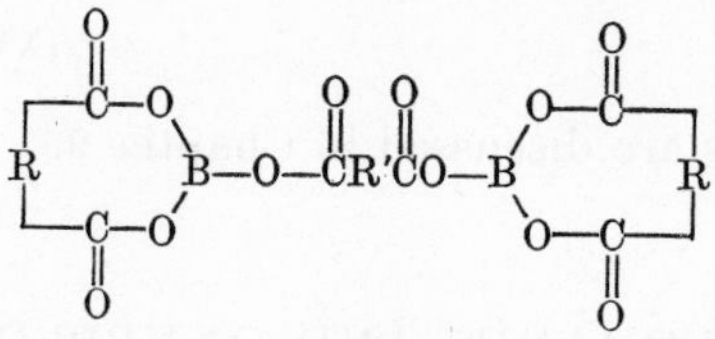 (VI) 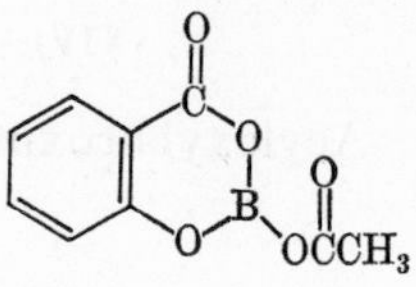 (VII)

acyloxyalkoxyboranes of definite structure have not yet been isolated; however, the mixed species (VIII) and (IX) were postulated

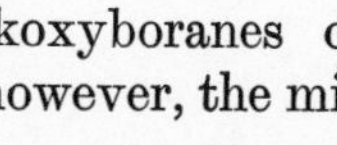

$$(C_4H_9O)_2BOC(=O)CH_3 \qquad C_4H_9OB(OC(=O)CH_3)_2$$

(VIII) 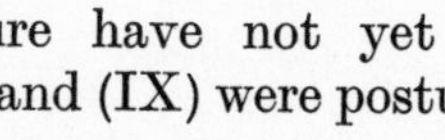 (IX)

as intermediates in the reactions of the butoxychloroboranes with acetic acid,[31] the reactions of triethoxyborane with acetic acid were reported to yield residues of this nature,[18] and various other examples have been claimed.[49]

Anhydride counterparts of hydroxydioxaborolanes and alkoxyhaloboranes (X and XI) also have not yet been reported; although

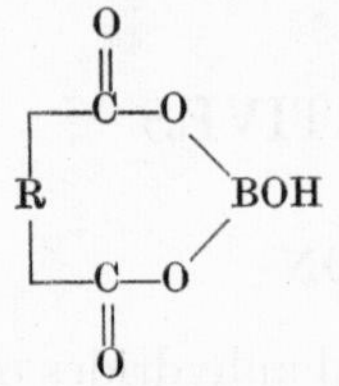

(X) 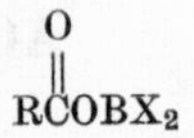 (XI) $RC(=O)OBX_2$

the salts (XII) have been described[68] and (XIII) is a possible intermediate in the reaction of propionic acid and ethylene-1,2-bis(dichloroborane).[54]

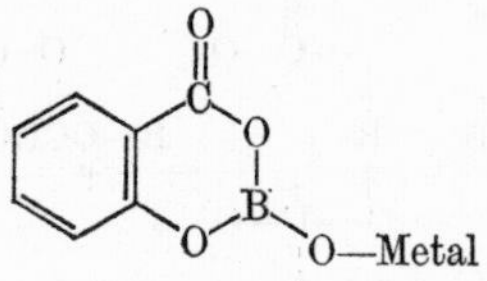

(XII) 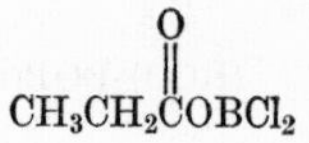 (XIII) $CH_3CH_2C(=O)OBCl_2$

Numerous acyloxyborolanes (XIV)[8,9] and acetoxyaryloxyboranes (XV)[24,25] have been reported.

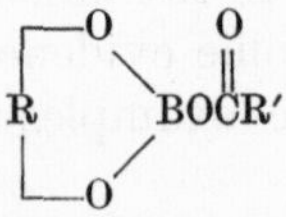

(XIV) 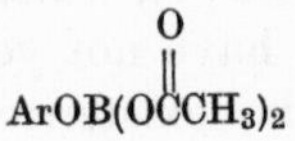 (XV) $ArOB(OC(=O)CH_3)_2$

Acyloxyboroxines are discussed in Chapter 9.

II. TRIACYLOXYBORANES AND OXYBIS(DIACYLOXYBORANES)

A. Historical

In 1861, Schützenberger observed that a compound was formed from the reaction of boric oxide and acetic anhydride.[71] The product was not characterized. Repetition of this work by Schiff,[69] six years later, resulted in the isolation of a glassy mass; however it

$$B_2O_3 + 3\,(CH_3C(=O))_2O \rightarrow 2\,(CH_3C(=O)O)_3B \qquad (8\text{-}1)$$

remained for Pictet and Geleznoff in 1903 to identify the product as triacetoxyborane.[64] The tetraacetoxy species (XVI) was reported twenty-three years later by Dimroth.[24]

$$\underset{\text{(XVI)}}{(CH_3\overset{\overset{O}{\|}}{C}O)_2BOB(O\overset{\overset{O}{\|}}{C}CH_3)_2}$$

B. Properties

1. GENERAL

The acyloxyboranes are hygroscopic,[64] monomeric[16,36,64] species which are odorless when pure.[21] If exposed to humid air, they quickly develop the odor of the carboxylic acid from which they are derived.[21] They cannot be distilled without decomposition even at reduced pressure.[64]

The electrophilicity of the boron atoms in oxybis(diacetoxyborane)* was believed to have been shown by the acid colors developed with more than twenty different indicators in benzonitrile solution.[77] However, the validity of the conclusion is clouded by the extreme difficulty of freeing the acyloxyborane from acetic acid.

Oxybis(diacetoxyborane) is very soluble in chloroform, acetone and ethyl acetate; moderately soluble in dioxane and glacial acetic acid; slightly soluble in benzene, nitrobenzene and the polyglycol ethers; and insoluble in ether, carbon tetrachloride and ligroin.[16]

As might be expected, the Raman spectrum of triacetoxyborane shows little similarity to the spectra of the lower trialkoxyboranes.[48]

2. STRUCTURE

The ^{11}B nuclear magnetic resonance chemical shift of oxybis(diacetoxyborane) is found at higher field ($\delta - 1.1 \pm 1.0$, $CHCl_3$ soln.) than most alkoxy and aryloxyboranes ($\delta - 14$ to -19). The oxybis(diacetoxyborane) resonance line would be expected to occur at slightly lower field than the alkoxyboranes if only an inductive effect were operative. However, chelation would increase the tetrahedral character and the shielding of the boron atoms and result in a shift to higher field. Indeed the oxybis(diacetoxyborane) resonance line occurs in the region characteristic of a tetrahedral boron atom

* The actual compound which was stated to have been used was triacetoxyborane. However, the American Potash and Chemical Corporation was acknowledged as the source of the compound, and available information indicates this company was marketing the tetraacetoxy and not the triacetoxy derivative at the time the work was performed.

bonded to four oxygen atoms: $B(OH)_4^-$, $\delta - 1.3$; $LiB(OCH_3)_4$, $\delta - 2.9$.[62]

Further evidence of intramolecular coordination of the carbonyl group and the vacant *p* orbital of the boron atom is indicated by the infrared spectrum which exhibits two carbonyl stretching bands. The band at the lower wavelengths is due to the normal unassociated carbonyl group and the band at the higher wavelengths is attributed to the associated carbonyl group (XVII).[27]

$$\begin{array}{c} \text{O} \qquad\quad | \quad\;\; \\ \| \qquad\quad | \quad\;\; \\ CH_3C\text{—O—B}\leftarrow\text{O} \\ \qquad\quad | \quad \| \\ \qquad\qquad \text{O—C—}CH_3 \end{array}$$

(XVII)

The fulfillment of the tendency of boron to attain sp^3 hybridization in this manner rather than as occurs routinely in the alkoxyboranes (XVIII) appears logical in view of the fact that the strong electron-attracting power of the carbonyl group (XIX) would tend to deter the back coordination of the electron pair on the ether oxygen (XX).

$$>\text{B}\!\leftarrow\!\ddot{\text{O}}\text{—R} \qquad >\text{B—}\ddot{\text{O}}\text{—}\overset{\text{O}}{\overset{\|}{\text{C}}}\text{—R} \qquad >\text{B}\!\leftarrow\!\ddot{\text{O}}\text{—}\overset{\text{O}}{\overset{\|}{\text{C}}}\text{—R}$$

(XVIII) (XIX) (XX)

The electron shift as shown in (XVII) has the added advantage over that in (XVIII) in that resonance stabilization of the resulting chelated ring (XXI) is possible.[27] Electronegative groups such as

$$\overset{-}{\text{B}}\langle\overset{\overset{+}{\text{O}}}{\underset{\text{O}}{}}\rangle\text{C—}CH_3 \longleftrightarrow \overset{-}{\text{B}}\langle\overset{\text{O}}{\underset{\underset{+}{\text{O}}}{}}\rangle\text{C—}CH_3$$

(XXI)

trifluoromethyl (XXII) tend to negate the electron transfer of (XVII) and, indeed, lead to coordinated carbonyl stretching bands intermediate in value to the coordinated carbonyl band and the normal carbonyl band for the unsubstituted acetoxy derivatives (Table 8-1).[27]

$$\begin{array}{c} \text{O} \qquad\quad | \quad\;\; \\ \| \qquad\quad | \quad\;\; \\ CF_3C\text{O—B}\leftarrow\text{O} \\ \qquad\quad | \quad \| \quad \longrightarrow \\ \qquad\qquad \text{O—C—}CF_3 \end{array}$$

(XXII)

Table 8-1. Infrared carbonyl stretching assignments for acyloxyboranes

Acyloxyborane	λ (μ) Normal	Coordinated
$(CH_3\overset{O}{\overset{\Vert}{C}}O)_2BOB(O\overset{O}{\overset{\Vert}{C}}CH_3)_2$	5.82	6.23
$(CF_3\overset{O}{\overset{\Vert}{C}}O)_2BOB(O\overset{O}{\overset{\Vert}{C}}CF_3)_2$	5.65	6.04
$(CF_3\overset{O}{\overset{\Vert}{C}}O)_3B$	5.64	6.02

The tetraacyloxy derivatives are capable of two different intramolecularly coordinated structures (XXIII and XXIV) which are

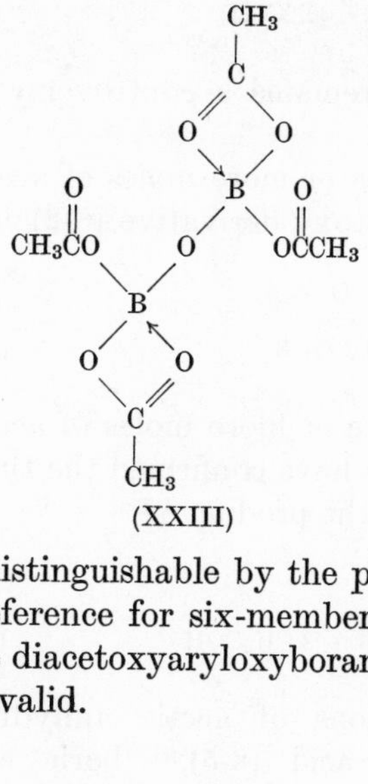

(XXIII) 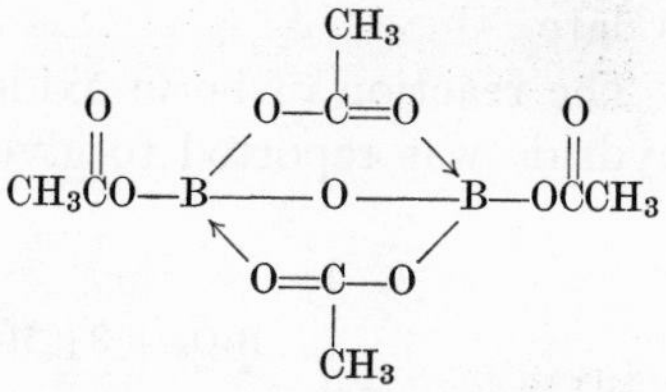 (XXIV)

indistinguishable by the present data.[27] In addition, in view of the preference for six-membered ring intramolecular coordination with the diacetoxyaryloxyboranes (see Section IV) structure (XXV) may be valid.

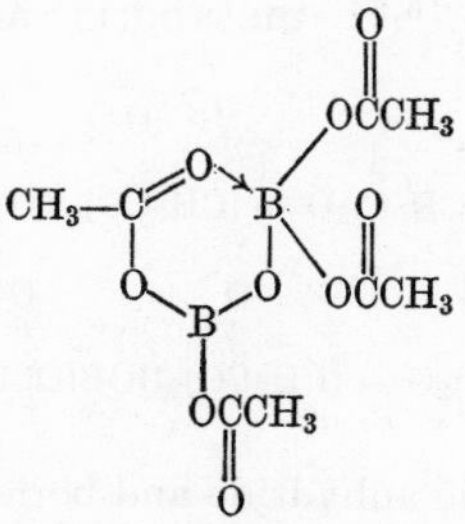

(XXV)

C. Methods of Preparation

In contrast to the preparation of alkoxyboranes, acyloxyboranes cannot be prepared by the simple dehydration of a mixture of boric acid and a carboxylic acid. In addition, acyloxyborane syntheses seldom involve the removal of water.*

1. FROM CARBOXYLIC ACID ANHYDRIDES

The reactions of a variety of boron sources with acetic anhydride have given either triacetoxyborane (XXVI) or the product of a 2:1 ratio of acetoxy groups to boron atoms, oxybis(diacetoxyborane) (XXVII). Both of these products have been called "boron acetate,"

$$\underset{\text{(XXVI)}}{(CH_3\overset{\overset{O}{\|}}{C}O)_3B} \qquad \underset{\text{(XXVII)}}{(CH_3\overset{\overset{O}{\|}}{C}O)_3BOB(O\overset{\overset{O}{\|}}{C}CH_3)_2}$$

and which structure is indeed obtained remains a controversy to this date.

The reaction of boric oxide with three or more moles of acetic anhydride was reported to give the triacetoxy derivative (8-2)[64] as

$$B_2O_3 + 3\,(CH_3\overset{\overset{O}{\|}}{C})_2O \rightarrow 2\,(CH_3\overset{\overset{O}{\|}}{C}O)_3B \tag{8-2}$$

was the treatment of boric acid with three or more moles of acetic anhydride (8-3).[3,21,64] Subsequent workers have confirmed the three to one ratio of acetic acid to boric acid in the product.[1,2]

$$H_3BO_3 + 3\,(CH_3\overset{\overset{O}{\|}}{C})_2O \rightarrow (CH_3\overset{\overset{O}{\|}}{C}O)_3B + 3\,CH_3\overset{\overset{O}{\|}}{C}OH \tag{8-3}$$

In direct contradiction, the reactions of acetic anhydride with boric oxide (8-4),[16,24] metaboric acid (8-5),[51] boric acid

$$B_2O_3 + 2\,(CH_3\overset{\overset{O}{\|}}{C})_2O \rightarrow (CH_3\overset{\overset{O}{\|}}{C}O)_2BOB(O\overset{\overset{O}{\|}}{C}CH_3)_2 \tag{8-4}$$

$$2\,HBO_2 + 3\,(CH_3\overset{\overset{O}{\|}}{C})_2O \rightarrow (CH_3\overset{\overset{O}{\|}}{C}O)_2BOB(O\overset{\overset{O}{\|}}{C}CH_3)_2 + 2\,CH_3\overset{\overset{O}{\|}}{C}OH \tag{8-5}$$

* The fusion of phthalic anhydride and boric acid to produce a biborate type anhydride is a rare example of water removal.[64]

(8-6),[16,32,36,48,51,63] boron trichloride (8-7),[16,30,57] triacetylboroxine (8-8),[24] and trialkoxyboranes (8-9)[16,17,55,73,75] have given the tetraacetoxy derivative.

$$2\,H_3BO_3 + 5\,(CH_3\overset{O}{\overset{\|}{C}})_2O \rightarrow (CH_3\overset{O}{\overset{\|}{C}}O)_2BOB(O\overset{O}{\overset{\|}{C}}CH_3)_2 + 6\,CH_3\overset{O}{\overset{\|}{C}}OH \quad (8\text{-}6)$$

$$2\,BCl_3 + 5\,(CH_3\overset{O}{\overset{\|}{C}})_2O \rightarrow (CH_3\overset{O}{\overset{\|}{C}}O)_2BOB(O\overset{O}{\overset{\|}{C}}CH_3)_2 + 6\,CH_3\overset{O}{\overset{\|}{C}}Cl \quad (8\text{-}7)$$

$$2\,(CH_3\overset{O}{\overset{\|}{C}}OBO)_3 + 3\,(CH_3\overset{O}{\overset{\|}{C}})_2O \rightarrow 3\,(CH_3\overset{O}{\overset{\|}{C}}O)_2BOB(O\overset{O}{\overset{\|}{C}}CH_3)_2 + 6\,CH_3\overset{O}{\overset{\|}{C}}Cl \quad (8\text{-}8)$$

$$2\,(RO)_3B + 5\,(CH_3\overset{O}{\overset{\|}{C}})_2O \rightarrow (CH_3\overset{O}{\overset{\|}{C}}O)_2BOB(O\overset{O}{\overset{\|}{C}}CH_3)_2 + 6\,CH_3\overset{O}{\overset{\|}{C}}OR \quad (8\text{-}9)$$

A plausible explanation for the apparent contradiction is that under certain conditions triacetoxyborane may eliminate acetic anhydride to give the tetraacetoxy derivative (8-10).[2] Tris(trifluoro-

$$2\,(CH_3\overset{O}{\overset{\|}{C}}O)_3B \rightarrow (CH_3\overset{O}{\overset{\|}{C}})_2O + (CH_3\overset{O}{\overset{\|}{C}}O)_2BOB(O\overset{O}{\overset{\|}{C}}CH_3)_2 \quad (8\text{-}10)$$

acetoxy)borane (XXVIII), which was prepared by the reaction of boric oxide and trifluoroacetic anhydride, undergoes the same elimination.[31,61]

$$(CF_3\overset{O}{\overset{\|}{C}}O)_3B$$
$$\text{(XXVIII)}$$

Reaction (8-9) with trimethoxyborane as the boron source was used to prepare the derivatives from propionic, butyric, isobutyric and n-caproic anhydride.[55]

2. FROM CARBOXYLIC ACID CHLORIDES

The triacetoxy–tetraacetoxy controversy also applies to the preparation from acetyl chloride. Both derivatives have been reported from the reaction of acetyl chloride and boric acid (8-11[64] and 8-12[32]). Other workers stated that reaction (8-12) did not proceed unless acetic acid or aluminum chloride were present in the reaction

$$H_3BO_3 + 3\,CH_3\overset{O}{\overset{\|}{C}}Cl \rightarrow (CH_3\overset{O}{\overset{\|}{C}}O)_3B + 3\,HCl \quad (8\text{-}11)$$

$$3\,H_3BO_3 + 5\,CH_3\overset{O}{\overset{\|}{C}}Cl \rightarrow (CH_3\overset{O}{\overset{\|}{C}}O)_2BOB(O\overset{O}{\overset{\|}{C}}CH_3)_2 + 5\,HCl + CH_3\overset{O}{\overset{\|}{C}}OH \quad (8\text{-}12)$$

mixture.[16] The benzoic acid derivative (XXIX) also was prepared by reaction (8-11).[64]

$$(C_6H_5\overset{\overset{O}{\|}}{C}O)_3B$$
(XXIX)

Cinnamoyl chloride, prepared *in situ* from cinnamic acid and thionyl chloride, reacted with boric acid to give (XXX).[41]

$$(C_6H_5CH{=}CH\overset{\overset{O}{\|}}{C}O)_3B$$
(XXX)

Acetate ion is readily displaced from boron by a variety of acyl halides.[64]

$$(CH_3\overset{\overset{O}{\|}}{C}O)_3B + 3\,R\overset{\overset{O}{\|}}{C}Cl \rightarrow (R\overset{\overset{O}{\|}}{C}O)_3B + 3\,CH_3\overset{\overset{O}{\|}}{C}Cl \qquad (8\text{-}13)$$

3. FROM CARBOXYLIC ACIDS

a. *And Chloroboranes.* An early reference to the reaction of acetic acid and boron trichloride claimed acetyl chloride as the product.[35] Later work showed that both the tetraacetoxy (8-14)[16,32] and triacetoxy (8-15)[6] derivatives were formed. The tetraacetoxy

$$5\,CH_3\overset{\overset{O}{\|}}{C}OH + 2\,BCl_3 \rightarrow (CH_3\overset{\overset{O}{\|}}{C}O)_2BOB(O\overset{\overset{O}{\|}}{C}CH_3)_2 + 5\,HCl + CH_3\overset{\overset{O}{\|}}{C}Cl \qquad (8\text{-}14)$$

$$3\,CH_3\overset{\overset{O}{\|}}{C}OH + BCl_3 \rightarrow (CH_3\overset{\overset{O}{\|}}{C}O)_3B + 3\,HCl \qquad (8\text{-}15)$$

$$3\,C_4H_9OBCl_2 + 6\,CH_3\overset{\overset{O}{\|}}{C}OH \xrightarrow{-6\,HCl} 3\left\{C_4H_9OB(O\overset{\overset{O}{\|}}{C}CH_3)_2\right\} \rightarrow$$
$$(CH_3\overset{\overset{O}{\|}}{C}O)_2BOB(O\overset{\overset{O}{\|}}{C}CH_3)_2 + (C_4H_9O)_3B + CH_3\overset{\overset{O}{\|}}{C}O\overset{\overset{O}{\|}}{C}CH_3 \qquad (8\text{-}16)$$

derivative also was formed from the reactions of acetic acid and the butoxychloroboranes (8-16 and 8-17), presumably by disproportiona-

$$6\,(C_4H_9O)_2BCl + 6\,CH_3\overset{\overset{O}{\|}}{C}OH \xrightarrow{-6\,HCl} 6\left\{(C_4H_9O)_2BO\overset{\overset{O}{\|}}{C}CH_3\right\} \rightarrow$$
$$(CH_3\overset{\overset{O}{\|}}{C}O)_2BOB(O\overset{\overset{O}{\|}}{C}CH_3)_2 + 4\,(C_4H_9O)_3B + CH_3\overset{\overset{O}{\|}}{C}O\overset{\overset{O}{\|}}{C}CH_3 \qquad (8\text{-}17)$$

tion of the intermediate acetoxybutoxyboranes,[31] or the acetoxy-chloro species (XXXI).[33]

$$\begin{matrix} CH_3\overset{\overset{O}{\|}}{C}O & & O\overset{\overset{O}{\|}}{C}CH_3 \\ & \diagdown BOB \diagup & \\ & \diagup \quad \diagdown & \\ Cl & & Cl \end{matrix}$$

(XXXI)

Trifluoroacetic acid and boron trichloride resulted in the triacyl derivative (XXXII).[31] This same compound, or the tetraacyl

$$\left(CF_3\overset{\overset{O}{\|}}{C}O\right)_3B$$

(XXXII)

derivative from its decomposition, also was obtained by the reaction of trifluoroacetic acid and dichloro(phenyl)borane (8-18).[31] Boron–

$$C_6H_5BCl_2 + 3\ CF_3\overset{\overset{O}{\|}}{C}OH \rightarrow (CF_3\overset{\overset{O}{\|}}{C}O)_3B + C_6H_6 + 2\ HCl \qquad (8\text{-}18)$$

carbon cleavage in this manner is not without precedent since acetic acid cleaves the boron carbon bond in trimethyl- and triethylborane to give the acetoxydialkylboranes.[34,58]

b. *And Boron Tribromide.* The triacyloxyboranes from acetic acid, propionic acid and butyric acid were prepared in essentially quantitative yield from the reaction of the appropriate acid and boron tribromide in benzene solution.[76]

$$3\ R\overset{\overset{O}{\|}}{C}OH + BBr_3 \rightarrow (R\overset{\overset{O}{\|}}{C}O)_3B + 3\ HBr \qquad (8\text{-}19)$$

c. *And Diborane.* Treatment of a carboxylic acid with one-sixth of a mole of diborane results in the evolution of one mole of hydrogen and the formation of the anhydride.[12,14]

$$6\ R\overset{\overset{O}{\|}}{C}OH + B_2H_6 \rightarrow 2\ (R\overset{\overset{O}{\|}}{C}O)_3B + 6\ H_2 \qquad (8\text{-}20)$$

d. *And Trialkylboranes.* A convenient non-catalytic procedure for the hydrogenation of double bonds involves the hydroboration of an olefin followed by treatment of the resulting trialkylborane with glacial acetic or propionic acid. The other product of the protonolysis is the triacyloxyborane (8-21).[13,15,22] However, no

$$R_3B + 3\ R\overset{\overset{O}{\|}}{C}OH \rightarrow 3\ RH + (R\overset{\overset{O}{\|}}{C}O)_3B \qquad (8\text{-}21)$$

actual isolation of a triacyloxyborane by this procedure has been reported as yet.

e. *And Triacetoxyborane.* Acetate ion is readily displaced from boron by a variety of aliphatic and aromatic acids.[1,64]

$$(CH_3\overset{O}{\overset{\|}{C}}O)_3B + 3\,R\overset{O}{\overset{\|}{C}}OH \xrightarrow{\Delta} (R\overset{O}{\overset{\|}{C}}O)_3B + 3\,CH_3\overset{O}{\overset{\|}{C}}OH \qquad (8\text{-}22)$$

Salicyclic acid was presumed to give the anhydride (XXXIII)[3]

$$\left[o\text{-}HOC_6H_4\overset{O}{\overset{\|}{C}}O \right]_3 B$$

(XXXIII)

by this method; however, comparison of the reported melting point of the product, 258–259°, with values recorded for the carboxyester (XXXIV), 258°,[42] 260–270°,[20] raises doubt as to the validity of

$$\left[o\text{-}HO_2CC_6H_4O\text{—} \right]_3 B$$

(XXXIV)

preferential reaction at the carboxyl group. More definitive proof of the formation of the ester (XXXIV) and not the anhydride (XXXIII) was shown by the presence of a carboxyl group and the absence of an hydroxyl group.[1]

The triacetoxyborane may be prepared *in situ* (8-23).[39,41]

$$3\,CH_3\overset{O}{\overset{\|}{C}}O\overset{O}{\overset{\|}{C}}CH_3 + H_3BO_3 + 3\,R\overset{O}{\overset{\|}{C}}OH \rightarrow (R\overset{O}{\overset{\|}{C}}O)_3B + 6\,CH_3\overset{O}{\overset{\|}{C}}OH \qquad (8\text{-}23)$$

However, prior reaction of the acetic anhydride and carboxylic acid to give a higher molecular weight anhydride which then reacts with the boric acid to give the product precludes the necessity of triacetoxyborane formation.

4. FROM CARBOXYLIC ACID ESTERS

No reaction resulted from the attempted acylation of boric oxide with amyl acetate.[16,17]

5. FROM CARBOXYLIC ACID SALTS

The metathetical reaction of silver acetate and boron trichloride in dioxane solution resulted in a small yield of the tetraacetoxy

$$6\,CH_3\overset{O}{\overset{\|}{C}}OAg + 2\,BCl_3 \rightarrow (CH_3\overset{O}{\overset{\|}{C}}O)_2BOB(O\overset{O}{\overset{\|}{C}}CH_3)_2 + CH_3\overset{O}{\overset{\|}{C}}O\overset{O}{\overset{\|}{C}}CH_3 + 6\,AgCl \quad (8\text{-}24)$$

derivative. Sodium acetate did not react.[17]

6. FROM KETENE

A poor yield of impure oxybis(diacetoxyborane) was claimed to be a product from the reaction of ketene and boric acid in chloroform solution (8-25).[16] An essentially quantitative yield was obtained in

$$2\,H_3BO_3 + 5\,CH_2{=}C{=}O \rightarrow (CH_3\overset{O}{\overset{\|}{C}}O)_2BOB(O\overset{O}{\overset{\|}{C}}CH_3)_2 + CH_3\overset{O}{\overset{\|}{C}}OH \quad (8\text{-}25)$$

acetone–tetrahydrofuran solution (8-26).[17]

Reaction (8-26) may be the first and, as yet, only example of the

$$2\,H_3BO_3 + 6\,CH_2{=}C{=}O \rightarrow (CH_3\overset{O}{\overset{\|}{C}}O)_2BOB(O\overset{O}{\overset{\|}{C}}CH_3)_2 + CH_3\overset{O}{\overset{\|}{C}}O\overset{O}{\overset{\|}{C}}CH_3 \quad (8\text{-}26)$$

addition of boric acid to a carbon–carbon double bond via hydrogen–oxygen cleavage (8-27). However, a more plausible path for the

$$CH_2{=}\overset{O}{\overset{\|}{C}} + H{-}OB(OH)_2 \rightarrow CH_3\overset{O}{\overset{\|}{C}}OB(OH)_2 \xrightarrow[\text{etc.}]{CH_2=C=O} \quad (8\text{-}27)$$

reaction may involve initial attack on boron by the carbonyl oxygen or attack on the carbonyl carbon by hydroxyl followed by collapse of the resulting enol (8-28).

$$CH_2{=}\overset{O\;\rightarrow\;B(OH)_2\text{—}OH}{\overset{\|}{C}} \rightarrow CH_2{=}\underset{OH}{\underset{|}{C}}{-}O{-}B(OH)_2 \rightarrow CH_3\underset{O}{\underset{\|}{C}}OB(OH)_2 \quad (8\text{-}28)$$

D. *Reactions*

1. HYDROLYSIS

Acyloxyboranes are readily hydrolyzed to give the original mixture of acids from which they are derived (8-29).[14,16,21,31,64] Unlike the trialkoxyboranes, the reverse reaction does not proceed.

$$(R\overset{O}{\overset{\|}{C}}O)_3B + 3\,H_2O \rightarrow 3\,R\overset{O}{\overset{\|}{C}}OH + H_3BO_3 \quad (8\text{-}29)$$

2. ALCOHOLYSIS

The reaction of alcohols with triacetoxyborane affords a convenient method of preparation of boric acid esters. This conversion is discussed in Chapters 4 and 5.

In general, the treatment of phenolic materials with oxybis(diacetoxyborane) results in the acetylation of the hydroxyl group (8-30); however, if certain structural features are present, such as an

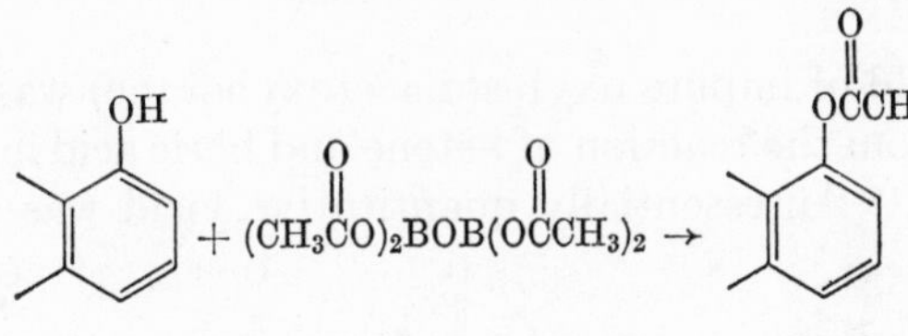

$$\text{(2,3-dimethylphenol, OH)} + (CH_3\overset{O}{\overset{\|}{C}}O)_2BOB(O\overset{O}{\overset{\|}{C}}CH_3)_2 \rightarrow \text{(2,3-dimethylphenyl, } O\overset{O}{\overset{\|}{C}}CH_3\text{)} \qquad (8\text{-}30)$$

adjacent carbonyl group, borylation of the hydroxyl group may occur (8-31).[8] This phenomenon is discussed in Section IV-B.

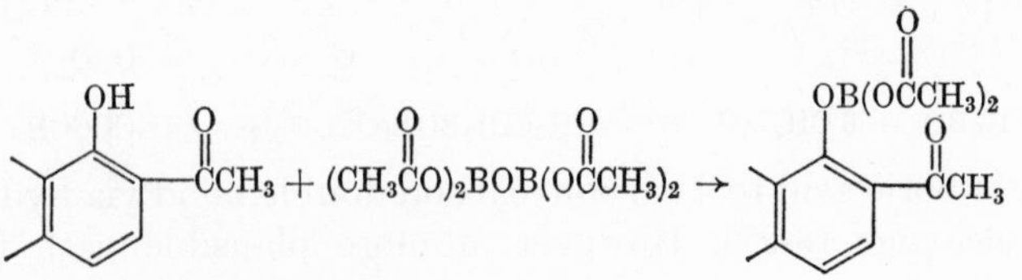

$$\text{(OH, } \overset{O}{\overset{\|}{C}}CH_3\text{ aryl)} + (CH_3\overset{O}{\overset{\|}{C}}O)_2BOB(O\overset{O}{\overset{\|}{C}}CH_3)_2 \rightarrow \text{(} OB(O\overset{O}{\overset{\|}{C}}CH_3)_2\text{, } \overset{O}{\overset{\|}{C}}CH_3\text{ aryl)} \qquad (8\text{-}31)$$

The reaction of salicyclic acid and oxybis(diacetoxyborane) resulted in the tetravalent species (XXXV).[24]

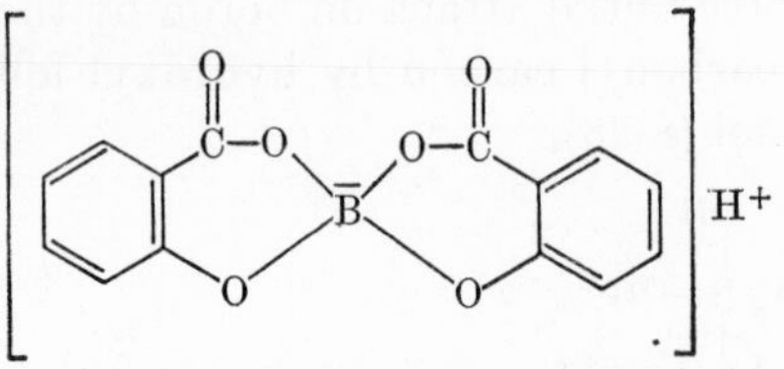

$$\left[\text{bis(salicylato)borate: } \overset{O}{\overset{\|}{C}}\text{—O}\diagdown\overset{-}{B}\diagup\text{O—}\overset{O}{\overset{\|}{C}} \right] H^+$$

(XXXV)

3. THERMAL STABILITY

Sublimation of tris(trifluoroacetoxy)borane at 100° and 10^{-4} mm. resulted in the elimination of trifluoroacetic anhydride and the formation of oxybis[di(trifluoroacetoxyborane)] (8-32).[31,61] Triacetoxyborane is believed to behave in a similar manner.[2]

$$2\,(CF_3\overset{O}{\overset{\|}{C}}O)_3B \rightarrow CF_3\overset{O}{\overset{\|}{C}}O\overset{O}{\overset{\|}{C}}CF_3 + (CF_3\overset{O}{\overset{\|}{C}}O)_2BOB(O\overset{O}{\overset{\|}{C}}CF_3)_2 \qquad (8\text{-}32)$$

A possible path for the decomposition is postulated to involve an initial heterolytic acyl-oxygen cleavage (8-33) followed by displacement of acetate ion by the resulting diacetoxyboryloxy anion (8-34).[31]

$$CH_3\overset{O}{\overset{\|}{C}}-O-B(O\overset{O}{\overset{\|}{C}}CH_3)_2 \rightleftarrows CH_3\overset{O}{\overset{\|}{C}}^+ + {}^-\!:\!OB(O\overset{O}{\overset{\|}{C}}CH_3)_2 \qquad (8\text{-}33)$$

$$(CH_3\overset{O}{\overset{\|}{C}}O)_2B\bar{O}: \; B(O\overset{O}{\overset{\|}{C}}CH_3)_2-O\overset{O}{\overset{\|}{C}}CH_3 \rightarrow (CH_3\overset{O}{\overset{\|}{C}}O)_2BOB(O\overset{O}{\overset{\|}{C}}CH_3)_2 + CH_3\overset{O}{\overset{\|}{C}}O:^- \qquad (8\text{-}34)$$

$$CH_3\overset{O}{\overset{\|}{C}}O:^- + CH_3\overset{O}{\overset{\|}{C}}^+ \rightarrow CH_3\overset{O}{\overset{\|}{C}}O\overset{O}{\overset{\|}{C}}CH_3 \qquad (8\text{-}35)$$

The diacetoxyboryloxy anion has not yet been demonstrated to be a valid entity in molecules of this kind, that is, carbon oxygen cleavage in B–O–C compounds is rare indeed. Since trialkoxyboranes do not undergo thermal decomposition to give B–O–B compounds and ethers, even when the alkyl radical is highly capable of tolerating a positive charge, such as *t*-butyl, benzyl, etc., it becomes apparent that the carbonyl group in the acetoxy boron compounds must play an important role in the transformation. Possibly the carbonyl group initiates the entire transformation (XXXVI) by virtue of its successful competition with boron for the

$$CH_3-C(=O^{\delta-})-O-B^{\delta+}(O\overset{O}{\overset{\|}{C}}CH_3)_2 \cdots O=C(CH_3)-O-B(O\overset{O}{\overset{\|}{C}}CH_3)_2$$

(XXXVI)

available pair of electrons and tends to induce an incipient boronium ion. In any event, the concerted mechanism implied in (XXXVI) need not call upon the diacetoxyboryloxy anion as an intermediate.

Oxybis(diacetoxyborane) decomposes at 150° to give acetic

anhydride and a residue formulated to be the monomeric metaborate (8-36),[24] Similar results were obtained in the attempted

$$(CH_3\overset{O}{\overset{\|}{C}}O)_2BOB(O\overset{O}{\overset{\|}{C}}CH_3)_2 \rightarrow CH_3\overset{O}{\overset{\|}{C}}O\overset{O}{\overset{\|}{C}}CH_3 + 2\,CH_3\overset{O}{\overset{\|}{C}}OB{=}O \qquad (8\text{-}36)$$

acetylation of the tetraacetoxy derivative with acetic anhydride.[36]

The monomeric metaborate in equation (8-36), which could arise by the cyclic transformation represented by (XXXVII), is best formulated as the boroxine (XXXVIII) (see Chapter 9).

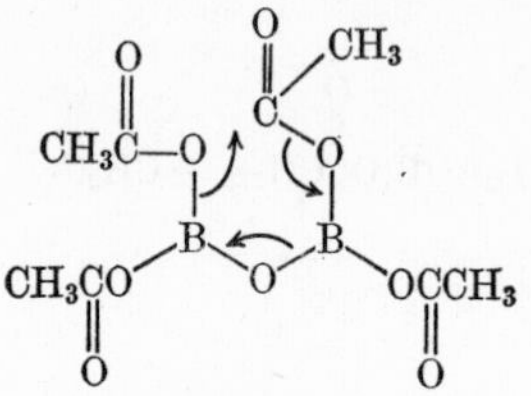

(XXXVII) 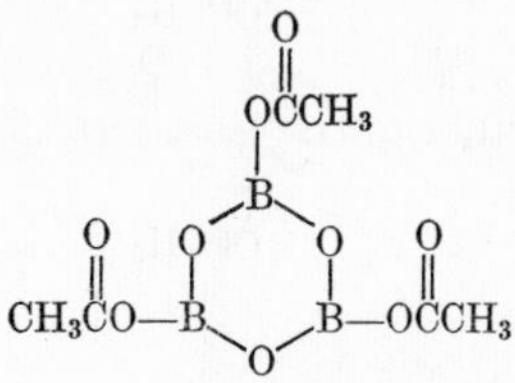 (XXXVIII)

4. WITH AMINES

Oxybis(diacetoxyborane) and crude higher molecular weight derivatives prepared from it and stearic acid and anisic acid have been used as a source of acyl radical for the preparation of amides.[29,70]

$$(R\overset{O}{\overset{\|}{C}}O)_2BOB(O\overset{O}{\overset{\|}{C}}R)_2 + 4\,R'_2NH \rightarrow 4\,R\overset{O}{\overset{\|}{C}}NR'_2 + H_3BO_3 + HBO_2 \qquad (8\text{-}37)$$

5. WITH CARBOXYLIC ACIDS AND CARBOXYLIC ACID CHLORIDES

These reactions have been discussed in Sections II-C-1 and II-C-2.

6. FRIEDEL–CRAFTS

Triacyloxyboranes derived from acetic, propionic and butyric acid have been used as acylating agents in a Friedel–Crafts type reaction. Yields of ketones from the reactions with benzene ranged from 56 to 66%.[76]

$$(R\overset{O}{\overset{\|}{C}}O)_3B + 3\,C_6H_6 \xrightarrow{AlCl_3} 3\,C_6H_5\overset{O}{\overset{\|}{C}}R + H_3BO_3 \qquad (8\text{-}38)$$

7. WITH SODIUM METHOXIDE

Titration of triacetoxyborane with sodium methoxide in methanol solution to the phenolphthalein endpoint, an acid base reaction shown to be valid for boric acid esters (see Chapter 14), revealed a 1:4 stoichiometry which was interpreted as displacement of acetate ion (8-39) followed by neutralization of the resulting

$$(CH_3\overset{\overset{O}{\|}}{C}O)_3B + 3\,CH_3O^- \rightarrow (CH_3O)_3B + 3\,CH_3\overset{\overset{O}{\|}}{C}O^- \qquad (8\text{-}39)$$

trimethoxyborane (8-40).[77] However, since the starting material probably was oxybis(diacetoxyborane) and not triacetoxyborane (see footnote p. 391), and since the acetoxyborane would solvolyze rapidly

$$(CH_3O)_3B + CH_3O^- \rightarrow (CH_3O)_4B^- \qquad (8\text{-}40)$$

in methanol solution, it is suggested that the actual sequence of reactions involved an initial conversion to trimethoxyborane and acetic acid (8-41) followed by neutralization of these substances (8-42).

$$(CH_3\overset{\overset{O}{\|}}{C}O)_2BOB(O\overset{\overset{O}{\|}}{C}CH_3)_2 + 6\,CH_3OH \rightarrow 2\,(CH_3O)_3B + 4\,CH_3\overset{\overset{O}{\|}}{C}OH + H_2O \qquad (8\text{-}41)$$

$$2\,(CH_3O)_3B + 4\,CH_3\overset{\overset{O}{\|}}{C}OH + 6\,NaOCH_3 \rightarrow 2\,(CH_3O)_4BNa + 4\,CH_3\overset{\overset{O}{\|}}{C}ONa + 4\,CH_3OH \qquad (8\text{-}42)$$

The stoichiometry is thus 1:6 and not 1:4. However, if one believed he was dealing with the triacetoxy derivative, the apparent stoichiometry would be 1:4.1.

8. REDUCTION

a. *Hydrogenation.* Catalytic hydrogenation of triacyloxyboranes to give alcohols has been claimed.[40] No experimental details were given.

b. *With Diborane or Sodium Borohydride.* Triacyloxyboranes are readily reduced to the alcohol with diborane or sodium borohydride.[12,14]

9. WITH ESTERS OF INORGANIC ACIDS

Polymeric materials have been obtained by the condensation of dialkoxydialkylsilanes with triacetoxyborane.[3] Other reactions with diethoxydimethylsilane[37] and tetramethoxysilane are discussed in Chapter 13.

$$R_2Si(OR')_2 + B(O\overset{\overset{O}{\|}}{C}CH_3)_3 \rightarrow R_2\overset{\overset{OR'}{|}}{Si}OB(O\overset{\overset{O}{\|}}{C}CH_3)_2 + CH_3\overset{\overset{O}{\|}}{C}OR' \qquad (8\text{-}43)$$

$$R_2\overset{\overset{OR'}{|}}{Si}OB(O\overset{\overset{O}{\|}}{C}CH_3)_2 + R_2Si(OR')_2 \rightarrow R_2\overset{\overset{OR'}{|}}{Si}OB\underset{\underset{\underset{O}{\|}}{OCCH_3}}{|}O\overset{\overset{OR'}{|}}{Si}R_2 + CH_3\overset{\overset{O}{\|}}{C}OR' \qquad (8\text{-}44)$$

$\downarrow$ etc., to give:

$$\left[-\underset{\underset{R}{|}}{\overset{\overset{R}{|}}{Si}}-O-\underset{\underset{\underset{\underset{|}{RSiR}}{|}}{O}}{B}-O- \right]_n$$

A series of polymeric mixed anhydrides were derived from the condensation reactions of triacetoxyborane and ethyl phosphate or some ethyl phosphonates.[38] The reactions are idealized in equation (8-45).

$$B(O\overset{\overset{O}{\|}}{C}CH_3)_3 + R\overset{\overset{O}{\|}}{P}(OC_2H_5)_2 \longrightarrow \left[\begin{array}{c} B\underset{|}{O}\overset{\overset{O}{\|}}{P}O- \\ \underset{|}{O}\quad R \\ R-\underset{\underset{O}{\|}}{P}-O- \end{array} \right]_n + CH_3\overset{\overset{O}{\|}}{C}OC_2H_5 \qquad (8\text{-}45)$$

10. AS A CATALYST

Diazomethane is converted to polymethylene, $(CH_2)_n$, under the catalytic influence of oxybis(diacetoxyborane).[56] The tetraacetoxy derivative also catalyzes the Perkin condensation of aldehydes with acetic anhydride, presumably by promoting the addition of the acetic anhydride methyl group to the aldehyde carbonyl group via the complex (XXXIX).[60]

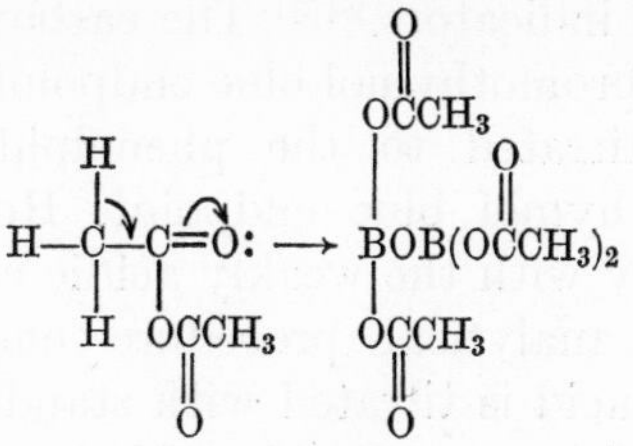

$$\mathrm{H{-}\underset{H}{\overset{H}{C}}{-}\underset{OCCH_3\,(\parallel O)}{C}{=}\ddot{O}: \longrightarrow \underset{O\overset{\parallel}{C}CH_3\;(\parallel O)}{\overset{O\overset{\parallel}{C}CH_3\;(\parallel O)}{B}}OB(O\overset{O}{\overset{\parallel}{C}}CH_3)_2}$$

(XXXIX)

It has been claimed that a mixed anhydride derived from boric oxide and acetic anhydride catalyzes the reaction of acetic acid with α- and β-pinene[28] and camphene.[46] The use of triacetoxyborane in the reactions of α-pinene with acetic acid[44,45] and oxalic acid[43] also has been recorded.

11. COMPLEX FORMATION

Complex formation of tris(trifluoroacetoxy)borane with acetone, acetaldehyde, acetonitrile, and hydrogen cyanide has been indicated. Complex formation with trimethylamine or ether presumably was followed by extensive secondary reaction.[61]

12. MISCELLANEOUS

Attempts to produce boron–hydrogen, boron–carbon, or boron–boron bonded materials from oxybis(diacetoxyborane) by electrolysis, fusion with alkali, or reaction with sodium hydride were unsuccessful.[16] The reaction of sodium hydride with triacetoxyborane is discussed in Chapter 17.

The tetraacetoxy derivative does not react with aldehydes.[50] Products from the reaction with hydrogen fluoride were not characterized.[60]

E. Analytical

1. BORON

Early workers determined the boron content of triacetoxyborane gravimetrically.[64] Pyrolytic decomposition served to drive off acetic anhydride and leave a residue of boric oxide which was calcined with magnesia to destroy any residual carbonaceous material. The acetic acid content was determined volumetrically by hydrolysis, precipitation of the resulting boric acid with barium hydroxide, and acidification and distillation of the filtrate.

This rather tedious procedure is unnecessary since the two acids may be titrated with indicators.[24,31] The carboxylic acid is titrated to the neutral red or bromothymol blue endpoint, mannitol is added, and boric acid is titrated to the phenolphthalein, α-naphtholphthalein or bromothymol blue endpoint. However, special precautions are necessary with the weakly acidic carboxylic acids, and the most accurate analytical procedure employs electrometric titration. The acetic acid is titrated with standard base to a pH in the range of 6.7 to 7.5, mannitol is added and the boric acid is titrated to the phenolphthalein endpoint[36] or to pH 8.7.[16]

Tris(trifluoroacetoxy)borane offers no particular analytical problem due to the enhanced acidity of trifluoroacetic acid.

Traces of triacetoxyborane in acetic acid were determined by a Parr oxygen bomb procedure followed by a spectrophotometric analysis.[5]

2. KARL FISCHER

The Karl Fischer reagent reacts with oxybis(diacetoxyborane) to liberate one mole of water.[36,51]* Since it does not react with triacetoxyborane, the reagent is a rapid diagnostic tool for differentiating between the two species.

$$(CH_3\overset{\overset{O}{\|}}{C}O)_2BOB(O\overset{\overset{O}{\|}}{C}CH_3)_2 + 2\,CH_3OH \rightarrow 2\,(CH_3\overset{\overset{O}{\|}}{C}O)_2BOCH_3 + H_2O \qquad (8\text{-}46)$$

III. ACYLOXYHYDROXYBORANES

A solution of boric acid and potassium acid oxalate at pH 3 yielded brilliant prisms of the composition $B_2O_3 \cdot 2C_2O_4KH \cdot H_2O$. They were interpreted as being the hydrogen bonded structure (XL).[65] Structures (XLI) and (XLII) seem as plausible.

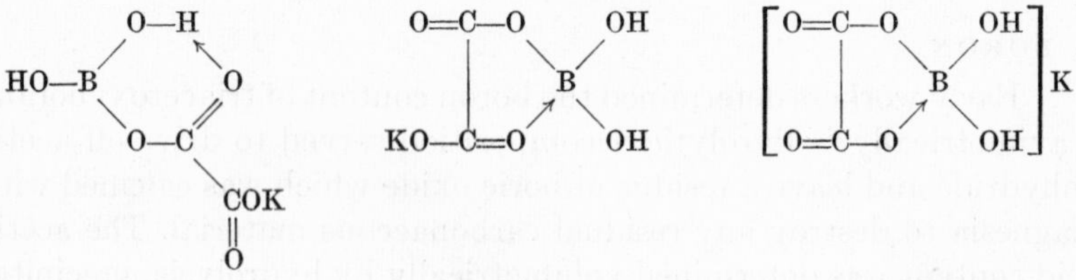

```
      O—H                  O═C—O      OH        ┌O═C—O        OH┐
     /    ↖                 |     \   /          | |     \    /   |
HO—B        O               |      B             | |      B       | K
     \     //               |    ↗   \           | |    ↗   \     |
      O—C                  KO—C═O     OH        └O═C—O        OH┘
          \
           COK
           ‖
           O
   (XL)                    (XLI)                      (XLII)
```

* Chapter 7 contains a general discussion of the use of the Karl Fischer reagent.

IV. DIACYLOXYARYLOXYBORANES

A. Properties

To date compounds in this class are limited to the diacetoxymonoaryloxy derivatives (XLIII). A further distinction is that in every

$$ArOB(O\overset{O}{\overset{\|}{C}}CH_3)_2$$

(XLIII)

case reported, with the possible exception of 8-hydroxyquinoline,[24] the aromatic group either has a carbonyl group on the carbon atom adjacent to the one bearing the boron residue or the aromatic group contains a keto group in the *peri*-position. Thus intramolecular coordination (XLIV and XLV) similar to that proposed for tri-

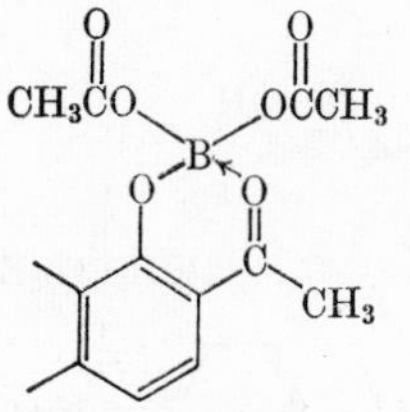

(XLIV) 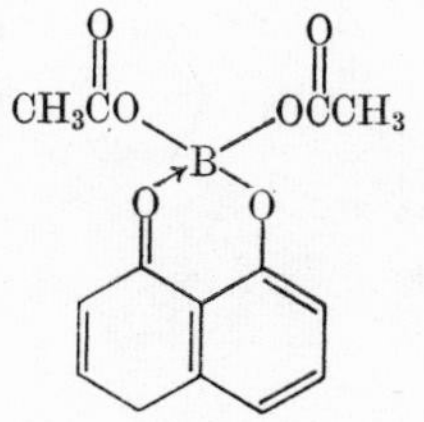 (XLV)

acetoxyborane and oxybis(diacetoxyborane)[27] is indicated as the stabilizing influence.

B. Methods of Preparation

A variety of properly substituted naphthols, hydroxynaphthoquinones, thionaphthenes, hydroxyanthraquinones, hydroxyphenanthraquinones, and phenol derivatives and related compounds on treatment with triacetoxyborane or oxybis(diacetoxyborane) in acetic anhydride solution have been converted to the diacetoxyboryl derivative (8-47).[4,10,19,23,24,25,26,47,52,66,67,74]

$$2\,ArOH + (CH_3\overset{O}{\overset{\|}{C}}O)_2BOB(O\overset{O}{\overset{\|}{C}}CH_3)_2 + (CH_3\overset{O}{\overset{\|}{C}})_2O \rightarrow 2\,ArOB(O\overset{O}{\overset{\|}{C}}CH_3)_2 + 2\,CH_3\overset{O}{\overset{\|}{C}}OH \qquad (8\text{-}47)$$

In every case, with the exclusion of 8-hydroxyquinoline, borylation occurs preferentially at the hydroxyl group in the β or *peri*-position to the carbonyl group and does not occur at all when this configuration is not present. Thus (XLVI) is converted to

(XLVII) and not (XLVIII),[24] indicating the relative unimportance of the configuration (XLIX) in stabilization of molecules of this

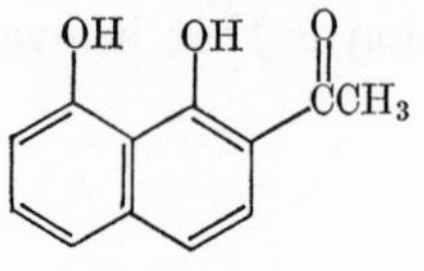

(XLVI)

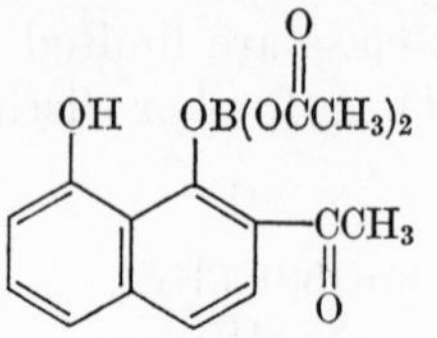

(XLVII)

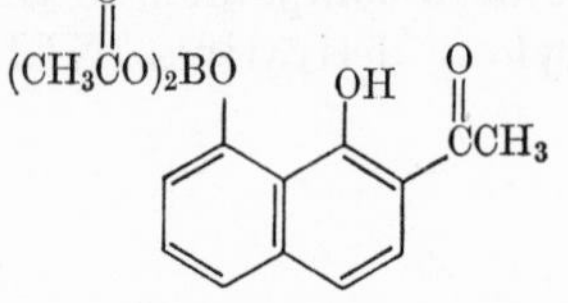

(XLVIII)

kind. Similarly, 2,3,4-trihydroxybenzophenone (L) is converted to (LI).[24] 1-Hydroxyxanthone (LII) was successfully borylated to

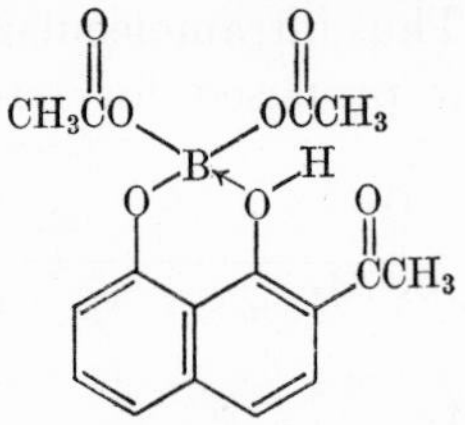

(XLIX)

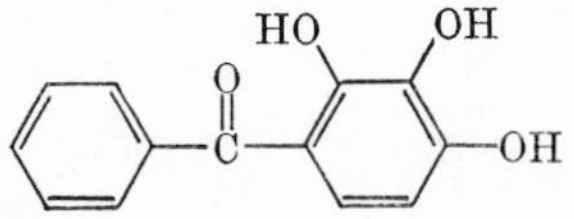

(L)

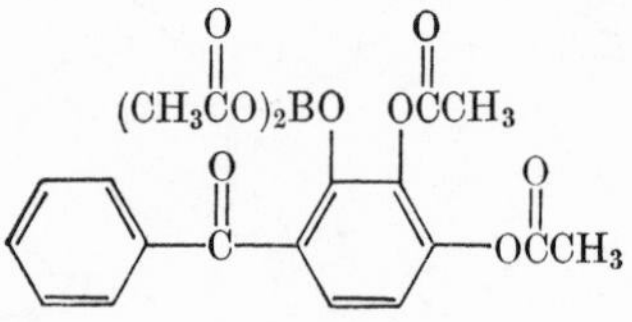

(LI)

give (LIII), but the 2- and 4- derivatives (LIV and LV) could not be made to react.[24] The lack of reaction with (LV) indicates that

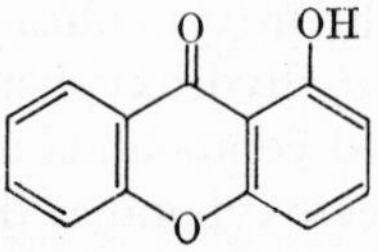

(LII)

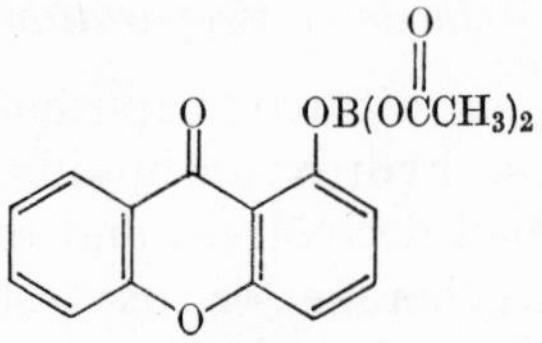

(LIII)

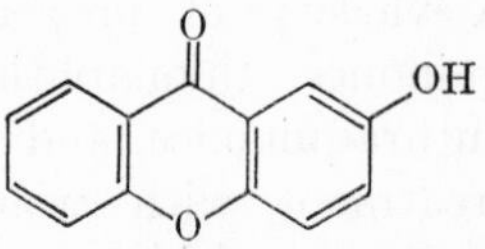

(LIV)

intramolecular complexes of the type (LVI), in addition to the type (XLIX), are ineffective in inducing stabilization in molecules of this kind. Similarly, (LVII) could not be borylated.[66] In contrast, 8-hydroxyquinoline was reported to react with oxybis(diacetoxyborane) to give the diacetoxyboryl derivative (LVIII).[24] The stability of (LVIII) as compared to (LVI) and (LIX) may be due to the greater ability of nitrogen to donate its free electron pair as compared to oxygen and sulfur.

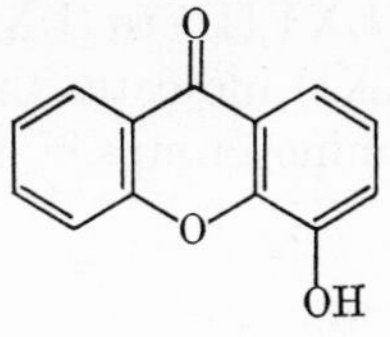

(LV) 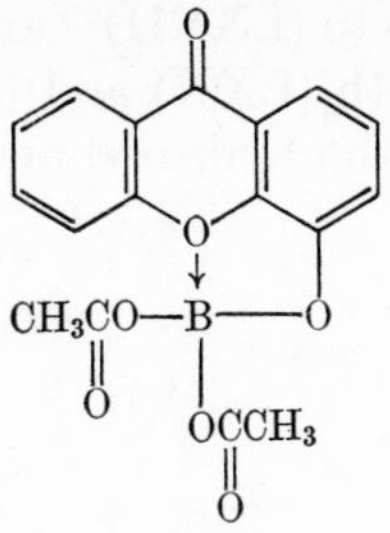 (LVI) 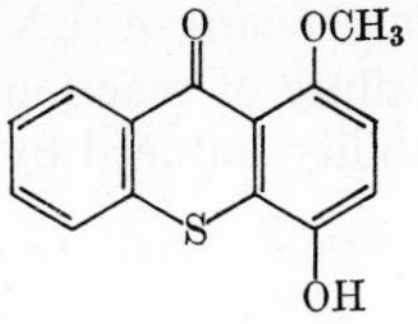 (LVII)

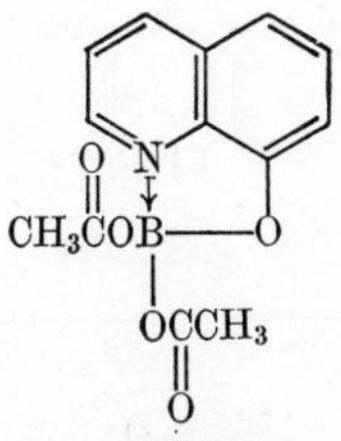

(LVIII) 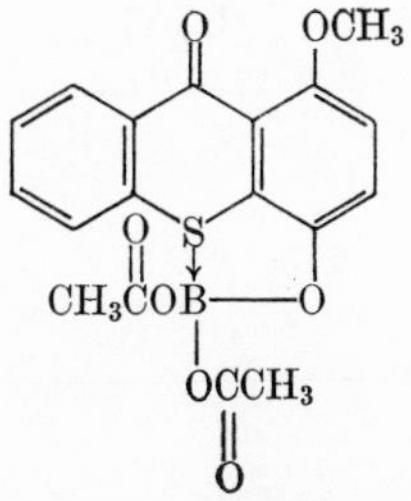 (LIX) 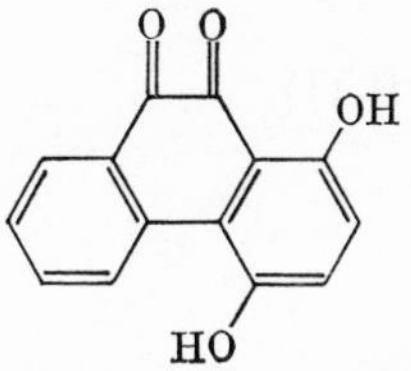 (LX)

Other examples demonstrating the specific nature of the borylation reaction include the conversion of (LX) and (LXI),[24] the transformations (LXII) to (LXIII)[24] and (LXIV) to (LXV),[4] and

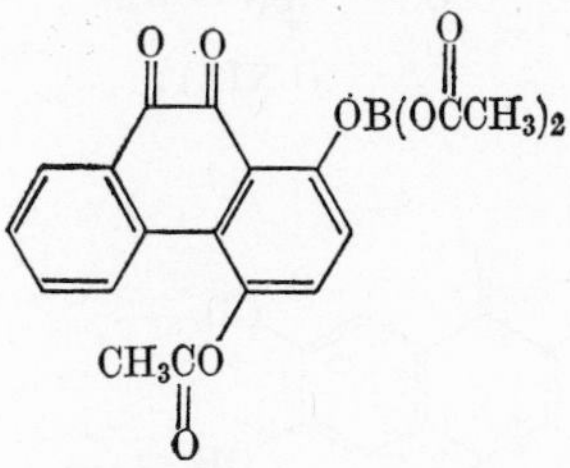

(LXI) 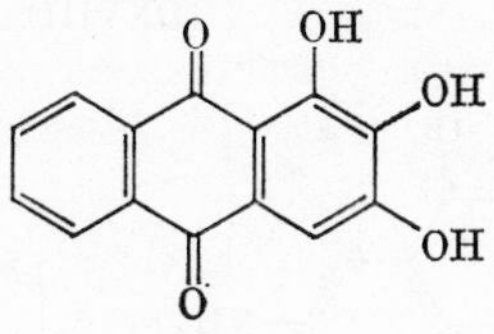 (LXII)

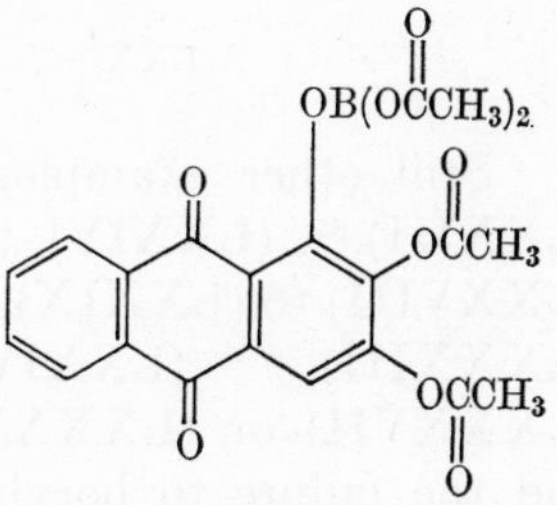

(LXIII)

the conversions of (LXVI) to (LXVII)[23] and (LXVIII) to (LXIX).[26] The failure of reaction with (LXX) and (LXXI) indicates the lack of stability induced by ortho hydroxyl and amino groups.[24]

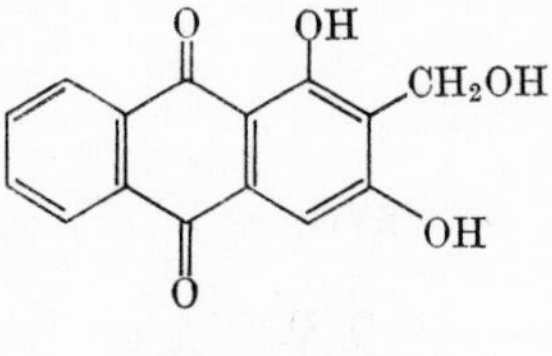

(LXIV) 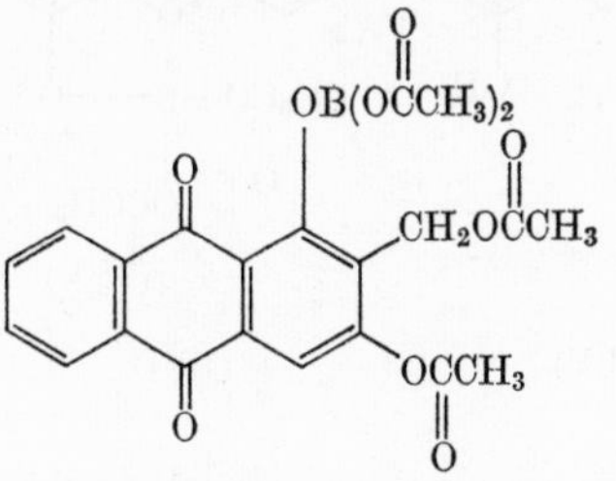 (LXV) 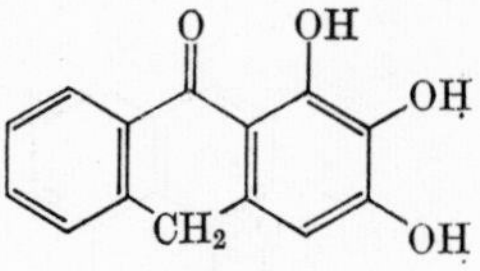 (LXVI)

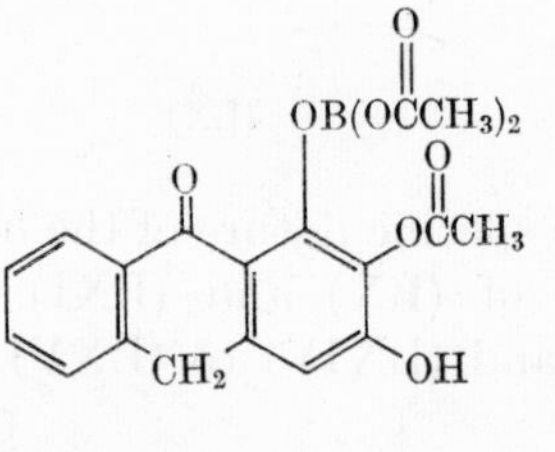

(LXVII) 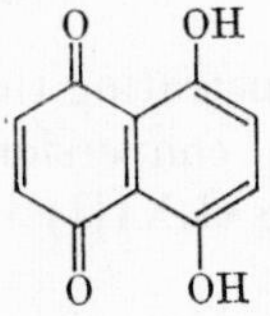 (LXVIII) 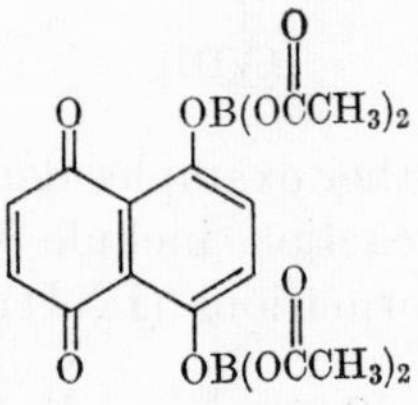 (LXIX)

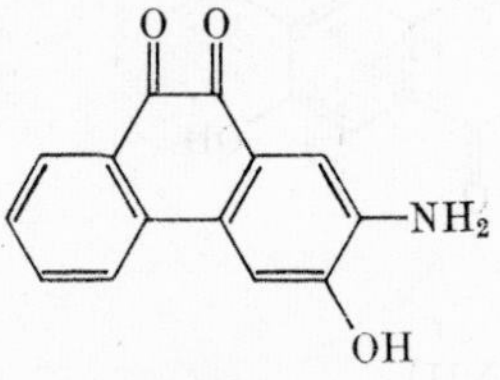

(LXX) 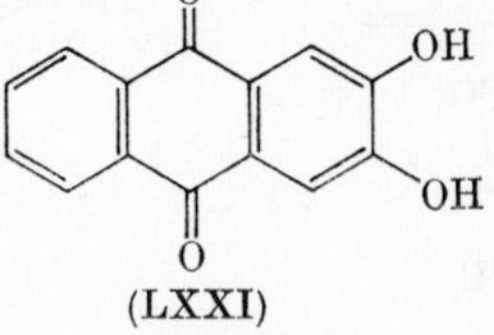 (LXXI)

Still other examples include the conversions of (LXXII) to (LXXIII),[67] (LXXIV) to (LXXV),[52] (LXXVI) to (LXXVII),[24] (LXXVIII) to (LXXIX),[24] (LXXX) to (LXXXI) but (LXXXII) to (LXXXIII),[25] (LXXIV) to (LXXXV),[10] (LXXXVI) to (LXXXVII) or (LXXXVIII),[25] (LXXXIX) to (XC) or (XCI),[25] and the failure to borylate (XCII).[52] Borylation with triacetoxyborane or oxybis(diacetoxyborane) thus has become a diagnostic

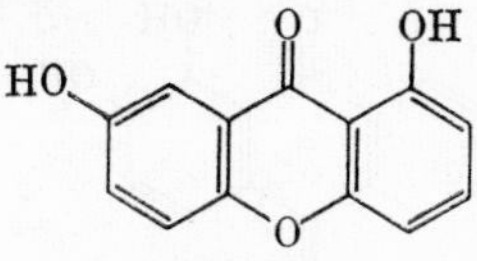

(LXXII)

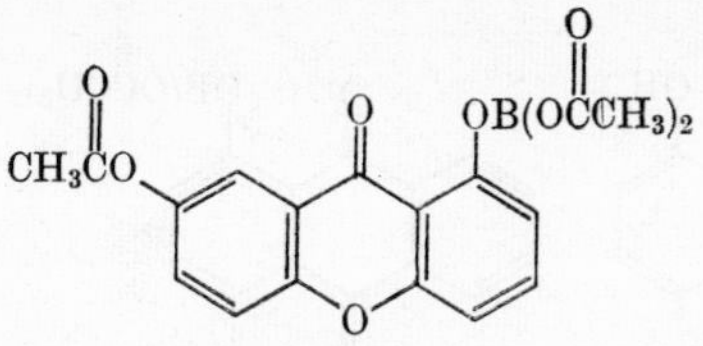

(LXXIII)

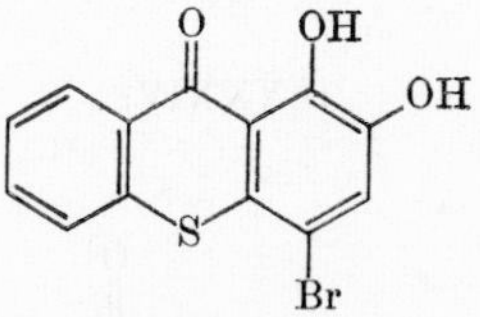

(LXXIV)

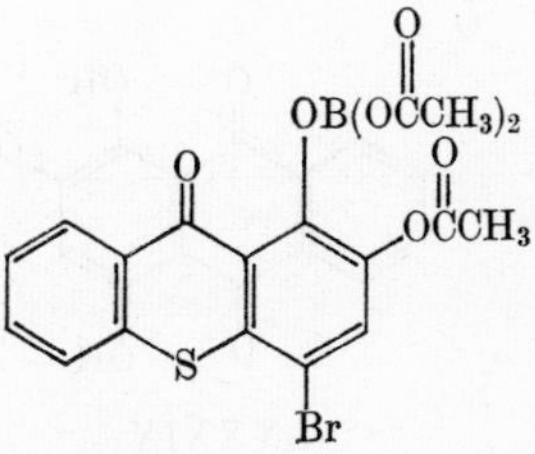

(LXXV)

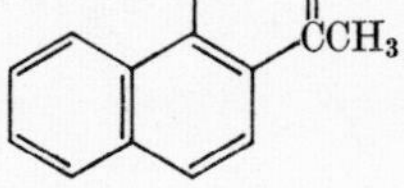

(LXXVI)

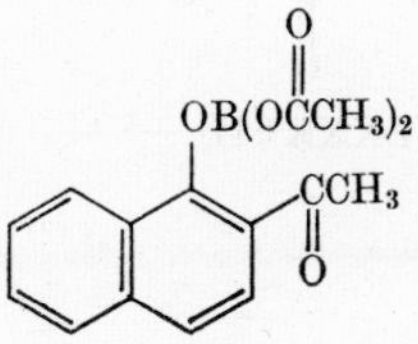

(LXXVII)

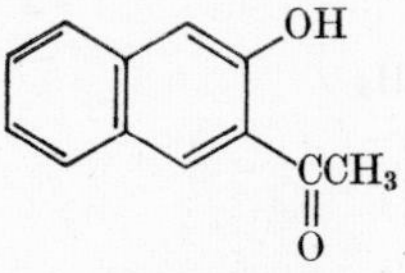

(LXXVIII)

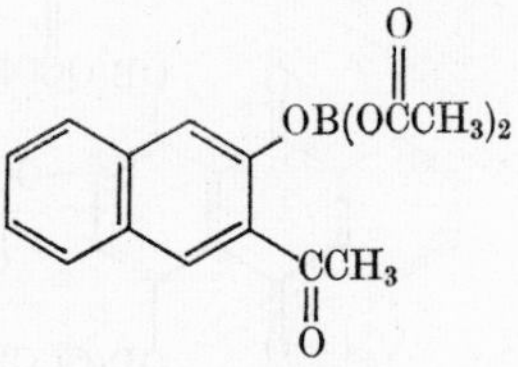

(LXXIX)

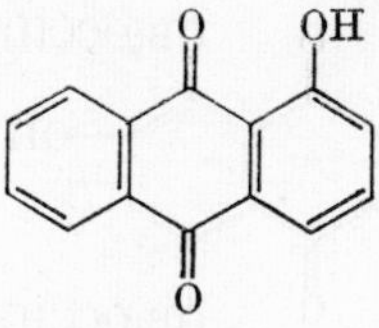

(LXXX)

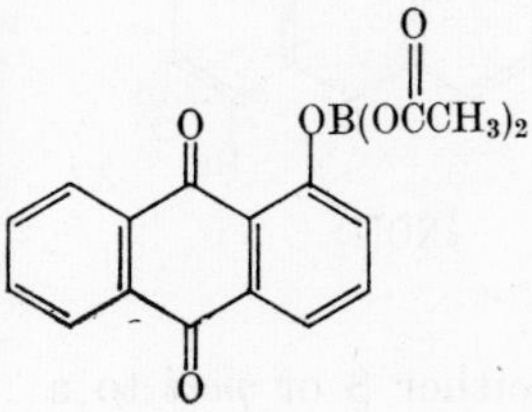

(LX XI)

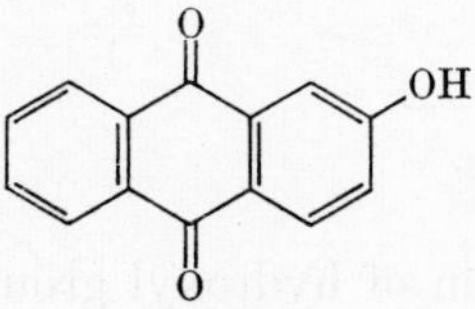

(LXXXII)

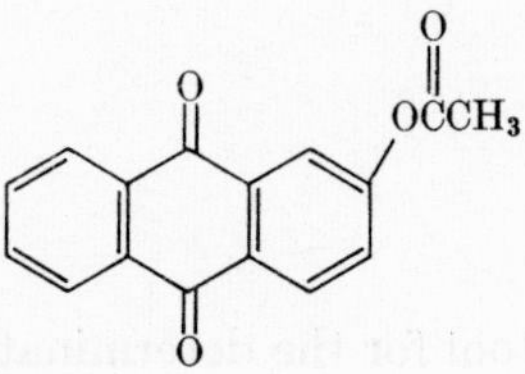

(LXXXIII)

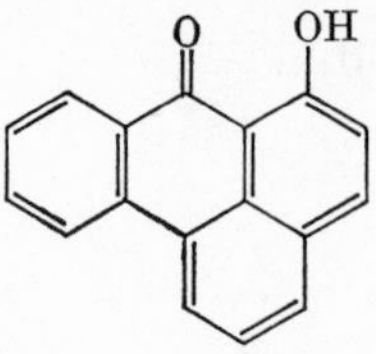

(LXXXIV) 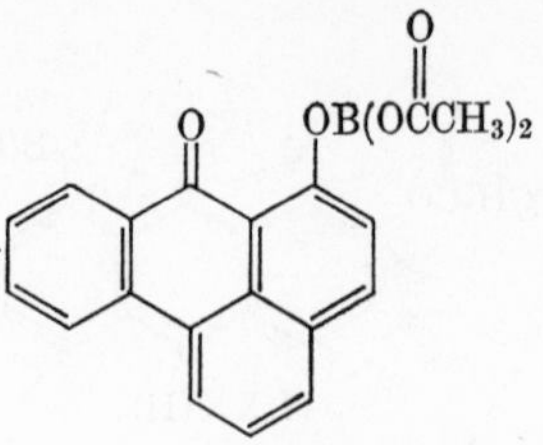 (LXXXV) 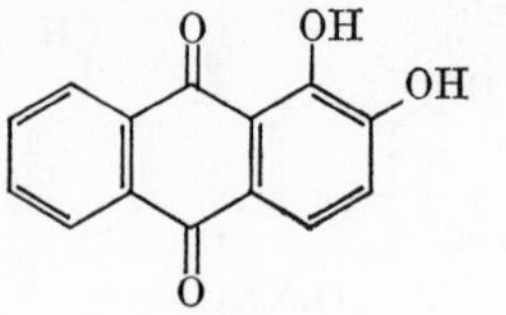 (LXXXVI)

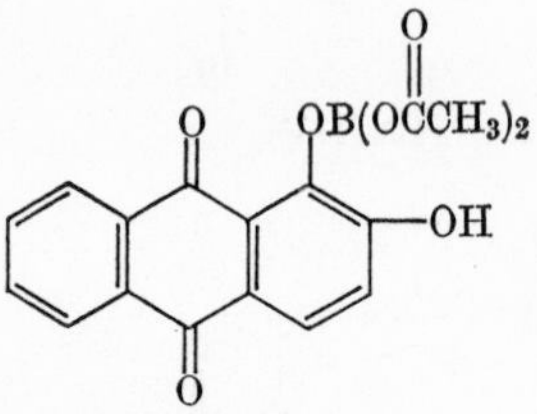

(LXXXVII) 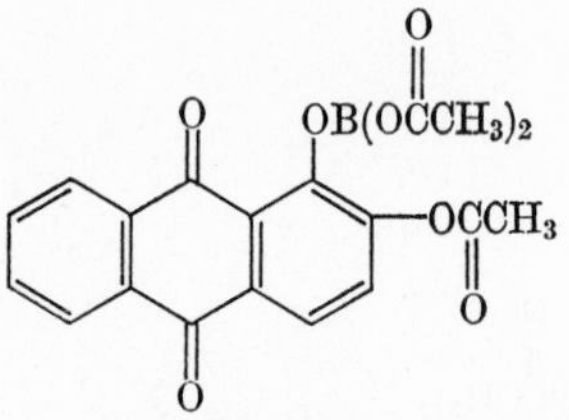 (LXXXVIII) 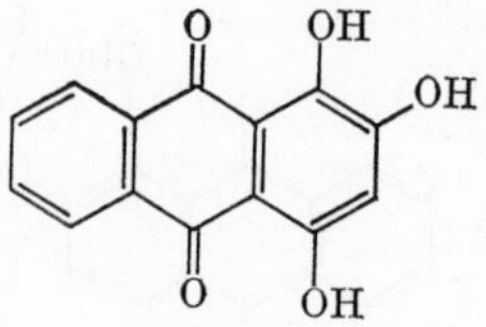 (LXXXIX)

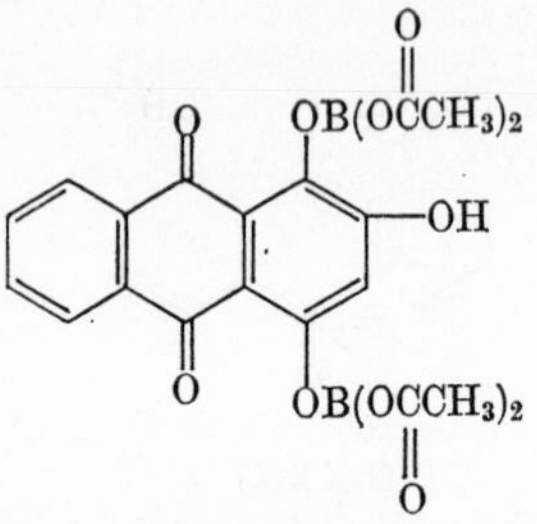

(XC) 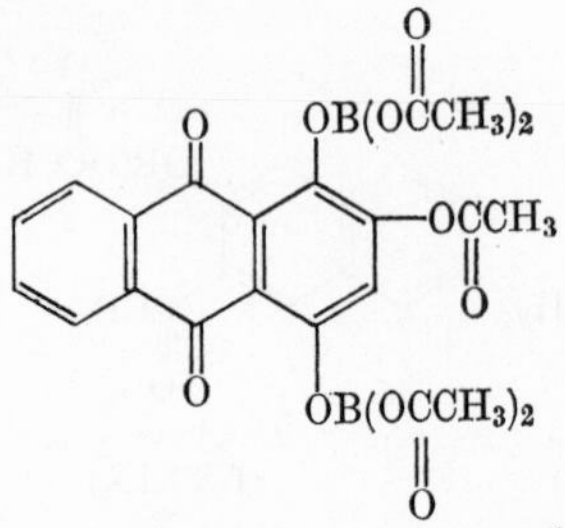 (XCI) 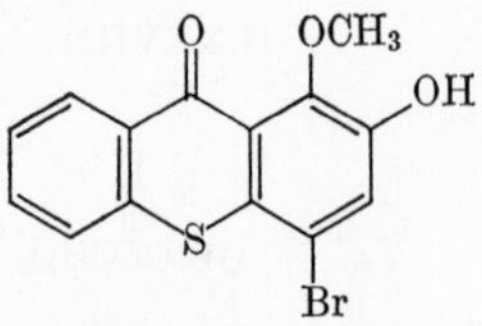 (XCII)

tool for the determination of hydroxyl groups either β or *peri* to a carbonyl group.

Enols also are capable of forming the diacetoxyboryl derivative as evidenced by the conversion of 2-benzoyl-3-keto-2,3-dihydrothionaphthen (XCIII) to (XCIV).[19]

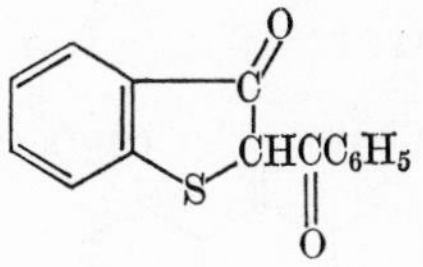

(XCIII) 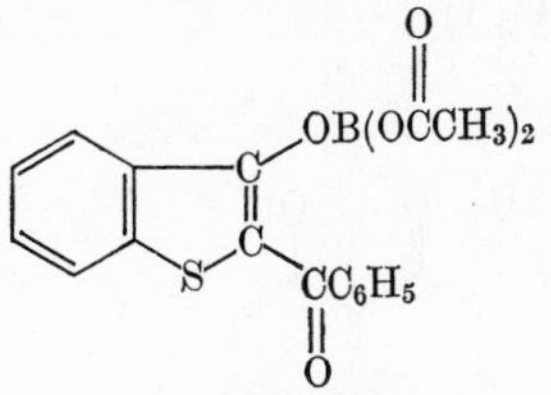 (XCIV)

The inability of one carbonyl function to stabilize two diacetoxyboryl residues was shown by the monoborylation of (XCV) to (XCVI),[24] the conversion of (XCVII) to (XCVIII) or (XCIX),[25] and the conversion of (C) to (CI).[25]

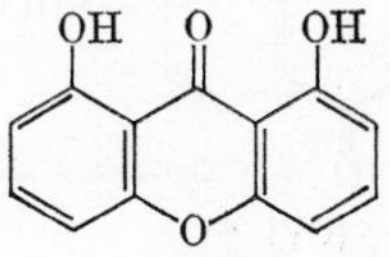

(XCV) 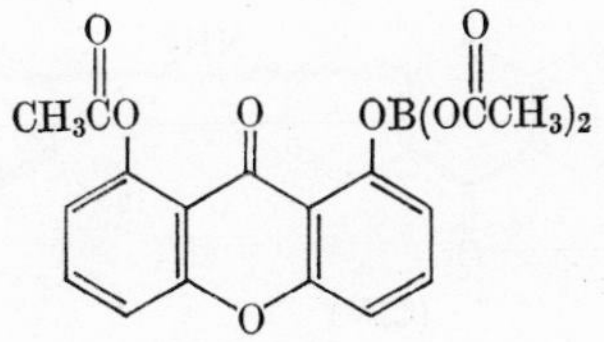 (XCVI)

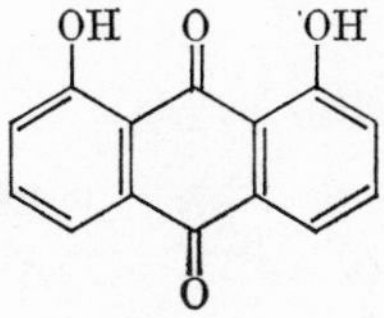

(XCVII) 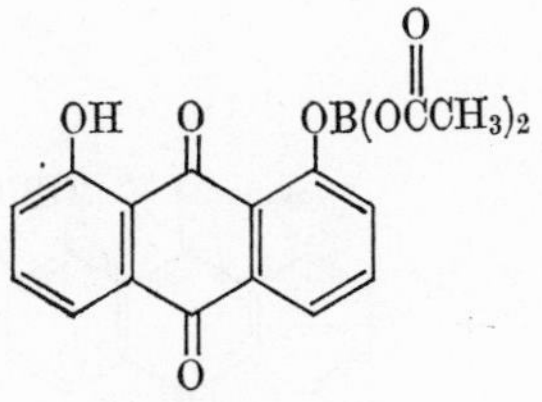 (XCVIII) 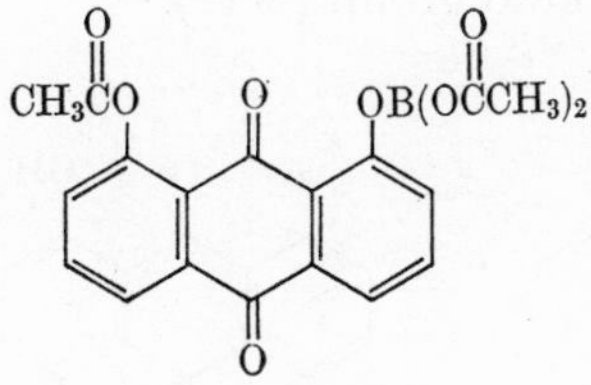 (XCIX)

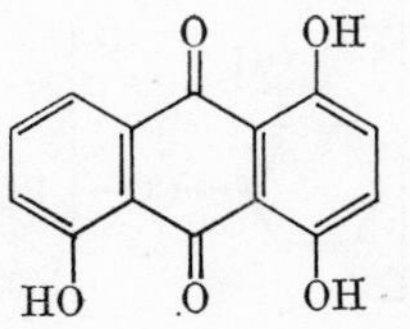

(C) 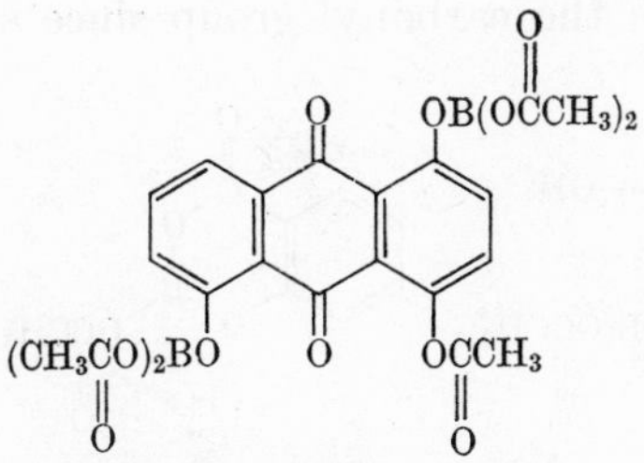 (CI)

The preferential reaction with hydroxyl groups as compared to amino groups is evident by the conversions of (CII) to (CIII) and (CIV) to (CV).[11]

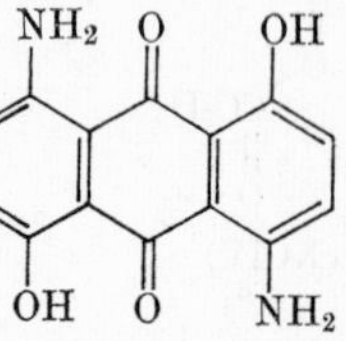

(CII) 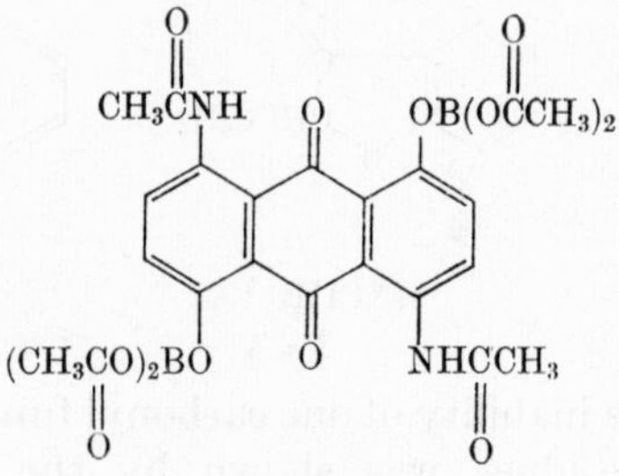 (CIII)

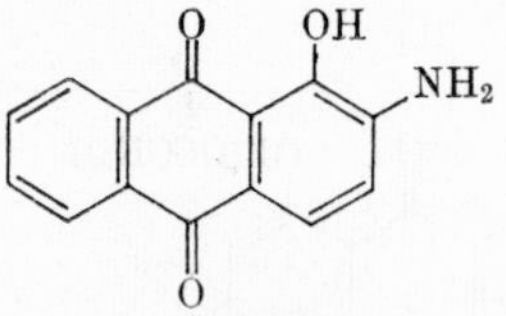

(CIV) 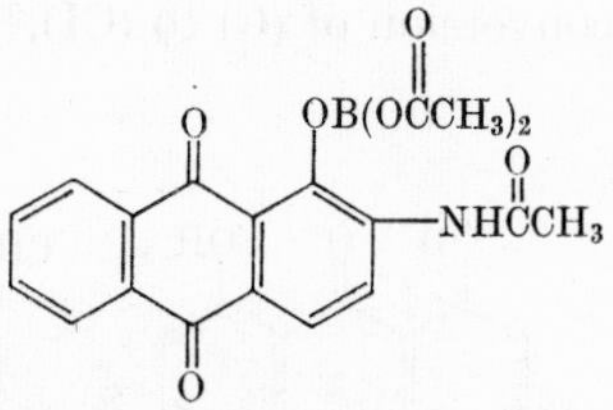 (CV)

The amino groups are capable of borylation if they are not competing with the hydroxyl groups for the stabilizing effect of a keto group (8-48).[11]

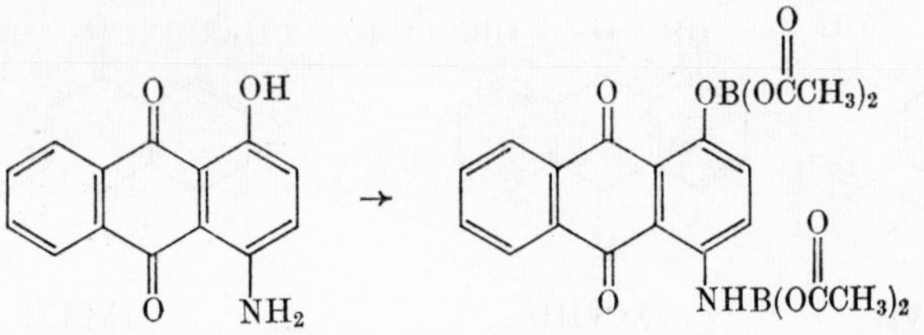

(8-48)

Ortho carboxy groups evidently do not play a stabilizing role similar to the carbonyl group since salicylic acid on reaction with

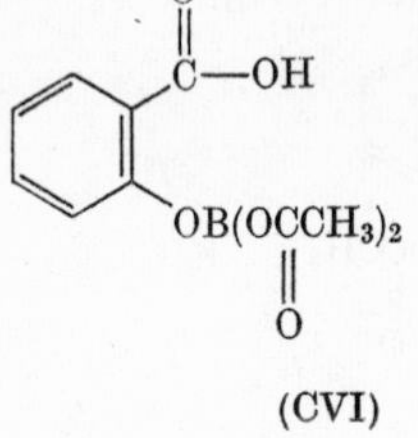

(CVI) 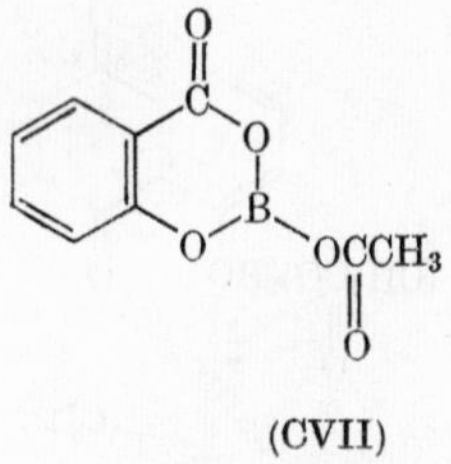 (CVII) 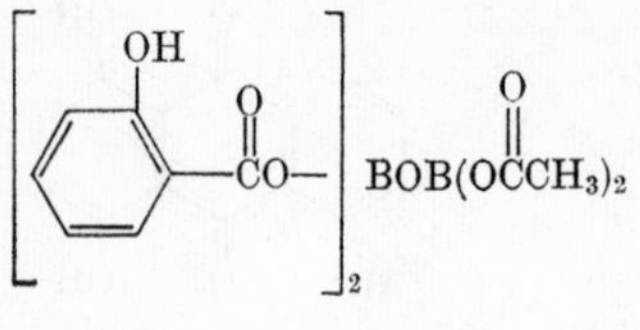 (CVIII)

oxybis(diacetoxyborane) in acetic anhydride solution did not give (CVI) but gave either (CVII) or (CVIII) as evidenced by the presence of equimolar amounts of the three acids involved.[24] However, in view of the reaction of salicylic acid and triacetoxyborane resulting in tri(carboxyphenoxy)borane and not the anhydride,[1] the product (CVIII) might best be formulated as (CIX) or indeed not formulated

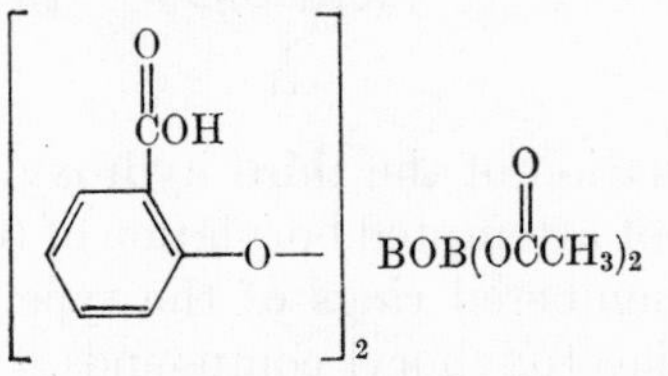

$$\left[o\text{-}HOOC{-}C_6H_4{-}O{-} \right]_2 BOB(OCCH_3)_2 \quad (C=O \text{ on acetyl})$$

(CIX)

at all since *m*- and *p*-hydroxybenzoic acid did not form similar derivatives;[24] thus indicating (CVII) to be the product. If (CVII) is indeed the product, it represents the only example of an anhydride of boric acid with two different carboxylic acids.

Cleavage of the B–O–B bond of oxybis(diacetoxyborane) to give a diacetoxyaryloxyborane also has been accomplished by an acetyl

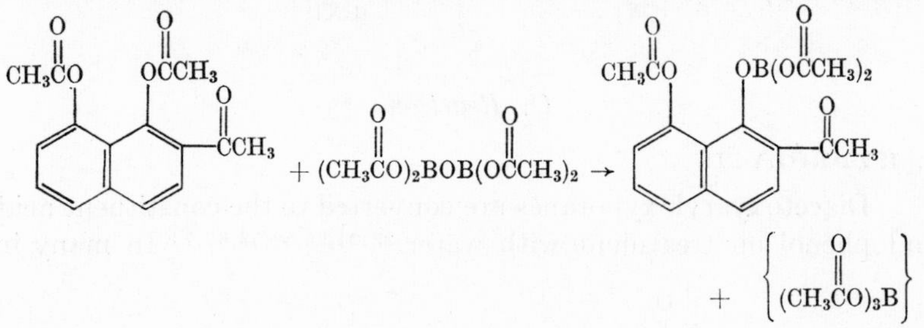

$$\text{1,8-di}(CH_3COO)\text{-2-}(CH_3CO)C_{10}H_5 + (CH_3CO)_2BOB(OCCH_3)_2 \rightarrow \text{8-}(CH_3COO)\text{-1-}[OB(OCCH_3)_2]\text{-2-}(CH_3CO)C_{10}H_5 + \{(CH_3CO)_3B\} \quad (8\text{-}49)$$

derivative of a phenol (8-49).[24] Once again the diacetoxyboryl group enters the position ortho to the carbonyl group.

The borylation reaction also has been carried out with acetic anhydride and boric acid (8-50 and 8-51). Possibly oxybis(diacetoxyborane) is formed *in situ*.[53]

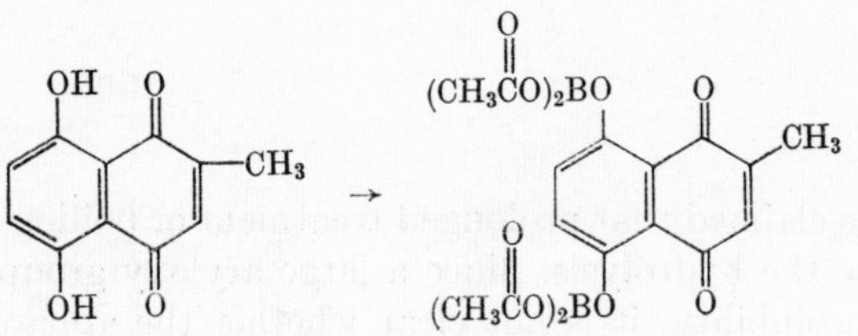

$$\text{5,8-(OH)}_2\text{-2-}CH_3\text{-1,4-naphthoquinone} \rightarrow \text{5,8-}[(CH_3CO)_2BO]_2\text{-2-}CH_3\text{-1,4-naphthoquinone} \quad (8\text{-}50)$$

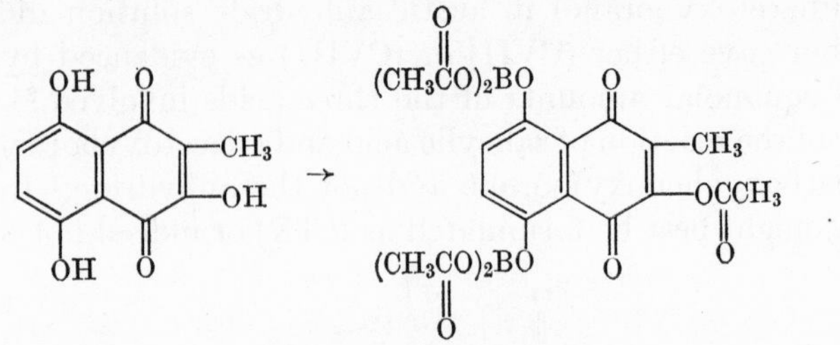

$$\text{(8-51)}$$

The lack of borylation of the third hydroxyl group in equation (8-51) and the failure of attempted borylation of (CX)[53] point out the ineffectiveness of 5-membered rings of the type (CXI) in inducing stabilization of the diacetoxyboryl compounds.

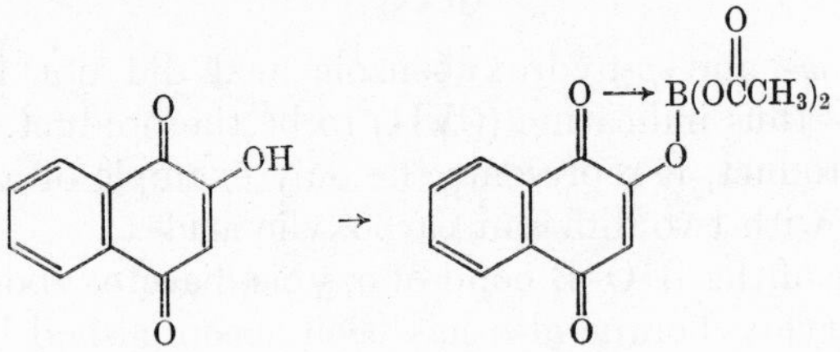

(CX) (CXI)

C. Reactions

1. HYDROLYSIS

Diacetoxyaryloxyboranes are converted to the constituent acids and phenol on treatment with water.[23,24,25,52,53,67,74] In many in-

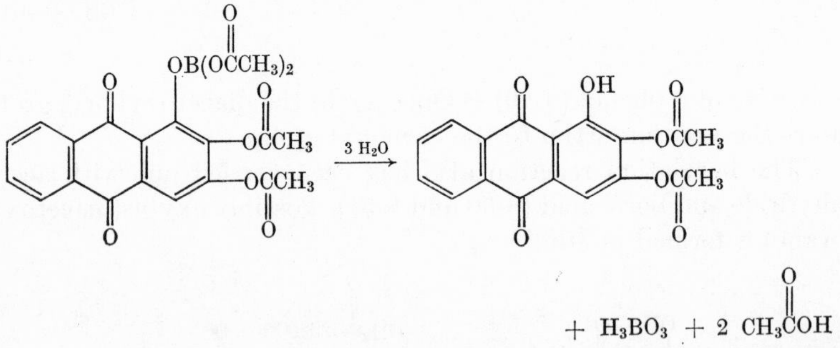

$$\xrightarrow{3\ H_2O} \quad + H_3BO_3 + 2\ CH_3COOH \qquad \text{(8-52)}$$

stances it is claimed that prolonged treatment or boiling is necessary to complete the hydrolysis. Since a large aryloxy group would lead to water insolubility, it is not clear whether the apparent stability of some of the members is due to the sp^3 nature of the boron deterring entry of water or just due to non-wetting of the sample.

The influence of the nature of the heterocyclic atoms present in the aryloxy group upon the rate of hydrolysis was suggested by the facile decomposition of (CXII) in cold water versus the slow decomposition of (CXIII) in boiling water.[19]

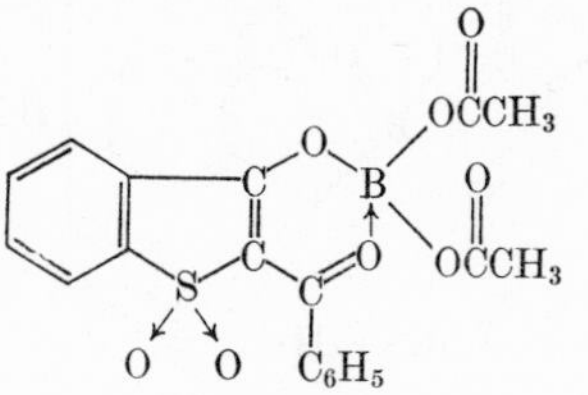

(CXII) 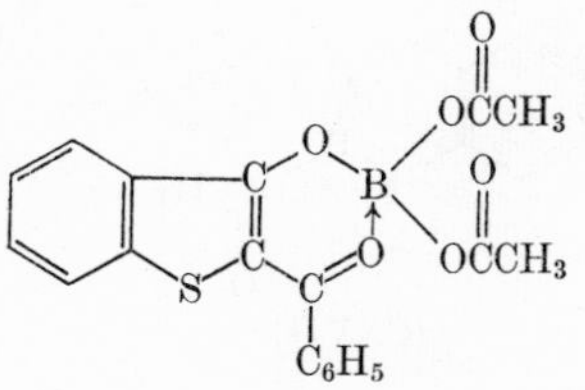 (CXIII)

It was believed the greater $+I$ effect of the sulfur atom in (CXIII) as compared to the sulfone group in (CXII) contributed to the greater nucleophilicity of the carbonyl oxygen in (CXIII) and consequently the stability of the resulting intramolecular complex. This effect may or may not be operative, but since sulfones are more water soluble than sulfides, no further explanation of the difference in the rates of hydrolysis of (CXII) and (CXIII) may be necessary.

2. THERMAL STABILITY

Treatment of (CXIV) at 140° in vacuum resulted in the removal of acetic anhydride and the formation of a residue formulated as the metaborate (CXV).[25]

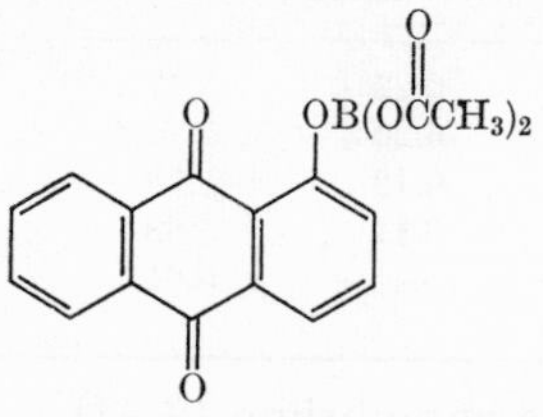

(CXIV) 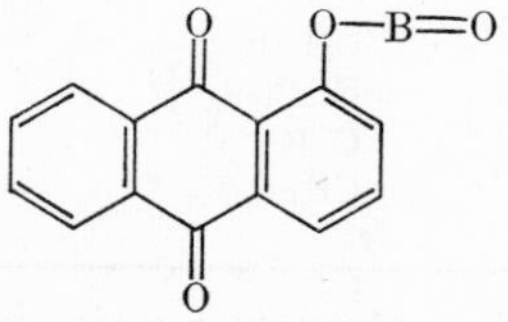 (CXV)

The 8-hydroxyquinoline derivative (CXVI) can be boiled in acetic anhydride solution without change.[24]

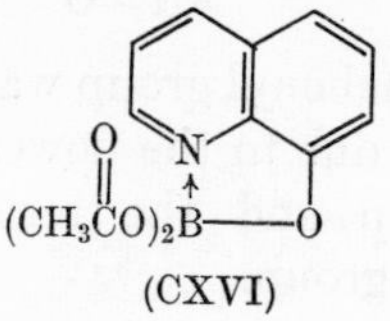

(CXVI)

3. WITH CARBOXYLIC ACIDS

The reaction product of salicylic acid and oxybis(diacetoxyborane), presumably structure (CXVII), on treatment with acetic acid and a trace of water was recorded to give the tetravalent species (CXVIII).[24]

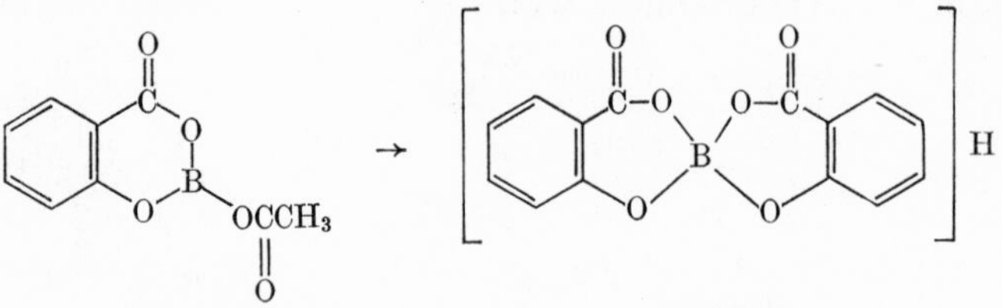

(CXVII) → [(CXVIII)]H (8-53)

(CXVII) (CXVIII)

V. 2-ACYLOXY-1,3,2-DIOXABOROLANES

A. Properties

The acetyl and haloacetyl derivatives of 2-hydroxy-1,3,2-dioxaborolane, with the exception of the trifluoroacetyl derivative, exhibit two carbonyl stretching frequencies (Table 8-2) which are

Table 8-2. Carbonyl stretching frequencies of 2-acetoxy-1,3,2-dioxaborolane and halogen derivatives

R in $(CH_2O)_2BOC(O)R$	λ (μ) Coordinated	Free
CH_3	6.23	5.77
CH_2Cl	6.20	5.74
$CHCl_2$	6.12	5.70
CCl_3	6.11	5.68
CF_3	—	5.61

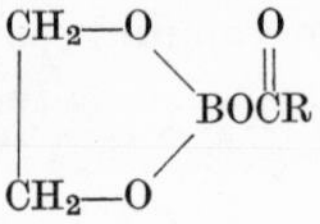

attributed to the two species in the equilibrium (8-54).[9]

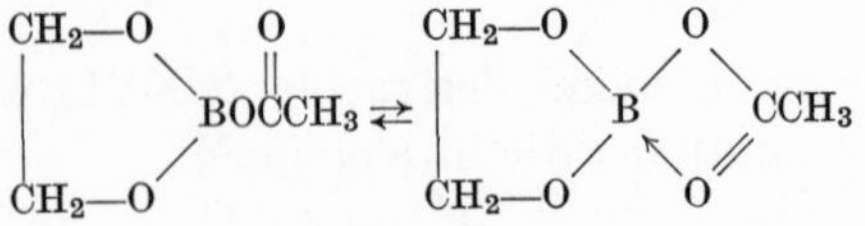

$$(CH_2O)_2BOC(O)CH_3 \rightleftarrows (CH_2O)_2B\leftarrow O{=}C(CH_3)O \text{ (chelate)} \quad (8\text{-}54)$$

Coordination of the carbonyl group was believed to be precluded in the trifluoro derivative due to the powerful electron attraction of the trifluoromethyl group and the resulting lower nucleophilic character of the carbonyl group.

B. *Methods of Preparation*

Slow addition of glacial acetic acid to 2-chloro-1,3,2-dioxaborolane in methylene chloride solution resulted in a 95% yield of the acetoxy derivative (8-55). Chloroacetic and trifluoroacetic acid behaved similarly.[8]

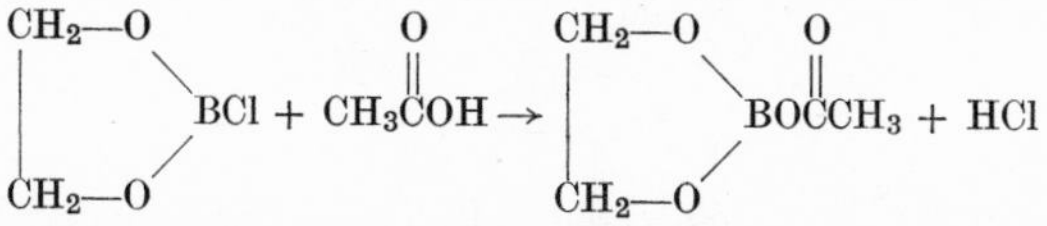

$$\begin{matrix} CH_2-O \\ | \quad\quad\; \diagdown \\ | \quad\quad\quad BCl \\ | \quad\quad\; \diagup \\ CH_2-O \end{matrix} + CH_3\overset{O}{\overset{\|}{C}}OH \rightarrow \begin{matrix} CH_2-O \\ | \quad\quad\; \diagdown \\ | \quad\quad\quad BO\overset{O}{\overset{\|}{C}}CH_3 \\ | \quad\quad\; \diagup \\ CH_2-O \end{matrix} + HCl \qquad (8\text{-}55)$$

It has been reported that hydroxyborylene derivatives of certain 16,17-dihydroxy sterols are capable of acylation with acetic anhydride to give structures of type (CXIX).[72]

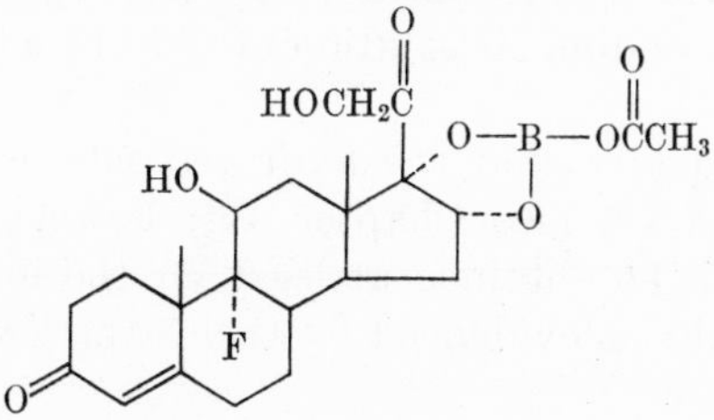

(CXIX)

C. *Reactions*

Pyrolysis of 2-acetoxy-1,3,2-dioxaborolane at 100° and 0.5 mm. for 9.5 hours resulted in the loss of acetic anhydride leaving a glassy residue whose analysis was consistent with reaction (8-56).[8]

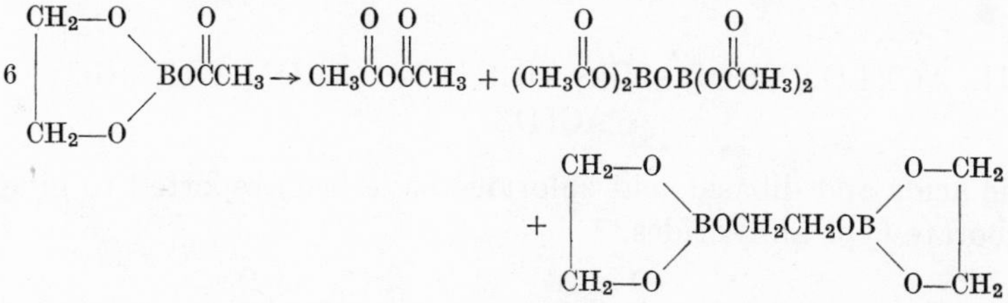

$$6 \begin{matrix} CH_2-O \\ | \quad\quad\; \diagdown \\ | \quad\quad\quad BO\overset{O}{\overset{\|}{C}}CH_3 \\ | \quad\quad\; \diagup \\ CH_2-O \end{matrix} \rightarrow CH_3\overset{O}{\overset{\|}{C}}O\overset{O}{\overset{\|}{C}}CH_3 + (CH_3\overset{O}{\overset{\|}{C}}O)_2BOB(O\overset{O}{\overset{\|}{C}}CH_3)_2$$

$$+ \begin{matrix} CH_2-O \\ | \quad\quad\; \diagdown \\ | \quad\quad\quad BOCH_2CH_2OB \\ | \quad\quad\; \diagup \\ CH_2-O \end{matrix} \begin{matrix} O-CH_2 \\ \diagup \quad\quad | \\ \\ \diagdown \quad\quad | \\ O-CH_2 \end{matrix} \qquad (8\text{-}56)$$

VI. ACYLOXYBORANES DERIVED FROM HYDROXY ACIDS

Treatment of an equimolar aqueous solution of lithium salicylate and boric acid with a concentrated solution of lithium chloride resulted in crystallization of the hydrated salt upon standing for some days.[68] The anhydrous salt (CXX) was obtained by treatment of the hydrate with phosphorus pentoxide under vacuum at 200°. The potassium salts, dihydrate and anhydrous, were prepared similarly. Magnesium, cobalt, nickel and zinc tetrahydrate salts were obtained from solutions of the metal sulfates with boric acid

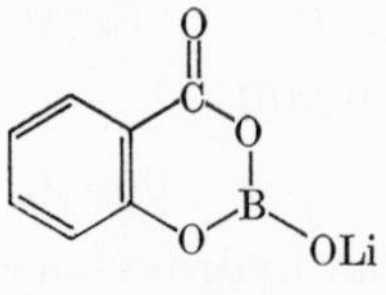

(CXX)

and sodium salicylate. The sodium salt was obtained by concentrating an aqueous equimolar solution of sodium salicylate and boric acid.[59]

It is most probable that the hydrated salts exist in the tetracovalent form (CXXI) (see Chapter 16); however trigonal forms such as (CXX) can be obtained at least for the lithium, potassium and magnesium salts as evidenced by their complete dehydration.

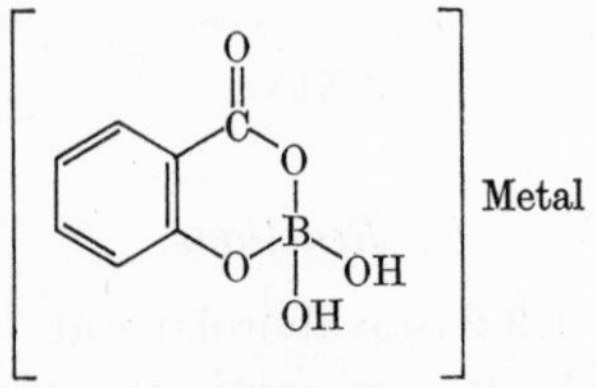

Metal

(CXXI)

VII. ACYLOXYBORANES DERIVED FROM DIBASIC ACIDS

Dibasic acids and dibasic acid chlorides have been reported to give the biborate type anhydrides.[64]

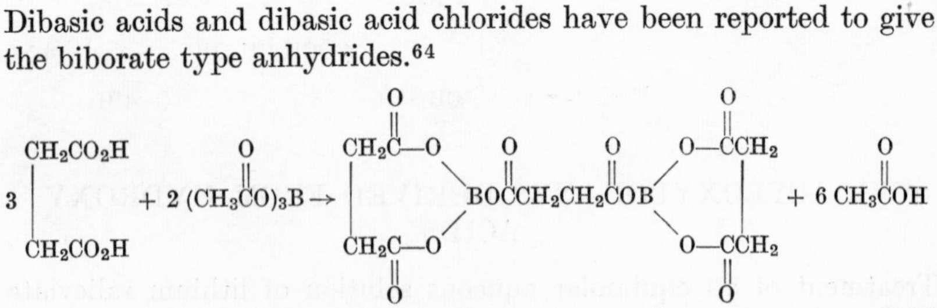

$$3\,\begin{matrix} CH_2CO_2H \\ | \\ CH_2CO_2H \end{matrix} + 2\,(CH_3\overset{O}{\overset{\|}{C}}O)_3B \rightarrow \begin{matrix} CH_2\overset{O}{\overset{\|}{C}}{-}O \\ | \qquad\quad \\ CH_2\underset{\|}{\underset{O}{C}}{-}O \end{matrix} \!\!>\! BO\overset{O}{\overset{\|}{C}}CH_2CH_2\overset{O}{\overset{\|}{C}}OB \!<\!\! \begin{matrix} O{-}\overset{O}{\overset{\|}{C}}CH_2 \\ \qquad\quad | \\ O{-}\underset{\|}{\underset{O}{C}}CH_2 \end{matrix} + 6\,CH_3\overset{O}{\overset{\|}{C}}OH \qquad (8\text{-}57)$$

Reaction (8-57) could not be confirmed.[1]

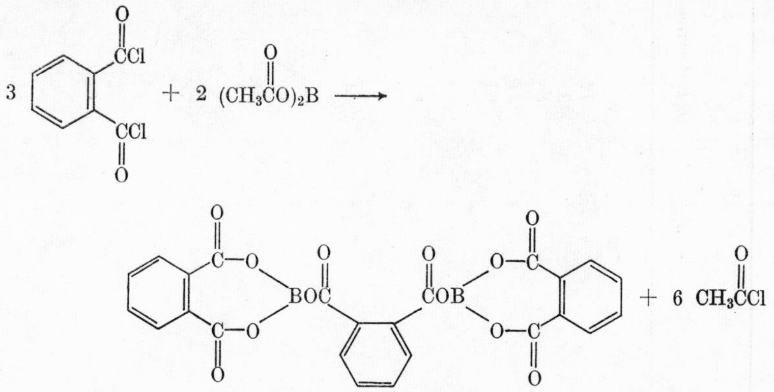

3 $C_6H_4(COCl)_2$ + 2 $(CH_3CO)_2B$ ⟶

[phthalyl boric anhydride structure: BOC, COB] + 6 CH_3CCl (O)

(8-58)

The boric anhydride of phthalic acid also was prepared by treatment of phthaloyl chloride with boric acid or fusion of phthalic anhydride with boric acid.[64]

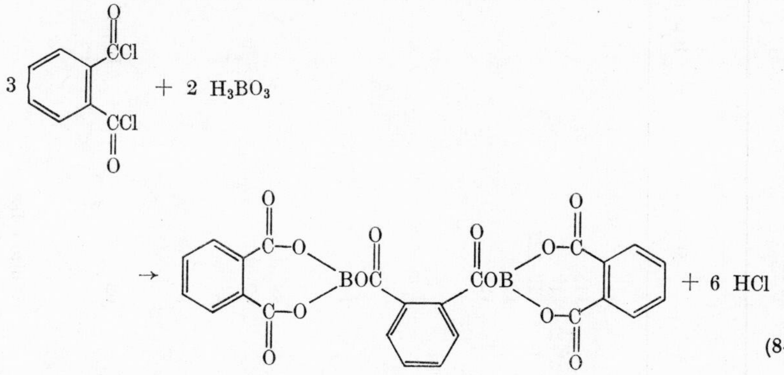

3 $C_6H_4(COCl)_2$ + 2 H_3BO_3

→ [phthalyl boric anhydride structure: BOC, COB] + 6 HCl

(8-59)

3 $C_6H_4(CO)_2O$ + 2 H_3BO_3

→ [phthalyl boric anhydride structure: BOC, COB] + 3 H_2O

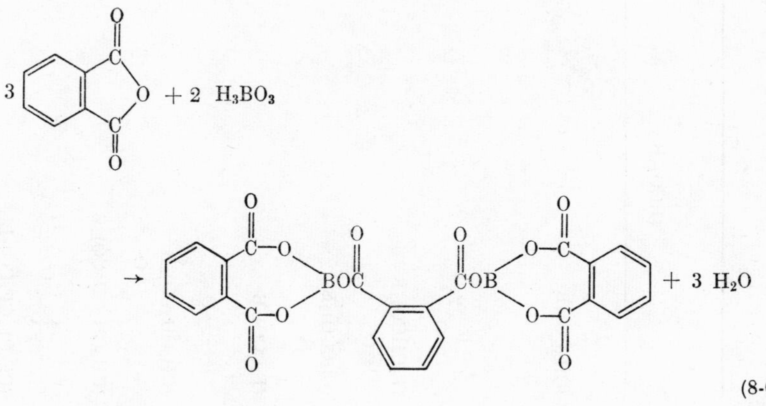

(8-60)

VIII. PHYSICAL CONSTANTS

$(R\overset{O}{\overset{\Vert}{C}}O)_3B$	M.p. (°C)	B.p. (°C)	d_4^t	n_D^t	Reference
$(CH_3\overset{O}{\overset{\Vert}{C}}O)_3B$	118				76
	119				3
	119–122				6
	120				21
	121				64
$(F_2CH\overset{O}{\overset{\Vert}{C}}O)_3B$	Tan solid				61
$(Cl_3C\overset{O}{\overset{\Vert}{C}}O)_3B$	165				64
$(F_3C\overset{O}{\overset{\Vert}{C}}O)_3B$	88 (d.)				31
	99 (d.)				61
$(CH_3CH_2\overset{O}{\overset{\Vert}{C}}O)_3B$	87				76
$(CH_3CH_2CH_2\overset{O}{\overset{\Vert}{C}}O)_3B$	63	Liquid	1.064^{23}		76
	—	—	—	—	64
$(CF_3CF_2CF_2\overset{O}{\overset{\Vert}{C}}O)_3B$	White solid				61

$(CH_3CH(CH_3)CH_2C(=O)O)_3B$		Liquid	$1.024^{21.5}$		64
$(C_6H_5CH{=}CHC(=O)O)_3B$	125–130				39, 41
$[CH_3(CH_2)_{10}C(=O)O]_3B$	Crystalline				39, 41
$[CH_3(CH_2)_{16}C(=O)O]_3B$	71				39, 41
	73				64

$(ArC(=O)O)_3B$	M.p. (°C)	B.p. (°C)	d_4^t	n_D^t	Reference
$[C_6H_5C(=O)O]_3B$	145				1, 64
	166				39, 41

$(RC(=O)O)_2BOB(OC(=O)R)_2$	M.p. (°C)	B.p. (°C)	d_4^t	n_D^t	Reference
$(CH_3C(=O)O)_2BOB(OC(=O)CH_3)_2$	140–150				16
	147–148				48
	147–148, 149–150				36
	150–152				24

(*Table continued*)

$(R\overset{O}{\overset{\|}{C}}O)_2BOB(O\overset{O}{\overset{\|}{C}}R)_2$	M.p. (°C)	B.p. (°C)	d_4^t	n_D^t	Reference
$(F_3C\overset{O}{\overset{\|}{C}}O)_2BOB(O\overset{O}{\overset{\|}{C}}CF_3)_2$	113–120				31
$(C_2H_5\overset{O}{\overset{\|}{C}}O)_2BOB(O\overset{O}{\overset{\|}{C}}C_2H_5)_2$	Crystalline				55
$(n\text{-}C_3H_7\overset{O}{\overset{\|}{C}}O)_2BOB(O\overset{O}{\overset{\|}{C}}\text{-}n\text{-}C_3H_7)_2$	Solid				55
$(i\text{-}C_3H_7\overset{O}{\overset{\|}{C}}O)_2BOB(O\overset{O}{\overset{\|}{C}}\text{-}i\text{-}C_3H_7)_2$	Solid				55
$(n\text{-}C_5H_{11}\overset{O}{\overset{\|}{C}}O)_2BOB(O\overset{O}{\overset{\|}{C}}\text{-}n\text{-}C_5H_{11})_2$	—	—	—	—	55

$R\overset{O}{\overset{\|}{C}}OB(OH)_2$	M.p. (°C)	B.p. (°C)	d_4^t	n_D^t	Reference
$KO\overset{O}{\overset{\|}{C}}\overset{O}{\overset{\|}{C}}OB(OH)_2$	Prisms				65

$ArOB(O\overset{O}{\overset{\Vert}{C}}CH_3)_2$	M.p. (°C)	B.p. (°C)	d_4^t	n_D^t	Reference
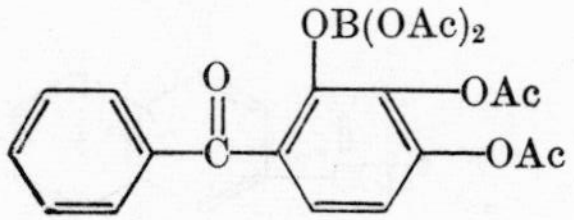 OB(OAc)$_2$; O; C; OAc; OAc	Orange-red solid				24
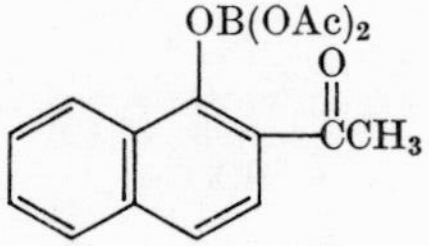 OB(OAc)$_2$; O; CCH$_3$	Yellow prisms				24
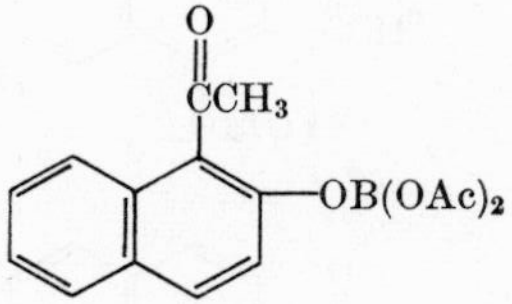 O; CCH$_3$; OB(OAc)$_2$	Orange-yellow octahedra				24
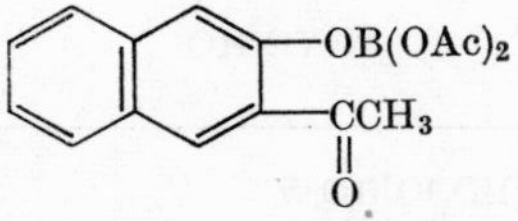 OB(OAc)$_2$; CCH$_3$; O	Orange crystals				24

(*Table continued*)

$ArOB(O\overset{O}{\overset{\|}{C}}CH_3)_2$	M.p. (°C)	B.p. (°C)	d_4^t	n_D^t	Reference
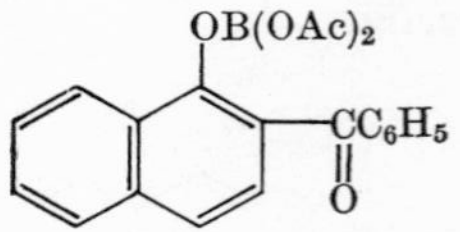 $OB(OAc)_2$; $\overset{}{C}C_6H_5$ (=O)	Orange prisms				24
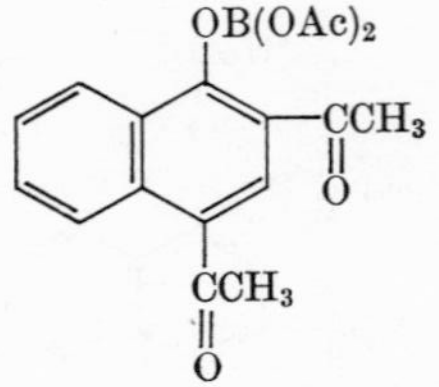 $OB(OAc)_2$; CCH_3 (=O); CCH_3 (=O)	Red-brown plates				24
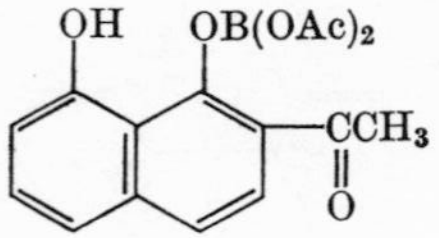 OH; $OB(OAc)_2$; CCH_3 (=O)	Red cubes				24
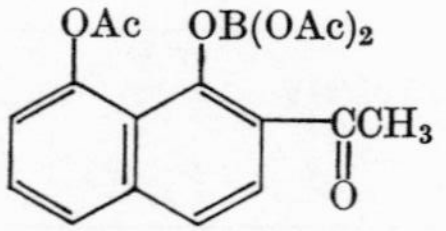 OAc; $OB(OAc)_2$; CCH_3 (=O)	Yellow leaflets				24

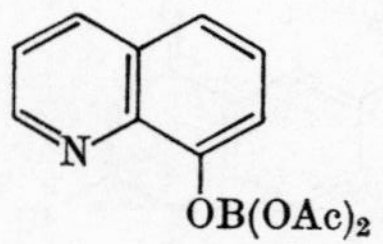 (quinoline, N) $OB(OAc)_2$	—	—	—	—	24
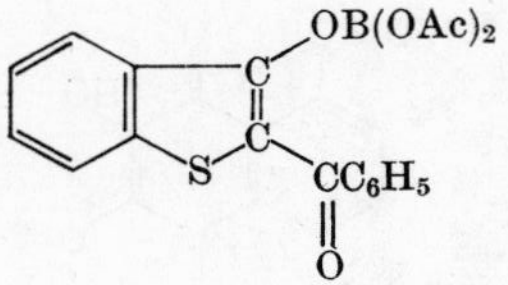 $OB(OAc)_2$; C=C; S; $\overset{O}{\parallel}CC_6H_5$	Red prisms				19
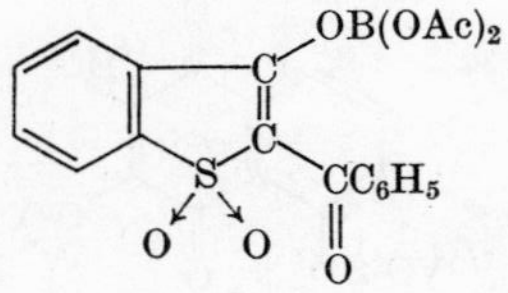 $OB(OAc)_2$; C=C; S(→O)(→O); $\overset{O}{\parallel}CC_6H_5$	220, Yellow needles				19
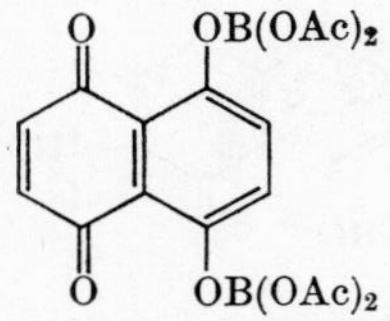 O, $OB(OAc)_2$; O, $OB(OAc)_2$	Brick-red prisms				26

(Table continued)

$ArOB(O\overset{O}{\overset{\parallel}{C}}CH_3)_2$	M.p. (°C)	B.p. (°C)	d_4^t	n_D^t	Reference
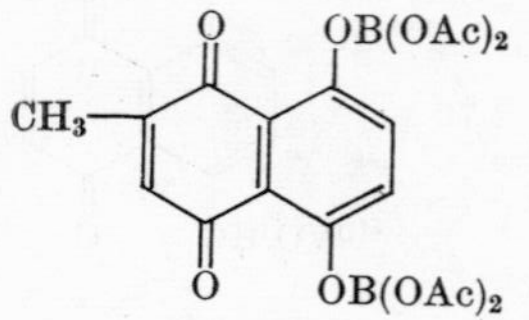 O, $OB(OAc)_2$, CH_3, O, $OB(OAc)_2$	Reddish-violet plates				53
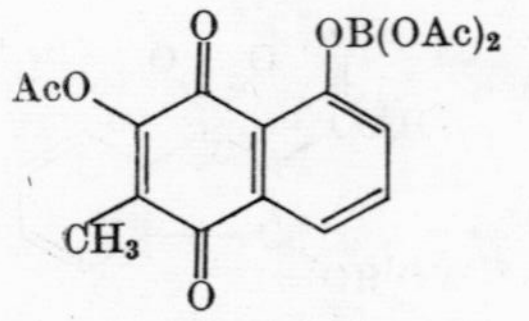 O, $OB(OAc)_2$, AcO, CH_3, O	—	—	—		53
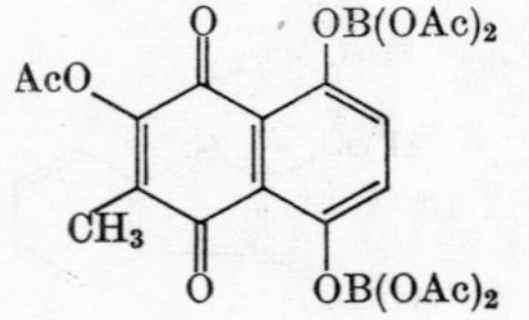 O, $OB(OAc)_2$, AcO, CH_3, O, $OB(OAc)_2$	Red crystalline powder				53
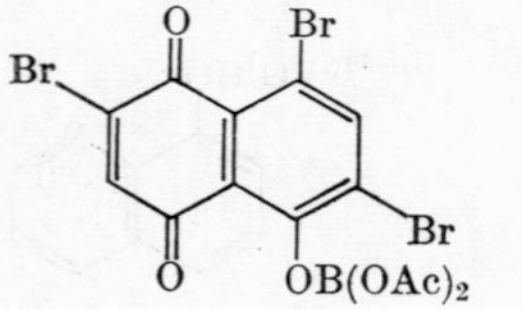 O, Br, Br, Br, O, $OB(OAc)_2$	Green hexagonal plates				53

Compound	Description	Ref.
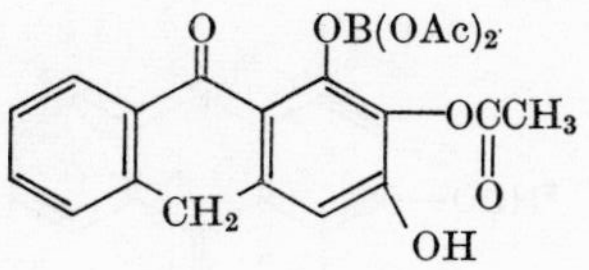	Orange crystalline powder	23
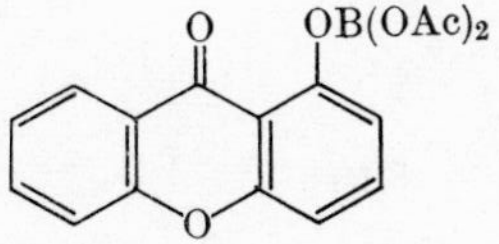	Yellow plates	24
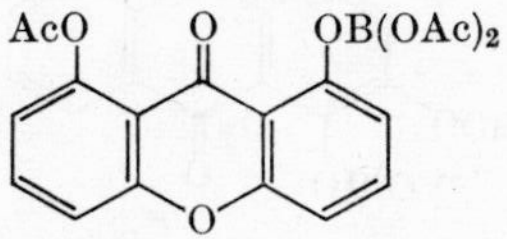	Yellow prisms	24
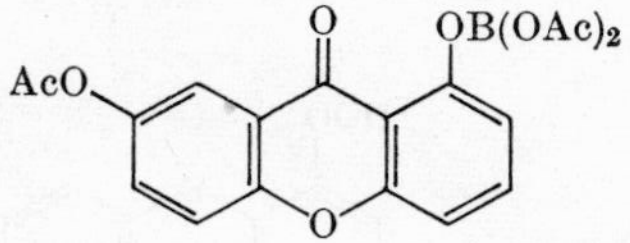	Golden needles	67
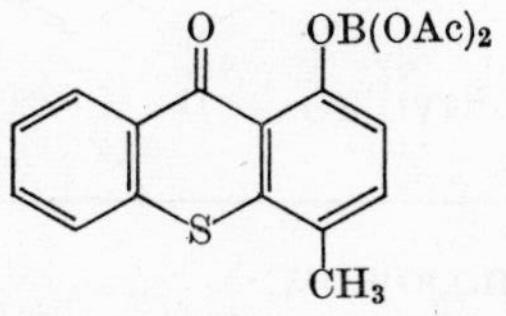	236, Red needles	52

(Table continued)

$ArOB(O\overset{O}{\overset{\|\|}{C}}CH_3)_2$	M.p. (°C)	B.p. (°C)	d_4^t	n_D^t	Reference
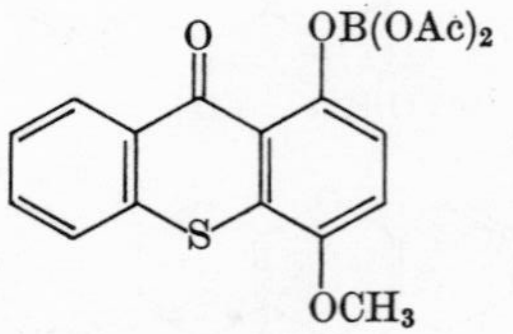 O, $OB(OAc)_2$, S, OCH_3	205, Red needles				66
O, $OB(OAc)_2$, OCH_3, S, CH_3	Purple				52
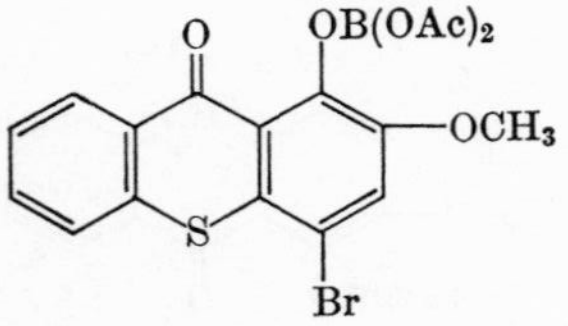 O, $OB(OAc)_2$, OCH_3, S, Br	Red crystals				52

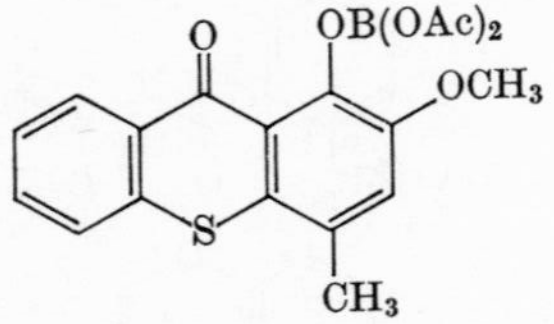

Compound	Properties	Ref.
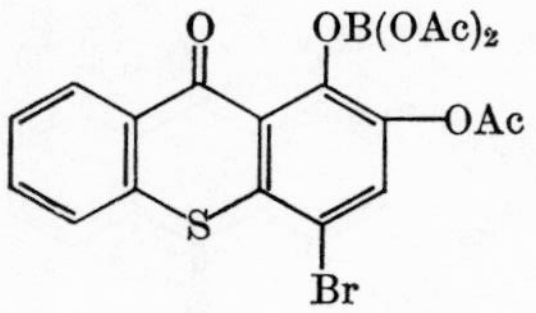 O, OB(OAc)₂, OAc, S, Br	Red crystals	52
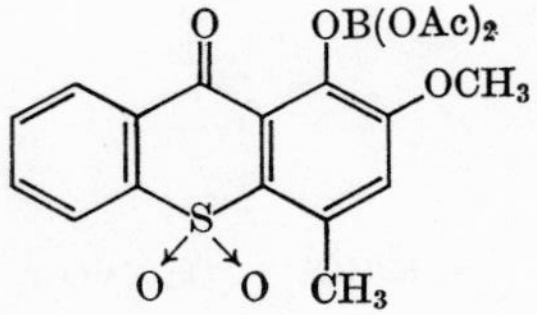 O, OB(OAc)₂, OCH₃, S, O, O, CH₃	222, Red	52
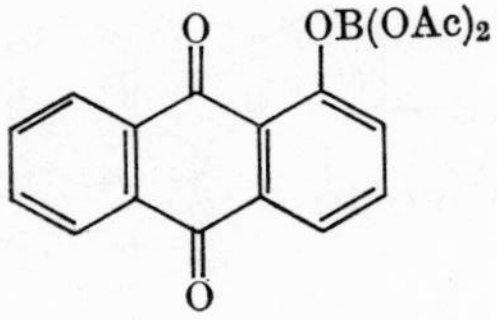 O, OB(OAc)₂, O	Orange-red tablets	25
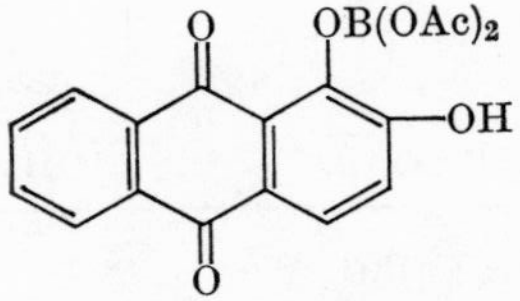 O, OB(OAc)₂, OH, O	Deep red crystals	25

(*Table continued*)

$ArOB(OC(=O)CH_3)_2$	M.p. (°C)	B.p. (°C)	d_4^t	n_D^t	Reference
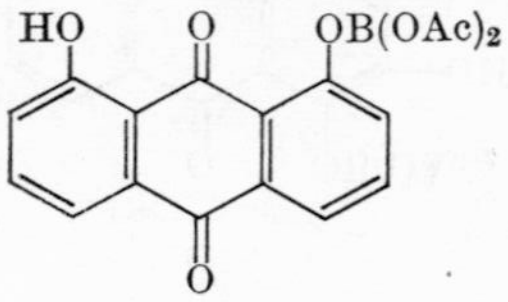 HO, O, $OB(OAc)_2$, O	Light red crystals				25
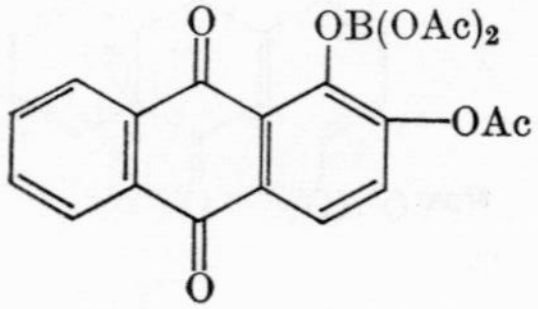 O, $OB(OAc)_2$, OAc, O	Orange-red crystals				25
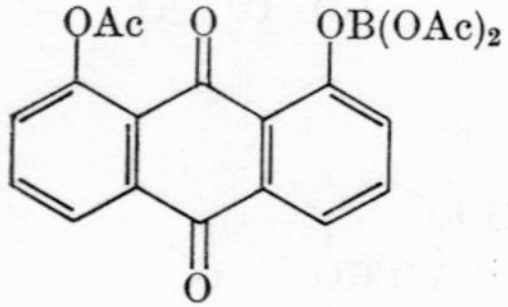 OAc, O, $OB(OAc)_2$, O	Red crystals				25
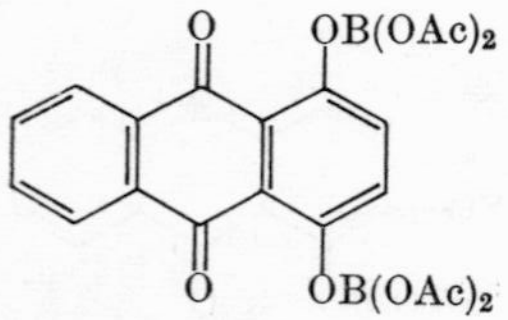 O, $OB(OAc)_2$, O, $OB(OAc)_2$	Ruby-red crystals				25

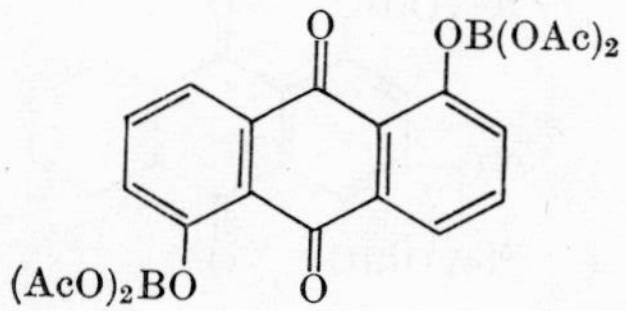 (AcO)$_2$BO, O, O, OB(OAc)$_2$	Yellow leaflets	25
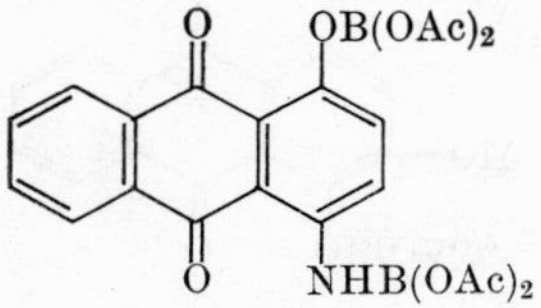 O, OB(OAc)$_2$, O, NHB(OAc)$_2$	Light blue leaflets or needles	11
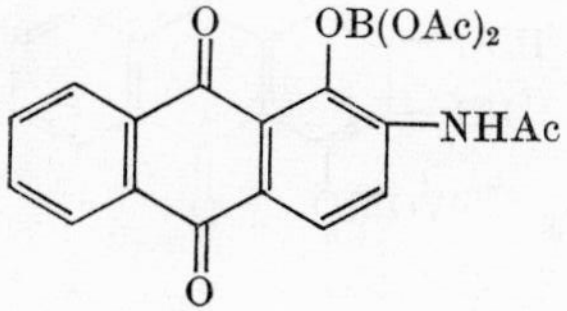 O, OB(OAc)$_2$, NHAc, O	Dark brown solid	11
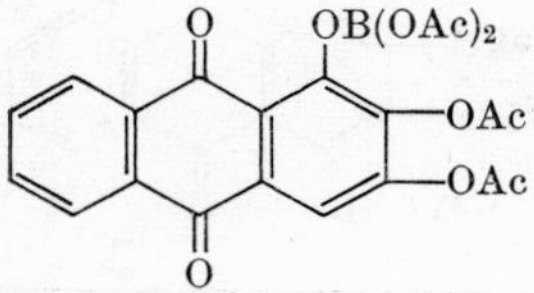 O, OB(OAc)$_2$, OAc, OAc, O	214	24

(*Table continued*)

$ArOB(O\overset{O}{\overset{\|\|}{C}}CH_3)_2$	M.p. (°C)	B.p. (°C)	d_4^t	n_D^t	Reference
$OB(OAc)_2$, CH_2OAc, OAc	Crystalline				4
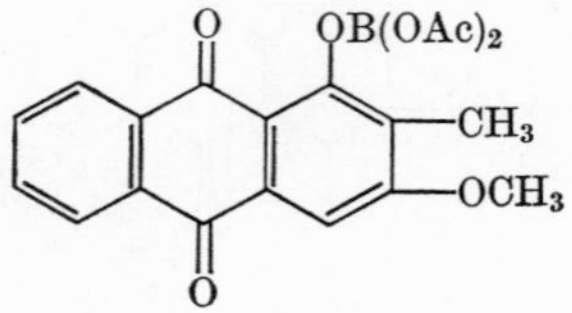 $OB(OAc)_2$, CH_3, OCH_3	Orange-red prisms				47
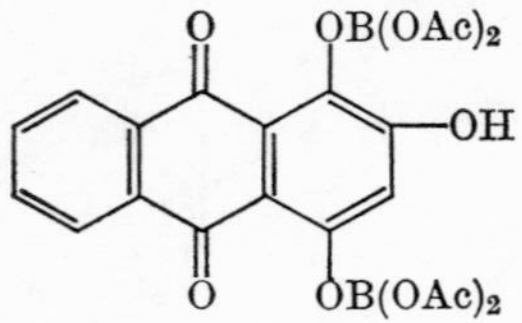 $OB(OAc)_2$, OH, $OB(OAc)_2$	Purple-red crystals				25
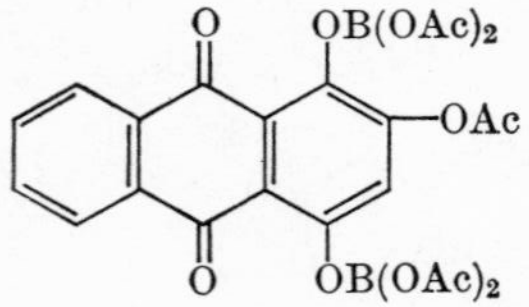 $OB(OAc)_2$, OAc, $OB(OAc)_2$	Violet-red crystals				25

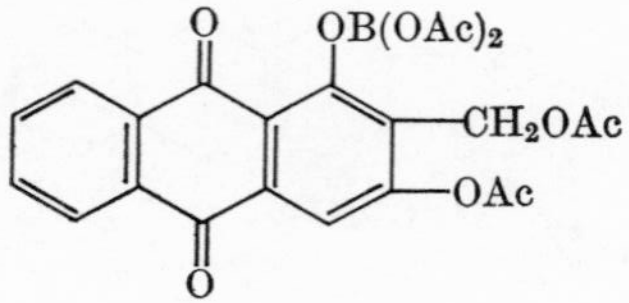

O, $OB(OAc)_2$, $(AcO)_2BO$, O, OAc	Red-brown crystals				25
AcNH, O, $OB(OAc)_2$, $(AcO)_2BO$, O, NHAc	Brown prisms				24
O O, $OB(OAc)_2$, OAc	—	—	—	—	24
O O, $OB(OAc)_2$, NHAc	—	—	—	—	24

(*Table continued*)

$ArOB(OC(=O)CH_3)_2$	M.p. (°C)	B.p. (°C)	d_4^t	n_D^t	Reference
$OB(OAc)_2$	268, Yellow needles				10

$R(O)_2BOC(=O)R'$	M.p. (°C)	B.p. (°C)	d_4^t	n_D^t	Reference
$(CH_2O)_2BOC(=O)CH_3$	~77				8, 9
$(CH_2O)_2BOC(=O)CH_2Cl$	—	—	—	—	8, 9
$(CH_2O)_2BOC(=O)CHCl_2$	—	—	—	—	9

Compound	M.p. (°C)	B.p. (°C)	d_4^t	n_D^t	Reference
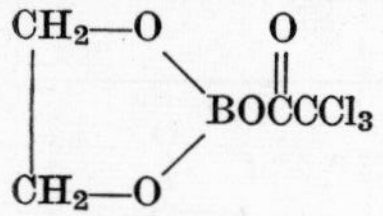 CH_2—O, CH_2—O (ring) $BOC(=O)CCl_3$	—	—	—	—	9
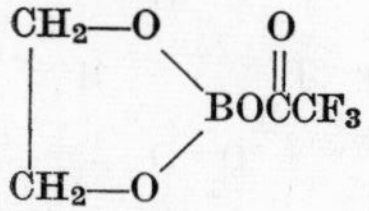 CH_2—O, CH_2—O (ring) $BOC(=O)CF_3$	—	—	—	—	8, 9
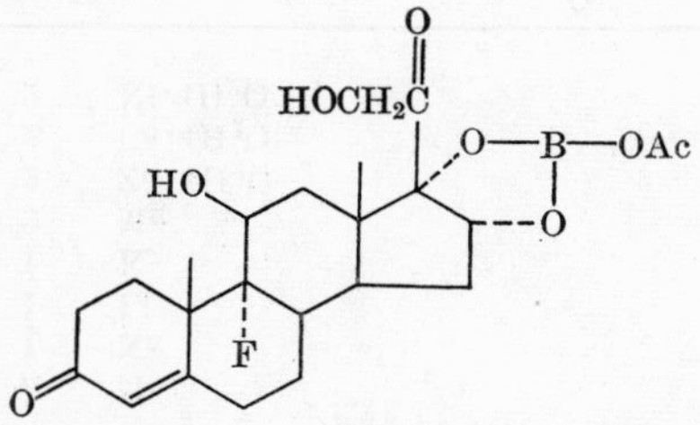 $HOCH_2C(=O)$, O—B—OAc, O, HO, F (steroid)	—	—	—	—	30

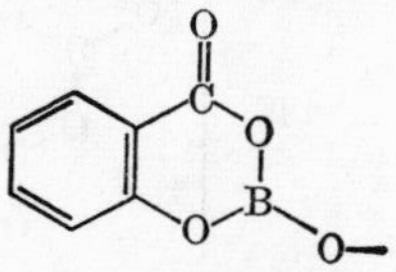

$C_6H_4C(=O)OB(O)$—O—	M.p. (°C)	B.p. (°C)	d_4^t	n_D^t	Reference
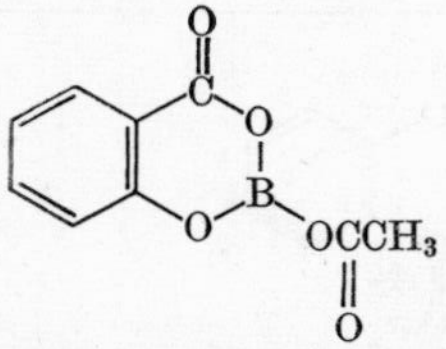 $C_6H_4C(=O)OB(O)OC(=O)CH_3$	Structure in doubt				24

(*Table continued*)

	M.p. (°C)	B.p. (°C)	d_4^t	n_D^t	Reference
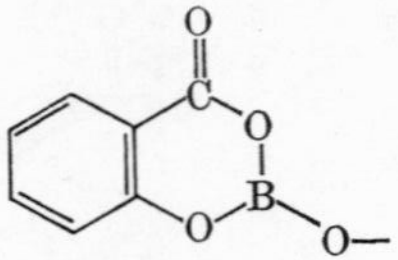					
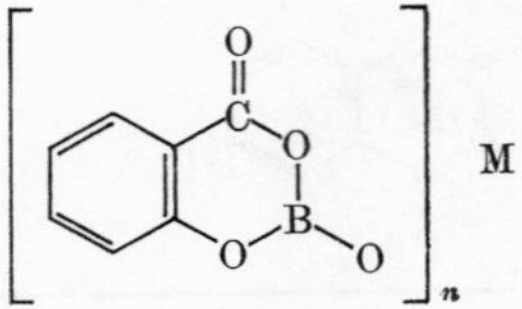					
n M					
1 Na	—	—	—	—	68
1 Li	—	—	—	—	68
1 K	—	—	—	—	68
2 Mg	—	—	—	—	68
2 $Zn \cdot 4H_2O$	—	—	—	—	68
2 $Co \cdot 4H_2O$	—	—	—	—	68
2 $Ni \cdot 4H_2O$	—	—	—	—	59

	M.p. (°C)	B.p. (°C)	d_4^t	n_D^t	Reference
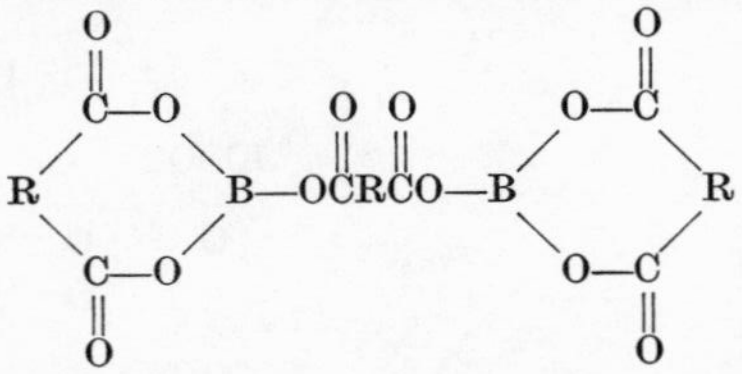					

$[CH_2C(O)O]_2$B—OC(O)CH_2CH_2C(O)O—B$[OC(O)CH_2]_2$ (cyclic: CH₂—C(=O)—O / CH₂—C(=O)—O rings on each B)	164	7, 64
$[CHC(O)O]_2$BOC(O)CH=CHC(O)OB$[OC(O)CH]_2$ (cyclic: CH—C(=O)—O ‖ CH—C(=O)—O rings on each B)	145–146	7
$C_6H_4[C(O)O]_2$BOC(O)C_6H_4C(O)OB$[OC(O)]_2C_6H_4$	165	7, 64

IX. REFERENCES

1. Ahmad, T., S. Z. Haider, and M. H. Khundkar, *J. Appl. Chem.*, **4**, 543 (1954).
2. Ahmad, T., and M. H. Khundkar, *Chem. & Ind.* (*London*), 248 (1954).
3. Andrianov, K. A., and L. M. Volkova, *Izv. Akad. Nauk S.S.S.R. Otd. Khim. Nauk*, 303 (1957).
4. Ayyangar, N. R., B. S. Joshi, and K. Venkataraman, *Tetrahedron*, **6**, 331 (1959).
5. Bailey, J. J., and D. G. Gehring, *Anal. Chem.*, **33**, 1760 (1961).
6. Bastin, E. L., *et al.*, Shell Development Co., Final Report on Potential CW Agents, Chemical Corps Procurement Agency, Contract No. CML-4564, Project No. 4-08-03-001, April 30, 1954.
7. Beran, F., V. Prey, and H. Böhm, Mitt. *Chem. Forschungsinst. Wirtsch. Oesterr.*, **6**, 54 (1952).
8. Blau, J. A., W. Gerrard, and M. F. Lappert, *J. Chem. Soc.*, 667 (1960).
9. Blau, J. A., W. Gerrard, M. F. Lappert, B. A. Mountfield, and H. Pyszora, *J. Chem. Soc.*, 380 (1960).
10. Bradley, W., and G. V. Jadhav, *J. Chem. Soc.*, 1791 (1937).
11. Brass, K., and O. Ziegler, *Ber.*, **58**, 755 (1925).
12. Brown, H. C., and W. Korytnyk, *J. Am. Chem. Soc.*, **82**, 3867 (1960).
13. Brown, H. C., and K. Murray, *J. Am. Chem. Soc.*, **81**, 4108 (1959).
14. Brown, H. C., and B. C. Subba Rao, *J. Am. Chem. Soc.*, **82**, 681 (1960).
15. Brown, H. C., and G. Zweifel, *J. Am. Chem. Soc.*, **83**, 3834 (1961).
16. Carpenter, R. A., *et al.*, Midwest Research Institute, Report No. CCC-1024-TR-6, Feb. 10, 1954; Astia Document 138,308.
17. Chappelow, C. C., Jr., F. J. Bergman, and R. A. Carpenter, *J. Chem. Eng. Data*, **5**, 567 (1960).
18. Cherbuliez, E., J. P. Leber, and A. M. Ulrich, *Helv. Chim. Acta*, **36**, 910 (1953).
19. Cohen, A., and S. Smiles, *J. Chem. Soc.*, 406 (1930).
20. Cohn, G., *Pharm. Zentralhalle*, **52**, 479 (1911).
21. Cook, H. G., J. D. Ilett, B. C. Saunders, and G. J. Stacey, *J. Chem. Soc.*, 3125 (1950).
22. Crighton, J., A. K. Holliday, A. G. Massey, and N. R. Thompson, *Chem. & Ind.* (*London*), 347 (1960).
23. Cross, E. J., and A. G. Perkin, *J. Chem. Soc.*, 292 (1930).
24. Dimroth, O., *Ann.*, **446**, 97 (1926).
25. Dimroth, O., and T. Faust, *Ber.*, **54**, 3020 (1921).
26. Dimroth, O., and F. Ruck, *Ann.*, **446**, 123 (1926).
27. Duncanson, L. A., W. Gerrard, M. F. Lappert, H. Pyszora, and R. Shafferman, *J. Chem. Soc.*, 3652 (1958).
28. Dupont and Pascaud, *Industrie chimique*, **14**, 117 (1927).
29. General Aniline and Film Corporation, Brit. Pat. 824,545 (1959).
30. Gerrard, W., and M. F. Lappert, *Chem. Rev.*, **58**, 1081 (1958).
31. Gerrard, W., M. F. Lappert, and R. Shafferman, *J. Chem. Soc.*, 3648 (1958).
32. Gerrard, W., and M. A. Wheelans, *Chem. & Ind.* (*London*), 758 (1954).
33. Gerrard, W., and M. A. Wheelans, *J. Chem. Soc.*, 4296 (1956).
34. Goubeau, J., R. Epple, D. Ulmschneider, and H. Lehmann, *Angew. Chem.* **67**, 710 (1955).

35. Gustavson, G., *Ber.*, **3**, 426 (1870).
36. Hayter, R. G., A. W. Laubengayer, and P. G. Thompson, *J. Am. Chem. Soc.*, **79**, 4243 (1957).
37. Henglein, F. A., R. Lang, and K. Scheinost, *Makromol. Chem.*, **15**, 177 (1955).
38. Henglein, F. A., R. Lang, and L. Schmack, *Makromol. Chem.*, **22**, 103 (1957).
39. Henkel and Cie., Brit. Pat. 398,064 (1933).
40. Henkel and Cie., G.m.b.H., French Pat. 746,954 (1933).
41. Hintermaier, A., U.S. Pat. 1,987,559 (1935, to Henkel and Cie.).
42. Hirao, N., and Y. Yabuuchi, *J. Pharm. Soc. Japan*, **74**, 1073 (1954).
43. Imoto, M., *J. Soc. Chem. Ind., Japan*, **41**, Suppl. binding, 251 (1938); through *Chem. Abstracts*, **33**, 552 (1939).
44. Imoto, M., *J. Soc. Chem. Ind., Japan*, **41**, Suppl. binding, 443 (1938); through *Chem. Abstracts*, **33**, 3359 (1939).
45. Imoto, M., *J. Soc. Chem. Ind., Japan*, **42**, Suppl. binding, 183, 185 (1939); through *Chem. Abstracts*, **33**, 7766 (1939).
46. Imoto, M., *J. Soc. Chem. Ind., Japan*, **42**, Suppl. binding, 230 (1939); through *Chem. Abstracts*, **33**, 3359 (1939).
47. Jones, E. T., and A. Robertson, *J. Chem. Soc.*, 1699 (1930).
48. Kahovec, L., *Ber.*, **43**, 109 (1939).
49. Konig, O., E. G. Gordon, and D. F. Herman, U.S. Pat. 2,969,342 (1961, to National Lead Company).
50. Kuskov, V. K., *Dokl. Akad. Nauk S.S.S.R.*, **110**, 223 (1956).
51. Levens, E., and R. M. Washburn, U.S. Pat. 2,891,993 (1959, to American Potash and Chemical Corporation).
52. Levi, A. A., and S. Smiles, *J. Chem. Soc.*, 520 (1931).
53. Macbeth, A. K., and F. L. Winzor, *J. Chem. Soc.*, 334 (1935).
54. Massey, A. G., *J. Chem. Soc.*, 5264 (1960).
55. May, F. H., and V. V. Levasheff, U.S. Pat. 2,941,000 (1960).
56. Meerwein, H., *Angew. Chem.*, **60**, 78 (1948).
57. Meerwein, H., and H. Maier-Hüser, *J. Prakt. Chem.*, **134**, 51 (1932).
58. Meerwein, H., and H. Sönke, *J. Prakt. Chem.*, **147**, 251 (1936).
59. Meulenhoff, J., *Rec. Trav. Chim.*, **44**, 161 (1925).
60. Muetterties, E. L., *J. Am. Chem. Soc.*, **80**, 4526 (1958).
61. Muetterties, E. L., U.S. Pat. 2,782,233 (1957, to E. I. duPont de Nemours & Co.).
62. Onak, T. P., H. Landesman, R. E. Williams, and I. Shapiro, *J. Phys. Chem.*, **63**, 1533 (1959).
63. Perotti, A., M. Cola, and A. Parmigiani, *Gazz. Chim. Ital.*, **90**, 1028 (1960).
64. Pictet, A., and A. Geleznoff, *Ber.*, **36**, 2219 (1903).
65. Ploquin, J., *Bull. Soc. Pharm. Bordeaux*, **95**, 13 (1956).
66. Roberts, K. C., and S. Smiles, *J. Chem. Soc.*, 1322 (1929).
67. Robertson, A., and R. B. Waters, *J. Chem. Soc.*, 2239 (1929).
68. Schäfer, H., *Z. Anorg. Allgem. Chem.*, **250**, 96 (1942).
69. Schiff, H., *Ann. Suppl.*, **5**, 154 (1867).
70. Schulze, H., U.S. Pat. 2,898,353 (1959, to General Aniline and Film Corporation).
71. Schützenberger, M., *Compt. Rend.*, **53**, 538 (1861).
72. Thomas, G. H., U.S. Pat. 2,831,003 (1958, to Olin Mathieson Chemical Corp.).

73. Washburn, R. M., E. Levens, C. F. Albright, and F. A. Billig, "Preparation, Properties, and Uses of Borate Esters," in *Metal-Organic Compounds, Advances in Chemistry Series No. 23,* American Chemical Society, Washington, 1959, p. 129.
74. Wheeler, A. S., and D. R. Ergle, *J. Am. Chem. Soc.*, **52**, 4872 (1930).
75. Willcockson, G. W., and W. G. Woods, Unpublished results.
76. Yur'ev, Y. K., Z. V. Belyakova, P. V. Kostetskii, and A. I. Prokof'ev, *Zh. Obshch. Khim.*, **30**, 415 (1960).
77. Zuffanti, S., R. T. Oliver, and W. F. Luder, *J. Phys. Chem.*, **63**, 1537 (1959).

9

TRIALKOXYBOROXINES AND RELATED COMPOUNDS

I. TRIALKOXYBOROXINES

A. Introduction

Esters of metaboric acid have a 1 : 1 ratio of alkoxy groups to boron atoms in contrast to the 3 : 1 ratio present in esters of orthoboric acid. The simplest formulation of an ester of metaboric acid contains a boron–oxygen double bond (I); however, the monomer has not yet

$$\text{ROB=O}$$
(I)

been demonstrated to have more than transitory existence, and all metaborates to date are best formulated as the trimer (II) containing

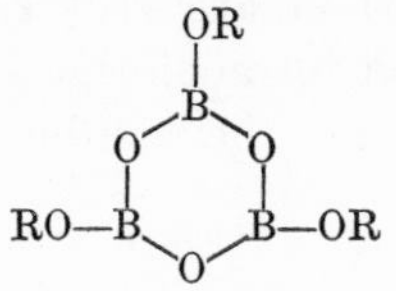

```
          OR
          |
          B
        /   \
       O     O
       |     |
  RO—B       B—OR
        \   /
          O
```
(II)

the boroxine ring. Thus the term "trialkoxyboroxines." Only primary and secondary alkyl derivatives of the boroxine ring have been reported to date.[1]

B. Historical

In 1865 Schiff and Bechi[60] reported the preparation of ethyl metaborate from the treatment of triethoxyborane with boric oxide. The reaction was formulated to give the monomeric species (9-1). These

$$(C_2H_5O)_3B + B_2O_3 \rightarrow 3\ C_2H_5OBO \qquad (9\text{-}1)$$

authors also recorded that the metaborate was formed along with the orthoborate from the reaction of alcohol with excess boric anhydride. Two years later an expanded version of their paper described a series of preparations and reactions of a variety of aliphatic and aromatic metaborates.[59] The metaborates were still formulated as monomeric species.

In 1898 Copaux[15] suggested that the molecular weights of the metaborates were greater than monomeric. The next metaborate publication did not appear until 1921.[19]

C. Properties

1. GENERAL

Most metaborates are viscous, hygroscopic liquids. Some of those derived from secondary alcohols, as well as triphenoxyboroxine, are solids at room temperature. Their solubility in organic media is dependent upon their origin. Those prepared from non-hydroxylic reagents, for the most part, are soluble in organic solvents.*[39] However, if alcohol was present in their synthesis, a small amount of hydroxyl groups remain in the product as evidenced by their infrared spectra, viscosity is increased, and solubility in non-polar solvents is not complete.[63]

Trimethoxyboroxine is miscible in all proportions with trimethoxyborane, methanol, ether, acetone, ligroin, benzene, toluene, xylene and dioxane,[7] very soluble in chloroform and carbon tetrachloride, and slightly soluble in petroleum ether.[63] Both the isopropyl and n-butyl derivatives are very soluble in acetone, ether, benzene, chloroform, carbon tetrachloride and petroleum ether.[63]

Equation (9-2), where n is the number of carbon atoms in the

$$R_{obsd.} = 13.90n + 20.38 \quad (9\text{-}2)$$

alkyl group, has been recorded as an empirical expression for the molar refraction of the homologous series $(ROBO)_3$.[10] Other molar refraction and magnetic susceptibility data have been recorded for the methyl, ethyl and isopropyl derivatives.[25] Dipole moments for these esters in dioxane solution are 2.18, 2.32, and 2.41 D respectively.[25,41]

The ^{11}B nuclear magnetic resonance chemical shift of trimethoxyboroxine and tributoxyboroxine have been recorded, $\delta = -17.3$ and -17.5 respectively.[49]

2. STRUCTURE

Although metaborates have been formulated as monomeric species (I) as late as 1939,[62] molecular weight determinations by

* It is interesting that trimethoxyboroxine contains a higher percentage of boron (18.7%) than boric acid itself. This fact coupled with its solubility in organic media allows the introduction of high boron contents into nonpolar solvents.

cryoscopic, ebullioscopic, and isopiestic methods indicate the trimeric structure (II).[1,20,23,39,47,63,67]

Further evidence for the trimeric structure is found in the Raman spectrum[23] of trimethoxyboroxine which exhibits characteristic lines of the boroxine ring, and the infrared spectra[47] of cyclohexyl and *l*-menthyl metaborate which do not exhibit absorption for a boron oxygen double bond.* In addition, the metaborates possess a characteristic absorption in the infrared in the region 13.82 to 13.87μ which is absent in orthoborates and oxybisboranes.[63] These data are consistent with the reported absorptions at 13.6 and 13.9 μ for a variety of metaborates believed to be due to out-of-plane vibrations of the boroxine ring.[1,39]

Bond strength data calculated from Raman spectral data indicated 10–20% aromatic character for trimethoxyboroxine as compared to benzene.[24] ^{11}B quadropole coupling constants for trimethoxyboroxine indicated that the structure can be represented as 40% (III) and 60% (IV).[54] Bond angles in the boroxine ring have not been determined.

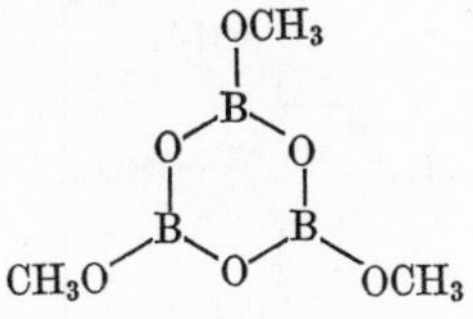

(III) 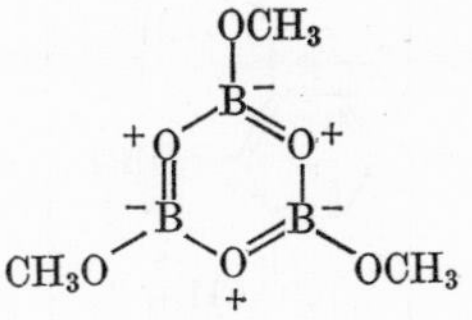 (IV)

Much difficulty has been experienced in assigning definitive structures to the metaborates because of the difficulty in purification. They cannot be distilled without decomposition,[12,23,39,47,60,61,63] and for the most part they cannot be crystallized. In addition, recrystallization procedures are hampered by the extreme hydrolytic instability of the compounds. The melting point of trimethoxyboroxine is very sensitive to traces of water or the slightest deviations from the theoretical stoichiometry.[7]

D. Methods of Preparation

1. FROM MONOHYDRIC ALCOHOLS OR PHENOLS AND BORIC ACID OR EQUIVALENT

The fallacy that orthoboric acid and boric oxide are esterified to give orthoborates and that metaboric acid yields metaborates, as

* It was expected that the B=O absorption would be in the region of the C=O absorption. As yet there has not been isolated an unequivocal structure possessing a B=O group.

discussed in Chapter 4, is again pointed out by the conversion of all three of these materials to metaborates by treatment with alcohols.

$$3\,ROH + 3\,H_3BO_3 \rightarrow (ROBO)_3 + 6\,H_2O \quad (9\text{-}3)$$

$$3\,ROH + 3\,HBO_2 \rightarrow (ROBO)_3 + 3\,H_2O \quad (9\text{-}4)$$

$$6\,ROH + 3\,B_2O_3 \rightarrow 2\,(ROBO)_3 + 3\,H_2O \quad (9\text{-}5)$$

Boric acid has been esterified with primary and secondary alcohols by simply heating[42] or evacuating[21] the admixture or by removing the water as a toluene or benzene azeotrope.[20,47,63] Cyclohexanol was esterified with boric acid by passage of the reflux vapors through calcium chloride.[11,12]

If the alcohol to boric acid ratio is greater than unity, mixtures of ortho and metaborates result (9-6),[5] except in the case of the

$$4\,ROH + 2\,H_3BO_3 \rightarrow (RO)_3B + \tfrac{1}{3}\,(ROBO)_3 + 5\,H_2O \quad (9\text{-}6)$$

hindered phenols, 2,6-di-*t*-butylphenol and 2,6-di-*t*-butyl-4-methylphenol, which result in the metaborates (V) and (VI) regardless of the stoichiometry employed.[28]

$[2,6\text{-}(C(CH_3)_3)_2C_6H_3\text{—OBO}]_3$

(V)

$[4\text{-}CH_3\text{-}2,6\text{-}(C(CH_3)_3)_2C_6H_2\text{—OBO}]_3$

(VI)

Both alkyl and phenyl derivatives have been prepared from metaboric acid by azeotropic removal of the water with toluene.[20,63]

With boric oxide, the water has been removed from the system as such (9-5),[59] as metaboric acid (9-7),[2] and as boric acid (9-8).[43,59,63] Mixtures of the orthoborate and metaborate were

$$3\,C_6H_5OH + 3\,B_2O_3 \rightarrow (C_6H_5OBO)_3 + 3\,HBO_2 \quad (9\text{-}7)$$

$$3\,ROH + 2\,B_2O_3 \rightarrow (ROBO)_3 + H_3BO_3 \quad (9\text{-}8)$$

obtained from the reaction of boric oxide with less than four moles of methanol.[61]

It was suggested that the reaction of an alcohol and boric oxide to produce a metaborate and boric acid proceeded in a stepwise fashion through the orthoborate.[59] However, since the hindered

$$3\,ROH + B_2O_3 \rightarrow (RO)_3B + H_3BO_3 \quad (9\text{-}9)$$

$$(RO)_3B + B_2O_3 \rightarrow (ROBO)_3 \quad (9\text{-}10)$$

$$3\,ROH + 2\,B_2O_3 \rightarrow (ROBO)_3 + H_3BO_3 \quad (9\text{-}11)$$

phenolic metaborates (V and VI) also can be prepared from boric oxide and the phenols,[63] and since orthoborate formation is sterically precluded in these systems, it is clear that an alternative path to the metaborates other than the sequence (9-9) and (9-10) must be available.

2. FROM DIOLS OR TRIOLS AND BORIC ACID OR EQUIVALENT

An elaborate series of metaborates was claimed to have been formed by the sequence of esterifications and transesterifications shown in Figure 9-1.[30] Since only one molecular weight value was presented, and in view of the low probability of formation of fused 9- and 10-membered rings, it must be concluded that polymeric products were formed to some appreciable degree if not completely.

Attempts to prepare the biborate of 2,5-dimethyl-2,5-hexanediol by the azeotropic removal of water with toluene from a 3:2 molar mixture of the diol and boric acid led to the deposition of a solid material with a boron analysis consistent with structure (VII) or (VIII).[64]

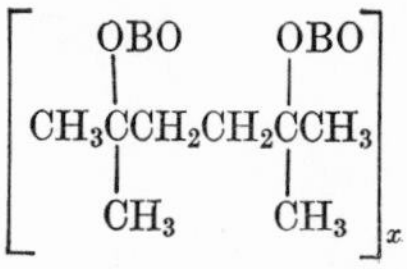

$$\left[\begin{array}{c} \text{OBO} \quad\quad \text{OBO} \\ | \quad\quad\quad\quad | \\ CH_3CCH_2CH_2CCH_3 \\ | \quad\quad\quad\quad | \\ CH_3 \quad\quad CH_3 \end{array}\right]_x$$

(VII)

$$\left[\begin{array}{l} \quad CH_3 \;\; CH_3 \\ \quad\quad\; \diagdown\,\diagup \\ \quad\quad\;\; C\text{—}O \\ CH_2 \quad\quad\;\; \diagdown \\ | \quad\quad\quad\quad\quad BOBO \\ CH_2 \quad\quad\;\; \diagup \\ \quad\quad\;\; C\text{—}O \\ \quad\quad\; \diagup\,\diagdown \\ \quad CH_3 \;\; CH_3 \end{array}\right]_x$$

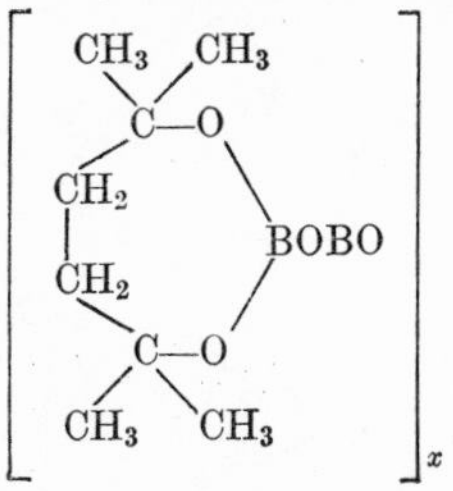

(VIII)

3. FROM TRIALKOXYBORANES

Trialkoxyboranes have been converted to metaborates on treatment with boric acid,[43] metaboric acid,[63] boric oxide,[20,23,37,59,60,63,67] and boron bromide.[22]

With boric acid, the stoichiometry employed resulted in an alcohol as the second product (9-12). With metaboric acid, the resulting water was removed as a toluene azeotrope (9-13). Both alkyl and aryl derivatives were prepared in this manner.[63] With boric oxide, an equimolar reaction (9-14) results only in the meta-

$$2\,(i\text{-}C_3H_7O)_3B + H_3BO_3 \rightarrow (i\text{-}C_3H_7OBO)_3 + 3\,i\text{-}C_3H_7OH \tag{9-12}$$

$$(RO)_3B + 2\,HBO_2 \rightarrow (ROBO)_3 + H_2O \tag{9-13}$$

$$(RO)_3B + B_2O_3 \rightarrow (ROBO)_3 \tag{9-14}$$

borate. This procedure stands as the most useful preparative method in the laboratory and results in the purest products. Metaborates

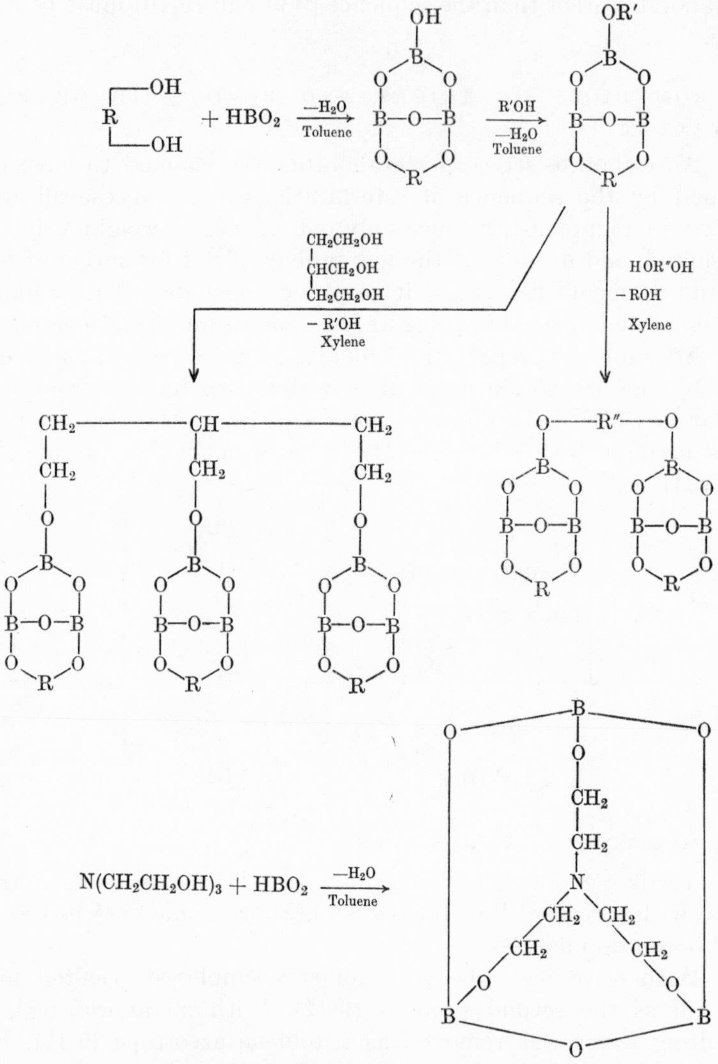

$$\text{R(OH)}_2 + HBO_2 \xrightarrow[\text{Toluene}]{-H_2O} \text{(RO}_2\text{B}_3\text{O}_2\text{)OH} \xrightarrow[-H_2O,\ \text{Toluene}]{R'OH} \text{(RO}_2\text{B}_3\text{O}_2\text{)OR}'$$

$$\xrightarrow[-R'OH,\ \text{Xylene}]{CH_2CH_2OH\text{—}CHCH_2OH\text{—}CH_2CH_2OH} \qquad \xrightarrow[-ROH,\ \text{Xylene}]{HOR''OH}$$

$$N(CH_2CH_2OH)_3 + HBO_2 \xrightarrow[\text{Toluene}]{-H_2O}$$

Fig. 9-1. Diol and Triol metaborates.

prepared from hydroxylic reagents always have some residual free hydroxyl groups present; whereas products from the orthoborate–boric oxide reaction as a rule do not. Thus the product from the reaction of boric oxide and trimethoxyborane–methanol azeotrope (9-15)[48] would be expected to contain some residual hydroxyl groups.

$$6\,B_2O_3 + 3\,[B(OCH_3)_3 + CH_3OH] \rightarrow 4\,(CH_3OBO)_3 + 3\,HBO_2 \qquad (9\text{-}15)$$

A method of "removing" the hydroxyl content by refluxing the crude trimethoxyboroxine with trimethoxyborane has been recorded.[58] Presumably the trimethoxyborane is hydrolyzed by the water freed in the reaction of two hydroxyl groups and by so doing provides driving force for the condensation. The resulting boric acid is removed by filtration and the methanol and excess trimethoxyborane are removed as hexane azeotropes.

Conditions necessary to effect reaction (9-14) include heating at 100 to 150°[20] or at 70° in a bomb[23] for undisclosed periods of time, heating under reflux or pressure for three to fourteen hours,[39] and heating at 150 to 250° for three to ten hours.[37] *t*-Butyl metaborate could not be prepared in this manner,[39] and indeed no metaborates derived from tertiary alcohols have yet been described.[1]*

The reaction of boric oxide and an orthoborate in general requires vigorous conditions over long periods of time. Presumably this is due to the insolubility and unreactivity of the oxide which is usually a vitreous product prepared by fusion of boric acid. However, the metaborate preparation can be greatly accelerated by using an oxide prepared by vacuum dehydration of boric acid which results in a product of high surface area.[23] The reaction also can be catalyzed by trace amounts of an alcohol.[63] Presumably the alcohol serves to solubilize the oxide by introducing alkoxyl and hydroxyl groups at intervals along the B_2O_3 matrix (9-16).

```
       |           |                            |           |
       O           O                            O           O
       |           |                            |           |
       B           B                            B           B—OR
     /   \       /   \                        /   \       /
    O     O     O     O                      O     O     O    OH
    |     |     |     |        ROH           |     |     |     |
 —O—B     B—O—B     B—O—     ——→     —O—B     B—O—B     B—O—
      \   /       \   /                        \   /       \   /
        O           O                            O           O
```

(9-16)

* The reaction of equimolar quantities of tri-*t*-pentoxyborane and boric oxide at 90–114° in the presence of a trace of methanol resulted in a viscous liquid which presumably was the metaborate of *t*-amyl alcohol. On standing for several days the liquid deposited metaboric acid.[63]

Trimethyl and triethylsilyl metaborate have been prepared by digestion of the tris(trialkylsiloxy)boranes and boric oxide for thirty hours in sealed tubes at 225°.[1]

$$(R_3SiO)_3B + B_2O_3 \rightarrow (R_3SiOBO)_3$$

The conversion of trimethoxyborane and boron tribromide to trimethoxyboroxine was formulated as involving an initial redistribution reaction (9-17) followed by decomposition of the resulting bromodimethoxyborane (9-18, see Chapter 12).[22]

$$2\,(CH_3O)_3B + BBr_3 \rightarrow 3\,[(CH_3O)_2BBr] \qquad (9\text{-}17)$$

$$3\,[(CH_3O)_2BBr] \rightarrow (CH_3OBO)_3 + 3\,CH_3Br \qquad (9\text{-}18)$$

The thermal decomposition of dialkoxyhaloboranes subsequently has been developed as a general preparative method of metaborates and is discussed in Section I-D-5 of this chapter.

Trialkoxyboranes also have been converted to metaborates by partial hydrolysis. With trimethoxyborane, the resulting methanol was removed from the residual metaborate either as a 2,3-dimethylbutane azeotrope (9-19)[57] or trimethoxyborane azeotrope (9-20).[63]

$$3\,(CH_3O)_3B + 3\,H_2O + x\,C_6H_{14} \rightarrow (CH_3OBO)_3 + [6\,CH_3OH \cdot xC_6H_{14}] \qquad (9\text{-}19)$$

$$9\,(CH_3O)_3B + 3\,H_2O \rightarrow (CH_3OBO)_3 + 6\,[(CH_3O)_3B \cdot CH_3OH] \qquad (9\text{-}20)$$

The coproduct alcohol was distilled as such in the preparation from triisopropoxyborane (9-21).[43] The partial hydrolysis of tri-n-butoxy-

$$3\,(i\text{-}C_3H_7O)_3B + 3\,H_2O \rightarrow (i\text{-}C_3H_7OBO)_3 + 6\,i\text{-}C_3H_7OH \qquad (9\text{-}21)$$

borane failed to give the metaborate.[39]

4. FROM TRIALKOXYBOROXINES

Hindered phenolic metaborates (IX) were prepared by transesterification of tributoxyboroxine.[28] The butanol was removed as such or as a toluene azeotrope.

$$3\,R\text{-}C_6H_2(C(CH_3)_3)_2\text{-}OH + (C_4H_9OBO)_3 \rightarrow [R\text{-}C_6H_2(C(CH_3)_3)_2\text{-}OBO]_3 + 3\,C_4H_9OH \qquad (9\text{-}22)$$

(IX, R = H, CH_3)

Transesterification of various trialkoxyboroxines with hindered bisphenols such as 1,1-bis-(3,5-di-*t*-butyl-4-hydroxyphenyl)methane produced a series of polymeric metaborates.[31]

5. FROM ALKOXYHALOBORANES

a. By Decomposition. The thermal or Lewis-acid catalyzed decomposition of dialkoxyhaloboranes appears to be a general method of preparation of trialkoxyboroxines.[37,38,39] The reaction is effected

$$3\,(RO)_2BCl \rightarrow (ROBO)_3 + 3\,RCl \qquad (9\text{-}23)$$

by heating the alkoxyhaloborane in a sealed tube at 250° or by treatment with catalytic amounts of ferric chloride or aluminum chloride at room temperature. The instability of di-*t*-butoxychloroborane[38] precludes its use by this method for the attempted preparation of tri-*t*-butoxyboroxine, and the alternative mode of decomposition of diaryloxyhaloboranes[13] (see Chapter 12) precludes the preparation of aromatic metaborates by this path.

The mechanism of the decomposition was considered to involve an initial rate determining heterolytic cleavage of the boron–halogen bond, assisted by the push of the alkoxyl groups and the pull of a neighboring boron atom or Lewis acid (9-24), followed by attack of halide on the dialkoxyboronium ion (9-25).[38]

$$(R\ddot{O})_2B\text{—}Cl \;\; FeCl_3 \rightarrow (RO)_2B^+ + Cl^- \qquad (9\text{-}24)$$

$$\bar{C}l\!: \;\; R\text{—}O\text{—}\overset{+}{B}OR \rightarrow RCl + \{O{=}BOR\} \rightarrow \tfrac{1}{3}\,(ROBO)_3 \qquad (9\text{-}25)$$

b. Reaction with Sodium. The treatment of chlorodiisopentoxyborane with sodium shavings in benzene solution was believed to give triisopentoxyboroxine via decomposition of an intermediate dialkoxyboryl radical.[34]

$$(i\text{-}C_5H_{11}O)_2BCl + Na \rightarrow (i\text{-}C_5H_{11}O)_2B\cdot + NaCl \qquad (9\text{-}26)$$

$$(i\text{-}C_5H_{11}O)_2B\cdot \rightarrow i\text{-}C_5H_{11}OBO + i\text{-}C_5H_{11}\cdot \qquad (9\text{-}27)$$

The metaborate subsequently disproportionated to triisopentoxyborane and boric oxide on attempted distillation. The pentyl radical gave pentylene and hydrogen.

The same products can arise via the ionic path (9-28) through (9-31).

$$(i\text{-}C_5H_{11}\text{—}O)_2B\text{—}Cl \rightarrow i\text{-}C_5H_{11}^+ + Cl^- + i\text{-}C_5H_{11}OBO \qquad (9\text{-}28)$$

$$i\text{-}C_5H_{11}OBO \rightarrow \tfrac{1}{3}\,(i\text{-}C_5H_{11}O)_3B + \tfrac{1}{3}\,B_2O_3 \quad (9\text{-}29)$$

$$i\text{-}C_5H_{11}^+ \rightarrow \text{pentylene} + H^+ \quad (9\text{-}30)$$

$$H^+ + Cl^- + Na \rightarrow NaCl + \tfrac{1}{2}\,H_2 \quad (9\text{-}31)$$

c. *Reaction with Bis(trialkyltin) Oxides.* The reaction of dichloroethoxyborane with bis(triethyltin) oxide has been reported to yield triethoxyboroxine (9-32).[2] The reaction can be formulated as an

$$3\,C_2H_5OBCl_2 + 3\,[(C_2H_5)_3Sn]_2O \rightarrow (C_2H_5OBO)_3 + 6\,(C_2H_5)_3SnCl \quad (9\text{-}32)$$

"ether" cleavage (9-33) (see Chapter 4) followed by decomposition of the dialkoxychloroborane (9-34 and 9-35).

$$(C_2H_5)_3Sn{-}O{-}Sn(C_2H_5)_3 \;\; C_2H_5OB(Cl){-}Cl \rightarrow (C_2H_5)_3SnOB(Cl)OC_2H_5 + (C_2H_5)_3SnCl \quad (9\text{-}33)$$

$$\big((C_2H_5)_3SnO\big)(C_2H_5O)B{-}Cl \rightarrow \big((C_2H_5)_3SnO\big)(C_2H_5O)B^+ + Cl^- \quad (9\text{-}34)$$

$$Cl^- + \big((C_2H_5)_3SnO\big)(C_2H_5O)B^+ \rightarrow (C_2H_5)_3SnCl + \{C_2H_5OB{=}O\} \rightarrow \tfrac{1}{3}\,(C_2H_5OBO)_3 \quad (9\text{-}35)$$

6. FROM DIOXANE–BORON TRIBROMIDE COMPLEX

The dioxane–boron tribromide complex on heating to 30° decomposed according to equation (9-36).[14]

$$O(CH_2CH_2)_2O{:}BBr_3 \rightarrow BrCH_2CH_2Br + \tfrac{1}{3}\,(BrCH_2CH_2OBO)_3 \quad (9\text{-}36)$$

7. FROM DIACETOXYARYLOXYBORANES

The diacetoxyboryl derivatives of 1-hydroxy- and 1,4-dihydroxyanthraquinone lose acetic anhydride on heating *in vacuo* to give the metaborates. They were formulated as the monomers (X) and (XI).[19]

No evidence was presented for the monomeric formulation. Stabilization of the monomeric form by an intramolecular coordination (XII)* common to the starting diacetoxyboryl derivatives (see Chapter 8) conceivably could overcome the tendency of the boron oxygen double bond to trimerize to a boroxine ring.

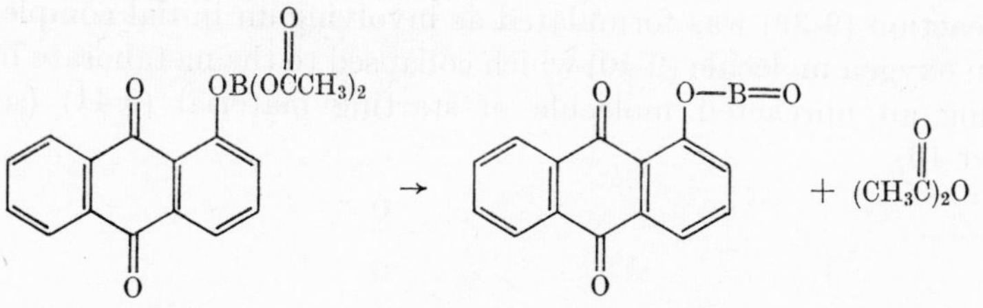

$$\text{1-}[OB(OCCH_3)_2]\text{-anthraquinone} \rightarrow \text{1-}(O\text{—}B{=}O)\text{-anthraquinone (X)} + (CH_3\overset{O}{\overset{\|}{C}})_2O \quad (9\text{-}37)$$

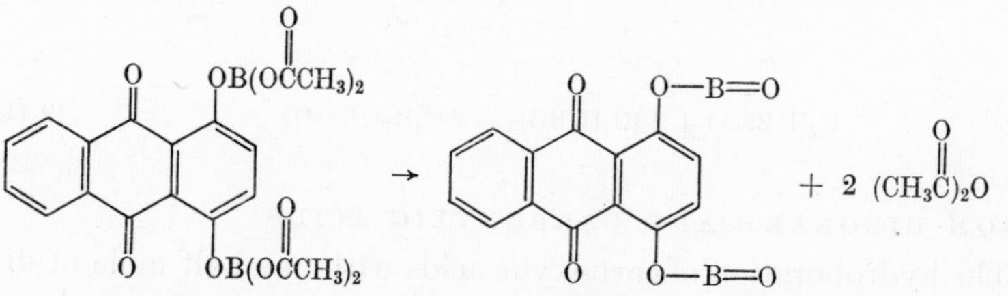

$$\text{1,4-bis}[OB(OCCH_3)_2]\text{-anthraquinone} \rightarrow \text{1,4-bis}(O\text{—}B{=}O)\text{-anthraquinone (XI)} + 2\ (CH_3\overset{O}{\overset{\|}{C}})_2O \quad (9\text{-}38)$$

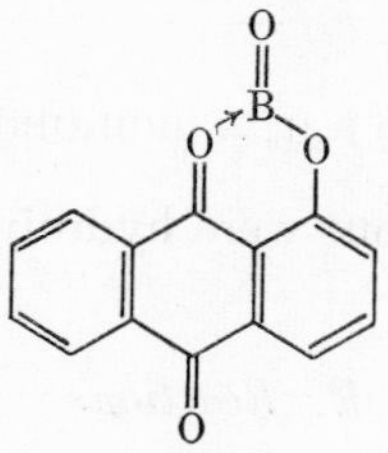

(XII)

8. FROM TRIALKYLBOROXINES

Evidence for monomeric n-butyl metaborate has been presented.[26] The oxidation of tributylboroxine (9-39) led to an oily liquid

$$(C_4H_9BO)_3 + \tfrac{3}{2}\,O_2 \rightarrow 3\ C_4H_9OB{=}O \quad (9\text{-}39)$$

with a faint ester odor and a cryoscopic molecular weight in benzene of 97.6 as compared to a theoretical value of 99.9 for monomeric butyl metaborate. However, until corroborative evidence is presented it must be assumed that the determined molecular weight was an

* A complex of oxytetracycline and boric acid was formulated to be stabilized in this manner.[55]

artifact due to hydrolysis of the trimeric metaborate.* Under the usual techniques for a Beckmann cryoscopic molecular weight determination,[53] as little as 0.086 grams of water could account for the value obtained.

Reaction (9-39) was formulated as involving an initial complex with an oxygen molecule (9-40) which collapsed to the metaborate by oxidizing an unreacted molecule of starting material (9-41) (see Chapter 10).

$$\tfrac{1}{3}(C_4H_9BO)_3 + O_2 \rightarrow C_4H_9\overset{\overset{\displaystyle O}{|}\atop\overset{\displaystyle O}{|}}{B}{=}O \qquad (9\text{-}40)$$

$$C_4H_9\overset{\overset{\displaystyle O}{|}\atop\overset{\displaystyle O}{|}}{B}{=}O + \tfrac{1}{3}(C_4H_9BO)_3 \rightarrow 2\ C_4H_9OB{=}O \qquad (9\text{-}41)$$

9. FROM DIBORANE AND CARBOXYLIC ACIDS

The hydroboration of carboxylic acids with one-half mole of diborane was formulated as resulting in the metaborate.[5] The products

$$3\ R\overset{\overset{\displaystyle O}{\|}}{C}OH + \tfrac{3}{2}B_2H_6 \rightarrow (RCH_2OBO)_3 + 3\ H_2 \qquad (9\text{-}42)$$

were not isolated as such but were hydrolyzed to the alcohols.

E. Reactions

1. HYDROLYSIS

In general, metaborates are readily hydrolyzed to their constituent alcohol or phenol and boric acid.[12,23,26,39,47,63]

$$(ROBO)_3 + 6\ H_2O \rightarrow 3\ ROH + 3\ H_3BO_3 \qquad (9\text{-}43)$$

The kinetics of the hydrolysis and mechanistic details are discussed in Chapter 21.

2. ALCOHOLYSIS

The conversion of metaborates to orthoborates on treatment with alcohols or metal alcoholates is discussed in Chapter 4.

* Tributoxyboroxine has been prepared by a number of workers[37,39,63] and found to have a molecular weight consistent with the trimer $(C_4H_9OBO)_3$.[39,63]

3. DISPROPORTIONATION

Attempted distillation of the metaborates results in disproportionation to the orthoborate and boric oxide (9-44) (see Chapter 4). Some decomposition to olefin may accompany the disproportionation (9-45).[63]

$$(ROBO)_3 \rightarrow (RO)_3B + B_2O_3 \tag{9-44}$$

$$(RCH_2CH_2OBO)_3 \rightarrow 3\ RCH{=}CH_2 + 3\ HBO_2 \tag{9-45}$$

The orthoborate must be removed from the reaction zone in order to effect the disproportionation as evidenced by the refluxing of tributoxyboroxine for six hours at 290° without change[39] and the heating of trialkylsilyl metaborates at 250° for 50 hours in a sealed tube without decomposition.[1] Table 9-2 records the temperature at which disproportionation sets in for the lower trialkoxyboroxines.[63]

Table 9-2. Initial decomposition temperatures of the lower trialkoxyboroxines

$(ROBO)_3$	Initial decomposition temperature (°C)
$(CH_3OBO)_3$	130
$(i\text{-}C_3H_7OBO)_3$	210
$(i\text{-}C_4H_9OBO)_3$	260
$(n\text{-}C_4H_9OBO)_3$	280

4. ELIMINATION

The thermal decomposition of metaborates to olefins is closely related to the thermal stability of orthoboric acid esters and consequently is discussed in a general fashion in Chapter 4.

The mechanism of the transformation for the conversion of l-menthyl metaborate to 2-menthene and racemized 3-menthene (9-46), with the 3-isomer produced in abundance, was believed to

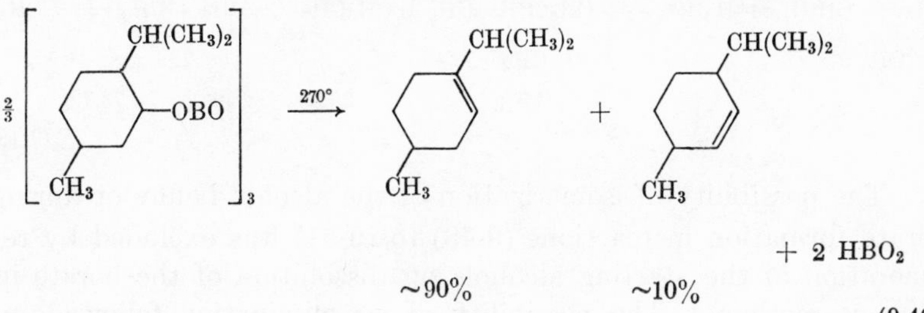

$$\frac{2}{3}\left[\text{menthyl–OBO (ring with } CH(CH_3)_2 \text{ and } CH_3)\right]_3 \xrightarrow{270^\circ} \underset{\sim 90\%}{\text{menthene } (CH(CH_3)_2,\ CH_3)} + \underset{\sim 10\%}{\text{menthene } (CH(CH_3)_2,\ CH_3)} + 2\ HBO_2 \tag{9-46}$$

involve a *cis* elimination from a cyclic transition state of the monomeric metaborate species (9-47).[47] Evidence for an equilibrium of the monomeric and trimeric metaborate species was based upon cryoscopic molecular weight determinations of tricyclohexyloxyboroxine in naphthalene at 80° and in anthracene at 218°. At the lower temperature only a trace of monomer was indicated; whereas at the

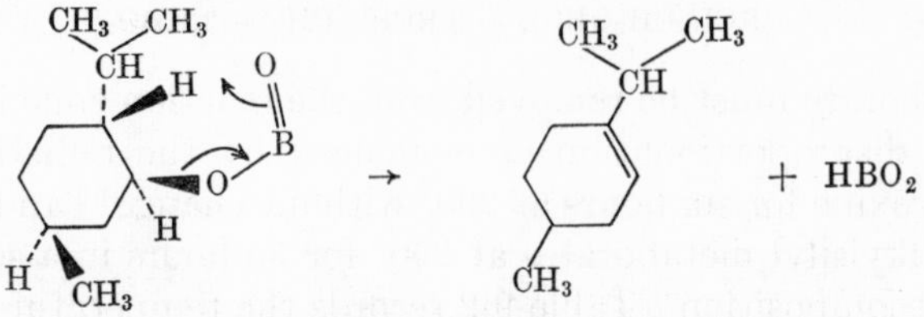

$$\rightarrow \quad + \; HBO_2 \qquad (9\text{-}47)$$

higher temperature the data indicated a 6% dissociation to monomer. It was felt unlikely that the lower molecular weight at 218° was due to some olefin formation since independent experiments indicated no appreciable elimination occurred below 260°. The distortion of the O—B=O angle from non-linearity was not thought unlikely at the temperatures involved.

In opposition to this rationale, the isomer distribution reported for the dehydration of menthol is not one which is characteristic of ester pyrolyses in that system. In addition, the fact that the 3-menthene was racemized, either during or after the elimination, shows that the reaction is proceeding under acidic conditions. Thus an acid catalyzed elimination was considered to be a possibility.[16]

Further evidence for a carbonium ion mechanism[16] versus the pyrolytic *cis* elimination of equation (9-47) is shown by the essentially exclusive formation of rearranged products from the treatment of *t*-butylmethylcarbinol, borneol, cyclohexylcarbinol, and cyclobutylcarbinol under conditions of borate pyrolysis.[8,9]

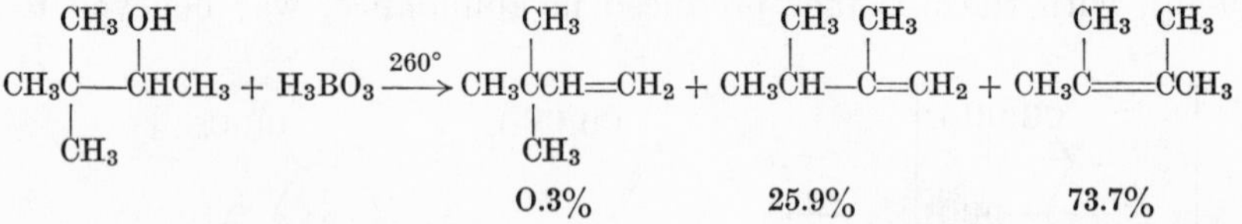

$$(CH_3)_3C\text{—}CH(OH)CH_3 + H_3BO_3 \xrightarrow{260^\circ} \underset{0.3\%}{(CH_3)_3CCH{=}CH_2} + \underset{25.9\%}{CH_3CH(CH_3)\text{—}C(CH_3){=}CH_2} + \underset{73.7\%}{(CH_3)_2C{=}C(CH_3)_2} \qquad (9\text{-}48)$$

The possibility of isomerization of the alcohol before or during borate formation in reactions (9-48) to (9-51) was excluded by regeneration of the starting alcohols on dissolution of the borate in aqueous methanol. The possibility of *cis* elimination followed by

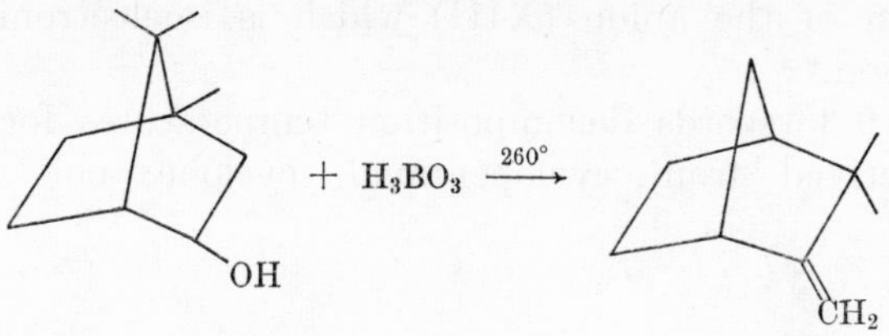

$$\text{(2-hydroxy-1,7,7-trimethylbicyclo[2.2.1]heptane)} + H_3BO_3 \xrightarrow{260°} \text{(camphene, =CH}_2\text{)} \qquad (9\text{-}49)$$

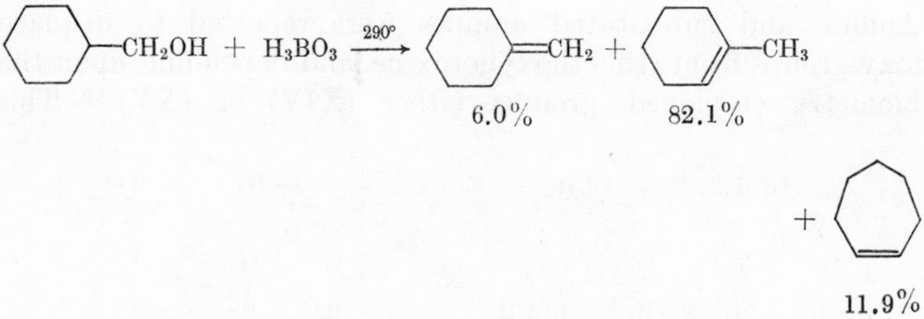

OH

CH_2

$$C_6H_{11}\text{—}CH_2OH + H_3BO_3 \xrightarrow{290°} C_6H_{10}{=}CH_2 + C_6H_9\text{—}CH_3 + \text{cycloheptene} \qquad (9\text{-}50)$$

6.0% 82.1% 11.9%

$$C_4H_7\text{—}CH_2OH + H_3BO_3 \xrightarrow{245\text{–}255°} \text{cyclopentene} \qquad (9\text{-}51)$$

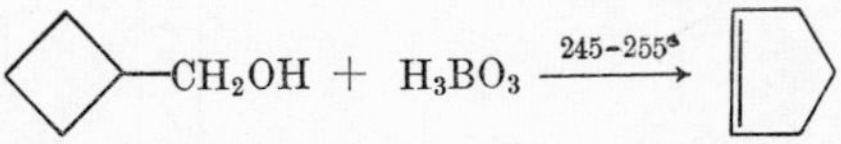

boric acid-catalyzed isomerization of the olefin initially produced was excluded since this sequence of events would not be expected to produce ring expanded products.

The ionization path (9-52) was pictured as proceeding via the

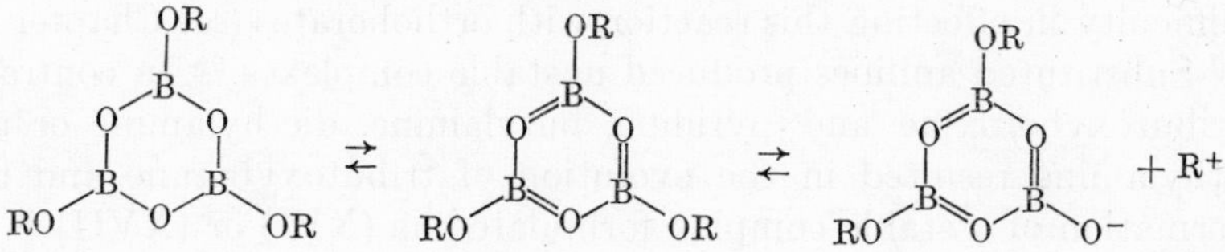

$$(ROBO)_3 \rightleftarrows \text{(XIII)} \rightleftarrows RO\text{—}B(OR)\text{—}O\text{—}B(=O)\text{—}O^- + R^+ \qquad (9\text{-}52)$$

(XIII)

doubly bonded resonance form of the trialkoxyboroxine. Some small amount of driving force for this ionization would be gained by the

Table 9-3. Decomposition temperatures of metaborates derived from cyclic alcohols

Metaborate of	Decomposition temperature (°C) Initial	In progress
Cyclopentanol	220	185–190
Cyclohexanol	235–240	215
Cycloheptanol	220–225	200

stabilization of the anion (XIII) which is isoelectronic with the phenoxide ion.[8]

Table 9-3 records decomposition temperatures for the metaborates derived from cyclopentanol, cyclohexanol, and cycloheptanol.[17]

5. WITH AMINES

Aniline and substituted anilines were reported to displace methoxy groups from trimethoxyboroxine, and depending upon the stoichiometry employed, produce either (XIV) or (XV).[52] This

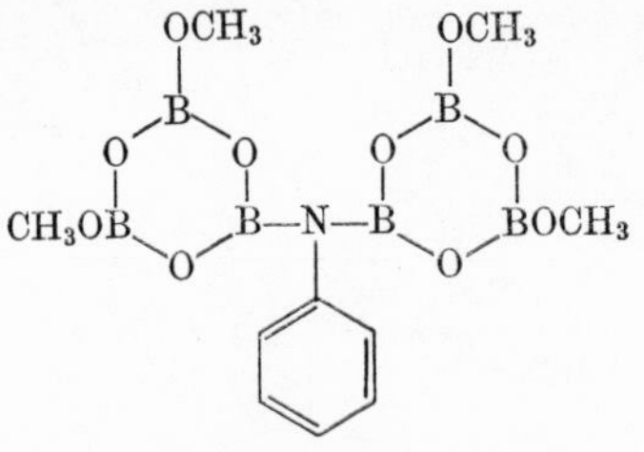

(XIV) 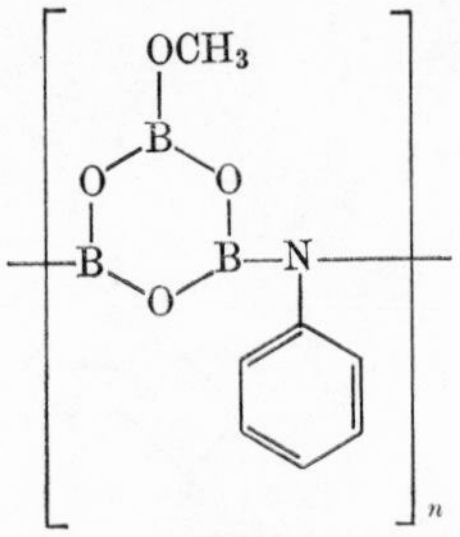 (XV)

apparently facile conversion of a metaborate boron–oxygen bond to a boron–nitrogen bond with aniline is to be compared to the difficulty in effecting this reaction with orthoborates (see Chapter 4). *N*-Substituted anilines produced unstable complexes.[52] In contrast, tributoxyboroxine and pyridine, butylamine, diethylamine or triethylamine resulted in the evolution of tributoxyborane and the formation of a stable complex formulated as (XVI) or (XVII).[40]

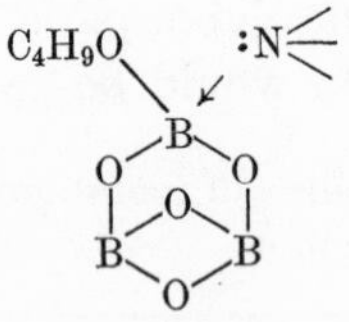

(XVI) 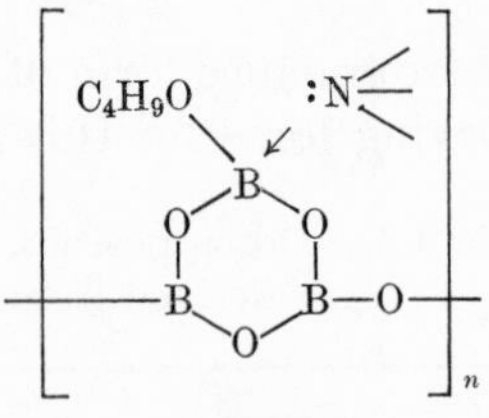 (XVII)

An earlier interpretation of the reaction with aniline was formulated as in equation (9-53) with a noncommittal structure for the complex.[59]

$$3\,C_2H_5OBO + C_6H_5NH_2 \rightarrow C_6H_5NH_2 \cdot B_2O_3 + (C_2H_5O)_3B \qquad (9\text{-}53)$$

6. WITH CARBOXYLIC ACIDS AND DERIVATIVES

Metaborates can serve as the alcohol source for the esterification of carboxylic acids, anhydrides and acid halides.[40,59]

$$\tfrac{1}{3}\,(C_2H_5OBO)_3 + CH_3\overset{O}{\overset{\|}{C}}OH \xrightarrow{\Delta} CH_3\overset{O}{\overset{\|}{C}}OC_2H_5 + HBO_2 \tag{9-54}$$

$$\tfrac{2}{3}\,(C_4H_9OBO)_3 + (CH_3\overset{O}{\overset{\|}{C}})_2O \xrightarrow{\Delta} 2\,CH_3\overset{O}{\overset{\|}{C}}OC_4H_9 + B_2O_3 \tag{9-55}$$

$$\tfrac{2}{3}\,(C_4H_9OBO)_3 + C_6H_5\overset{O}{\overset{\|}{C}}Cl \rightarrow C_6H_5\overset{O}{\overset{\|}{C}}OC_4H_9 + 1\,(\underset{\sim 90\%}{C_4H_9Cl} + \underset{\sim 10\%}{s\text{-}C_4H_9Cl}) + B_2O_3 \tag{9-56}$$

The presence of *s*-butyl chloride in the products of the reaction (9-56) suggest the formation of n-$BuOBCl_2$ as an intermediate which subsequently decomposes via a butyl carbonium ion (see Chapter 12).

7. WITH HALOGEN COMPOUNDS

a. *Chlorine.* Treatment of trimethoxyboroxine with excess chlorine for twenty-four hours at room temperature was reported to be a simple method of preparation of boron trichloride.[44]

$$(CH_3OBO)_3 + 9\,Cl_2 \rightarrow BCl_3 + 3\,COCl_2 + 9\,HCl + B_2O_3 \tag{9-57}$$

b. *Hydrogen Halides.* Tributoxyboroxine and hydrogen chloride or bromide could not be made to react at 20°. However, the bromide did effect rapid dealkylation when the reaction was carried out in a sealed vessel.[40] This concentration effect was believed to be

$$\tfrac{1}{3}\,(C_4H_9OBO)_3 + HBr \rightarrow C_4H_9Br + HBO_2 \tag{9-58}$$

consistent with a mechanism involving a rate determining S_N2 attack of bromide ion on the protonated metaborate.

$$CH_3CH_2CH_2CH_2\text{—}\overset{+}{\underset{}{\overset{H}{\overset{|}{O}}}}\text{—(boroxine ring)} + \bar{B}r{:}^{-} \rightarrow C_4H_9Br + HO\text{—(boroxine ring)} \tag{9-59}$$

Trimethoxyboroxine was converted by hydrogen fluoride to a product that could not be vacuum distilled without decomposition. It appeared to be a labile mixture of $2CH_3OH \cdot BF_3$, $2H_2O \cdot BF_3$ and possibly $H_2O \cdot CH_3OH \cdot BF_3$.[46]

c. *Boron Trihalides.* The conversion of metaborates to alkoxyhaloboranes by reaction with boron trihalides is discussed in Chapter 12.

d. *Other Halides.* Trialkoxyboroxines have been converted to alkyl halides and boric oxide by treatment with aluminum chloride in a sealed tube,[33] or by treatment with phosphorus pentachloride, phosphorus pentabromide, phosphorus trichloride, or thionyl chloride in the presence of ferric chloride.[40] The reactions can be formulated as follows:

$$2\,(CH_3OBO)_3 + 2\,AlCl_3 \rightarrow 6\,CH_3Cl + Al_2O_3 + 3\,B_2O_3 \quad (9\text{-}60)$$

$$\tfrac{1}{3}\,(C_4H_9OBO)_3 + PCl_5 \rightarrow C_4H_9Cl + POCl_3 + \{BOCl\} \quad (9\text{-}61)$$

$$2\,(C_4H_9OBO)_3 + 2\,PCl_3 \rightarrow 6\,C_4H_9Cl + P_2O_3 + 3\,B_2O_3 \quad (9\text{-}62)$$

$$\tfrac{2}{3}\,(C_4H_9OBO)_3 + SOCl_2 \rightarrow 2\,C_4H_9Cl + SO_2 + B_2O_3 \quad (9\text{-}63)$$

In the reactions involving tributoxyboroxine, the butyl chloride produced contained 5–10% of the *s*-butyl isomer, once again indicating an S_N1 mechanism to be operative.[40]

8. WITH ORGANOMETALLIC REAGENTS

The reactions of metaborates with organometals to produce trialkylboranes and other boron–carbon bonded materials are discussed in Volume III of this series.

9. WITH TRIALKYLBORANES

A variety of trialkylboranes were converted to the corresponding boronic acids by heating in a sealed tube with trimethoxyboroxine and subsequent hydrolysis of the reaction mixture.[29] Presumably trialkylboroxines are intermediates.

$$R_3B + (CH_3OBO)_3 \rightarrow (RBO)_3 + (CH_3O)_3B \xrightarrow{H_2O} 3\,RB(OH)_2 + 3\,CH_3OH + H_3BO_3 \quad (9\text{-}64)$$

10. WITH ALKYLDIBORANES

The reaction of trimethoxyboroxine and dioctadecyldiborane at 200° in a closed vessel was reported to give a 92% yield of the boronic acid after hydrolysis of the resulting trioctadecylboroxine.[45]

11. OXIDATION

The use of trimethoxyboroxine in extinguishing metals fires[56] depends, at least in part, upon its oxidation to yield glassy boric oxide.[7]

$$2\,(CH_3OBO)_3 + 9\,O_2 \rightarrow 3\,B_2O_3 + 9\,H_2O + 6\,CO_2 \quad (9\text{-}65)$$

12. REDUCTION

The treatment of trimethoxyboroxine with hydrogen at elevated temperature and pressure in the presence of aluminum trichloride, aluminum powder, and potassium chloride was reported as a means of producing diborane.[32]

The reactions of trimethoxyboroxine with sodium hydride, sodium borohydride, or sodium trimethoxyhydroborate can serve as a preparative method for trimethoxyborane (see Chapter 4) or dimethoxyborane (see Chapter 11).

Lithium aluminum hydride reduction of the metaborate was stated to give 70–90% yields of lithium borohydride.[35]

13. MISCELLANEOUS

Tributoxyboroxine and propionamide heated at 220° for forty-eight hours in a sealed tube resulted in a small yield of propionitrile.[40] This ability to promote water forming reactions is a characteristic shared with the orthoborates (see Chapter 4).

Trimethoxyboroxine reportedly reacts with epoxides.[6] It has been claimed as a crosslinking agent for epoxidized fatty acids or esters.[65] Tributoxyboroxine did not react with butyl chloride at 20° or with butyl ether under reflux.[40] The reaction of trimethoxyboroxine with sodium hydride has been discussed in Chapter 4. In contrast to orthoborates, metaborates do not serve as alkylating agents in Friedel–Crafts reactions.[36]

F. Analytical

Analysis of the trialkoxyboroxines[39] is performed by the method of hydrolysis, neutralization to the methyl orange endpoint with carbonate free base, and titration of the boric acid with phenolphthalein in the presence of mannitol.[38] The method is not applicable to triphenoxyboroxine since the phenol produced in the hydrolysis is weakly acidic and interferes with the titration for boric acid. The aromatic metaborate was analyzed[39] by reaction with methanol in the presence of sulfuric acid to give trimethoxyborane which was distilled as the methanol azeotrope, hydrolyzed, and titrated for boric acid in the usual manner.[66]

The sodium carbonate fusion method[27] (see Chapter 4) also is applicable to the phenyl derivative as well as a variety of alkyl metaborates.[63]

II. POLYBORATES

A. Introduction

The trialkoxyboroxines (II) have a 1:1 ratio of boron atoms to alkoxy groups. Polyborates are compounds of a similar nature with a boron to alkoxy group ratio greater than unity. Clearly an infinite series of polyborates can be envisaged with increasing ratios of boron to alkoxyl, with the ultimate member being a single alkoxyl buried in a boron oxide type matrix (XVIII). Thus, a polyborate is, in essence,

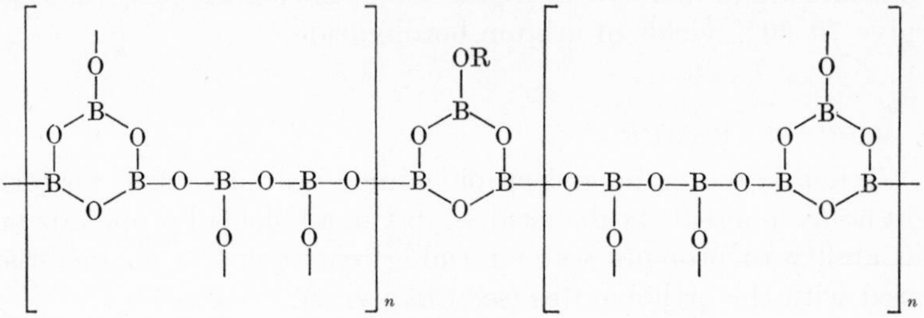

(XVIII)

any alkoxylated boron oxide matrix. A discussion of this broad class of materials is not instructive; therefore this section is concerned in the main with those polyborates of a comparatively well defined nature; those compounds with a 4:3 ratio of boron to alkoxyl groups (XIX and XX).

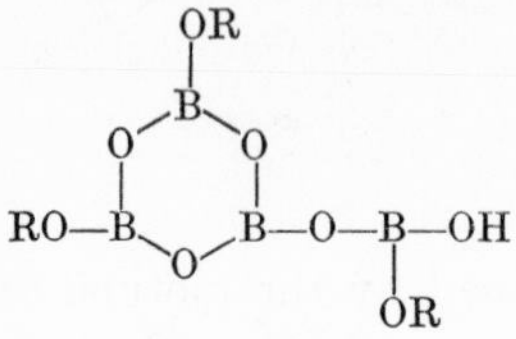

(XIX) 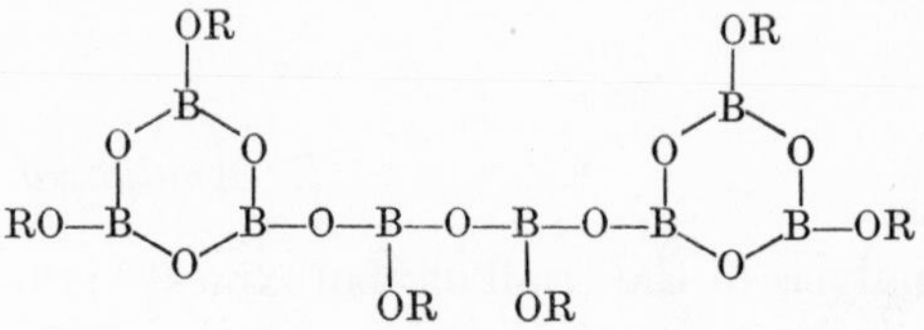 (XX)

B. Historical

In 1864 the reaction of boric oxide and ethyl orthocarbonate was reported to give diethyl carbonate and a borate, $(C_2H_5)_2B_4O_7$.[4] This formula can be rewritten as the product from the reaction of triethoxyboroxine and 1.5 moles of boric oxide, $(C_2H_5OBO)_3 \cdot \frac{3}{2}B_2O_3$.

C. Properties

Methyl polyborate (type XX) is very soluble in acetone, ether and benzene; soluble in chloroform and carbon tetrachloride; and slightly soluble in petroleum ether.[63] The isopropyl derivative is soluble in ether, acetone, benzene, toluene and acetonitrile; partially soluble in chloroform and carbon tetrachloride; and slightly soluble in petroleum ether.[63]

D. *Methods of Preparation*

1. FROM ALCOHOLS AND BORIC ACID OR EQUIVALENT

The earliest worker in the field stated, without a true knowledge of the product, that the minimum amount of n-amyl alcohol that would react with one mole of boric acid was 0.76 mole.[3] Possibly a product such as (XIX) or (XX) was involved.

The first definitive work involved the azeotropic removal of water from a xylene or toluene solution of cyclohexanol and 1.5 molar equivalents of boric acid. The excess boric acid was removed by filtration leaving a product with a 4:3 ratio of boron atoms to cyclohexyl groups.[47] The analytical data were interpreted as being consistent with $C_{18}H_{34}O_8B_4$, presumably structure (XXI). However, since the molecular weight was not determined, structure (XXII) cannot be ruled out.

```
            OC6H11
            |
           B
         /   \
        O     O
        |     |
C6H11O—B      B—O—B—OH
         \   /     |
           O       OC6H11
```

(XXI)

```
                OC6H11                                   OC6H11
                |                                        |
               B                                        B
             /   \                                    /   \
            O     O                                  O     O
            |     |                                  |     |
   C6H11O—B       B—O——B—O—B—O——B       B—OC6H11
             \   /          |      |            \   /
               O            C6H11O  OC6H11         O
```

(XXII)

The procedure of azeotropic water removal subsequently was used to prepare a variety of alkyl polyborates.[63] The amount of water removed indicated the reaction to be (9-66) rather than (9-67).

Other alkyl polyborates were prepared from alcohols and boric oxide by removing the water azeotropically (9-68) or by reaction with excess oxide (9-69).[63]

$$6\,\mathrm{ROH} + 8\,\mathrm{H_3BO_3} \rightarrow \mathrm{ROB\langle O{-}B(OR){-}O\rangle B{-}O{-}B(OR){-}O{-}B(OR){-}O{-}B\langle O{-}B(OR){-}O\rangle B{-}OR} + 15\,\mathrm{H_2O} \tag{9-66}$$

$$3\,\mathrm{ROH} + 4\,\mathrm{H_3BO_3} \rightarrow \mathrm{ROB\langle O{-}B(OR){-}O\rangle B{-}O{-}B(OR)OH} + 7\,\mathrm{H_6O} \tag{9-67}$$

$$6\,\mathrm{ROH} + 4\,\mathrm{B_2O_3} \xrightarrow{\text{Xylene}} \left[\mathrm{ROB\langle O{-}B(OR){-}O\rangle B{-}O{-}B(OR){-}}\right]_2\mathrm{O} + 3\,\mathrm{H_2O} \tag{9-68}$$

$$6\,\mathrm{ROH} + 5\,\mathrm{B_2O_3} \rightarrow \left[\mathrm{ROB\langle O{-}B(OR){-}O\rangle B{-}O{-}B(OR){-}}\right]_2\mathrm{O} + 2\,\mathrm{H_3BO_3} \tag{9-69}$$

With isopropyl alcohol, the method of conversion of equation (9-69) was reported to give a product, $(C_3H_7O)_3B \cdot 2.3B_2O_3$,[43] as compared to $(C_3H_7O)_3B \cdot 1.5B_2O_3$ for the 4 : 3 polyborate.

2. FROM TRIALKOXYBORANES

The conversion of orthoborates to polyborates by direct reaction with boric oxide, analogously to the conversion of orthoborates to metaborates, had been performed for the lower alkyl members.[63] This conversion, as is the transformation to the metaborates, is catalyzed by hydroxylic reagents.

$$2\,(RO)_3B + 3\,B_2O_3 \rightarrow \left[\begin{array}{c} OR \\ | \\ B \\ O \quad\; O \\ RO{-}B \quad\; B{-}O{-}B{-} \\ O \quad\quad\;\; | \\ \quad\quad\quad\; OR \end{array} \right]_2 O \qquad (9\text{-}70)$$

3. FROM TRIALKOXYBOROXINES

The attempted distillation of impure triisopropoxyboroxine resulted in a distillate of triisopropoxyborane and a residue corresponding to $(C_3H_7O)_3B \cdot 1.78B_2O_3$.[43]

E. Reactions

1. HYDROLYSIS

Polyborates hydrolyze rapidly in aqueous dioxane at room temperature with half lives of the order of one or two seconds to give boric acid and the corresponding alcohol.[63]

2. THERMAL DECOMPOSITION

Methyl polyborate begins to decompose in air at 165°;[63] 35° above the decomposition point of trimethoxyboroxine. It might be predicted that polyborates in general should be more thermally stable than the corresponding metaborates since they are closer to boric oxide, a highly thermally stable species, in the continuum $(RO)_3B \ldots (ROBO)_3 \ldots (ROBO)_6B_2O_3 \ldots B_2O_3$.

III. TRIACYLOXYBOROXINES

When oxybis(diacetoxyborane) was slowly heated in vacuum at 150°, acetic anhydride distilled leaving a residue believed to be triacetoxyboroxine (XXXIII) as evidenced by hydrolysis to equimolar quantities of acetic acid and boric acid.[18] The reaction (9-71)

$$3\,(CH_3\overset{O}{\overset{\|}{C}}O)_2BOB(O\overset{O}{\overset{\|}{C}}CH_3)_2 \rightleftarrows 3\,(CH_3\overset{O}{\overset{\|}{C}})_2O + \begin{array}{c} O\overset{O}{\overset{\|}{C}}CH_3 \\ | \\ B \\ O \quad\; O \\ CH_3\overset{O}{\overset{\|}{C}}O{-}B \quad\; B{-}O\overset{O}{\overset{\|}{C}}CH_3 \\ O \end{array} \qquad (9\text{-}71)$$

(XXIII)

is formulated as being reversible since (XXIII) could be converted to the tetraacetoxy derivative by dissolution in acetic anhydride.

The same product has been prepared from the reaction of metaboric acid and acetyl chloride in acetic acid solution.[50]

$$3\ CH_3\overset{\overset{\large O}{\|}}{C}Cl + 3\ HBO_2 \rightarrow (CH_3\overset{\overset{\large O}{\|}}{C}OBO)_3 + 3\ HCl \tag{9-72}$$

Dehydration of an equimolar aqueous solution of boric acid and potassium acid oxalate was recorded to give a salt formulated as (XXIV).[51] The boroxine (XXV or XXVI) may have been the product (see Chapter 8).

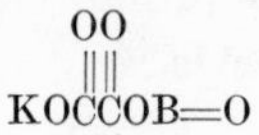

$$KO\overset{\overset{\large O}{\|}}{C}\overset{\overset{\large O}{\|}}{C}OB{=}O$$

(XXIV)

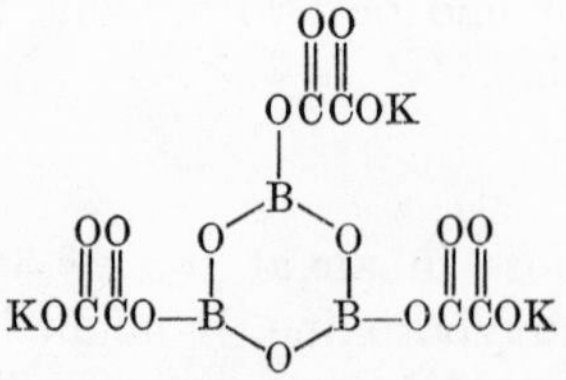

(XXV)

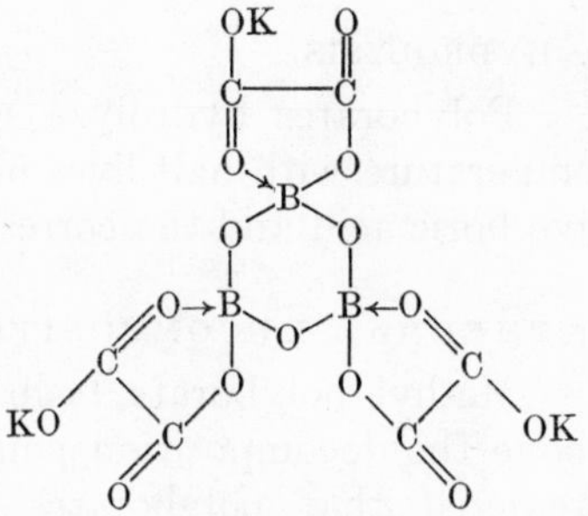

(XXVI)

IV. PHYSICAL CONSTANTS

ROB=O	M.p. (°C)	B.p. (°C)	d_4^t	n_D^t	Reference
n-C_4H_9OB=O		Oily liquid			26

$(ROBO)_3$	M.p. (°C)	B.p. (°C)	d_4^t	n_D^t	Reference
$(CH_3OBO)_3$	10	Decomposes			23
	10–11	150 (decomp.)	1.216^{25}	1.3986^{20}	7
		130 (decomp.)	1.22^{25}	1.3989^{25}	63
			1.233^{20}	1.4038^{20}	39
				1.3940^{25}	67
			1.2286^{25}	1.5010^{25}	25
	—	—	—	—	59
$(C_2H_5OBO)_3$			1.113^{22}	1.4069^{22}	37
			1.113^{20}	1.4071^{20}	39
			1.109^{25}	1.4064^{25}	25
	—	—	—	—	59
$(C_2H_5OCH_2CH_2OBO)_3$		Oily liquid			20
(n-$C_3H_7OBO)_3$			1.025^{20}	1.4129^{20}	39
			1.017^{22}	1.4133^{22}	37
$[Cl(CH_2)_3OBO]_3$				1.4645	21
(i-$C_3H_7OBO)_3$	47–59	210 (decomp.)			63
	50				20
	52–54				37, 39
	52.5				25
(n-$C_4H_9OBO)_3$		280 (decomp.)	0.99^{25}	1.4200^{25}	63
			1.014^{20}	1.4236^{20}	37, 39

(*Table continued*)

$(ROBO)_3$	M.p. (°C)	B.p. (°C)	d_4^t	n_D^t	Reference
$(i\text{-}C_4H_9OBO)_3$		260 (decomp.)		1.4159^{25}	63
			0.997^{20}	1.4170^{20}	39
$(s\text{-}C_4H_9OBO)_3$			0.985^{20}	1.4151^{20}	39
			0.985^{22}	1.4160^{22}	37
$(n\text{-}C_5H_{11}OBO)_3$	—	—	—	—	59
$[(C_2H_5)_2CHOBO]_3$		Liquid			63
[(cyclopentyl)—OBO]$_3$	80				17
$(HCF_2CF_2CF_2CF_2CH_2OBO)_3$		Viscous liquid			63
$(n\text{-}C_6H_{11}OBO)_3$	140				20
	140-154				63
	165–167				47
$(CH_3CH(CH_3)CH_2CH(CH_3)OBO)_3$		Viscous liquid			63
[(cyclohexyl)—OBO]$_3$	215–225				17
$[(n\text{-}C_3H_7)_2CHOBO]_3$		Liquid			63
$[(i\text{-}C_3H_7)_2CHOBO]_3$		Liquid			63
$(n\text{-}C_4H_9CH(C_2H_5)OBO)_3$		Liquid			63
$(C_6H_5CH_2OBO)_3$	—	—	—	—	20

	M.p. (°C)	B.p. (°C)	d_4^t	n_D^t	Reference
$[\text{(cycloheptane ring)}\text{—OBO}]_3$	100				17
l $[\text{(cyclohexane ring with } CH(CH_3)_2\text{, —OBO, } CH_3)]_3$	150–152				47
$[(CH_3)_2CHCH_2CH(CH_3)CH_2CH(CH_2CH(CH_3)_2)OBO]_3$		Viscous liquid			63
$(n\text{-}C_{16}H_{33}OBO)_3$	—	—	—	—	42, 59
$(n\text{-}C_{18}H_{37}OBO)_3$	—	—	—	—	20
$[CH_3(CH_2)_7CH{=}CH(CH_2)_7CH_2OBO]_3$	—	—	—	—	42

$(ArOBO)_3$	M.p. (°C)	B.p. (°C)	d_4^t	n_D^t	Reference
$(C_6H_5OBO)_3$	96–120				63
	98–101				39
	—	—	—	—	59
$[\text{(benzene ring with } C(CH_3)_3\text{, —OBO, } C(CH_3)_3)]_3$	310–323				23

(Table continued)

$(ArOBO)_3$	M.p. (°C)	B.p. (°C)	d_4^t	n_D^t	Reference
$[4\text{-}CH_3\text{-}2,6\text{-}(C(CH_3)_3)_2C_6H_2OBO]_3$	246–268				28
$[1\text{-}OBO\text{-anthraquinone}]_3$ (9,10-dioxo; O, O, OBO)	Brown solid				19

Diol and Triol Metaborates	M.p. (°C)	B.p. (°C)	d_4^t	n_D^t	Reference
$(CH_3C(OBO)(CH_3)CH_2CH_2C(OBO)(CH_3)CH_3)_x$	119–125				64

OR B O O B O B O O CH_3C-CH_2-$CHCH_3$ CH_3	R = H, C_6H_{11}	—	—	—	—	30
OR B O O B O B O O $CH_3C(CH_2)_2CHCH_3$	R = H, n—C_4H_9, (i-$C_4H_9)_2CH$	—	—	—	—	30
OR B O O B O B O O CH_3HC-CH_2-CH_2	R = H, $CH_3OCH_2CH_2$, *p*-$CH_3C_6H_5$	—	—	—	—	30

(*Table continued*)

Diol and Triol Metaborates	M.p. (°C)	B.p. (°C)	d_4^t	n_D^t	Reference
Cyclic metaborate: B–OR ring bridged through O–CH₂CH₂–NH–CH₂CH₂–O; $R = H, C_6H_5CH_2$	—	—	—	—	30
Two metaborate rings, each with O–$CH_3CH(CH_2)_2CHCH_3$–O, linked O–R–O; $R = —CH_2CH_2—, —CH_2CH_2NHCH_2CH_2—$	—	—	—	—	30

CH_2—CH—CH_2 (each bearing CH_2—O—B ring B_3O_3, ring B atoms bearing O—$CH_3C(CH_3)$—CH_2—$CHCH_3$)	—	—	—	—	30
B(O)(O)—O—CH_2—CH_2—N(CH_2—CH_2—O—B)$_2$; B—O—B bridges	Large plates				30

(Table continued)

Diol and Triol Metaborates	M.p. (°C)	B.p. (°C)	d_4^t	n_D^t	Reference
$CH(CH_2CH_2O)_3B_3O_3$ (cage structure)	Viscous liquid				30
$[C_{14}H_6O_2(OBO)_2]_x$ (1,4-bis(OBO)anthraquinone polymer)	Rust brown solid				19

$(RCOBO)_3$ (C=O)	M.p. (°C)	B.p. (°C)	d_4^t	n_D^t	Reference
$(CH_3COBO)_3$ (C=O)	Decomposes 102–104				50
	Hard brittle mass				18

$(KO\overset{O}{\overset{\Vert}{C}}—\overset{O}{\overset{\Vert}{C}}OBO)_3$	Solid				51

Polyborates	M.p. (°C)	B.p. (°C)	d_4^t	n_D^t	Reference
$(CH_3OBO)_6 \cdot B_2O_3$		Viscous liquid Decomposes at 165°	1.31^{25}	1.4135^{25}	63
$(C_2H_5OBO)_3 \cdot \frac{3}{2}B_2O_3$	—	—	—	—	4
$(i\text{-}C_3H_7OBO)_6 \cdot B_2O_3$	49–135	Decomposes at 170°			63
$(n\text{-}C_4H_9OBO)_6 \cdot B_2O_3$		Viscous liquid			63
$(i\text{-}C_4H_9OBO)_6 \cdot B_2O_3$		Viscous liquid			63
$(C_6H_{11}OBO)_6 \cdot B_2O_3$	138–148				63
$(C_6H_{11}OBO)_3 \cdot HBO_2$	141–143				47
$(\underset{CH_3}{\underset{\vert}{CH_3CH}}CH_2\underset{CH_3}{\underset{\vert}{CH}}OBO)_6 \cdot B_2O_3$		Viscous liquid			63

V. REFERENCES

1. Abel, E. W., and A. Singh, *J. Chem. Soc.*, 690 (1959).
2. Anderson, H. H., *J. Org. Chem.*, **19**, 1766 (1954).
3. Anderson, J. R., K. G. O'Brien, and F. H. Reuter, *J. Appl. Chem.*, **2**, 241 (1952).
4. Bassett, H., *Ann. Chem. Pharm.*, **132**, 54 (1864).
5. Brown, H. C., and W. Korytnyk, *J. Am. Chem. Soc.*, **82**, 3866 (1960).
6. Callery Chemical Co., *Chem. Eng. News*, **36**, 57 (1958).
7. Callery Chemical Co., Technical Data Sheet.
8. Chapman, O. L., and G. W. Borden, *J. Org. Chem.*, **26**, 4193 (1961).
9. Chapman, O. L., and G. W. Borden, Private Communication to C. H. Depuy and R. W. King, *Chem. Rev.*, **60**, 431 (1960).
10. Christopher, P. M., *J. Chem. Eng. Data*, **5**, 568 (1960).
11. Clark, M. M., U.S. Pat. 2,613,219 (1952, one half to A. R. Clark).
12. Clark, M. M., U.S. Pat. 2,769,746 (1956, one half to A. R. Clark).
13. Colclough, T., W. Gerrard, and M. F. Lappert, *J. Chem. Soc.*, 907 (1955).
14. Cooper, S., M. J. Frazer, and W. Gerrard, *J. Chem. Soc.*, 5545 (1961).
15. Copaux, H., *Compt. Rend.*, **127**, 719 (1898).
16. Depuy, C. H., and R. W. King, *Chem. Rev.*, **60**, 431 (1960).
17. Dev, S., *J. Indian Chem. Soc.*, **33**, 769 (1956).
18. Dimroth, O., *Ann.*, **446**, 97 (1925).
19. Dimroth, O., and T. Faust, *Ber.*, **54**, 3020 (1921).
20. Dykstra, F. J., U.S. Pat. 2,862,879 (1958, to Ethyl Corporation); see also Brit. Pat. 828,941; Fr. Pat. 1,174,148.
21. Finch, A., J. C. Lockhart, and J. Pearn, *J. Org. Chem.*, **26**, 3250 (1961).
22. Goubeau, J., H. J. Becher, and F. Griffel, *Z. Anorg. Allgem. Chem.*, **282**, 86 (1955).
23. Goubeau, J., and H. Keller, *Z. Anorg. Allgem. Chem.*, **267**, 1 (1951).
24. Goubeau, J., and H. Keller, *Z. Anorg. Allgem. Chem.*, **272**, 303 (1953).
25. Grau, A., and H. Lumbroso, *Bull. Soc. Chim. France*, 1860 (1961).
26. Grummitt, O., *J. Am. Chem. Soc.*, **64**, 1811 (1942).
27. Hunter, D. L., L. L. Petterson, and H. Steinberg, *Anal. Chim. Acta*, **21**, 523 (1959).
28. Hunter, D. L., and H. Steinberg, Fr. Pat. 1,203,698 (1960, to United States Borax and Chemical Corporation).
29. Iloff, P. M., Jr., U.S. Pat. 2,010,989 (1961, to Callery Chemical Company); see also Fr. Pat. 1,245,242.
30. Irish, G. E., and M. S. Baylerian, U.S. Pat. 2,866,811 (1958, to Ethyl Corp.); U.S. Pat. 2,996,451 (1961, to Ethyl Corp.).
31. Irish, G. E., J. B. Hinkamp, and J. D. Bartleson, U.S. Pat. 3,014,061 (1961, to Ethyl Corporation).
32. Kalb, G. H., U.S. Pat. 2,985,510 (1961, to E. I. duPont de Nemours and Company); see also Brit. Pat. 832,134; Ger. Pat. 1,054,080 (1959).
33. Keller, R. N., and E. M. Vander Wall, 133rd Meeting American Chemical Society, San Francisco, April, 1958, Abstracts of Papers, p. 31-L.
34. Kinney, C. R., H. T. Thompson, and L. C. Cheney, *J. Am. Chem. Soc.*, **57**, 2396 (1935).
35. Kollonitsch, J., *Nature*, **189**, 1005 (1961).
36. Kuskov, V. K., and G. F. Filippova, *Zh. Obshch. Khim.*, **29**, 4063 (1959).
37. Lappert, M. F. Brit Pat. 815,140 (1959).

38. Lappert, M. F., *J. Chem. Soc.*, 1768 (1956).
39. Lappert, M. F., *J. Chem. Soc.*, 2790 (1958).
40. Lappert, M. F., *J. Chem. Soc.*, 3256 (1958).
41. Lumbroso, H., and A. Grau, *Bull. Soc. Chim. France*, 1866 (1961).
42. Mauersberger, E. A., U.S. Pat. 2,042,952 (1936, to The Richards Chemical Works).
43. May, F. H., U.S. Pat. 2,839,565 (1958, to American Potash and Chemical Corp.).
44. McElroy, A. D., U.S. Pat. 2,943,916 (1960, to Callery Chemical Company).
45. McElroy, A. D., and R. M. Hunt, U.S. Pat. 2,996,539 (1961, to Callery Chemical Company).
46. Meutterties, E. L., *J. Am. Chem. Soc.*, **80**, 4526 (1958).
47. O'Connor, G. L., and H. R. Nace, *J. Am. Chem. Soc.*, **77**, 1578 (1955).
48. Olmsted, P. B., and C. A. Thomas, U.S. Pat. 2,927,124 (1960, to Callery Chemical Company).
49. Onak, T. P., H. Landesman, R. E. Williams, and I. Shapiro, *J. Phys. Chem.*, **63**, 1533 (1959).
50. Perotti, A., M. Cola, and A. Parmigiani, *Gazz. Chim. Ital.*, **90**, 1028 (1960).
51. Ploquin, J., *Bull. Soc. Pharm. Bordeaux*, **95**, 13 (1956).
52. Quill, L. L., P. R. Ogle, L. G. Kallander, and W. T. Lippincott, 129th Meeting American Chemical Society, Dallas, April, 1956, Abstracts of Papers, p. 40-N.
53. Reilly, J., and W. N. Rae, *Physico-Chemical Methods*, Vol. III, 4th Ed., D. Van Nostrand Co., Inc., New York, 1943, p. 94.
54. Ring, M. A., and W. S. Koski, *J. Chem. Phys.*, **35**, 381 (1961).
55. Sakaguchi, T., K. Sekiguchi, A. Hanaki, and A. Saito, *Yakugaku Zasshi*, **79**, 461 (1959).
56. Schechter, W. H., U.S. Pat. 2,787,329 (1957, to Callery Chemical Co.).
57. Schechter, W. H., U.S. Pat. 2,891,086 (1959, to Callery Chemical Co.).
58. Schechter, W. H., and T. B. Williams, U.S. Pat. 2,926,186 (1960, to Callery Chemical Company); see also Brit. Pat. 872,140 (1961).
59. Schiff, H., *Ann. Suppl.*, **5**, 154 (1867).
60. Schiff, H., and E. Bechi, *Compt. Rend.*, **61**, 697 (1865).
61. Schlesinger, H. I., H. C. Brown, D. L. Mayfield, and J. R. Gilbreath, *J. Am. Chem. Soc.*, **75**, 213 (1953).
62. Schomaker, B. H., and C. M. Loane, U.S. Pat. 2,160,917 (1939, to Standard Oil Co., Chicago, Ill.).
63. Steinberg, H., and D. L. Hunter, Unpublished results.
64. Steinberg, H., and L. L. Petterson, Unpublished results.
65. Swift and Company, Brit. Pat. 877,137 (1961).
66. Thomas, L. H., *J. Chem. Soc.*, 820 (1946).
67. Vander Wall, E. M., Ph.D. Dissertation, University of Colorado (R. N. Keller); Technical Report OMCC-HEF-44, June, 1957.

10

PEROXY DERIVATIVES

I. INTRODUCTION

This chapter is concerned with boron–oxygen compounds which contain at least one alkylperoxy group bonded to boron. Types (I) to (V) have been reported.

$B(OOR)_3$	$HOB(OOR)_3$	$(RO)_2BOOR$	$ArOB(OOR)_2$	$(ArO)_2BOOR$
(I)	(II)	(III)	(IV)	(V)

II. PROPERTIES

Tri-n-butyl and tri-*t*-butylperoxyborane are colorless liquids which are stable for extended periods at room temperature or for short periods at 100°. Molecular weights determined ebullioscopically in benzene were consistent with monomeric species; however it was stated that the partially esterified species, $(t\text{-}C_4H_9OO)_2BOH$, showed an anomalous molecular weight* indicating some molecular association.[7]

The alkylperoxyboranes absorb strongly in the infrared in the 7.42 to 7.49 μ region[6,7] which is identical with the B–O stretching frequency assigned for the trialkoxyboranes.[9]

Proton magnetic resonance chemical shifts for diisobutoxyisobutylperoxyborane have been recorded.[5]

III. METHODS OF PREPARATION

A. *From Alkyl Hydroperoxides and Various Boron Sources*

Boron trichloride is readily converted to the trialkylperoxyborane in good yield by treatment with an alkyl hydroperoxide in pentane solution at room temperature.[6,7]

$$BCl_3 + 3\,ROOH \rightarrow (ROO)_3B + 3\,HCl, \qquad R = n\text{-}C_4H_9,\ t\text{-}C_4H_9 \qquad (10\text{-}1)$$

The corresponding reaction with boric acid or its esters in place of the boron trichloride, in contrast to the ready alcoholysis of these

* It would be surprising if anomalous behaviour were not evident in boiling benzene due to anhydride formation: $2\ {>}BOH \rightarrow B{-}O{-}B{<} + H_2O$.

materials, did not result in the trialkylperoxyborane.[7] Other dissimilarity to the alcoholysis of boron trichloride is shown by the isolation of phenol from the reaction with phenyldimethylcarbinyl hydroperoxide. Presumably the peroxyborane once formed decomposed via heterolytic cleavage of the oxygen–oxygen bond accompanied by phenyl migration to oxygen (10-2)[6,7] as was

$$(CH_3)_2C(C_6H_5)OOH + Cl{-}B\langle \xrightarrow{-HCl} (CH_3)_2C(C_6H_5){-}O{-}O{-}B\langle \rightarrow (CH_3)_2C(OC_6H_5)(OB\langle) \qquad (10\text{-}2)$$

previously recorded for benzoyl-α-cumyl peroxide on standing (10-3).[8]

$$(CH_3)_2C(C_6H_5){-}O{-}OC(=O)C_6H_5 \rightarrow (CH_3)_2C(OC_6H_5)(OC(=O)C_6H_5) \qquad (10\text{-}3)$$

Reactions similar to (10-1) were performed with the *o*-nitrophenoxy derivatives of boron trichloride (VI and VII) to give (VIII) and (IX).[6,7]

$$o\text{-}NO_2C_6H_4OBCl_2 \quad \text{(VI)}$$

$$[o\text{-}NO_2C_6H_4O{-}]_2BCl \quad \text{(VII)}$$

$$o\text{-}NO_2C_6H_4OB(OO\text{-}t\text{-}C_4H_9)_2 \quad \text{(VIII)}$$

$$[o\text{-}NO_2C_6H_4O{-}]_2BOO\text{-}t\text{-}C_4H_9 \quad \text{(IX)}$$

In contrast to the alcoholysis of oxybis(diacetoxyborane) which produces trialkoxyboranes, the reaction of *t*-butyl hydroperoxide with oxybis(diacetoxyborane) resulted in the partially "esterified" species (X).[6,7]

$$(t\text{-}C_4H_9OO)_2BOH$$
(X)

B. By Rearrangement of Alkyl(alkylperoxy)boranes

Alkyldialkylperoxyboranes (XI), prepared by the oxidation of trialkylboranes[1,2,3,7] are converted to dialkoxyalkylperoxyboranes (XII) by treatment with pyridine, piperidine or water.[1,2,3,7]

$$\underset{\text{(XI)}}{RB(OOR)_2} \qquad \underset{\text{(XII)}}{(RO)_2BOOR}$$

It was believed that coordination of the nucleophile with the boron atom induced the migration of the alkyl group from boron to oxygen.[1,2*]

$$R_3N\!: \rightarrow \underset{\displaystyle OOR}{\overset{\displaystyle R}{B}}\text{—O—OR} \longrightarrow R_3N\!: \rightarrow \underset{\displaystyle OOR}{\overset{+}{B}}\text{—OR} + \bar{O}R \rightarrow R_3N + (RO)_2BOOR \qquad (10\text{-}4)$$

The reaction of perbenzoic acid with butoxy(butyl)butylperoxyborane† to give dibutoxybutylperoxyborane (10-5) was offered as

$$C_6H_5\overset{O}{\overset{\|}{C}}OOH + \underset{\displaystyle OC_4H_9}{\overset{\displaystyle C_4H_9}{B}}\text{—}OOC_4H_9 \rightarrow \left[C_6H_5\overset{O}{\overset{\|}{C}}\text{—O—O—}\underset{\displaystyle OC_4H_9}{\overset{\displaystyle C_4H_9}{B}}\text{—}OOC_4H_9\right]^{-}H^{+}$$

$$\rightarrow (C_4H_9O)_2BOOC_4H_9 + C_6H_5\overset{O}{\overset{\|}{C}}OH \qquad (10\text{-}5)$$

further evidence for the proposed mechanism.[2] The preferential migration of the butyl group to the benzoylperoxy group as compared

* A similar rearrangement was proposed in the reaction of *t*-butyl(diisobutyl)borane with hydrogen peroxide.[4]

$$[(CH_3)_2CHCH_2]_2B\text{—}C(CH_3)_3 + H_2O_2 \rightarrow \left[(CH_3)_2CHCH_2\text{—}\underset{\displaystyle CH_2CH(CH_3)_2}{\overset{\displaystyle C(CH_3)_3}{B}}\text{—O—OH}\right]^{-}H^{+}$$

$$\rightarrow [(CH_3)_2CHCH_2]_2B\text{—O—}C(CH_3)_3 + H_2O$$

† Presumably this species arises in the oxidation of tributylborane by the reaction[2]

$$RB(OOR)_2 + R_3B \rightarrow RB(OOR)(OR) + R_2BOR$$

to the butylperoxy group was believed to be due to electron attraction in the benzoylperoxy group.

A mechanism similar to reaction (10-4) was proposed to explain the loss of peroxide content on storage of isobutyldiisobutylperoxyborane.[5]

$$(CH_3)_2CHCH_2OOB(CH_2CH(CH_3)_2)-O-CH_2CH(CH_3)_2 \longrightarrow (CH_3)_2CHCH_2OOB[OCH_2CH(CH_3)_2]_2 \quad (10\text{-}6)$$

C. *Other Attempts*

1. FROM DIALKYL PEROXIDES

An attempt to parallel the cleavage of ethers with boron trichloride (10-7) with the cleavage of di-*t*-butylperoxide (10-8) resulted

$$BCl_3 + 3\ ROR \rightarrow (RO)_3B + 3\ RCl \quad (10\text{-}7)$$

$$BCl_3 + 3\ t\text{-}C_4H_9OO\text{—}t\text{-}C_4H_9 \rightarrow (t\text{-}C_4H_9OO)_3B + 3\ t\text{-}C_4H_9Cl \quad (10\text{-}8)$$

instead in a vigorous reaction yielding boric acid, hydrogen chloride, isobutylene and a trace of *t*-butyl chloride.[7]

2. FROM PERACIDS AND BORON TRICHLORIDE

An attempt to prepare (XIII) from the reaction of boron tri-

$$[CH_3(CH_2)_6\overset{\overset{\displaystyle O}{\|}}{C}OO]_3B$$

(XIII)

chloride and peroxycaprylic acid resulted in the formation of caprylic acid, boric oxide and chlorine.[7]

IV. REACTIONS

A. *Hydrolysis*

Trialkylperoxyboranes hydrolyze rapidly and completely liberating the corresponding alkyl hydroperoxides.[6,7]

$$(ROO)_3B + 3\ H_2O \rightarrow H_3BO_3 + 3\ ROOH \quad (10\text{-}9)$$

B. *Alcoholysis*

Tri-*t*-butylperoxyborane on treatment with ethanol was converted to *t*-butyl hydroperoxide and triethoxyborane.[7]

$$(t\text{-}C_4H_9OO)_3B + 3\ C_2H_5OH \rightarrow 3\ t\text{-}C_4H_9OOH + (C_2H_5O)_3B \quad (10\text{-}10)$$

C. *With Amines*

Tri-*t*-butylperoxyborane, but not the n-butyl derivative, on treatment with ammonia, pyridine or diethylamine in pentane solution resulted in the formation of insoluble but rather unstable complexes. The pyridine complex (XIV) was the most stable.[7]

$$C_5H_5N{:}B(OO\text{—}t\text{-}C_4H_9)_3$$
$$\text{(XIV)}$$

D. *Catalysis of Polymerization*

Homolytic cleavage of the oxygen–oxygen bonds in both tri-n-butyl and tri-*t*-butylperoxyborane is indicated by their catalysis of the polymerization of styrene and methyl methacrylate.[6,7]

V. ANALYTICAL

The ready hydrolysis of the alkylperoxyboranes permits their analysis by a straightforward volumetric procedure. After dissolution in water, the alkyl hydroperoxide is destroyed by refluxing in dilute hydrochloric acid. The cooled solution is neutralized with dilute sodium hydroxide and titrated for boron in the usual manner.

VI. PHYSICAL CONSTANTS

	M.p. (°C)	B.p. (°C)	d_4^t	n_D^t	Reference
$(n\text{-}C_4H_9OO)_3B$	−80	$40\text{–}60/10^{-3}$			7
		$50\text{–}60/10^{-3}$			6
$(t\text{-}C_4H_9OO)_3B$	15–18				7
		$60\text{–}70/10^{-3}$			6
$(t\text{-}C_4H_9OO)_3B{:}NC_5H_5$	—	—			7
$(t\text{-}C_4H_9OO)_2BOH$	38–40				6
	38–42				7
$n\text{-}C_4H_9OOB(O\text{—}n\text{-}C_4H_9)_2$					2
$i\text{-}C_4H_9OOB(O\text{—}i\text{-}C_4H_9)_2$					5
$t\text{-}C_4H_9OOB(O\text{—}t\text{-}C_4H_9)_2$					1, 2
$(t\text{-}C_4H_9OO)_2BO(C_6H_4NO_2)$		Red liquid			6, 7
$t\text{-}C_4H_9OOB[O(C_6H_4NO_2)]_2$	~15	Red liquid			7

VII. REFERENCES

1. Abraham, M. H., and A. G. Davies, *Chem. & Ind.* (*London*), 1622 (1957).
2. Abraham, M. H., and A. G. Davies, *J. Chem. Soc.*, 429 (1959).
3. Davies, A. G., and D. G. Hare, *J. Chem. Soc.*, 438 (1959).
4. Davies, A. G., D. G. Hare, and R. F. M. White, *Chem. & Ind.* (*London*). 556 (1960).
5. Davies, A. G., D. G. Hare, and R. F. M. White, *J. Chem. Soc.*, 1040 (1960),
6. Davies, A. G., and R. B. Moodie, *Chem. & Ind.* (*London*), 1622 (1957).
7. Davies, A. G., and R. B. Moodie, *J. Chem. Soc.*, 2372 (1958).
8. Hock, H., and H. Kropf, *Ber.*, **88**, 1544 (1955).
9. Werner, R. L., and K. G. O'Brien, *Australian J. Chem.*, **8**, 355 (1955).

11

ALKOXYBORANES

I. INTRODUCTION

Alkoxyboranes are the mono- (I) and dialkoxy derivatives (II) of borane (III). Unlike borane, they are capable of more than momentary existence in the monomeric form.

$ROBH_2$	$(RO)_2BH$	BH_3
(I)	(II)	(III)

In contrast to the alkoxyalkanes or ethers of conventional carbon compounds, in which the hydrogen atoms on the α-carbon atom play only a minor role, the chemistry of the alkoxyboranes is to a large extent dependent upon the boron–hydrogen bonds and their unique properties.

This chapter will attempt to delineate the interplay of these unique properties and the more exoteric boron–oxygen characteristics. As stated in the general introduction in Chapter 1, this chapter will not be concerned with "boron hydrides" as such and does not treat the chemistry of three-centered orbitals.

II. HISTORICAL

The first and simplest member of the dialkoxyboranes was prepared and characterized by Burg and Schlesinger[8] in 1933 by the methanolysis of diborane (11-1) and the equilibration of trimethoxyborane and diborane (11-2).

$$4\,CH_3OH + B_2H_6 \rightarrow 2\,(CH_3O)_2BH + 4\,H_2 \tag{11-1}$$

$$4\,(CH_3O)_3B + B_2H_6 \rightleftarrows 6\,(CH_3O)_2BH \tag{11-2}$$

An unstable white solid formed as a by-product in reaction (11-1) was believed to be polymeric methoxyborane (IV). To date well

$$(CH_3OBH_2)_n$$
(IV)

defined monomeric monoalkoxyboranes have not been reported

although products of this type derived from polyether alcohols (V) have been described.[36]

$$\mathrm{H(\overset{R}{\overset{|}{C}}HCH_2O)_nBH_2}$$

(V, R = H, CH_3)

III. PROPERTIES

Dialkoxyboranes are monomeric,[5,8,36] colorless, volatile liquids. In contrast to the boron hydrides, they are not spontaneously flammable in air.[8] Their odor is a composite of diborane and the alcohol from which they are derived.[8]

The infrared spectra of the lower members exhibit very strong bands due to asymmetric B–O stretching at 6.90 to 7.35 μ,[21,22,23] as compared to 7.00 to 7.35 μ for the corresponding trialkoxyboranes. The methoxy and ethoxy derivatives have strong bands due to B–H stretching at 3.98 and 3.99 μ,[21,22] as compared to 3.96 μ[28] for diborane.*

The ^{11}B nuclear magnetic resonance chemical shifts for dimethoxyborane and its deutero derivative, $DB(OCH_3)_2$, are -26.1 ± 0.5 and -26.7 ± 0.5 respectively.[27]

Monoalkoxyboranes, with the possible exclusion of those derived from polyethers, $H[CH_2CH_2O]_nBH_2$, are unstable solids of polymeric nature.[5,8] It is postulated that they are complexes involving the electron pair on oxygen and the vacant p orbital of boron (VI).[5,8]

$$\left[\begin{array}{cccccc} & \mathrm{H} & & \mathrm{H} & & \mathrm{H} \\ & | & & | & & | \\ :\mathrm{O}— & \mathrm{B}:\mathrm{O}— & & \mathrm{B}:\mathrm{O}— & & \mathrm{B} \\ | & | & | & | & | & | \\ \mathrm{R} & \mathrm{H} & \mathrm{R} & \mathrm{H} & \mathrm{R} & \mathrm{H} \end{array}\right] \text{etc.}$$

(VI)

IV. METHODS OF PREPARATION

A. From Diborane

1. AND ALCOHOLS

Methanol and excess diborane react rapidly in the cold to give good yields of dimethoxyborane (11-3).[8,13,21] The reaction necessarily

$$B_2H_6 + 4\,CH_3OH \rightarrow 2\,(CH_3O)_2BH + 4\,H_2 \qquad (11\text{-}3)$$

* B–H stretching in monoalkoxyboranes, $H[CH_2CH_2O]_nBH_2$, occurs at 3.82 and 3.97 μ.[36]

must proceed via the monomethoxy derivative and should continue to the trimethoxy derivative, and indeed monomethoxyborane (in the polymeric form, IV) and trimethoxyborane are by-products.[8]

Derivatives with secondary and tertiary alkyl groups also have been obtained by reaction (11-3). Diisopropoxyborane with ^{10}B was prepared by the addition of isopropyl alcohol to diborane-^{10}B, and di-*t*-butoxyborane was obtained by treatment of diborane with *t*-butyl alcohol.[34]

The mechanism of the alcoholysis, by analogy to the proposed paths for the hydrolysis[37] of diborane or the reaction of diborane and carbonyl compounds,[5] may involve coordination of the free electron pair on oxygen (11-5) with the equilibrium concentration of borane (11-4), or with larger concentrations of borane produced on demand of the nucleophilic reagent, followed by loss of hydrogen in a rate determining step (11-6). The resulting monomethoxyborane then either reacts with a second molecule of methanol in a similar manner (11-7) or undergoes disproportionation to the dimethoxy derivative (11-8).

$$B_2H_6 \rightleftarrows 2\,BH_3 \qquad (11\text{-}4)$$

$$CH_3\ddot{O}H + BH_3 \rightarrow CH_3\overset{+}{O}(H)\text{—}\overset{-}{B}H_3 \qquad (11\text{-}5)$$

$$CH_3\overset{+}{O}(H)\text{—}\overset{-}{B}H_2(H) \rightarrow CH_3OBH_2 + H_2 \qquad (11\text{-}6)$$

$$CH_3OBH_2 + CH_3OH \rightarrow CH_3\overset{+}{O}(H)\text{—}\overset{-}{B}(OCH_3)(H)\text{—}H \rightarrow \text{etc.} \qquad (11\text{-}7)$$

$$H_2B(\mu\text{-}OCH_3)(\mu\text{-}H)BH(OCH_3) \rightarrow BH_3 + (CH_3O)_2BH \qquad (11\text{-}8)$$

The ethanolysis of diborane in an infrared gas cell afforded a convenient means of "observing" the path of the reaction.[22,35] Even with a large excess of diborane, a detectable concentration of $C_2H_5OBH_2$ was not observed. The only visible changes on incremental addition of the ethanol to the diborane were due to a decrease in diborane concentration and formation of diethoxyborane. Triethoxyborane did not form in significant amounts in the very early stages of the ethanolysis, but its concentration increased rapidly after all the diborane had been converted to diethoxyborane. Of further significance, there was no evidence of absorption peaks due to unreacted alcohol until alcoholysis of the diborane was essentially complete nor was there any evidence of an intermediate containing a B–H bridge group. Thus the probability of disproportionation of the monoethoxyborane is not as great as the probability of further alcoholysis.

2. AND OTHER OXYGEN COMPOUNDS

Diborane is converted to dialkoxyboranes on treatment with aldehydes (11-9),[2,5] ketones (11–10),[2,3,5] esters (11-11),[5] and epoxides (11-12).[36,38] An amine–borane complex also has been used for the reduction of benzoquinone (11-13).[26] The reactions with aldehydes,

$$4\,CH_3\overset{\overset{O}{\|}}{C}H + B_2H_6 \rightarrow 2\,(C_2H_5O)_2BH \qquad (11\text{-}9)$$

$$4\,CH_3\overset{\overset{O}{\|}}{C}CH_3 + B_2H_6 \rightarrow 2\,(i\text{-}C_3H_7O)_2BH \qquad (11\text{-}10)$$

$$2\,CH_3\overset{\overset{O}{\|}}{C}OC_2H_5 + B_2H_6 \rightarrow 2\,(C_2H_5O)_2BH \qquad (11\text{-}11)$$

$$4\,\overset{\diagup O \diagdown}{CH_2CH_2} + B_2H_6 \rightarrow 2\,(C_2H_5O)_2BH \qquad (11\text{-}12)$$

$$2\,O{=}C_6H_4{=}O + t\text{-}C_4H_9NH_2{:}BH_3 \rightarrow \left[HO\text{-}C_6H_4\text{-}O\text{—}\right]_2 BH{:}NH_2\text{-}t\text{-}C_4H_9 \qquad (11\text{-}13)$$

ketones and epoxides are rapid and complete at room temperature or below; the reaction with esters is slow.

Two different mechanisms were postulated to rationalize these results.[5] With aldehydes and ketones, hydride transfers from boron to carbon via a complex of borane and the carbonyl oxygen. None of the proposed steps (11-14 to 11-16) require any appreciable energy of activation and the reactions proceed rapidly. With esters, a

$$B_2H_6 \rightleftarrows 2\,BH_3 \tag{11-14}$$

$$>C{=}O\colon + BH_3 \rightarrow >C{=}\overset{+}{O}{-}\overset{-}{B}H_3 \tag{11-15}$$

$$>C{=}\overset{+}{O}{-}\overset{-}{B}H_2(H) \rightarrow >CHOBH_2 \xrightarrow{>C=O} \text{etc.} \tag{11-16}$$

complex involving the ether oxygen (11-17) is envisaged. The subsequent step requires fission of the carbon–oxygen bond (11-18) which

$$RC(=O)OR' + BH_3 \rightarrow RC(=O){-}\overset{+}{O}(R'){-}\overset{-}{B}H_3 \tag{11-17}$$

$$R{-}C(=O){-}\overset{+}{O}(-\overset{-}{B}H_3){-}R' \rightarrow RC(=O)H + R'OBH_2;\quad RCHO \xrightarrow{BH_3} \text{etc.};\quad R'OBH_2 \xrightarrow{RC(=O)OR'} \text{etc.} \tag{11-18}$$

may involve a high energy of activation and the overall reaction proceeds slowly.[5] In addition, any transfer of hydride from boron to carbon via a carbonyl–borane complex will be hindered by the stabilization provided the carbonyl group by resonance with the oxygen atom of the alkoxy group (11-19).[7]

$$-C(={}^{+}\ddot{O}{-}{}^{-}BH_3){-}OR \longleftrightarrow -C(-\ddot{O}{-}{}^{-}BH_3){=}\overset{+}{O}R \tag{11-19}$$

Inertness[5] of chloral, acetyl chloride and phosgene to diborane subsequently was attributed[7] to the decreased basic properties of the oxygen atom of the carbonyl group resulting from the powerful inductive effect of the halogen substituents.

$$-C(Cl){=}\overset{\delta+}{O} + BH_3 \longleftrightarrow -C(Cl){=}\overset{+}{O}\colon\overset{-}{B}H_3 \tag{11-20}$$

Attempts to isolate monoalkoxy derivatives from the reactions of diborane with aldehydes and ketones resulted in the production of unstable, white, crystalline substances believed to be polymeric monoalkoxyboranes.[5] However, a monomeric *t*-butylamine complex of a monoalkoxyborane (VII) was produced by the reduction of benzoyl chloride with *t*-butylamine-borane.[26]

$$C_6H_5CH_2OBH_2{:}NH_2C(CH_3)_3$$
(VII)

Reactions (11-21) and (11-22) were postulated to account for the production of diethoxyborane and diisopropoxyborane from the

$$\begin{array}{l}CH_2\\ |\quad\diagdown\\ |\quad\;\; O{:} + BH_3 \rightarrow\\ |\quad\diagup\\ CH_2\end{array}\begin{array}{l}CH_2\\ |\quad\diagdown\\ |\quad\;\; \overset{+}{O}{:}\overset{-}{B}H_3\\ |\quad\diagup\\ CH_2\end{array} \qquad (11\text{-}21)$$

$$\begin{array}{l}CH_2\\ |\;\;\searrow O^{+}\!\!\cdot\cdot\;\; H\\ CH_2\swarrow\;\; B\!\!-\\ \quad H \qquad H\end{array} \rightarrow CH_3CH_2OBH_2 \qquad (11\text{-}22)$$

reactions of ethylene oxide and propylene oxide with diborane.[36] Polymeric by-products which exhibited B–H stretching frequencies in the infrared identical with those for terminal BH_2 groups in diborane were believed to arise by ring fission without hydride transfer (11-23). The resulting carbonium ion would effect further ring cleavage and polymerization (11-24). The chain termination step (11-25) was not defined.

$$\begin{array}{l}CH_2\\ |\quad\diagdown\\ |\quad\;\; O{:}\\ |\quad\diagup\\ CH_2\end{array} + BH_3 \rightarrow \overset{+}{C}H_2CH_2O{:}\overset{-}{B}H_3 \qquad (11\text{-}23)$$

$$\begin{array}{l}CH_2\\ |\quad\diagdown\\ |\quad\;\; O{:}\\ |\quad\diagup\\ CH_2\end{array} + \overset{+}{C}H_2CH_2O{:}\overset{-}{B}H_3 \rightarrow \overset{+}{C}H_2CH_2OCH_2CH_2O{:}\overset{-}{B}H_3 \qquad (11\text{-}24)$$

$$\downarrow n\ \overset{O}{CH_2\!-\!CH_2}$$

$$^{+}CH_2CH_2O(CH_2CH_2O)_n{:}\overset{-}{B}H_3$$

$$^{+}CH_2CH_2O(CH_2CH_2O)_n{:}BH_3 \xrightarrow[\text{termination}]{\text{Chain}} H(CHCH_2O)_nBH_2 + H_2 \qquad (11\text{-}25)$$

3. AND TRIALKOXYBORANES

Diborane and trimethoxyborane equilibrate slowly at room temperature to give dimethoxyborane.[8,32]

$$B_2H_6 + 4\,(CH_3O)_3B \rightleftarrows 6\,(CH_3O)_2BH \qquad (11\text{-}26)$$

The slow transfer of ethoxy groups from triethoxyborane to diborane was followed in an infrared cell.[22] After thirty-six hours, the growth of diethoxyborane became discernible. No peaks that might be attributable to monoethoxyborane were observed. Thus, the initial transfer of an ethoxy group to diborane (VII) is more difficult than subsequent transfers to ethoxyborane (IX).

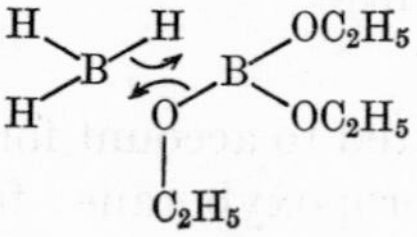

H, H, B, B, OC_2H_5, H, O, OC_2H_5, C_2H_5

(VIII)

H, H, B, B, OC_2H_5, C_2H_5O, O, OC_2H_5, C_2H_5

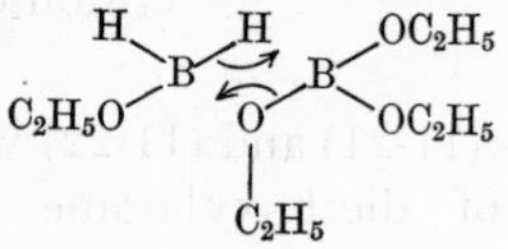

(IX)

B. From Higher Boron Hydrides

The treatment of tetraborane with approximately four molar equivalents of ethanol at $-78°$ resulted in the formation of a colorless polymer, diethoxyborane (28% yield), and triethoxyborane (61% yield).[9] Equation (11-27) is an idealized formulation.

$$B_4H_{10} + 8\ C_2H_5OH \rightarrow 4\ (C_2H_5O)_2BH + 7\ H_2 \qquad (11\text{-}27)$$

The alcoholysis of pentaborane with ten molar equivalents of ethanol resulted in a 40% yield of diethoxyborane (11-28).[39] The

$$B_5H_9 + 10\ C_2H_5OH \rightarrow 5\ (C_2H_5O)_2BH + 7\ H_2 \qquad (11\text{-}28)$$

methanolysis of excess pentaborane at $-30°$ gave a trace of dimethoxyborane and a solid material, non-volatile at $-30°$, believed to be monomethoxyborane.[33] The reaction of pentaborane and *t*-butyl alcohol at 0° gave di-*t*-butoxyborane.[34]

Experiments using isotopically labeled reagents showed the conversions (11-27) and (11-28) to involve rupture of B–B bonds present in the boron hydrides.[35] The addition of either isotopically normal or deuterated ethanol to isotopically normal diborane resulted in the formation of diethoxyborane, $(C_2H_5O)_2BH$. When isotopically normal ethanol was added to excess tetraborane or pentaborane, $(C_2H_5O)_2BH$ was found as a product; but when deuterated ethanol, C_2H_5OD, was added to these hydrides, both $(C_2H_5O)_2BH$ and $(C_2H_5O)_2BD$ were formed. In the case of tetraborane the concentration of the protonated ethoxyborane was approximately twice as great as that of the deuterated ethoxyborane. With pentaborane, essentially equivalent amounts of the two species were produced. Additionally, an appreciable amount of triethoxyborane was observed even though the amount of ethanol added was comparatively small with respect to the boron hydride.

The formation of $(C_2H_5O)_2BD$ from C_2H_5OD and tetraborane or pentaborane and the absence of this product in the case of diborane were presented as evidence for its formation from the breaking of boron–boron bonds (11-29) which are present in both tetraborane and pentaborane but absent in diborane.

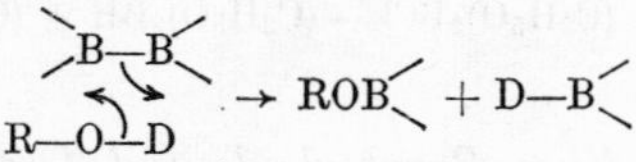

$$\begin{array}{c} >B{-}B< \\ R{-}O{-}D \end{array} \rightarrow ROB< + D{-}B< \qquad (11\text{-}29)$$

The relative amounts of the protonated and deuterated alkoxyboranes produced are consistent with the number of boron–boron bonds in tetraborane[25] and pentaborane[14,15] if the rate determining step of the overall reaction is the rupture of the B–B bond and not the alcoholysis of the B–H bonds (Fig. 11-1).

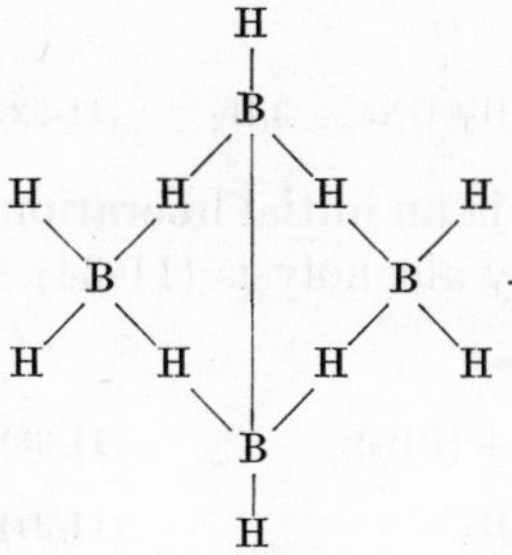

$$B_4H_{10} + 8\,C_2H_5OD \rightarrow 2\,(C_2H_5O)_2BH + (C_2H_5O)_2B{-}B(OC_2H_5)_2 + 8\,HD$$

$$(C_2H_5O)_2B{-}B(OC_2H_5)_2 + C_2H_5OD \rightarrow (C_2H_5O)_2BD + (C_2H_5O)_3B$$

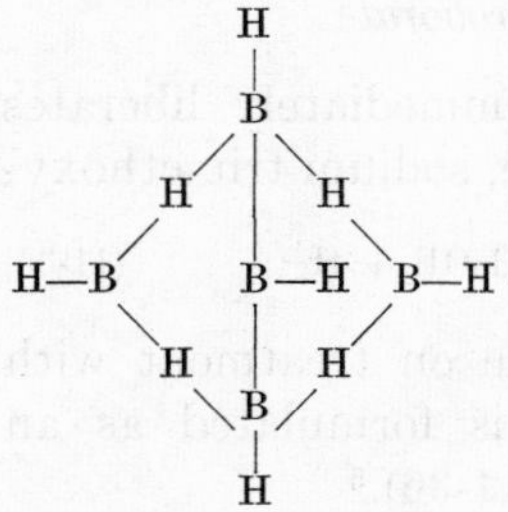

$$B_5H_9 + 9\,C_2H_5OD \rightarrow 2\,(C_2H_5O)_2BH + (C_2H_5O)_2B{-}B(OC_2H_5){-}B(OC_2H_5)_2 + 7\,HD + D_2$$

$$(C_2H_5O)_2B{-}B(OC_2H_5){-}B(OC_2H_5)_2 + 2\,C_2H_5OD \rightarrow 2\,(C_2H_5O)_2BD + (C_2H_5O)_3B$$

Fig. 11-1. Reaction of ethanol-d with tetraborane to give

$$[(C_2H_5O)_2BH]/[(C_2H_5O)_2BD] = 2$$

and with pentaborane to give

$$[(C_2H_5O)_2BH]/[(C_2H_5O)_2BD] = 1.$$

C. From Dialkoxyhaloboranes

Chlorodiethoxyborane reportedly is quantitatively reduced to diethoxyborane by treatment with sodium hydride at 180° in the presence of catalytic amounts of triethoxyborane.[18] Perhaps the actual reducing agent is sodium triethoxyhydroborate.

$$(C_2H_5O)_3B + NaH \rightarrow [(C_2H_5O)_3BH]Na \quad (11\text{-}30)$$

$$[(C_2H_5O)_3BH]Na + (C_2H_5O)_2BCl \rightarrow (C_2H_5O)_2BH + (C_2H_5O)_3B + NaCl \quad (11\text{-}31)$$

D. From Sodium Borohydride and Tertiary Alcohols

Sodium borohydride in the presence of one equivalent of acetic acid reacts smoothly at room temperature with primary and secondary alcohols to give good yields of trialkoxyboranes (Chapter 4). Under the same conditions, tertiary alcohols lead to the production of dialkoxyboranes (11-32).[4]

$$2\,ROH + NaBH_4 + CH_3\overset{\overset{O}{\|}}{C}OH \rightarrow (RO)_2BH + CH_3\overset{\overset{O}{\|}}{C}ONa + 3\,H_2 \quad (11\text{-}32)$$

The reaction is formulated as proceeding via an initial liberation of borane by the acetic acid (11-33) followed by alcoholysis (11-34).[4]

$$NaBH_4 + CH_3\overset{\overset{O}{\|}}{C}OH \rightarrow CH_3\overset{\overset{O}{\|}}{C}ONa + H_2 + \{BH_3\} \quad (11\text{-}33)$$

$$\{BH_3\} + 2\,ROH \rightarrow (RO)_2BH + 2\,H_2 \quad (11\text{-}34)$$

E. From Sodium Trimethoxyhydroborate

In contrast to sodium borohydride, which immediately liberates hydrogen on treatment with hydrogen chloride, sodium trimethoxy-

$$[(CH_3O)_3BH]Na + HCl \rightarrow (CH_3O)_2BH + CH_3OH + H_2 \quad (11\text{-}35)$$

hydroborate is converted to dimethoxyborane on treatment with hydrogen chloride at −80°.[6] The reaction is formulated as an electrophilic attack of the proton on oxygen (11-36).[6]

$$H^+ + :\underset{\underset{CH_3}{|}}{O}-\overset{\overset{H}{|}}{\underset{\underset{OCH_3}{|}}{B^-}}-OCH_3 \rightarrow H:\underset{\underset{CH_3}{|^+}}{O}-\overset{\overset{H}{|}}{\underset{\underset{OCH_3}{|}}{B^-}}-OCH_3 \rightarrow CH_3OH + (CH_3O)_2BH \quad (11\text{-}36)$$

The thermal decomposition of sodium trimethoxyhydroborate to sodium borohydride and sodium tetramethoxyborate (Chapter 14) is accompanied by the formation of dimethoxyborane and sodium methoxide in 19% yield.[31]

$$NaBH(OCH_3)_3 \xrightarrow{230^\circ} (CH_3O)_2BH + NaOCH_3 \quad (11\text{-}37)$$

A trace of diethoxyborane was obtained from the pyrolysis of sodium triethoxyhydroborate.[31]

F. From Trialkoxyboranes and Reducing Agents

Reaction of trimethoxyborane and sodium hydride in at least a 2:1 molar ratio for several hours at total reflux under two atmospheres pressure was reported to result in a high conversion to dimethoxyborane (11-38). Sodium borohydride or sodium trimethoxyhydroborate also can serve as the reducing agent (11-39).[11,17]

$$2\,(CH_3O)_3B + NaH \rightarrow (CH_3O)_2BH + [(CH_3O)_4B]Na \quad (11\text{-}38)$$

$$[BH_n(OCH_3)_{4-n}]Na + n\,(CH_3O)_3B \rightarrow n\,(CH_3O)_2BH + [(CH_3O)_4B]Na \quad (11\text{-}39)$$

G. From Trialkoxyboroxines and Reducing Agents

Trimethoxyboroxine reacts with sodium hydride, sodium borohydride or sodium trimethoxyhydroborate in the absence of a solvent in an analogous manner to trimethoxyborane (see Section IV-F) to produce dimethoxyborane.[17] The reactions were formulated as follows:[10]

$$6\,NaH + 10\,(CH_3OBO)_3 \rightarrow 6\,(CH_3O)_2BH + 6\,(CH_3O)_3B + 3\,Na_2B_6O_{10} \quad (11\text{-}40)$$

$$3\,NaBH_4 + 2\,(CH_3OBO)_3 + 6\,(CH_3O)_3B \rightarrow 12\,(CH_3O)_2BH + 3\,NaBO_2 \quad (11\text{-}41)$$

$$6\,NaBH_4 + 7\,(CH_3OBO)_3 + 9\,(CH_3O)_3B \rightarrow 24\,(CH_3O)_2BH + 3\,Na_2B_4O_7 \quad (11\text{-}42)$$

$$6\,NaBH_4 + 10\,(CH_3OBO)_3 + 6\,(CH_3O)_3B \rightarrow 24\,(CH_2O)_2BH + 3\,Na_2B_6O_{10} \quad (11\text{-}43)$$

$$6\,NaBH(OCH_3)_3 + 10\,(CH_3OBO)_3 \rightarrow 6\,(CH_3O)_2BH + 12\,(CH_3O)_3B + 3\,Na_2B_6O_{10} \quad (11\text{-}44)$$

Higher yields than any other known method were claimed for he preparation of dialkoxyboranes from the sodium borohydride reduction of trialkoxyboroxines in polyethylene glycol dialkyl ether solution.[24]

V. REACTIONS

A. Hydrolysis

Dialkoxyboranes are rapidly hydrolyzed to boric acid and an alcohol

$$(RO)_2BH + 3\,H_2O \rightarrow H_3BO_3 + 2\,ROH + H_2 \quad (11\text{-}45)$$

with the evolution of one molar equivalent of hydrogen.[5,8,13,34,39] The heat of hydrolysis of the dimethoxy derivative is 24.2 ± 1.5 kcal/mole.[13]

Complexing of the boron with an amine does not preclude hydrolysis, at least for the aromatic members, since compound (X) turns brown and hydrolyzes on standing in air.[26]

$$\left[HO-C_6H_4-O \right]_2 BH{:}NH_2\text{-}t\text{-}C_4H_9$$

(X)

B. *Alcoholysis*

The alcoholysis of dialkoxyboranes to produce trialkoxyboranes is discussed in Chapter 4.

C. *Disproportionation*

The disproportionation of dialkoxyboranes to diborane and the corresponding trialkoxyboranes is discussed in Chapter 4.

D. *With Amines*

Diisopropoxyborane forms an unstable addition product (XI) with trimethylamine.[5]

$$(i\text{-}C_3H_7O)_2BH{:}N(CH_3)_3$$

(XI)

E. *With Hydrides, Tetraalkoxyborates, and Tetra(alkoxyhydro)borates*

Dialkoxyboranes react with alkaline earth or alkali metal hydrides (11-46) or tetraalkoxyborates (11-47) to produce a metal borohydride and trialkoxyborane.[16]

$$3n\,(RO)_2BH + MH_n \rightarrow M(BH_4)_n + 2n\,(RO)_3B \qquad (11\text{-}46)$$

$$4n\,(RO)_2BH + M[B(OR)_4]_n \rightarrow M(BH_4)_n + 4n\,(RO)_3B \qquad (11\text{-}47)$$

Dimethoxyborane reacts quantitatively with sodium trimethoxyhydroborate to produce sodium borohydride and trimethoxyborane.[32]

$$3\,(CH_3O)_2BH + NaBH(OCH_3)_3 \rightarrow NaBH_4 + 3\,(CH_3O)_3B \qquad (11\text{-}48)$$

F. *With Olefins and Acetylenes*

The hydroboration of olefins with diborane to produce trialkylboranes (11-49) has been extensively documented[1] (see Volume III of this

$$3\ \rangle C{=}C\langle\ + \{BH_3\} \rightarrow (\ \rangle CH\overset{|}{\underset{|}{C}}\langle\ )_3B \qquad (11\text{-}49)$$

series). In an analogous manner, the addition of dimethoxyborane to olefins (11-50) offers a convenient method of synthesis of a variety of dimethoxyalkylboranes.[19,29,30] Acetylenes were both mono- (11-51)

$$(CH_3O)_2BH + \rangle C{=}C\langle \rightarrow (CH_3O)_2B\overset{|}{\underset{|}{C}}CH\langle \qquad (11\text{-}50)$$

and di-substituted (11-52) depending upon the stoichiometry of the reactants.

$$CH_3CH_2CH_2CH_2C{\equiv}CH + (CH_3O)_2BH \rightarrow C_6H_{11}B(OCH_3)_2 \qquad (11\text{-}51)$$

$$CH_3CH_2CH_2CH_2C{\equiv}CH + 2\,(CH_3O)_2BH \rightarrow C_6H_{12}[B(OCH_3)_2]_2 \qquad (11\text{-}52)$$

G. *With Carbonyl Compounds and Nitriles*

In a manner analogous to the hydroboration of olefins (Section V-F), dimethoxyborane adds to aldehydes, ketones, esters, acid chlorides, and nitriles to give alcohols or amines on subsequent hydrolysis.[12]

$$R\overset{O}{\overset{\|}{C}}R + (CH_3O)_2BH \rightarrow R_2CHOB(OCH_3)_2 \xrightarrow{H_2O} R_2CHOH + H_3BO_3 + 2\,CH_3OH \qquad (11\text{-}53)$$

$$RCN + 2\,(CH_3O)_2BH \rightarrow RCH_2N[B(OCH_3)_2]_2 \xrightarrow{H_2O} RCH_2NH_2 + 2\,H_3BO_3 + 4\,CH_3OH \qquad (11\text{-}54)$$

H. *Hydrogen Exchange*

Spectral experiments with $(C_2H_5O)_2BD$ in an infrared gas cell indicated a rapid exchange of deuterium with hydrogen from diborane or $(C_2H_5O)_2BH$.[22] The concentration of the proposed transitory dimers containing a double hydrogen bridge (XII and XIII) were too low for actual detection.

$$\begin{array}{ccccc} C_2H_5O & & D & & OC_2H_5 \\ & \diagdown & \diagup\ \cdot\cdot\ \diagdown & \diagup & \\ & B & & B & \\ & \diagup & \cdot\cdot\ \diagup\ \diagdown & \diagdown & \\ C_2H_5O & & H & & OC_2H_5 \end{array}$$

(XII)

$$\begin{array}{ccccc} C_2H_5O & & D & & H \\ & \diagdown & \diagup\ \cdot\cdot\ \diagdown & \diagup & \\ & B & & B & \\ & \diagup & \cdot\cdot\ \diagup\ \diagdown & \diagdown & \\ C_2H_5O & & H & & H \end{array}$$

(XIII)

VI. ANALYTICAL

Dimethoxyborane has been analyzed by hydrolysis and measurement of the resulting hydrogen (11-55) followed by distillation of the

$$(CH_3O)_2BH + 3\,H_2O \rightarrow H_3BO_3 + 2\,CH_3OH + H_2 \tag{11-55}$$

methanol and titration of the residual boric acid with standard barium hydroxide in the presence of excess mannitol.[8] A possible complication of trimethoxyborane–methanol azeotrope distillation was not mentioned.

A titrimetric method for the determination of hydrolyzable hydrogen in dimethoxyborane based on the reaction of hydridic hydrogen with iodine in the presence of excess iodine and a subsequent titration of unreacted iodine with thiosulfate has been recorded.[20]

Diethoxyborane has been analyzed by both the above hydrolysis method and by a nitric oxide catalyzed oxidation followed by the removal of volatile constituents and final titration of the residual boric oxide.[5]

VII. PHYSICAL CONSTANTS

$ROBH_2$	V.p. (mm./°C)	M.p. (°C)	B.p. (°C)	d_4^t	n_D^t	Reference
$(CH_3OBH_2)_n$		White solid				8
$(C_2H_5OBH_2)_n$		White crystalline solid				5
$(i\text{-}C_3H_7OBH_2)_n$		White crystalline solid				5
$C_6H_5CH_2OBH_2:NH_2\text{-}t\text{-}C_4H_9$		24–25				26
$H(CH_2CH_2O)_8BH_2$		White solid				36
$H(CH(CH_3)CH_2O)_6BH_2$			Liquid			36

$(RO)_2BH$	V.p. (mm./°C)	M.p. (°C)	B.p. (°C)	d_4^t	n_D^t	Reference
$(CH_3O)_2BH$		−130.6	25.9 (calc.)			8
	275/0					5, 13
$(CH_3O)_2BD$	—	—	—	—	—	21
$(C_2H_5O)_2BH$	35.5/0					36
	36.5/0					9
	37.5/0					5
	—	—	—	—	—	22, 39
$(C_2H_5O)_2{}^{10}BH$	—	—	—	—	—	22
$(C_2H_5O)_2BD$	—	—	—	—	—	22
$(i\text{-}C_3H_7O)_2BH$	10/0					5
	10.1/0					36
$(i\text{-}C_3H_7O)_2{}^{10}BH$	—	—	—	—	—	23
$(i\text{-}C_3H_7O)_2BH:N(CH_3)_3$		−19 to −10				5
$(t\text{-}C_4H_9O)_2BH$		−44.6				34
	—	—	—	—	—	4
$(t\text{-}C_5H_{11}O)_2BH$	—	—	—	—	—	4
$[(CH_3)_3CCH_2O]_2BH$	3/25					5

(*Table continued*)

$(RO)_2BH$	V.p. (mm./°C)	M.p. (°C)	B.p. (°C)	d_4^t	n_D^t	Reference
$[C_4H_3O\text{–}CH_2O]_2BH$	—	—	—	—	—	2
$(C_6H_{11}O)_2BH$	—	—	—	—	—	2
$(C_6H_5CH_2O)_2BH$	—	—	—	—	—	2
$(n\text{-}C_6H_{13}CH(CH_3)O)_2BH$	—	—	—	—	—	2
$[(C_6H_5)_2CHO]_2BH$	—	—	—	—	—	2
[pregnenolone-3-O]$_2$BH	—	—	—	—	—	2

$(ArO)_2BH$	V.p. (mm./°C)	M.p. (°C)	B.p. (°C)	d_4^t	n_D^t	Reference
$[HO\text{–}C_6H_4\text{–}O]_2BH\!:\!NH(CH_3)_2$		Decomposes 170				26

$[HO-C_6H_4-O]_2BH:NH_2\text{-}t\text{-}C_4H_9$	Decomposes > 150	26

VIII. REFERENCES

1. Brown, H. C., *Hydroboration*, W. A. Benjamin, Inc., New York, 1962.
2. Brown, H. C., U.S. Pat. 2,709,704 (1955).
3. Brown, H. C., and W. Korytnyk, *J. Am. Chem. Soc.*, **82**, 3866 (1960).
4. Brown, H. C., E. J. Mead, and C. J. Shoaf, *J. Am. Chem. Soc.*, **78**, 3613 (1956).
5. Brown, H. C., H. I. Schlesinger, and A. B. Burg, *J. Am. Chem. Soc.*, **61**, 673 (1939).
6. Brown, H. C., H. I. Schlesinger, I. Sheft, and D. M. Ritter, *J. Am. Chem. Soc.*, **75**, 192 (1953).
7. Brown, H. C., and B. C. Subba Rao, *J. Am. Chem. Soc.*, **82**, 681 (1960).
8. Burg, A. B., and H. I. Schlesinger, *J. Am. Chem. Soc.*, **55**, 4020 (1933).
9. Burg, A. B., and F. G. A. Stone, *J. Am. Chem. Soc.*, **75**, 228 (1953).
10. Bush, J. D., U.S. Pat. 3,014,060 (1961, to Callery Chemical Company).
11. Bush, J. D., R. A. Carpenter, and W. H. Schechter, U.S. Pat. 3,014,059 (1961, to Callery Chemical Company).
12. Callery Chemical Company, Fr. Pat. 1,264,478 (1961).
13. Cooper, W. J., and J. F. Masi, *J. Phys. Chem.*, **64**, 682 (1960).
14. Dulmage, W. J., and W. N. Lipscomb, *J. Am. Chem. Soc.*, **73**, 3539 (1951).
15. Hedberg, K., M. E. Jones, and V. Schomaker, *J. Am. Chem. Soc.*, **73**, 3538 (1951).
16. Huff, G. F., Can. Pat. 626,249 (1961, to Callery Chemical Company).
17. Huff, G. F., and W. H. Schechter, U.S. Pat. 2,992,072 (1961, to Callery Chemical Company).
18. Jenkner, H., Ger. Pat. 1,044,055 (1956, to Kali-Chemie Aktiengesellschaft).
19. Jenkner, H., Ger. Pat. 1,115,249 (1961, to Kali-Chemie Aktiengesellschaft).
20. Krol, A. J., L. B. Eddy, D. R. Mackey, and A. E. Weber, Callery Chemical Company Report No. CCC-1024-TR-239 to Navy Dept. Bur. of Aeronautics, May 1, 1957.
21. Lehmann, W. J., T. P. Onak, and I. Shapiro, *J. Chem. Phys.*, **30**, 1215 (1959).
22. Lehmann, W. J., H. G. Weiss, and I. Shapiro, *J. Chem. Phys.*, **30**, 1222 (1959).
23. Lehmann, W. J., H. G. Weiss, and I. Shapiro, *J. Chem. Phys.*, **30**, 1226 (1959).
24. McElroy, A. D., and R. M. Adams, U.S. Pat. 2,992,266 (1961, to Callery Chemical Company).
25. Nordman, C. E., and W. N. Lipscomb, *J. Am. Chem. Soc.*, **75**, 4117 (1953).
26. Nöth, H., and H. Beyer, *Ber.*, **93**, 1078 (1960).
27. Onak, T. P., H. Landesman, R. E. Williams, and I. Shapiro, *J. Phys. Chem.*, **63**, 1533 (1959).
28. Price, W. C., *J. Chem. Phys.*, **16**, 894 (1948).
29. Schechter, W. H., Can. Pat. 610,163 (1960, to Callery Chemical Company).
30. Schechter, W. H., Ger. Pat. 1,111,181 (1961, to Callery Chemical Company).
31. Schlesinger, H. I., H. C. Brown, and A. E. Finholt, *J. Am. Chem. Soc.*, **75**, 205 (1953).

32. Schlesinger, H. I., H. C. Brown, H. R. Hockstra, and L. R. Rapp, *J. Am. Chem. Soc.*, **75**, 199 (1953).
33. Schlesinger, H. I., R. Schaeffer, *et al.*, University of Chicago, Hydrides and Borohydrides of Light Weight Elements and Related Compounds, Final Report for period Aug. 1, 1950 to June 30, 1951, Contract N6ori-20, Project 052-255.
34. Schlesinger, H. I., R. Schaeffer, *et al.*, University of Chicago, Hydrides and Borohydrides of Light Weight Elements and Related Compounds, Technical Report for period Aug. 1, 1951 to July 31, 1952, Contract N6ori-20, Project 052-255.
35. Shapiro, I., and H. G. Weiss, *J. Phys. Chem.*, **63**, 1319 (1959).
36. Stone, F. G. A., and H. J. Emeléus, *J. Chem. Soc.*, 2755 (1950).
37. Weiss, H. G., and I. Shapiro, *J. Am. Chem. Soc.*, **75**, 1221 (1953).
38. Wirth, H. E., Syracuse University, for Olin Mathieson Chemical Corporation, Technical Research Report, Project Zip, OMCC-HEF-105, Feb. 6, 1958.
39. Zhigach, A. F., E. B. Kazakova, and R. A. Kigel, *Proc. Acad. Sci. U.S.S.R.*, **106**, 9 (1956).

12

ALKOXYHALOBORANES AND RELATED COMPOUNDS

I. INTRODUCTION

This chapter is concerned with the trigonal coplanar compounds of boron in which boron is bonded to one or more halogens and to at least one organic residue through oxygen. Examples of such species are (I) to (IV) and the silicon analogs (V) and (VI). Only one example with different alkyl groups (VII) has been reported.[14]

$ROBX_2$	$ArOBX_2$	$(RO)_2BX$	$(ArO)_2BX$
(I)	(II)	(III)	(IV)

R_3SiOBX_2	$(R_3SiO)_2BX$	$n\text{-}C_4H_9OB(Cl)OCH_2CH_2OBCl_2$
(V)	(VI)	(VII)

Alkoxydichloroboranes (I) derived from primary alkyl groups are relatively stable at 20°; whereas those derived from secondary alkyl groups have only momentary stability at −80°.[53,86] The dialkoxychloroboranes (III), both primary and secondary, appear to be stable at 20° with the primary derivatives the more stable of the two.[88] No evidence exists for (I) or (III) with tertiary alkyl groups[53,86,88] or where the halogen is iodine. An example of the completely unsymmetrical species (VIII) has not been reported.

$$RO{-}B(X){-}OH$$

(VIII)

Species derived from 1,2- and 1,3-glycols (IX) and catechol (X) also have been described.

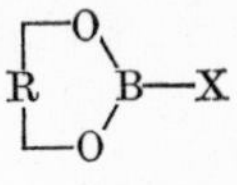

(IX) 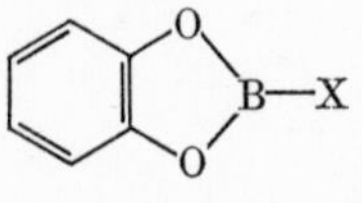 (X)

Only one acyloxyhaloborane (XI) has been reported.

$$\begin{array}{ccc} CH_3\overset{O}{\overset{\|}{C}}O & & O\overset{O}{\overset{\|}{C}}CH_3 \\ & \diagdown \quad \diagup & \\ & BOB & \\ & \diagup \quad \diagdown & \\ Cl & & Cl \end{array}$$

(XI)

This chapter will not be concerned with the many examples of complexes formed from boron halides and oxygenated organic compounds. Chapter 18 contains a discussion of coordination compounds which appear to have alkoxy- and acyloxytrihaloborate structures.

II. HISTORICAL

The first alkoxyhaloboranes were prepared by Gasselin in 1894 by the alcoholysis of boron trifluoride with methanol and ethanol (12-1).[48] The conversion of the monoalkoxy derivative to the di-

$$ROH + BF_3 \rightarrow ROBF_2 + HF \qquad (12\text{-}1)$$

alkoxy derivative was accomplished by treatment with a sodium alcoholate (12-2). Redistribution reactions involving boron tri-

$$ROBF_2 + NaOR \rightarrow (RO)_2BF + NaF \qquad (12\text{-}2)$$

fluoride and trimethoxyborane or triethoxyborane also were recorded.

$$BF_3 + 2\,(RO)_3B \rightarrow 3\,(RO)_2BF \qquad (12\text{-}3)$$

$$2\,BF_3 + (RO)_3B \rightarrow 3\,ROBF_2 \qquad (12\text{-}4)$$

The first alkoxychloroboranes were prepared by Wiberg and coworkers in 1930 by cleavage of ethers with boron trichloride (12-5)[112,130] or by alcoholysis of boron trichloride (12-6 and 12-7).[129]

$$R_2O + BCl_3 \rightarrow R_2O{:}BCl_3 \xrightarrow{\Delta} ROBCl_2 + RCl \qquad (12\text{-}5)$$

$$ROH + BCl_3 \rightarrow ROBCl_2 + HCl \qquad (12\text{-}6)$$

$$2\,ROH + BCl_3 \rightarrow (RO)_2BCl + 2\,HCl \qquad (12\text{-}7)$$

III. PROPERTIES

A. General

The alkoxy- and aryloxyhaloboranes are colorless liquids or solids[13,112,118,130] which fume in air[1,13,48,85,99,115,118] and burn with a green flame.[48] 2-Chloro-1,3,2-dioxaborinane rapidly darkens on storage.[42] Recorded solubilities are summarized in Table 12-1.

Table 12-1. Solubilities of alkoxyhaloboranes and related compounds

	Water	Meth-anol	Ethanol	Ace-tone	Ether	Ben-zene	Methylene chloride	Chloro-form	n-Pentane	n-Hexane	Hydro-carbons	Pet. ether	Ref.
$\underline{ROBX_2}$													
CH_3OBF_2		S	S								I		48
						S				S			96
$C_2H_5OBF_2$						S				S			96
$(C_2H_5)_2O \cdot 2\ C_2H_5OBCl_2$					VS								112
$CH_2{=}CHCH_2OBCl_2{:}C_5H_5N$	SS												56
$Cl(CH_2)_4OBCl_2{:}C_5H_5N$	S												38
$CH_3\overset{O}{\overset{\|}{C}}CH{=}\underset{CH_3}{\underset{\|}{C}}OBF_2$						VS						I	107
$C_6H_5\overset{O}{\overset{\|}{C}}CH{=}\underset{C_6H_5}{\underset{\|}{C}}OBF_2$						SS						I	107
$\underline{(RO)_2BX}$													
$(CH_3O)_2BF$											I		48
$[(C_2H_5)_3SiO]_2BBr$						S							126
$(ClCH_2CH_2O)_2BCl$			S		S								91
$(CH_2{=}CHCH_2O)_2BCl{:}C_5H_5N$									I				56

$HOC_6H_4O[B(Cl)OC_6H_4O]_9H$ (m-phenylene)	S	I	I		I	I	54
$(CH_2O)_2BCl$ (cyclic, B—Cl)		I		S			13

VS = Very soluble, S = Soluble, SS = Slightly soluble, I = Insoluble.

B. Structure

1. ALKOXYCHLOROBORANES AND HALOSILOXYBORANES

Alkoxydichloroboranes[112, 127, 128, 129, 130] and dialkoxychloroboranes[127,128,129] have been shown to be monomeric in the vapor state. Chlorinated alkoxychloroboranes were found to be monomeric in cyclohexane solution.[1] A variety of halosiloxyboranes also were shown to be monomeric in the vapor state[41] and in benzene solution.[99,126]

2. ALKOXYFLUOROBORANES

Gasselin, the earliest worker in the field, formulated the methoxy and ethoxy derivatives as monomeric (XII)[48] on the basis of vapor

$$ROBF_2$$
(XII)

phase data. Mass spectral data corroborated the monomeric form in the gas phase.[134] These observations, of course, did not preclude higher states of aggregation in condensed states, and subsequently the dimeric formula with bridged fluorine atoms (XIII) was pro-

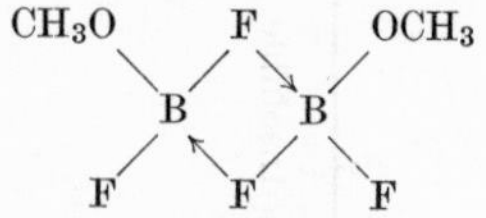

```
CH3O     F      OCH3
    \   / \↘   /
     B         B
    / ↖ \   /   \
   F      F      F
```
(XIII)

posed to explain the abnormal parachor value for liquid difluoro(methoxy)borane.[2]

A more complete picture of the structural relationships of the fluoro(methoxy)boranes, based on vapor pressure data and Raman spectra, showed difluoro(methoxy)borane to be dimeric below 75°. In addition, fluorodimethoxyborane was shown to exist only in the gaseous state, disproportionating to the difluoro derivative on condensation (12-8). The dimer (XIV) was formulated as an addition compound involving the unshared pairs of electrons on the oxygen atoms and the electron deficient boron atoms.[64,65]

The monobutoxy derivative subsequently was shown by cryoscopic measurements in cyclohexane to be dimeric in the liquid state and was formulated with bridged oxygens as in (XIV).[87]

Recent cryoscopic molecular weight determinations for methoxy-, ethoxy- and butoxydifluoroboranes in benzene and cyclohexane solution indicated trimeric compositions. On the basis of electric dipole moments, molar refractions, distillation characteristics, and reactions with ammonia and pyridine they were formulated as the addition compounds (XV)[96] and not the simple trimers (XVI).[95] The ethoxy derivative was monomeric in dioxane as evidenced by its cryoscopic molecular weight in that solvent.[96]

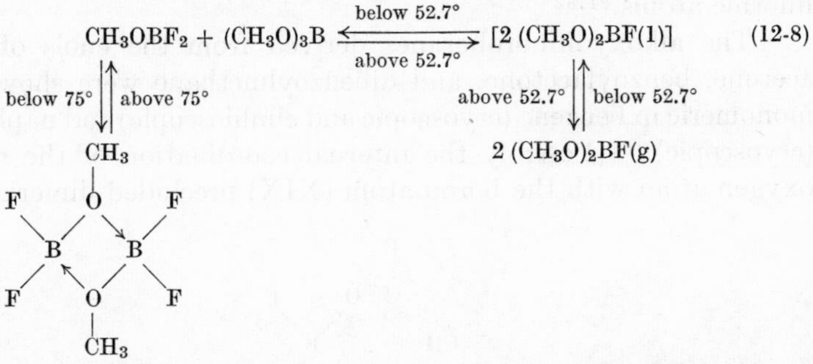

$$CH_3OBF_2 + (CH_3O)_3B \underset{\text{above } 52.7°}{\overset{\text{below } 52.7°}{\rightleftarrows}} [2\,(CH_3O)_2BF(l)] \quad (12\text{-}8)$$

below 75° / above 75° (between CH_3OBF_2 and XIV); above 52.7° / below 52.7° (between $[2\,(CH_3O)_2BF(l)]$ and $2\,(CH_3O)_2BF(g)$)

$$2\,(CH_3O)_2BF(g)$$

(XIV) — dimer: two F_2B groups bridged by two O–CH_3 groups

$$\underset{(XV)}{(RO)_3B\cdot 2BF_3} \qquad \underset{(XVI)}{(ROBF_2)_3}$$

More recently [11]B nuclear magnetic resonance shifts of the compounds in question revealed only one type of boron in an apparently tetrahedral environment. In addition, redistribution of ethoxydifluoroborane and [10]B enriched boron trifluoride was found to take place more rapidly than in the boron trifluoride–boron trifluoride etherate system, and the triethoxyborane liberated after removing the exchanged boron trifluoride was enriched in [10]B.[82]

$$(C_2H_5O)_3B\cdot 2BF_3 + {}^{10}BF_3 \xrightarrow[\text{Room temp.}]{\text{5 min.}} (C_2H_5O)_3B\cdot 2BF_3 + BF_3 \quad (12\text{-}9)$$

$(C_2H_5O)_3B\cdot 2BF_3$: 80% ^{11}B, 20% ^{10}B; $^{10}BF_3$: 17.9% ^{11}B, 82.1% ^{10}B; product: 54.0% ^{11}B, 46.0% ^{10}B

$$\xrightarrow{2\,C_5H_5N} (C_2H_5O)_3B + 2\,C_5H_5N{:}BF_3$$

65% ^{11}B, 35% ^{10}B

These data would tend to rule out the $(RO)_3B\cdot 2BF_3$ formulation, which is best represented as in structure (XVII), and are consistent with the boroxine-like trimer (XVIII). It was felt that analogous

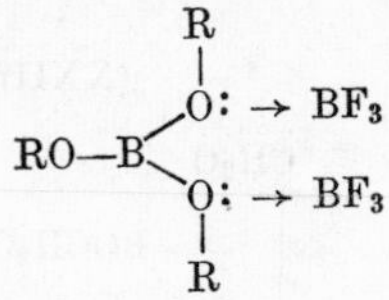

$$RO{-}B\begin{cases}\overset{R}{|}\,O{:} \rightarrow BF_3\\ O{:} \rightarrow BF_3\,\underset{R}{|}\end{cases}$$

(XVII)

(XVIII) — six-membered ring of alternating BF_2 and O–R units

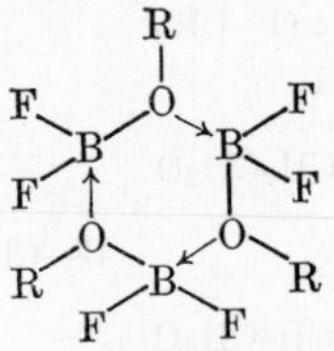

(XVIII)

trimers in the chlorine series, $(ROBCl_2)_3$, were precluded due to the greater steric requirements of the chlorine atoms as compared to the fluorine atoms.[81,82]

The alkoxydifluoroboranes derived from the enols of acetylacetone, benzoylacetone, and dibenzoylmethane were shown to be monomeric in benzene (cryoscopic and ebullioscopic) and naphthalene (cryoscopic).[107] Possibly the internal coordination of the carbonyl oxygen atom with the boron atom (XIX) precluded dimerization.

```
        R
        |
        C=O     F
       /    ↘  /
    CH        B
      \\    /  \
        C—O     F
        |
        R′
```

(XIX)

3. 2-CHLORO-1,3,2-DIOXABOROLANES AND BORINANES

The extremely viscous nature of (XX) as well as its high boiling

```
    CH2—O
    |     \
    |      BCl
    |     /
    CH2—O
```

(XX)

point (74° at 1 mm.) indicated a high degree of association in the liquid phase. This was borne out by a cryoscopic molecular weight determination of 209 in benzene (monomer = 107, dimer = 213).[22] A plausible structure for the dimer is (XXI) although evidence is not available to unequivocally rule out (XXII) to (XXIV).[22]

```
CH2—O     Cl
|     \  /
|      B
|     / ↖
CH2—O     O—CH2
      ↘  /
       B
      /  \
    Cl    O—CH2
```

(XXI)

```
CH2—O     Cl      O—CH2
|     \  /  ↘   /    |
|      B      B      |
|     / ↖   /  \     |
CH2—O     Cl      O—CH2
```

(XXII)

```
        OCH2CH2O
       /        \
  Cl—B            B—Cl
       \        /
        OCH2CH2O
```

(XXIII)

```
CH2O
|    \
|     BOCH2CH2OBCl2
|    /
CH2O
```

(XXIV)

In contrast to the dimeric nature of (XX), the dioxaborinane (XXV) exhibits a monomeric molecular weight in benzene.[22]

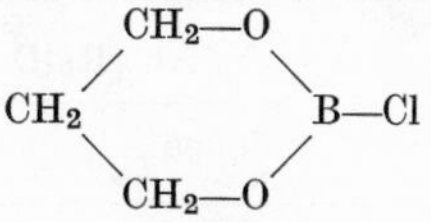

CH₂—O
CH₂ B—Cl
CH₂—O
(XXV)

More information is needed on the conformations of the 1,3,2-dioxaborolane and 1,3,2-dioxaborinane rings before any rational explanation can be given for the dimerization of the five- and not of the six-membered ring.

The absence of an absorption band for (XXVI) in the infrared region normally associated with the B–Cl bond was attributed to contribution of the canonical structure (XXVII).[16]

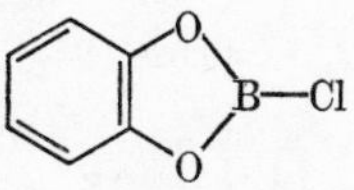

O
B—Cl
O
(XXVI)

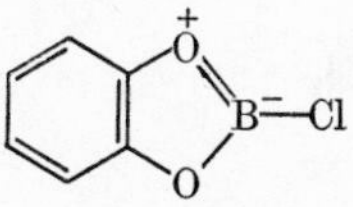

+
O
B̄—Cl
O
(XXVII)

4. OXYBIS(ACETOXYCHLOROBORANE)

The long wavelength carbonyl stretching band of oxybis(acetoxychloroborane) (6.30 μ) has been attributed to intramolecular coordination of the carbonyl oxygen atoms and the boron atoms (XXVIII or XXIX, see Chapter 8).[36]

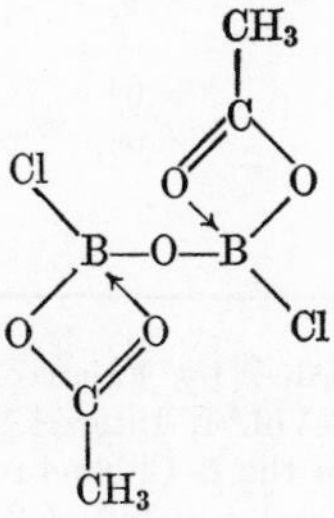

CH₃
C
Cl O O
B—O—B
O O Cl
C
CH₃
(XXVIII)

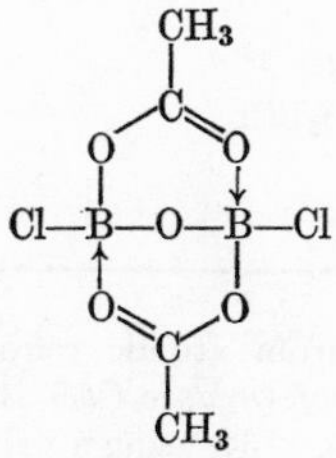

CH₃
C
O O
Cl—B—O—B—Cl
O O
C
CH₃
(XXIX)

C. Molecular Refractivities

Molar refractivity data for a variety of alkoxychloro and chlorosiloxyboranes appear to be in good agreement with the calculated

Table 12-2. Molecular refractivities

	$[R_L]D$ Found	$[R_L]D$ Calc.	Reference
$ROBCl_2$			
$n\text{-}C_3H_7OBCl_2$	30.62	31.46[a]	27
$Cl(CH_2)_3OBCl_2$	35.9	35.8[b]	1
$n\text{-}C_4H_9OBCl_2$	36.02	36.09[a]	27
$i\text{-}C_4H_9OBCl_2$	36.54	36.00[a]	27
$Cl(CH_2)_4OBCl_2$	40.74	40.90[a]	27
$n\text{-}C_5H_{11}OBCl_2$	40.2	40.2[b]	1
$(CH_3)_3CCH_2OBCl_2$	40.52	40.60[a]	27
$Cl(CH_2)_5OBCl_2$	44.7	45.1[b]	1
$n\text{-}C_8H_{17}OBCl_2$	53.87	54.61[a]	27
$(CH_3)_2SiOBCl_2$ (Si–Cl)	40.43	39.76[c]	99
$(C_2H_5)_2SiOBCl_2$ (Si–Cl)	48.67	49.02[c]	99
$(RO)_2BCl$			
$(n\text{-}C_3H_7O)_2BCl$	41.8	41.8[d]	88
$[Cl(CH_2)_3O]_2BCl$	51.1	51.4[b]	1
$(n\text{-}C_4H_9O)_2BCl$	51.0	51.0[d]	88
$(i\text{-}C_4H_9O)_2BCl$	50.6	51.0[d]	88
$(s\text{-}C_4H_9O)_2BCl$	50.7	51.0[d]	88
$[Cl(CH_2)_4O]_2BCl$	60.6	60.6[b]	1
$(n\text{-}C_5H_{11}O)_2BCl$	59.8	60.3[b]	1
$[(CH_3)_3CCH_2O]_2BCl$	60.2	60.3[d]	88
$[Cl(CH_2)_5O]_2BCl$	70.5	69.9[b]	1
$[(CH_3)_3CCHO]_2BCl$ (C–CH_3)	69.3	69.5[d]	88
$(n\text{-}C_8H_{17}O)_2BCl$	88.7	88.0[d]	88
$(n\text{-}C_6H_{13}CHO)_2BCl$ (C–CH_3)	87.3	88.0[d]	88

[a] Calculated from atomic refractivities recorded by Fajans in Weissberger, A., *Physical Methods of Organic Chemistry*, 2nd Ed., Vol. 1, Interscience Publishers, Inc., New York, 1949, p. 1164, using a value of 6.98[94] for the B–Cl bond refraction.

[b] Based on atomic refractivities of Vogel[122] and a value of 2.65[88] for the atomic refractivity of boron.

[c] Calculated from Warrick's data for silicon compounds,[123] a 1.67[109] value for the B–O bond refraction calculated from data on tri-n-butoxy and tri-n-pentoxyborane, and a value of 6.98[94] for the B–Cl bond refraction derived from data on n-amyldichloroborane and dichloro-(n-hexyl)borane.

[d] Derived from carbon, hydrogen, oxygen and chlorine atomic refractivities of Eisenlohr[40] and an average value for boron of 2.65 calculated from Cowley and Partington[34] and Arbuzov and Vinogradova.[5]

values (Table 12-2). Equations for molar refraction as a function of the number of carbon atoms in the alkyl group are recorded in Table 12-3.[26]

Table 12-3. Molar refraction of alkoxydichloro- and dialkoxychloroboranes as a function of the number of carbon atoms, n, in the alkyl group

Compound	$R_{obsd.}$
$ROBCl_2$	$4.57n + 17.47$
$(RO)_2BCl$	$9.22n + 14.05$
$Cl(CH_2)_nOBCl_2$	$4.42n + 22.83$
$[Cl(CH_2)_nO]_2BCl$	$9.71n + 22.06$

D. Nuclear Magnetic Resonance Data

^{11}B nuclear magnetic resonance chemical shifts for some ethoxy derivatives are recorded in Table 12-4.

Table 12-4. Nuclear magnetic resonance chemical shifts[a]

	δ	Reference
$C_2H_5OBCl_2$	-23.3 ± 1.0	108
$(C_2H_5O)_2BCl$	-32.5 ± 1.0	108
$(C_2H_5O)_2BBr$	-18.5	82

[a] $(C_2H_5)_2O{:}BF_3$, $\delta = 0$.

E. Bond Energies

It was determined from the heats of hydrolysis of BCl_3, $C_2H_5OBCl_2$, $(C_2H_5O)_2BCl$ and $(C_2H_5O)_3B$ that the bond-energy term values of the B–Cl and B–O bonds in the chloro(ethoxy)boranes are not constant. The molecules $C_2H_5OBCl_2$ and $(C_2H_5O)_2BCl$ are more stable by 4.8 and 4.0 kcal/mole, respectively, than would be the case if the bonds had the same energies as B–Cl in BCl_3 and as B–O in $B(OC_2H_5)_3$.[116]

A molecular-orbital treatment of the back coordination in the chloro(ethoxy)boranes indicated that the oxygen atoms are appreciably more effective in donating their unbonded pair of electrons to boron than are the chlorine atoms.[116]

IV. ALKOXY- AND ARYLOXYDIHALOBORANES

A. Methods of Preparation

1. INTRODUCTION

Most of the recorded preparations of alkoxy and aryloxydihaloboranes have utilized boron halides as the source of the halogen. In some instances, such as reactions with alcohols and ethers, the boron halide is the sole source of boron. In other instances, such as reactions with trialkoxyboranes and trialkoxyboroxines, the boron halide is a partial source of boron.

2. FROM BORON TRIHALIDES

a. *And Alcohols, Glycols and Phenols.* Primary alkyl[51,53,129] and ω-chloroalkyl[37] derivatives have been prepared by an equimolar reaction of boron trichloride and the appropriate alcohol at room temperature or below (12-10). Evidence was obtained at −80°

$$BCl_3 + ROH \rightarrow ROBCl_2 + HCl \qquad (12\text{-}10)$$

for the preparation of the secondary alkyl derivatives, dichloro(isopropoxy)borane[53] and *s*-butoxydichloroborane.[51]

Attempts to prepare carbethoxy substituted alkoxydichloroboranes (XXX) from the reaction of boron trichloride with various

$$C_2H_5O\overset{\overset{\displaystyle O}{\|}}{C}CH_2OBCl_2$$
(XXX)

hydroxy esters were unsuccessful, presumably due to concomitant acyl–oxygen cleavage of the carbethoxy group (12-11, see Section IV-A-2h).[44]

$$HOCH_2\overset{\overset{\displaystyle O}{\|}}{C}OC_2H_5 + BCl_3 \rightarrow HOCH_2\overset{\overset{\displaystyle O}{\|}}{C}Cl + C_2H_5OBCl_2 \qquad (12\text{-}11)$$

Boron trifluoride is alcoholized by the lower alcohols (12-12),[48,134] by enolizable diketones (see Section IV-A-2f),[107] and by methyl salicylate (12-13).[106] These data contradict the statement that this

$$BF_3 + ROH \rightarrow ROBF_2 + HF \qquad (12\text{-}12)$$

$$BF_3 + o\text{-}HOC_6H_4\overset{\overset{\displaystyle O}{\|}}{C}OCH_3 \rightarrow o\text{-}F_2BOC_6H_4\overset{\overset{\displaystyle O}{\|}}{C}OCH_3 + HF \qquad (12\text{-}13)$$

method of preparation of alkoxydifluoroboranes is precluded by formation of the complexes $BF_3{:}ROH$ and $BF_3{:}2ROH$.[87]

Dibromo(methoxy)borane was produced by the methanolysis of boron tribromide. Unlike the chloro and fluoro derivatives, it is unstable and decomposes to give methyl bromide, boron tribromide and boric oxide.[63]* Dibromo(butoxy)borane prepared from butanol and boron tribromide behaved similarly.[25]

$$BBr_3 + CH_3OH \rightarrow HBr + \{CH_3OBBr_2\} \qquad (12\text{-}14)$$

$$\{CH_3OBBr_2\} \rightarrow CH_3Br + \{Br{-}B{=}O\} \qquad (12\text{-}15)$$

$$\{BrB{=}O\} \rightarrow \tfrac{1}{3}\,BBr_3 + \tfrac{1}{3}\,B_2O_3 \qquad (12\text{-}16)$$

The equimolar reaction of phenol and boron trichloride resulted in a quantitative yield of hydrogen chloride based on reaction 12-17;

$$C_6H_5OH + BCl_3 \rightarrow C_6H_5OBCl_2 + HCl \qquad (12\text{-}17)$$

however, the dichlorophenoxyborane was too unstable to isolate.[28] Similar attempts to prepare aryloxydichloroboranes from *p*-nitrophenol, *o*-chlorophenol and *o*-cresol led to unstable products which disproportionated at 20°.[29] Dichloro-(*o*-nitrophenoxy)borane, however, is inordinately stable and did not disproportionate or decompose when heated at 100°. The stability is attributed to intramolecular complexing of the boron atom (XXXI).[29] Similar chelation has

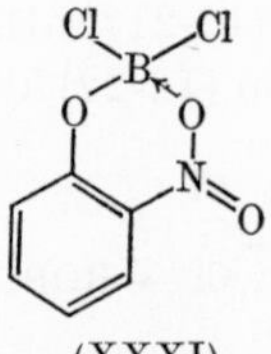

(XXXI)

been postulated to explain the abnormally weak acidity of *o*-nitrobenzeneboronic acid.[12] *o*-Nitrophenol also reacts with the acetonitrile complex of boron trichloride to produce (XXXI).[59]

Attempts to prepare the hindered phenolic derivative (XXXII) from 2,6-di-*t*-butylphenol and boron trichloride were unsuccessful.[118] (See Section IV-A-2b).

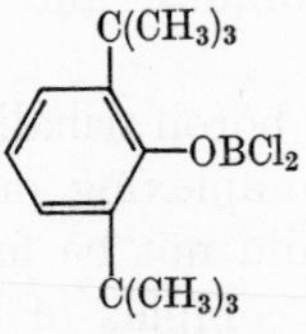

(XXXII)

* The residue from the decomposition was formulated as B_3O_4Br, but it probably was boric oxide contaminated with a bromine-containing impurity.

The reaction of resorcinol with two moles of boron trichloride in methylene chloride solution was claimed to yield a trinuclear product which was formulated as arising via disproportionation of an intermediate bis(dichloroboryloxy) derivative.[54]

$$1,3\text{-}C_6H_4(OH)_2 + 2\ BCl_3 \rightarrow \{1,3\text{-}C_6H_4(OBCl_2)_2\} + 2\ HCl \qquad (12\text{-}18)$$

$$\{1,3\text{-}C_6H_4(OBCl_2)_2\} \rightarrow \tfrac{1}{3}\ Cl_2BOC_6H_4\text{—}OB(Cl)O\text{—}C_6H_4\text{—}OB(Cl)O\text{—}C_6H_4OBCl_2 + \tfrac{2}{3}\ BCl_3 \qquad (12\text{-}19)$$

Ethylene glycol and boron trichloride result in a similar bis(dichloroboryl) derivative.[14,15]

$$HOCH_2CH_2OH + 2\ BCl_3 \rightarrow Cl_2BOCH_2CH_2OBCl_2 + 4\ HCl \qquad (12\text{-}20)$$

The mechanism of the alcoholysis reaction was postulated to be four-centered and concerted (12-21) rather than a two-stage process with initial complex formation (12-22).[51] This is in contrast to earlier

$$R\text{—}O(H)\cdots Cl\text{—}BCl_2 \rightarrow ROBCl_2 + HCl \qquad (12\text{-}21)$$

$$ROH + BCl_3 \rightarrow R(H)O\rightarrow BCl_3 \rightarrow ROBCl_2 + HCl \qquad (12\text{-}22)$$

statements that the equimolar reaction of boron trichloride and an alcohol proceeds through a 1:1 complex and thus accounts for the absence of dialkoxyhaloboranes and trialkoxyboranes in the product.[131]

Prior complexing of the boron trihalide with an amine evidently can preclude subsequent complexing or reaction with an alcohol since alkoxyhaloboranes could not be formed from (XXXIII) and an alcohol.[131] The pyridine complex of boron trichloride, however,

$$(CH_3)_3N{:}BCl_3$$

(XXXIII)

did react with a variety of alcohols on prolonged refluxing in chloroform solution to give the pyridine complex of the alkoxydihaloborane.[86]

$$C_4H_9OH + C_5H_5N\!:\!BCl_3 \rightarrow HCl + C_4H_9OBCl_2\!:\!C_5H_5N \qquad (12\text{-}23)$$

The mechanisms proposed[86] for the alcoholysis of the amine complex appear to be inadequate. An S_N2 displacement of chloride by alcohol seems unlikely in view of the necessity of a quinquevalent boron atom in the transition state (XXXIV). An S_N1 pre-ionization

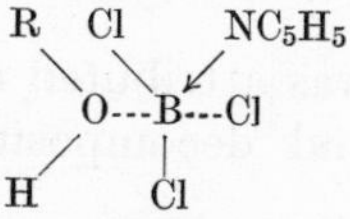

```
R   Cl      NC5H5
 \   \     /
  O---B---Cl
 /    |
H     Cl
```

(XXXIV)

(12-24) in chloroform solution seems energetically unfavorable.

$$C_5H_5N\!:\!BCl_3 \rightarrow C_5H_5N\!:\!BCl_2^+ + Cl^- \qquad (12\text{-}24)$$

Possibly all that is involved is a simple prior dissociation of the pyridine complex in refluxing chloroform followed by reaction of the liberated boron trichloride with the alcohol.

$$C_5H_5N\!:\!BCl_3 \rightleftarrows C_5H_5N + BCl_3 \qquad (12\text{-}25)$$

$$BCl_3 + ROH \rightleftarrows ROH\!:\!BCl_3 \qquad (12\text{-}26)$$

$$ROH\!:\!BCl_3 \rightarrow \text{products} \qquad (12\text{-}27)$$

b. *And Sodium Phenoxides.* The hindered phenolic derivative (XXXV), which could not be prepared from the reaction of boron trichloride with 2,6-di-*t*-butylphenol, was obtained in good yield from the reaction of boron chloride with the corresponding sodium salt (XXXVI) in toluene solution at $-60°$.[118]

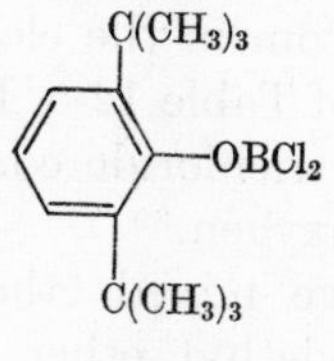

$C(CH_3)_3$ — $OBCl_2$ — $C(CH_3)_3$

(XXXV)

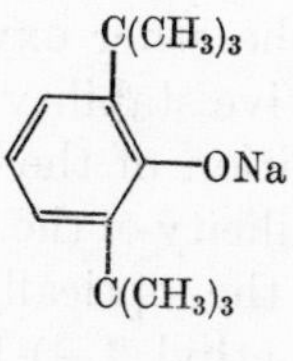

$C(CH_3)_3$ — ONa — $C(CH_3)_3$

(XXXVI)

c. *And Ethers.* The boron trichloride cleavage of ethers often precludes their use as solvents for boron halide reactions.[24] The reaction (12-28), however, does offer a means of preparing alkoxydihaloboranes.[57,91,112]

$$ROR + BCl_3 \rightarrow ROBCl_2 + RCl \qquad (12\text{-}28)$$

In some instances, the intermediate ether complex (XXXVII) is isolated and converted to the alkoxydihaloborane by heating at

$$R_2O\!:\!BCl_3$$
(XXXVII)

moderate temperatures.[39,91,112] However, the complex of chloromethyl ether did not afford the dichloro(chloroalkoxy)borane on pyrolysis but reacted according to equation (12-29).[39] The origin

$$6\ ClCH_2OCH_3\!:\!BCl_3 \rightarrow 6\ CH_3Cl + 3\ (ClCH_2)_2O + 4\ BCl_3 + B_2O_3 \qquad (12\text{-}29)$$

of the symmetrical ether was attributed to the intermediate formation (12-30 and 12-31) and decomposition (12-32) of tri(chloromethoxy)borane.[39] The formation of an ether from an alkoxyborane is a rare event in born chemistry.[45,92]

$$6\ ClCH_2OCH_3\!:\!BCl_3 \rightarrow 6\ CH_3Cl + 6\ ClCH_2OBCl_2 \qquad (12\text{-}30)$$

$$6\ ClCH_2OBCl_2 \rightarrow 4\ BCl_3 + 2\ (ClCH_2O)_3B \qquad (12\text{-}31)$$

$$2\ (ClCH_2O)_3B \rightarrow B_2O_3 + 3\ ClCH_2OCH_2Cl \qquad (12\text{-}32)$$

Bischloromethyl ether did not react with boron trichloride up to the reflux temperature. The inertness was attributed to a lowered electron density on the ether oxygen atom due to electron withdrawal by the chlorine atoms.[39] Similar reasoning was offered for the unreactivity of diphenyl ether* (XXXVIII) towards boron trichloride.[28]

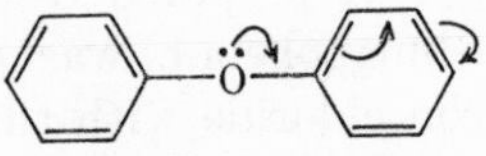

(XXXVIII)

The role of the ether oxygen atom in the cleavage reaction is shown in the relative stability data of Table 12-5. It is seen that the ease of decomposition of the boron trichloride complexes increases with the nucleophilicity of the ether oxygen.[39]

Cleavage of the optically active mixed ethers, ethyl (+)-2-octyl ether and ethyl (−)-1-phenylethyl ether, with boron trichloride results in the formation of dichloro(ethoxy)borane in excellent yield. Concomitant formation of (−)-2-chlorooctane of greatly reduced activity and totally racemized 1-chloro-1-phenylethane is observed.[50] The proposed mechanism assumed heterolytic cleavage

* In contrast to other ethers, diphenyl ether does not form a complex with boron trifluoride.[20,103]

Table 12-5. Relative stability of ether–boron trichloride complexes

Time	% Decomposition					
	20°			100°		
	$CH_3OCH_2CH_2Cl:BCl_3$	$C_2H_5OCH_2CH_2Cl:BCl_3$	$(n\text{-}C_4H_9)_2O:BCl_3$	$(ClCH_2CH_2)_2O:BCl_3$	$CH_3OCH_2CH_2Cl:BCl_3$	$C_2H_5OCH_2CH_2Cl:BCl_3$
(min.)						
2			12			
2.25			12			
2.5				18		
4.98					100	100
9				37		
19.25			63			
24				61		
25.25			91			
62				77		
(hr.)						
1.75		65				
2.92				90		
20.1	40					
29.0	75					
41.75	85					
68.1	100					

between oxygen and the alkyl group leading to the most stable carbonium ion.[50,52]

$$(C_6H_5)(CH_3)CHOC_2H_5 + BCl_3 \rightarrow (C_6H_5)(CH_3)CH\text{—}\underset{C_2H_5}{O}:\rightarrow BCl_3 \rightarrow C_2H_5OBCl_2 + C_6H_5\overset{+}{C}HCH_3 + Cl^- \quad (12\text{-}33)$$

$$C_6H_5\overset{+}{C}HCH_3 + Cl^- \rightarrow C_6H_5CHCl(CH_3) \quad (12\text{-}34)$$

The retention of some activity in the 2-chlorooctane was attributed to a portion of the reaction proceeding through an S_Ni mechanism (XXXIX).

$$C_6H_{13}CH(CH_3)\text{—}\underset{\downarrow}{\ddot{O}}\text{—}C_2H_5 \quad Cl\text{—}B(Cl)\text{—}Cl$$

(XXXIX)

In general the cleavage of mixed ethers involves fission of the

Table 12-6. Fission products of boron trichloride and mixed ethers

Ether	Fission products		Reference
	$ROBCl_2$	RCl	
n-C_4H_9, i-C_4H_9	n-$C_4H_9OBCl_2$	i-C_4H_9Cl + *t*-C_4H_9Cl	52
n-C_4H_9, *s*-C_4H_9	n-$C_4H_9OBCl_2$	*s*-C_4H_9Cl	52
n-C_4H_9, *t*-C_4H_9	n-C_4H_9OBCl	*t*-C_4H_9Cl	52
i-C_4H_9, *s*-C_4H_9	i-$C_4H_9OBCl_2$	*s*-C_4H_9Cl	52
i-C_4H_9, *t*-C_4H_9	i-$C_4H_9OBCl_2$	*t*-C_4H_9Cl	52
C_2H_5, n-C_8H_{17}	$C_2H_5OBCl_2$	n-$C_8H_{17}Cl$	52
C_2H_5, *s*-C_8H_{17}	$C_2H_5OBCl_2$	*s*-$C_8H_{17}Cl$	52
C_2H_5, $C_6H_5CH_2CH_2$	$C_2H_5OBCl_2$	$C_6H_5CH_2CH_2Cl$	52
CH_3, C_6H_5	$C_6H_5OBCl_2$	—	52
C_2H_5, C_6H_5	$C_6H_5OBCl_2$	—	52
CH_3, CH_2CH_2Cl	$ClCH_2CH_2OBCl_2$	CH_3Cl	39
C_2H_5, CH_2CH_2Cl	$ClCH_2CH_2OBCl_2$	C_2H_5Cl	39
$CH_2{=}CHCH_2$, α-tocopheryl	α-tocopherol (after hydrolysis)	—	66
n-C_3H_7, α-tocopheryl	α-tocopherol (after hydrolysis)	—	66
n-C_4H_9, $CH_2{=}CHCH_2$	n-$C_4H_9OBCl_2$	—	57

oxygen-alkyl bond involving that alkyl group with the greatest $+I$ effect. This is shown by the results in Table 12-6 for the equimolar reaction of boron trichloride with a series of mixed ethers. In addition, it is evident from the formation of dichloro(phenoxy)-borane in the cleavage of anisole and phenetole, and the production of α-tocopherol in the cleavage of the allyl and n-propyl tocopheryl ethers, that the phenyl group promotes the transformation (XL).

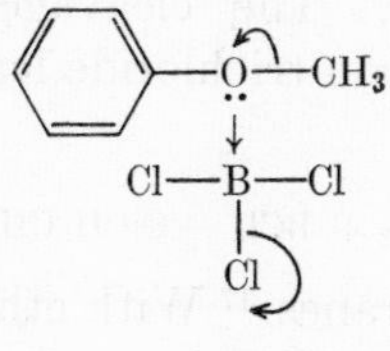

$$C_6H_5-\ddot{O}-CH_3 \quad \downarrow \quad Cl-B(Cl)-Cl$$

(XL)

Of further significance, it is seen that the cleavage of n-butyl isobutyl ether produces some *t*-butyl chloride from rearrangement of the isobutyl to the *t*-butyl carbonium ion.

Cleavage of ethers with boron trichloride for synthetic purposes other than the preparation of alkoxy or aryloxyhaloboranes has been reported. Thus, the *p*-hydroxy group in the sequence (12-35) was

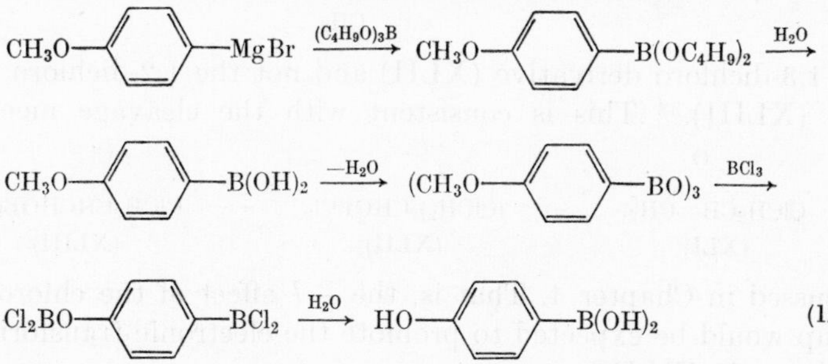

$$CH_3O-C_6H_4-MgBr \xrightarrow{(C_4H_9O)_3B} CH_3O-C_6H_4-B(OC_4H_9)_2 \xrightarrow{H_2O}$$

$$CH_3O-C_6H_4-B(OH)_2 \xrightarrow{-H_2O} (CH_3O-C_6H_4-BO)_3 \xrightarrow{BCl_3}$$

$$Cl_2BO-C_6H_4-BCl_2 \xrightarrow{H_2O} HO-C_6H_4-B(OH)_2 \qquad (12\text{-}35)$$

protected as the methyl ether which was subsequently cleaved with boron chloride.[35] In addition, methylated sugars, with the exception of fructose, are degraded to the parent sugar on treatment with boron trichloride and subsequent methanolysis or hydrolysis of the dichloroboryl derivative.[3,17] Methyl α-D-fructofuranoside was converted to 5-hydroxymethylfurfuraldehyde.[17]

Cleavage of ethers with boron tribromide to give alkoxydibromoboranes has not been reported. However, this does not mean that cleavage with boron tribromide is not possible since reaction (12-36) has been reported (see Chapter 4).[11]

$$3\,ROR + BBr_3 \rightarrow (RO)_3B + 3\,RBr \qquad (12\text{-}36)$$

Cleavages with boron trifluoride to give alkoxyfluoroboranes in general have not been recorded. However, the feasibility of the reaction is demonstrated in the thermal decomposition of the isopropyl ether–boron trifluoride complex at 50–68° (12-37).[23]

$$(i\text{-}C_3H_7)_2O{:}BF_3 \rightarrow i\text{-}C_3H_7OBF_2 + i\text{-}C_3H_7F \qquad (12\text{-}37)$$

Presumably the formation of stable complexes, $R_2O{:}BF_3$, precludes this path as a general method for producing $ROBF_2$ compounds.[87]

d. *And Cyclic Ethers.* The cleavage of cyclic ethers with equimolar quantities of boron trichloride leads to the preparation of

$$\overset{O}{\overbrace{CH_2\text{—}CH_2}} + BCl_3 \rightarrow ClCH_2CH_2OBCl_2 \qquad (12\text{-}38)$$

dichloro-ω-chloroalkoxyboranes.[37] With ethylene oxide, the reaction proceeds to the chloroethoxy derivative.*

$$2\ ROBCl_2 \rightleftarrows (RO)_2BCl + BCl_3$$

With propylene oxide, the electronic and steric influences of the methyl group apparently are not definitive and both possible products result (12-39).[38] In contrast, epichlorohydrin (XLI) afforded

$$2\ CH_3\overset{O}{\overbrace{CH\text{—}CH_2}} + 2\ BCl_3 \rightarrow ClCH_2\underset{CH_3}{\underset{|}{C}}HOBCl_2 + CH_3\overset{Cl}{\overset{|}{C}}HCH_2OBCl_2 \qquad (12\text{-}39)$$

the 1,3-dichloro derivative (XLII) and not the 1,2-dichloro derivative (XLIII).[38] This is consistent with the cleavage mechanism

$$ClCH_2\overset{O}{\overbrace{CH\text{—}CH_2}} \quad (XLI) \qquad (ClCH_2)_2CHOBCl_2 \quad (XLII) \qquad ClCH_2\overset{Cl}{\overset{|}{C}}HCHOBCl_2 \quad (XLIII)$$

discussed in Chapter 4. That is, the $-I$ effect of the chloromethyl group would be expected to promote the electronic transformations as shown in (XLIV).

$$\begin{array}{c} Cl \\ | \\ Cl\text{—}B\text{—}Cl \\ \vdots \\ O \\ ClCH_2CH\text{—}CH_2 \end{array}$$

(XLIV)

* A 1:1 addition product of ethylene oxide and boron trichloride which decomposed reversibly in the range 0–90° had been reported earlier;[67] however, it was felt that the product actually was the isomeric $ClCH_2CH_2OBCl_2$ which subsequently underwent reversible disproportionation in the temperature cycle.[37]

The equimolar reaction of trimethylene oxide and boron trichloride at $-80°$ produced a 51% yield of a product with an analysis consistent with (XLV).[38]

$$ClCH_2CH_2CH_2OBCl_2$$
(XLV)

An insoluble 1:1 complex is obtained with tetrahydrofuran at $-80°$ in pentane solution; this is converted to the chlorobutoxy derivative when heated at reduced pressure (12-40).[37] In addition,

$$C_4H_8O + BCl_3 \rightarrow C_4H_8O{:}BCl_3 \xrightarrow[1\text{–}2\ mm.]{100\text{–}120°} Cl(CH_2)_4OBCl_2 \quad (12\text{-}40)$$

the reaction mixture is contaminated with 1,4-dichlorobutane resulting from subsequent partial decomposition of the product.

$$Cl(CH_2)_4OBCl_2 \rightarrow Cl(CH_2)_4Cl + \tfrac{1}{3}\,BCl_3 + \tfrac{1}{3}\,B_2O_3 \quad (12\text{-}41)$$

Reactions (12-40) and (12-41) are in contrast to the reported evolution of hydrogen chloride and boron trichloride from the reaction of tetrahydrofuran and boron trichloride via scheme (12-42).[67]

$$C_4H_8O{:}BCl_3 \rightarrow \{\overset{+}{C}H_2CH_2CH_2CH_2O\overset{-}{B}Cl_3\} \rightarrow CH_2{=}CHCH_2CH_2OH + BCl_3 \rightarrow$$
$$\tfrac{1}{3}\,(CH_2{=}CHCH_2CH_2O)_3B + \tfrac{2}{3}\,BCl_3 + HCl \quad (12\text{-}42)$$

A facile cleavage of the tetrahydrofuran ring is realized by treatment of the boron trichloride complex with pyridine at room temperature or below.[38]

$$C_4H_8O{:}BCl_3 + C_5H_5N \rightarrow Cl(CH_2)_4OBCl_2{:}C_5H_5N \quad (12\text{-}43)$$

Perfluoro-1-butyltetrahydrofuran did not react with boron trichloride when heated to 350° for 24 hours.[121]

Pyrolysis of the tetrahydropyran–boron trichloride complex at 90° resulted in evolution of hydrogen chloride, but not boron trichloride. Reaction (12-44) was suggested.[67] The trichlorosilylmethyl

$$C_5H_{10}O{:}BCl_3 \rightarrow CH_2{=}CH(CH_2)_2CH_2OBCl_2 + HCl \quad (12\text{-}44)$$

derivative (XLVI) reacted with boron trichloride to produce the alkoxyhaloborane (XLVII). The product was not isolated but was converted to 1,5-dichloro-3-trichlorosilylmethylpentane by treatment with thionyl chloride.[117]

$$\text{(XLVI): tetrahydropyran ring with } CH_2SiCl_3 \text{ substituent at C-4} \qquad \underset{\text{(XLVII)}}{(Cl_3SiCH_2)(ClCH_2CH_2)CHCH_2CH_2OBCl_2}$$

The 1:1 dioxane–boron trichloride complex melts at about 80° to a deep blue liquid with evolution of hydrogen chloride and formation of a viscous liquid whose analysis is consistent with that of structure (XLVIII).[73] The chlorinated derivative (XLIX) might

$$\underset{\text{(XLVIII)}}{CH_2{=}CHOCH_2CH_2OBCl_2}$$

$$\underset{\text{(XLIX)}}{ClCH_2CH_2OCH_2CH_2OBCl_2}$$

be initially formed, it then could generate (XLVIII) by dehydrohalogenation. 1,3-Dioxolane did not form an isolable complex with boron trichloride, but immediately underwent fission to give chloromethoxyethyl esters.[33]

$$n\ \overset{CH_2-CH_2}{\underset{\diagdown CH_2 \diagup}{O\qquad O}} + BCl_3 \rightarrow (ClCH_2OCH_2CH_2O)_nBCl_{3-n} \tag{12-45}$$

The cleavage of tri-*O*-methylenehexitols by boron trichloride was formulated as in equation (12-46).[18]

$$\text{hexitol chain with two } -C-O-CH_2-O-C- \text{ rings} + BCl_3 \rightarrow \text{(ring O}^{+}\text{–}\bar{B}Cl_3 \text{ adduct)} \rightarrow \text{(one ring opened: } -C-OCH_2Cl,\ \overset{+}{O}\text{–}\bar{B}Cl_2\text{)} \rightarrow \text{(both rings opened: two } -C-OCH_2Cl \text{ groups, } -C-O-BCl-O-C- \text{ ring)} \tag{12-46}$$

Definite cleavage reactions with boron tribromide have not been described although its reaction with dioxane is violent.[83]

It was reported that ethylene oxide, propylene oxide, tetrahydropyran and dioxane are not cleaved by boron trifluoride.[68]

Subsequent workers found that ethylene oxide and trimethylene oxide polymerized on contact with boron trifluoride;[101] however the reaction products were not identified.

The reaction of (L) with boron trifluoride etherate resulted in the rearranged and unsaturated product (LI).[74]

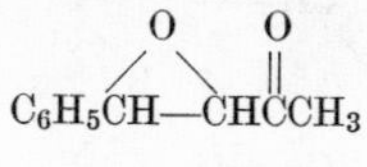

$$\underset{\text{(L)}}{C_6H_5\overset{O}{CH}\text{—}\overset{}{C}H\overset{O}{\overset{\|}{C}}CH_3} \qquad \underset{\text{(LI)}}{C_6H_5\text{—}C\begin{matrix}\diagup\!\!\!\!\diagup CH\text{—}O\diagdown \\ \diagdown C{=}O\nearrow \\ |\\ CH_3\end{matrix}BF_2}$$

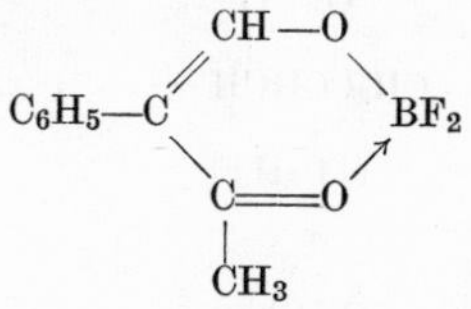

e. *And Aldehydes.* Chloroalkoxydichloroboranes are stated to be intermediates in the synthesis of tri(chloroalkoxy)boranes involving the reaction of boron trichloride and di- and trichloroacetaldehyde.[45] The reactions are formulated as an addition of boron chloride to the carbonyl group followed by disproportionation of the product.

$$Cl_2CH\overset{O}{\overset{\|}{C}}H + BCl_3 \rightarrow Cl_2CH\underset{Cl}{\underset{|}{C}}HOBCl_2 \rightarrow \tfrac{1}{3}\,(Cl_2CH\underset{Cl}{\underset{|}{C}}HO)_3B + \tfrac{2}{3}\,BCl_3 \qquad (12\text{-}47)$$

In the reactions of acetaldehyde, monochloroacetaldehyde, n-butyraldehyde, and isobutyraldehyde, symmetrical α-chloroethers and boric oxide were formed in addition to boron trichloride. This sequence of reactions was formulated as in equation (12-48) followed by decomposition of the intermediate borate (12-49, see Chapter 4).

$$CH_3\overset{O}{\overset{\|}{C}}H + BCl_3 \rightarrow ClCH_2OBCl_2 \rightarrow \tfrac{2}{3}\,BCl_3 + \tfrac{1}{3}\,(ClCH_2O)_3B \qquad (12\text{-}48)$$

$$\tfrac{1}{3}\,(ClCH_2O)_3B \rightarrow \tfrac{1}{2}\,(ClCH_2)_2O + \tfrac{1}{6}\,B_2O_3 \qquad (12\text{-}49)$$

Crotonaldehyde was claimed to form either the 1,2 (LII) or 1,4 (LIII) addition product. The ready hydrolysis of only two-thirds of the chlorine of the product would appear to rule out (LII) since

$$\underset{\text{(LII)}}{CH_3CH{=}CH\underset{Cl}{\underset{|}{C}}HOBCl_2} \qquad \underset{\text{(LIII)}}{CH_3\underset{Cl}{\underset{|}{C}}HCH{=}CHOBCl_2}$$

the α-chloroether structure would be expected to have a third labile chlorine atom.[45] The instability of allyloxydichloroboranes (see Section IV-B) also would tend to rule out structure (LII). Structure

(LIII), however, is unique in that it is the only known example of a vinyloxyborane without a γ-keto group.

The ketoaldehyde (LIV) was converted to (LV) by treatment with boron trifluoride etherate.[74]

$$CH_3C(=O)CH(C_6H_5)CH(=O)$$

(LIV)

$$C_6H_5\text{—}C\!\begin{cases} =CH\text{—}O \\ \text{—}C(CH_3)=O \end{cases}\!BF_2$$

(LV)

f. *And Ketones.* Benzophenone and boron trichloride gave a 1:1 reaction product which was believed to have the structure (LVI) due to the absence of carbonyl absorption in the infrared.[55]

$$(C_6H_5)_2C(Cl)OBCl_2$$

(LVI)

An interesting preparative technique involves the conversion of an enol ester to a β-diketone by an intramolecular acyl rearrangement promoted by boron trifluoride. The diketone is isolated as the difluoroboryl derivative of the enol (12-50).[133] It is of further interest

$$2\ CH_3C(OCCH_3)=CHCH(CH_3)CH_3 \xrightarrow[2.\ H_2O,\ NaOAc]{1.\ BF_3} CH_3C(OBF_2)=C(CH(CH_3)_2)CCH_3(=O) \qquad (12\text{-}50)$$

that the product survives vigorous shaking with cold aqueous sodium acetate solution, presumably due to the stabilizing influence of intramolecular coordination with the carbonyl oxygen as in (LVII) below.

Diketones also have reacted with boron halides to produce alkoxydihaloboranes. Boron trifluoride reacted with a series of enolizable β-diketones to give difluoro-α-β-unsaturated-γ-ketoalkoxy-

$$RC(=O)CH(R'')C(=O)R' \rightleftarrows RC(=O)C(R'')=C(OH)R' \xrightarrow{BF_3} RC(=O)C(R'')=C(R')OBF + HF \qquad (12\text{-}51)$$

boranes (12-51).*[7,74,107] The products were formulated as internal complexes (LVII).

$$\begin{array}{c} R \\ | \\ C{=}O \rightarrow BF_2 \\ R''{-}C \quad\quad \\ \| \\ C{-}O \\ | \\ R' \end{array}$$

(LVII)

Enol esters of β-diketones react with boron trifluoride to produce substituted difluoro(vinyloxy)boranes (12-52).[71] The mechanism was

$$C_6H_5C(=O)O{-}C(C_6H_5){=}CHC(=O)CH_3 + BF_3 \rightarrow F_2BO{-}C(C_6H_5){=}CHC(=O)CH_3 + C_6H_5C(=O)F \quad (12\text{-}52)$$

formulated as involving the β-elimination of the acid fluoride from the intermediate boron trifluoride–ester complex with driving force supplied by the resonance stabilization of the product (12-53).[71]

$$C_6H_5C(=O)OC(C_6H_5){=}CHC(=O)CH_3 + BF_3 \rightarrow C_6H_5C(=O){-}O(\rightarrow BF_3){-}C(C_6H_5){=}CHC(=O)CH_3 \xrightarrow{-C_6H_5C(=O)F}$$

$$F_2B(O{-}C(C_6H_5){=}CH{-}C(CH_3){=}O\rightarrow) \rightleftharpoons F_2B(\leftarrow O{=}C(C_6H_5){-}CH{=}C(CH_3){-}O) \quad (12\text{-}53)$$

g. *And β-Ketoamides.* Enolizable β-ketoamides react with boron trifluoride in a manner analogous to the reaction with diketones discussed in Section IV-A-2g above.[70]

$$C_6H_5C(=O)CH_2C(=O)NH_2 + BF_3 \rightarrow CH[{=}C(C_6H_5){-}O{-}]BF_2[\leftarrow O{=}C(NH_2){-}] \text{ or } CH[{=}C(C_6H_5){-}O{-}]BF_2[\leftarrow NH_2{-}C(=O){-}] + HF \quad (12\text{-}54)$$

h. *And Carboxylic Acid Esters.* The equimolar reaction of boron trichloride and a carboxylic acid ester derived from a primary

* In contrast, benzoylacetone and boron trifluoride were reported to give a 1:1 complex.[105] Boron trichloride reacts with enolizable diketones to form boronium salts (see Chapter 19).

alcohol or phenol results in the formation of a 1 : 1 complex. Heating of the complex results in acyl–oxygen cleavage* to give acid chloride and an alkoxy or aryloxydihaloborane.[44,62]

$$RC(=O)OR' + BCl_3 \rightarrow RC(=O)OR' \cdot BCl_3 \xrightarrow{\Delta} RC(=O)Cl + R'OBCl_2 \qquad (12\text{-}55)$$

The reaction, however, is not a practical preparative method since the temperatures necessary to effect decomposition of the ester–boron chloride complex lead to decomposition of the alkoxydihaloboranes and disproportionation of the aryloxydihaloboranes. *o*-Nitrophenyl acetate, however, gives a stable dichloro-(*o*-nitrophenoxy)borane,[62] presumably due to intramolecular coordination between the nitro oxygen and the boron atom.[29]

Ester fission with boron trichloride has been used as a synthetic tool for the preparation of compounds which do not contain boron. Thus, cellulose acetate and amylopectin acetate were converted to glucose by treatment with boron trichloride and subsequent hydrolysis of the dichloroborylglucose.[3]

i. *And Alkoxysilanes.* n-Butoxydichloroborane was obtained in 61% yield from the equilibration of tetra-n-butoxysilane and boron trichloride (12-56).[61] A 36% yield was realized when two moles of

$$(C_4H_9O)_4Si + BCl_3 \rightarrow C_4H_9OBCl_2 + (C_4H_9O)_3SiCl \qquad (12\text{-}56)$$

boron trichloride were employed. A 75% yield was obtained from tributoxychlorosilane (12-57).[47] The isobutyl derivative was prepared similarly.

$$(C_4H_9O)_3SiCl + BCl_3 \rightarrow C_4H_9OBCl_2 + (C_4H_9O)_2SiCl \qquad (12\text{-}57)$$

Alkoxytrialkylsilanes are cleaved by boron trihalides to give alkoxydihaloboranes and trialkylsilylhalides (12-58) rather than trialkylsiloxydihaloboranes and alkyl halides.[124] Methoxysilane behaves similarly (12-59).[119]

$$R_3SiOR' + BX_3 \rightarrow R'OBX_2 + R_3SiX \qquad (12\text{-}58)$$

$$H_3SiOCH_3 + BF_3 \rightarrow CH_3OBF_2 + H_3SiF \qquad (12\text{-}59)$$

* Chloroesters appear to be an exception.[62] Ethyl dichloroacetate was recovered in 75% yield when its boron trichloride complex was heated; ethyl trichloroacetate did not form a complex. Either the halogens interfere sterically with the complexing of the boron atom with the carbonyl oxygen or their large total $-I$ effect reduces the availability of electrons so as to preclude complex formation with boron.

j. *And Alkyl Phosphites.* Tri-n-butyl phosphite and boron trichloride react immediately and irreversibly at $-80°$ to give butoxydichloroborane (isolated as the pyridine complex).[60]

$$(n\text{-}C_4H_9O)_3P + BCl_3 \rightarrow n\text{-}C_4H_9OBCl_2 + (n\text{-}C_4H_9O)_2PCl \quad (12\text{-}60)$$

k. *And Boronic Acid Esters.* The 2:1 and 1:1 molar reactions of boron trifluoride and boron trichloride with dialkyl boronates result in an exchange of halogen and alkoxyl groups in a manner analogous to the preparation of alkoxydihaloboranes from boron halides and trialkoxyboranes (see Section IV-A-3a).[21]

$$2\ BF_3 + C_4H_9B(OC_4H_9)_2 \rightarrow 2\ C_4H_9OBF_2 + C_4H_9BF_2 \quad (12\text{-}61)$$

$$BF_3 + C_6H_5B(OC_4H_9)_2 \rightarrow C_4H_9OBF_2 + C_6H_5BF(OC_4H_9) \quad (12\text{-}62)$$

$$BCl_3 + C_4H_9B(OC_4H_9)_2 \rightarrow C_4H_9OBCl_2 + C_4H_9BCl(OC_4H_9) \quad (12\text{-}63)$$

$$BCl_3 + C_6H_5B(OC_4H_9)_2 \rightarrow C_4H_9OBCl_2 + C_6H_5BCl(OC_4H_9) \quad (12\text{-}64)$$

l. *And Trialkoxyboroxines.* The reaction of tributoxyboroxine with excess boron trichloride or boron trifluoride gave 50 and 73% yields, respectively, of the butoxydihaloboranes.[89]

$$(C_4H_9OBO)_3 + 3\ BCl_3 \rightarrow 3\ C_4H_9OBCl_2 + \{ClBO\}_3 \quad (12\text{-}65)$$

$$(C_4H_9OBO)_3 + 2\ BF_3 \rightarrow \tfrac{3}{2}\ (C_4H_9OBF_2)_2 + B_2O_3 \quad (12\text{-}66)$$

3. FROM TRIALKOXYBORANES

a. *And Boron Trihalides.* A convenient and essentially quantitative method of preparation involves the low temperature 2:1 molar reaction of boron trichloride and a trialkoxyborane derived from a primary or secondary* alcohol or chloroalcohol (12-67).[1,37,51,53,127,128] The mode of addition of the reactants or the use of pentane as a solvent does not influence the course of the reaction.[53]

$$2\ BCl_3 + (RO)_3B \rightarrow 3\ ROBCl_2 \quad (12\text{-}67)$$

The butenyl derivative (LVIII)[58] was stable and could be isolated; the allylic derivatives (LIX and LX)[56] were not isolable at 20°

$CH_2{=}CHCH_2CH_2OBCl_2$ (LVIII) $CH_2{=}CHCH_2OBCl_2$ (LIX) $CH_2{=}C(CH_3)CH_2OBCl_2$ (LX)

but formed stable pyridine complexes. In contrast to (LX), the 1- and 3-methylallyl compounds (LXI and LXII) were completely

* *s*-Butoxydichloroborane[51] and dichloro(2-octoxy)borane[53] are stable at $-80°$.

unstable and could not be stabilized even as the pyridine complexes.[58]

$$CH_2{=}CHCH(CH_3)OBCl_2 \quad \text{(LXI)} \qquad CH_3CH{=}CHCH_2OBCl_2 \quad \text{(LXII)}$$

The equimolar reaction of boron trichloride and tri-*t*-butoxyborane at −80° afforded boric oxide and *t*-butyl chloride as the decomposition products and none of the desired *t*-butoxydichloroborane.[51]

Attempts to prepare carbethoxy-substituted alkyldichloroboranes (LXIII) from reactions of boron trichloride with tri(carb-

$$C_2H_5OC(=O)CH_2OBCl_2 \quad \text{(LXIII)}$$

ethoxyalkoxy)boranes were unsuccessful, presumably due to concomitant acyl–oxygen cleavage of the carbethoxy group (see Section IV-A-2h).

$$(C_2H_5OC(=O)CH_2O)_3B + 3\,BCl_3 \rightarrow (ClC(=O)CH_2O)_3B + 3\,C_2H_5OBCl_2 \qquad (12\text{-}68)$$

The instability of dichlorophenoxyborane did not permit its isolation from a reaction mixture of one mole of triphenoxyborane and two moles of boron trichloride. However, the addition of pyridine to the reaction mixture resulted in a stable pyridine–dichlorophenoxyborane complex (12-69).[28] The pyridine–aryloxydichloroborane complexes derived from *p*-nitrophenol, *o*-chlorophenol and *o*-cresol were prepared similarly.[29]

$$(ArO)_3B + 2\,BCl_3 + 3\,C_5H_5N \rightarrow 3\,ArOBCl_2{:}C_5H_5N \qquad (12\text{-}69)$$

The redistribution reaction also has been applied to boron trichloride and 2-alkoxy-1,3,2-dioxaborolanes and borinanes derived from both glycols[13] and catechol.[54]

$$\begin{matrix}CH_2{-}O\\ |\\ CH_2{-}O\end{matrix}\!\!>BOC_4H_9 + BCl_3 \rightarrow \begin{matrix}CH_2{-}O\\ |\\ CH_2{-}O\end{matrix}\!\!>BCl + C_4H_9OBCl_2 \qquad (12\text{-}70)$$

$$C_6H_4O_2BOC_4H_9 + BCl_3 \rightarrow C_6H_4O_2BCl + C_4H_9OBCl_2 \qquad (12\text{-}71)$$

Due to decomposition to methyl bromide, dibromo(methoxy)-borane could not be isolated from the reaction of boron tribromide and trimethoxyborane.[63] The isobutyl and n-butyl derivatives behaved similarly. However, a pyridine complex (LXIV) was obtained from the n-butyl derivative.[25]

$$\text{n-}C_4H_9OBBr_2\text{:}NC_5H_5$$
(LXIV)

Dibromo(phenoxy)borane was obtained from the reaction of triphenoxyborane and boron tribromide, but it could not be completely separated from the diphenoxy compound.[46]

Boron trifluoride–trialkoxyborane reactions are a convenient means of preparation of alkoxydifluoroboranes (12-72).[9,48,65,87]

$$2\ BF_3 + (RO)_3B \rightarrow 3\ ROBF_2{}^{*} \qquad (12\text{-}72)$$

Butoxydifluoroborane was obtained along with unchanged tri-butoxyborane even when the stoichiometry was that which normally leads to the dialkoxyhaloborane (12-73).[87]

$$BF_3 + 2\ (C_4H_9O)_3B \rightarrow \tfrac{3}{2}\ C_4H_9OBF_2 + \tfrac{3}{2}\ (C_4H_9O)_3B \qquad (12\text{-}73)$$

The equimolar reaction of trimethoxyborane and boron trifluoride etherate was stated to give both the methoxy and dimethoxy derivatives.[113]

$$(CH_3O)_3B + BF_3\text{:}(C_2H_5)_2O \rightarrow CH_3OBF_2 + (CH_3O)_2BF + (C_2H_5)_2O \qquad (12\text{-}74)$$

The products of the reactions of trimethoxy, triethoxy and tri-n-butoxyborane with two moles of boron trifluoride were formulated as the addition compounds (LXV).[96†]

$$(RO)_3B\cdot 2BF_3$$
(LXV)

When boron trifluoride gas was bubbled into the complex, $BF_3\cdot(C_4H_9O)_3B\cdot C_4H_9OH$, an exothermic reaction took place and butoxydifluoroborane was obtained on distillation.[87]

$$3\ BF_3 + 2\,[BF_3\cdot(C_4H_9O)_3B\cdot C_4H_9OH] \rightarrow 6\ C_4H_9OBF_2 + BF_3\cdot 2C_4H_9OH \qquad (12\text{-}75)$$

* Difluoromethoxyborane was shown to be dimeric below 75°.[16] Butoxy-difluoroborane also was shown to be dimeric.[22] See Section III-B-2 for a discussion of the structure of alkoxydifluoroboranes.

† It has been proposed that the initial product of the reaction of one mole of a trialkoxyborane and two moles of boron trifluoride is the complex $(RO)_3B\cdot 2BF_3$. This type of complex is unstable, with the exception of $(ClCH_2CH_2O)_3B\cdot 2BF_3$, and disproportionates to $ROBF_2$.[102]

b. *And Diphenyl Phosphonate.* Trialkyl phosphates[49] and dialkyl phosphonates[10] react to give intermediate species formulated as (LXVI) and (LXVII) which ultimately react further to give

$$\underset{\text{(LXVI)}}{(RO)_2\overset{\overset{O}{\|}}{P}OBCl_2} \qquad \underset{\text{(LXVII)}}{RO\overset{\overset{O}{\|}}{P}HOBCl_2}$$

boron phosphate, BPO_4. On the other hand, the equimolar reaction of diphenyl phosphonate and boron trichloride resulted in the evolution of one mole of hydrogen chloride and the formation of a yellow liquid believed to be (LXVIII). Assignment of structure

$$\underset{\text{(LXVIII)}}{(C_6H_5O)_2POBCl_2}$$

(LXVIII) was based on elemental analyses and conversion on heating to triphenoxyborane, phenyl phosphinodichloridite, and phosphorus trichloride.[10]

c. *And Various Chlorides.* The reactions of trimethoxyborane with excess carbon tetrachloride or phosphorus trichloride at temperatures of 280–350° resulted in 32 and 28% yields, respectively, of chlorodimethoxyborane. Trace yields were obtained with silicon tetrachloride, sulfuryl chloride, and phosgene.[111]

4. FROM DIALKOXYHALOBORANES

a. *And Boron Halides.* Dialkoxyhaloboranes undergo an equimolar redistribution reaction with boron trichloride and boron trifluoride to give the alkoxydihaloborane.[48,53]

$$(RO)_2BX + BX_3 \rightarrow 2\ ROBX_2 \qquad (12\text{-}76)$$

b. *Disproportionation.* The dialkoxychloroboranes derived from n-propyl, n-butyl and isobutyl alcohol undergo disproportionation when heated under reflux at 1 mm. to give the corresponding monoalkoxy compounds.[88] Distillation of chlorodiphenoxyborane at

$$2\ (RO)_2BCl \rightarrow ROBCl_2 + (RO)_3B \qquad (12\text{-}77)$$

reduced pressure resulted in a small fraction of the dichlorophenoxy derivative[28] as did heating of chlorodi-2-chloroethoxyborane at 120° and 1 mm.[37]

Chlorodimethoxyborane did not disproportionate even when heated at 200° for several hours; but the trimethylamine complex of chlorodimethoxyborane disproportionated when heated at 100° for four hours.[132]

$$2\ (CH_3O)_2BCl{:}N(CH_3)_3 \rightarrow CH_3OBCl{:}N(CH_3)_3 + (CH_3O)_3B + N(CH_3)_3 \qquad (12\text{-}78)$$

B. Reactions

1. HYDROLYSIS

Due to the extreme hydrolytic instability of the boron–halogen bond, alkoxydichloro-, alkoxydifluoro- and alkoxydibromoboranes are readily hydrolyzed in the cold to boric acid, alcohol, and hydrogen halide (12-79).[1,25,48,51,52,112,116,129] The heat of hydrolysis of chlorodimethoxyborane has been recorded.[78]

$$ROBX_2 + 3\,H_2O \rightarrow H_3BO_3 + ROH + 2\,HX \qquad (12\text{-}79)$$

Complexing of the alkoxydihaloborane with pyridine does not prevent hydrolysis since (LXIX),[86] (LXX),[53] (LXXI),[56] and (LXXII)[56] were readily decomposed by water to boric acid, pyridine, the corresponding alcohol, and hydrogen chloride.

$n\text{-}C_4H_9OBCl_2{:}NC_5H_5$ (LXIX)

$n\text{-}C_6H_{13}CH(CH_3)OBCl_2{:}NC_5H_5$ (LXX)

$CH_2{=}CHCH_2OBCl_2\cdot 2\,C_5H_5N$ (LXXI)

$CH_2{=}C(CH_3)CH_2OBCl_2\cdot 2\,C_5H_5N$ (LXXII)

The aromatic addition compound (LXXIII), due to its insolubility, or possibly due to some more subtle cause such as an intra-

$o\text{-}NO_2C_6H_4OBCl_2{:}C_5H_5N$

(LXXIII)

molecular interaction of the nitro group and boron atom required four days of agitation in water for complete hydrolysis.[29]

Internal complex formation with a carbonyl oxygen does not preclude hydrolysis (12-80)[107] but may be partially responsible for

$$CH[C(CH_3){=}O{\rightarrow}]\,[C(CH_3){-}O]{=}BF_2 \text{ (chelate)} + 3\,H_2O \rightarrow CH_3COCH_2COCH_3 + H_3BO_3 + 2\,HF \qquad (12\text{-}80)$$

the stability of the similar derivatives (LXXIV) to treatment with cold aqueous sodium acetate solution.[71,133]

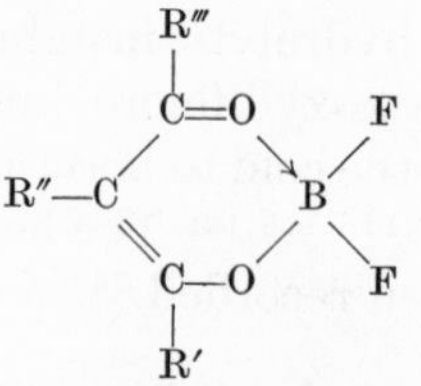

R‴
C=O F
R″—C B
C—O F
R′

(LXXIV, $R' = R'' = R''' = CH_3$
$R' = R''' = CH_3$, $R'' = CH(CH_3)_2$
$R' = R''' = C_6H_5$, $R'' = H$)

The hydrolysis of butoxydifluoroborane with a limited amount of water resulted in the 2:1 butyl alcohol–boron trifluoride complex (12-81).[87] On heating butoxydifluoroborane with solid sodium

$$2\,C_4H_9OBF_2 + 3\,H_2O \rightarrow BF_3 \cdot 2\,C_4H_9OH + H_3BO_3 + HF \qquad (12\text{-}81)$$

hydroxide at 130°, a mixture of water and butanol was distilled.[87]

The hindered phenolic derivative (LXXV) is unique in its reaction

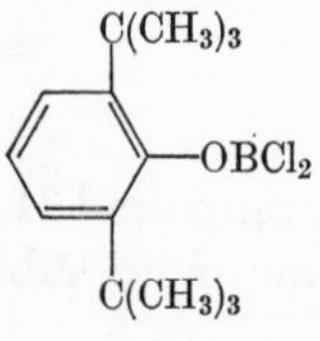

$C(CH_3)_3$
—$OBCl_2$
$C(CH_3)_3$

(LXXV)

with water.[118] In aqueous dioxane containing an excess of water, complete hydrolysis to the hindered phenol, boric acid and hydrochloric acid takes place. In dioxane solution with two molar equivalents of water, hydrolysis to the phenol, metaboric acid and hydrogen chloride takes place. Presumably the initial reaction produces chlorohydroxyphenoxyborane (12-82) which dehydrohalogenates to triphenoxyboroxine (12-83) which is then further hydrolyzed by the second mole of water (12-84). If the hindered phenolic derivative

$$ArOBCl_2 + H_2O \rightarrow ArOBCl(OH) + HCl \qquad (12\text{-}82)$$

$$ArOBCl(OH) \rightarrow \tfrac{1}{3}\,(ArOBO)_3 + HCl \qquad (12\text{-}83)$$

$$\tfrac{1}{3}\,(ArOBO)_3 + H_2O \rightarrow ArOH + HBO_2 \qquad (12\text{-}84)$$

(LXXV) is triturated in water only, the partially hydrolyzed species, $ArOB(OH)_2$, is insoluble and can be isolated (see Chapter 7).

2. ALCOHOLYSIS

The halogens of the alkoxydihaloboranes are readily replaced by alkoxyl groups to give, depending upon the stoichiometry employed, either dialkoxyhaloboranes or trialkoxyboranes.

$$ROBCl_2 + ROH \rightarrow (RO)_2BCl + HCl \qquad (12\text{-}85)$$

$$ROBCl_2 + 2\ ROH \rightarrow (RO)_3B + 2\ HCl \qquad (12\text{-}86)$$

Reaction (12-85) is a preparative method for dialkoxyhaloboranes and is treated in Section V-A-2a. Reaction (12-86) is a preparative method for trialkoxyboranes and is discussed in Chapter 4. Mixed esters derived from alcoholysis of hindered phenolic dichloroboranes are described in Chapter 6. The treatment of alkoxydichloroboranes with glycols to form 2-alkoxy-1,3,2-dioxaborolanes also is discussed in Chapter 6.

The treatment of (LXXVI) with glycols to form biborates is discussed in Chapter 5. Reaction with four moles of an alcohol to form mixed esters is treated in Chapter 6.

$$Cl_2BOCH_2CH_2OBCl_2$$
(LXXVI)

The alcoholysis of butoxydifluoroborane with butanol produces an unusual series of complex products.[87]

$$3\ C_4H_9OBF_2 + 3\ C_4H_9OH \rightarrow BF_3\cdot(C_4H_9O)_3B\cdot C_4H_9OH + BF_3\cdot 2C_4H_9OH \qquad (12\text{-}87)$$

3. WITH ALKOXIDES

The reaction of alkoxydihaloboranes with two moles of a sodium alkoxide to produce trialkoxyboranes is discussed in Chapter 4. The reaction with one mole of alkoxide is discussed in Section V-A-2b.

4. WITH *t*-BUTYL HYDROPEROXIDE

The conversion of dichloro-(*o*-nitrophenoxy)borane to the di-*t*-butylperoxy derivative by treatment with *t*-butyl hydroperoxide is discussed in Chapter 10.

5. WITH ETHERS

Dichloromethoxy- and dichloroethoxyborane were reported to form 2 : 1 molar complexes with dimethyl ether at $-80°$ (12-88).[129,130]

$$2\ ROBCl_2 + (CH_3)_2O \rightarrow (CH_3)_2O\cdot 2\ ROBCl_2 \qquad (12\text{-}88)$$

The ethoxy derivative also formed a 2 : 1 complex with diethyl ether (LXXVII).[112] The structure of the complex was speculated as

$$(C_2H_5)_2O\cdot 2C_2H_5OBCl_2$$
(LXXVII)

involving a double coordination of the ether oxygen and the boron atoms (LXXVIII).

$$\begin{array}{c} C_2H_5 \\ | \\ \text{Cl} \quad \text{Cl} \\ C_2H_5OB:O:BOC_2H_5 \\ \text{Cl} \quad \text{Cl} \\ | \\ C_2H_5 \end{array}$$

(LXXVIII)

6. WITH CYCLIC ETHERS

See Section V-A-2c.

7. WITH BIS(TRIETHYLTIN) OXIDE

The reaction of dichloro(ethoxy)borane with bis(triethyltin) oxide to give triethyltin chloride and triethoxyboroxine[4] is reminiscent of ether cleavage with boron trichloride (see Section IV-A-2c) and dialkoxyhaloborane decomposition to give metaborates (see Chapter 9).

$$C_2H_5OBCl_2 + [(C_2H_5)_3Sn]_2O \rightarrow (C_2H_5)_3SnCl + C_2H_5OB(Cl)OSn(C_2H_5)_3 \quad (12\text{-}89)$$

$$C_2H_5OB(Cl)OSn(C_2H_5)_3 \rightarrow (C_2H_5)_3SnCl + \tfrac{1}{3}\,(C_2H_5OBO)_3 \quad (12\text{-}90)$$

$$C_2H_5OBCl_2 + [(C_2H_5)_3Sn]_2O \rightarrow \tfrac{1}{3}\,(C_2H_5OBO)_3 + 2\,(C_2H_5)_3SnCl \quad (12\text{-}91)$$

8. THERMAL DECOMPOSITION AND DISPROPORTIONATION

a. *Introduction.* The fate of an alkoxydihaloborane when heated is dependent upon the experimental conditions employed.[1,53] In general, reflux at atmospheric pressure or pyrolysis in sealed tubes results in decomposition to the alkyl halide and unstable trichloroboroxine (12-92); whereas reflux at reduced pressure leads to disproportionation to the dialkoxyhaloborane (12-93). Distillation

$$3\,ROBCl_2 \rightarrow 3\,RCl + \{(ClBO)_3\} \quad (12\text{-}92)$$

$$\{(ClBO)_3\} \rightarrow B_2O_3 + BCl_3$$

$$2\,ROBCl_2 \rightarrow (RO)_2BCl + BCl_3 \quad (12\text{-}93)$$

at atmospheric or reduced pressure can give all the products of equations (12-92) and (12-93).

Further disproportionation of the product of equation (12-93) leads to trialkoxyboranes (12-94). Equation 12-95, the sum of

$$2\,(RO)_2BCl \rightarrow (RO)_3B + ROBCl_2 \tag{12-94}$$

$$3\,ROBCl_2 \rightarrow (RO)_3B + 2\,BCl_3 \tag{12-95}$$

equation (12-93) taken twice and equation (12-94), is a preparative method for trialkoxyboranes and is discussed in Chapter 4.

The details of reaction 12-92 are discussed below. Reaction (12-93) is discussed in Section V-A-2d.

b. *Decomposition to Alkyl Halides.* Table 12-7 records the percentage decomposition of a variety of primary* alkoxydichloroboranes according to equation (12-92) as a function of time and temperature. It is seen that in the saturated unsubstituted alkyl series, the general order of stability at 150° is $n\text{-}C_8H_{17} > n\text{-}C_4H_9 > n\text{-}C_3H_7 > C_2H_5$, which could indicate either steric control or electronic control in which the alkyl groups with the greatest electron releasing properties are the most stable. The ω-chloroalkyl compounds, however, fall in the order $Cl(CH_2)_2 > Cl(CH_2)_3 \gg Cl(CH_2)_5 > Cl(CH_2)_4$, and in addition $Cl(CH_2)_2 \gg C_2H_5$, $Cl(CH_2)_3 > n\text{-}C_3H_7$, $n\text{-}C_4H_9 > Cl(CH_2)_4$, and $n\text{-}C_5H_{11} > Cl(CH_2)_5$. Thus, there is no clear indication of a pure electronic or steric control. These orders, however, can be rationalized by an electronic control in which the compounds with alkyl groups with the greatest electron releasing powers are the most stable if special stabilities are ascribed the $Cl(CH_2)_2$ and $Cl(CH_2)_3$ compounds by virtue of intramolecular coordination (LXXIX).[1]

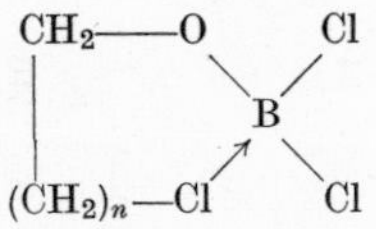

```
CH2——O      Cl
|      \   /
|        B
|      ↗   \
(CH2)n—Cl     Cl
```

(LXXIX, $n = 1, 2$)

The greater stability of (LXXIX) when $n = 1$ as compared to $n = 2$ is consistent with other intramolecular stabilizations of certain acyloxyboranes (see Chapter 8).

With dichloro(octoxy)borane, the decomposition was accompanied by elimination of hydrogen chloride and resulted in a 34% yield of octene.[53]

$$3\,n\text{-}C_8H_{17}OBCl_2 \rightarrow B_2O_3 + BCl_3 + 3\,n\text{-}C_6H_{13}CH{=}CH_2 + 3\,HCl \tag{12-96}$$

* Secondary alkoxydichloroboranes appear to be stable only at −80°.[51,58] Tertiary alkoxyhaloboranes have not been demonstrated to be isolable.[21,25,27] Aryloxydihaloboranes do not decompose via path 12-92.[25]

Table 12-7. Thermal stability of primary alkoxydichloroboranes

Time (hr.)	R in $ROBCl_2$ % Decomposed 150°							
	C_2H_5[1]	$Cl(CH_2)_2$[1]	n-C_3H_7[53]	$Cl(CH_2)_3$[1]	n-C_4H_9[53]	i-C_4H_9[53]	$(CH_3)_3CCH_2$[53]	n-C_8H_{17}[53]
0.17								
0.25								
0.33								
0.5			14		2	5.5	2	1
0.67								
0.83								
1.0	39							
1.17								
1.25								
1.33								
1.50			46		24	62	29	15
1.83								
2.1								
2.25								
2.5								
3.0	94	9		19				
3.2								
3.5								
4.2								
4.5								
5.00			93		100	92	81	95
5.2								
6.0		17		46				
6.1								

6.5								
7.1								
7.9								
8.4								
9.0								
9.4								
10.0		21		90				
10.9								
12.6								
15.5								
15.9								
21.0								
24.2								
30.0								
40.0								
25 days								

	100°							
	n-C_4H_9		$Cl(CH_2)_4$[37]	$Cl(CH_2)_4$[1]	i-C_4H_9	n-C_5H_{11}[1]	$Cl(CH_2)_5$[1]	$(CH_3)_3CCH_2$[53]
Time (hr.)	$FeCl_3$ present[51]	No $FeCl_3$[53]			$FeCl_3$ present[51]			
0.17				6				
0.25						0	0	
0.33				9				
0.5				24				
0.67				41				
0.83				56				
1.0			63	63	6.0	2	11	
1.17				72				

(*Table continued*)

Table 12-7 (*continued*)

	100°							
	n-C_4H_9		$Cl(CH_2)_4$[37]	$Cl(CH_2)_4$[1]	i-C_4H_9	n-C_5H_{11}[1]	$Cl(CH_2)_5$[1]	$(CH_3)_3CCH_2$[53]
Time (hr.)	$FeCl_3$ present[51]	No $FeCl_3$[53]			$FeCl_3$ present[51]			
1.25	6.6							
1.33				85				
1.50								
1.83			95					
2.1					7.0			
2.25	29.9							
2.5						8	35	
3.0								
3.2					8.0			
3.5	46.7							
4.2					11.0			
4.5	64.8							
5.00						24	68	
5.2					21.0			
6.0								
6.1					30.0			
6.5	69.2					40	87	
7.1					36.0			
7.9	74.0							
8.4					39.0			
9.0		<5						
9.4					41.4			
10.0								
10.9	76.3							

12.6			46.0		
15.5	80.5				
15.9			50.0		
21.0					
24.2			62.0		
30.0					
40.0					
25 days					75

	70°	50°	20°		
Time (hr.)	CH_3[129]	C_2H_5[112]	$CH_2{=}CHCH_2$[56]	$CH_2{=}C(CH_3)CH_2$[56]	$CH_2{=}CHCH_2CH_2$[58]
0.17					
0.25					
0.33					
0.5				91.8	
0.67					
0.83					
1.0			97.1		
1.17					
1.25					
1.33					
1.50					
1.83					
2.1					
2.25					
3.0					11
3.2					

(*Table continued*)

Table 12-7 (*continued*)

	70°	50°	20°		
Time (hr.)	CH_3[129]	C_2H_5[112]	$CH_2{=}CHCH_2$[56]	$CH_2{=}C(CH_3)CH_2$[56]	$CH_2{=}CHCH_2CH_2$[58]
3.5					
4.2					
4.5					
5.00					
5.2					
6.0					
6.1					
6.5					
7.1					
7.9					
8.4					
9.0					
9.4					
10.0					
10.9					
12.6					
15.5					
15.9					
21.0				—	92
24.2					
30.0	80.0				
40.0		26.8			
25 days					

The pyrolytic decomposition of dichloro-(4-chlorobutoxy)borane at 100° in a sealed tube results in the formation of 1,4-dichloro-

$$Cl(CH_2)_4OBCl_2 \rightarrow Cl(CH_2)_4Cl + \tfrac{1}{3} B_2O_3 + \tfrac{1}{3} BCl_3 \qquad (12\text{-}97)$$

butane.[37] A general method of converting ω-chloroalcohols to α,ω-dichloroalkanes thus is indicated.

The product of the reaction of crotonaldehyde and boron trichloride, either (LXXX) or (LXXXI), gave 1,3-dichloro-1-butene

$$\underset{\underset{\displaystyle Cl}{|}}{CH_3CH}CH{=}CHOBCl_2 \quad \text{or}$$

(LXXX)

$$CH_3CH{=}CH\underset{\underset{\displaystyle Cl}{|}}{CH}OBCl_2 \rightarrow CH_3\underset{\underset{\displaystyle Cl}{|}}{CH}CH{=}CHCl + \tfrac{1}{3} BCl_3 + \tfrac{1}{3} B_2O_3 \qquad (12\text{-}98)$$

(LXXXI)

when heated.[45] The product does not dictate a choice of (LXXX) or (LXXXI) due to the equilibrium (12-99).[80]

$$CH_3CH{=}CHCHCl_2 \rightleftarrows CH_3\underset{\underset{\displaystyle Cl}{|}}{CH}CH{=}CHCl \qquad (12\text{-}99)$$

Decomposition of the pyridine complex of butoxydichloroborane by heating at 150° for forty-five hours results in the same products as the thermal decomposition of the uncomplexed haloborane except that the unstable intermediate species, O═B—Cl, apparently is rendered isolable by complexing with the pyridine.

$$C_4H_9OBCl_2{:}C_5H_5N \rightarrow C_4H_9Cl + C_5H_5N{:}BOCl^* \qquad (12\text{-}100)$$

It was felt that the products arose by disproportionation of the complex (12-101) followed by subsequent reaction of the products of the disproportionation (12-102).[86]

$$3\ C_4H_9OBCl_2{:}C_5H_5N \rightarrow (C_4H_9O)_3B + 2\ C_5H_5N{:}BCl_3 + C_5H_5N \qquad (12\text{-}101)$$

$$(C_4H_9O)_3B + 2\ C_5H_5N{:}BCl_3 + C_5H_5N \rightarrow 3\ C_4H_9Cl + 3\ C_5H_5N{:}BOCl \qquad (12\text{-}102)$$

Prior dissociation of the pyridine complex followed by the usual decomposition path of the liberated butoxydichloroborane does not seem to be precluded.

* This product was not rigorously characterized. Monomeric boron oxychloride has not been shown to have more than momentary existence at room temperature. Possibly the product is a pyridine-stabilized trichloroboroxine.

[Structure: six-membered B_3O_3 ring; each B bears Cl and a coordinated C_5H_5N (arrow $C_5H_5N \rightarrow B$)]

Alkoxydibromoboranes (methyl,[61] n-butyl, i-butyl and *s*-butyl) appear to be completely unstable at ambient temperatures. The 1:1 pyridine complex of dibromo-(n-butoxy)borane decomposed slowly at 15°.[25]

The proposed mechanism for the decomposition of alkoxydihaloboranes involves an initial ionization of halide accompanied by heterolytic cleavage of the alkyl oxygen bond to give a carbonium ion.[50,51,53] This mechanism accounts for the instability of *s*-butoxy-

$$\text{—}\overset{|}{\underset{|}{C}}\text{—O—B(Cl)—Cl} \rightarrow \text{—}\overset{|}{\underset{|}{C}}^{+} + Cl^{-} + \tfrac{1}{3}(OBCl)_3 \qquad (12\text{-}103)$$

dichloroborane as compared to the methyl, ethyl, n-butyl and isobutyl derivatives since it results in a secondary carbonium ion and thus provides more driving force than the production of primary carbonium ions from the other derivatives. The mechanism, in addition, accounts for the considerable production of *t*-butyl chloride in the decomposition of isobutoxydichloroborane (12-104),[51,62] the

$$CH_3\underset{\underset{CH_3}{|}}{CH}CH\text{—O—B(Cl)—Cl} \rightarrow CH_3\underset{\underset{CH_3}{|}}{CH}CH_2^{+} + Cl^{-} + \tfrac{1}{3}(OBCl)_3 \;\downarrow\; CH_3\overset{+}{\underset{\underset{CH_3}{|}}{C}}CH_3 \qquad (12\text{-}104)$$

formation of *t*-amyl chloride in the decomposition of the neopentyl[53,62] and methylisopropylcarbinyl[53] derivatives, and the production of 2,3-dimethyl-2-chlorobutane from the methyl-*t*-butylcarbinyl derivative[53] as a result of rearrangement of primary and secondary to tertiary carbonium ions.

The production of a mixture of 1-chloro-2-butene and 3-chloro-1-butene from the decompositions of both the 1-methylallyl and 3-methylallyl derivatives is another case in point.[58]

$$CH_2{=}CH\underset{\underset{CH_3}{|}}{CH}OBCl_2 \rightarrow CH_3\overset{+}{C}HCH{=}CH_2 + Cl^- + \tfrac{1}{3}(OBCl)_3$$

$$CH_3CH{=}CHCH_2OBCl_2 \rightarrow CH_3CH{=}CHCH_2^{+} + Cl^- + \tfrac{1}{3}(OBCl)_3$$

$$\rightarrow CH_3CH{=}CHCH_2Cl + CH_3\overset{\overset{Cl}{|}}{C}HCH{=}CH_2 + \tfrac{1}{3}(OBCl)_3 \qquad (12\text{-}105)$$

The instability of the allyl derivatives (Table 12-7) also is consistent with the carbonium ion mechanism since the production of an allyl carbonium ion would introduce considerable driving force by virtue of the decreased energy of the resonating system (12-106) relative to alkyl carbonium ions.

$$CH_2{=}CHCH_2^+ \longleftrightarrow \overset{+}{C}H_2CH{=}CH_2 \qquad (12\text{-}106)$$

The marked catalysis of the decomposition by the Lewis acids, ferric chloride and aluminum chloride[1,21,51,53] (Tables 12-7 and 12-8[53]), also is consistent with the proposed mechanism in that the

Table 12-8. Effect of Lewis acids on alkoxydihaloborane decomposition

R in $ROBCl_2$	Time	Temp. (°C)	Catalyst	% Decomposition
n-C_4H_9	<1 min.	20	1% $FeCl_3$	100
	1 hr.	100	0.2% $FeCl_3$	98
	1 hr.	100	0.2% $AlCl_3$	96
	9 hr.	100	—	<5
$(CH_3)_3CCH_2$	5 hr.	17	0.7% $AlCl_3$	20
	4 days	17	0.7% $AlCl_3$	65
	25 days	100	—	75

metal halides would be expected to assist in removal of the chloride ion. Similarly, it was proposed that a second molecule of alkoxyhalo-

$$\text{R—O(Cl)B—Cl} \; FeCl_3 \rightarrow R^+ + \{O{=}B{-}Cl\} + FeCl_4^- \qquad (12\text{-}107)$$

borane could serve as the chloride acceptor and catalyze the reaction.[53] This possibility is consistent with the apparent increased stability of the alkoxydihaloboranes with bulky or branched chain alkyl groups which prevent close approach to a second molecule and inhibit the catalytic effect.

Combinations of S_N1 and S_N2 reactions involving chloride ionization (12-108) and subsequent attack on alkyl (12-109), as well

$$\text{—}\overset{|}{\underset{|}{C}}\text{—O(Cl)B—Cl} \rightarrow \{\text{—}\overset{|}{\underset{|}{C}}\text{—O—B—Cl}\}^+ + Cl^- \qquad (12\text{-}108)$$

$$Cl^- \; \text{>C—O—}\overset{+}{B}\text{—Cl} \rightarrow \text{—}\overset{|}{\underset{|}{C}}\text{—Cl} + \tfrac{1}{3}(OBCl)_3 \qquad (12\text{-}109)$$

as S_Ni reactions (12-110), were proposed as companion mechanisms to account for unrearranged products.[51]

$$>C\text{—}O\text{—}B(Cl)\text{—}Cl \rightarrow \text{—}\overset{|}{\underset{|}{C}}\text{—}Cl + \tfrac{1}{3}\,(OBCl)_3 \qquad (12\text{-}110)$$

c. *Other Decompositions.* When (LXXXII) is heated in a dry tube it decomposes with the evolution of acetylacetone, boric acid, and acid fumes which burn with a green flame.[107]

$$CH_3\text{—}C(=O\rightarrow BF_2)\text{—}CH{=}C(\text{—}O\text{—}BF_2)\text{—}CH_3$$

(LXXXII)

9. WITH AMINES

a. *Ammonia.* The ready reaction of ethoxydifluoroborane with ammonia to give triethoxyborane and the ammonia–boron trifluoride complex was interpreted as evidence for the structure (LXXXIII) for this compound.[96]

$$\underset{\text{(LXXXIII)}}{(C_2H_5O)_2B\cdot 2BF_3} + 2\,NH_3 \rightarrow (C_2H_5O)_3B + 2\,NH_3{:}BF_3 \qquad (12\text{-}111)$$

It is not clear why the other structures proposed for alkoxydifluoroboranes, $ROBF_2$ and $(ROBF_2)_3$, would not give the same products on reaction with ammonia since the ammonia would be expected to promote their disproportionation via formation of the ammonia–boron trifluoride complex.

b. *Primary and Secondary Amines.* The aminolysis of alkoxydihaloboranes should offer a convenient method of synthesis of alkoxy(amino)boranes due to the reactivity of the halogen and the relative difficulty of displacing an alkoxyl group from boron with an amino group.[93] The reaction, however, has been employed only twice.[6,14]

$$C_4H_9OBCl_2 + 4\,C_2H_5NH_2 \xrightarrow[\text{pentane}]{-78^\circ} C_4H_9OB(NHC_2H_5)_2 + 2\,C_2H_5NH_2\cdot HCl \qquad (12\text{-}112)$$

$$Cl_2BOCH_2CH_2OBCl_2 + 8\,(C_2H_5)_2NH \xrightarrow[-100^\circ]{CH_2Cl_2}$$

$$[(C_2H_5)_2N]_2BOCH_2CH_2OB[N(C_2H_5)_2]_2 + 4\,(C_2H_5)_2NH\cdot HCl \qquad (12\text{-}113)$$

c. *Tertiary Amines.* Alkoxydichloroboranes form 1:1 (LXXXIV) and 1:2 (LXXXV) complexes with pyridine. With

$$ROBCl_2{:}C_5H_5N \qquad ROBCl_2{:}2C_5H_5N$$
(LXXXIV) (LXXXV)

dichloro-(2-chloroethoxy)borane[37] and allyloxydichloroborane,[56] the product is dependent upon the stoichiometry employed. Dichloro-(2-methylallyloxy)borane,[56] dichloro-(5-chloropentoxy)borane,[1] and ethylenedioxybis(dichloroborane)[14] appear to form only the 1:2 complex; whereas dichloro-(3-chloropropoxy)borane,[1] butoxydichloroborane,[86] and dichloro-(4-chlorobutoxy)borane[37] form the 1:1 complex. The thermally unstable dichloro-(2-octoxy)borane appears to be stabilized as the 1:1 pyridine complex.[53]

Dibromobutoxyborane forms a 1:1 complex with pyridine which slowly decomposes at 15°.[25] In contrast to this and the ease with which butoxydichloroborane forms a pyridine complex, the reaction of pyridine with butoxydifluoroborane, even at 20°, leads to disproportionation instead of complex formation.[87]

The formation of the pyridine–boron trifluoride complex and the liberation of the trialkoxyborane from the reaction of pyridine and the methoxy, ethoxy and n-butoxydifluoro derivatives was offered as partial proof of structure (LXXXVI) for these com-

$$(RO)_3B{:}2BF_3$$
(LXXXVI)

pounds.[96] As discussed in Section IV-B-9a above, this conclusion is not necessarily justified.

Dichloro(phenoxy)borane, which is too unstable to isolate, forms a stable solid 1:1 addition complex with pyridine,[28] as do the *o*-nitro,[29,62] *p*-nitro, *o*-chloro, and *o*-methyl derivatives.[28]

Dichloro(methoxy)borane reacts with excess trimethylamine to give a solid 1:1 complex (LXXXVII).[132]

$$CH_3OBCl_2{:}N(CH_3)_3$$
(LXXXVII)

d. *Phenylhydrazine.* Treatment of (LXXXVIII) with phenylhydrazine produced the pyrazole (LXXXIX).[74]

```
           CH—O     F              C6H5—C———CH
          //    \  /                    ‖     ‖
   C6H5—C        B                 CH3—C      N
          \    ↗  \                      \   /
           C==O    F                       N
           |                               |
           CH3                             C6H5
      (LXXXVIII)                      (LXXXIX)
```

10. WITH CARBOXYLIC ACIDS

The reaction of dibutoxychloroborane with acetic acid affords a synthesis of both tributoxyborane and oxybis(diacetoxyborane). See Chapters 4 and 8.

11. WITH HYDROGEN CHLORIDE

Alkoxydichloroboranes[35] and phenoxydichloroboranes[30] do not react with hydrogen chloride at 20°.

12. WITH THIONYL CHLORIDE

Although the generality of the reaction is not yet known, it appears that alkoxydichloroboranes can be cleaved to the alkyl halide by reaction with thionyl chloride.[117]

$$\underset{\displaystyle ClCH_2CH_2CHCH_2CH_2OBCl_2}{\overset{CH_2SiCl_3}{|}} \xrightarrow{SOCl_2} \underset{\displaystyle ClCH_2CH_2CHCH_2CH_2Cl}{\overset{CH_2SiCl_3}{|}} \qquad (12\text{-}114)$$

13. REDUCTION

a. *With Sodium Borohydride.* Reduction of butoxydifluoroborane and difluoropentoxyborane with sodium borohydride in the presence of propylene was claimed as a method of preparation of borinic acid esters.[84] Presumably the alkoxyborane, $ROBH_2$, is

$$2\ ROBF_2 + NaBH_4 + 4\ C_3H_6 \rightarrow 2\ (C_3H_7)_2BOR + NaBF_4 \qquad (12\text{-}115)$$

formed and subsequently adds to the olefin to give the borinate.

b. *With Sodium Trimethoxyhydroborate.* Reduction of dichloro(methoxy)borane with sodium trimethoxyhydroborate in the presence of triethylamine resulted in the borane–amine complex (XC).[77]

$$\underset{(XC)}{(C_2H_5)_3N\!:\!BH_3}$$

c. *With Sodium.* Difluoro(methoxy)borane did not react with sodium at 100° in a sealed tube.[48] Dichloro(ethoxy)borane on treatment with sodium amalgam resulted in a trace of a slightly volatile, chlorine-free product.[127]

14. WITH TRIALKOXYBORANES

The equilibration of alkoxydihaloboranes and trialkoxyboranes to give dialkoxyhaloboranes is discussed in Section V-A-2e.

15. WITH DIALKOXYALKYLBORANES

Alkoxydihaloboranes react with two molar equivalents of a boronic acid ester at room temperature or below to produce good yields of symmetrical trialkoxyboranes and completely unsymmetrical alkoxy-(alkyl)haloboranes.[21]

$$C_4H_9OBF_2 + 2\ C_4H_9B(OC_4H_9)_2 \rightarrow (C_4H_9O)_3B + 2\ C_4H_9BF(OC_4H_9) \quad (12\text{-}116)$$

$$C_4H_9OBCl_2 + 2\ C_4H_9B(OC_4H_9)_2 \rightarrow (C_4H_9O)_3B + 2\ C_4H_9BCl(OC_4H_9) \quad (12\text{-}117)$$

The equimolar reaction of the boronate and alkoxydihaloborane also has been recorded.[21]

$$C_4H_9OBCl_2 + C_4H_9B(OC_4H_9)_2 \rightarrow (C_4H_9O)_2BCl + C_4H_9BCl(OC_4H_9) \quad (12\text{-}118)$$

V. DIALKOXY- AND DIARYLOXYHALOBORANES

A. Methods of Preparation

1. FROM BORON TRIHALIDES

a. *And Alcohols or Phenols.* A variety of dialkoxychloroboranes derived from primary and secondary alcohols and phenols have been prepared from the low temperature reaction of boron trichloride and two moles of the alcohol[37,51,88,127,129] or phenol (12-119).[29] Chloroform[79] and methylene chloride[1,29] have been used as solvents.

$$BCl_3 + 2\ ROH \rightarrow (RO)_2BCl + 2\ HCl \quad (12\text{-}119)$$

The reaction was postulated as proceeding via 1 : 1 alcohol complexes of both the boron trichloride and the intermediate alkoxyhaloborane.[131] Prior complexing of the boron halide with

$$BCl_3 + ROH \rightarrow \begin{matrix} R \\ \diagdown \\ O{:}BCl_3 \\ \diagup \\ H \end{matrix} \rightarrow ROBCl_2 + HCl \quad (12\text{-}120)$$

$$ROBCl_2 + ROH \rightarrow \begin{matrix} R & & OR \\ \diagdown & & | \\ & O{:} & B\text{—}Cl \\ \diagup & & | \\ H & & Cl \end{matrix} \rightarrow (RO)_2BCl + HCl \quad (12\text{-}121)$$

trimethylamine precluded reaction with ethanol. The ether complex, however, did react with ethanol to give the ether complex of chlorodiethoxyborane.[131]

$$C_2H_5OH + (C_2H_5)_2O{:}BCl_3 \rightarrow \tfrac{1}{2}\ (C_2H_5O)_2BCl{:}(C_2H_5)_2O + \tfrac{1}{2}\ (C_2H_5)_2O{:}BCl_3 + HCl \quad (12\text{-}122)$$

Reaction of the acetonitrile complex of boron trichloride and butanol in methylene chloride solution resulted in butoxydichloroborane regardless of the stoichiometry employed.[59]

$$CH_3CN{:}BCl_3 + 2\,C_4H_9OH \rightarrow (C_4H_9O)_2BCl + 2\,HCl + CH_3CN \quad (12\text{-}123)$$

$$CH_3CN{:}BCl_3 + C_4H_9OH \rightarrow \tfrac{1}{2}\,CH_3CN{:}BCl_3 + \tfrac{1}{2}\,(C_4H_9O)_2BCl + HCl + \tfrac{1}{2}\,CH_3CN \quad (12\text{-}124)$$

The dibutoxy derivative in the equimolar reaction (12-124) probably arises via reaction of the $C_4H_9OBCl_2$ intermediate with acetonitrile, as was shown in an independent reaction (12-125).[59]

$$2\,C_4H_9OBCl_2 + CH_3CN \rightarrow CH_3CN{:}BCl_3 + (C_4H_9O)_2BCl \quad (12\text{-}125)$$

An equimolar reaction of resorcinol and boron trichloride gave a polymeric material whose analysis was consistent with (XCI).[54]

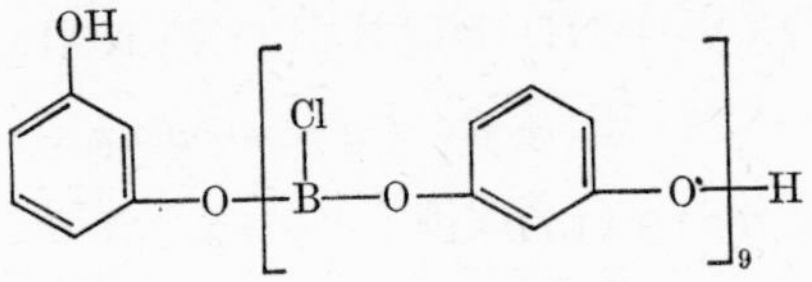

(XCI)

The hydroquinone product was similarly formulated (XCII).[54]

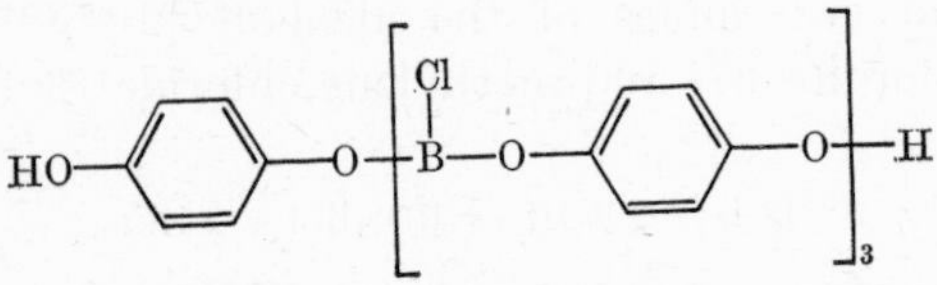

(XCII)

b. *And Ethers.* The cleavage of ethers with boron trichloride is a common method of preparation of alkoxydihaloboranes. The dihaloborane also is capable of cleavage and if a second mole of ether is employed a dialkoxyhaloborane results.[57]

$$CH_2{=}CHCH_2OCH_2CH_2CH_3 + BCl_3 \rightarrow CH_2{=}CHCH_2Cl + CH_3CH_2CH_2OBCl_2 \quad (12\text{-}126)$$

$$CH_3CH_2CH_2OBCl_2 + CH_2{=}CHCH_2OCH_2CH_2CH_3 \rightarrow CH_2{=}CHCH_2Cl + (CH_3CH_2CH_2O)_2BCl \quad (12\text{-}127)$$

$$2\,CH_2{=}CHCH_2OCH_2CH_2CH_3 + BCl_3 \rightarrow 2\,CH_2{=}CHCH_2Cl + (CH_3CH_2CH_2O)_2BCl \quad (12\text{-}128)$$

The production of the chlorodipropoxyborane in reaction (12-128) (the allyl chloride actually was not isolated) is consistent with the proposed mechanism of the cleavage reaction discussed in Chapter 4 in which the alkyl moiety of the ether which is best able to form a carbonium ion leads to the alkyl halide product.

c. *And Cyclic Ethers.* The cleavage of cyclic ethers with boron trichloride offers a means of preparation of chlorodi-(ω-chloroalkoxy)boranes.

$$2\,\overset{\displaystyle O}{\widehat{CH_2\text{—}CH_2}} + BCl_3 \rightarrow (ClCH_2CH_2O)_2BCl \qquad (12\text{-}129)$$

With propylene oxide, both possible modes of cleavage occur to give (XCIII) and (XCIV).[38,67]

$$\underset{\text{(XCIII)}}{(CH_3\overset{\overset{\displaystyle Cl}{|}}{C}HCH_2O)_2BCl} \qquad \underset{\text{(XCIV)}}{(ClCH_2\overset{\overset{\displaystyle CH_3}{|}}{C}HO)_2BCl}$$

When the 1 : 1 dioxane–boron trichloride complex is heated just above the melting point (95°), an exothermic decomposition occurs with the formation of (XCV). The 2 : 3 complex behaves similarly.[33]

$$\underset{\text{(XCV)}}{(ClCH_2CH_2O)_2BCl}$$

d. *And Alkoxysilanes.* Boron halides cleave alkoxysilanes in a manner reminiscent of the cleavage of ethers to give dialkoxyhaloboranes and silyl halides.[124]

$$BBr_3 + 2\,(CH_3)_3SiOC_2H_5 \xrightarrow{50°} (C_2H_5O)_2BBr + 2\,(CH_3)_3SiBr \qquad (12\text{-}130)$$

$$BCl_3 + 2\,(CH_3)_3SiOC_2H_5 \xrightarrow{80°} (C_2H_5O)_2BCl + 2\,(CH_3)_3SiCl \qquad (12\text{-}131)$$

$$BF_3 + (CH_3O)_4Si \xrightarrow[\text{temp.}]{\text{Room}} \text{complex} \xrightarrow{80°} (CH_3O)_2BF + (CH_3O)_2SiF_2 \qquad (12\text{-}132)$$

A small yield of dibutoxychloroborane was isolated from the equimolar reaction of boron trichloride and tetrabutoxysilane.[61]

The absence of siloxyborane products can be rationalized by a mechanism in which the available *d* orbitals of silicon are utilized. The empty *d* orbitals of silicon can accommodate the unbonded electron pair on the halide atom. Thus scheme (12-133) is promoted to the exclusion of path (12-134).

```
      X                X
      |                |
   X—B—X    →     X—B   X
      ↑  ..  ↓         |     |
  >C—Ö—Si<       >C—O   Si<
```
(12-133)

```
       X                   X
       |                   |
   X—B—X     →     X   B—X
   ..  ↓  ↑            |    |
  >C—Ö—Si<        >C   O—Si<
```
(12-134)

e. *And Trialkoxy- and Triaryloxyboranes.* Dialkoxyhaloboranes containing both primary and secondary alkyl groups and haloalkyl groups are prepared conveniently and quantitatively from the 1:2 molar reaction of boron trichloride and a trialkoxyborane at low temperature.[1,51,79,88,115,127,128] Pentane has been used as a solvent.[37]

$$BCl_3 + 2\,(RO)_3B \rightarrow 3\,(RO)_2BCl \qquad (12\text{-}135)$$

Chlorodiphenoxyborane and its pyridine complex and chlorodi-(*o*-nitrophenoxy)borane were prepared similarly with methylene chloride as a solvent.[28,29]

$$BCl_3 + 2\,(C_6H_5O)_3B \rightarrow 3\,(C_6H_5O)_2BCl \qquad (12\text{-}136)$$

$$BCl_3 + 2\,(C_6H_5O)_3B + 3\,C_5H_5N \rightarrow 3\,(C_6H_5O)_2BCl{:}C_5H_5N \qquad (12\text{-}137)$$

The monochloroboranes derived from unsaturated alcohols (allyl,[56] 2-methallyl[56] and 1-methallyl[58]) decomposed slowly at 20° but could be stabilized as pyridine complexes.

$$BCl_3 + 2\,(CH_2{=}CHCH_2O)_3B \rightarrow 3\,(CH_2{=}CHCH_2O)_2BCl \begin{cases} \xrightarrow{3\,C_5H_5N} 3\,[(CH_2{=}CHCH_2O)_2BCl{:}C_5H_5N] \\ \xrightarrow[6\,C_5H_5N]{} 3\,[(CH_2{=}CHCH_2O)_2BCl{:}2C_5H_5N] \end{cases} \qquad (12\text{-}138)$$

$$BCl_3 + 2\,(CH_2{=}C(CH_3)CH_2O)_3B \rightarrow 3\,(CH_2{=}C(CH_3)CH_2O)_2BCl \xrightarrow{3\,C_5H_5N} 3\,[(CH_2{=}C(CH_3)CH_2O)_2BCl{:}C_5H_5N] \qquad (12\text{-}139)$$

$$BCl_3 + 2\,(CH_2{=}CHCH(CH_3)O)_3B \rightarrow 3\,(CH_2{=}CHCH(CH_3)O)_2BCl \xrightarrow{3\,C_5H_5N} 3\,[(CH_2{=}CHCH(CH_3)O)_2BCl{:}C_5H_5N] \qquad (12\text{-}140)$$

The 3-methallyl derivative (XCVI) could not be stabilized even as the pyridine complex; whereas the butenyl derivative (XCVII) was isolable as such.[58]

$(CH_3CH{=}CHCH_2O)_2BCl$ (XCVI) $\qquad$ $(CH_2{=}CHCH_2CH_2O)_2BCl$ (XCVII)

Boron trifluoride reacts with two moles of trimethoxyborane in

$$BF_3 + 2\,(CH_3O)_3B \rightarrow 3\,(CH_3O)_2BF^* \qquad (12\text{-}141)$$

* Fluorodimethoxyborane has been shown to be stable only in the gaseous phase and to disproportionate to trimethoxyborane and difluoro(methoxy)borane in the condensed phase.[65]

the usual manner[48,65] but behaves peculiarly with tributoxyborane. Butoxydifluoroborane and not dibutoxyfluoroborane is isolated from the reaction, although the stoichiometry is designed to give the dialkoxy derivative.[87] Impure dibutoxyfluoroborane, however, was

$$BF_3 + 2\,(C_4H_9O)_3B \rightarrow \tfrac{3}{2}\,C_4H_9OBF_2 + \tfrac{3}{2}\,(C_4H_9O)_3B \qquad (12\text{-}142)$$

obtained from the reaction of tributoxyborane with the ether complex of boron trifluoride. Attempts to isolate dibenzyloxyfluoroborane by a similar reaction were unsuccessful, probably due to disproportionation of the product.[32]

The equimolar reaction of trimethoxyborane and boron trifluoride etherate was stated to give both the mono- and dimethoxy products.[113]

$$(CH_3O)_3B + BF_3\!:\!(C_2H_5)_2O \rightarrow (CH_3O)_2BF + CH_3OBF_2 + (C_2H_5)_2O \qquad (12\text{-}143)$$

Bromodimethoxyborane, prepared by the reaction of boron tribromide and trimethoxyborane, could not be isolated due to decomposition.[63] The normal and isobutyl derivatives behaved

$$BBr_3 + 2\,(CH_3O)_3B \rightarrow 3\,\{(CH_3O)_2BBr\} \qquad (12\text{-}144)$$

$$3\,\{(CH_3O)_2BBr\} \rightarrow 3\,CH_3Br + (CH_3OBO)_3 \qquad (12\text{-}145)$$

similarly;[25] however an essentially quantitative yield of the phenoxy derivative was obtained at 18° in methylene chloride solution.[46]

$$2\,(C_6H_5O)_3B + BBr_3 \rightarrow 3\,(C_6H_5O)_2BBr \qquad (12\text{-}146)$$

2. FROM ALKOXY AND ARYLOXYDIHALOBORANES

a. *And Alcohols and Phenols.* The treatment of an alkoxy or aryloxydihaloborane with one mole of an alcohol or phenol results in the displacement of one of the halogens to give the dialkoxy* or diaryloxy derivatives.[51,85,129] Due to the instability of the dibutoxy derivative, the reaction must be performed below 0° to prevent decomposition of the product to tributoxyborane[51] (see Chapter 4).

$$ROBX_2 + ROH \rightarrow (RO)_2BX + HX \qquad (12\text{-}147)$$

An interesting example of alcoholysis involves an ethylene glycol derivative (12-148).[14]

$$Cl_2BOCH_2CH_2OBCl_2 + C_4H_9OH \rightarrow Cl_2BOCH_2CH_2OB\begin{matrix} \diagup Cl \\ \diagdown OC_4H_9 \end{matrix} + HCl \qquad (12\text{-}148)$$

* Methods of preparation of dialkoxychloroboranes from alkoxydichloroboranes essentially are limited to the production of compounds with primary alkyl groups since only primary alkoxydihaloboranes are stable.[85]

The product is the only known example of a dialkoxyhaloborane involving different alkoxyl groups.

b. *And Alkoxides.* Alkoxydihaloboranes are converted to the dialkoxy derivative on treatment with one mole of an alkoxide.[48]

$$ROBF_2 + RONa \rightarrow (RO)_2BF + NaF, \quad R = CH_3, C_2H_5 \quad (12\text{-}149)$$

This reaction can be contrasted to the formation of the salt (XCVIII) from the reaction of sodium methylate and boron trifluoride in ether solution.[104]

$$CH_3OBF_3^-Na^+$$
(XCVIII)

c. *And Cyclic Ethers.* Reaction (12-150) has been reported.[33]

$$\begin{array}{c} CH_2\text{—}CH_2 \\ | \quad\quad | \\ O \quad\quad O \\ \diagdown \;\; \diagup \\ CH_2 \end{array} + ClCH_2OCH_2CH_2OBCl_2 \rightarrow (ClCH_2OCH_2CH_2O)_2BCl \quad (12\text{-}150)$$

d. *Disproportionation.* Dialkoxyhaloboranes are obtained from the disproportionation of alkoxydihaloboranes (12-151). Thus the

$$2\ ROBCl_2 \rightarrow (RO)_2BCl + BCl_3 \quad (12\text{-}151)$$

attempted preparation of dichloro-(2-chloroethoxy)borane from the equimolar reaction of boron trichloride and 2-chloroethanol resulted instead in the formation of chlorodi-(2-chloroethoxy)borane and tri-2-chloroethoxyborane, presumably by the following series of reactions:[37,91]

$$BCl_3 + ClCH_2CH_2OH \rightarrow HCl + ClCH_2CH_2OBCl_2 \quad (12\text{-}152)$$

$$2\ ClCH_2CH_2OBCl_2 \rightleftarrows (ClCH_2CH_2O)_2BCl + BCl_3 \quad (12\text{-}153)$$

$$2\ (ClCH_2CH_2O)_2BCl \rightleftarrows (ClCH_2CH_2O)_3B + ClCH_2CH_2OBCl_2 \quad (12\text{-}154)$$

Dichloro-(4-chlorobutoxy)borane behaves similarly to the ethyl derivative when distilled at reduced pressure.[37] Dichloro(neopentoxy)borane and butoxydichloroborane gave 100% and 68% yields, respectively, of the dialkoxy derivative on refluxing for 4.5 and 7.5 hr. at reduced pressure.[53] Dichloro-(2-chloromethoxyethoxy)-borane resulted in a 75% yield of the dialkoxy derivative when heated at 45–50° for four hours under reduced pressure.[33]

The ether complexes of dichloro(ethoxy)borane and dichloro-(methoxy)borane disproportionate at room temperature to give the dialkoxy derivatives.[112,130]

$$(C_2H_5)_2O{:}2C_2H_5OBCl_2 \rightarrow (C_2H_5O)_2BCl + (C_2H_5)_2O{:}BCl_3 \quad (12\text{-}155)$$

$$(CH_3)_2O{:}2CH_3OBCl_2 \rightarrow (CH_3)_2O{:}BCl_3 + (CH_3O)_2BCl \quad (12\text{-}156)$$

Dichloro(phenoxy)borane[53] and the *p*-nitro derivative[29] are incapable of decomposition to chlorobenzene (see Section IV-B-8b) and disproportionate to the diphenoxy derivatives.

Acetonitrile promotes the disproportionation of butoxydichloroborane by virtue of formation of an acetonitrile–boron trichloride complex (12-157). This effect is not observed with dichloro-(*o*-

$$2\ C_4H_9OBCl_2 + CH_3CN \rightarrow CH_3CN{:}BCl_3 + (C_4H_9O)_2BCl \qquad (12\text{-}157)$$

nitrophenoxy)borane presumably due to intramolecular coordination (XXXI).[59]

e. *And Trialkoxyboranes.* A series of dialkoxyhaloboranes derived from both primary and secondary alcohols was obtained as undistilled oils from the equimolar redistribution reaction of an alkoxydihaloborane and a trialkoxyborane.[88]

$$ROBCl_2 + (RO)_3B \rightarrow 2\ (RO)_2BCl \qquad (12\text{-}158)$$

Due to the existence of difluoromethoxyborane as a dimer, its boiling point is higher than that of fluorodimethoxyborane. Consequently the dimethoxy derivative could be distilled from a mixture of the difluoro compound and trimethoxyborane (12-159).[65] Butoxy-

$$CH_3OBF_2 + (CH_3O)_3B \rightarrow 2\ (CH_3O)_2BF \qquad (12\text{-}159)$$

difluoroborane, which also is dimeric, could not similarly be converted to the dibutoxy derivative.[87]

f. *And Boronic Acid Esters.* Impure dibutoxychloroborane was obtained from the equimolar equilibration of butoxydichloroborane and dibutoxybutylborane.[21]

$$C_4H_9OBCl_2 + C_4H_9B(OC_4H_9)_2 \rightarrow (C_4H_9O)_2BCl + C_4H_9BCl(OC_4H_9) \qquad (12\text{-}160)$$

3. FROM TRI(POLYFLUOROALKOXY)BORANES

Chlorination of the fluorinated esters (XCIX) under ultraviolet light gave the α-chloro derivatives (C) as well as the dialkoxychloroboranes (CI).[115]

$$(RCH_2O)_3B \quad \text{(XCIX)} \qquad (R\overset{Cl}{\overset{|}{C}}HO)_3B \quad \text{(C)} \qquad (R\overset{Cl}{\overset{|}{C}}HO)_2BCl \quad \text{(CI)}$$

$$R = CF_3,\ C_2H_5,\ C_3F_7$$

B. Reactions

1. HYDROLYSIS

Like the monoalkoxydihalo derivatives, the dialkoxy-[1,48,79,91,116,129] and diaryloxyhaloboranes[29] are rapidly hydrolyzed in cold water or moist air to give boric acid, two moles of an alcohol or phenol, and one mole of hydrogen halide.

$$(RO)_2BX + 3\ H_2O \rightarrow H_3BO_3 + 2\ ROH + HX \tag{12-161}$$

The polymeric products derived from diphenols (CII and CIII) similarly gave boric acid, diphenol, and hydrochloric acid when treated with water in ether solution.[54]

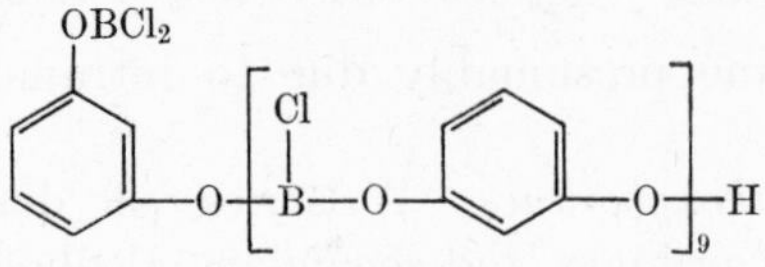

OBCl$_2$ Cl O B O O H 9

(CII)

HO O Cl B O O H 3

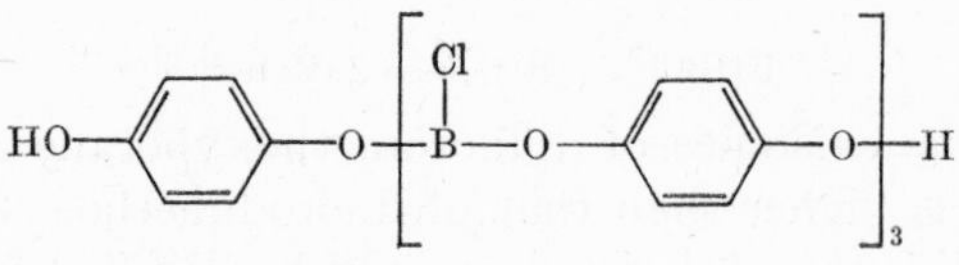

(CIII)

2. ALCOHOLYSIS

The conversion of dialkoxy- and diaryloxyhaloboranes to trialkoxy- and triaryloxyboranes by reaction with alcohols and phenols is discussed in Chapter 4. The reaction of dialkoxyhaloboranes with a glycol to produce alkylenedioxybis(dialkoxyboranes) is treated in Chapter 6.

3. WITH ALKOXIDES

The treatment of dialkoxyhaloboranes with metal alkoxides to produce trialkoxyboranes is discussed in Chapter 4.

4. WITH *t*-BUTYL HYDROPEROXIDE

The conversion of chlorodi-(*o*-nitrophenoxy)borane to the *t*-butylperoxy derivative by treatment with *t*-butyl hydroperoxide is recorded in Chapter 10.

5. WITH ETHERS

Chlorodimethoxyborane does not react with diglyme at 25° or with dimethyl ether up to 80°, nor does the diethoxy derivative react with dimethyl ether up to 100°.[129] Dibutoxychloroborane does not cleave n-butyl isobutyl ether.[50] In general, dialkoxychloroboranes and trialkoxyboranes do not react with ethers; whereas boron trichloride and alkoxydichloroboranes do react. Thus, in the series BCl_3, $ROBCl_2$, $(RO)_2BCl$, $(RO)_3B$, it appears that the electrophilicity of the boron atom is reduced in the dialkoxy derivative to the point where coordination with an ether is precluded. However, exceptions have been recorded. Chlorodiethoxyborane has been reported to react with both tetrahydrofuran and diglyme as shown by the decrease in the amount of hydrolyzable chlorine present as a function of time (Table 12-9),[92] and reaction (12-162) has been reported.[33]

$$\begin{matrix} CH_2\text{—}CH_2 \\ | \quad\quad | \\ O \quad\quad O \\ \diagdown \ \diagup \\ CH_2 \end{matrix} + (ClCH_2OCH_2CH_2O)_2BCl \rightarrow (ClCH_2OCH_2CH_2O)_3B \qquad (12\text{-}162)$$

Table 12-9. Reaction of chlorodiethoxyborane with tetrahydrofuran and diglyme

$(C_2H_5O)_2BCl$ (moles)	Solvent (moles)		Temp. (°C)	Time (hr.)	% $(C_2H_5O)_2BCl$ reacted
0.0652	None		Room temp.	0	0
0.0713	THF	(0.12)	,,	2	26
0.0790	,,	(0.12)	,,	24	58
0.0358	,,	(0.12)	,,	24	72
0.0362	,,	(0.55)	,,	2	38
0.0362	,,	(0.55)	,,	24	68
0.0362	,,	(0.55)	,,	48	76
0.0712	,,	(0.12)	55–65	2	51
0.0722	Diglyme	(0.07)	Room temp.	2	0
0.0716	,,	(0.07)	55–65	2	12
0.0359	,,	(0.32)	Room temp.	2	25
0.0359	,,	(0.32)	,,	24	19
0.0359	,,	(0.32)	,,	48	36

6. DISPROPORTIONATION

The disproportionation of dialkoxy- and diaryloxyhaloboranes to trialkoxy- and triaryloxyboranes (12-163) is treated in Chapter 4 and Section IV-A-4b of this chapter.

$$2\,(RO)_2BCl \rightarrow ROBCl_2 + (RO)_3B \qquad (12\text{-}163)$$

7. THERMAL DECOMPOSITION

In general, the thermal decomposition of dialkoxyhaloboranes at atmospheric or higher pressures yields trialkoxyboranes. Thus,

reaction (12-164) is discussed in Chapter 4. The reaction, however, can be stopped at an intermediate metaborate stage (12-165, see Chapter 9).

$$3\,(RO)_2BCl \rightarrow (RO)_3B + 3\,RCl + B_2O_3 \qquad (12\text{-}164)$$

$$3\,(RO)_2BCl \rightarrow (ROBO)_3 + 3\,RCl \qquad (12\text{-}165)$$

In contrast to the alkoxydihaloboranes, chlorodimethoxyborane and chlorodiethoxyborane are thermally stable at 78° and 100°, respectively.[129] A series of dialkoxychloroboranes derived from both primary and secondary alkyl groups (n-propyl, n-butyl, i-butyl, neopentyl, and methyl-*t*-butylcarbinyl) could be distilled at 30–40° at reduced pressure without significant decomposition.[88]

The chloromethoxyethoxy derivative (CIV) when heated at 50° and 20 mm. was reported to give the alkyl halide (CV) as one of the decomposition products.[33] Since alkyl halides are not a common

$$\underset{\text{(CIV)}}{(ClCH_2OCH_2CH_2O)_2BCl} \qquad \underset{\text{(CV)}}{ClCH_2OCH_2CH_2Cl}$$

decomposition product of dialkoxyhaloboranes, but are well known products in the decomposition of alkoxydihaloboranes, it is possible that the decomposition path of (CIV) is as follows:

$$2\,(RO)_2BCl \rightarrow (RO)_3B + ROBCl_2 \qquad (12\text{-}166)$$

$$3\,ROBCl_2 \rightarrow 3\,RCl + B_2O_3 + BCl_3 \qquad (12\text{-}167)$$

8. WITH AMINES

a. *Primary and Secondary.* Primary amines react readily with haloboranes to displace the halogen atom. The aminolysis of dialkoxyhaloboranes thus offers a convenient method of synthesis of dialkoxy(amino)boranes.[6]

$$(C_4H_9O)_2BCl + 2\,C_2H_5NH_2 \xrightarrow[-78^\circ]{\text{Pentane}} (C_4H_9O)_2BNHC_2H_5 + C_2H_5NH_2\cdot HCl \qquad (12\text{-}168)$$

An attempt to aminolyze chlorodiethoxyborane with dimethylamine led to isolation of the disproportionation products of the dialkoxyaminoborane.[116]

$$(C_2H_5O)_2BCl + (CH_3)_2NH \rightarrow HCl + \{(C_2H_5O)_2BN(CH_3)_2\} \rightarrow \tfrac{2}{3}\,(C_2H_5O)_3B + \tfrac{1}{3}\,[(CH_3)_2N]_3B \qquad (12\text{-}169)$$

b. *Tertiary.* One-to-one pyridine complexes (CVI) have been reported for dialkoxychloroboranes derived from primary ω-chloro-

$$\underset{\text{(CVI)}}{(RO)_2BCl\!:\!C_5H_5N}$$

alcohols,[1,37] and for diaryloxychloroboranes derived from chlorophenols.[28,29] The allyl and 2-methylallyl derivatives formed either 1:1 or 1:2 (CVII) complexes with pyridine depending upon the

$$(CH_2{=}CHCH_2O)_2BCl{:}2C_5H_5N$$
(CVII)

stoichiometry employed.[56] The 1-methylallyl derivative formed a 1:1 complex with pyridine.[58]

The reaction of chlorodimethoxyborane with excess trimethylamine resulted in the 1:1 complex (CVIII).[132]

$$(CH_3O)_2BCl{:}N(CH_3)_3$$
(CVIII)

9. WITH CARBOXYLIC ACIDS

The acylation of dialkoxyhaloboranes with a carboxylic acid affords a synthesis of anhydrides and is discussed in Chapter 8.

10. WITH HYDROGEN CHLORIDE

Dialkoxychloroboranes[35] at 20° and diphenoxychloroboranes[30] do not react with hydrogen chloride.

11. WITH BORON TRIHALIDES

The conversion of dialkoxyhaloboranes to alkoxydihaloboranes by reaction with an equimolar quantity of boron halide is discussed in Section IV-A-4a.

12. REDUCTION

a. *With Sodium.* The conversion[127] and attempted conversions[79] of dialkoxyhaloboranes to boron–boron bonded materials by treatment with metallic sodium and other metals will be discussed in a subsequent volume of this series.

$$(RO)_2BCl + 2\,Na \rightarrow (RO)_2B{-}B(OR)_2 + 2\,NaCl \qquad (12\text{-}170)$$

b. *With Sodium Hydride.* The reduction of dialkoxyhaloboranes to dialkoxyboranes with sodium hydride is discussed in Chapter 11.

$$(RO)_2BCl + NaH \rightarrow (RO)_2BH + NaCl \qquad (12\text{-}171)$$

c. *With Sodium Borohydride.* The conversion of chlorodimethoxyborane to trimethoxyborane by reaction with sodium borohydride in diglyme solution[24] is treated in Chapter 4.

Reduction of dibutoxyfluoroborane and fluorodipentoxyborane

with sodium borohydride in the presence of propylene in tetrahydrofuran solution was claimed as a method of preparation of boronic acid esters.[84] Presumably the dialkoxyborane, $(RO)_2BH$, is

$$4\,(RO)_2BF + NaBH_4 + 4\,C_3H_6 \rightarrow 4\,C_3H_7B(OR)_2 + NaBF_4 \qquad (12\text{-}172)$$

formed and adds to the olefin to give the boronate. In contrast, no dimethoxyborane was detected in the reduction of chlorodimethoxyborane with sodium borohydride in diglyme solution.[24]

13. WITH SODIUM TETRAMETHOXYBORATE

Halodimethoxyboranes are converted to trimethoxyborane by treatment with sodium tetramethoxyborate. See Chapter 4.

VI. TRIALKYLSILOXYHALOBORANES

A. Methods of Preparation

1. BORON TRIHALIDE CLEAVAGE OF DISILOXANES, TRISILOXANES AND TETRASILOXANES

Cleavage of a hexaalkyldisiloxane with one mole of boron tribromide results in the silicon analog of a tertiary alkoxydibromo-

$$[(CH_3)_3Si]_2O + BBr_3 \xrightarrow{-40^\circ} \text{complex} \xrightarrow[\text{temp.}]{\text{Room}} (CH_3)_3SiOBBr_2 + (CH_3)_3SiBr \qquad (12\text{-}173)$$

borane (12-173). If excess disiloxane is present, the bis(trialkylsiloxy) bromoborane is formed (12-174).[126]

$$2\,[(C_2H_5)_3Si]_2O + BBr_3 \xrightarrow{80^\circ} [(C_2H_5)_3SiO]_2BBr + 2\,(C_2H_5)_3SiBr \qquad (12\text{-}174)$$

In contrast to organic ethers, which complex with boron trifluoride but do not react further, the silyl ethers, $(CH_3SiH_2)_2O$, $[(CH_3)_2SiH]_2O$ and $[(CH_3)_3Si]_2O$, are cleaved by boron trifluoride to give the difluorosiloxyboranes.[41]

$$(CH_3SiH_2)_2O + BF_3 \rightarrow CH_3SiH_2OBF_2 + CH_3SiH_2F \qquad (12\text{-}175)$$

However, the difluorosiloxyboranes are unstable and rapidly decompose.[41] Similar products have been obtained from boron tri-

$$3\,CH_3SiH_2OBF_2 \rightarrow 3\,CH_3SiH_2F + BF_3 + B_2O_3 \qquad (12\text{-}176)$$

chloride. In this case the dichlorosiloxy derivative (CIX) is only slowly decomposed at room temperature.[41]

$$(CH_3)_3SiOBCl_2$$
(CIX)

The inability of organic silicon compounds to form siliconium ions ruled out the carbonium ion type mechanism for the cleavage reaction and an S_Ni type mechanism (12-177) was proposed.[41]

$$\begin{matrix} >\!Si\!-\!O\!-\!Si\!< \\ \vdots \\ Cl\!-\!B\!-\!Cl \\ | \\ Cl \end{matrix} \rightarrow\ >\!SiCl + >\!SiOBCl_2 \tag{12-177}$$

The cyclic siloxanes, hexamethyl- and hexaethylcyclotrisiloxane and octamethyl- and octaethylcyclotetrasiloxane, are cleaved by boron trichloride[99,100] and tribromide[98] in an exothermic reaction.[97,99] In these cases, each R_2SiO unit results in a dialkylhalosiloxydihaloborane.

$$(R_2SiO)_3 + 3\,BX_3 \rightarrow 3\,R_2Si(X)OBX_2 \tag{12-178}$$

$$(R_2SiO)_4 + 4\,BX_3 \rightarrow 4\,R_2Si(X)OBX_2 \tag{12-179}$$

Intermediate siloxane–boron trichloride complexes in reactions (12-178) and (12-179), if formed at all, were too short-lived to be determined by cryoscopic measurements.[99] In contrast, siloxane–boron trifluoride complexes, $(R_2SiO)_3{:}3BF_3$ and $(R_2SiO)_4{:}4BF_3$, were shown to be present. However, the dialkylfluorosiloxydifluoroboranes, $R_2Si(F)OBF_2$, if formed at all, were too unstable to isolate.[100]

The relative rates of reactions (12-178) and (12-179) with boron trichloride were found to be strongly affected by steric factors. The methylcyclosiloxanes reacted more rapidly than the ethyl derivatives and the trimers reacted more rapidly than the tetramers. These results are in agreement with greatest accessibility of the oxygen atoms in the trimeric methyl derivative and least accessibility in the tetrameric ethyl derivative as indicated by Fisher–Hirschfelder–Taylor models.[99]

2. ATTEMPTED PREPARATION FROM BORON TRIHALIDES AND SILANOLS

Unlike alcohols which undergo hydrogen–oxygen cleavage with boron trihalides, silanols do not react with boron tribromide to give siloxyboranes but result in silicon–oxygen cleavage to give boric acid and silyl halides.[125]

$$3\,(C_2H_5)_3SiOH + BBr_3 \rightarrow 3\,(C_2H_5)_3SiBr + H_3BO_3 \qquad (12\text{-}180)$$

Sodium triethylsiloxide does result in Si–O–B bond formation in reaction with boron tribromide, but the reaction has not specifically been used to prepare $R_3SiOBBr_2$ or $(R_3SiO)_2BBr$.[125]

B. Reactions

1. HYDROLYSIS

Although specific data are not available, it is most probable that the trialkylsiloxyhaloboranes are readily hydrolyzed as in equation (12-181).

$$R_3SiOBX_2 + 3\,H_2O \rightarrow R_3SiOH + H_3BO_3 + 2\,HX \qquad (12\text{-}181)$$

The dialkylchlorosiloxyboranes (CX) react with water with the formation of a cyclosiloxane and boric acid.[99]

$$R_2Si(Cl)OBCl_2$$
$$(CX,\ R = CH_3,\ C_2H_5)$$

2. ALCOHOLYSIS

The conversion of (CXI) to an unsymmetrical ester on treatment with methanol is discussed in Chapter 13.

$$[(C_2H_5)_3SiO]_2BBr$$
$$(CXI)$$

3. DISPROPORTIONATION

The disproportionation of dialkylhalosiloxydihaloboranes to tris(dialkylhalosiloxy)boranes is discussed in Chapter 13.

4. THERMAL DECOMPOSITION

Dibromo(trimethylsiloxy)borane decomposes in a manner analogous to the alkoxydihaloboranes when heated at 80°.[126]

$$(CH_3)_3SiOBBr_2 \rightarrow (CH_3)_3SiBr + \{BrBO\} \qquad (12\text{-}182)$$

$$\{BrBO\} \rightarrow \tfrac{1}{3}\,BBr_3 + \tfrac{1}{3}\,B_2O_3 \qquad (12\text{-}183)$$

The fluorine and chlorine derivatives, $CH_3SiH_2OBF_2$, $(CH_3)_2$-$SiHOBF_2$, $(CH_3)_3SiOBF_2$, $CH_3SiH_2OBCl_2$, and $(CH_3)_2SiHOBCl_2$ were too unstable to isolate; $(CH_3)_3SiOBCl_2$ decomposed slowly at room temperature.[41]

The mechanism of the decomposition has not been elucidated; however, the inability of silicon to form siliconium ions would rule out the path (12-184) analogous to that proposed for $ROBX_2$ compounds.

$$\geq Si-O-B\langle^{X}_{X} \rightarrow \geq Si^{+} + \{O{=}BX\} + X^{-} \qquad (12\text{-}184)$$

VII. 2-HALO-1,3,2-DIOXABOROLANES AND BORINANES

A. Methods of Preparation

1. FROM BORON TRIHALIDES AND DIOLS OR CATECHOL

Vicinal and 1,3-glycols are capable of reacting with boron trichloride to produce five- and six-membered rings. Thus, the equimolar reaction of ethylene glycol and boron trichloride at −80° afforded a 72% yield of the dioxaborolane (12-185).[13] A similar yield was

$$HOCH_2CH_2OH + BCl_3 \rightarrow \begin{matrix} CH_2{-}O \\ | \\ CH_2{-}O \end{matrix}\rangle BCl + 2\,HCl \qquad (12\text{-}185)$$

obtained at 0° with excess boron trichloride.[9] Similar reactions were performed with propylene glycol,[9,31] trimethylene glycol,[22,31,43,114] and 1,3-butanediol.[22]

If two moles of boron trichloride are used with ethylene glycol, an intermediate linear product is formed (12-186) which disproportionates to the cyclic product on distillation (12-187).

$$HOCH_2CH_2OH + 2\,BCl_3 \rightarrow Cl_2BOCH_2CH_2OBCl_2 + 2\,HCl \qquad (12\text{-}186)$$

$$Cl_2BOCH_2CH_2OBCl_2 \rightarrow \begin{matrix} CH_2{-}O \\ | \\ CH_2{-}O \end{matrix}\rangle BCl + BCl_3 \qquad (12\text{-}187)$$

2-Chloro-1,3,2-dioxaborolane also was stated to have been prepared by passing boron trichloride through ethylene glycol.[114]

Catechol readily forms the cyclic derivative (CXII) with one or more moles of boron trichloride or boron tribromide.[54]

$$C_6H_4\langle^{O}_{O}\rangle B{-}X$$

(CXII, X = Cl, Br)

2. FROM BORON TRICHLORIDE OR ALKOXYCHLOROBORANES AND 2-ALKOXY-1,3,2-DIOXABOROLANES

The redistribution of trialkoxyboranes and boron trihalides to give linear alkoxyhaloboranes has its counterpart in the cyclic derivatives (12-188, 12-189, and 12-190).[13,43,54] The formation of

$$C_6H_4O_2BOC_4H_9 + BCl_3 \rightarrow C_6H_4O_2BCl + C_4H_9OBCl_2 \quad (12\text{-}188)$$

$$\begin{array}{l} CH_2{-}O \\ | \qquad\quad \diagdown \\ | \qquad\qquad BOBC_4H_9 \\ | \qquad\quad \diagup \\ CH_2{-}O \end{array} + BCl_3 \rightarrow \begin{array}{l} CH_2{-}O \\ | \qquad\quad \diagdown \\ | \qquad\qquad BCl \\ | \qquad\quad \diagup \\ CH_2{-}O \end{array} + C_4H_9OBCl_2 \quad (12\text{-}189)$$

$$CH_2(CH_2O)_2BO(CH_2)_3Cl + BCl_3 \rightarrow \underset{\text{(CXIII)}}{CH_2(CH_2O)_2BCl} + Cl(CH_2)_3OBCl_2 \quad (12\text{-}190)$$

(CXIII) and not some linear product such as (CXIV) testifies to the relative stability of the dioxaborolane ring.

$$Cl_2BOCH_2CH_2OB\begin{array}{l} \diagup Cl \\ \diagdown OC_4H_9 \end{array}$$

(CXIV)

Alkoxydichloroboranes (12-191) and dialkoxychloroboranes (12-192) can serve as the source of halogen.[43]

$$CH_2(CH_2O)_2BO(CH_2)_3Cl + Cl(CH_2)_3OBCl_2 \rightarrow CH_2(CH_2O)_2BCl + (ClCH_2O)_2BCl \quad (12\text{-}191)$$

$$CH_2(CH_2O)_2BO(CH_2)_3Cl + [Cl(CH_2)_3O]_2BCl \rightarrow CH_2(CH_2O)_2BCl + (ClCH_2O)_3B \quad (12\text{-}192)$$

3. FROM 2,2′ OXYBIS-(1,3,2-BENZODIOXABOROLE)

The anhydride (CXV) was converted to both the chloro and bromo derivatives (CXVI and CXVII) in good yield on treatment with either boron trichloride or bromide. The reaction could not be effected with boron trifluoride. Phosphorus pentachloride also effected the transformation of (CXV) to (CXVI).[54]

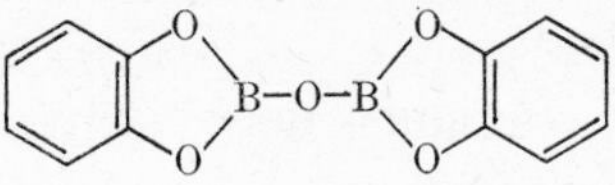

(CXV) 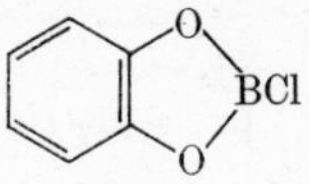 (CXVI) 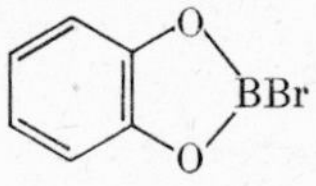 (CXVII)

4. FROM ETHYLENEDIOXYBISBORANES

Attempted distillation of the chloroboranes (CXVIII) and (CXIX) resulted in their disproportionation to the cyclic monochloroborane.[14,15]

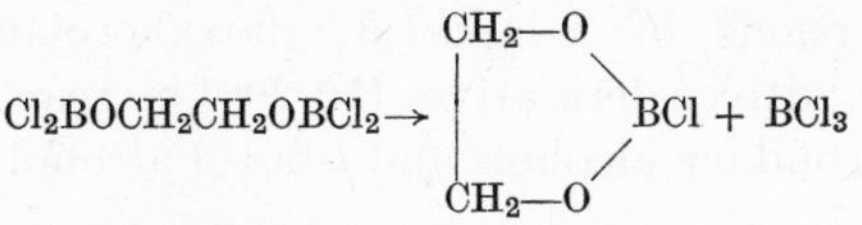

$$\underset{\text{(CXVIII)}}{Cl_2BOCH_2CH_2OBCl_2} \rightarrow \begin{matrix} CH_2{-}O \\ | \\ CH_2{-}O \end{matrix} \!\!> BCl + BCl_3 \qquad (12\text{-}193)$$

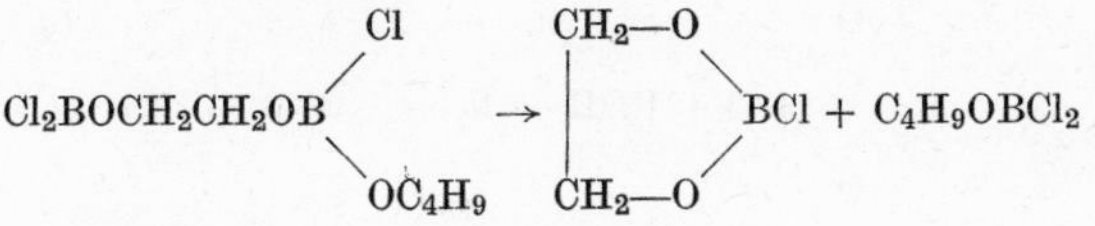

$$\underset{\text{(CXIX)}}{Cl_2BOCH_2CH_2OB\begin{matrix} Cl \\ OC_4H_9 \end{matrix}} \rightarrow \begin{matrix} CH_2{-}O \\ | \\ CH_2{-}O \end{matrix} \!\!> BCl + C_4H_9OBCl_2 \qquad (12\text{-}194)$$

B. *Reactions*

1. HYDROLYSIS

The cyclic alkoxyhaloboranes are readily hydrolyzed to the starting glycol, boric acid and halogen acid.[9,13,42,54]

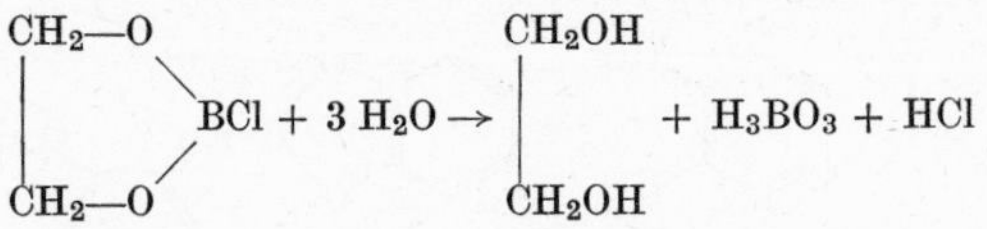

$$\begin{matrix} CH_2{-}O \\ | \\ CH_2{-}O \end{matrix} \!\!> BCl + 3\ H_2O \rightarrow \begin{matrix} CH_2OH \\ | \\ CH_2OH \end{matrix} + H_3BO_3 + HCl \qquad (12\text{-}195)$$

$$C_6H_4O_2BBr + 3\ H_2O \rightarrow C_6H_4(OH)_2 + H_3BO_3 + HBr \qquad (12\text{-}196)$$

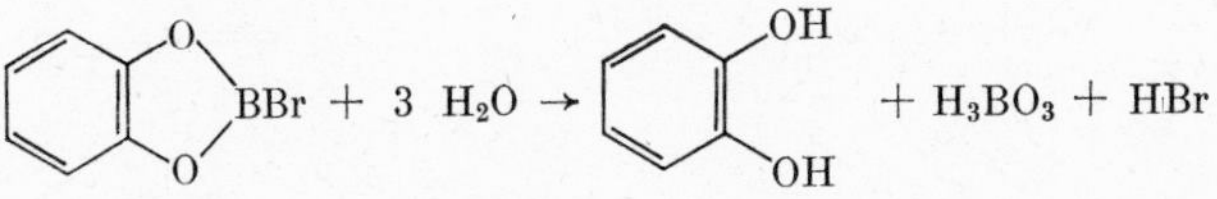

Complex formation with pyridine (CXX[13] and CXXI[54]) does not preclude hydrolysis.

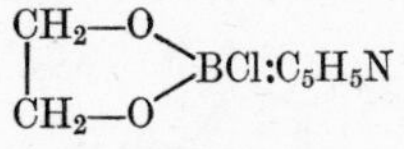

$$\begin{matrix} CH_2{-}O \\ | \\ CH_2{-}O \end{matrix} \!\!> BCl{:}C_5H_5N \qquad C_6H_4O_2BBr{:}C_5H_5N$$

(CXX) 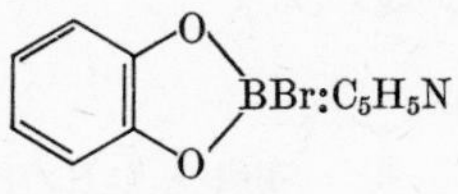 (CXXI)

Reaction with an insufficient amount of water leads to preferential destruction of the boron–halogen bond.[13,54]

$$\begin{array}{l}CH_2\text{—}O\\ |\qquad\qquad \backslash\\ |\qquad\qquad\quad BCl\\ |\qquad\qquad /\\ CH_2\text{—}O\end{array} + H_2O \rightarrow \begin{array}{l}CH_2\text{—}O\\ |\qquad\qquad \backslash\\ |\qquad\qquad\quad BOH\\ |\qquad\qquad /\\ CH_2\text{—}O\end{array} + HCl \qquad (12\text{-}197)$$

$$C_6H_4O_2BCl + H_2O \rightarrow C_6H_4O_2BOH + HCl \qquad (12\text{-}198)$$

2. ALCOHOLYSIS

The conversions of 2-halo-1,3,2-dioxaborolanes to 2-alkoxy (12-199) and 2-hydroxy derivatives (12-200) by reaction with various primary and secondary alcohols and *t*-butyl alcohol are discussed in Chapters 6 and 7.

$$R(O)_2BCl + ROH \rightarrow R(O)_2BOR + HCl \qquad (12\text{-}199)$$

$$R(O)_2BCl + t\text{-}C_4H_9OH \rightarrow R(O)_2BOH + t\text{-}C_4H_9Cl \qquad (12\text{-}200)$$

Similar reactions with the catechol derivative are discussed in Chapters 5 and 6.

$$2\ C_6H_4O_2BCl + C_6H_4(OH)_2 \rightarrow C_6H_4O_2B\text{—}O\text{—}C_6H_4\text{—}O\text{—}BO_2C_6H_4 + 2\ HCl \qquad (12\text{-}201)$$

$$C_6H_4O_2BCl + ROH \rightarrow C_6H_4O_2BOR + HCl \qquad (12\text{-}202)$$

$$C_6H_4O_2BCl + C_6H_5OH \rightarrow C_6H_4O_2BOC_6H_5 + HCl \qquad (12\text{-}203)$$

3. WITH THIOLS

The transformation of (CXXII) to (CXXIII) is discussed in Chapter 20.

$$R\langle\begin{smallmatrix}O\\O\end{smallmatrix}\rangle B{-}X \quad \text{(CXXII)} \qquad\qquad R\langle\begin{smallmatrix}O\\O\end{smallmatrix}\rangle BSR \quad \text{(CXXIII)}$$

4. THERMAL DECOMPOSITION

In contrast to the linear dialkoxyhaloboranes and diaryloxyhaloboranes, the cyclic members (CXXIV,[9,13] CXXV,[42,43] and CXXVI[54]) have exceptional thermal stability even in the presence of ferric chloride. Thus (CXXIV) was recovered in 69% yield when

$$\begin{matrix}CH_2{-}O\\ |\\ CH_2{-}O\end{matrix}\!\!>BCl \quad \text{(CXXIV)} \qquad CH_2\langle\begin{matrix}CH_2{-}O\\ CH_2{-}O\end{matrix}\rangle BCl \quad \text{(CXXV)} \qquad C_6H_4\langle\begin{matrix}O\\ O\end{matrix}\rangle B{-}X \quad \text{(CXXVI, X = Cl, Br)}$$

heated for two hours at 120° in the presence of ferric chloride. Extensive decomposition according to equation (12-204) did take place in thirty hours at 300°. In one experiment ethylene was formed.[13]

$$\begin{matrix}CH_2{-}O\\ |\\ CH_2{-}O\end{matrix}\!\!>BCl \rightarrow \{ClCH_2CH_2OBO\} \rightarrow \tfrac{1}{3}\,(ClCH_2CH_2O)_3B + \tfrac{1}{3}\,B_2O_3 \qquad (12\text{-}204)$$

This is reminiscent of the thermal decomposition of metaborates (see Chapter 9).

The propylene glycol derivative (CXXVII) is less stable than the ethylene glycol derivative (CXXIV).[9]

$$\begin{matrix}CH_2{-}O\\ |\\ CH_3CH{-}O\end{matrix}\!\!>BCl \quad \text{(CXXVII)}$$

The decomposition products (CXXVIII) and (CXXIX) were isolated from the pyrolysis of (CXXV) at 100° (see Chapter 4).[42,43]

$$CH_2\langle\begin{matrix}CH_2{-}O\\ CH_2{-}O\end{matrix}\rangle BO(CH_2)_3Cl \quad \text{(CXXVIII)} \qquad\qquad [Cl(CH_2)_3O]_3B \quad \text{(CXXIX)}$$

The aromatic derivative (CXXVI) required prolonged heating at elevated temperature to effect decomposition to tricatechol biborate and boron trihalide.[54] It was suggested that the stability of the catechol derivatives, at least in part, could be due to resonance as a result of the six π-electrons in the borolane ring (12-205).[54]

$$C_6H_4(\ddot{O})_2B{-}Cl \longleftrightarrow C_6H_4(\overset{+}{O})(\ddot{O})B{=}Cl \longleftrightarrow C_6H_4(\ddot{O})(\overset{+}{O})B{=}Cl \qquad (12\text{-}205)$$

5. WITH AMINES

In a manner analogous to the linear alkoxyhaloboranes, the cyclic ethylene glycol[13] and catechol[54] derivatives form 1:1 complexes with pyridine (CXXX and CXXXI).

$$\begin{array}{l}CH_2{-}O\\ |\qquad\qquad \rangle BCl:C_5H_5N\\ CH_2{-}O\end{array} \qquad\qquad C_6H_4(O)_2BBr:C_5H_5N$$

(CXXX) (CXXXI)

Primary and secondary amines yield the 2-amino derivatives.[9,14,31,54]

$$\begin{array}{l}CH_2{-}O\\ |\qquad\qquad \rangle BCl\\ CH_2{-}O\end{array} + 2\,(CH_3)_2NH \rightarrow \begin{array}{l}CH_2{-}O\\ |\qquad\qquad \rangle BN(CH_3)_2\\ CH_2{-}O\end{array} + (CH_3)_2NH\cdot HCl \qquad (12\text{-}206)$$

$$C_6H_4(O)_2BCl + 2\,(C_2H_5)_2NH \rightarrow C_6H_4(O)_2BN(C_2H_5)_2 + (C_2H_5)_2NH\cdot HCl \qquad (12\text{-}207)$$

$$\begin{array}{l}CH_2{-}O\\ |\qquad\qquad \rangle BCl\\ CH_3CH{-}O\end{array} + 2\,CH_3NH_2 \rightarrow \begin{array}{l}CH_2{-}O\\ |\qquad\qquad \rangle NHCH_3\\ CH_3CH{-}O\end{array} + CH_3NH_2\cdot HCl \qquad (12\text{-}208)$$

6. WITH CARBOXYLIC ACIDS

The acetylation of cyclic alkoxyhaloboranes with carboxylic acids is recorded in Chapter 8.

7. WITH ORGANOMETALLIC REAGENTS

The conversion of (CXXXII) to (CXXXIII) by treatment with butyl magnesium chloride is discussed in Volume III of this series.

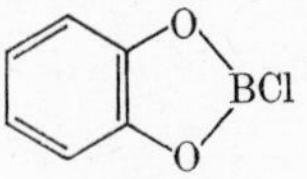

$$\text{(CXXXII)}\quad C_6H_4O_2BCl \qquad \text{(CXXXIII)}\quad C_6H_4O_2BC_4H_9$$

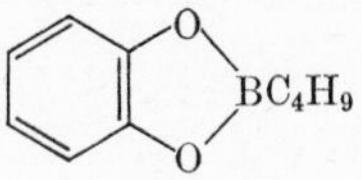

8. WITH 2-HYDROXY-1,3,2-DIOXABOROLANES

The reactions of 2-chlorodioxaborolanes with 2-hydroxydioxaborolanes are discussed in Chapter 7.

VIII. OXYBIS(ACETOXYCHLOROBORANE)

A. Methods of Preparation

1. FROM BORON TRICHLORIDE AND ACETIC ACID ESTERS

Acetates of secondary alcohols and of *t*-butyl alcohol react with boron trichloride at $-80°$ to form 1:1 complexes* which on warming in the presence of excess ester give oxybis(acetoxychloroborane).[62]

$$2\,[CH_3C(=O)OR{:}BCl_3] + CH_3C(=O)OR \rightarrow CH_3C(=O)OB(Cl)OB(Cl)OC(=O)CH_3 + 3\,RCl + CH_3C(=O)Cl \qquad (12\text{-}209)$$

The fact that the products shown in equation (12-209) arise only when R is secondary or tertiary indicates that the reaction proceeds via acyl–oxygen cleavage. When R is primary, the intermediate alkoxydichloroborane reacts with the acetyl chloride to give oxybis-(acetoxychloroborane).[62]

2. FROM BORON TRICHLORIDE AND ACETIC ACID OR ANHYDRIDE

It has been stated, without presentation of experimental data,

* The infrared spectrum of the ethyl acetate–boron trichloride complex indicates coordination through the carbonyl oxygen and not the alkyl oxygen.[90]

that oxybis(acetoxychloroborane) is obtained from the 3 : 2 reactions of acetic acid or acetic anhydride and boron trichloride.[35,62]

$$3\,CH_3\overset{\overset{O}{\|}}{C}OH + 2\,BCl_3 \rightarrow CH_3\overset{\overset{O}{\|}}{C}O\underset{\underset{Cl}{|}}{B}O\underset{\underset{Cl}{|}}{B}O\overset{\overset{O}{\|}}{C}CH_3 + CH_3\overset{\overset{O}{\|}}{C}Cl + 3\,HCl \qquad (12\text{-}210)$$

$$3\,(CH_3\overset{\overset{O}{\|}}{C})_2O + 2\,BCl_3 \rightarrow CH_3\overset{\overset{O}{\|}}{C}O\underset{\underset{Cl}{|}}{B}O\underset{\underset{Cl}{|}}{B}O\overset{\overset{O}{\|}}{C}CH_3 + 4\,CH_3\overset{\overset{O}{\|}}{C}Cl \qquad (12\text{-}211)$$

B. Reactions

1. PYROLYSIS

Pyrolysis of oxybis(acetoxychloroborane) at 150° results in elimination of acetyl chloride and deposition of boric oxide.[62]

$$CH_3\overset{\overset{O}{\|}}{C}O\underset{\underset{Cl}{|}}{B}O\underset{\underset{Cl}{|}}{B}O\overset{\overset{O}{\|}}{C}CH_3 \rightarrow 2\,CH_3\overset{\overset{O}{\|}}{C}Cl + B_2O_3 \qquad (12\text{-}212)$$

2. WITH ACETIC ACID

Acetic acid converts oxybis(acetoxychloroborane) to oxybis-(diacetoxyborane) (see Chapter 8).[62]

$$CH_3\overset{\overset{O}{\|}}{C}O\underset{\underset{Cl}{|}}{B}O\underset{\underset{Cl}{|}}{B}O\overset{\overset{O}{\|}}{C}CH_3 + 2\,CH_3\overset{\overset{O}{\|}}{C}OH \rightarrow (CH_3\overset{\overset{O}{\|}}{C}O)_2BOB(O\overset{\overset{O}{\|}}{C}CH_3)_2 + 2\,HCl \qquad (12\text{-}213)$$

IX. ANALYTICAL

A. Fluorine Derivatives

The original method[48] for the analysis of boron in alkoxyfluoroboranes involved hydrolysis, precipitation of the fluorine as calcium fluoride with calcium nitrate, and evaporation and incineration of the filtrate. The residue was then taken up in acetic acid and water and the remaining calcium removed as the oxalate. The filtrate was evaporated and calcined with a calculated amount of magnesium oxide to a constant weight of MgO and B_2O_3.

An alternative method involved fusion of the alkoxyfluoroborane with calcium chloride and an equimolar amount of potassium chloride and sodium. The melt was then taken up in water and the precipitates of calcium fluoride and calcium borate were separated by dissolution in a concentrated ammoniacal solution of calcium nitrate.[48]

Volumetric methods for alkoxyfluoroboranes also have been reported. An early procedure[107] for some diketone derivatives adopted from a nineteenth century procedure[76] involved basic hydrolysis followed by acidification and removal of the fluoride with barium chloride solution. After addition of potassium iodide and sodium iodate, the liberated iodine was titrated with sodium thiosulfate. Strong acids then were titrated with standard sodium hydroxide to the phenolphthalein endpoint followed by addition of mannitol and further titration of the boric acid to the phenolphthalein endpoint. A later method[9] involved fusion in a sodium peroxide bomb[72] followed by the usual titration for boric acid.

Methoxy- and ethoxydifluoroborane were analyzed by digestion in an alkaline calcium chloride solution followed by the usual titration for boric acid.[96] The method was adapted from the procedure for the determination of boron in boron trifluoride.[19]

B. Chlorine Derivatives

The analysis of an alkoxychloroborane does not suffer from fluoride interference and straightforward hydrolytic methods have been employed involving titration of the hydrochloric acid with sodium hydroxide to methyl orange endpoint and subsequent titration of the boric acid to the phenolphthalein endpoint in the presence of mannitol.[13,38,45,56,79,88,91] Barium hydroxide titrations also have been employed.[112,128,129,130]

The production of weakly acidic phenols from (CXXXIV)[28] and (CXXXV)[118] precluded straightforward hydrolytic and titrimetric

$C_6H_5OBCl_2$ (CXXXIV)

2,6-$(C(CH_3)_3)_2C_6H_3OBCl_2$ (CXXXV)

procedures. Dichloro(phenoxy)borane (CXXXIV) was analyzed[28] by the method of Thomas[120] involving methanolysis and distillation of trimethoxyborane as the methanol azeotrope followed by hydrolysis of the distillate and the usual titration for boric acid. The hindered phenolic derivative (CXXXV) was analyzed[118] by fusion in potassium carbonate[75] followed by dissolution of the melt and the usual titration for boric acid.

Alkylsiloxychloroboranes evidently offer no particular problems, since they also have been analyzed for hydrochloric acid and boric acid by straightforward hydrolytic and titrimetric procedures.[99]

X. PHYSICAL CONSTANTS

$ROBX_2$	M.p. (°C)	B.p. (°C)	d_4^t	n_D^t	Reference
CH_3OBCl_2	−15	0/66			128
		18/72			130
		58.0			129
$CH_3OBCl_2:N(CH_3)_3$	120				132
$2\,CH_3OBCl_2:O(CH_3)_2$	< 0				130
	—	—	—	—	129
CH_3OBBr_2	Unstable				63
CH_3OBF_2, $(CH_3OBF_2)_2$, $(CH_3OBF_2)_3$ or $(CH_3O)_3B:2\,BF_3$	37.0–39.5	85.2–85.4/745			96
	41–42	85.4			64
	41–42				119
	41.5	87			48
	41.9	85.2			65
	42	86			9
		85–86			134
		86			2
$C_2H_5OBCl_2$		0/26			127
		77.9			129
		78	1.125^{20}	1.3968^{20}	1
		78–80			50, 52
$2\,C_2H_5OBCl_2:O(CH_3)_2$	—	—	—	—	129
$2\,C_2H_5OBCl_2:O(C_2H_5)_2$	—	—	—	—	112, 130
$ClCH_2CH_2OBCl_2$		20/0.5	1.358^{18}	1.4429^{20}	37
$ClCH_2CH_2OBCl_2:C_5H_5N$	Solid				37
$ClCH_2CH_2OBCl_2:2C_5H_5N$	Solid				37
$ClCH_2OCH_2CH_2OBCl_2$			1.369_{20}^{20}	1.4587^{20}	33

(*Table continued*)

$ROBX_2$	M.p. (°C)	B.p. (°C)	d_4^t	n_D^t	Reference
$C_2H_5OBF_2$, $(C_2H_5OBF_2)_3$ or $(C_2H_5O)_3B{:}2\ BF_3$	19–21	82.4–82.7/745	1.2452^{25}	1.3495^{25}	96
	23	82			48
		82–83			134
$n\text{-}C_3H_7OBCl_2$			1.138^{20}	1.4094^{20}	53
$ClCH_2CH_2CH_2OBCl_2$		26/0.5		1.4460^{21}	38
			1.293^{20}	1.4432^{20}	1
$Cl(CH_2)_3OBCl_2{:}C_5H_5N$		Viscous oil			1
$CH_2\overset{Cl}{C}HCH_2OBCl_2$	Not isolated pure				38
$CH_2{=}CHCH_2OBCl_2$	Unstable at 20°				56
$CH_2{=}CHCH_2OBCl_2{:}C_5H_5N$	61				56
$CH_2{=}CHCH_2OBCl_2{:}2C_5H_5N$	White solid				56
$i\text{-}C_3H_7OBCl_2$		Stable at −80°			53
$ClCH_2\underset{CH_3}{C}HOBCl_2$	Not isolated pure				38
$(ClCH_2)_2CHOBCl_2$			1.424^{18}	1.4708^{21}	38
$n\text{-}C_4H_9OBCl_2$		34/12	1.066^{18}	1.4135^{20}	62
		35–38/12			52
		38–39/15		1.4164^{20}	52
		38–40/20	1.079^{20}	1.4162^{20}	51, 53
		42/12			47
$n\text{-}C_4H_9OBCl_2{:}C_5H_5N$		Oil			60, 86
$Cl(CH_2)_4OBCl_2$		Decomposes	1.254^{20}	1.4522^{20}	37
$Cl(CH_2)_4OBCl_2{:}C_5H_5N$	Solid				37, 38
$CH_2{=}CHCH_2CH_2OBCl_2$		36/15		1.4261^{20}	58
$CH_3CH{=}CHCH_2OBCl_2$	Unstable at 20°				58
$CH_3CH{=}CHCH_2OBCl_2{:}C_5H_5N$	Unstable at 20°				58
$CH_3CH{=}CH\underset{Cl}{C}HOBCl_2$ or $CH_3\underset{Cl}{C}HCH{=}CHOBCl_2$	White solid				45

$n\text{-}C_4H_9OBBr_2$	Unstable at 15°				25
$n\text{-}C_4H_9OBBr_2{:}C_5H_5N$	Unstable at 15°				25
$(n\text{-}C_4H_9OBF)_2$, $(n\text{-}C_4H_9OBF_2)_3$ or $(C_4H_9O)_3B{:}2BF_3$		36/20	1.047^{20}	1.4099^{18}	51
		43/11, 55–57/32	1.122^{20}	1.3858^{22}	87
		45–48/10		1.3882^{14}	89
		50–53/23		1.3840^{23}	21
		51.5–51.8/26	1.1302^{25}	1.3835^{25}	96
$i\text{-}C_4H_9OBCl_2$		32–34/20	1.042^{20}	1.4087^{20}	52
			1.046^{20}	1.4088^{20}	53
$CH_2{=}CCH_2OBCl_2$ $\mid$ CH_3	Unstable at 20°				56
$CH_2{=}CCH_2OBCl_2{:}2\ C_5H_5N$ $\mid$ CH_3	White solid				56
$i\text{-}C_4H_9OBBr_2$	Unstable at 20°				25
$s\text{-}C_4H_9OBCl_2$		Stable at −80°			51
$CH_2{=}CHCHOBCl_2$ $\mid$ CH_3	Unstable at 20°				58
$CH_2{=}CHCHOBCl_2{:}C_5H_5N$ $\mid$ CH_3	Unstable at 20°				58
$(CH_3)_3COBCl_2$	Unstable at 20°				51, 88
$n\text{-}C_5H_{11}OBCl_2$		52–55/28	1.056^{20}	1.4170^{20}	1
$Cl(CH_2)_5OBCl_2$			1.228^{20}	1.4533^{20}	1
$Cl(CH_2)_5OBCl_2{:}2C_5H_5N$	Crystalline				1
$(CH_3)_2CHCHOBCl_2$ $\mid$ CH_3	Not isolated				53
$(CH_3)_3CCH_2OBCl_2$			1.032^{20}	1.4097^{20}	53

(Table continued)

$ROBX_2$	M.p. (°C)	B.p. (°C)	d_4^t	n_D^t	Reference
$CH_3C(=O)CH{=}C(CH_3)OBF_2$	43				107
$(CH_3)_3CCH(CH_3)OBCl_2$	Not isolated				53
$ClCH_2CH_2CH(CH_2SiCl_3)CH_2CH_2OBCl_2$	Not isolated				117
$CH_3C(=O)C(CH_3){=}C(CH_3)OBF_2$	94–94.5				71
$C_6H_5CH_2OBCl_2$	Unstable at 20°				8
n-$C_8H_{17}OBCl_2$			1.015^{20}	1.4316^{20}	53
n-$C_6H_{13}CH(CH_3)OBCl_2$	Not isolated pure	Stable at −80°			53
n-$C_6H_{13}CH(CH_3)OBCl_2{:}C_5H_5N$	Not isolated pure				53
$C_6H_5CH(CH_3)OBCl_2$	Unstable at 20°				50
$CH_3C(=O)C(CH(CH_3)_2){=}C(CH_3)OBF_2$	113–113.5				133

2-Thienyl—C(OBF_2)=CHC(=O)CH_3	174–175	7
	176–177	69
$H_2NC(=O)CH{=}C(C_6H_5)OBF_2$	186.5–189.5	70
$CH_3C(=O)CH{=}C(C_6H_5)OBF_2$	155	107
$CH_3C(=O)C(C_6H_5){=}CHOBF_2$	100–101.5	74
$C_6H_5C(=O)CH{=}C(C_6H_5)OBF_2$	189–190	71
	191	107
$C_6H_5C(=O)C(C_6H_5){=}C(C_6H_5)OBF_2$	313–315	74

(Table continued)

$X_2BOROBX_2$	M.p. (°C)	B.p. (°C)	d_4^t	n_D^t	Reference
$Cl_2BOCH_2CH_2OBCl_2$				1.4392^{20}	14
	—	—	—	—	15
$Cl_2BOCH_2CH_2OBCl_2 : 2C_5H_5N$	White solid				14

$ArOBX_2$	M.p. (°C)	B.p. (°C)	d_4^t	n_D^t	Reference
$C_6H_5OBCl_2$		Decomposes			28, 52
$C_6H_5OBCl_2 : C_5H_5N$	98–102				28
2-$ClC_6H_4OBCl_2$	Unstable at 20°				29
2-$ClC_6H_4OBCl_2 : C_5H_5N$	67–70				29
2-$CH_3C_6H_4OBCl_2$	Unstable at 24°				29
2-$CH_3C_6H_4OBCl_2 : C_5H_5N$	50–55				29

o-$O_2NC_6H_4OBCl_2$	63		62
o-$O_2NC_6H_4OBCl_2:C_5H_5N$	160		62
	172		29
p-$O_2NC_6H_4OBCl_2$	Unstable at 20°		29
p-$O_2NC_6H_4OBCl_2:C_5H_5N$	194–196		29
$2,6$-$[C(CH_3)_3]_2C_6H_3OBCl_2$	1.301	160–161/26	118
$C_6H_5OBBr_2$	Not isolated pure		46
o-$CH_3OC(=O)C_6H_4OBF_2$	128		106

(Table continued)

$(RO)_2BX$	M.p. (°C)	B.p. (°C)	d_4^t	n_D^t	Reference
$(CH_3O)_2BCl$	−87.5	74.7			129
	—	—	—	—	110, 128, 130
$(CH_3O)_2BCl:N(CH_3)_3$	34				132
$(CH_3O)_2BBr$	Unstable				63
$(CH_3O)_2BF$		52.7 (Stable only in gas phase)			65
		53	1.053^{0}		48
	—	—	—	—	124
$(C_2H_5O)_2BCl$		0/5			127
		45.5–46/60			116
		112.3			129
			0.972^{20}	1.3878^{20}	1
$(C_2H_5O)_2BCl:(C_2H_5)_2O$	56				131
$(ClCH_2CH_2O)_2BCl$		76–83/18		1.4550^{20}	33
		Glass	1.2770^{20}		91
		Decomposes	1.320^{18}	1.4551^{20}	37
$(ClCH_2CH_2O)_2BCl:C_5H_5N$	Low melting solid				37
$(ClCH_2OCH_2CH_2O)_2BCl$		46/0.15	1.301_{20}^{20}	1.4611^{20}	33
$(CF_3\underset{\mathrm{Cl}}{\underset{\vert}{C}}HO)_2BCl$		77/200		1.3490^{25}	115
$(C_2H_5O)_2BBr$	—	—	—	—	82, 124
$(C_2H_5O)_2BF$		78			48
$(n\text{-}C_3H_7O)_2BCl$		36/6	0.959^{20}	1.4028^{20}	88
		38.5/6		1.4036^{20}	56
$(CH_3\overset{\mathrm{Cl}}{\overset{\vert}{C}}HCH_2O)_2BCl$	Not isolated pure				38

$(ClCH_2CH_2CH_2O)_2BCl$		84/0.1	1.240^{20}	1.4564^{20}	1
$(CF_3CF_2CHO)_2BCl$ (Cl on CH)				1.3330^{25}	115
$(CH_2{=}CHCH_2O)_2BCl$	Not isolated				56
$(CH_2{=}CHCH_2O)_2BCl{:}C_5H_5N$	—	—	—	—	56
$(CH_2{=}CHCH_2O)_2BCl{:}2C_5H_5N$		White solid			56
$(ClCH_2CHO)_2BCl$ (CH_3 on CH)	Not isolated pure				38
$(n\text{-}C_4H_9O)_2BCl$		Decomposes at 20°	0.941^{20}	1.4141^{20}	51
		39–40/0.3		1.4125^{20}	59
		40/0.25		1.4132^{20}	88
$[Cl(CH_2)_4O]_2BCl$		101/0.04	1.181^{20}	1.4622^{20}	1
$(CF_3CF_2CF_2CHO)_2BCl$ (Cl on CH)				1.3360^{20}	115
$(CH_2{=}CHCH_2CH_2O)_2BCl$		47/0.2	0.9745^{23}	1.4338^{20}	58
$(CH_3CH{=}CHCH_2O)_2BCl$	Unstable at 20°				58
$(CH_3CH{=}CHCH_2O)_2BCl{:}C_5H_5N$	Unstable at 20°				58
$(n\text{-}C_4H_9O)_2BBr$	Unstable				25
$(n\text{-}C_4H_9O)_2BF$		77/18			32
$(i\text{-}C_4H_9O)_2BCl$		Decomposes	0.938^{20}	1.4060^{19}	51
$(CH_2{=}CCH_2O)_2BCl{:}C_5H_5N$ (CH_3 on C)	Solid				56
$(i\text{-}C_4H_9O)_2BBr$	Unstable				25
$(s\text{-}C_4H_9O)_2BCl$		Decomposes	0.924^{20}	1.4017^{20}	51, 88
$(CH_2{=}CHCHO)_2BCl$ (CH_3 on CH)	Unstable at 20°				58
$(CH_2{=}CHCHO)_2BCl{:}C_5H_5N$ (CH_3 on CH)	Impure solid				58

(Table continued)

$(RO)_2BX$	M.p. (°C)	B.p. (°C)	d_4^t	n_D^t	Reference
$(t\text{-}C_4H_9O)_2BCl$	Not stable at 20°				88
$n\text{-}C_5H_{11}O)_2BCl$		62–64/0.2	0.933^{20}	1.4202^{20}	1
$[Cl(CH_2)_5O]_2BCl$		128/0.1	1.127^{20}	1.4621^{20}	1
$[(CH_3)_2CHCH_2CH_2O]_2BCl$		110–115/14			79
$[(CH_3)_3CCH_2O]_2BCl$		30/0.2	0.906^{20}	1.4102^{20}	88
$[(CH_3)_3CCH(CH_3)O]_2BCl$		35/0.015	0.901^{20}	1.4165^{20}	88
$(C_6H_5CH_2O)_2BF$	Unstable				32
$(n\text{-}C_8H_{17}OB)_2Cl$			0.906^{20}	1.4380^{20}	88
$(n\text{-}C_6H_{13}CH(CH_3)O)_2BCl$		40–75/0.01 With disproportionation	0.897^{20}	1.4277^{20}	88

$RO(R'O)BX$	M.p. (°C)	B.p. (°C)	d_4^t	n_D^t	Reference
$Cl_2BOCH_2CH_2OB(Cl)OC_4H_9$				1.4339^{20}	14

$(ArO)_2BX$	M.p. (°C)	B.p. (°C)	d_4^t	n_D^t	Reference
$(C_6H_5O)_2BCl$		104–116/0.2 (d.)			28
$(C_2H_5O)_2BCl{:}C_5H_5N$	116–118				28
$[2,4,6\text{-}Cl_3C_6H_2O]_2BCl$	115				29

$[2,4,6\text{-}Cl_3C_6H_2O]_2BCl:C_5H_5N$	89–91	29
$[4\text{-}NO_2C_6H_4O]_2BCl$	187–190	29
$[2\text{-}NO_2C_6H_4O]_2BCl$	Not isolated	29
$3\text{-}Cl_2BOC_6H_4OB(Cl)OC_6H_4OB(Cl)OC_6H_4\text{-}3\text{-}OBCl_2$	Solid	54
$3\text{-}HOC_6H_4O[B(Cl)OC_6H_4O]_9H$	Solid	54

(*Table continued*)

$(ArO)_2BX$	M.p. (°C)	B.p. (°C)	d_4^t	n_D^t	Reference
$HO{-}C_6H_4{-}O{-}[B(Cl){-}O{-}C_6H_4{-}O]_3{-}H$	Solid				54
$(C_6H_5O)_2BBr$	22				46

R_3SiOBX_2	M.p. (°C)	B.p. (°C)	d_4^t	n_D^t	Reference
$CH_3SiH_2OBCl_2$	Unstable				41
$(CH_3)_2SiHOBCl_2$	Unstable				41
$(CH_3)_3SiOBCl_2$		0/10.5			41
$(CH_3)_2SiOBCl_2$ with Cl on Si			1.199^{20}	1.4210^{20}	99
$(CH_3)_3SiOBr_2$	—	—	—	—	126
$(CH_3)_2SiOBBr_2$ with Br on Si	—	—	—	—	98
$CH_3SiH_2OBF_2$	Unstable				41
$(CH_3)_2SiHOBF_2$	Unstable				41
$(CH_3)_3SiOBF_2$	Unstable				41
$(C_2H_5)_2SiOBCl_2$ with Cl on Si		67.5–68/18	1.172^{20}	1.4333^{20}	99
$(C_2H_5)_2SiOBBr_2$ with Br on Si	—	—	—	—	98

$(R_3SiO)_2BX$	M.p. (°C)	B.p. (°C)	d_4^t	n_D^t	Reference
$[(C_2H_5)_3SiO]_2BBr$		Colorless liquid			126

R(O)(O)B—X (cyclic: R bonded to two O, both O bonded to B—X)	M.p. (°C)	B.p. (°C)	d_4^t	n_D^t	Reference
1,2-diols					
CH_2—O, CH_2—O (cyclic) BCl		70–74/1	1.4640[20]		13
		74/20			9
	—	—	—	—	22
CH_2—O, CH_2—O (cyclic) $BCl:C_5H_5N$	91				13
CH_2—O, CH_3CH—O (cyclic) BCl	—	—	—		9, 31

(Table continued)

R(O)(O)B—X	M.p. (°C)	B.p. (°C)	d_4^t	n_D^t	Reference
1,3-diols					
$CH_2(CH_2O)_2BCl$		20°/0.01		1.4340^{25}	43
		Room temp./0.5			42
		28–31/0.5		1.4361^{24}	22
	—	—	—	—	31
$CH_2(CH_2O)(CH(CH_3)O)BCl$	—	—	—	—	31
Catechol					
$C_6H_4O_2BCl$	57	64/10			54
$C_6H_4O_2BCl{:}C_5H_5N$	80–90				54

	M.p. (°C)	B.p. (°C)	d_4^t	n_D^t	Reference
$C_6H_4O_2BBr$	47	76/9			54
$C_6H_4O_2BBr:C_5H_5N$	80–85				54

$RC(=O)O-B(X)-O-B(X)-OC(=O)R$	M.p. (°C)	B.p. (°C)	d_4^t	n_D^t	Reference
$CH_3C(=O)OB(Cl)OB(Cl)OC(=O)CH_3$	Crystalline				62

XI. REFERENCES

1. Abel, E. W., J. D. Edwards, W. Gerrard, and M. F. Lappert, *J. Chem. Soc.*, 501 (1957).
2. Allen, E. G., and S. Sugden, *J. Chem. Soc.*, 760 (1932).
3. Allen, S., T. C. Bonner, E. J. Bourne, and N. M. Saville, *Chem. & Ind. (London)*, 630 (1958).
4. Anderson, H. H., *J. Org. Chem.*, **19**, 1766 (1954).
5. Arbuzov, B. A., and V. S. Vinogradova, *Compt. rend. acad. sci. U.R.S.S.*, **55**, 411 (1947).
6. Aubrey, D. W., and M. F. Lappert, *J. Chem. Soc.*, 2927 (1959).
7. Badger, G. M., and J. M. Sasse, *J. Chem. Soc.*, 746 (1961).
8. Barrett, G. W., W. Gerrard, and M. F. Lappert, in W. Gerrard, and M. F. Lappert, *Chem. Rev.*, **58**, 1081 (1958).
9. Bastin, E. L., *et al.*, Shell Development Company, Chemical Corps Procurement Agency, Final Report, Contract No. CML-4564, Project No. 4-08-03-001, April 30, 1954.
10. Bedell, R., N. J. Frazer, and W. Gerrard, *J. Chem. Soc.*, 4037 (1960).
11. Benton, F. L., and T. E. Dillon, *J. Am. Chem. Soc.*, **64**, 1128 (1942).
12. Bettman, B., G. E. K. Branch, and D. L. Yabroff, *J. Am. Chem. Soc.*, **56**, 1865 (1934).
13. Blau, J. A., W. Gerrard, and M. F. Lappert, *J. Chem. Soc.*, 4116 (1957).
14. Blau, J. A., W. Gerrard, and M. F. Lappert, *J. Chem. Soc.*, 667 (1960).
15. Blau, J. A., W. Gerrard, and M. F. Lappert, in W. Gerrard, and M. F. Lappert, *Chem. Rev.*, **58**, 1081 (1958).
16. Blau, J. A., W. Gerrard, M. F. Lappert, B. A. Mountfield, and H. Pyszora, *J. Chem. Soc.*, 380 (1960).
17. Bonner, T. G., E. J. Bourne, and S. McNally, *J. Chem. Soc.*, 2929 (1960).
18. Bonner, T. G., and N. M. Saville, *J. Chem. Soc.*, 2851 (1960).
19. Booth, H. S., and D. R. Martin, *Boron Trifluoride and Its Derivatives*, Wiley, New York, 1949, p. 245.
20. Bowlus, H., and J. A. Nieuwland, *J. Am. Chem. Soc.*, **53**, 3835 (1931).
21. Brindley, P. B., W. Gerrard, and M. F. Lappert, *J. Chem. Soc.*, 824 (1956).
22. Brotherton, R. J., and A. L. McCloskey, *J. Org. Chem.*, **26**, 1668 (1961).
23. Brown, H. C., and R. M. Adams, *J. Am. Chem. Soc.*, **64**, 2557 (1942).
24. Brown, H. C., and P. A. Tierney, *J. Am. Chem. Soc.*, **80**, 1552 (1958).
25. Bujwid, Z. J., W. Gerrard, and M. F. Lappert, *Chem. & Ind. (London)*, 1386 (1957).
26. Christopher, P. M., *J. Chem. Eng. Data*, **5**, 568 (1960).
27. Christopher, P. M., and T. J. Tully, *J. Am. Chem. Soc.*, **80**, 6516 (1958).
28. Colclough, T., W. Gerrard, and M. F. Lappert, *J. Chem. Soc.*, 907 (1955).
29. Colclough, T., W. Gerrard, and M. F. Lappert, *J. Chem. Soc.*, 3006 (1956).
30. Colclough, T., W. Gerrard, and M. F. Lappert, in W. Gerrard, and M. F. Lappert, *Chem. Rev.*, **58**, 1081 (1958).
31. Conklin, G. W., and R. C. Morris, Brit. Pat. 790,090 (1958, to N.V. De Bataafsche Petroleum Maatschappij); Ger. Pat. 1,108,235 (1961).
32. Cook, H. G., J. D. Ilett, B. C. Saunders, and G. J. Stacey, *J. Chem. Soc.*, 3125 (1950).
33. Cooper, S., M. J. Frazer, and W. Gerrard, *J. Chem. Soc.*, 5545 (1961).

34. Cowley, E. G., and J. R. Partington, *Nature*, **136**, 643 (1935).
35. Dandegaonker, S. H., W. Gerrard, and M. F. Lappert, in W. Gerrard, and M. F. Lappert, *Chem. Rev.*, **58**, 1081 (1958).
36. Duncanson, L. A., W. Gerrard, M. F. Lappert, H. Pyszora, and R. Shafferman, *J. Chem. Soc.*, 3652 (1958).
37. Edwards, J. D., W. Gerrard, and M. F. Lappert, *J. Chem. Soc.*, 1470 (1955).
38. Edwards, J. D., W. Gerrard, and M. F. Lappert, *J. Chem. Soc.*, 348 (1957).
39. Edwards, J. D., W. Gerrard, and M. F. Lappert, *J. Chem. Soc.*, 377 (1957).
40. Eisenlohr, F., *Z. Physik. Chem.*, **75**, 585 (1910).
41. Emeléus, H. J., and M. Onyszchuk, *J. Chem. Soc.*, 604 (1958).
42. Finch, A., J. C. Lockhart, and J. Pearn, *Chem. & Ind.* (*London*), 471 (1960).
43. Finch, A., J. C. Lockhart, and J. Pearn, *J. Org. Chem.*, **26**, 3250 (1961).
44. Frazer, M. J., and W. Gerrard, *J. Chem. Soc.*, 2959 (1955).
45. Frazer, M. J., W. Gerrard, and M. F. Lappert, *J. Chem. Soc.*, 739 (1957).
46. Frazer, M. J., W. Gerrard, and J. K. Patel, *Chem. & Ind.* (*London*), 728 (1959).
47. Frazer, M. J., W. Gerrard, and J. A. Strickson, *J. Chem. Soc.*, 4701 (1960).
48. Gasselin, V., *Ann. chim. et phys.*, **3**, 5 (1894).
49. Gerrard, W., and P. F. Griffey, *Chem. & Ind.* (*London*), 55 (1959).
50. Gerrard, W., and M. F. Lappert, *J. Chem. Soc.*, 1020 (1951).
51. Gerrard, W., and M. F. Lappert, *J. Chem. Soc.*, 2545 (1951).
52. Gerrard, W., and M. F. Lappert, *J. Chem. Soc.*, 1486 (1952).
53. Gerrard, W., and M. F. Lappert, *J. Chem. Soc.*, 3084 (1955).
54. Gerrard, W., M. F. Lappert, and B. A. Mountfield, *J. Chem. Soc.*, 1529 (1959).
55. Gerrard, W., M. F. Lappert, and R. Nutkins, in W. Gerrard, and M. F. Lappert, *Chem. Rev.*, **58**, 1081 (1958).
56. Gerrard, W., M. F. Lappert, and H. B. Silver, *J. Chem. Soc.*, 3285 (1956).
57. Gerrard, W., M. F. Lappert, and H. B. Silver, *J. Chem. Soc.*, 4987 (1956).
58. Gerrard, W., M. F. Lappert, and H. B. Silver, *J. Chem. Soc.*, 1647 (1957).
59. Gerrard, W., M. F. Lappert, and J. W. Wallis, *J. Chem. Soc.*, 2178 (1960).
60. Gerrard, W., and M. Lindsay, *Chem. & Ind.* (*London*), 152 (1960).
61. Gerrard, W., and J. A. Strickson, *Chem. & Ind.* (*London*), 860 (1958).
62. Gerrard, W., and M. A. Wheelans, *J. Chem. Soc.*, 4296 (1956).
63. Goubeau, J., H. J. Becher, and F. Griffel, *Z. Anorg. Allgem. Chem.*, **282**, 86 (1955).
64. Goubeau, J., and D. Hummel, *Z. Physik. Chem.*, **20**, 15 (1959).
65. Goubeau, J., and K. E. Lücke, *Ann.*, **575**, 37 (1952).
66. Green, J., S. Marcinkiewicz, P. Mamolis, and D. McHale, in W. Gerrard, and M. F. Lappert, *Chem. Rev.*, **58**, 1081 (1958).
67. Grimley, J., and A. K. Holliday, *J. Chem. Soc.*, 1212 (1954).
68. Grimley, J., and A. K. Holliday, *J. Chem. Soc.*, 1215 (1954).
69. Hartough, H. D., and A. I. Kosak, *J. Am. Chem. Soc.*, **70**, 867 (1948).
70. Hauser, C. R., and C. J. Eby, *J. Am. Chem. Soc.*, **79**, 725 (1957).
71. Hauser, C. R., F. C. Frostick, Jr., and E. H. Man, *J. Am. Chem. Soc.*, **74**, 3231 (1952).

72. Hillebrand, W. F., and G. E. F. Lundell, *Applied Inorganic Analysis*, John Wiley and Sons, Inc., New York, 1929, p. 610.
73. Holliday, A. K., and J. Sowler, *J. Chem. Soc.*, 11 (1952).
74. House, H. O., and D. J. Reif, *J. Am. Chem. Soc.*, **77**, 6525 (1955).
75. Hunter, D. L., L. L. Petterson, and H. Steinberg, *Anal. Chim. Acta*, **21**, 523 (1959).
76. Jones, L. C., *Am. J. Sci.*, **7**, 147 (1899).
77. Kali-Chemie Aktiengesellschaft, Brit. Pat. 830,768 (1960).
78. Kilday, M. V., W. H. Johnson, and E. J. Prosen, *J. Res. Nat. Bur. Std.*, **A**, **65**, 435 (1961).
79. Kinney, C. R., H. T. Thompson, and L. C. Cheney, *J. Am. Chem. Soc.*, **57**, 2396 (1935).
80. Kirrman, A., *Compt. Rend.*, **199**, 1228 (1934).
81. Landesman, H., and R. E. Williams, 138th Meeting American Chemical Society, New York, Sept. 1960, Abstracts of Papers, p. 39-N.
82. Landesman, H., and R. E. Williams, *J. Am. Chem. Soc.*, **83**, 2663 (1961).
83. Lane, T. J., P. A. McCusker, and B. C. Curran, *J. Am. Chem. Soc.*, **64**, 2076 (1942).
84. Lang, K., A. Bürger, E. M. Horn, and K. Nützel, Ger. Pat. 1,094,747 (1960, to Farbenfabriken Bayer Aktiengesellschaft).
85. Lappert, M. F., *Chem. Rev.*, **56**, 959 (1956).
86. Lappert, M. F., *J. Chem. Soc.*, 667 (1953).
87. Lappert, M. F., *J. Chem. Soc.*, 784 (1955).
88. Lappert, M. F., *J. Chem. Soc.*, 1768 (1956).
89. Lappert, M. F., *J. Chem. Soc.*, 3256 (1958).
90. Lappert, M. F., in W. Gerrard, and M. F. Lappert, *Chem. Rev.*, **58**, 1081 (1958).
91. Martin, D. R., and L. S. Mako, *J. Am. Chem. Soc.*, **73**, 2674 (1951).
92. McCloskey, A. L., R. J. Brotherton, *et al.*, U.S. Borax Research Corp., WADC Technical Report 59-761, Materials Laboratory Contract No. AF 33(616)-5931, Project No. 7340, December, 1959.
93. McCloskey, A. L., H. Goldsmith, R. J. Brotherton, H. Steinberg, and G. W. Willcockson, 135th Meeting American Chemical Society, Boston, April, 1959, Abstracts of Papers, p. 34-M.
94. McCusker, P. A., E. C. Ashby, and H. S. Makowski, *J. Am. Chem. Soc.*, **79**, 5182 (1957).
95. McCusker, P. A., and M. Laeticia Kilzer, 136th Meeting American Chemical Society, Atlantic City, Sept. 1959, Abstracts of Papers, p. 54-N.
96. McCusker, P. A., and S. M. Laeticia Kilzer, *J. Am. Chem. Soc.*, **82**, 372 (1960).
97. McCusker, P. A., and T. Ostdick, 132nd Meeting American Chemical Society, New York, Sept. 1957, Abstracts of Papers, p. 17-N.
98. McCusker, P. A., and T. Ostdick, 133rd Meeting American Chemical Society, San Francisco, April, 1958, Abstracts of Papers, p. 36-L.
99. McCusker, P. A., and T. Ostdick, *J. Am. Chem. Soc.*, **80**, 1103 (1958).
100. McCusker, P. A., and T. Ostdick, *J. Am. Chem. Soc.*, **81**, 5550 (1959).
101. McLaughlin, D. E., M. Tamres, and S. Searles, Jr., *J. Am. Chem. Soc.*, **82**, 5621 (1960).
102. Meerwein, H., E. Battenberg, H. Gold, E. Pfeil, and G. Willfang, *J. Prakt. Chem.*, **154**, 83 (1939).

103. Meerwein, H., and Maier-Huser, *J. Prakt. Chem.*, **134**, 51 (1932).
104. Meerwein, H., and W. Pannwitz, *J. Prakt. Chem.*, **141**, 123 (1934).
105. Meerwein, H., and D. Vossen, *J. Prakt. Chem.*, **141**, 149 (1934).
106. Morgan, G. T., and R. Taylor, *J. Chem. Soc.*, 1497 (1932).
107. Morgan, G. T., and R. B. Tunstall, *J. Chem. Soc.*, **125**, 1963 (1924).
108. Onak, T. P., H. Landesman, R. E. Williams, and I. Shapiro, *J. Phys. Chem.*, **63**, 1533 (1959).
109. Otto, M. M., *J. Am. Chem. Soc.*, **57**, 1476 (1935).
110. Peach, M. E., and T. C. Waddington, *J. Chem. Soc.*, 1238 (1961).
111. Pearson, R. K., T. W. Platt, J. C. Renforth, N. J. Sheetz, and L. J. Edwards, Callery Chemical Company, Report No. CCC-1024-TR-227, March 1, 1957.
112. Ramser, H., and E. Wiberg, *Ber.*, **63**, 1136 (1930).
113. Schlesinger, H. I., H. C. Brown, J. R. Gilbreath, and J. J. Katz, *J. Am. Chem. Soc.*, **75**, 195 (1953).
114. Schlesinger, H. I., and G. Urry, Univ. of Chicago, "Hydrides and Borohydrides of Light Weight Elements and Related Compounds," Annual Technical Report, Aug. 1, 1954 to July 31, 1955, Contract N6ori-20, Project NR 356-255.
115. Schroeder, H., *J. Org. Chem.*, **25**, 1682 (1960).
116. Skinner, H. A., and N. B. Smith, *J. Chem. Soc.*, 3930 (1954).
117. Sommer, L. H., and O. F. Bennett, *J. Am. Chem. Soc.*, **79**, 1008 (1957).
118. Steinberg, H., and D. L. Hunter, Unpublished results.
119. Sternbach, B., and A. G. MacDiarmid, *J. Am. Chem. Soc.*, **83**, 3384 (1961).
120. Thomas, L. H., *J. Chem. Soc.*, 820 (1946).
121. Van Dyke Tiers, G., *J. Am. Chem. Soc.*, **77**, 4837 (1955).
122. Vogel, A. I., *J. Chem. Soc.*, 133 (1946); 616, 644, 654 (1948).
123. Warrick, E. L., *J. Am. Chem. Soc.*, **68**, 2455 (1946).
124. Wiberg, E., and U. Krüerke, *Z. Naturforsch.*, **8b**, 608 (1953).
125. Wiberg, E., and U. Krüerke, *Z. Naturforsch.*, **8b**, 609 (1953).
126. Wiberg, E., and U. Krüerke, *Z. Naturforsch.*, **8b**, 610 (1953).
127. Wiberg, E., and W. Ruschmann, *Ber.*, **70**, 1393 (1937).
128. Wiberg, E., and H. Smedsrud, *Z. Anorg. Allgem. Chem.*, **225**, 204 (1935).
129. Wiberg, E., and W. Sütterlin, *Z. Anorg. Allgem. Chem.*, **202**, 1 (1931).
130. Wiberg, E., and W. Sütterlin, *Z. Anorg. Allgem. Chem.*, **202**, 22 (1931).
131. Wiberg, E., and W. Sütterlin, *Z. Anorg. Allgem. Chem.*, **202**, 31 (1931).
132. Wiberg, E., and W. Sütterlin, *Z. Anorg. Allgem. Chem.*, **222**, 92 (1935).
133. Young, F. G., F. C. Frostick, Jr., J. J. Sanderson, and C. R. Hauser, *J. Am. Chem. Soc.*, **72**, 3635 (1950).
134. Zmbov, K. F., and S. V. Ribnikar, *Bull. Inst. Nucl. Sci. "Boris Kidrich" (Belgrade)*, **11**, 146 (1961).

13

SILOXY DERIVATIVES

I. INTRODUCTION

Compounds containing Si–O–B bonds are the second most prevalent type* of organic boron–oxygen materials. Orthoborates with two (I) and three (II) silyl groups as well as silyl metaborates (III) have been described.

$ROB(OSiR_3)_2$ (I) $B(OSiR_3)_3$ and $B(OSiAr_3)_3$ (II) R_3SiO–[boroxine ring with B–$OSiR_3$ substituents] (III)

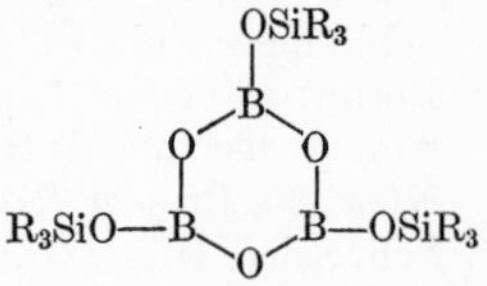

II. HISTORICAL

The earliest recorded example, tris(trimethylsiloxy)borane,[11] described in 1948, was obtained by the cleavage of ethoxytrimethylsilane with boric acid in the presence of an acid catalyst followed by fractional distillation of the products.†

$$3\,(CH_3)_3SiOC_2H_5 + H_3BO_3 \xrightarrow{H^+} [(CH_3)_3SiO]_3B + 3\,C_2H_5OH \qquad (13\text{-}1)$$

* Boron–oxygen compounds containing other group IVA atoms have been described.[25] Removal of water from a mixture of dibutyltin oxide and boric acid reportedly resulted in the tin borate.

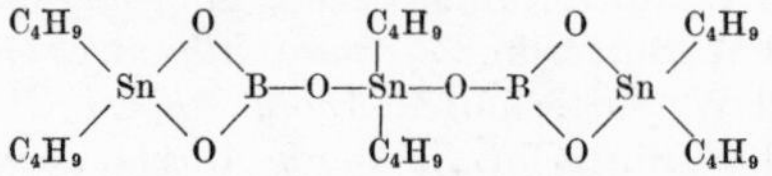

$$(C_4H_9)_2Sn(O)_2B\text{—O—}Sn(C_4H_9)_2\text{—O—}B(O)_2Sn(C_4H_9)_2$$

In the presence of 2-ethylhexanol the mixed alkyl tin borate was obtained.

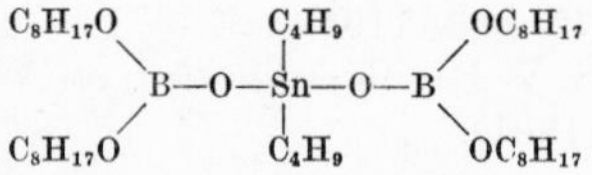

$$(C_8H_{17}O)_2B\text{—O—}Sn(C_4H_9)_2\text{—O—}B(OC_8H_{17})_2$$

† Ref. 11 recorded a boiling point of 90° for tris(trimethylsiloxy)borane. Since tri-*t*-butoxyborane boils at 175°,[14] and tris(trimethylsiloxy)borane has a slightly higher molecular weight, the intended value may have been 190°. Subsequent workers,[28] however, were unable to repeat the preparation, obtaining triethoxyborane (b.p. 117°) and hexamethyldisiloxane as the products. It is conceivable, therefore, that the material boiling at 90° was impure triethoxyborane. The triethoxyborane–ethanol azeotrope boils at 76.6°.

III. PROPERTIES

Silyl borates, with the exclusion of tris(triphenylsiloxy)borane,[21] are colorless liquids[4,6,7,28] with an odor described as characteristic[6] and similar to that of trialkylsilanes;[28] somewhat burnt[31] or ester-like.[32] They burn with a green flame,[28] are insoluble in water,[28,31] and soluble in organic solvents.[7,28,31,32] The chlorosiloxyboranes are fuming liquids which become tacky in air.[18]

The orthoborates, with the exception of some of the halosilyl derivatives,[19] are distillable.[4,6] The metaborates cannot be distilled.[1] The monomeric nature of the orthoborates[18,19,31] and the trimeric nature of the metaborates[1] have been established by molecular weight measurements. Further evidence for the trimeric nature of the metaborates is shown by strong absorption in the infrared at 13.6 to 13.9 μ,[1] which is consistent with out-of-plane vibrations of the boroxine ring.[13]

Tris(trimethylsiloxy)borane and tris(triethylsiloxy)borane exhibit their B–O stretching absorption in the infrared at 7.46 and 7.52 μ,[1] which is comparable to the assignment of bands at 7.40 to 7.58 μ[30] for the asymmetrical stretching frequency of the BO_3 group in trialkoxyboranes. The B–O absorption in the silyl metaborates is shifted to shorter wavelengths at 7.25 μ.[1] Comparison with the B–O absorption in the trialkoxyboroxines is difficult due to strong absorption in these compounds in the range 6.93–7.50 μ.[13]

Octet refractivities for the B–O–Si structure have been recorded.[29]

IV. SILYL ORTHOBORATES

A. Methods of Preparation

1. FROM BORIC ACID

a. *And Silanols.* Tris(trialkylsiloxy)-[1,21,22,23] and tris(triarylsiloxy)boranes[21,22,23] are readily obtained by the esterification of boric acid with a variety of trialkyl- and triarylsilanols by continuous azeotropic removal of water.

$$3\ R_3SiOH + H_3BO_3 \rightarrow (R_3SiO)_3B + 3\ H_2O \qquad (13\text{-}2)$$

The relative ease of preparing "tertiary alkyl" silyl borates can be contrasted with the difficulty of preparing tertiary alkyl borates (see Chapter 4).

A peculiar reaction product, putty-like in the range 35–50° and pasty below 35°, was obtained from an equimolar reaction of boric acid and tetramethyldisiloxane-1,3-diol.[15] Presumably polymeric silyl borates (IV) are involved.

$$\left[\begin{array}{c} CH_3 \quad\; CH_3 \\ | \qquad\quad | \\ -Si-O-Si-O-B-O- \\ | \qquad\quad | \qquad\quad | \\ CH_3 \quad\; CH_3 \quad\; O \\ \qquad\qquad\qquad\quad | \end{array} \right]_n$$

(IV)

b. *And Alkoxyalkylsilanes.* In contrast to dialkyl ethers, which are inert to boric acid, alkoxytrialkylsilanes are cleaved in a 3:1 molar reaction with boric acid to give the corresponding tris(trialkylsiloxy)borane and alcohol.[11,28]

$$3\, R_3SiOR + H_3BO_3 \rightarrow (R_3SiO)_3B + 3\, ROH \qquad (13\text{-}3)$$

The reaction, first reported[11] for ethoxytrimethylsilane in the presence of an acid catalyst, could not be confirmed;[28] triethoxyborane and hexamethyldisiloxane resulted (13-4).* However, a series of alkoxyethyl- and alkoxypropylsilanes was converted to the silyl borates (13-5).[28]

$$3\, (CH_3)_3SiOC_2H_5 + H_3BO_3 \xrightarrow{H^+} (C_2H_5O)_3B + 3\, (CH_3)_3SiOH \qquad (13\text{-}4)$$
$$\downarrow$$
$$\tfrac{3}{2}\, [(CH_3)_3Si]_2O + \tfrac{3}{2}\, H_2O$$

$$3\, R_3SiOCH_3 + H_3BO_3 \rightarrow (R_3SiO)_3B + 3\, CH_3OH \qquad (13\text{-}5)$$

It is possible that reaction (13-4) did indeed yield ethanol and the desired tris(trimethylsiloxy)borane (13-6) but that the ethanol then transesterified the silyl borate to give the observed triethoxyborane and trimethylsilanol, or equivalent hexamethyldisiloxane (13-7).

$$3\, (CH_3)_3SiOC_2H_5 + H_3BO_3 \rightarrow [(CH_3)_3SiO]_3B + 3\, C_2H_5OH \qquad (13\text{-}6)$$

$$[(CH_3)_3SiO]_3B + 3\, C_2H_5OH \rightarrow (C_2H_5O)_3B + 3\, (CH_3)_3SiOH \qquad (13\text{-}7)$$

A similar secondary reaction of methanol and tris(triethylsiloxy)-borane in reaction (13-5) would be precluded, or at least retarded, by the greater steric requirements of the tris(triethylsiloxy)borane.

A 2:1 molar reaction of diethoxydimethylsilane with boric acid resulted in a polymer formulated as (V); a 3:2 molar reaction led to the polymer (VI).[10] The equimolar reaction of triethoxymethylsilane

* Similar exchange of hydroxyl and alkoxyl groups takes place with alkyl silicates: $3\, Si(OR)_4 + 4\, H_3BO_3 \rightarrow 3\, Si(OH)_4 + 4\, B(OR)_3$. See Chapter 4.

and boric acid was reported by two different investigators to result in (VII)[28] and (VIII).[10]

$[B_2O_3 \cdot 6(CH_3)_2SiO]_n$ (V) $[B_2O_3 \cdot 3(CH_3)_2SiO]_n$ (VI) $[B_2O_3 \cdot 4CH_3SiO_{1.5}]_n$ (VII)

$[\frac{1}{2} B_2O_3 \cdot CH_3SiO_{1.5}]$ (VIII)

The mechanism of reaction (13-3) has not been studied, but some speculations are possible. It is improbable that the reaction involves an initial nucleophilic attack on boron by the silyl ether oxygen due to the involvement of the free pair of electrons on that oxygen with the vacant *d* orbitals of the silicon atoms. Possibly the *d* orbital of the silicon atom accepts a pair of electrons from an oxygen atom of the boric acid resulting in a configuration which facilitates the loss of alcohol.

$$R_2Si(OR)_2 + :O(H)\text{—}B(OH)_2 \rightarrow [R_2Si^{-}(OR)(R)\text{—}O^{+}(H)\text{—}B(OH)_2] \rightarrow R_3SiOB(OH)_2 + ROH \xrightarrow{R_3SiOR} \text{etc.} \quad (13\text{-}8)$$

Pentacovalent intermediates such as in reaction (13-8) are well known in organosilicon chemistry.

c. *And Alkylchlorosilanes.* Tris(trimethylsiloxy)borane and tris(triethylsiloxy)borane were obtained in approximately 25% yield from the reactions of boric acid and the appropriate trialkylchlorosilane.[28] A 62% yield was realized when the reaction time was increased from fifteen to forty hours.[5] This transformation (13-9) can be contrasted to the inertness of boric acid towards alkyl halides.

$$3\ R_3SiCl + H_3BO_3 \rightarrow (R_3SiO)_3B + 3\ HCl \quad (13\text{-}9)$$

The conversion of (IX) to (X)[5] and not (XI) with boric acid indicates the greater lability of the silicon–chlorine bond as compared to the silicon–oxygen linkage.

$$C_2H_5OSi(CH_3)_2Cl \quad \text{(IX)} \qquad (C_2H_5OSi(CH_3)_2O)_3B \quad \text{(X)} \qquad (ClSi(CH_3)_2O)_3B \quad \text{(XI)}$$

With dialkyldichlorosilanes,[27,28] the corresponding reaction results in a polymer with the properties of "bouncing putty."[33,34]

$$3\,(CH_3)_2SiCl_2 + 2\,H_3BO_3 \rightarrow 6\,HCl + \left[\begin{array}{ccccccccc} CH_3 & & & & CH_3 & & & & \\ | & & & & | & & & & \\ -Si & -O- & B & -O- & Si & -O- & B & -O- & \\ | & & | & & | & & | & & \\ CH_3 & & O & & CH_3 & & O & & \\ & & | & & & & | & & \\ & CH_3- & Si & -CH_3 & & & & & \\ & & | & & & & & & \end{array}\right]_{\text{etc.}} \qquad (13\text{-}10)$$

The idealized stoichiometric reaction has been formulated to give the polymer (XII).[27]

$$\begin{array}{ccccccccc} & CH_3\;CH_3 & & & CH_3\;CH_3 & & & CH_3\;CH_3 & \\ & OSiO & & CH_3 & OSiO & & CH_3 & OSiO & \\ HOB & & BO & \left[-SiOB\right. & & BO & -SiOB & & BOH \\ & OSiO & & CH_3 & OSiO & & CH_3 & OSiO & \\ & CH_3\;CH_3 & & & CH_3\;CH_3 &]_n & & CH_3\;CH_3 & \end{array}$$

(XII)

Other polymeric materials similarly have been prepared from boric acid and (XIII).[24]

$$Cl\left[\begin{array}{c} CH_3 \\ | \\ -Si-O- \\ | \\ CH_3 \end{array}\right]_n\begin{array}{c} CH_3 \\ | \\ Si-Cl \\ | \\ CH_3 \end{array}$$

(XIII)

d. *And Trialkylsilanes.* Treatment of boric acid with a trialkylsilane at 100–130° in the presence of colloidal nickel or a nickel, platinum, or palladium halide has been stated to result in 90–95% yields of a tris(trialkylsiloxy)borane.[6,21,22,33]

$$3\,R_3SiH + H_3BO_3 \rightarrow (R_3SiO)_3B + 3\,H_2 \qquad (13\text{-}11)$$

It is of interest to speculate on the mechanism of the transformation. Silicon, by virtue of its vacant d orbitals, can expand its valence shell to accommodate a pair of electrons from the oxygen

$$\begin{array}{c} H \quad H \\ R_2(R)Si + :O-B(OH)_2 \end{array} \rightarrow \begin{array}{c} H \quad H \\ R_2(R)\overset{-}{Si}-\overset{+}{O}-B(OH)_2 \end{array} \rightarrow R_3SiOB(OH)_2 + H_2 \xrightarrow{R_3SiH} \text{etc.} \qquad (13\text{-}12)$$

atom of the boric acid. The resulting pentacovalent configuration would permit the evolution of hydrogen.

e. *And Dimethylpolysiloxanes.* Low molecular weight dimethylpolysiloxanes are further polymerized to "bouncing putty"[33,34] when heated at 150–200° with boric acid.[9] Presumably Si–O–B crosslinks are formed.

$$\left[-\overset{CH_3}{\underset{CH_3}{\overset{|}{\underset{|}{Si}}}}-O-\right]_n + H_3BO_3 \xrightarrow[-H_2O]{\Delta} \left[-\overset{CH_3}{\underset{CH_3}{\overset{|}{\underset{|}{Si}}}}-O-B(-O-Si(CH_3)_2-O-)-O-\right]_n \qquad (13\text{-}13)$$

2. FROM BORIC OXIDE

a. *And Silanols.* Boric oxide is esterified with trialkyl- and triarylsilanols by azeotropic removal of water.[21,22,23] Tris(triethylsiloxy)borane was prepared by removal of the water with anhydrous copper sulfate.[35]

$$6\ R_3SiOH + B_2O_3 \rightarrow 2\ (R_3SiO)_3B + 3\ H_2O \qquad (13\text{-}14)$$

b. *And Alkoxytrialkylsilanes.* Ethoxytrimethylsilane is cleaved by boric oxide to give a mixture of alkyl and silyl borates (13-15).[1]

$$3\ C_2H_5OSi(CH_3)_3 + B_2O_3 \rightarrow (C_2H_5O)_3B + [(CH_3)_3SiO]_3B \qquad (13\text{-}15)$$

Once again an expansion of the silicon valence shell followed by a four-centered collapse (13-16) can be called upon to account for the products.

$$(CH_3)_3Si-OC_2H_5 + :O(-B<)-B< \rightarrow [(CH_3)_3\overset{-}{Si}(OC_2H_5)-\overset{+}{O}(-B<)-B<] \rightarrow (CH_3)_3SiOB< + C_2H_5OB< \qquad (13\text{-}16)$$

c. *And Hexaalkyldisiloxanes.* Tris(trimethylsiloxy)borane has been obtained in 20% yield by the cleavage of hexamethyldisiloxane with boric oxide in an autoclave at 350°.[28]

$$3\ (CH_3)_3SiOSi(CH_3)_3 + B_2O_3 \rightarrow 2\ [(CH_3)_3SiO]_3B \qquad (13\text{-}17)$$

The molecular weights of polymeric silicones have been increased by reaction with boric oxide.[20] Presumably a reaction similar to (13-17) occurs to give crosslinked polymers similar to (XIV).

```
 ┌ R                  ┐
 │ |                  │
—Si—O—B—O—
 │ |    |             │
 │ R    O             │
 │   ┌  |   ┐         │
 │   │ RSiR │         │
 │   │  |   │         │
 │ R └  O   ┘n        │
 │ |    |             │
—Si—O—B—O—
 │ |                  │
 │ R                  │
 └                    ┘m
```

(XIV)

3. FROM BORON HALIDES

a. *And Silanols.* The "alcoholysis" of boron trichloride with triethylsilanol in the presence of pyridine resulted in a 34% yield of the silyl borate (13-18).[1] The poor yield, presumably due to the

$$BCl_3 + 3\,(C_2H_5)_3SiOH + 3\,C_5H_5N \rightarrow [(C_2H_5)_3SiO]_3B + 3\,C_5H_5N \cdot HCl \qquad (13\text{-}18)$$

formation of hexaethyldisiloxane, can be doubled by the use of sodium triethoxysilanolate.[1]

$$BCl_3 + 3\,(C_5H_5)_3SiONa \rightarrow [(C_2H_5)_3SiO]_3B + 3\,NaCl \qquad (13\text{-}19)$$

The straightforward alcoholysis of boron tribromide with triethylsilanol (13-20) was unsuccessful, but substitution of the sodium salt again led to a good yield of the silyl borate (13-21).[31]

$$BBr_3 + 3\,(C_2H_5)_3SiOH \rightarrow B(OH)_3 + 3\,(C_2H_5)_3SiBr \qquad (13\text{-}20)$$

$$BBr_3 + 3\,(C_2H_5)_3SiONa \rightarrow [(C_2H_5)_3SiO]_3B + 3\,NaBr \qquad (13\text{-}21)$$

b. *And Alkoxydialkylhalosilanes or Alkoxytrihalosilanes.* Treatment of *s*-butoxychlorodimethylsilane with boron trichloride resulted in a small yield of tris(chlorodimethylsiloxy)borane. Alkoxytrialkylsilanes did not react similarly but resulted in trialkoxyboranes (see Chapter 4) and trialkylchlorosilanes.[7]

Reaction (13-22) was performed for the isopropyl and butyl derivatives.[7]

$$3\,ROSiCl_3 + BCl_3 \rightarrow (Cl_3SiO)_3B + 3\,RCl \qquad (13\text{-}22)$$

c. *And Cyclosiloxanes.* The silicon analogs of the trialkylboroxines are cleaved by boron bromide,[17] boron chloride,[16,18] or boron fluoride[16,19] to give dialkylhalosiloxydihaloboranes which then disproportionate to the dialkylhalosilyl borate (13-23). The eight-membered rings behave similarly.

$$\text{cyclo-}(R_2SiO)_3 + 3\,BX_3 \rightarrow 3\,R_2Si(X)OBX_2 \rightarrow (R_2Si(X)O)_3B + 2\,BX_3 \quad (13\text{-}23)$$

The similar cleavage of hexamethyldisiloxane with boron bromide did not result in formation of a silyl borate; decomposition of the intermediate trialkylsiloxydibromoborane occurred rather than disproportionation.[32]

$$(CH_3)_3SiOSi(CH_3)_3 + BBr_3 \rightarrow \{(CH_3)_3SiOBBr_2\} + (CH_3)_3SiBr \quad (13\text{-}24)$$

$$\{(CH_3)_3SiOBBr_2\} \rightarrow (CH_3)_3SiBr + \{BrBO\} \quad (13\text{-}25)$$

4. FROM TRIALKOXYBORANES

a. *And Silanols.* A 23.5% yield of tris(triethylsiloxy)borane was obtained by the "transesterification" of tri-n-butoxyborane with triethylsilanol in the presence of a catalytic amount of sodium.[28]

$$(n\text{-}C_4H_9O)_3B + 3\,(C_2H_5)_3SiOH \rightarrow [(C_2H_5)_3SiO]_3B + 3\,n\text{-}C_4H_9OH \quad (13\text{-}26)$$

Sodium is not necessary since subsequent preparations of tris(trimethylsiloxy)borane[1] and tris(triethylsiloxy)borane[2] resulted in 38 and 52% yields, respectively, from the same reaction in the absence of sodium.

The reaction of a boron ester corresponding in composition to (XV), prepared from the 2:1 molar reaction of triethylsilanol and triethoxyborane, with diethylsilanediol resulted in the diborasiloxane (XVI).[2]

$$2\,[([C_2H_5]_3SiO)_2BOC_2H_5]\ (\text{XV}) + (C_2H_5)_2Si(OH)_2 \rightarrow 2\,C_2H_5OH + [(C_2H_5)_3SiO]_2BOSi(C_2H_5)_2OB[OSi(C_2H_5)_3]_2\ (\text{XVI}) \quad (13\text{-}27)$$

b. *And Trialkylhalosilanes.* In contrast to the inertness of trialkoxyboranes to alkyl halides (Chapter 4), triethylchlorosilane in the presence of ferric chloride converted tri-n-butoxyborane to the silyl borate in 10% yield.[28]

$$(n\text{-}C_4H_9O)_3B + 3\,(C_2H_5)_3SiCl \xrightarrow{FeCl} [(C_2H_5)_3SiO]_3B + 3\,n\text{-}C_4H_9Cl \quad (13\text{-}28)$$

The ferric chloride presumably facilitates the transfer of electrons from oxygen to silicon by aiding in the removal of the chlorine atom.

$$(C_4H_9O)_2B\text{—}\overset{C_4H_9}{\overset{|}{O}}: + \overset{FeCl_3 \curvearrowleft Cl}{\overset{|}{Si}}(C_2H_5)_3 \rightarrow (C_4H_9O)_2B\overset{C_4H_9}{\overset{|+}{O}}Si(C_2H_5)_3 + FeCl_4^- \longrightarrow (C_4H_9O)_2BOSi(C_2H_5)_3 + C_4H_9Cl + FeCl_3 \xrightarrow{(C_2H_5)_3SiCl + FeCl_3} \text{etc.} \quad (13\text{-}29)$$

c. *And Diacetoxydialkylsilanes.* Diacetoxydialkylsilanes reacted with tributoxyborane[3] and triethoxyborane in the presence of sodium ethoxide[8] to give low molecular weight siloxyborane polymers, ideally formulated as (XVII).

$$(CH_3\overset{O}{\overset{\|}{C}}O)_2SiR_2 + (R'O)_3B \rightarrow CH_3\overset{O}{\overset{\|}{C}}OR' + CH_3\overset{O}{\overset{\|}{C}}\left[\text{—}O\underset{R}{\overset{R}{\overset{|}{\underset{|}{Si}}}}O\underset{OR'}{\underset{|}{B}}\text{—}\right]_n OR' \quad (13\text{-}30)$$

(XVII)

The reaction of a boron ester corresponding in composition to (XVIII), prepared from the 2 : 1 molar reaction of triethylsilanol and triethoxyborane, with dimethyl- or diethyldiacetoxysilane, resulted in distillable products believed to be (XIX).[2]

$$2\,[([C_2H_5]_3SiO)_2BOC_2H_5] + (CH_3\overset{O}{\overset{\|}{C}}O)_2SiR_2 \rightarrow$$

(XVIII)

$$2\,CH_3\overset{O}{\overset{\|}{C}}OC_2H_5 + [(C_2H_5)_3SiO]_2BO\underset{R}{\overset{R}{\overset{|}{\underset{|}{Si}}}}OB[OSi(C_2H_5)_3]_2 \quad (13\text{-}31)$$

(XIX)

The reaction of diacetoxydiethylsilane and trimethoxyborane-^{18}O proceeded as recorded in equation (13-32) with the ^{18}O

$$3\,(C_2H_5)_2Si(O\overset{O}{\overset{\|}{C}}CH_3)_2 + 2\,(CH_3{}^{18}O)_3B \rightarrow 6\,CH_3\overset{O}{\overset{\|}{C}}{}^{18}OCH_3 + \left[\text{—}O\underset{R}{\overset{R}{\overset{|}{\underset{|}{Si}}}}OB\underset{|}{}O\underset{R}{\overset{R}{\overset{|}{\underset{|}{Si}}}}OB\underset{|}{}O\underset{R}{\overset{R}{\overset{|}{\underset{|}{Si}}}}\text{—}\right]_n \quad (13\text{-}32)$$

ending up in the methyl acetate. It was concluded that the reaction proceeded via B–O and acyl–oxygen cleavage (13-33),[12] indicating

$$-\overset{|}{\underset{|}{Si}}-O-\overset{O}{\overset{\|}{C}}CH_3 \;\; -\overset{|}{B}-{}^{18}O-CH_3 \rightarrow -\overset{|}{\underset{|}{Si}}-O-\overset{|}{B}- + CH_3\overset{O}{\overset{\|}{C}}{}^{18}OCH_3 \qquad (13\text{-}33)$$

that nucleophilic attack by boric acid ester oxygen on a carbonyl carbon is preferred to a pentacovalent silicon intermediate.

5. FROM TRIACETOXYBORANE

a. *And Dialkoxydialkylsilanes.* Low molecular weight polymers (XX) similar to (XVII) were obtained from the reaction of tri-

$$(RO)_2SiR'_2 + (CH_3\overset{O}{\overset{\|}{C}}O)_3B \rightarrow CH_3\overset{O}{\overset{\|}{C}}OR + RO\left[\overset{R'}{\underset{R'}{Si}}O\underset{\underset{|}{O}}{B}O\right]_n\overset{O}{\overset{\|}{C}}CH_3 \qquad (13\text{-}34)$$

(XX)

acetoxyborane and a dialkoxydialkylsilane in the presence[16] and absence[15] of a sodium alcoholate.

b. *And Methyl Silicate.* The reaction of triacetoxyborane and methyl silicate–^{18}O proceeded as recorded in equation (13-35) with

$$4\,B(O\overset{O}{\overset{\|}{C}}CH_3)_3 + 3\,Si({}^{18}OCH_3)_4 \rightarrow 12\,CH_3\overset{O}{\overset{\|}{C}}{}^{18}OCH_3 + \left[OB\underset{|}{O}\overset{|}{Si}OB\underset{|}{O}\overset{|}{Si}OB\underset{|}{O}\overset{|}{Si}OB\underset{|}{O}\right]_n \qquad (13\text{-}35)$$

the ^{18}O ending up in the methyl acetate. Thus it was concluded that the reaction proceeded via Si–O and acyl–oxygen cleavage (13-36).[12] Acyl–oxygen cleavage has not yet been demonstrated

$$-\overset{|}{B}-O-\overset{O}{\overset{\|}{C}}CH_3 \;\; -\overset{|}{\underset{|}{Si}}-{}^{18}OCH_3 \rightarrow -\overset{|}{B}-O-\overset{|}{\underset{|}{Si}}- + CH_3\overset{O}{\overset{\|}{C}}{}^{18}OCH_3 \qquad (13\text{-}36)$$

unequivocally in acyloxyboranes (see Chapter 8). The necessity for this path could be avoided by an exchange of acetoxy and methoxy groups via a cyclic mechanism (13-37) followed by B–O and acyl–

$$>BOC(=O)CH_3 + -\overset{|}{\underset{|}{Si}}{}^{18}OCH_3 \rightarrow CH_3{-}O \cdots [>B{-}O{-}C(CH_3){=}O \cdots Si<] \rightarrow\ >B^{18}OCH_3 + -\overset{|}{\underset{|}{Si}}OC(=O)CH_3 \qquad (13\text{-}37)$$

oxygen cleavage in the silicon species (13-38). Reaction (13-38) is analogous to reaction (13-33).

$$>B^{18}OCH_3 + -\overset{|}{\underset{|}{Si}}OC(=O)CH_3 \rightarrow CH_3C(=O)^{18}OCH_3 +\ >BO\overset{|}{\underset{|}{Si}}- \qquad (13\text{-}38)$$

6. FROM TRIS(ALKYLAMINO)BORANES

"Alcoholysis" of tris(diethylamino)borane with triethylsilanol at 0° resulted in a 98% yield of tris(triethylsiloxy)borane.[1]

$$[(C_2H_5)_2N]_3B + 3\ (C_2H_5)_3SiOH \rightarrow [(C_2H_5)_3SiO]_3B + 3\ (C_2H_5)_2NH \qquad (13\text{-}39)$$

7. FROM OTHER TRIS(TRIALKYLSILOXY)BORANES

"Transesterification" of tris(trimethylsiloxy)borane with triethylsilanol proceeded readily.[1]

$$[(CH_3)_3SiO]_3B + 3\ (C_2H_5)_3SiOH \rightarrow [(C_2H_5)_3SiO]_3B + 3\ (CH_3)_3SiOH \qquad (13\text{-}40)$$

8. FROM DIALKYLHALOSILOXYDIHALOBORANES

Dimethyl- and diethylchlorosiloxydichloroboranes[18] and the bromosiloxydibromoboranes[17] disproportionate rapidly to the symmetrical trisiloxyboranes and boron trihalide on attempted vacuum distillation.

$$3\ R_2\underset{\underset{X}{|}}{Si}OBX_2 \rightarrow (R_2\underset{\underset{X}{|}}{Si}O)_3B + 2\ BX_3, \qquad R = CH_3, C_2H_5;\ X = Cl, Br \qquad (13\text{-}41)$$

The fluorine analogs (XXI) are too unstable to isolate.[19]

$$R_2\underset{\underset{F}{|}}{Si}OBF_2$$

(XXI)

9. FROM BIS(TRIALKYLSILOXY)HALOBORANES

The only recorded example of a mixed alkylsilyl borate was obtained by the methanolysis of bromobis(triethylsiloxy)borane.[32] If the product is indeed a mixed ester, as its vapor pressure of 2.5 mm.

$$BrB[OSi(C_2H_5)_3]_2 + CH_3OH \rightarrow CH_3OB[OSi(C_2H_5)_3]_2 + HBr \qquad (13\text{-}42)$$

at 150° indicates, it can be concluded that silyl borates are less prone to disproportionation than alkyl borates (see Chapter 6). Since disproportionation involves the intermolecular complexing of boron with oxygen, this conclusion is consistent with the lowered electron density on the oxygen atoms in the mixed alkyl silyl borate due to p_π–d_π bonding of the oxygen and silicon atoms. It also is consistent with the greater steric requirements in the silyl borates.

B. Reactions

1. HYDROLYSIS

Silyl borates are hydrolyzed slowly in water or in the presence of atmospheric moisture.[1,6,8,27,31] The rate of hydrolysis is increased

$$(R_3SiO)_3B + \tfrac{3}{2}\,H_2O \rightarrow H_3BO_3 + \tfrac{3}{2}\,(R_3Si)_2O \qquad (13\text{-}43)$$

in alkaline or acidic solution[3,28,31] or in hot water[8] and, as with the trialkoxyboranes,[26] appears to be subject to steric control.[1,28]

Tris(trichlorosiloxy)borane is violently hydrolyzed by water.[7]

Tris(dialkylhalosiloxy)boranes are rapidly hydrolyzed with the formation of boric acid and hexaalkylcyclotrisiloxanes.[18]

$$(R_2\overset{X}{\overset{|}{Si}})_3B + 3\,H_2O \rightarrow H_3BO_3 + \underbrace{R_2Si\text{–}O\text{–}Si(R_2)\text{–}O\text{–}SiR_2\text{–}O}_{\text{ring}} + 3\,HX \qquad (13\text{-}44)$$

The polymers (XXII) normally hydrolyze on contact with atmospheric moisture but are rendered essentially hydrolytically

```
     CH3  CH3              CH3  CH3               CH3  CH3
       \  /      [CH3        \  /      ]CH3         \  /
       OSiO       |          OSiO       |           OSiO
HOB          BO--SiOB              BO--SiOB               BOH
       OSiO       |          OSiO       |           OSiO
       /  \      [CH3        /  \      ]n CH3       /  \
     CH3  CH3              CH3  CH3               CH3  CH3
```

(XXII)

stable by irradiation with a 4 Mev electron beam.[27] The attendant water insolubility induced by the radiation may account for the apparent hydrolytic stability.

A rough comparison can be made of the relative stabilities of the siloxy- and alkoxyboranes under heterogeneous conditions. Tris(trimethylsiloxy)borane when shaken with water is 39% hydrolyzed in two hours,[1] which corresponds to a half life of 2.8 hours. The carbon analog, tri-*t*-butoxyborane, has an identical heterogeneous half life in water.[26]

Under homogeneous conditions it might be expected that the siloxyboranes would hydrolyze more rapidly than their carbon analogs due to the lowered electron density on boron resulting from p_π–d_π bonding of the electron pair on oxygen and the silicon $3d$ orbitals. However, it is possible that this effect is more than offset by the greater steric requirements of the silicon compounds.

2. THERMAL STABILITY

Tris(trialkylsiloxy)boranes have been recovered unchanged after being heated in sealed tubes at 275°.[1] At 300–350° they are recovered "practically unchanged"; however, decomposition to boric oxide and a hexaalkyldisiloxane takes place in the presence of ferric chloride.[28]

$$3\,(R_3SiO)_3B \xrightarrow{FeCl_3} B_2O_3 + 3\,R_3SiOSiR_3 \qquad (13\text{-}45)$$

The dialkylhalosiloxy derivatives are not as stable as the tris(trialkylsiloxy)boranes and decompose to boric oxide and *sym*-tetraalkyldichlorodisiloxanes on distillation at atmospheric pressure (13-46).[16,17,18,19] The chloro derivatives have a thermal

$$2\,(R_2\overset{\displaystyle X}{\overset{|}{Si}}O)_3B \rightarrow B_2O_3 + 3\,R_2\overset{\displaystyle X}{\overset{|}{Si}}O\overset{\displaystyle X}{\overset{|}{Si}}R_2 \qquad (13\text{-}46)$$

threshold of about 100° and are much more stable than the fluorine compounds, which decompose at room temperature.[19] In turn, the bromide analogs also are more stable than the fluorine compounds.[17] This phenomenon possibly is a function of the ability of the halogen to form an intramolecular p_π–d_π bond with silicon, which would promote the transfer of oxygen and its electron pair to a neighboring boron atom (13-47). The ability to form a double bond with silicon

$$\begin{matrix} R_2\overset{\displaystyle X}{\overset{|}{Si}}O & & O\overset{\displaystyle X}{\overset{|}{Si}}R_2 & & O\overset{\displaystyle X}{\overset{|}{Si}}R_2 \\ & B & & B & \\ R_2\underset{\displaystyle X}{\underset{|}{Si}}O & & O{-}Si(\ddot{X})R_2 & & O\underset{\displaystyle X}{\underset{|}{Si}}R_2 \end{matrix} \rightarrow R_2\overset{\displaystyle X}{\overset{|}{Si}}O\overset{\displaystyle X}{\overset{|}{Si}}R_2 + (R_2\overset{\displaystyle X}{\overset{|}{Si}}O)_2B\underset{\displaystyle \text{etc.}}{\underset{\downarrow}{O}}B(O\overset{\displaystyle X}{\overset{|}{Si}}R_2)_2 \qquad (13\text{-}47)$$

would decrease in going from fluorine to iodine, and consequently the ease of decomposition (disproportionation in this case) would decrease in going from fluorine to iodine.

3. WITH HYDROGEN HALIDES

Hydrogen chloride and bromide react rapidly and completely with tris(trimethylsiloxy)borane to produce boric acid and the corres-

$$[(CH_3)_3SiO]_3B + 3\ HX \rightarrow H_3BO_3 + 3\ (CH_3)_3SiX \qquad (13\text{-}48)$$

ponding trimethylhalosilanes.[1] Reaction (13-48) is analogous to the conversion of tertiary alkoxyboranes to tertiary alkyl halides (Chapter 4).

The polymer (XX) reacted with hydrogen chloride in carbon tetrachloride solution; however the reaction is not completely analogous to (13-48) since dichlorodimethylsilane was not a product.[27]

4. WITH BORIC OXIDE

The conversion of a silyl orthoborate to a silyl metaborate by reaction with boric oxide is discussed in Section V-A.

5. WITH TRIALKYLSILANOLS

"Transesterification" of a tris(trialkylsiloxy)borane with a different trialkylsilanol is discussed in Section IV-A-7.

V. SILYL METABORATES

A. Methods of Preparation

Silyl metaborates, like alkyl metaborates (Chapter 9), can be prepared by digestion of the orthoborate with boric oxide in a sealed tube at elevated temperature.[1]

$$(R_3SiO)_3B + B_2O_3 \rightarrow \begin{array}{ccccc} & & O & & \\ & \diagup & & \diagdown & \\ R_3SiOB & & & & BOSiR_3 \\ | & & & & | \\ O & & & & O \\ & \diagdown & & \diagup & \\ & & B & & \\ & & | & & \\ & & OSiR_3 & & \end{array} \qquad (13\text{-}49)$$

B. Reactions

Silyl metaborates have been heated in sealed tubes at 250° for 50 hours without decomposition but decompose to boric oxide and the corresponding orthoborate on attempted distillation.[1]

$$(R_3SiOBO)_3 \rightarrow B_2O_3 + (R_3SiO)_3B \qquad (13\text{-}50)$$

VI. ANALYTICAL

The boron content of both monomeric and polymeric silyl borates was determined by hydrolysis of the ester in aqueous dioxane or aqueous alcohol and titration of the resulting boric acid with standard base in the presence of mannitol to thymol blue[6,28] or phenolphthalein[22] endpoint. Chlorine-containing polymers which could give acidic hydrolysates were titrated to the methyl red endpoint before the addition of mannitol.[27] A second procedure applied to the polymeric products involved decomposition in a bomb followed by titration of the resulting boric acid in the presence of mannitol.[8]

VII. PHYSICAL CONSTANTS

$(R_3SiO)_3B$	M.p. (°C)	B.p. (°C)	d_4^t	n_D^t	Reference
$[(CH_3)_3SiO]_3B$		47/5		1.3852^{25}	5
		48/5			28
		90		1.3859^{20}	11
		184.5	0.8285^{20}	1.3860^{20}	28
		186		1.3840^{20}	1
$[C_2H_5Si(CH_3)_2O]_3B$		93–94/6	0.8598^{20}	1.4072^{20}	22, 23
$[(C_2H_5)_2Si(CH_3)O]_3B$		131–133/5	0.8751^{20}	1.4225^{20}	28
		138–140/6	0.8773^{20}	1.4240^{20}	22
$[(C_2H_5)_3SiO]_3B$		120/1			1
		145–146/2			2
		152–154/3	0.8962^{18}	1.4375^{21}	35
		154–155/4	0.8915^{20}	1.4373^{20}	22
		172–174/6	0.8904^{20}	1.4378^{20}	21
		178–179/13			28
		184/20		1.4370^{20}	1
		195/9.5	0.8921^{20}	1.4380^{20}	6
		310–312/780	0.8918^{20}	1.4379^{20}	28
$[(n\text{-}C_3H_7)_2Si(CH_3)O]_3B$		157–160/1	0.8668^{20}	1.4332^{20}	28
		185/3	0.8661^{20}	1.4308^{20}	6
$[(n\text{-}C_3H_7)_2Si(C_2H_5)O]_3B$		214/3	0.8768^{20}	1.4410^{20}	6
$[(n\text{-}C_3H_7)_3SiO]_3B$		215–217/1	0.8662^{20}	1.4425^{20}	6
$[(n\text{-}C_4H_9)_2Si(C_2H_5)O]_3B$		235/3	0.8875^{20}	1.4462^{20}	6
$[(n\text{-}C_5H_{11})_2Si(CH_3)O]_3B$		273–274/9	0.8613^{20}	1.4410^{20}	6
$[(n\text{-}C_4H_9)_3SiO]_3B$		273–274/3	0.8753^{20}	1.4488^{20}	6
$[(i\text{-}C_5H_{11})_2Si(C_2H_5)O]_3B$		297–298/11	0.8753^{20}	1.4480^{20}	6

(Table continued)

$[R_2Si(X)O]_3B$	M.p. (°C)	B.p. (°C)	d_4^t	n_D^t	Reference
$[(CH_3)_2Si(Cl)O]_2B$		60/0.1			7
		81.5–82/2			18
		98–98.5/11	1.0966^{20}	1.4130^{20}	7
$[(CH_3)_2Si(Br)O]_3B$	—	—	—	—	17
$[(CH_3)_2Si(F)O]_3B$			1.0797^{20}	1.3649^{20}	19
$[(C_2H_5)_2Si(Cl)O]_3B$		137.5–138/2	1.0665^{20}	1.4401^{20}	18
$[(C_2H_5)_2Si(Br)O]_3B$	—	—	—	—	17
$[(C_2H_5)_2Si(F)O]_3B$			1.0419^{20}	1.4019^{20}	19

$(X_3SiO)_3B$	M.p. (°C)	B.p. (°C)	d_4^t	n_D^t	Reference
$(Cl_3SiO)_3B$		98–102/12, 124–128/35	1.586^{20}		7

$[R_2Si(OR')O]_3B$	M.p. (°C)	B.p. (°C)	d_4^t	n_L^t	Reference
$[(CH_3)_2Si(OC_2H_5)O]_3B$	—	—	—	—	5

$[ArSi(R)_2O]_3B$	M.p. (°C)	B.p. (°C)	d_4^t	n_D^t	Reference
$[C_6H_5Si(C_2H_5)_2O]_3B$		250–255/6	1.0125^{20}	1.5200^{20}	22, 23
$[(C_6H_5)_2Si(CH_3)O]_3B$		320–325/3	1.120^{20}	1.5850^{20}	21, 22
$[(C_6H_5)_2Si(C_2H_5)O]_3B$		354–358/8	1.086^{20}	1.5796^{20}	6

$(Ar_3SiO)_3B$	M.p. (°C)	B.p. (°C)	d_4^t	n_D^t	Reference
$[(C_6H_5)_3SiO]_3B$	150				21. 22

$(R_3SiO)_2BOSiR_2OB(OSiR_3)_2$	M.p. (°C)	B.p. (°C)	d_4^t	n_D^t	Reference
$[(C_2H_5)_3SiO]_2BOSi(CH_3)_2OB[OSi(C_2H_5)_3]_2$	169–175/8			1.4320^{20}	2
$[(C_2H_5)_3SiO]_2BOSi(C_2H_5)_2OB[OSi(C_2H_5)_3]_2$		170–175/8		1.4384^{20}	2
		176–179/12		1.4390^{20}	2

$(R_3SiO)_2BOR'$	M.p. (°C)	B.p. (°C)	d_4^t	n_D^t	Reference
$[(C_2H_5)_3SiO]_2BOCH_3$		V.p. 2.5 mm at 115°			32

$(R_3SiOBO)_3$	M.p. (°C)	B.p. (°C)	d_4^t	n_D^t	Reference
$[(CH_3)_3SiOBO]_3$		Viscous liquid	0.988^{20}	1.4101^{20}	1
$[(C_2H_5)_3SiOBO]_3$			0.955^{20}	1.4360^{20}	1

VIII. REFERENCES

1. Abel, E. W., and A. Singh, *J. Chem. Soc.*, 690 (1959).
2. Andrianov, K. A., and M. N. Ermakova, *Zh. Obshch. Khim.*, **31**, 1310 (1961).
3. Andrianov, K. A., and L. M. Volkova, *Izv. Akad. Nauk. S.S.S.R. Otd. Khim. Nauk*, 303 (1957).
4. Anonymous. *Angew. Chem.*, **71**, 288 (1959).
5. Barry, A. J., U.S. Pat. 2,611,775 (1952, to Dow Corning Corporation).
6. Dolgov, B. N., I. I. Khudobin, and N. P. Kharitonov, *Proc. Acad. Sci. U.S.S.R.*, **122**, 717 (1958).
7. Frazer, M. J., W. Gerrard, and J. A. Strickson, *J. Chem. Soc.*, 4701 (1960).
8. Henglein, F. A., R. Lang, and K. Scheinost, *Makromol. Chem.*, **15**, 177 (1955).
9. Jedlicka, H., Ger. Pat. 1,045,092 (1956).
10. Kreshkov, A. P., D. A. Karateev, and V. Fyurst, *Zh. Obshch. Khim.*, **31**, 2139 (1961).
11. Krieble, R. H., U.S. Pat. 2,440,101 (1948, to General Electric Co.).
12. Kudryavtsev, R. V., D. N. Kursanov, and K. A. Andrianov, *Zh. Obshch. Khim.*, **29**, 1497 (1959).
13. Lappert, M. F., *J. Chem. Soc.*, 2790 (1958).
14. Lippincott, S. B., U.S. Pat. 2,642,453 (1953, to Standard Oil Development Co., Delaware).
15. Martin, R. W., U.S. Pat. 2,644,805 (1953, to General Electric Co.).
16. McCusker, P. A., and T. Ostdick, 132nd Meeting American Chemical Society, New York, Sept. 1957, Abstracts of Papers, p. 17-N.
17. McCusker, P. A., and T. Ostdick, 133rd Meeting American Chemical Society, San Francisco, April, 1958, *Abstracts of Papers*, p. 36-L.
18. McCusker, P. A., and T. Ostdick, *J. Am. Chem. Soc.*, **80**, 1103 (1958).
19. McCusker, P. A., and T. Ostdick, *J. Am. Chem. Soc.*, **81**, 5550 (1959).
20. McGregor, R. R., and E. L. Warrick, U.S. Pat. 2,431,878 (1947, to Corning Glass Works).
21. Orlov, N. F., and B. N. Dolgov, Russ. Pat. 115,167 (1958); *Chem. Abstracts*, **53**, 13107 (1959).
22. Orlov, N. F., B. N. Dolgov, and M. G. Voronkov, *Izv. Akad. Nauk S.S.S.R. Otd. Khim. Nauk*, 1607 (1960).
23. Orlov, N. F., B. N. Dolgov, and M. G. Voronkov, *Khim. i Prakt. Primenenie Kremneorgan. Soedinen., Tr. Konf. Leningrad*, 161 (1958); through *Chem. Abstracts*, **54**, 4360 (1960).
24. Patnode, W. I., U.S. Pat. 2,434,953 (1948, to General Electric Co.).
25. Ramsden, H. E., U.S. Pat. 2,867,641 (1959, to Metal and Thermit Corp.).
26. Steinberg, H., and D. L. Hunter, *Ind. Eng. Chem.*, **49**, 174 (1957).
27. Vale, R. L., *J. Chem. Soc.*, 2252 (1960).
28. Voronkov, M. G., and V. N. Zgonnik, *Zh. Obshch. Khim.*, **27**, 1476 (1957).
29. Weidmann, H., and H. K. Zimmerman, Jr., *J. Phys. Chem.*, **64**, 182 (1960).
30. Werner, R. L., and K. G. O'Brien, *Australian J. Chem.*, **8**, 355 (1955).
31. Wiberg, E., and U. Krüerke, *Z. Naturforsch.*, **8b**, 609 (1953).
32. Wiberg, E., and U. Krüerke, *Z. Naturforsch.*, **8b**, 610 (1953).
33. Wick, M., *Kunststoffe*, **50**, 433 (1960).
34. Wright, J. G. E., U.S. Pat. 2,541,851 (1951, to General Electric Co.).
35. Yakovlev, B. I., and N. V. Vinogradova, *Zh. Obshch. Khim.*, **29**, 695 (1959).

14

COORDINATION COMPOUNDS DERIVED FROM MONOHYDRIC ALCOHOLS AND PHENOLS

I. INTRODUCTION

Reactions of trigonal coplanar boron compounds are characterized by acceptance of a nucleophile which causes the rehybridization of the boron atom from sp^2 to sp^3 (14-1).

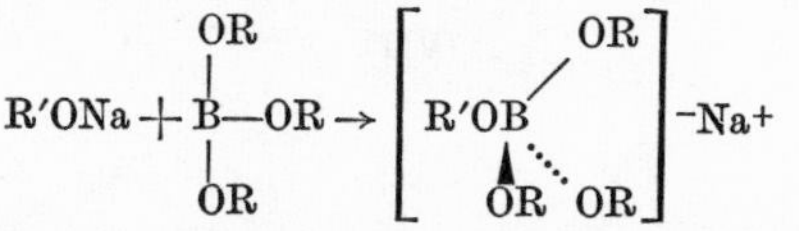

$$R'ONa + B(OR)_3 \rightarrow [R'OB(OR)_3]^- Na^+ \quad (14\text{-}1)$$

This chapter is concerned with those tetracovalent compounds of boron in which the four ligands to boron are alkoxyl (I). Tetra-

$$[(RO)_4B]^- M^+$$
(I)

alkoxyborates with different alkoxyl ligands (II and III) have been reported,[27] but the products were not well characterized. The parent acids (IV) are unstable[7] and have not been isolated.

$[(RO)_3BOR']M$ (II) $\quad$ $[R(-O-)_3BOR']M$ (III) $\quad$ $[(RO)_4B]H$ (IV)

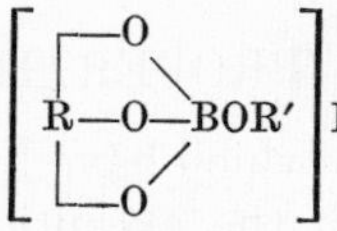

A few examples of coordination compounds with hydroxy and formoxy ligands in addition to alkoxy ligands have been described. A very early paper[9] stated that triethoxyborane reacted with alcoholic solutions of sodium hydroxide and barium hydroxide. Possibly the species (V) and (VI) were formed.

$[(C_2H_5O)_3BOH]\,Na$ (V) $\quad$ $[(C_2H_5O)_3BOH]_2Ba$ (VI)

Recently, the reaction of sodium borohydride with excess carbon dioxide in the absence of solvent, and the reaction of lithium borohydride with excess carbon dioxide in ether solvent were formulated as in equation (14-2).[25,34,35] The product also was formulated as the coordination compound (VII).[35]

$$MBH_4 + 2\,CO_2 \rightarrow MBO(OCH_3)(OCH{=}O) \qquad (14\text{-}2)$$

$$\left[\begin{array}{c} \text{cyclic } B_3O_3 \text{ ring; each B bearing } OCH_3 \text{ and } OCH{=}O \end{array}\right]M_3$$

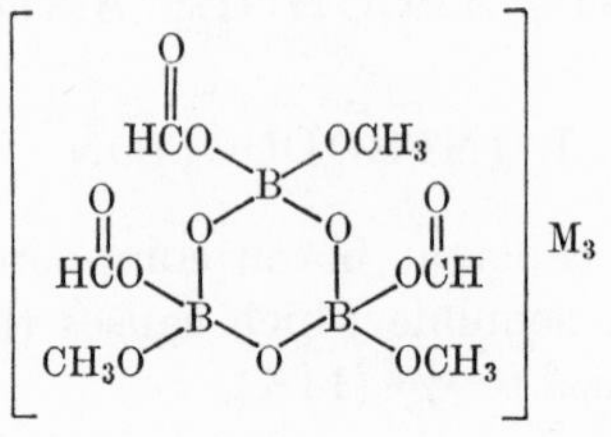

(VII)

II. HISTORICAL

In 1898, Copaux[9] described a crystalline product obtained from the treatment of triethoxyborane with sodium ethylate in alcohol solution. He formulated the product with a pentavalent boron atom (VIII).

$$(C_2H_4O)_4B{-}Na$$

(VIII)

III. PROPERTIES

The tetraalkoxyborate salts which have been isolated are crystalline or amorphous solids.[36] With the exception of sodium tetraoctoxy- and tetrastearoxyborate,[26] and presumably some of the higher alkoxy derivatives, they do not possess characteristic melting points but decompose on heating.

The tetraalkoxyborates crystallize from alcohol solution as the alcoholates. They can be freed of alcohol by heating at reduced pressure.[7,26] In general, they are sparingly soluble in the common organic solvents with the exception of the alcohols and tetrahydrofuran (Tables 14-1 and 14-2[13]). Small concentrations in benzene cause an appreciable increase in viscosity.[26]

The ^{11}B nuclear magnetic resonance chemical shift of lithium tetramethoxyborate has been recorded and indicates a high degree of shielding.[24]

Table 14-1. Solubility of tetraalkoxyborate salts in organic solvents

Solubility, $g./l.^t$ (reference)

	$[(CH_3O)_4B]Na$	$[(CH_3O)_4B]Li$	$[(CH_3O)_4B]_2Mg$	$[(CH_3O)_4B]_2Ca$	$[(CH_3O)_4B]_2Sr$	$[(CH_3O)_4B]_2Ba$	$[(C_2H_5O)_4B]Na$	$[(C_2H_5O)_4B]_2Ca$	$[(C_2H_5O)_4B]_2Sr$	$[(C_2H_5O)_4B]_2Ba$	$[(i\text{-}C_3H_7O)_4B]Na$	$[(i\text{-}C_3H_7O)_4B]_2Ca$	$[(n\text{-}C_5H_{11}O)_4B]Na$	$[(i\text{-}C_5H_{11}O)_4B]Na$	$[(n\text{-}C_8H_{17}O)_4B]Na$	$[(C_6H_5O)_4B]Na$
Methanol	272^{0} (2) 334^{25} (2) 430^{25} (6)	s^{25} (26)	vs (36)	s (36)	ss (36)	11.4^{21} (35) 0.6^{60} (36)						s^{25} (26)	s^{25} (26)		s^{25} (26)	
Ethanol				vs (16)			96^{0} (2) 113^{25} (2)	s (37)	s (37)	s (37)						
Isopropanol											24^{0} (2) 29^{25} (2)					
Dimethyl ether												I^{25} (26)				
Diethyl ether	0^{25} (2)		I (36)	I (36)	I (36)	I (36)	0^{25} (2)	ss (37)	ss (37)	I (37)	0^{25} (2)					
Dibutyl ether			I (36)	I (36)	I (36)	I (36)										
Tetrahydrofuran	vs^{0} (2) 467^{25} (2) 840^{25} (2)						vs^{0} (2) vs^{25} (2)	s (37)	s (37)	I (37)	7^{0} (2) 10^{25} (2)	I^{25} (26)				
Dioxane	0.4 to 1.9^{25} (6)		I (36)	I (36)	I (36)	I (36)		I (37)	I (37)	I (37)		I^{25} (26)				
Diethylene glycol	8.4^{25} (6)															
Diglyme	I (4)										ss (27)					
Triglyme	9.6^{25} (6)										5.4^{25} (2)					
Acetone		s^{25} (26)										I^{25} (26)	I^{25} (26)			
Pet. ether	I^{25} (6)	I^{25} (6)	I (36)	I (36)	I (36)	I (36)		ss (37)	ss (37)	I (37)			I^{25} (26)			
Hexane								s (37)	s (37)	I (37)						
Benzene	0^{70} (2)		I (36)	I (36)	I (36)	I (36)	0^{70} (2)	s (37)	s (37)		0^{70} (2)	s^{25} (26)				
Toluene												s^{25} (26)	I^{25} (26)			
Xylene										I (37)				vs^{hot} (21)		ss^{hot} (21)
Chloroform		I^{25} (26)											s^{25} (26)			
Carbon tetrachloride	I^{25} (6)													s^{25} (26)		
Chlorobenzene	0.4^{25} (6)													s^{25} (26)		
Acetonitrile	0^{70} (2)						0^{70} (2)				0^{70} (2)	I^{25} (26)	I^{25} (26)		I^{25} (26)	
Dimethylformamide	778^{25} (6)															
Butylamine	1230^{25} (6)															
Ethanolamine	$> 1560^{25}$ (6)															
Pyridine	0.4^{25} (6)		I (36)	I (36)	I (36)	I (36)						s^{25} (26)	s^{25} (26)			

s = Soluble, ss = Slightly soluble, vs = Very soluble, I = Insoluble

Table 14-2. Solubility of sodium tetramethoxyborate in trimethoxyborane–methanol solution

Mole fraction $(CH_3O)_3B$ in CH_3OH	Solubility $NaB(OCH_3)_4$, g./100 g. solvent
0.00	54.50
0.25	21.50
0.50	18.58
0.75	5.06
1.00	0.09

IV. METHODS OF PREPARATION

A. From Trialkoxyboranes

1. AND METAL ALKOXIDES

The original transformation observed by Copaux [9] which involves the direct reaction of a boric acid ester and the corresponding metal alcoholate (14-3) subsequently was confirmed for a variety of mono-

$$(C_2H_5O)_3B + C_2H_5ONa \rightarrow (C_2H_5O)_4BNa \tag{14-3}$$

valent cations (Na^+, Li^+, K^+, Tl^+) and for calcium ion with methoxy, ethoxy, n-propoxy and isopropoxy ligands.[7,10,16,26,27,31,32]

Secondary alcohol derivatives such as sodium [2] and calcium [26] tetraisopropoxyborate also could be prepared by this method; however all attempts to convert *t*-butyl borate to sodium tetra-*t*-butoxyborate failed. It was concluded that the steric requirements of the *t*-butoxy group precluded the formation of the tetracovalent compound.[2]

The method evidently also is applicable to the aromatic members if the preparation of sodium tetraphenoxyborate [21] can be generalized. Xylene, instead of the usual excess alcohol, was used as the solvent in this case.

In situ preparation of the alkoxide (14-4) was successful for the

$$M + 2\,ROH + 2\,(RO)_3B \xrightarrow{ROH} [(RO)_4B]_2M + H_2 \tag{14-4}$$

preparation of calcium tetramethoxyborate,[7,36] magnesium, barium and strontium tetramethoxyborate,[36] and calcium, barium and strontium tetraethoxyborate.[37]

The formation of ammonium tetramethoxyborate from ammonia and trimethoxyborane–methanol azeotrope (14-5) can be considered a special case of reaction (14-4).[33]

$$NH_3 + CH_3OH + (CH_3O)_3B \rightarrow NH_4B(OCH_3)_4 \tag{14-5}$$

The alkoxyl ligand can be transferred to the orthoborate from an existing complex as evidenced by the formation of lithium tetraisobutoxyborate from the reaction of triisobutoxyborane and phenyllithium. Presumably the following sequence occurs:[22]

$$(i\text{-}C_4H_9O)_3B + C_6H_5Li \rightarrow [C_6H_5B(O\text{-}i\text{-}C_4H_9)_3]Li \tag{14-6}$$

$$[C_6H_5B(O\text{-}i\text{-}C_4H_9)_3]Li + (i\text{-}C_4H_9O)_3B \rightarrow [(i\text{-}C_4H_9O)_4B]Li + C_6H_5B(O\text{-}i\text{-}C_4H_9)_2 \tag{14-7}$$

The kinetics of reaction (14-3) have not been studied; however an indication of the rapidity of the transformation is seen in the titration of trimethoxyborane* with sodium methylate in methanol solution.[19,21]

The reversible nature of the reaction in alcoholic solution is shown by the incomplete titrations observed for a variety of esters with their corresponding sodium alcoholates (Table 14-3).[2,19,21]

Table 14-3. Titration of boric acid esters with corresponding sodium alcoholates

$(RO)_3B$	Solvent	Alkoxide	Indicator	Percent titrated
$(C_6H_5CH_2O)_3B$	$C_6H_5CH_2OH$	$C_6H_5CH_2ONa$	Thymolphthalein	98.5
$(CH_3O)_3B$	CH_3OH	CH_3ONa	Thymolphthalein	96.7
$(CH_3O)_3B$	CH_3OH	CH_3ONa	Phenolphthalein	90.6
$(CH_3O)_3B$	CH_3OH	CH_3ONa	Alizarin Yellow R	90.0
$(C_2H_5O)_3B$	C_2H_5OH	C_2H_5ONa	Thymolphthalein	13.0
$(C_2H_5O)_3B$	C_2H_5OH	C_2H_5ONa	Phenolphthalein	3.1
$(C_2H_5O)_3B$	C_2H_5OH	C_2H_5ONa	Alizarin Yellow R	0
$(n\text{-}C_3H_7O)_3B$	$n\text{-}C_3H_7OH$	$n\text{-}C_3H_7ONa$	Thymolphthalein	6.2
$(i\text{-}C_3H_7O)_3B$	$i\text{-}C_3H_7OH$	$i\text{-}C_3H_7ONa$	Thymolphthalein	0.7
$(i\text{-}C_3H_7O)_3B$	$i\text{-}C_3H_7OH$	$i\text{-}C_3H_7ONa$	Phenolphthalein	0
$(i\text{-}C_3H_7O)_3B$	$i\text{-}C_3H_7OH$	$i\text{-}C_3H_7ONa$	Alizarin Yellow R	0
$(i\text{-}C_3H_7O)_3B$	C_6H_6	CH_3ONa	Thymolphthalein	98.5
$(t\text{-}C_4H_9O)_3B$	$t\text{-}C_4H_9OH$	$t\text{-}C_4H_9ONa$	Phenolphthalein	0
$(t\text{-}C_4H_9O)_3B$	$t\text{-}C_4H_9OH$	$t\text{-}C_4H_9ONa$	Alizarin Yellow R	0

The incomplete titrations could not be rationalized, especially in view of the stability of the tetraalkoxy salts.[2] It is apparent that steric considerations are not operative since benzyl borate is more completely titrated than ethyl borate. The general order of reactivity

* Noller[23] prefers to look upon the titration as involving the neutralization of the acid species.

$$\begin{matrix} CH_3 & & OCH_3 \\ & \diagdown & | \\ & O{:} & B\text{—}OCH_3 \\ & \diagup & | \\ H & & OCH_3 \end{matrix}$$

$C_6H_5CH_2 > CH_3 > C_2H_5 > i\text{-}C_3H_7 > t\text{-}C_4H_9$ is consistent with increasing electron density on boron which would serve to deter the entry of the alkoxide ion. Another more general listing of the order of reactivity of boric acid esters to metal alcoholates has been recorded:[20] $Cl_3CCH_2 > ClCH_2CH_2 > C_6H_5CH_2 > CH_2{=}CHCH_2 > CH_3 > C_2H_5 > n\text{-}C_3H_7 > i\text{-}C_3H_7$. This sequence also is consistent with decreasing reactivity with increasing electron density on boron.

2. AND SODIUM HYDRIDE

Treatment of sodium hydride with a large excess of trimethoxyborane in tetrahydrofuran solution at 65° was reported to give an 83% yield of sodium borohydride.[1] Presumably sodium tetramethoxyborate was produced in equal yield (14-8).

$$4\ NaH + 4\ B(OCH_3)_3 \rightarrow NaBH_4 + 3\ NaB(OCH_3)_4 \qquad (14\text{-}8)$$

B. From Borohydrides

1. AND ALCOHOLS

Lithium,[28] sodium[31] and beryllium[36] borohydride have been converted to the corresponding tetramethoxyborates by treatment

$$MBH_4 + 4\ CH_3OH \rightarrow (CH_3O)_4BM + 4\ H_2 \qquad (14\text{-}9)$$

with methanol. The beryllium salt, however, could not be isolated due to its ready decomposition to methyl borate and beryllium methoxide. Secondary and tertiary alcohol derivatives evidently cannot be prepared at an appreciable rate by this method, since isopropyl and *t*-butyl alcohol were considered as solvents for the sodium borohydride reduction of ketones and esters.[3]

2. AND ALDEHYDES AND KETONES

The reduction of aldehydes[8] and ketones[3,8,31] to the corresponding alcohols with sodium borohydride undoubtedly proceeds via the tetraalkoxyborate which subsequently is hydrolyzed to the desired alcohol.

$$4\ R\overset{\overset{O}{\|}}{C}H + NaBH_4 \rightarrow (RCH_2O)_4BNa \xrightarrow{H_2O} 4\ RCH_2OH + NaBO_2 \qquad (14\text{-}10)$$

$$4\ R\overset{\overset{O}{\|}}{C}R + NaBH_4 \rightarrow (R_2CHO)_4BNa \xrightarrow{H_2O} 4\ R_2CHOH + NaBO_2 \qquad (14\text{-}11)$$

C. From Sodium Trimethoxyhydroborate

1. DISPROPORTIONATION

Sodium trimethoxyhydroborate disproportionates at 230° to compounds richer in hydrogen than the starting material (14-12).

$$4\,[(CH_3O)_3BH]Na \xrightarrow{\Delta} NaBH_4 + 3\,(CH_3O)_4BNa \qquad (14\text{-}12)$$

The reaction can be driven further by the continuous removal of the trimethoxyborane which results from the decomposition of the tetramethoxy derivative (14-13).[30]

$$(CH_3O)_4BNa \xrightarrow{\Delta} NaOCH_3 + (CH_3O)_3B \qquad (14\text{-}13)$$

A more facile disproportionation to sodium tetramethoxyborate and sodium borohydride can be effected by simple dissolution of sodium trimethoxyhydroborate in tetrahydrofuran or diglyme. The borohydride is insoluble and the tetramethoxyborate is soluble in tetrahydrofuran. Reverse solubilities are operative in diglyme.[4]

2. AND ALCOHOLS

Sodium trimethoxyhydroborate reacts rapidly and completely

$$[(CH_3O)_3BH]Na + CH_3OH \rightarrow (CH_3O)_4BNa + H_2 \qquad (14\text{-}14)$$

with methanol, even in the cold, to give the tetramethoxyborate.[5] A more complex example is given in equation (14-15).[27]

$$[(CH_3O)_3BH]Na + [N(CH_2CH_2OH)_4]Cl \rightarrow$$
$$NaCl + H_2 + (HOCH_2CH_2)_3\overset{+}{N}CH_2CH_2O\overset{-}{B}(OCH_3)_3 \qquad (14\text{-}15)$$

D. From Alkali Borates and Methanol

Anhydrous or hydrated alkali borates dissolve in methanol to give the tetramethoxyborate and water according to equation (14-16).[18]

$$MBO_2 + 4\,CH_3OH \rightarrow MB(OCH_3)_4 + 2\,H_2O \qquad (14\text{-}16)$$

If the metal to boron ratio of the alkali borate is less than unity, such as in borax, the excess boron is converted to trimethoxyborane.[18]

$$Na_2B_4O_7 + 14\,CH_3OH \rightarrow 2\,NaB(OCH_3)_4 + 2\,(CH_3O)_3B + 7\,H_2O \qquad (14\text{-}17)$$

E. From Other Tetraalkoxyborates

1. EXCHANGE OF CATIONS

The replacement of the cation of a given tetraalkoxyborate salt with a different cation is dependent upon the solubilities of the species involved. Thus, sodium and potassium tetramethoxyborate are converted to the lithium salt by treatment with lithium chloride in methanol solution due to the insolubility of the resulting sodium

$$(CH_3O)_4BK + LiCl \xrightarrow{CH_3OH} (CH_3O)_4BLi + \underline{KCl} \quad (14\text{-}18)$$

and potassium chloride.[7,12] Similarly, potassium tetraethoxyborate is converted to the less soluble thallium tetraethoxyborate by treatment with thallium acetate in ethanol solution (14-19).[7] Sodium

$$(C_2H_5O)_4BK + TlOAc \xrightarrow{C_2H_5OH} \underline{(C_2H_5O)_4BTl} + KOAc \quad (14\text{-}19)$$

tetramethoxyborate was converted to the beryllium salt in an analogous manner by treatment with beryllium chloride in methanol solution. As in the case of the preparation from beryllium borohydride and methanol, the product decomposed to methyl borate and beryllium methoxide.[36]

2. EXCHANGE OF ALKOXYL LIGANDS

"Transesterification" of a tetraalkoxyborate has been claimed.[11,14,27]

$$M[B(OR)_4]_n + 4n\ R'OH \rightarrow M[B(OR')_4]_n + 4n\ ROH \quad (14\text{-}20)$$

The partial "transesterification" of sodium tetramethoxyborate with a hydroxyl-containing tetraalkylammonium chloride has been claimed to give a mixed alkoxy betaine (14-21).[27] The product was

$$NaB(OCH_3)_4 + [CH_3N(CH_2CH_2OH)_3]Cl \rightarrow (CH_3O)_3\overset{-}{B}OCH_2CH_2\overset{+}{N}(CH_3)(CH_2CH_2OH)_2 + CH_3OH + NaCl \quad (14\text{-}21)$$

not characterized. Two (14-22) and three (14-23) ligands of sodium tetramethoxyborate also have been replaced.[27]

$$NaB(OCH_3)_4 + [N(CH_2CH_2OH)_4]Br \rightarrow Br^- (HOCH_2CH_2)_2\overset{+}{N}(CH_2CH_2O)_2\overset{-}{B}(OCH_3)_2\ Na^+ + 2\,CH_3OH \quad (14\text{-}22)$$

$$NaB(OCH_3)_4 + [CH_3N(CH_2CH_2OH)_3]\,I \rightarrow I^-\ CH_3\overset{+}{N}(CH_2CH_2O)(CH_2CH_2O)(H_2CH_2O)\overset{-}{B}OCH_3\ Na^+ + 3\,CH_3OH \quad (14\text{-}23)$$

The betaines (IX and X) were claimed from the reaction of sodium tetraethoxyborate and tetrakis-(2-hydroxyethyl)ammonium chloride.[27]

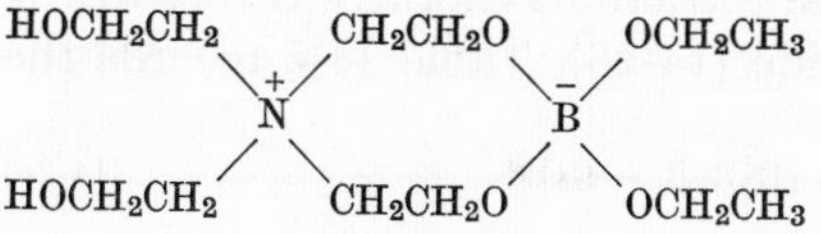

(IX)

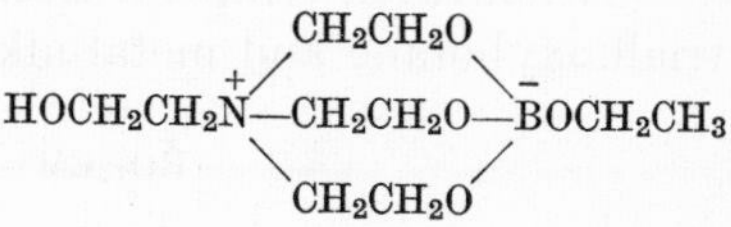

(X)

V. REACTIONS

A. *Hydrolysis*

The tetraalkoxyborates are readily hydrolyzed in water or by contact with moist air.[2,7,26,27,36,37]

$$(RO)_4BM + 2\,H_2O \rightarrow 4\,ROH + MBO_2 \qquad (14\text{-}24)$$

$$[(RO)_4B]_2M + 4\,H_2O \rightarrow 8\,ROH + MB_2O_4 \qquad (14\text{-}25)$$

An indication of steric dependence is seen in the half-lives of hydrolysis under heterogeneous conditions (Table 14-4). The half-

Table 14-4. Heterogeneous rate of hydrolysis of tetraalkoxyborates in water at 24°

Tetraalkoxyborate	$t_{1/2}$ (sec.)[a]
$(CH_3O)_4BLi$	Too fast to measure
$(CH_3O)_4BK$	Too fast to measure
$(CH_3O)_4BNa$	Too fast to measure
$(i\text{-}C_3H_7O)_4BNa$	Too fast to measure
$(n\text{-}C_8H_{17}O)_4BNa$	4
$(n\text{-}C_{18}H_{37}O)_4BNa$	420

[a] Water (50 ml.) containing 0.6 m.e. of hydrochloric acid and five drops phenolphthalein was added to 1.2 mmole of salt. Half-life shown is time for indicator change.

lives appear to increase with the molecular weight of the alcohols involved. However, the rate of solubility probably decreases with increasing molecular weight and the observed variation in half-lives may be due to this phenomenon rather than steric effects.[26]

B. *Thermal Stability*

With the exception of beryllium tetramethoxyborate[36] and magnesium tetraethoxyborate,[37] which decompose below 0°, the tetraalkoxyborates and sodium tetraphenoxyborate are stable at room temperature or on warming *in vacuo*.[7] Sodium tetramethoxyborate charred but did not decompose up to 200°.[9] It appears to be stable for a period of years when stored at room temperature in a sealed vial.[26]

At elevated temperatures, the tetraalkoxyborates revert to the trialkoxyborane and metal alkoxide (14-26). Table 14-5 records the

$$(RO)_4BM \xrightarrow{\Delta} (RO)_3B + ROM \tag{14-26}$$

Table 14-5. Decomposition temperatures of tetraalkoxyborate salts

Tetraalkoxyborate	Decomposition temperature (°C/mm.)	Reference
$(CH_3O)_4BLi$	50–140	18
	250/ < 63.5	10
$(CH_3O)_4BNa$	200	18
	210–240/Vacuum	31
	260–265/Vacuum	2
	280/ < 13	10
$[(CH_3O)_4B]_2Be$	−45	36
$[(CH_3O)_4B]_2Mg$	135/Vacuum	36
$[(CH_3O)_4B]_2Ca$	225/Vacuum	36
$[(CH_3O)_4B]_2Sr$	232/Vacuum	36
$[(CH_3O)_4B]_2Ba$	240/Vacuum	36
$(C_2H_5O)_4BNa$	340–345/Vacuum	2
$[(C_2H_5O)_4B]_2Mg$	< −10	37
$[(C_2H_5O)_4B]_2Ca$	145-160/Vacuum	37
$[(C_2H_5O)_4B]_2Sr$	155–180/Vacuum	37
$[(C_2H_5O)_4B]_2Ba$	165–200/Vacuum	37
$(i\text{-}C_3H_7O)_4BNa$	265–270/Vacuum	2
	300	26
$[(i\text{-}C_3H_7O)_4B]_2Ca$	60	26

decomposition temperatures. Table 14-6 lists the vapor pressure of trimethoxyborane over sodium and lithium tetramethoxyborate.[10] It is seen that for a given alkoxy group, the stability of the salt

Table 14-6. Vapor pressure of trimethoxyborane over sodium and lithium tetramethoxyborate

Temp. (°C)	Vapor pressure (mm.) of $(CH_3O)_3B$	
	Over $(CH_3O)_4BNa$	Over $(CH_3O)_4BLi$
230		25.5
250	3	63.5
260		96.5
280	13	
290	19	
300	27	

increases with the atomic weight of the metal for both the alkali metal and alkaline earth series. In addition, the alkali metal salts are more stable than the alkaline earth salts.

It is further apparent that the stability of a given alkaline earth salt decreases with increasing molecular weight of the alkoxy ligand. This situation does not appear to hold for the alkali metal salts, at least for the limited data available, since the stability of the sodium salts seems to be at a maximum at the ethoxy derivative.

The monomeric betaine (XI) was converted to the polymer (XII)

$$CH_3\overset{+}{N}(CH_2CH_2O)_3\overset{-}{B}OCH_3 \qquad \left[-CH_2CH_2-\overset{+}{N}(CH_3)(CH_2CH_2O)_2\overset{-}{B}(OCH_3)-O-\right]_n$$

(XI) (XII)

when heated at 240° *in vacuo* for one hour.[27] A similar transformation of (XIII) to (XIV) took place at 170°.[27]

$$Br^- \ (HOCH_2CH_2)_2\overset{+}{N}(CH_2CH_2O)_2\overset{-}{B}(OCH_3)_2 \qquad Na^+ \left[(-CH_2CH_2)_2\overset{+}{N}(CH_2CH_2O)_2\overset{-}{B}(O-)_2\right]_n$$

(XIII) (XIV)

C. *With Hydridic Materials*

Tetraalkoxyborate salts are readily reduced to metal borohydrides by treatment with diborane (14-27 and 14-28),[4,29,31,38] dimethoxy-borane (14-29),[17] sodium hydride (14-30),[30] or silane (14-31).[15]

$$3\,(CH_3O)_4BM + 2\,B_2H_6 \rightarrow 3\,MBH_4 + 4\,(CH_3O)_3B, \qquad M = Li, Na, K \qquad (14\text{-}27)$$

$$3\,[(CH_3O)_4B]_2M + 4\,B_2H_6 \rightarrow 3\,M(BH_4)_2 + 8\,(CH_3O)_3B, \qquad M = Mg, Ca, Sr, Ba \qquad (14\text{-}28)$$

$$[(RO)_4B]_nM + 4n\,(RO)_2BH \rightarrow M(BH_4)_n + 4n\,B(OR)_3 \qquad (14\text{-}29)$$

$$(CH_3O)_4BNa + 4\,NaH \rightarrow NaBH_4 + 4\,NaOCH_3 \qquad (14\text{-}30)$$

$$(CH_3O)_4BNa + SiH_4 \rightarrow NaBH_4 + (CH_3O)_4Si \qquad (14\text{-}31)$$

Reaction (14-28) proceeded without solvent, but improved yields were obtained in ether solution, and a quantitative yield was realized in tetrahydrofuran.[38] Other workers could not isolate calcium borohydride from reaction (14-28) without solvent and formulated the product as (XV).[16,32]

$$[(CH_3O)_4B]\,CaBH_4$$

(XV)

The partial solubility of sodium borohydride in a tetrahydrofuran solution of sodium tetramethoxyborate was attributed to a rapid equilibration of ligands (14-32 and 14-33), or, more likely, to the tridentate chelation of the sodium ion (XVI).[4]

$$NaBH_4 + NaB(OCH_3)_4 \rightleftharpoons NaBH_3(OCH_3) + NaBH(OCH_3)_3 \quad (14\text{-}32)$$

$$NaBH_3(OCH_3) + NaB(OCH_3)_4 \rightleftharpoons NaBH_2(OCH_3)_2 + NaBH(OCH_3)_3 \quad (14\text{-}33)$$

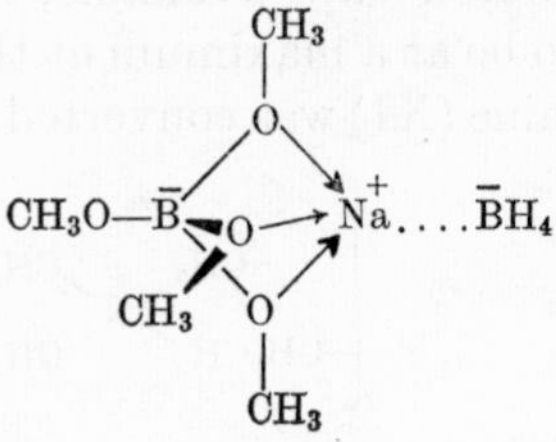

CH_3
O
$CH_3O—\bar{B}$ O → $\overset{+}{Na}$.... $\bar{B}H_4$
CH_3 O
CH_3

(XVI)

D. *With Carbon Dioxide*

The carbonation of tetraalkoxyborate salts as a preparative method for trialkyl borates has been discussed in Chapter 4.

E. *Miscellaneous*

Sodium tetramethoxyborate forms addition compounds of unknown structure with acetone, benzaldehyde and hexachlorobutadiene.[6] Sodium tetraethoxyborate did not react with ethyl iodide up to 140°.[9] The reaction product of triethoxyborane and sodium hydroxide, presumably $[(C_2H_5O)_3BOH]Na$, also was unreactive towards ethyl iodide.[9]

VI. ANALYTICAL

Cambis' original analytical procedure for the determination of boron in tetraalkoxyborates involved hydrolysis of the salt followed by neutralization of the resulting strong base with hydrochloric acid to the methyl orange endpoint and subsequent titration of the boric acid in the presence of mannitol with barium hydroxide to the phenolphthalein endpoint. The alkoxy groups were determined by the Zeisel method.[7]

Determination of the alkalinity by titration to the methyl red endpoint, destruction of carbonate by gentle boiling in acid medium, and final titration with sodium hydroxide to the methylene blue modified phenolphthalein endpoint appears more advisable. The higher molecular weight alkoxyborates should be hydrolyzed in alcohol–water solution to insure solubility of the resulting fatty alcohols.[26]

VII. PHYSICAL CONSTANTS

$(RO)_4BM$	M.p. (°C)	Reference
$(CH_3O)_4BLi$	> 310	26
	—	7, 18, 28
$(CH_3O)_4BLi \cdot 2CH_3OH$	—	26
$(CH_3O)_4BLi \cdot 2.5CH_3OH$	Long prisms	7
$(CH_3O)_4BNa$	> 200	9, 18
	253–258	27
	260–265 (d.)	2
	ca. 300 (d.)	6
$(CH_3O)_4BNa \cdot 1.5CH_3OH$	Prisms	7
$(CH_3O)_4BK$	Needles	31
	—	7, 18, 26
$(CH_3O)_4BK \cdot 1.5CH_3OH$	—	7
$(CH_3O)_4BRb$	—	18
$(CH_3O)_4BCs$	—	18
$(CH_3O)_4BNH_4$	Solid	33
$[(CH_3O)_4B]_2Be$	−45 (d.)	36
$[(CH_3O)_4B]_2Mg$	135 (d.)	36
$[(CH_3O)_4B]_2Ca$	225 (d.)	36
$[(CH_3O)_4B]_2Zn$	Needles	21
$[(CH_3O)_4B]_2Sr$	232 (d.)	36
$[(CH_3O)_4B]_2Ba$	240 (d.)	36
$(C_2H_5O)_4BNa$	340–345 (d.)	2
	348–351	27
	—	7
$(C_2H_5O)_4BNa \cdot C_2H_5OH$	Rhombic prisms	7
$(C_2H_5O)_4BNa \cdot 1.5C_2H_5OH$	—	26
$(C_2H_5O)_4BK$	—	7
$(C_2H_5O)_4BK \cdot 1.5C_2H_5OH$	Prisms	7
$(C_2H_5O)_4BTl$	Needles	7
$[(C_2H_5O)_4B]_2Mg$	< −10 (d.)	37
$[(C_2H_5O)_4B]_2Ca$	145–160 (d.)	37
$[(C_2H_5O)_4B]_2Sr$	155–180 (d.)	37
$[(C_2H_5O)_4B]_2Ba$	165–200 (d.)	37
$(n\text{-}C_3H_7O)_4BNa$	—	7
$(n\text{-}C_3H_7O)_4BNa \cdot n\text{-}C_3H_7OH$	Pearly scales	7
$(i\text{-}C_3H_7O)_4BNa$	265–270 (d.)	2
	287–292 (d.)	27
	300 (d.)	26
	—	26
$[(i\text{-}C_3H_7O)_4B]_2Ca$	—	26
$(n\text{-}C_4H_9O)_4Na$	Solid	11
$(i\text{-}C_4H_9O)_4BLi$	—	22
$(n\text{-}C_5H_{11}O)_4BNa$	Solid	26
$(i\text{-}C_5H_{11}O)_4BNa$	Solid	21
$(C_6H_5CH_2O)_4BK$	—	21
$(n\text{-}C_8H_{17}O)_4BNa$	37	26
$(n\text{-}C_{18}H_{37}O)_4BNa$	74.5–77	26

(Table continued)

$(ArO)_4BM$	M.p. (°C)	Reference
$(C_6H_5O)_4BNa$	Needles	21

$\left[R\left(\begin{smallmatrix}-O\\-O\end{smallmatrix}\right)B(OR')_2\right]M$	M.p. (°C)	Reference
$\left[Br^- \; (HOCH_2CH_2)_2\overset{+}{N}(CH_2CH_2O)_2\overset{-}{B}(OCH_3)_2\right]Na^+$	255–275 (d.)	27

$\left[R\left(\begin{smallmatrix}-O\\-O-\\-O\end{smallmatrix}\right)BOR'\right]M$	M.p. (°C)	Reference
$\left[I^- \; CH_3\overset{+}{N}(CH_2CH_2O)_3\overset{-}{B}OCH_3\right]Na^+$	228–230	27

Betaines	M.p. (°C)	Reference
$(HOCH_2CH_2)_2\overset{+}{N}(CH_3)CH_2CH_2O\overset{-}{B}(OCH_3)_3$	Clear colorless gum	27
$(HOCH_2CH_2)_3\overset{+}{N}CH_2CH_2O\overset{-}{B}(OCH_3)_3$	—	27
$CH_3CH(OH)CH_2\overset{+}{N}(CH_3)(CH_2CH(CH_3)O)_2\overset{-}{B}(OCH_3)_2$	Off-white foam	27
$CH_3\overset{+}{N}(CH_2CH(CH_3)O)_3\overset{-}{B}OCH(CH_3)_2$	135–150	27
$CH_3CH(OH)CH_2\overset{+}{N}(CH_3)(CH_2CH(CH_3)O)_2\overset{-}{B}[OCH(CH_3)_2]_2$	132–142	72
$(HOCH_2CH_2)_2\overset{+}{N}(CH_2CH_2O)_2\overset{-}{B}(OCH_3)_2$	Ca. 255–275	27

(*Table continued*)

Betaines	M.p.(°C)	Reference
$(CH_3)(C_{18}H_{37})\overset{+}{N}(CH_2CH_2O)_2\overset{-}{B}(OCH_3)_2$	Off-white powder	27
$(HOCH_2CH_2)_2\overset{+}{N}(CH_2CH_2O)_2\overset{-}{B}(OCH_2CH_3)_2$	Solid	27
$[-CH_2CH_2(CH_3)\overset{+}{N}(CH_2CH_2O)_2\overset{-}{B}(OCH_3)O-]_n$	Glass	27
$[(-CH_2CH_2)_2\overset{+}{N}(CH_2CH_2O)_2\overset{-}{B}(O-)_2]_n$	250–260 (d.)	27
$CH_3\overset{+}{N}(CH_2CH_2O)_3\overset{-}{B}OCH_3$	233–236 (d.)	27
$HOCH_2CH_2\overset{+}{N}(CH_2CH_2O)_3\overset{-}{B}OCH_2CH_3$	Solid	27
$[-CH_2CH_2\overset{+}{N}(CH_2CH_2O)_3\overset{-}{B}-O-]_n$	—	27
$[-OCH_2\overset{+}{P}(CH_2O)_3\overset{-}{B}-]_n$	Ca. 190	27

$[(RO)_3BOH]M$	M.p. (°C)	Reference
$[(C_2H_5O)_3BOH]Na$	—	9
$[(C_2H_5O)_3BOH]_2Ba$	—	9

(Table continued)

$[ROBO(O\overset{\overset{O}{\|}}{C}R)]_3M$	M.p. (°C)	Reference
$[(HC(=O)O)(CH_3O)BO]_3Na_3$ (cyclic trimer: three B atoms, each bearing $HC(=O)O$ and OCH_3, joined by three ring O atoms)	White solid	25, 34, 35

VIII. REFERENCES

1. Berner, R. G., R. P. Berni, and S. J. Klach, U.S. Pat. 2,939,762 (1960, to Callery Chemical Company).
2. Brown, H. C., and E. J. Mead, *J. Am. Chem. Soc.*, **78**, 3614 (1956).
3. Brown, H. C., E. J. Mead, and B. C. Subba Rao, *J. Am. Chem. Soc.*, **77**, 6209 (1955).
4. Brown, H. C., E. J. Mead, and P. A. Tierney, *J. Am. Chem. Soc.*, **79**, 5400 (1957).
5. Brown, H. C., H. I. Schlesinger, I. Sheft, and D. M. Ritter, *J. Am. Chem. Soc.*, **75**, 192 (1953).
6. Callery, Chemical Co., Technical Data Sheet C-920, August 1, 1957.
7. Cambi, L., *Atti accad. Lincei*, **23**, 244 (1914).
8. Chaikin, S. W., and W. G. Brown, *J. Am. Chem. Soc.*, **71**, 122 (1949).
9. Copaux, H., *Compt. Rend.*, **127**, 719 (1898).
10. Cunningham, G. L., U.S. Pat. 2,830,070 (1958, to Callery Chemical Co.).
11. Cunningham, G. L., and F. Pretka, Can. Pat. 631,509 (1961, to Callery Chemical Company).
12. Cunningham, G. L., and F. Pretka, U.S. Pat. 2,923,731 (1960, to Callery Chemical Company); See also Can. Pat. 615,642; Fr. Pat. 1,246,606.
13. Cunningham, G. L., and F. Pretka, U.S. Pat. 2,938,920 (1960, to Callery Chemical Company).
14. Cunningham, G. L., and F. Pretka, U.S. Pat. 2,996,534 (1960, to Callery Chemical Company); Can. Pat. 631,509 (1961).
15. Edwards, L. J., XVIIth International Congress of Pure and Applied Chemistry, Munich, Sept. 1959, Inorganic Chemistry Abstracts, p. 50.
16. Griggs, B., M.S. Thesis, University of California, Los Angeles, MCC-1023-TR-162, June 1955.
17. Huff, G. F., Can. Pat. 626,249 (1961, to Callery Chemical Company).
18. Lehmann, H. A., and D. Tiess, *Z. Anorg. Allgem. Chem.*, **304**, 89 (1960); See also *Wiss Z. Tech. Hochsch. Chem. Leuna-Merseburg*, **2**, 285 (1959/60); through *Chem. Abstracts*, **55**, 1257 (1961).
19. Mead, E. J., *Dissertation Abstr.*, **15**, 971 (1955).
20. Meerwein, H., *Angew. Chem.*, **60**, 78 (1948).
21. Meerwein, H., and T. Bersin, *Ann.*, **476**, 113 (1929).

22. Mikhailov, B. M., and P. M. Aronovich, *Dokl. Akad. Nauk S.S.S.R.*, **98,** 791 (1954).
23. Noller, C. R., *Chemistry of Organic Compounds,* W. B. Saunders Co., Philadelphia, 1951, p. 95.
24. Onak, T. P., H. Landesman, R. E. Williams, and I. Shapiro, *J. Phys. Chem.*, **63,** 1533 (1959).
25. Pearson, R. K., and T. Wartik, U.S. Pat. 2,872,474 (1959, to Callery Chemical Company).
26. Petterson, L. L., and H. Steinberg, Unpublished results.
27. Rudner, B., and M. S. Moores, U.S. Pat. 2,976,307 (1961, to Koppers Company, Inc.).
28. Schlesinger, H. I., and H. C. Brown, *J. Am. Chem. Soc.*, **62,** 3429 (1940).
29. Schlesinger, H. I., and H. C. Brown, U.S. Pat. 2,461,663 (1949, to The United States Atomic Energy Commission).
30. Schlesinger, H. I., H. C. Brown, and A. E. Finholt, *J. Am. Chem. Soc.*, **75,** 205 (1953).
31. Schlesinger, H. I., H. C. Brown, H. R. Hoekstra, and L. R. Rapp, *J. Am. Chem. Soc.*, **75,** 199 (1953).
32. Stone, H. W., and B. Griggs, XVIth International Congress of Pure and Applied Chemistry, Paris, July 1957, Div. of Phys. Chem. and Inorg. Chem. Handbook, p. 165.
33. Tiess, D., *Chem. Tech.*, **11,** 260 (1959).
34. Wartik, T., and R. K. Pearson, *J. Am. Chem. Soc.*, **77,** 1075 (1955).
35. Wartik, T., and R. K. Pearson, *J. Inorg. & Nucl. Chem.*, **7,** 404 (1958).
36. Wiberg, E., and R. Hartwimmer, *Z. Naturforsch.*, **10b,** 290 (1955).
37. Wiberg, E., and R. Hartwimmer, *Z. Naturforsch.*, **10b,** 291 (1955).
38. Wiberg, E., H. Nöth, and R. Hartwimmer, *Z. Naturforsch.*, **10b,** 292 (1955).

15

COORDINATION COMPOUNDS DERIVED FROM POLYHYDRIC ALCOHOLS AND PHENOLS

I. INTRODUCTION

Chapter 14 deals with the coordination compounds of boron in which all four ligands are unidentate (I). This chapter is concerned with the coordination compounds in which at least one ligand is bidentate (II and III) or terdentate (IV). The major portion of the chapter, however, is concerned with the chemistry of the tetracovalent compounds composed of two bidentate ligands (V).

$[(RO)_4B]^-M^+$

(I)

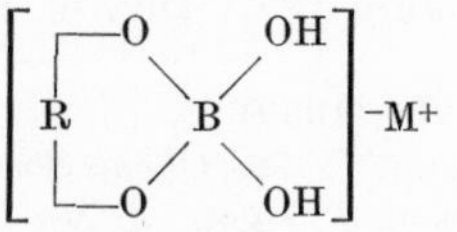

(II)

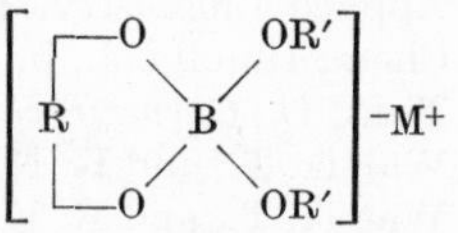

(III)

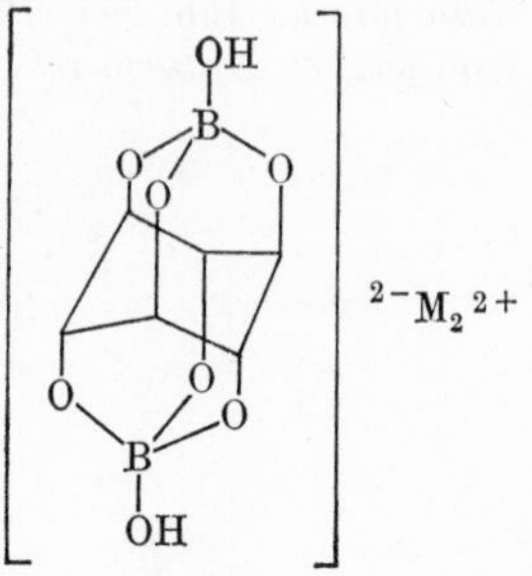

(IV)

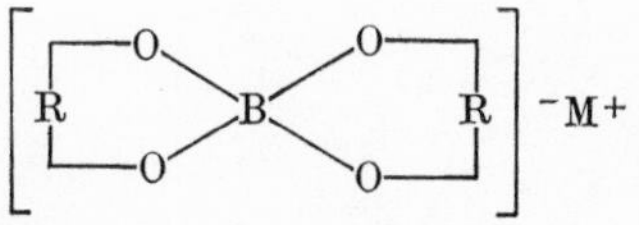

(V)

The bidentate ligands that have been reported include aliphatic, alicyclic, and aromatic 1,2-diols, aliphatic 1,3-diols, and aromatic *peri*-diols.* The recorded cations include protons, mono and divalent metallic ions, ammonium and substituted ammonium ions.

* The possibility of a complex from a *gem*-diol, hydrated thenoyltrifluoroacetone, has been reported.[63]

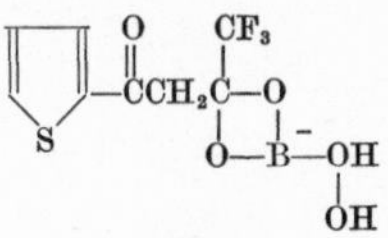

Examples with two different diols (VI) have been reported.[8]

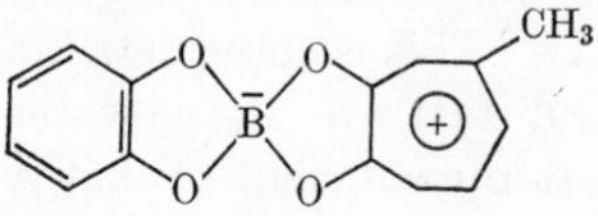

(VI)

Much of the chemistry of the coordination compounds of boron derived from diols and polyols stems from the series of equilibria (15-1) to (15-3).

$$H_3BO_3 + H_2O \rightleftarrows B(OH)_4^- + H^+ \qquad (15\text{-}1)^*$$

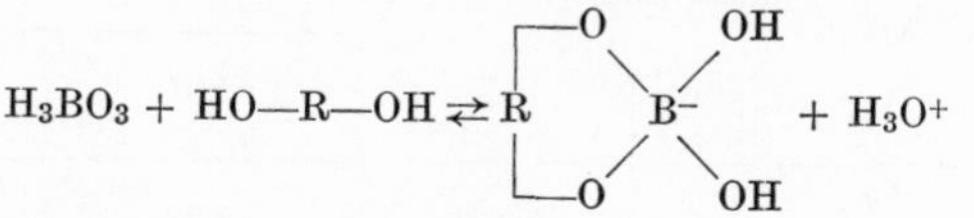

(15-2)

(VII)

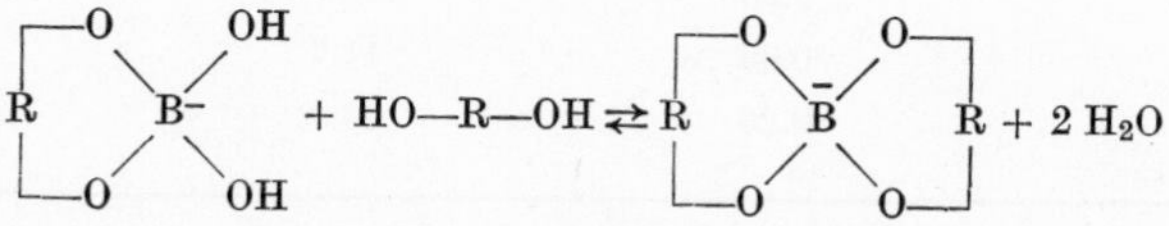

(15-3)

(VIII)

The enhanced acidity, conductivity and ionophoretic mobility of a large variety of diols and polyols in aqueous solutions of boric acid or sodium borate can be attributed to the formation of the ionic species (VII) and (VIII). In addition, the effects of boric acid on the optical rotation of various polyhydric materials and the increase in solubility of many polyols in the presence of boric acid also can be attributed to the formation of the coordination compounds (VII and VIII).†

* The existence of the tetrahydroxyborate ion has been established by Raman spectral data.[62] The concepts of the species[28,86] and the equilibrium[24] were established some years before.

† Theories which have ignored the equilibria (15-1) to (15-3) and have attempted to explain the observed phenomena of aqueous boric acid–diol solutions on the basis of solubility effects of the diol[9] or on the basis of the trigonal coplanar species[52] below have not received support and have been refuted.

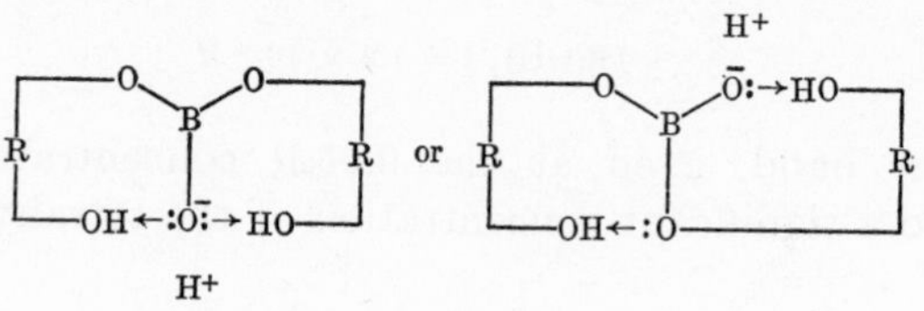

Much of the chemistry of the coordination compounds, at least in aqueous medium, does not involve boric acid as such but rather its conjugate base, $B(OH)_4^-$. This is shown strikingly in the study of the distribution of diethyl tartrate in a water–ether system (Table 15-1).[152] The distribution coefficient of diethyl tartrate between the

Table 15-1. Influence of boron compounds on the distribution of diethyl tartrate between ether and water

Boron compound in aqueous phase	Conc. of boron compound in aqueous phase (mole/l.)	Conc. of diethyl tartrate in water phase / Conc. of diethyl tartrate in ether phase	
		20°	15°
Blank	—	2.22	2.66
H_3BO_3	0.25	—	2.68
$Na_2B_4O_7$	0.05	11.7	—
KBO_2	0.25	24.7	34

aqueous and ether phases essentially is indifferent to the presence or absence of boric acid ($0.25M$) in the aqueous phase and to changes in temperature. On the other hand, a large shift of the tartrate to the aqueous phase is realized on the addition of borax to the system. There is an even more pronounced shift on the addition of potassium metaborate, and the shift is promoted by a decrease in temperature.

These observations are consistent with the postulated need for the presence of the tetrahydroxyborate anion. Boric acid has an ionization constant of 5.8×10^{-10} [123,124] and thus at a concentration of $0.25M$ supplies little of the tetrahydroxyborate species. Borax,

$$\frac{[B(OH)_4^-][H^+]}{[H_3BO_3]} = 5.8 \times 10^{-10} \tag{15-4}$$

$$[H_3BO_3] = 0.25 \tag{15-5}$$

$$[B(OH)_4^-] = 1.2 \times 10^{-5} M \tag{15-6}$$

on the other hand, even at the $0.05M$ concentration in Table 15-1, leads to a significant concentration of the tetrahydroxyborate ion.

$$Na_2B_4O_7 \xrightarrow{H_2O} 2\,B(OH)_4^- + 2\,H_3BO_3 + 2\,Na^+ \tag{15-7}$$

$$[B(OH)_4^-] = 2\,[Na_2B_4O_7] = 0.1M \tag{15-8}$$

Potassium metaborate is an even more efficient source of tetrahydroxyborate ion in that all of the boron is available as the tetracoordinated ion.

$$KBO_2 \xrightarrow{H_2O} K^+ + B(OH)_4^- \tag{15-9}$$

$$[B(OH)_4^-] = [KBO_2] \tag{15-10}$$

A second study which indicates the role of the tetrahydroxyborate species is concerned with the optical rotation of ethyl tartrate.[154] Boric acid did not affect the rotation of dextrorotatory ethyl tartrate in aqueous solution; whereas borax, and potassium metaborate even more strongly, caused a shift to the levorotatory species (Table 15-2).* Similar results were obtained with mannitol,

Table 15-2. Effect of boron compounds on optical rotation of aqueous ethyl tartrate

Boron compound	Conc. of boron compound (mole/l.)	$[\alpha]_{5461}^{20}$
Blank	—	+31.0°
H_3BO_3	0.25	+31.9°
$Na_2B_4O_7$	0.0625	− 6.9°
KBO_2	0.25	−22.0°

glucose and fructose,[153,156] and there now seems to be general agreement that the tetrahydroxyborate ion is the complexing species rather than boric acid.[60,122,131,132,143]

The covalent nonaqueous chemistry of boric acid–diol systems and the aqueous ionic chemistry of boric acid–diol systems do not form a continuum. There is a discontinuity which prevents extrapolation between the two. Fine stereochemical and conformational relationships which play an all important role in aqueous media at room temperature are lost in the twisting of bonds and angles that is permissible at higher temperatures in the absence of water,

* The changes in rotation were not a function of the pH since potassium carbonate was without effect.

and thus ring systems which are prohibited in aqueous solution are easily prepared under dehydrating conditions (15-11 and 15-12).

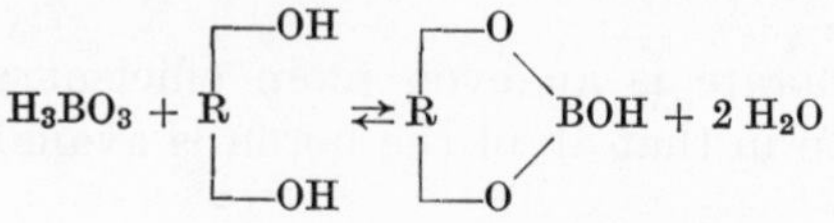

$$H_3BO_3 + R(OH)_2 \rightleftharpoons R(O)_2BOH + 2\,H_2O \quad (15\text{-}11)$$

$$R(O)_2BOH + R(OH)_2 \rightleftharpoons [R(O)_2B(O)_2R]H + H_2O \quad (15\text{-}12)$$

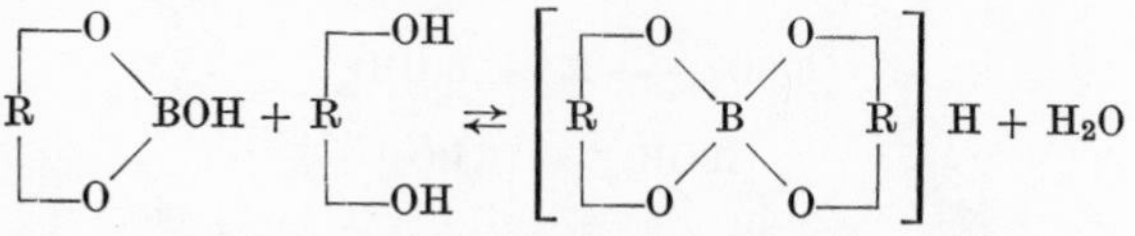

II. HISTORICAL

The influence of polyhydric materials on the acidity[94,148] and conductivity,[111] of boric acid and borax, and the influence of these boron compounds on the rotatory properties of diols[48,66,162] have been known since the nineteenth century. In addition, the concept of cyclic esters derived from polyols with adjacent hydroxyl groups was recorded in 1908.[158] However, it remained for Rosenheim and Vermehren[130] and Weil and Adler[163] in 1924 and Hermans[86] in 1925 to show that the salts originally isolated by Böseken and coworkers[41] in 1918 had the spiran structure (IX).

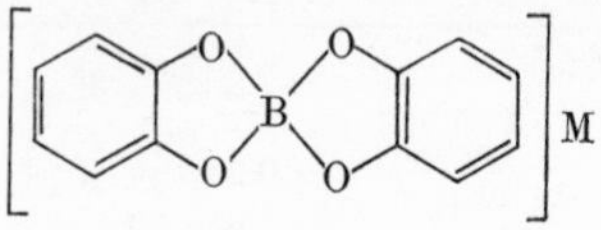

M

(IX)

A coordination compound with one bidentate ligand was prepared in 1925.[117] Twenty-four years later it was recognized as having structure (X).[138]

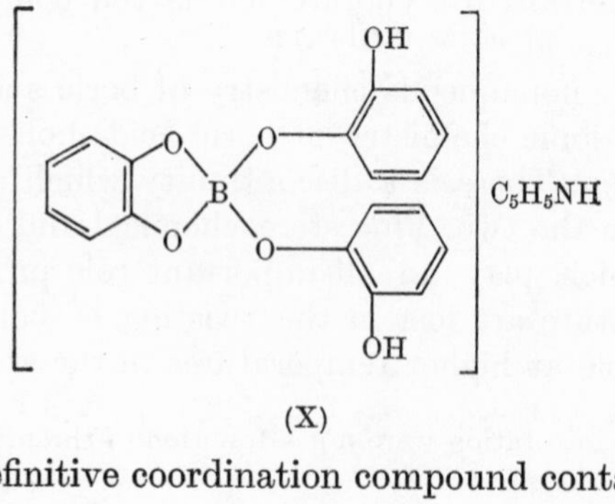

OH

C_5H_5NH

OH

(X)

The first definitive coordination compound containing hydroxyl ligands was prepared from mannitol in 1911,[78] and although no actual structure was recorded, it appears likely that it was (XI).[117]

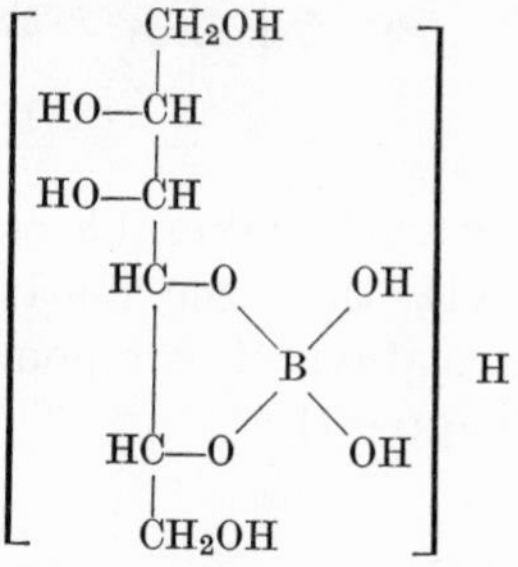

```
[    CH2OH                  ]
      |
 HO—CH
      |
 HO—CH
      |
    HC—O        OH
     |     \   /
     |      B            ] H
     |     /   \
    HC—O        OH
      |
    CH2OH                   ]
```

(XI)

The monumental work in this field undoubtedly is that of J. Böeseken who in the years 1912 [45] to 1944 published thirty or more papers on the chemistry of boric acid–polyol complexes and the significance of the stereochemical relationships involved.

III. BISDIOLBORATES

A. Properties

1. GENERAL

Coordination compounds derived from diols (XII) differ from those derived from monohydric species (XIII) in several respects.

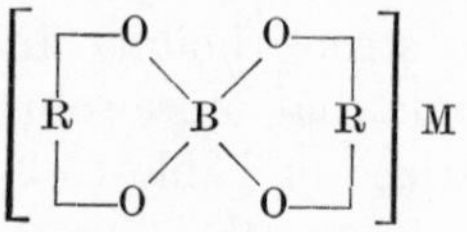

```
[ ┌—O     O—┐ ]
[ R    B    R ] M            [(RO)4B] M
[ └—O     O—┘ ]
```

(XII) (XIII)

The diols can participate in equilibria with boric acid in aqueous solution which permit the isolation of both the free acids (XIV) and salts (XV). The salts of the monohydric species (XIII) are unstable in water solution and to date no free acids have been isolated (see

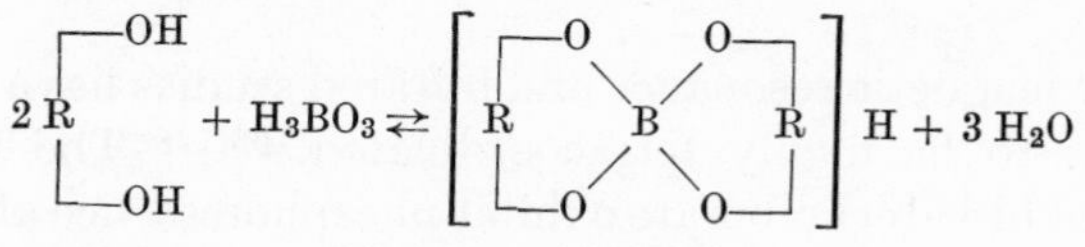

```
  ┌—OH              [ ┌—O     O—┐ ]
2 R     + H3BO3 ⇄   [ R    B    R ] H + 3 H2O        (15-13)
  └—OH              [ └—O     O—┘ ]
```

(XIV)

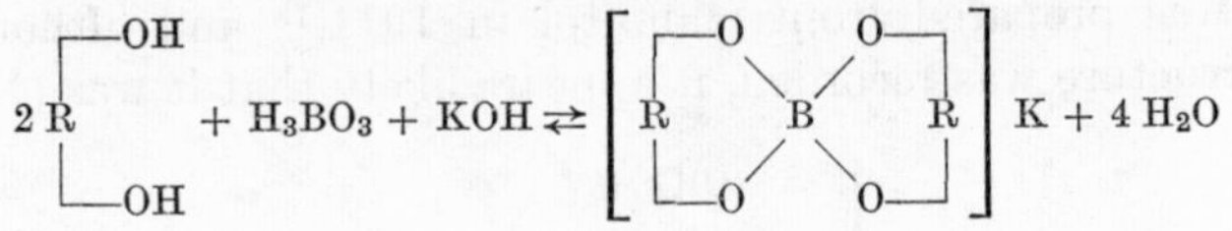

$$2\,R(OH)_2 + H_3BO_3 + KOH \rightleftarrows \left[R{<}^{O}_{O}{>}B{<}^{O}_{O}{>}R \right] K + 4\,H_2O \qquad (15\text{-}14)$$

(XV)

Chapter 14). Presumably a more favorable entropy relationship exists in the cyclic system (XII) than the linear system (XIII). This is consistent with the isolation of compounds of structure (XVI) but not (XVII) (see Chapter 7).

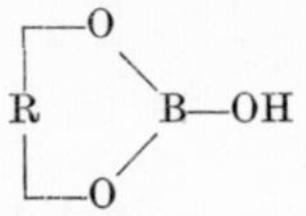

$$R{<}^{O}_{O}{>}B\text{—}OH \qquad\qquad (RO)_2BOH$$

(XVI) (XVII)

Another consequence of the equilibrium of diols and boric acid is the enhancement of the acidity or conductivity of boric acid in water–diol solution by the formation of the relatively strong acid (XIV). The significance and usefulness of this property is discussed in Sections VIII-B and E.

The monomeric nature of both the acids and the metallic and amine salts of the bisdiolborates has been demonstrated by cryoscopic and ebullioscopic molecular weight determinations.[40,117,136]

The salts of biscatecholborate are sparingly soluble in, and may be recrystallized from water.[84,90,117,137,166] Hydrogen biscatecholborate dissolves in water only on strong boiling and agitation.[117] The acid (XVIII) apparently is somewhat more soluble.[109] Solubilities in organic solvents are summarized in Table 15-3.

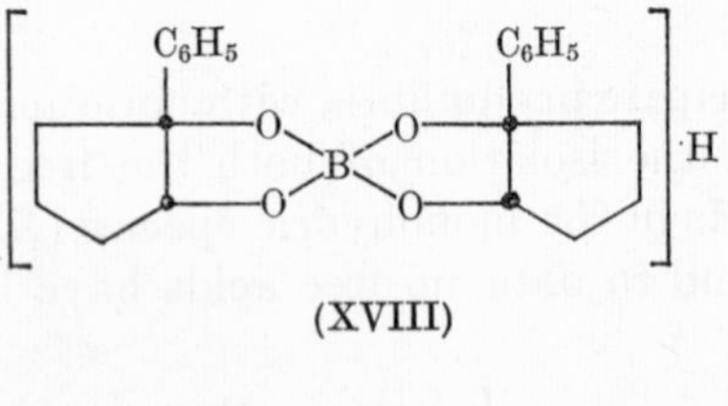

C_6H_5 C_6H_5 — [bis(1-phenylcyclopentane-1,2-diolato)borate] H

(XVIII)

Nuclear magnetic resonance and infrared studies have shown the sodium salts to be highly tetracoordinated.[106,128] The metal and amine salts of biscatecholborate exhibit phosphorescence after excitation with radiation from a quartz lamp.[137]

Table 15-3. Solubility of bisdiolborate salts and acids in organic solvents

	Ether	Pet. ether	Benzene	Chloroform	Acetone	Pyridine	Ethanol	Acetic acid	Mineral oil	Hexane	Reference
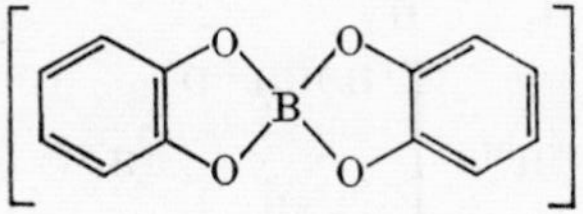 $[B(O_2C_6H_4)_2]^- H^+$	I	I	I	I	S	S					117
Na^+	I		I								137
K^+	I		I				S				137
Rb^+	I		I				S				137
Tl^+	I		I				S				137
NH_4^+ (a)	I		I								137
$CH_3NH_3^+$	I		I								137
$C_6H_5NH_3^+$	I		I								137
$C_6H_5CH_2NH_3^+$	I		I								137
$C_6H_5NH(CH_3)_2^+$	I	I	I		S						117, 137
α-$C_{10}H_7NH_3^+$	I		I								137
β-$C_{10}H_7NH_3^+$	I		I								137
Nitron H^+	I		I		R		R				137
Methylene Blue H^+	I		I								137
$NH_2\overset{NH_2^+}{\overset{\Vert}{C}}NH_2$	I		I								137
Quinolinium				R							138
Nicotine H^+				S	S		S	R			138
β-pyridylmethylcarbinol H^+				R							138
$C_{16}H_{33}NH_3^+$	I		S (hot)				VS		SS	I	150

(*Table continued*)

Table 15-3 (*continued*)

	Ether	Pet. ether	Ben-zene	Chloro-form	Acetone	Pyri-dine	Ethanol	Acetic acid	Mineral oil	Hexane	Reference
$[B(O_2C_6H_3OH)_2]^- C_6H_5NH_3^+$	I	I	I	SS	S		S				117
$C_5H_5NH^+$	I	I	I	SS	S		S				117
$[(CH_2O)_2B(OCH_2)_2]^- C_{16}H_{33}NH_3^+$	S		S				VS		SS	S	150
$C_6H_{11}NH_3^+$									SS	I	150
$(HOCH_2CH_2)_3NH^+$	I		I				VS		SS	I	150
$[(CH_2O)(CH_3CHO)B(OCH_2)(OCHCH_3)]^- C_{16}H_{33}NH_3^+$	SS (hot)		S				S		SS	S (hot)	150
$[(CH_2O)(CH_3CHO)B(OCHCOCH_3)(OCHCOCH_3)]^- K^{+(b)}$											90

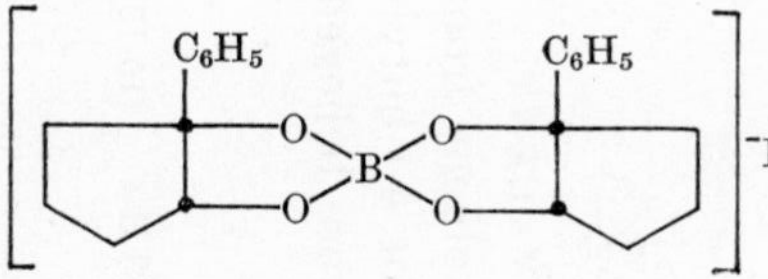

Compound									Ref.
$[(C_6H_5)C_5H_7O_2]_2B^-H^+$ (bis(1-phenylcyclopentane-1,2-diolato)borate)				S					109
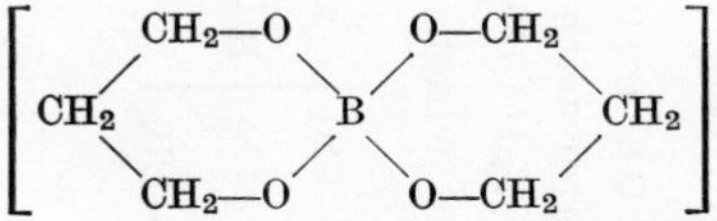 $[(CH_2)_3O_2]_2B^- \cdot C_{16}H_{33}NH_3^+$	S		SS			VS	SS	S	150
$(HOCH_2CH_2)_3NH^+$	I		SS			S	SS	I	150
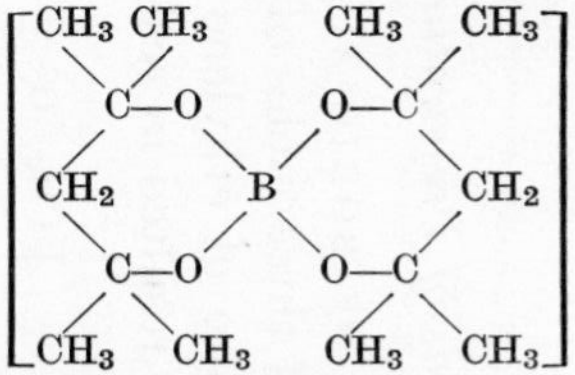 $[((CH_3)_2C\text{–}O)(CH_2)((CH_3)_2C\text{–}O)]_2B^-H^+$			S						147
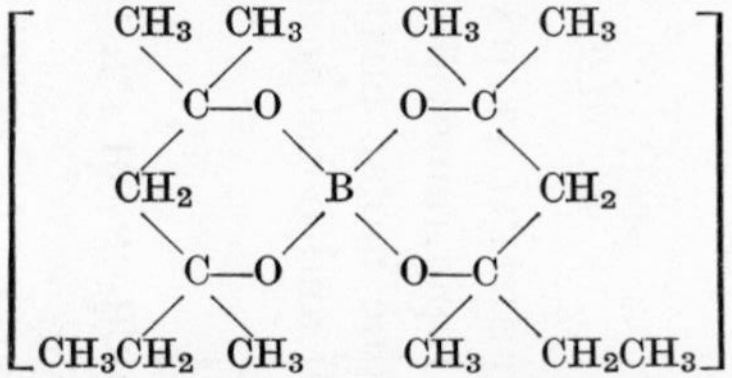 $[((CH_3)_2C\text{–}O)(CH_2)((CH_3)(CH_3CH_2)C\text{–}O)]_2B^-H^+$		S							147

I = insoluble
S = soluble
SS = slightly soluble
VS = very soluble

R = can be recrystallized from solvent
(a) Insoluble in common solvents, Ref. 117
(b) Low solubility in organic solvents

2. ASYMMETRY

Unsymmetrical substitution in the diol of a bisdiolborate creates overall molecular asymmetry[20] in the molecule (Fig. 15-1) and,

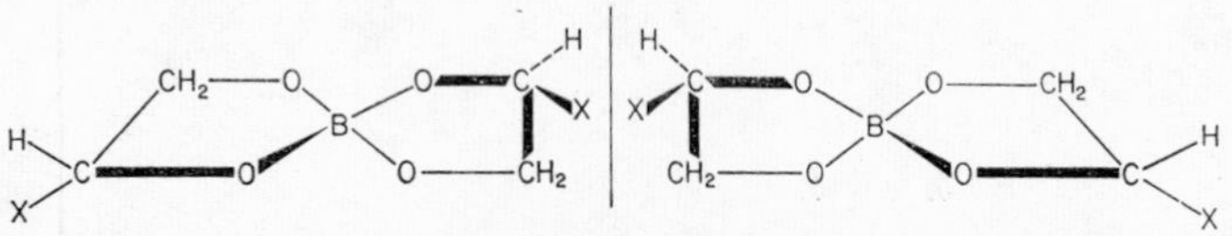

Fig. 15-1. Enantiomorphs of an unsymmetrically substituted bisdiolborate.

indeed, examples of bisdiolborates have been resolved into their optical isomers.

Fractional precipitation of the brucine salt of (XIX) from

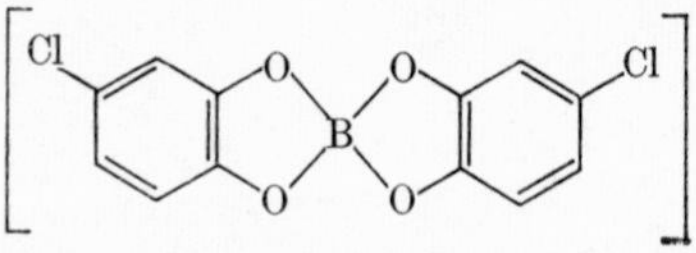

(XIX)

chloroform solution by addition of ligroin resulted in fractions with $[\alpha]_D$ ranging from -5.9 to $-19.7°$. Similar treatment of the strychnine salt of (XX) gave fractions with $[\alpha]_D$ of -68.7 to $-55.2°$.[40]

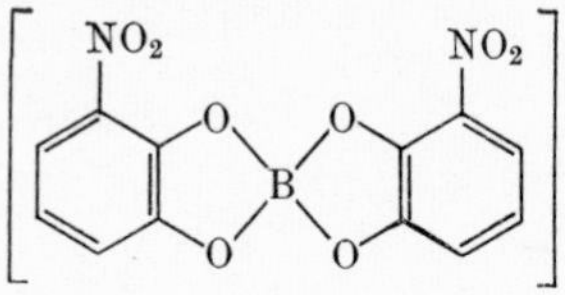

(XX)

B. *Methods of Preparation of Acids*

1. BY ESTERIFICATION OF BORIC ACID OR EQUIVALENT

Azeotropic removal of three moles of water with toluene from a two to one molar mixture of ethylene glycol[64,150] or 4-*t*-butylcatechol[147] and boric acid resulted in residues which were believed

$$2\,HOCH_2CH_2OH + H_3BO_3 \rightarrow \left[\begin{matrix} CH_2{-}O & & O{-}CH_2 \\ | & B & | \\ CH_2{-}O & & O{-}CH_2 \end{matrix}\right]H + 3\,H_2O \qquad (15\text{-}15)$$

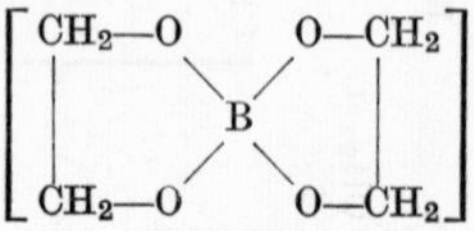

(XXI)

to be the acids (XXI) and (XXII).* Similar treatment of catechol resulted in both (XXIII) and (XXIV).[125]

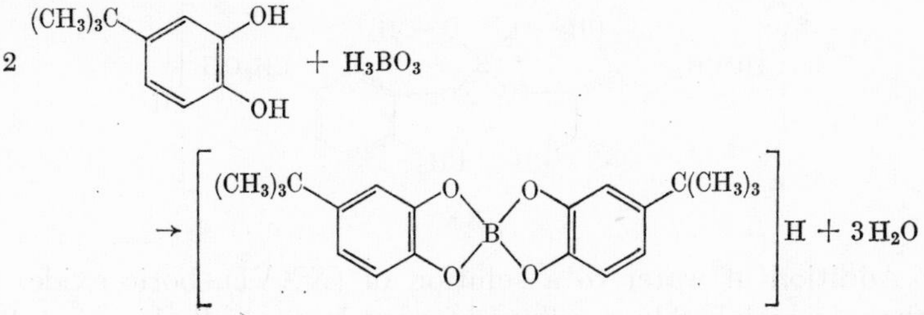

2 $(CH_3)_3C$-C$_6$H$_3$(OH)$_2$ + H_3BO_3

→ [$(CH_3)_3C$-C$_6$H$_3$O$_2$BO$_2$C$_6$H$_3$-$C(CH_3)_3$] H + 3 H_2O (15-16)

(XXII)

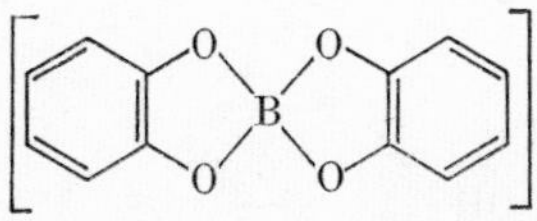

(XXIII)

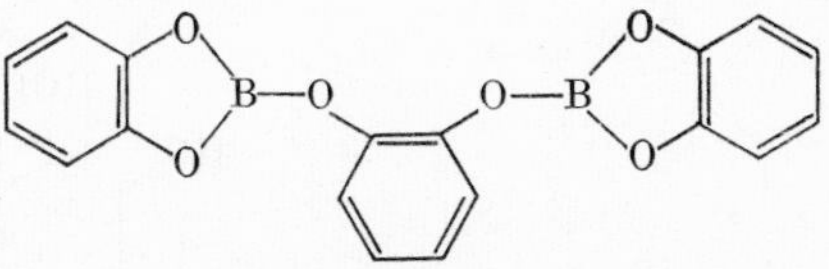

(XXIV)

Azeotropic removal of the calculated amount of water from a chloroform solution of two moles of ethylene glycol or 1,3-propanediol and one mole of boric acid resulted in viscous residues on evaporation of the chloroform. Attempted distillation of the residues resulted in disproportionation.[87]

Vacuum dehydration of a 2:1 molar mixture of diol and boric acid was employed to prepare the bisdiolborates of pinacol, 2,4-dimethyl-2,4-pentanediol, 2,4-dimethyl-2,4-hexanediol, and 2-methyl-2,4-pentanediol.[147]

* The difficulty of preparing 1,3,2-dioxaborolane derivatives with ethylene glycol (Chapter 7) indicates the possibility that the product is the polymer

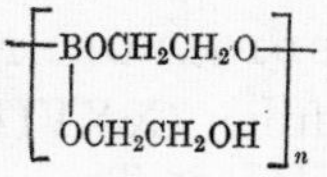

$$\left[\begin{array}{c} BOCH_2CH_2O \\ | \\ OCH_2CH_2OH \end{array} \right]_n$$

rather than the acid (XXI). However, the subsequent conversion of the product to an amine salt[64,150]

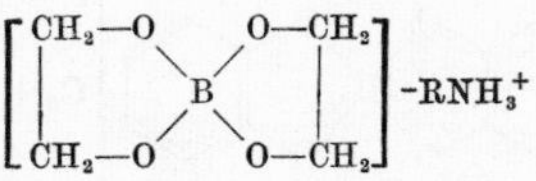

$$\left[\begin{array}{ccc} CH_2-O & & O-CH_2 \\ | & B & | \\ CH_2-O & & O-CH_2 \end{array} \right]^- RNH_3^+$$

would be easier to rationalize if the product indeed were (XXI).

The purification of vitamin B_6 by precipitation from water solution with boric acid was formulated as involving the tetracovalent borate (XXV).[51]

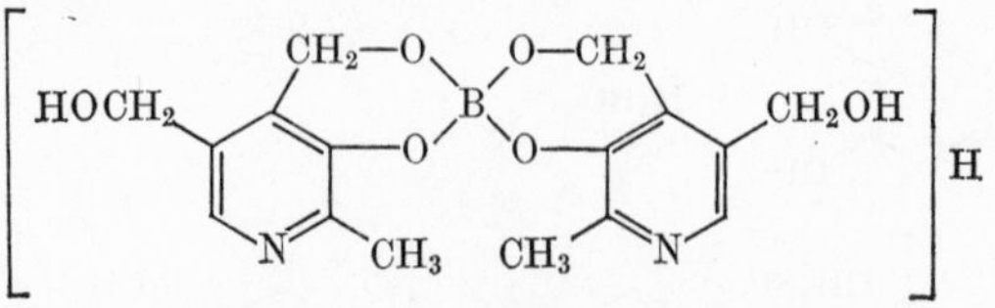

(XXV)

Addition of water to a solution of (XXVI), boric oxide, and methanol which had been refluxed for one hour resulted in crystallization of (XXVII) on standing overnight.[103]

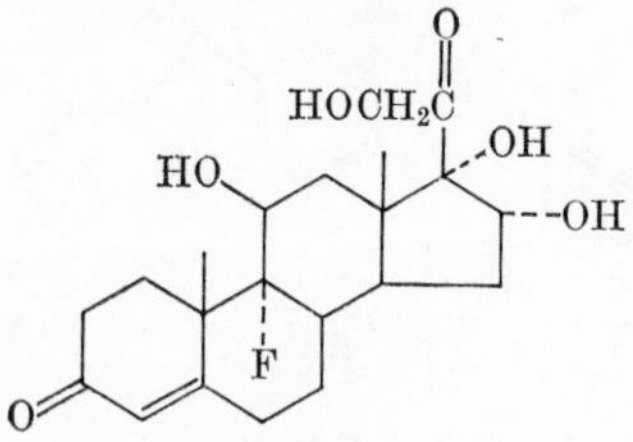

(XXVI)

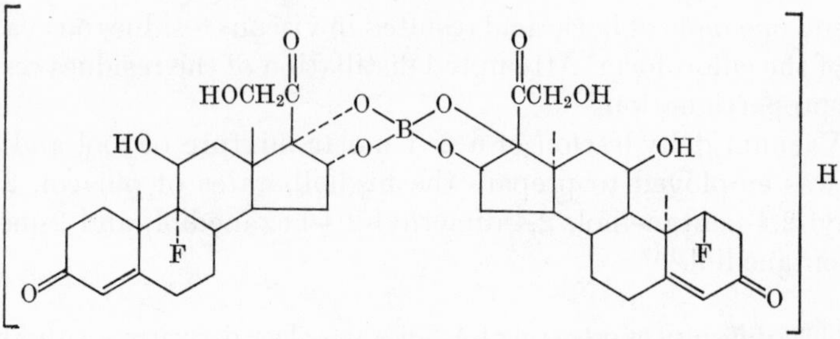

(XXVII)

2. BY PYROLYSIS OF BISDIOLBORATE SALTS

Aniline is volatilized from (XXVIII) at 140° or at 100° *in vacuo* leaving the acid (XXIII).[86] The product can be purified by vacuum sublimation at 200°.[84] The *p*-chloroaniline, dimethylaniline,

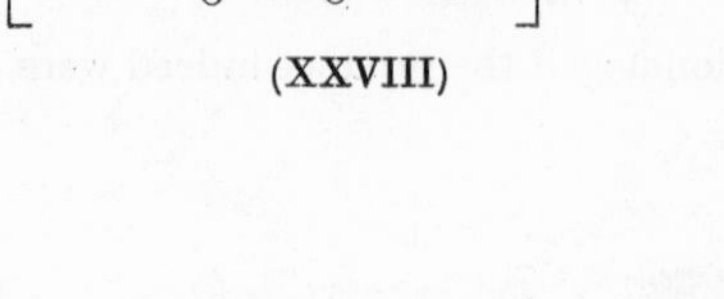

(XXVIII)

and pyridine salts[117] as well as the aniline salt of bis-(*cis*-1,2-cycloheptanediol)borate[84] behave similarly.

The aniline salts of the 3- and 4-nitrocatechol borates also lose aniline at 140° *in vacuo* but the pure acids could not be isolated[117] presumably due to their subsequent decomposition.[38]

The aniline and pyridine salts of the pyrogallol borate lose base slowly on being heated to 140° *in vacuo* for two hours. At higher temperatures the free acid sublimes as needles.[117]

3. FROM DIOLDIALKOXYBORATES

Attempts to prepare the acid (XXIX) from the pyridinium salt of (XXIX) by treatment with potassium bisulfate in chloroform

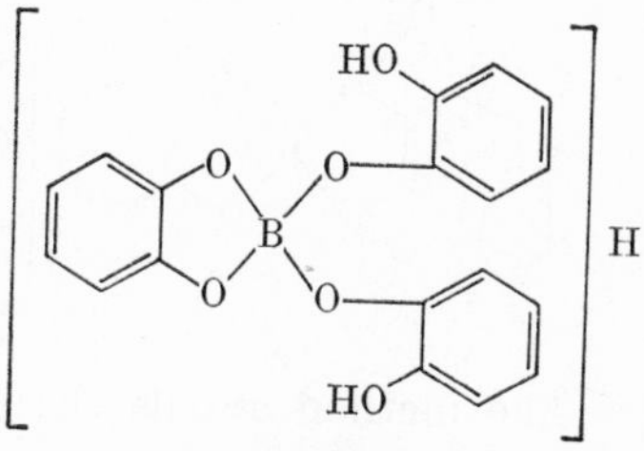

HO HO B O O O O H

(XXIX)

solution resulted in the formation of catechol and the acid (XXIII).[138] Similarly, pyridine is removed from the pyridinium salt of (XXIX)* when it is heated *in vacuo* leaving the acid (XXIX) which then sublimes.[117]

4. FROM 2-HYDROXY-1,3,2-DIOXABOROLANES

Chloroform extraction of a dilute potassium hydroxide solution of (XXX) resulted in an acidic product whose boron analysis was consistent with that of structure (XXXI).[109] Thus the equilibria between (XXX), (XXXI) and their potassium salts were shifted to (XXXI) by the latter's solubility in and removal by chloroform.

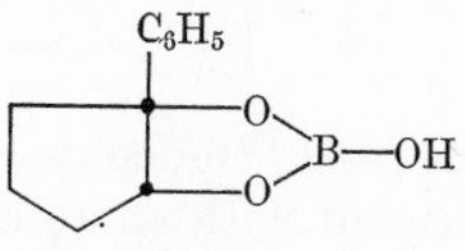

C_6H_5 O O B—OH

(XXX)

C_6H_5 C_6H_5 O O B O O H

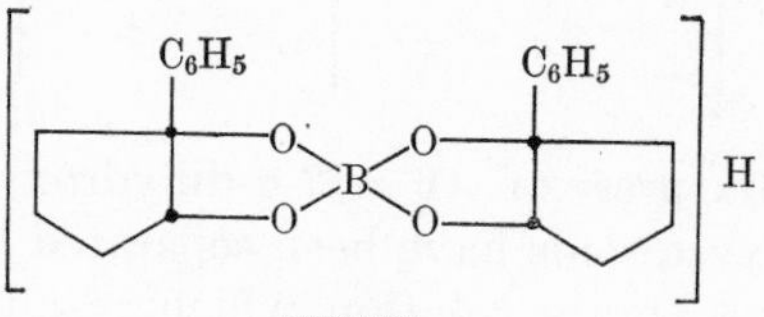

(XXXI)

* Ref. 117 erroneously recorded this salt as biscatechol borate.[99,138]

C. Methods of Preparation of Salts

1. BY REMOVAL OF WATER FROM MIXTURE OF DIOL, BORIC ACID AND BASE

When a mixture of two moles of diol, one mole of boric acid and one mole of a base is heated to temperatures appreciably above the melting point of the mixture, water is eliminated and a salt of the bisdiolborate is formed. This fusion method has been used to prepare a variety of amine salts of biscatecholborate (15-17) in essentially

$$2\,C_6H_4(OH)_2 + H_3BO_3 + (C_4H_9)_2NH \rightarrow [(C_6H_4O_2)_2B](C_4H_9)_2NH_2 + 3\,H_2O \qquad (15\text{-}17)$$

quantitative yields.[166] The method avoids the difficulty attending the isolation of the water-soluble salts from aqueous solution. The method also avoids problems associated with the slightly soluble nature of some amines.

A variation of the procedure involves azeotropic removal of water from the diol and boric acid (15-18) followed by reaction of the

$$2\,R(OH)_2 + H_3BO_3 \rightarrow [(RO_2)_2B]H + 3\,H_2O \qquad (15\text{-}18)$$

residue with an amine (15-19).[150]

$$[(RO_2)_2B]H + RNH_2 \rightarrow [(RO_2)_2B]RNH_3 \qquad (15\text{-}19)$$

Mixtures of 16-α,17-α-dihydroxysteroids and 16-deoxy-17-α-hydroxysteroids have been separated by treatment with an aqueous alkaline borate solution which results in solubilization of the dihydroxy species by virtue of complex formation (XXXII).[102,104,105] Lyophilization of the borate solution results in isolation of the salt.[103]

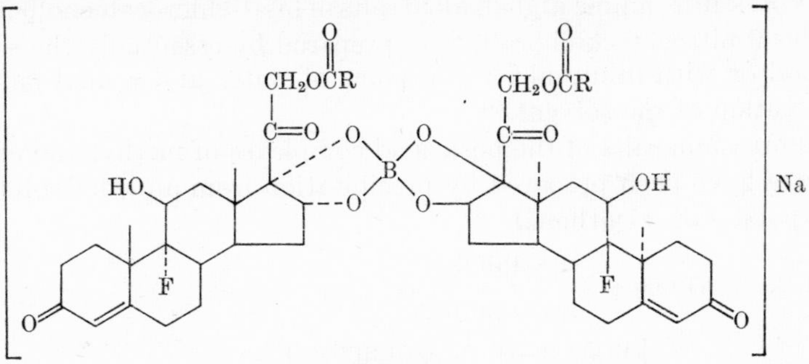

(XXXII)

Potassium bis(ascorbic acid)borate can be obtained by heating an aqueous solution of two molar equivalents of ascorbic acid, one molar equivalent of boric acid and one molar equivalent of potassium hydroxide and distilling the water under reduced pressure.[165]

2. BY CRYSTALLIZATION FROM AN AQUEOUS SOLUTION OF DIOL, BORIC ACID AND BASE

Metal and amine salts of biscatecholborate,[41,86,117,130,136,137] bis-3-nitrocatecholborate, and bis-4-nitrocatecholborate[117] and amine salts of bispyrogallolborate[117] have been prepared in aqueous solution. The calculated quantities (2:1:1) of catechol, boric acid and base (metal or ammonium hydroxide, metal carbonate or free amine) are dissolved in hot water, the solution is cooled, and the crystallized product removed by filtration.*

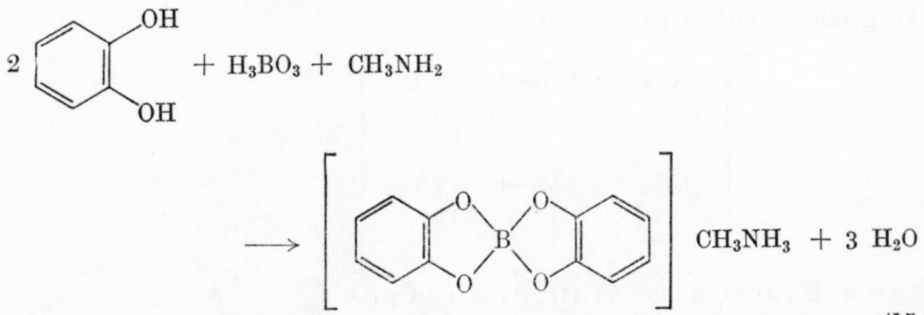

$$2\,C_6H_4(OH)_2 + H_3BO_3 + CH_3NH_2 \longrightarrow [(C_6H_4O_2)_2B]\,CH_3NH_3 + 3\,H_2O \quad (15\text{-}20)$$

* Ref. 117 erroneously records the pyridine salt as the biscatecholborate. With pyridine and triethylamine, the triscatecholborates are obtained.[99,138] With piperidine, quinoline, 8-hydroxyquinoline, nicotine and β-pyridylmethylcarbinol, the bisdiolborates are formed even if an excess of the amine is employed[138] (see Section V-B-1). With potassium hydroxide, the biscatechol salt is formed even with an equimolar ratio of catechol and boric acid.[117] With sodium carbonate, an excess of catechol is required to effect precipitation of the salt.[136]

Potassium, amine and alkaloid salts of bis-4-chlorocatecholborate and bis-3-nitrocatecholborate were prepared by essentially the same method or with dilute alcohol in place of water and a final partial evaporation of the solvent.[40]

Potassium salts of the boric acid complexes of methyl and ethyl tartrate have been prepared by precipitation from aqueous solution with potassium bicarbonate.[90]

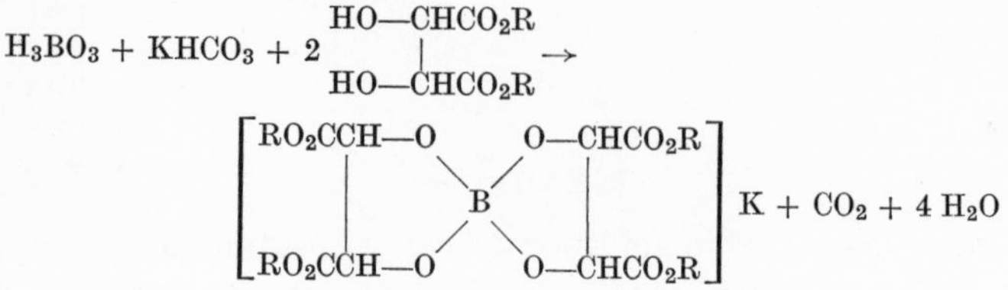

$$H_3BO_3 + KHCO_3 + 2\begin{array}{l} HO\text{—}CHCO_2R \\ \quad\;| \\ HO\text{—}CHCO_2R \end{array} \rightarrow$$

$$\left[\begin{array}{ccc} RO_2CCH\text{—}O & & O\text{—}CHCO_2R \\ | \quad\quad \diagdown & & \diagup \quad\quad | \\ & B & \\ | \quad\quad \diagup & & \diagdown \quad\quad | \\ RO_2CCH\text{—}O & & O\text{—}CHCO_2R \end{array}\right]K + CO_2 + 4\,H_2O \qquad (15\text{-}21)$$

The hydrated pinacol salt (XXXIII) crystallized from an aqueous solution of sodium borate and pinacol. Four moles of water

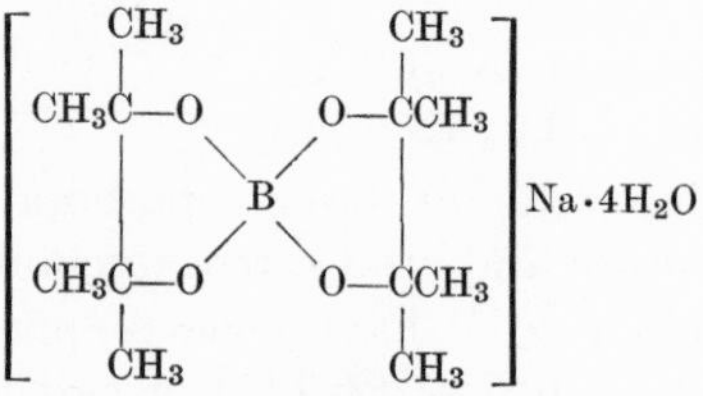

$$\left[\begin{array}{ccc} CH_3 & & CH_3 \\ | & & | \\ CH_3C\text{—}O & & O\text{—}CCH_3 \\ | \quad \diagdown & & \diagup \quad | \\ & B & \\ | \quad \diagup & & \diagdown \quad | \\ CH_3C\text{—}O & & O\text{—}CCH_3 \\ | & & | \\ CH_3 & & CH_3 \end{array}\right]Na\cdot 4H_2O$$

(XXXIII)

were lost when the hydrate was heated to 80°. A concentrated equimolar solution of pentaerythritol and sodium metaborate resulted in the polymer (XXXIV). The anhydrous product was obtained by heating the hexahydrate to 80°.[58]

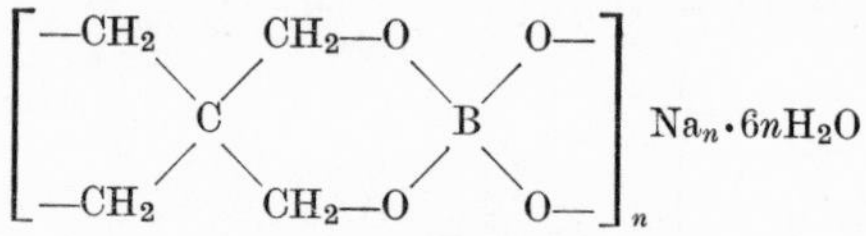

$$\left[\begin{array}{ccccc} \text{—}CH_2 & & CH_2\text{—}O & & O\text{—} \\ \diagdown & & \diagup \quad \diagdown & & \diagup \\ & C & & B & \\ \diagup & & \diagdown \quad \diagup & & \diagdown \\ \text{—}CH_2 & & CH_2\text{—}O & & O\text{—} \end{array}\right]_n Na_n\cdot 6nH_2O$$

(XXXIV)

3. FROM HYDROGEN BISDIOLBORATES

The aniline and *p*-chloroaniline salts of hydrogen biscatechol borate have been obtained by a direct acid–base reaction (15-22).[117]

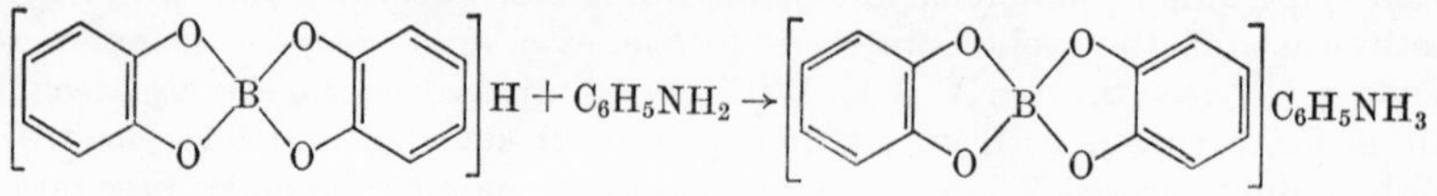

$$[(C_6H_4O_2)_2B]H + C_6H_5NH_2 \rightarrow [(C_6H_4O_2)_2B]C_6H_5NH_3 \qquad (15\text{-}22)$$

The aniline salt of hydrogen bis-*cis*-1,2-cycloheptanediolborate was obtained similarly.[84]

A variety of amine salts was prepared from the hydrogen diolborates of aliphatic 1,2- and 1,3-glycols and catechol by heating the amine with an excess of the acid.[64,107,150]

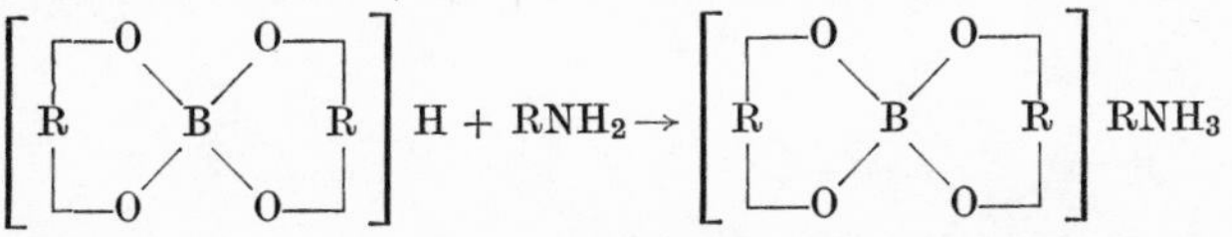

$$\left[R\begin{matrix}O & & O\\ & B & \\ O & & O\end{matrix}R\right]H + RNH_2 \rightarrow \left[R\begin{matrix}O & & O\\ & B & \\ O & & O\end{matrix}R\right]RNH_3 \qquad (15\text{-}23)$$

Treatment of a suspension of (XXXVa) in methanol with sodium hydroxide solution followed by filtration and lyophilization of the filtrate resulted in (XXXVb).[103]

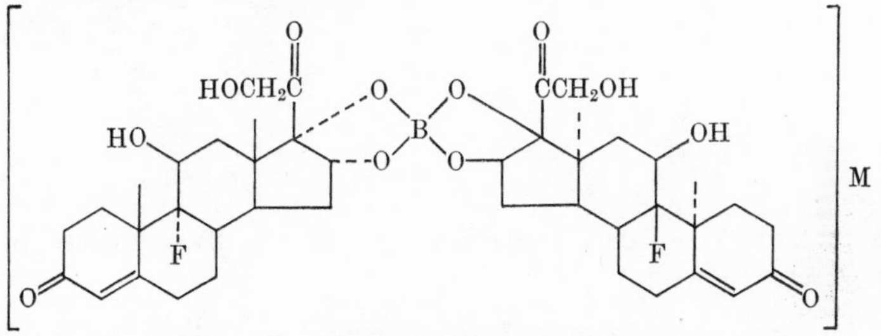

(XXXVa, M = H)
(XXXVb, M = Na)

The conversion of bisdiolborate acids derived from glycerol and pentaerythritol to their ammonium salts has been used to separate a process stream of ammonia and hydrogen cyanide[10] and to remove basic nitrogen impurities from hydrocarbons.[80]

4. FROM DIOLDIALKOXYBORATES

The pyridinium salt of triscatecholborate is converted to the bisdiolborate by warming in pyridine.[99,138]

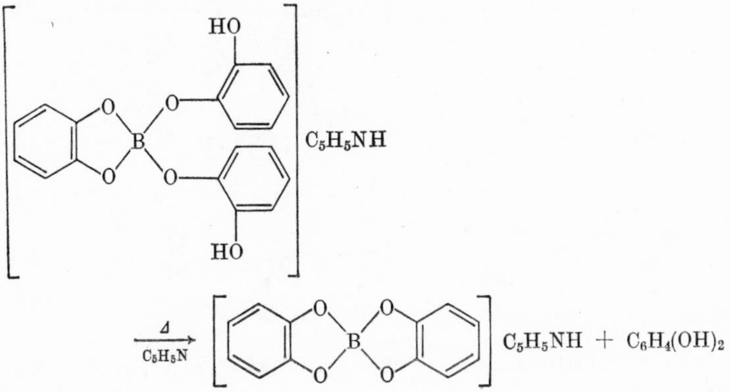

$$[(C_6H_4O_2)B(OC_6H_4OH)_2]C_5H_5NH \xrightarrow[C_5H_5N]{\Delta} [(C_6H_4O_2)_2B]C_5H_5NH + C_6H_4(OH)_2 \qquad (15\text{-}24)$$

5. BY HYDROLYSIS OF A TRIGLYCOL BIBORATE IN THE PRESENCE OF A BASE

Hydrolysis of tricatechol biborate in the presence of potassium hydroxide, ammonium hydroxide or pyridine gave the corresponding salt of biscatecholborate.[125]

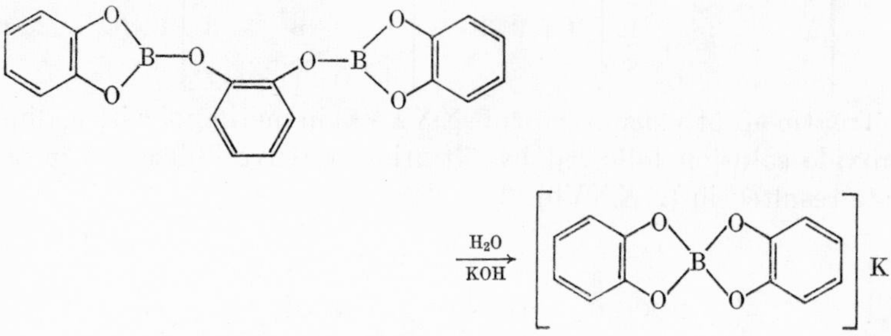

$\xrightarrow[\text{KOH}]{H_2O}$ K

(15-25)

6. BY REACTION OF TROPOLONES AND 2-ALKOXY-1,3,2-DIOXABOROLES

β-Methyltropolone and 2-butoxy-1,3,2-benzodioxaborole reacted exothermically to form a yellow crystalline product which was characterized as the internally compensated salt (XXXVI). Similarly, β-methyltropolone and colchicein resulted in (XXXVII), and β-methyltropolone and (XXXVIII) gave (XXXIX).[8]

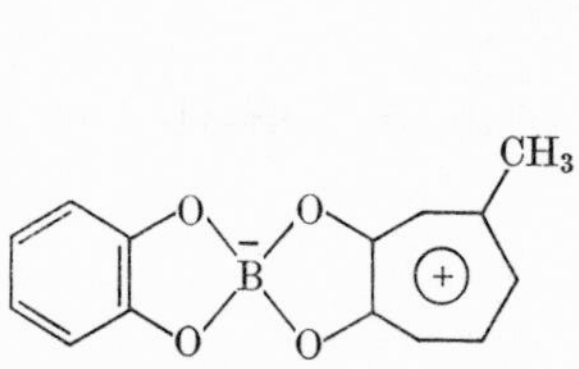

(XXXVI)

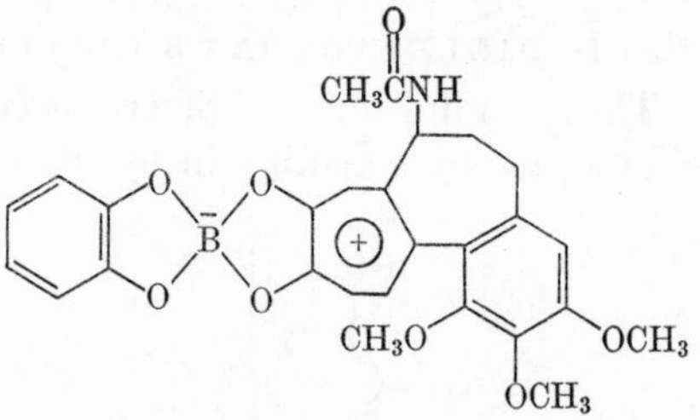

(XXXVII)

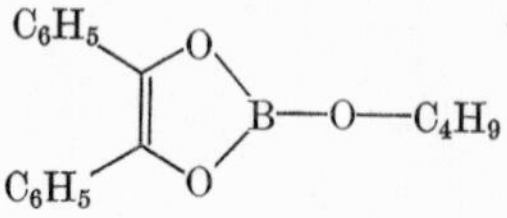

(XXXVIII)

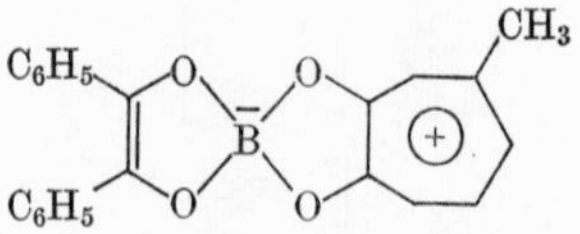

(XXXIX)

D. *Reactions of Acids*

The neutralization of hydrogen bisdiolborates with ammonia, amines, and sodium hydroxide to form salts is described in Section III-C-3.

The purification of vitamin B_6 involves final recovery of the vitamin from its borate by transesterification with methanol.[51]

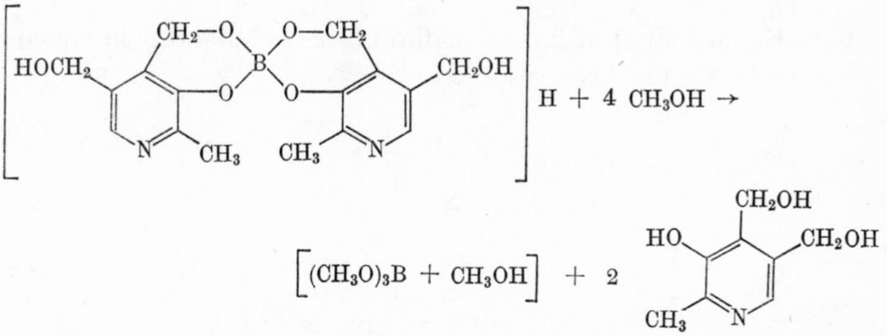

[bis(pyridoxine)borate: $HOCH_2$, CH_2—O, O—CH_2, B, O, O, CH_2OH, N, CH_3, CH_3, N] H + 4 CH_3OH →

$[(CH_3O)_3B + CH_3OH]$ + 2 [pyridoxine: CH_2OH, HO, CH_2OH, CH_3, N]

(15-26)

E. *Reactions of Salts*

1. HYDROLYSIS

The study of the hydrolytic stability of bisdiolborates has been limited to the salts of biscatecholborate, with the single exception that (XL) is stated to be unstable in aqueous solution.[90]

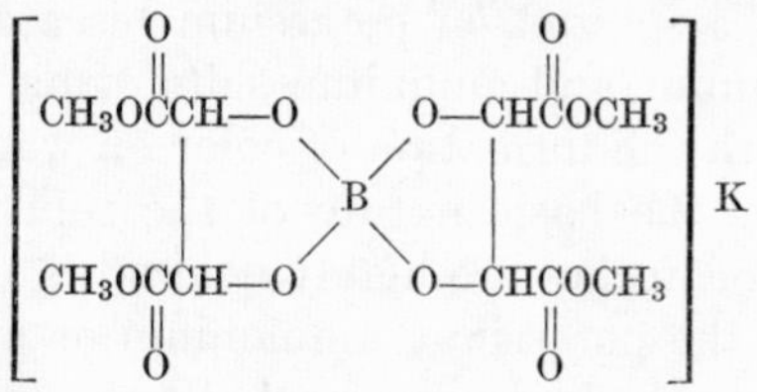

$$\left[\begin{array}{ccc} CH_3O\overset{O}{\overset{\|}{C}}CH—O & & O—CH\overset{O}{\overset{\|}{C}}OCH_3 \\ | & B & | \\ CH_3O\underset{O}{\underset{\|}{C}}CH—O & & O—CH\underset{O}{\underset{\|}{C}}OCH_3 \end{array}\right]K$$

(XL)

The ultraviolet absorption spectra of an aqueous solution of pyridinium biscatecholborate and that of a synthetic aqueous solution of pyridine, catechol and boric acid in the correct concentration are similar. Based on these data, it was concluded that the salt was completely dissociated into its constituents.[99]* It appears, however, that the similarity of the spectra is not sufficient evidence to justify this conclusion since it does not exclude the possibility of

* The spectra were recorded as ethanol solutions and it was stated that the spectra determined in aqueous solution showed the same agreement.

equilibrium (15-27). This equilibrium would lead to identical spectra whether one started with the salt or its constituents. Indeed, the

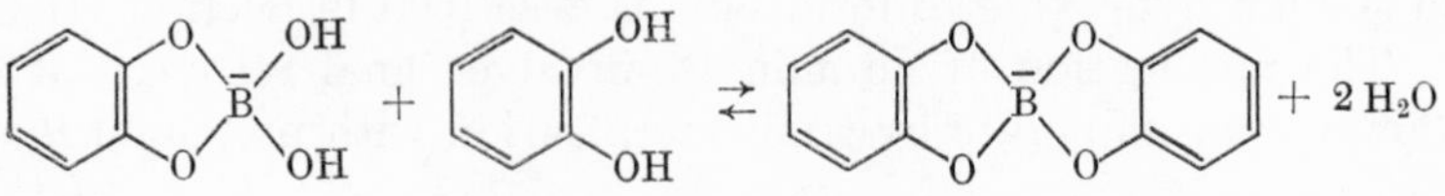

[Chemical equation: catecholboric acid (B with O, O, OH, OH) + catechol (OH, OH) ⇄ biscatecholborate (B with four O) + $2\,H_2O$]

(15-27)

dissociation constant at 25° for sodium biscatecholborate in aqueous solution (15-28) has been recorded.[136,137*]

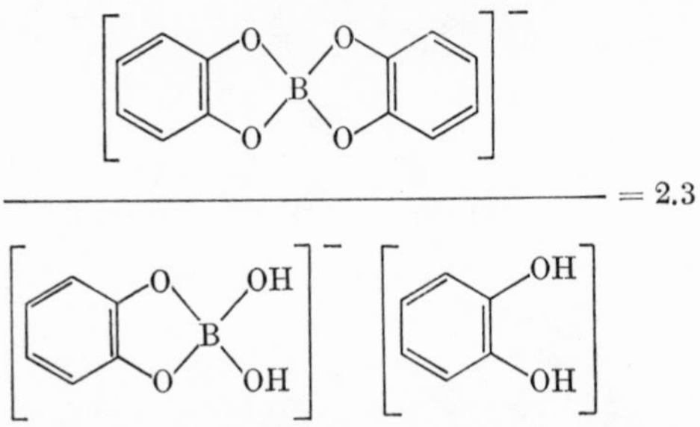

[Equation: [biscatecholborate]$^-$ / ([catecholboric acid anion]$^-$ [catechol]) = 2.3]

(15-28)

The weakly acidic character of hydrogen biscatecholborate is shown by the inability of both sodium hydroxide and pyridine to effect complete transformation to the salt in aqueous solution. Further indications are the evolution of ammonia on warming an aqueous solution of ammonium biscatecholborate[117] and the alkaline nature of a solution of potassium biscatecholborate.[84] The potassium, ammonium, and anilinium salts of bis-(3-nitrocatechol)-borate dissolve with the formation of color on warming in water.[117] This also indicates the basic nature of the solution since alkaline solutions of 3-nitrocatechol are highly colored.[83]

Reduction of the potassium, ammonium or pyridinium salts of biscatecholborate with hydrogen and Raney nickel in aqueous solution was reported to give *cis*-cyclohexanediol.[125]

2. ALCOHOLYSIS

The similarity of the ultraviolet spectra of (XLI) in ethanol and of an ethanol solution of catechol, boric acid and pyridine in cor-

* Ref. 99 further concluded that pyridinium biscatechol borate essentially was completely dissociated in ethanol solution ($0.0002M$) due to the absence of pyridinium ion absorption. On the basis of the similarity of spectra in aqueous and alcoholic solution, it might be concluded that complete dissociation also would prevail in aqueous solution.

responding concentrations was offered as proof of the complete dissociation of (XLI) into its constituents in alcoholic solution.[99]*

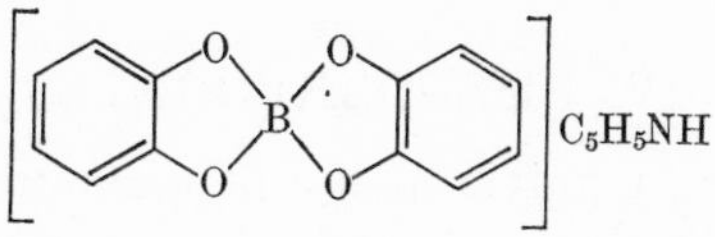

$$\left[(C_6H_4O_2)_2B \right] C_5H_5NH$$

(XLI)

This transformation was described as surprising since it is generally believed that the stability of complexes such as (XLI) is greater in non-aqueous solvents than in water. However, if the transformation is more accurately renamed an alcoholysis or transesterification reaction rather than a dissociation, the exchange of alkoxy groups for aryloxy groups (15-29) is predictable and should be rapid (see

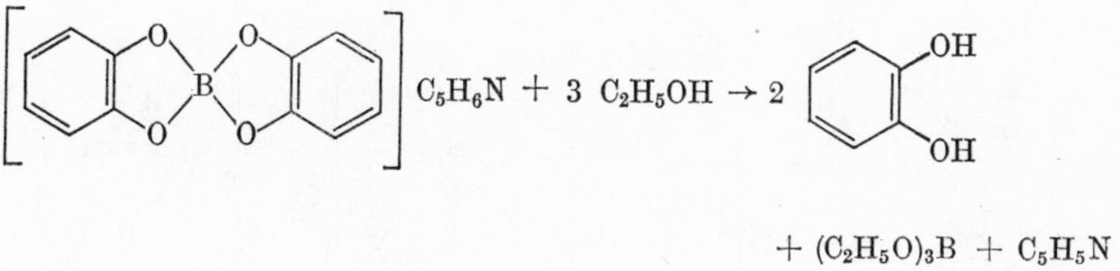

$$\left[(C_6H_4O_2)_2B \right] C_5H_6N + 3\ C_2H_5OH \rightarrow 2\ C_6H_4(OH)_2 + (C_2H_5O)_3B + C_5H_5N \qquad (15\text{-}29)$$

Chapter 4). The stability of complexes such as (XLI) in aprotic solvents still appears to be greater than in water or other hydroxylic solvents.

The reactions of various amine salts of biscatecholborate with catechol are discussed in Section V-B-2.

3. THERMAL STABILITY

The metallic salts of biscatecholborate char on heating.[137] Amine salts of biscatecholborate,[86,117] bispyrogallolborate[117] and the 3- and 4-nitro derivatives of biscatecholborate[117] lose amine on

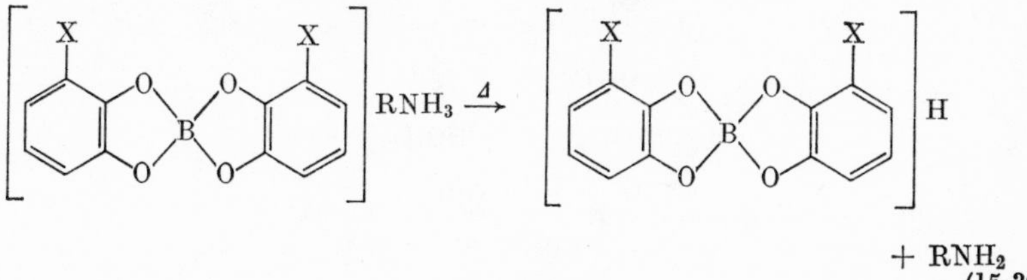

$$\left[(XC_6H_3O_2)_2B \right] RNH_3 \xrightarrow{\Delta} \left[(XC_6H_3O_2)_2B \right] H + RNH_2 \qquad (15\text{-}30)$$

$X = H, OH, NO_2$

* Arguments against this conclusion have been presented in Section III-E-1.

heating at reduced pressure to give the free acids. The nitro acids were not isolated.

IV. BISSUGARBORATES

In spite of the almost universal use of mannitol in the titrimetric determination of boric acid and the voluminous publications treating the chemistry of aqueous solutions of sugars and boric acid, few examples of well-defined tetracoordinate acids or salts derived from boric acid and sugars or sugar alcohols have been reported.

Ill-defined hydrates of the sodium, lithium and silver salts of di- and tri-mannitol, dulcitol and sorbitolborate have been reported.[82]

Acids derived from mannitol (XLII), fructose (XLIII), and xylose (XLIV) have been isolated by evaporation of aqueous

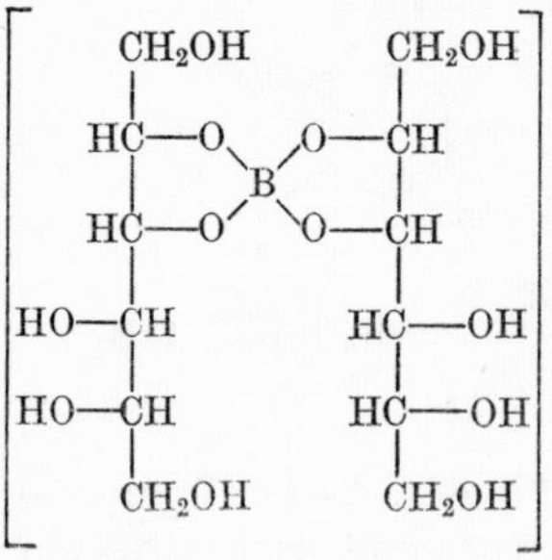

(XLII) 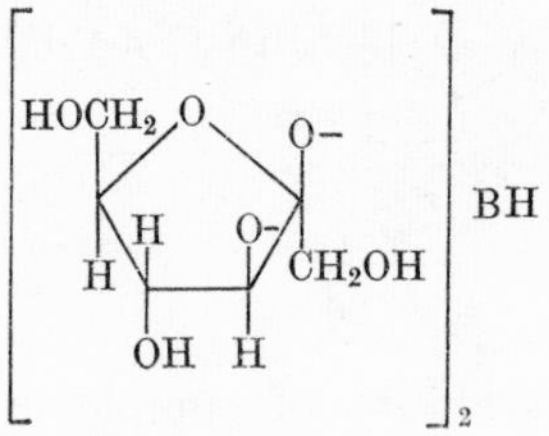 (XLIII) 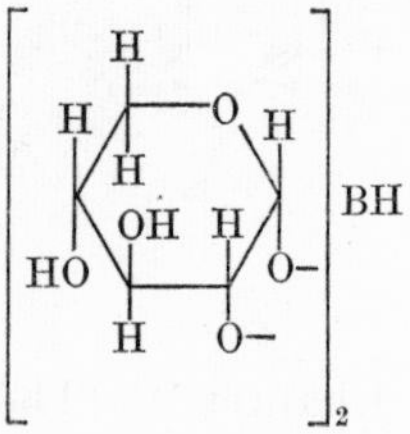 (XLIV)

solutions of the polyols and boric acid.[155] Molecular weights determined cryoscopically agreed with those for the monomeric structures (XLII–XLIV).

Evaporation to dryness of an aqueous solution of one mole of calcium gluconate and two moles of boric acid resulted in a crystalline residue which was formulated as (XLV).[7,61,110,145]

Structure (XLV) would be expected to exhibit a pH in aqueous

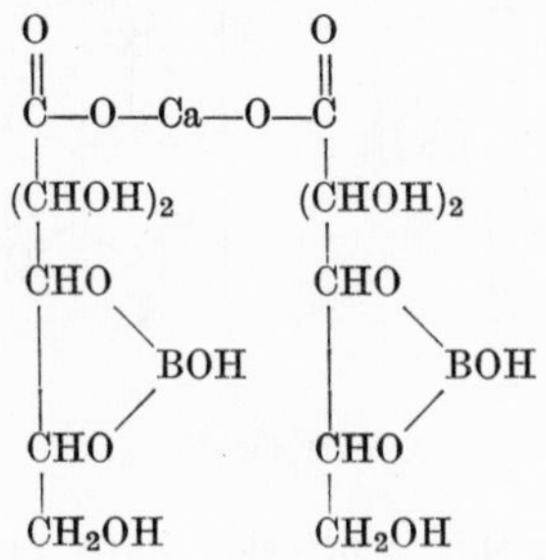

(XLV)

solution similar to that of calcium gluconate itself (pH 6.0[61]) since the hydroxyborolane structure (XLVI) has been shown to be

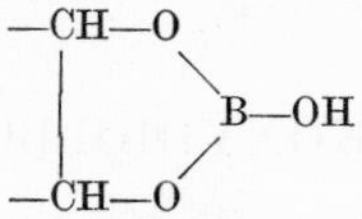

```
—CH—O
 |     \
 |      B—OH
 |     /
—CH—O
```

(XLVI)

essentially neutral.[86] Therefore, the pH value of 3.5 to 3.7[61,110] for calcium borogluconate solutions must be rationalized. The enhanced acidity could be due to the presence of tetracoordinate species. Structures (XLVII) and (XLVIII) (shown as monomeric species for simplicity) represent possible acidic configurations which maintain the gross stoichiometry of (XLV).

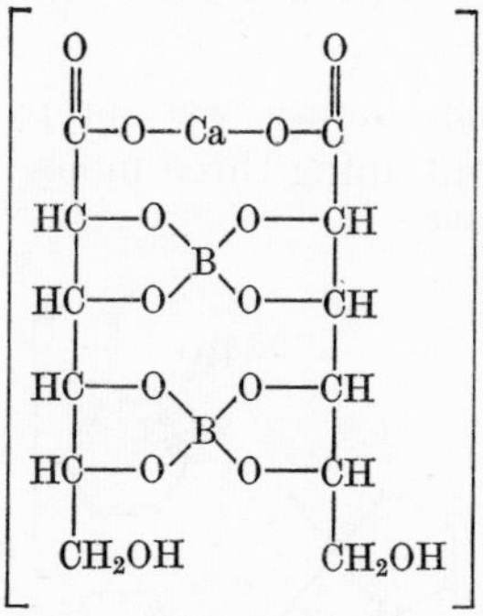

```
[ O              O   ]        [ O              O   ]
[ ‖              ‖   ]        [ ‖              ‖   ]
[ C—O—Ca—O—C         ]        [ COH          COH   ]
[ |              |   ]        [ |              |   ]
[ HC—O    O—CH       ]        [ HC—O    O—CH       ]
[ |    \B/       |   ]        [ |    \B/       |   ]
[ HC—O/   \O—CH      ] H2     [ HC—O/   \O—CH      ] Ca
[ |              |   ]        [ |              |   ]
[ HC—O    O—CH       ]        [ HC—O    O—CH       ]
[ |    \B/       |   ]        [ |    \B/       |   ]
[ HC—O/   \O—CH      ]        [ HC—O/   \O—CH      ]
[ |              |   ]        [ |              |   ]
[ CH2OH      CH2OH   ]        [ CH2OH      CH2OH   ]
```

(XLVII) 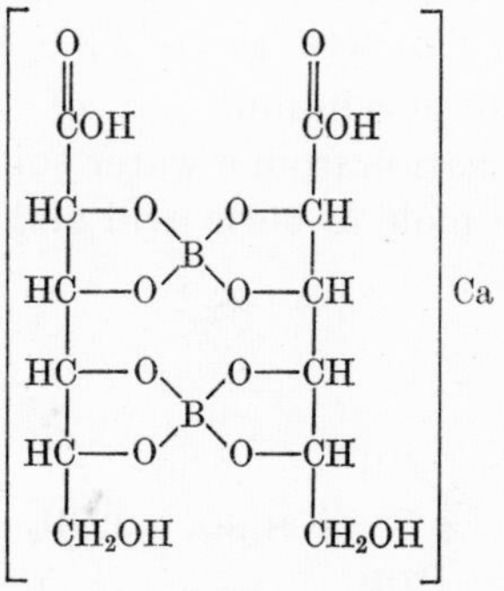 (XLVIII)

A series of ill-defined alkaloid salts of δ-gluconolactone were prepared by evaporation of an aqueous solution of the lactone

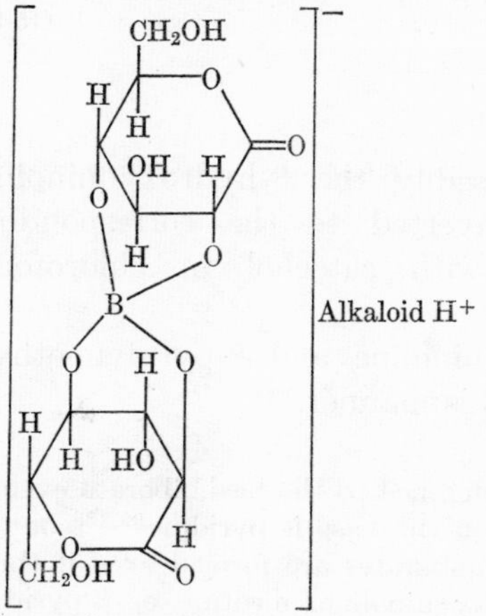

(XLIX) Alkaloid H⁺ (L) Alkaloid H⁺

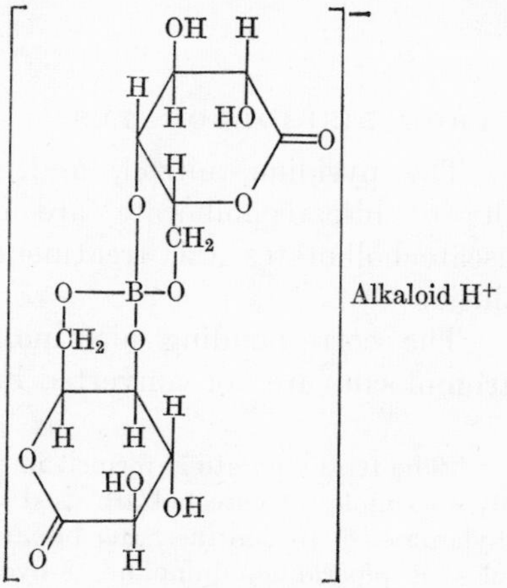

(2 moles), boric acid (1 mole) and amine (1 mole).[56] Presumably, 2,4- (XLIX) or 4,6- bridges (L) were involved.

V. DIALKOXYDIOLBORATES

A. Methods of Preparation of Acids

An attempt to convert pyridinium triscatecholborate to the acid is discussed in Section III-B-3.

B. Methods of Preparation of Salts

1. BY CRYSTALLIZATION FROM AN AQUEOUS SOLUTION OF DIOL, BORIC ACID AND BASE

The pyridinium salt of triscatecholborate was prepared by crystallization from a water solution containing three moles* of diol and one mole of boric acid and amine.[138]

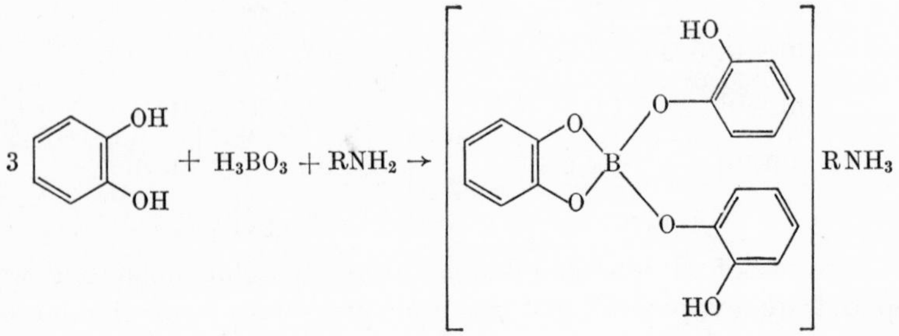

$$3\,C_6H_4(OH)_2 + H_3BO_3 + RNH_2 \rightarrow [(C_6H_4O_2)B(OC_6H_4OH)_2]\,RNH_3 \qquad (15\text{-}31)$$

2. FROM BISDIOLBORATES

The pyridine, nitron, and possibly the 8-hydroxyquinoline salts of biscatecholborate are converted to the corresponding triscatecholborates on treatment with catechol in chloroform solution.[138]

The corresponding nicotine, quinoline and β-pyridylmethylcarbinol salts are not converted in this manner.[138]

* The trisdiolborate is formed in preference to the bisdiolborate even if only two moles of catechol are used when the base is pyridine[99,138] or triethylamine.[138] In contrast, the biscatecholborates are formed even if three moles of piperidine, quinoline, 8-hydroxyquinoline, nicotine or β-pyridylmethylcarbinol are employed.[138]

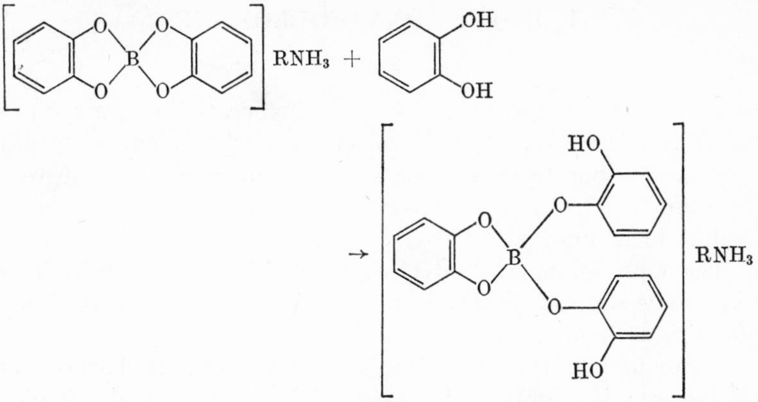

(15-32)

3. FROM TRI-(β-HYDROXYALKOXY)BORANES

An unusual example of salt formation was recorded (without experimental detail) in which one of the hydroxy groups of tri-β-hydroxyethoxyborane on treatment with ammonia in dioxane became the site of the fourth coordinate bond to boron. The sodium salt was prepared similarly.[113]

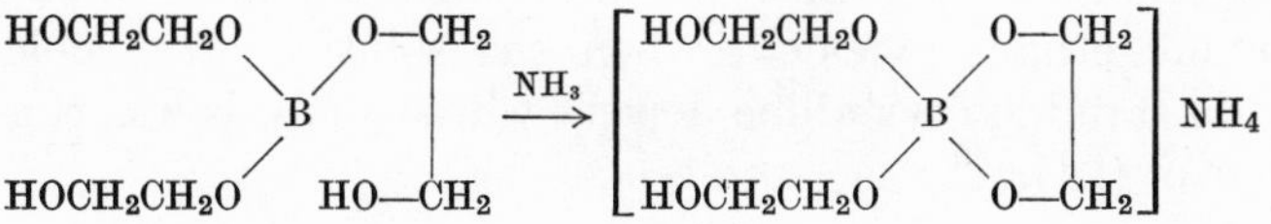

$$(HOCH_2CH_2O)_2B(OCH_2CH_2OH) \xrightarrow{NH_3} [(HOCH_2CH_2O)_2B(OCH_2CH_2O)]NH_4 \quad (15\text{-}33)$$

C. Reactions

1. CONVERSION TO BISDIOLBORATE SALTS AND ACIDS

The conversions of pyridinium triscatecholborate to the biscatecholborate salt by warming in pyridine and to the acid on heating *in vacuo* are discussed in Sections III-C-4 and III-B-3.

2. HYDROLYSIS AND ALCOHOLYSIS

The discussion and arguments for the hydrolysis and alcoholysis of pyridinium biscatecholborate are pertinent for pyridinium triscatecholborate. These results, based on ultraviolet spectral data, are given in sections III-E-1 and 2.

VI. DIHYDROXYDIOLBORATES

A. Properties

The monomeric nature of the dihydroxydiolborates has not been well established. The value of the molecular weight of hydrogen dihydroxymannitolborate in acetone solution indicated some degree of association.[78] The results, however, are doubtful due to the low solubility in acetone.

The ammonium and silver salts of dihydroxymannitolborate appear to decompose on standing; changing from crystals to a glassy mass with darkening.[78]

Compound (LII) (p. 653) is soluble in acetone, ethyl acetate and pyridine and is slightly soluble in ether, benzene and petroleum ether.[159] Compound (LIII) (p. 653) is soluble in pyridine and slightly soluble in acetone, chloroform and benzene.[160]

B. Methods of Preparation of Acids

Recorded examples of hydrogen dihydroxydiolborates are limited to sugar and sugar alcohol derivatives. In addition, all the recorded methods of preparation have involved the esterification of boric acid or its equivalent.

Treatment of one mole of mannitol with two moles of boric acid in refluxing ethanol yielded, when the solution was cooled and allowed to stand, a crystalline deposit whose analysis was consistent with that of (LI).*[78]

```
┌     CH₂OH           ┐
        |
  HO—CH
        |
  HO—CH
        |
     HC—O      OH
      |    \  /
      |     B         │ H
      |    /  \
     HC—O      OH
        |
     CH₂OH
└                     ┘
```

(LI)

* Meulenhoff[117] first formulated the product in this manner. He also believed that the cycloheptane derivative, formulated in Chapter 7 as

```
 ┌——CH—O                              ┌ ┌——CH—O    OH ┐
(CH₂)₅ |     \                          (CH₂)₅ |    \  /
 |     |      BOH·H₂O, probably was     |     |     B        H.
 |     |     /                          |     |    /  \
 └——CH—O                              └ └——CH—O    OH ┘
```

An equimolar acetone solution of glucose and boric acid in the presence of concentrated sulfuric acid yielded the 3,5-borate of 1,2-isopropylidene-α-D-glucofuranose (LII).[144,159] The same product was obtained from 1,2-isopropylidene-α-D-glucofuranose by treatment with boric acid and concentrated sulfuric acid.

```
┌                              ┐
        OH
        |
  HO—B——O
        |     |
        O   CHCH2OH
  H   /       |
  |  /H    H\             H
   \/          O
   O   H    /
   |    \  /
    \    O
     C
    / \
 CH3   CH3
└                              ┘
```

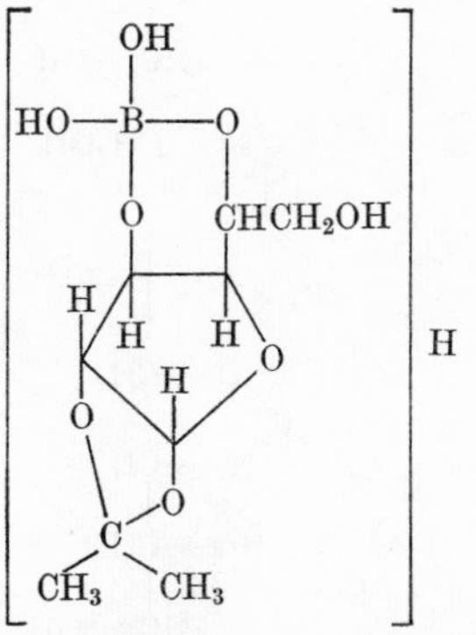

(LII)

The positions of the borate attachment were shown by the conversion of (LII) to the 6-benzoyl, 6-*p*-toluenesulfonyl and 6-trityl derivatives of the glucose acetonide.[144,159] The 6-acetyl derivative was prepared by treatment of (LII) with acetic anhydride and pyridine.[144]

Mannitol and boric acid in an acetone–sulfuric acid solution led to the isolation of (LIII).[160] The positions of the substituents were

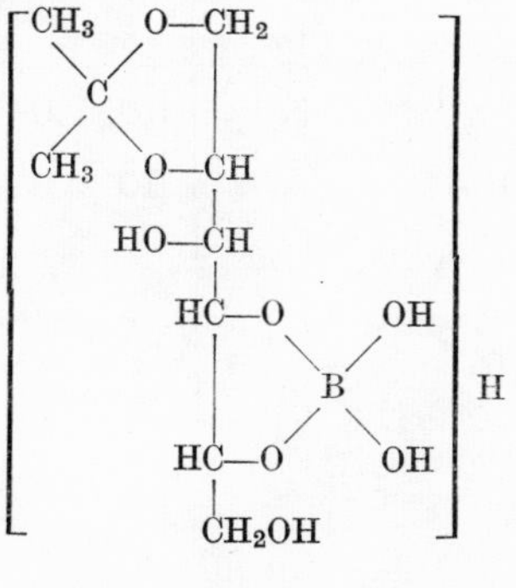

```
┌CH3   O—CH2                ┐
   \  /     |
    C       |
   /  \     |
 CH3   O—CH
        HO—CH
             |
           HC—O       OH
             |    \  /
             |     B          H
             |    /  \
           HC—O       OH
             |
           CH2OH
└                            ┘
```

(LIII)

shown by the following sequence of reactions.

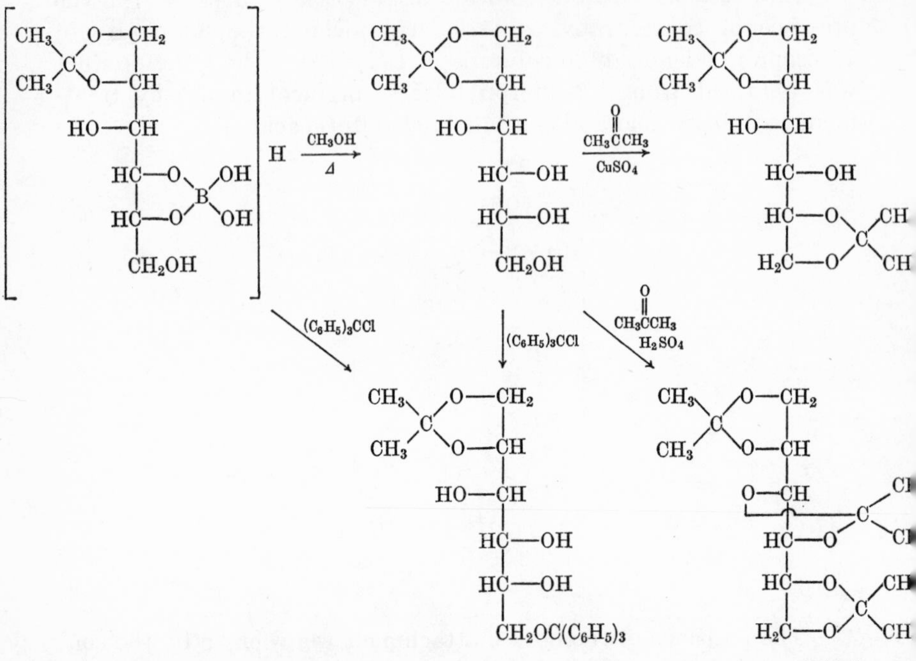

(15-34)

Treatment of glucose or mannitol with two moles of metaboric acid in acetone solution led to crystalline products.[50] On the basis of analytical and molecular weight data, they can be formulated as (LIV) and (LV).

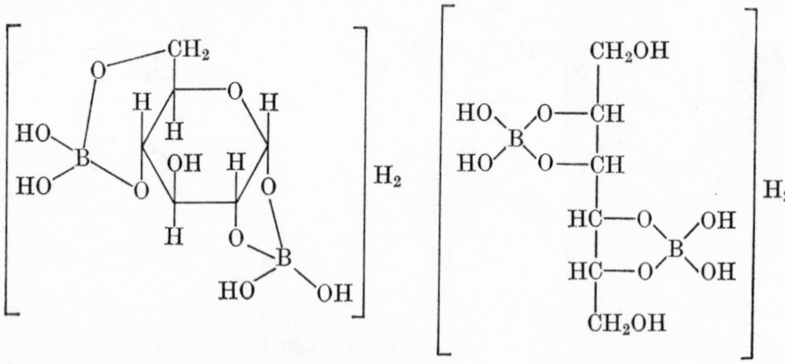

(LIV) (LV)

The substitution in (LV) is shown at the 2,3- and 4,5-positions to accommodate the fact that subsequent treatment of (LV) with benzoyl chloride followed by hydrolysis gave the 1,6-dibenzoate of mannitol. This assignment, however, does not necessarily follow since carboxylic acid halides react with boric acid esters.[139]

The 1,2- and 4,6-substituents in (LIV), therefore, are not necessarily inconsistent with the subsequent conversion of (LIV) to the 2,6-dibenzoate of glucose.

Treatment of methyl-α-D-glucopyranoside with an equimolar amount of metaboric acid in acetone solution followed by benzoylation and hydrolysis yielded 2,6-di-*O*-benzoyl-α-D-glucoside. The intermediate borate thus was formulated as the 3,4-derivative (LVI).*[146] It was felt that bridging of the *trans*-3,4-hydroxyls was

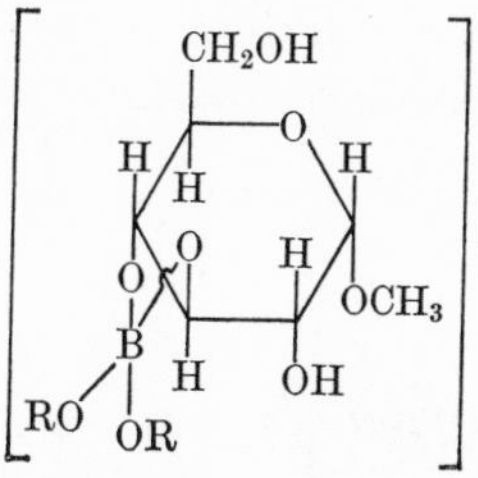
CH₂OH
H
H
O
H
O
O
H
OCH₃
H
B
H
OH
RO
OR

(LVI, R = H or C—)

possible in the anhydrous system involved even though it has been reported that methyl-α-D-glucopyranoside does not increase the conductivity of an aqueous boric acid solution.[29]

Methyl-β-D-glucopyranoside, on the basis of subsequent benzoylations and acetylations, was concluded to give a mixture of the tetravalent 3,4- and 4,6-borates (LVII and LVIII) on treatment with boric oxide or metaboric acid.[146]

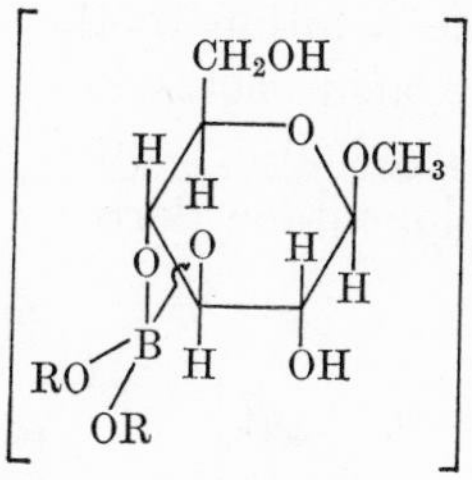
CH₂OH
O
OCH₃
H
H
H
O
O
H
H
H
B
H
OH
RO
OR

(LVII, R = H or C—)

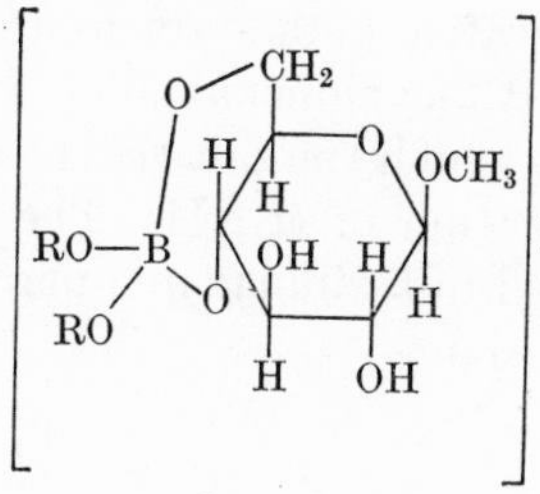
CH₂
O
O
OCH₃
H
H
RO—B
OH
H
H
O
H
RO
H
OH

(LVIII, R = H or C—)

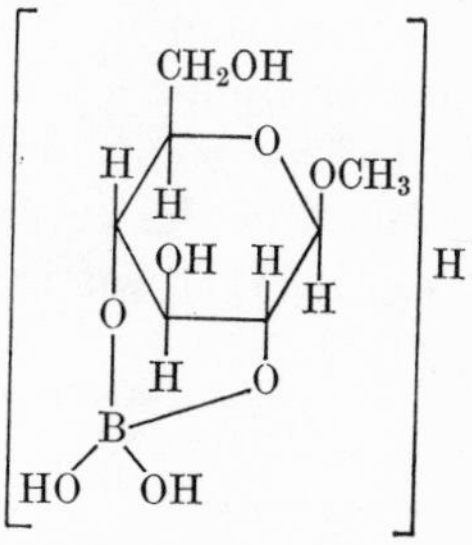
CH₂OH
O
OCH₃
H
H
OH
H
H
O
H
H
O
B
HO
OH

(LIX)

* No proof for the dihydroxyboryl nature of the compound was presented.

Examination of Fisher–Hirschfelder–Taylor atomic models indicates little if any strain involved in the 4,6-bridge (LVIII) or the 2,4-bridge (LIX) and a prohibitive amount of distortion in the *trans*-3,4-bridge (LVII). Since all assignments of the positions of the borates were based on subsequent benzoylations with benzoyl chloride in pyridine, and since carboxylic acid halides react with boric acid esters,[139] it is conceivable that the strain-free 4,6- and 2,4-derivatives did indeed give rise to all the observed benzoyl and acetyl derivatives.

Treatment of the α- and β-methylglucopyranosides with two moles of metaboric acid in acetone solution was believed to give a mixture of bisdihydroxyboryl derivatives of which (LX) would be one example.[11] Since the products analyzed for only one boron atom

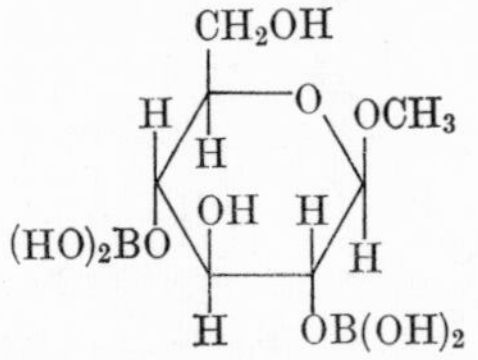

CH_2OH H O OCH_3 H OH H $(HO)_2BO$ H H $OB(OH)_2$

(LX)

per molecule and the predominant subsequent derivative on methylation was the 3,6-dimethyl methylglucoside, it can be concluded the actual intermediate borate may have been (LIX).

C. Methods of Preparation of Salts

1. FROM AN AQUEOUS SOLUTION OF DIOL, BORIC ACID AND BASE

Addition of a saturated potassium hydroxide solution to the mother liquor of a *cis*-1,2-cyclohexanediol, boric acid, potassium hydroxide solution from which the salt (LXI) already had deposited resulted in the crystallization of (LXII). The cyclopentane derivative (LXIII) was isolated in a similar manner.[86]

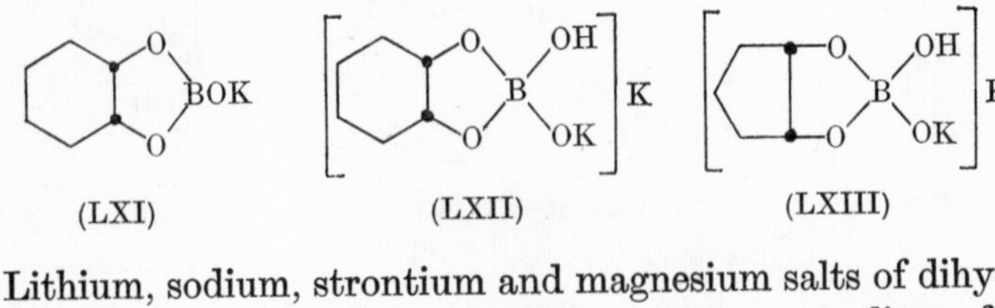

O BOK O | O OH B O OK K | O OH B O OK K

(LXI) (LXII) (LXIII)

Lithium, sodium, strontium and magnesium salts of dihydroxycatecholborate were isolated by evaporation or cooling of water solutions of catechol, boric acid, and the appropriate metal hydroxide, oxide or carbonate.*[136]

A series of sodium salt trihydrates (LXIV) was crystallized from

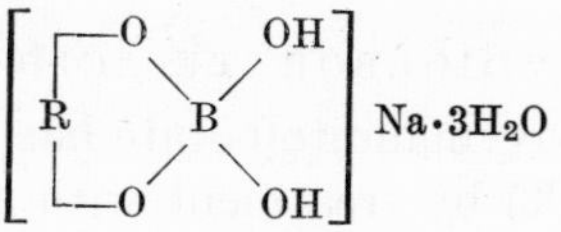

$$\left[R\begin{matrix} O \\ O \end{matrix} B \begin{matrix} OH \\ OH \end{matrix} \right] Na \cdot 3H_2O$$

(LXIV)

aqueous borate solutions of *racemic* or *meso*-2,4-pentanediol and 2,3-butanediol, *cis*-1,2-cyclopentanediol, and *cis*-1,2-cyclohexanediol. The anhydrous salts were obtained by heating the hydrates to 100°.[58]

Similar complexes could not be formed with 2,4-dimethyl-2,4-pentanediol and *cis*-1,3-cyclohexanediol, even though the corresponding 2-hydroxy derivatives (LXV) have been prepared (see

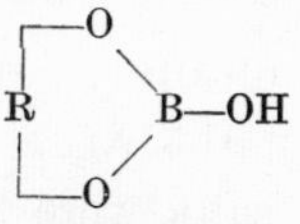

$$R\begin{matrix} O \\ O \end{matrix} B{-}OH$$

(LXV)

Chapter 7). This was attributed to the greater steric requirements in the complexes as compared to (LXV), due to the methyl–methyl and methyl–hydroxyl axial interactions (LXVI and LXVII).[58]

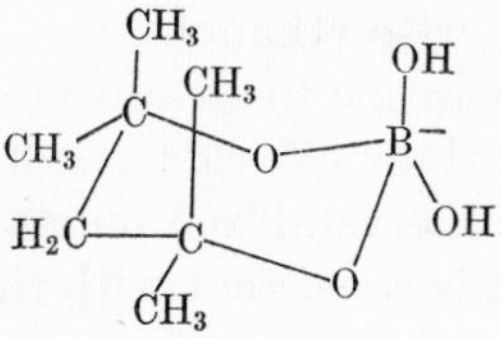

(LXVI) 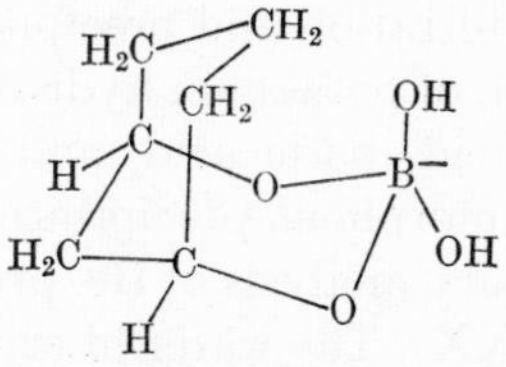 (LXVII)

An aqueous solution of pentaerythritol and substantially more than two molar equivalents of sodium metaborate resulted in the crystallization of the hydrated salt (LXVIII). If heated quickly, the

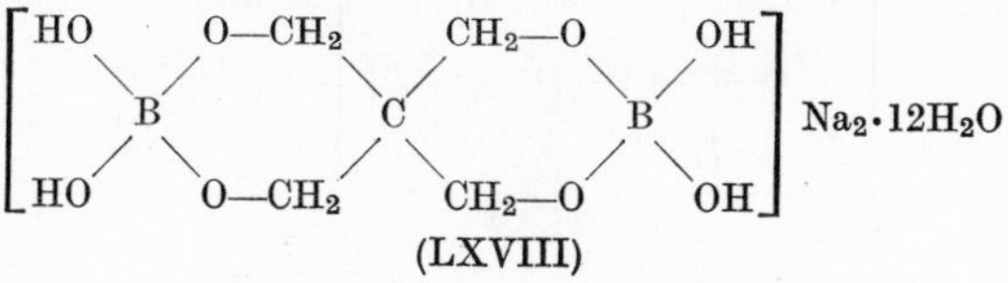

$$\left[\begin{matrix} HO \\ HO \end{matrix} B \begin{matrix} O{-}CH_2 \\ O{-}CH_2 \end{matrix} C \begin{matrix} CH_2{-}O \\ CH_2{-}O \end{matrix} B \begin{matrix} OH \\ OH \end{matrix} \right] Na_2 \cdot 12H_2O$$

(LXVIII)

* Schäfer chose to represent the compounds as hydrates of the trigonal coplanar salts.

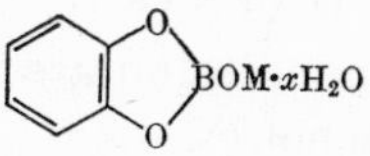

$$C_6H_4O_2BOM \cdot xH_2O$$

hydrate melts above 75°, then solidifies again as the water evaporates. If heated slowly, no melting occurs below 350°. The anhydrous salt is obtained at 95°.[58]

2. FROM DIHYDROXYDIOLBORATE ACIDS

Hydrogen dihydroxymannitolborate has been converted to the ammonium salt (LXIX) by treatment with ammonium hydroxide.

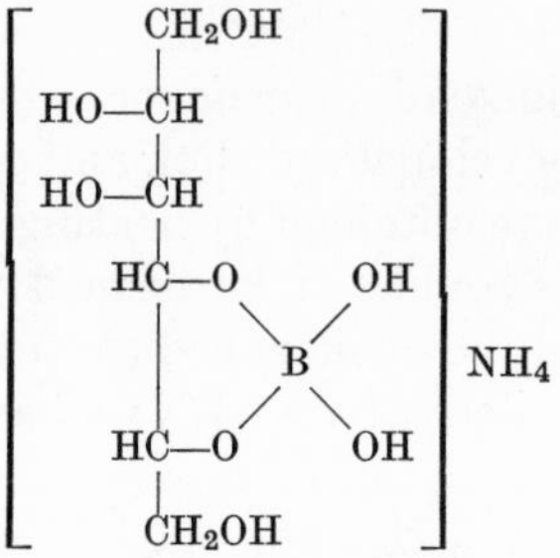

```
┌        CH2OH            ┐
          |
    HO—CH
          |
    HO—CH
          |
         HC—O      OH
          |    \   /
          |     B         NH4
          |    /   \
         HC—O      OH
          |
         CH2OH
└                         ┘
```

(LXIX)

Silver, calcium and barium salts were prepared by dissolving the acid in a stoichiometric quantity of sodium hydroxide solution and adding an excess of an aqueous solution of a soluble salt of the metal followed by precipitation with ethanol. They also could be prepared by grinding the metal hydroxides with the acid and a little water followed by filtration and precipitation with ethanol.[78]

Addition of potassium hydroxide solution to an aqueous solution of tartaric acid, boric acid, and strontium chloride resulted in an immediate amorphous precipitate which crystallized on standing.[142] The elementary analysis of the product is consistent with that calculated for (LXX). The water of crystallization was removed when the product was heated to 250-280°.

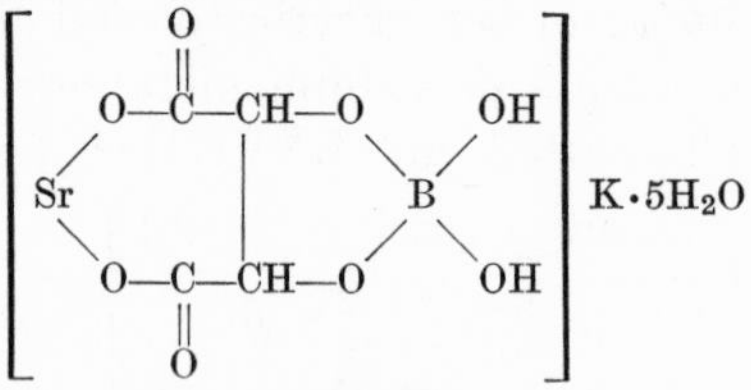

```
┌          O                    ┐
           ||
     O—C—CH—O      OH
    /        |     \   /
 Sr          |      B          K·5H2O
    \        |     /   \
     O—C—CH—O      OH
           ||
           O
└                               ┘
```

(LXX)

D. *Reactions of Acids*

1. WITH HYDROXYLIC SOLVENTS

Hydrogen dihydroxymannitolborate (LI) is decomposed by boiling alcohol, water or phenol.[78]

The 3,5-borate of 1,2-isopropylidene-α-D-glucofuranose (LII)[159] and the acetonide borate (LIII)[160] are hydrolyzed to boric acid and the acetonide on treatment with water.

Benzoate[146] and isopropylidene[144,159,160] derivatives of dihydroxydiolborate acids derived from sugars have been freed of boron by treatment with methanol and distillation of trimethoxyborane–methanol azeotrope.

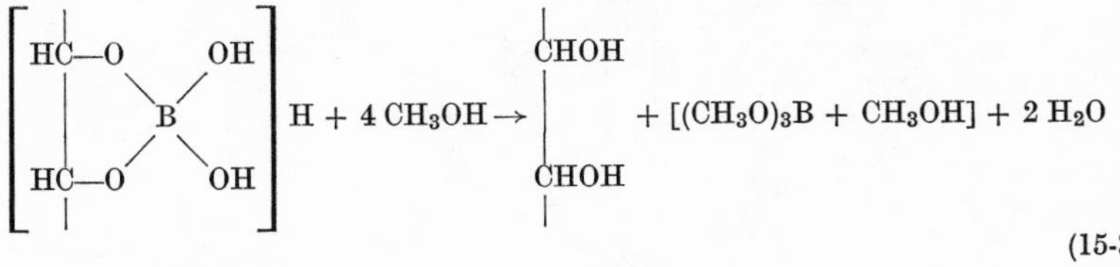

$$\left[\begin{array}{l} \text{HC—O} \quad\quad \text{OH} \\ \quad\quad\quad \text{B} \\ \text{HC—O} \quad\quad \text{OH} \end{array}\right]\text{H} + 4\,\text{CH}_3\text{OH} \rightarrow \begin{array}{l}\text{CHOH}\\ |\\ \text{CHOH}\end{array} + [(\text{CH}_3\text{O})_3\text{B} + \text{CH}_3\text{OH}] + 2\,\text{H}_2\text{O} \quad (15\text{-}35)$$

2. CONVERSION TO SALTS

The formation of salts from the dihydroxydiolborate acids is treated in Section VI-C-2.

3. DEHYDRATION

Dehydration to 2-hydroxy-1,3,2-dioxaborolane and borinane derivatives is discussed in Chapter 7.

E. Reactions of Salts

No definite reactions have been recorded.

VII. HYDROXYTRIOLBORATES

Complexes of sodium borate in aqueous solution with cyclitols possessing *cis*-hydroxyls in the 1,3,5-positions (LXXI) have been proposed to explain the reduction in pH[1] and the ionophoretic mobility.[2]

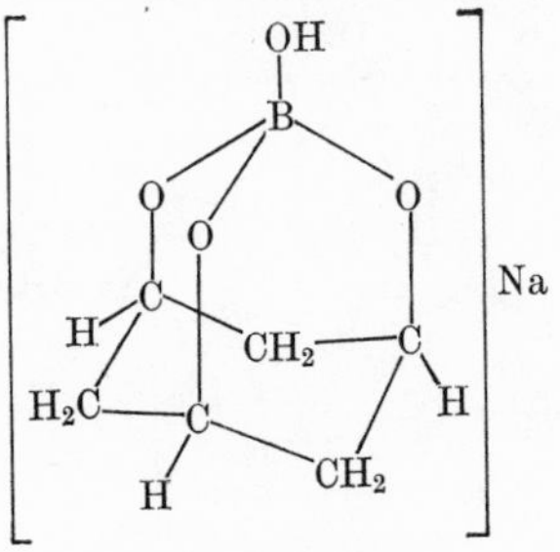

(LXXI)

Scyllitol diborate nonahydrate (LXXII) was isolated from the reduction of *scyllo-myo*-inosose with sodium borohydride.[164] Treatment of (LXXII) with methanol and sulfuric acid resulted in the

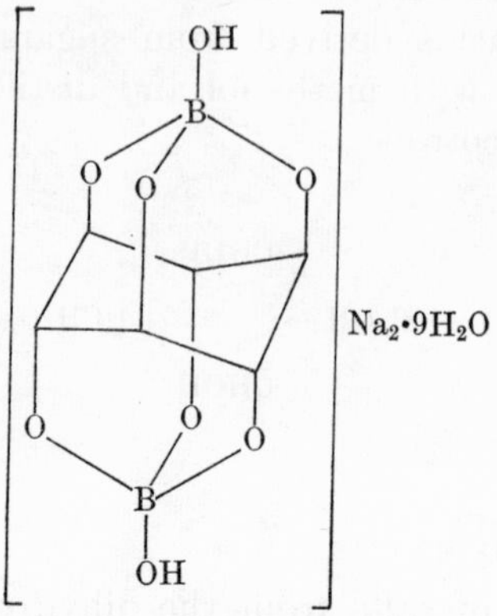

OH B O O O O O O B OH $Na_2 \cdot 9H_2O$

(LXXII)

removal of the boron as methyl borate and left a residue (after deionization) of scyllitol. Treatment with acetic anhydride and sulfuric acid converted (LXXII) to scyllitol hexaacetate.

1,1,1-Tris(hydroxymethyl)ethane gives a crystalline complex (LXXIII) with sodium borate. The water of hydration is lost at 47°.

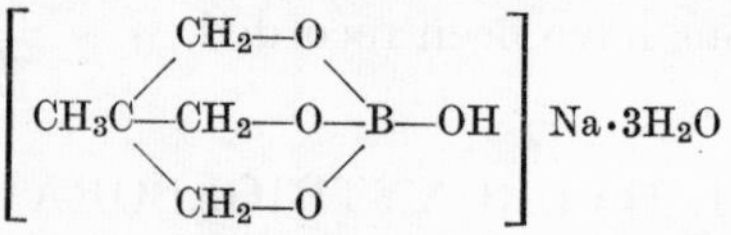

$$\left[CH_3C{-}CH_2{-}O{-}B{-}OH \right] Na \cdot 3H_2O$$
(CH_2—O above and CH_2—O below, linking C and B)

(LXXIII)

Cis-1,3,5-cyclohexanetriol behaved similarly to give (LXXIV).[58]

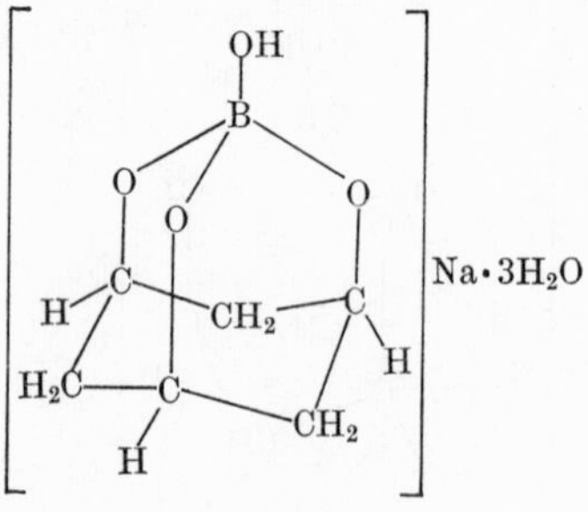

OH B O O O C H CH_2 C H H_2C C H CH_2 $Na \cdot 3H_2O$

(LXXIV)

VIII. STEREOCHEMICAL CONSIDERATIONS

A. Introduction

The ability of boric acid to coordinate with certain polyhydroxy materials in aqueous solution has served as a useful tool for the determination of the stereochemical relationships in the polyol. Clearly, the ability of the diol to form the spiran structure (LXXV) in equation (15-36) is a function of the stereochemical environment and relationship of the two hydroxyl groups.

$$2\ C_n\begin{matrix}\text{C—OH}\\ \text{C—OH}\end{matrix} + H_3BO_3 \rightleftharpoons \left[C_n\begin{matrix}\text{C—O}\\ \text{C—O}\end{matrix}B\begin{matrix}\text{O—C}\\ \text{O—C}\end{matrix}C_n \right]H + 3\ H_2O \qquad (15\text{-}36)$$

(LXXV)

Since a highly dissociated and acidic ionic species (LXXV) is formed in reaction (15-36) from two neutral or very weakly acidic molecules, the extent of the reaction and the attendant stereochemical implications can be indicated by conductivity, ionophoretic mobility, acidity, and, in some special cases, optical rotation measurements.

Unfortunately, structural conclusions obtained by these methods are not always of general validity since the preferred conformations of a polyol in aqueous solution cannot always be extrapolated to non-aqueous media. Indeed, a host of diols and polyols are known which do not effect an appreciable shift of equilibrium (15-36) in aqueous solution but which do form isolable cyclic derivatives of boric acid under dehydrating conditions.

B. Conductivity Considerations

1. 1,2-DIOLS

The primary requisite for enhancement of the conductivity of an aqueous solution of boric acid by a diol or polyol appears to be coplanarity of the oxygen–carbon atoms–oxygen system and a *cis* conformation of the hydroxyl groups.[15] Thus, simple aliphatic 1,2-diols do not enhance the conductivity of a boric acid solution (Table 15-4). This is consistent with the preferred conformation of ethylene glycol (LXXVI) which has the hydroxyl groups staggered at the positions of least steric interference and maximum repulsion of the negative oxygen atoms. Evidently this conformation or the

Table 15-4. Effect of polyols on conductivity of aqueous boric acid at 25°C.

Polyol	Conc. (mole/l.)	Δ[a]	Reference
1,2-Diols			
Ethylene glycol	0.5	0	16, 18, 34, 45
Methyl α-glyceryl ether	0.5	0	19
Propylene glycol	0.5	0	18, 22, 34
1,2-Dihydroxy-3-chloropropane	0.5	0	16, 27
	0.5	5.5	34
Phenyl α-glyceryl ether	0.125	0	27
Biacetyl dihydrate	0.25	160.6	35, 39
2-Methyl-2,3-butanediol	0.5	0	23
2-Methyl-2,4,5-pentanetriol	0.5	0	23
Pinacol	0.125	0	16, 18, 27
3,4-Dihydroxy-1,5-hexanediol	0.125	0	18
	0.5	0.5	16, 27
3,4-Dihydroxy-4-methyl-2-pentanone	0.5[b]	197.7	32
dl-Hydrobenzoin	0.5	10.3	85
meso-Hydrobenzoin	0.5	0	85
1,3-Diols			
1,3-Propanediol	0.5	0	16, 18, 27, 34
2-Methyl-2-nitro-1,3-propanediol	0.5	9.3	21
2-Hydroxymethyl-2-nitro-1,3-propanediol	0.5	122	16, 27
Pentaerythritol	0.5	72	18, 22, 45
	0.5	222	27
	0.5	231	16
2-Hydroxybenzyl alcohol (saligenin)	0.0625	79	33
	0.125	148	33
	0.25	267	33
2-Hydroxy-4-methylbenzyl alcohol (4-methylsaligenin)	0.00781	1.5	33
1,4-Diols			
1,4-Butanediol	0.5	0	16, 18, 27
Triols, tetrols, pentitols and hexitols			
Glycerol	0.5	9	16, 18, 27, 34, 45
Erythritol	0.5	64	16, 18
Adonitol	0.5	90	15
Arabitol	0.5	357	15
Xylitol	0.5	625	15
Mannitol	0.5	685	16, 18
Dulcitol	0.5	717	16, 18
Sorbitol	0.5	794	16, 18, 27
Alicyclic diols			
Five-membered rings			
cis-1,2-Cyclopentanediol	0.5	149	16, 18, 34
trans-1,2-Cyclopentanediol	0.5	0	18, 22

(*Table continued*)

Table 15-4 (*continued*)

Polyol	Conc. (mole/l.)	Δ[a]	Reference
cis-1-Methyl-1,2-cyclopentanediol	0.5	114	15, 109
trans-1-Methyl-1,2-cyclopentanediol	0.5	0	15, 109
cis-1-Phenyl-1,2-cyclopentanediol	0.025[c]	0.2	109
cis-1,2-Dihydroxyindane	0.143	63	18, 22
trans-1,2-Dihydroxyindane	0.143	0	18, 22
α-Mannitan	0.5	776	15, 157
N-Ethyl-*meso*-tartrimide	0.5	702	15
N-Methyl-*dextro*-tartrimide	0.5	0	15
N-Methyl-*dl*-tartrimide	0.2	0	19
cis-2,3-Dihydroxytetramethylenesulfone	0.5	494	15
trans-2,3-Dihydroxytetramethylenesulfone	0.5	0	15
cis-2-Methyl-2,3-dihydroxytetra-methylenesulfone	0.5	1096	15
trans-2-Methyl-2,3-dihydroxytetra-methylenesulfone	0.5	0	15
cis-1,4-Dimethyl-2,3-dihydroxytetra-methylenesulfone	0.5	1458	15
trans-1,4-Dimethyl-2,3-dihydroxytetra-methylenesulfone	0.5	0	15
4,5-Dihydroxyuric acid	0.00391	4.4	43
exo-exo-2,3-Dihydroxybicyclo-[2.2.1]heptane	0.25	594	101
endo-endo-2,3-Dihydroxybicyclo-[2.2.1]heptane	0.25[d]	93.9	101
exo-exo-2,3-Dihydroxy-1,7,7-trimethyl-bicyclo[2.2.1]heptane (camphor glycol)	0.25	0	101
exo-2-*syn*-7-Dihydroxybicyclo-[2.2.1]heptane	0.25	0	101
exo-2-*syn*-7-Dihydroxybicyclo-[2.2.1]heptane	0.25	0	101
Six-membered rings			
cis-1,2-Cyclohexanediol	0.5	0	15, 34, 44
trans-1,2-Cyclohexanediol	0.5	0	15, 44
cis-1-Methyl-1,2-cyclohexanediol	0.5	0	24, 109
trans-1-Methyl-1,2-cyclohexanediol	0.5	0	24, 109
cis-1-Phenyl-1,2-cyclohexanediol	0.025	0	24, 109
trans-1-Phenyl-1,2-cyclohexanediol	0.025	0	24, 109
cis-2,8-Dihydroxybicyclo[3.2.1]octane	0.127	0	101
cis-1,2-Dihydroxytetrahydronaphthalene	0.09	7	17
trans-1,2-Dihydroxytetrahydronaphthalene	0.05	0	17
cis-2,3-Dihydroxytetrahydronaphthalene	0.05	0	17
trans-2,3-Dihydroxytetrahydronaphthalene	0.05	0	17
Dialuric acid	0.00781	0	43
Alloxantin	0.00781	0	43
Alloxan	0.0312	0	43
Cyanuric acid	0.0128	0	43
Hydrated triquinoyl	0.01	2982	39

(*Table continued*)

Table 15-4 (*continued*)

Polyol	Conc. (mole/l.)	Δ^a	Reference
Seven-membered rings			
cis-1,2-Cycloheptanediol	0.05	138	17, 22, 31
trans-1,2-Cycloheptanediol	0.05	49	17, 22, 31
Aromatic derivatives			
Catechol	0.0625	137	38, 117
	0.5	516	16, 18, 22, 45
	1.0	681	15
3-Nitrocatechol	0.0625	1163	38, 117
4-Nitrocatechol	0.0625	311.8	38, 117
3,5-Dinitrocatechol	0.00390	122	18, 42
3,4-Dihydroxybenzoic acid	0.0312	68.7	15, 18, 42
(protocatechuric acid)	0.125	119	16, 42
Resorcinol	0.5	0	15, 16, 45
4-Nitroresorcinol	0.00781	0	42
Hydroquinone	0.5	0	15, 16, 45
1,2,3-Trihydroxybenzene	0.5	572	18
(pyrogallol)	0.5	573	16, 45
	1.0	909	15
1,2,4-Trihydroxybenzene	0.5	322	15,18,25
1,3,5-Trihydroxybenzene (phloroglucinol)	0.5	0	15, 16, 45
3,4,5-Trihydroxybenzoic acid	0.031	28	18
(gallic acid)	0.0312	41.1	15, 45
	0.125	181.6	42
Methyl 3,4,5-trihydroxybenzoate	0.0312	212	18, 22, 26
Tannin (digallic acid)	0.00459	230	18, 22, 26
1,2-Dihydroxynaphthalene	0.005	17	18, 22
	0.0156	46	22
	0.0312	65	15, 42
2,3-Dihydroxynaphthalene	0.005	92	15, 16, 18
1,8-Dihydroxynaphthalene	0.005	524	30
2,3-Dihydroxyquinoxaline	0.00252	0	43
Tetrahydroxy-*p*-quinone	0.01	59	39
Hexahydroxybenzene	0.01	1546	39
Sugars			
Furanoses, from hexoses			
α-D-Glucofuranose	0.5	70–23	15, 22, 29
α-D-Galactofuranose	0.5	55–49	15, 22
β-D-Mannofuranose	0.5	289–319	15, 22, 29
β-D-Fructofuranose	0.1	51–74	15, 22, 29
	0.5	774–778	15, 22, 29
β-L-Sorbofuranose	0.1	230	15
Furanoses, from pentoses			
α-L-Rhamnofuranose	0.5	23–40	15, 22, 29
β-L-Arabinofuranose	0.5	101–93	15, 22, 29
α-D-Xylofuranose	0.5	205–185	15, 22, 31

(*Table continued*)

Table 15-4 (*continued*)

Polyol	Conc. (mole/l.)	Δ[a]	Reference
Pyranoses			
Methyl-α-D-glucopyranoside	0.5	0	29
Methyl-β-D-glucopyranoside	0.5	0	29
Methyl tetramethyl-α-D-glucopyranoside	0.5	0	29
Methyl tetramethyl-β-D-glucopyranoside	0.5	0	29
Tetramethyl-α-D-glucopyranose	0.5	0	29
Polysaccharides			
Sucrose	0.5	0	22, 29
α-Lactose	0.5	0	15, 24
β-Lactose	0.5	0	15, 24
Maltose	0.5	0	15
Melibiose	—	0	161
Raffinose	0.5	0	15, 18, 22

[a] Δ = conductivity increment = observed conductivity of polyol–boric acid solution minus the sum of the conductivities of the individual polyol and boric acid solutions in Kohlrausch–Holborn[95] units $\times 10^6$.
[b] in 72% ethanol solution.
[c] in 70% ethanol solution.
[d] in 15% ethanol solution.

skew conformation (LXXVII) holds to some extent even when the hydrogen atoms are replaced by methyl groups, since neither propylene glycol nor pinacol gives a conductivity increment.

HO H
H····C····C◄H
H OH
(LXXVI)

HO CH₃
CH_3····C——C◄OH
CH_3 CH_3
(LXXVII)

The preponderance of hydroxyl groups in dihydrated biacetyl greatly increases the probability of the eclipsed conformation (LXXVIII) and a large conductivity increment is realized (Table 15-4).[35,39]

CH_3 CH_3
HO····C——C····OH
HO OH
(LXXVIII)

Meso-hydrobenzoin (Table 15-4) does not produce a conductivity increment (Δ = 0); the racemic isomer has a small effect (Δ = 10.3).[85]

There is some logic in this order since a *cis* disposition of the hydroxyl groups in the *meso* isomer results in eclipsed bulky phenyl groups (LXXIX) as compared to their displacement by 120° in the racemic isomer (LXXX).

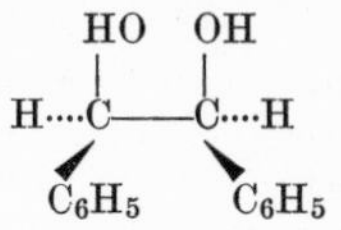

HO OH
H····C——C····H
C_6H_5 C_6H_5
(LXXIX)

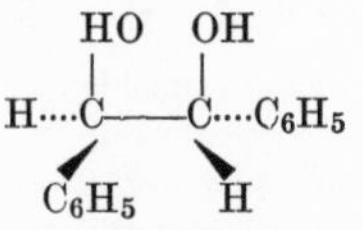

HO OH
H····C——C····C_6H_5
C_6H_5 H
(LXXX)

The large conductivity increment of 3,4-dihydroxy-4-methyl-2-pentanone (LXXXI) is not thought to be due to the presence of a favorable conformation in which the hydroxyl groups are eclipsed but rather to the formation of a trimethylene oxide ring with *cis*-hydroxyl groups (LXXXII).[32]

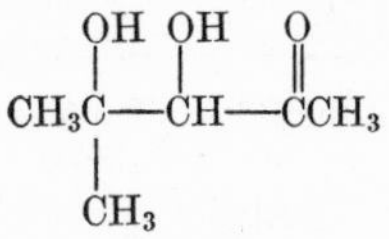

OH OH O
CH_3C—CH—CCH_3
CH_3
(LXXXI)

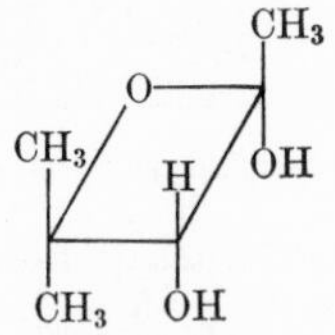

CH_3 O CH_3 H OH CH_3 OH
(LXXXII)

Since trimethylene oxide derivatives are relatively rare and difficult to prepare,[167] the ready formation of (LXXXII) in aqueous medium is doubtful and the large conductivity increment might best be ascribed either to the eclipsed conformation (LXXXIII), the ene-1,2-diol (LXXXIV), or the ene-1,3-diol (LXXXV).

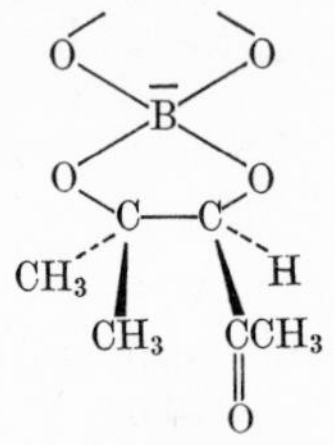

(LXXXIII) 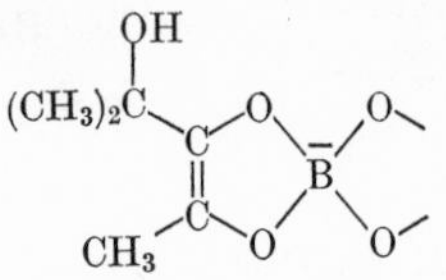 (LXXXIV) 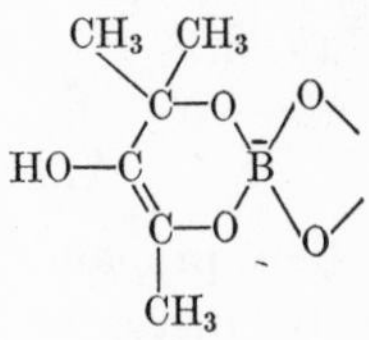 (LXXXV)

2. 1,3- AND 1,4-DIOLS

The inability of unsubstituted 1,3- and 1,4-diols to complex boric acid (Table 15-4) cannot be due to steric or electronic repulsions preventing favorable conformations. The unreactivity is probably due to unfavorable entropy relationships in the unsubstituted six- and seven-membered rings that would result from complex formation.

Substitution in the six-ring, which is known to favorably alter the entropy of cyclic systems and promote ring closure in a variety of cyclization reactions, seems to apply in the case of 1,3-diols. Thus *gem* substitution on the 2-carbon atom (LXXXVI–LXXXVIII),[16,21,22,27,45] does promote complex formation with 1,3-diols. A benzo substituent (LXXXIX)[33] produces the same effect.*

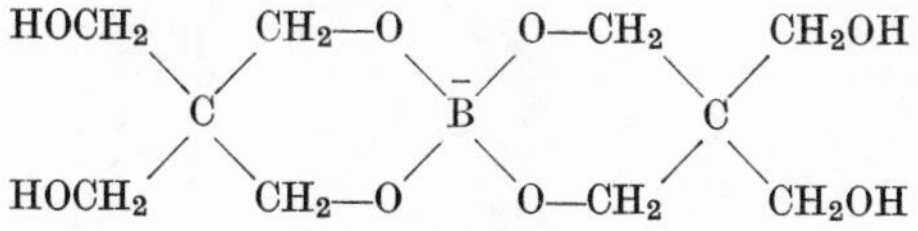

HOCH$_2$ CH$_2$—O O—CH$_2$ CH$_2$OH
C B$^-$ C
HOCH$_2$ CH$_2$—O O—CH$_2$ CH$_2$OH

(LXXXVI)

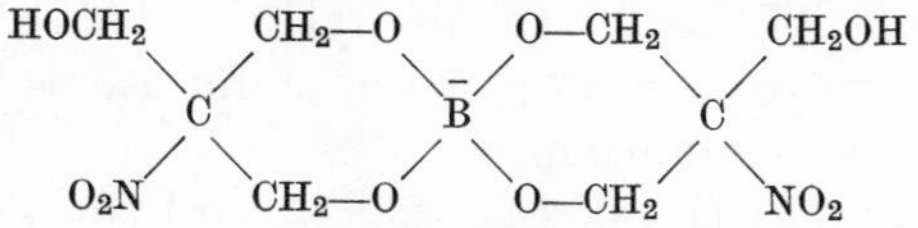

HOCH$_2$ CH$_2$—O O—CH$_2$ CH$_2$OH
C B$^-$ C
O$_2$N CH$_2$—O O—CH$_2$ NO$_2$

(LXXXVII)

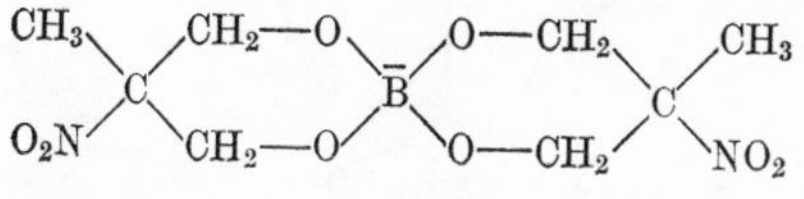

CH$_3$ CH$_2$—O O—CH$_2$ CH$_3$
C B$^-$ C
O$_2$N CH$_2$—O O—CH$_2$ NO$_2$

(LXXXVIII)

CH$_2$—O O—CH$_2$
B$^-$
O O
R R

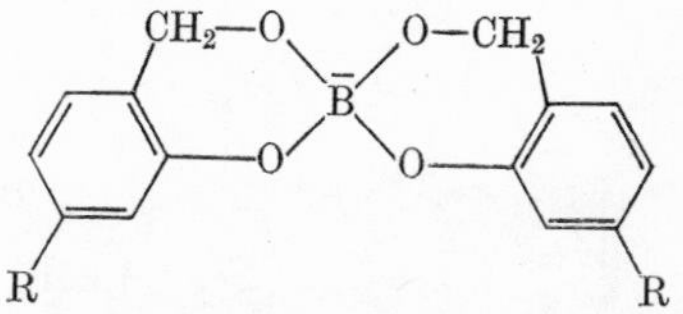

(LXXXIX, R = H, CH$_3$)

3. TRIOLS, TETROLS, PENTITOLS AND HEXITOLS

With triols, tetrols, pentitols and hexitols, the electronic and steric repulsions cannot keep all the vicinal hydroxyl groups diametrically opposed. Thus the probability of favorable positioning of two hydroxyl groups is greatly increased, and indeed a conductivity increment which increases with the number of hydroxyl groups is realized (Table 15-4).

4. ALICYCLIC DIOLS

Conductivity measurements with alicyclic diols are consistent with the known near planarity of the five-membered ring, the chair

* The small conductivity increment ($\Delta = 1.5$) experienced with 4-methylsaligenin (LXXXIX, R = CH$_3$) was attributed to the unfavorable influence of the methyl group.[33] However, based on a plot of Δ *vs.* conc. for saligenin (Table 15-4), the 1.5 value for methylsaligenin at a concentration of 0.00781 mole/l. is what is to be expected, and it can be concluded the methyl group exerts little influence on the equilibrium and resulting conductivity.

form of the six-membered ring, and the relative freedom of movement in the seven-membered ring. Thus, *cis*-1,2-cyclopentanediol (XC)[16,34] enhances the conductivity of boric acid; the *trans* isomer

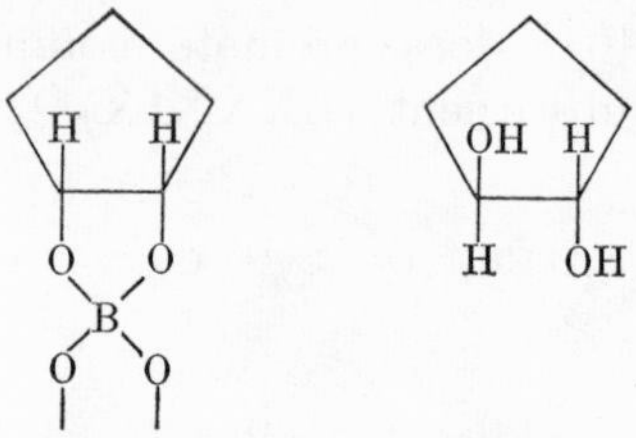

(XC) (XCI)

(XCI)[22] does not (Table 15-4). Methyl[15] or benzo[22] substituents on the five-ring, or oxygen, nitrogen or sulfur atoms in the five-ring do not change this relationship.[15]

Both *exo-exo-* (XCII) and *endo-endo*-2,3-dihydroxybicyclo[2.2.1]-heptane (XCIII) complex with boric acid.[101] Comparison of the

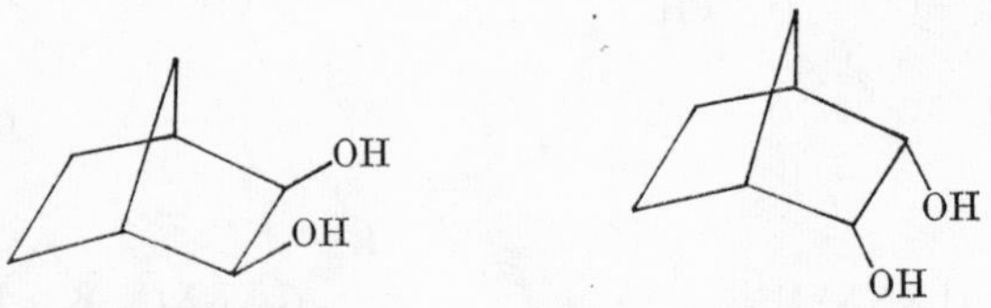

(XCII) (XCIII)

Δ values (Table 15-4) with the value for *cis*-1,2-cyclopentanediol, after correction for concentration differences, leads to the conclusion that the hydroxyl groups in (XCIII) are essentially equivalent in planarity to those in cyclopentanediol. The enhanced ability of (XCII) relative to (XCIII) to form the complex is in accord with the well-known ease of steric approach to the *exo* side rather than the *endo* in bicyclo[2.2.1]heptane systems.

The inability of (XCIV) to complex with boric acid was attri-

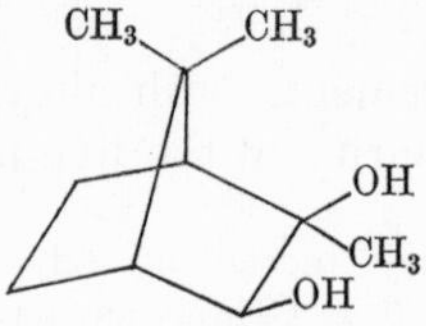

(XCIV)

buted to the steric interference of the *syn*-methyl group and was offered as proof of the *exo-exo* nature of camphor glycol since the *endo-endo* derivative would be expected to enhance the conductivity of boric acid.[101]

Neither *cis*- nor *trans*-1,2-cyclohexanediol enhances the conductivity of boric acid.[15,34,44] Thus, both the equatorial–polar conformation of the *cis*-diol (XCV) and the equatorial–equatorial conformation[129] of the *trans*-diol (XCVI) have the hydroxyl groups

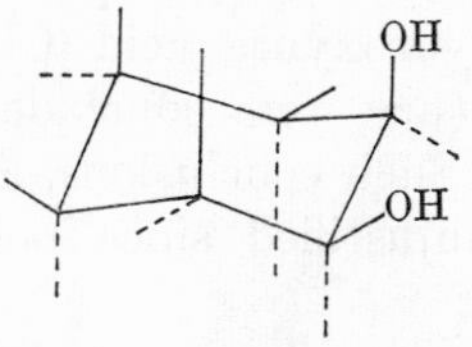

(XCV) 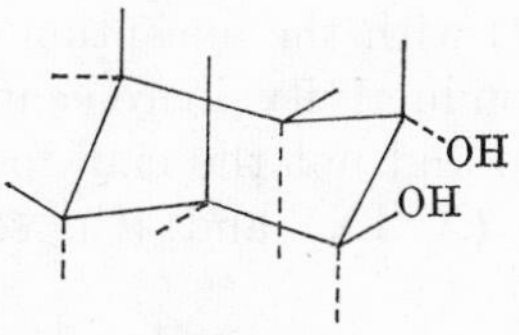 (XCVI)

thrust out from the rings at an angle sufficiently removed from coplanarity to prevent the formation of the necessary spiran system. Deviations from coplanarity in the cycloheptanediol systems evidently are lessened to the point where both the *cis*- and *trans*-1,2-cycloheptanediols effect an enhancement of conductivity.[17,22,31]

Two exceptions to the rule of the "inertness" of six-membered alicyclic diols appear to be the hexahydrate* of triquinoyl (XCVII),

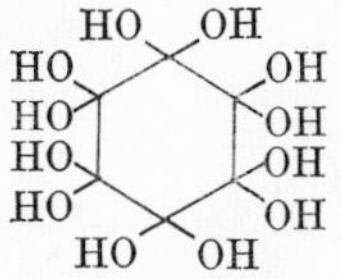

(XCVII)

which produces a remarkable increase in the conductivity of boric acid ($\Delta = 2982$ at 0.01 molar conc.),[39] and *cis*-1,2-dihydroxytetrahydronaphthalene, which exhibits a small conductivity increment ($\Delta = 7$).[17] The chair form of triquinoyl (XCVIII) seems to be ideally

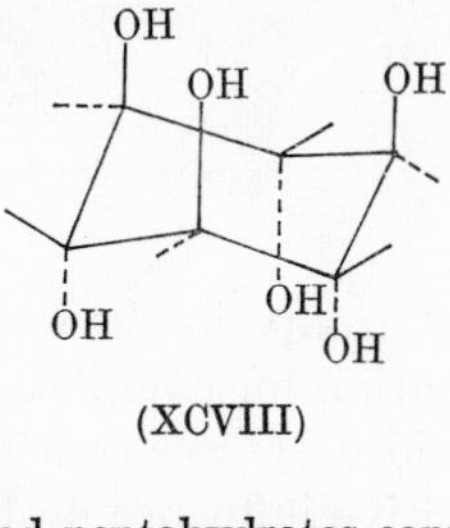

(XCVIII)

* The di-, tri-, tetra- and pentahydrates cannot be excluded as possible "active" intermediates.

constituted for the ready formation of 1,3-complexing with boric acid. The positive effect of *cis*-1,2-dihydroxytetrahydronaphthalene cannot be completely rationalized but may be related to the inability of the hydrogenated ring of tetrahydronaphthalene to assume the chair form.[100]

Nitrogen heterocycles containing the group —NHC=O (XCIX–CI) with the exception of dihydroxyuric acid (CII) did not effect a conductivity increment and thus were concluded to exist in the keto and not the enol forms.[43] Such conclusions, at least for structures (XCIX) and (C), seem unjustified since none of the

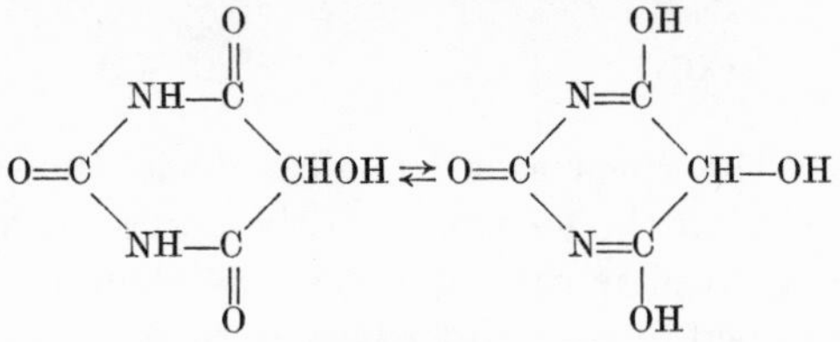

Dialuric acid
(XCIX)

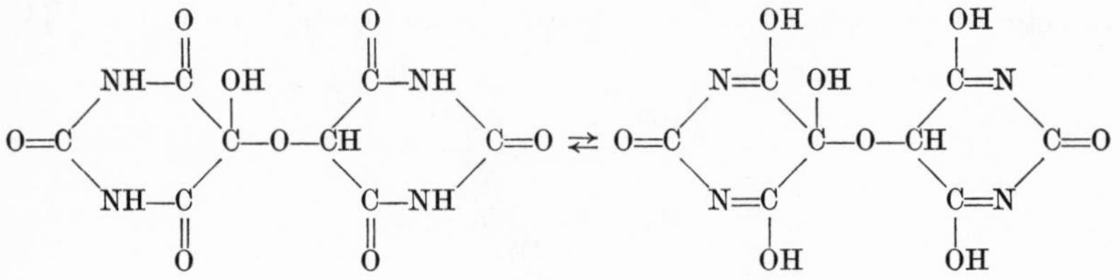

Alloxantin
(C)

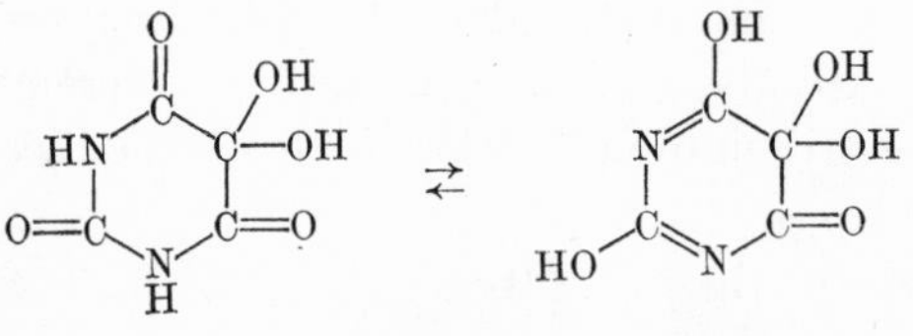

Alloxan
(CI)

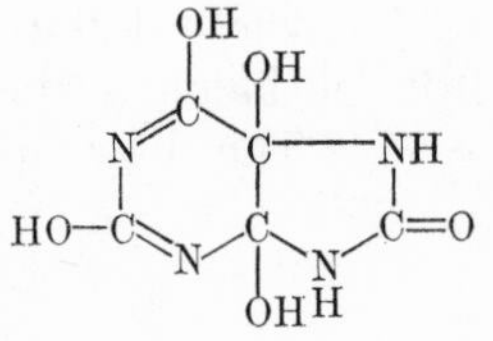

(CII)

possible pairs of hydroxyl groups in the enol forms are expected to be in the correct conformation for complex formation.

4,5-Dihydroxyuric acid (CII) was concluded to have a *cis* fusion of the rings due to its positive influence on the conductivity of boric acid.[43]

Cyanuric acid (CIII) would not be expected to enhance the conductivity of boric acid even if the enol form predominates, since the hydroxyl groups are improperly disposed for complexing a boron atom. No conductivity enhancement was found.[43]

(CIII)

5. AROMATIC DERIVATIVES

The increased resonance energy of aromatic systems in which the hydroxyl substituents are coplanar with the rings insures a favorable conformation for complex formation with boric acid. Thus, benzene and naphthalene derivatives with *ortho*- or *peri*-hydroxyl groups effect an enhancement of conductivity.[15,16,22,25,30,38,42,45] Clearly, *meta* and *para* derivatives are incapable of forming the necessary cyclic structure.

Nitro derivatives of catechol produce an enhancement of the conductivity of boric acid over that of catechol itself.[38,42]

2,3-Dihydroxyquinoxaline did not effect a conductivity increment and was concluded to be in the keto form (CIV).[43]

(CIV)

6. SUGARS

The fundamental relationships developed for five and six-membered alicyclic diols can be applied to more complex cyclic polyol systems such as the sugars. Furanoses possessing vicinal *cis*-hydroxyl groups should be capable of complexing with boric acid[15] due to the essentially planar conformation of the furanoid ring.[65] All pyranoses, on the other hand, should be insensitive to boric acid[15] due to the chair-form conformation (CV).[65] This conformation, as in the case of cyclohexanediol, precludes coplanarity of vicinal hydroxyl groups even though they have the *cis* configuration.* Thus, the change in

* X-ray investigations of methyl xylopyranosides indicate the five carbon atoms of the ring to be essentially coplanar with the ring oxygen displaced by about 0.8 Å.[112] If this conformation is valid in aqueous media, many of the arguments dealing with the conductivity of carbohydrate–boric acid solutions are invalid.

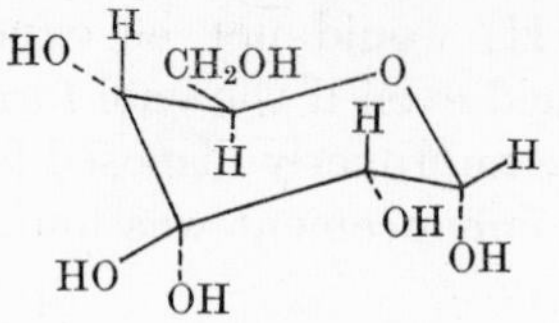

α-D-Glucopyranose
(CV)

conductivity with time of an aqueous solution of glucose and boric acid, that is, the decrease in Δ in the case of α-D-glucose and the increase in Δ in the case of β-D-glucose, changes which paralleled somewhat the rate of mutarotation of these sugars, was attributed to the cycle in Fig. 15-2. α-D-Glucofuranose contributed to the

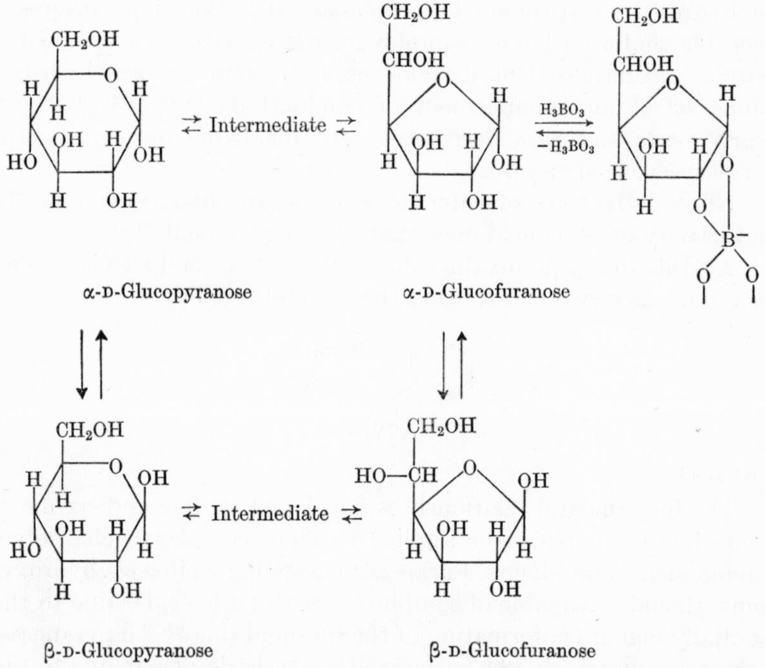

α-D-Glucopyranose ⇄ Intermediate ⇄ α-D-Glucofuranose $\underset{-H_3BO_3}{\overset{H_3BO_3}{\rightleftharpoons}}$ (borate complex)

β-D-Glucopyranose ⇄ Intermediate ⇄ β-D-Glucofuranose

Fig. 15-2. Conductivity cycle of aqueous solution of D-glucose and boric acid.

conductivity and neither β-D-glucofuranose nor the pyranoses enhanced the conductivity.[15,16,29] Similar reasoning was used to explain the variations with time in the conductivity of galactose-boric acid solutions.[15,22,36] In the case of mannose, the *cis* configuration of the 2- and 3-hydroxyl groups supports complexing with boric acid for both the α- and β-isomers (CVI and CVII) and a large Δ (Table 15-4) is observed.[15]

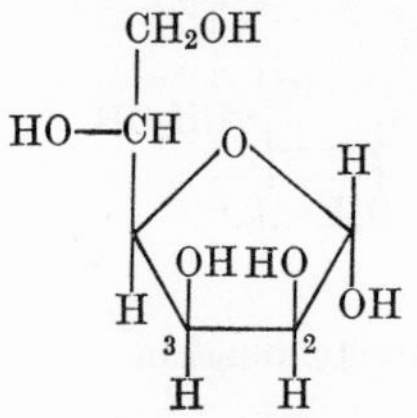

α-D-Mannofuranose
(CVI)

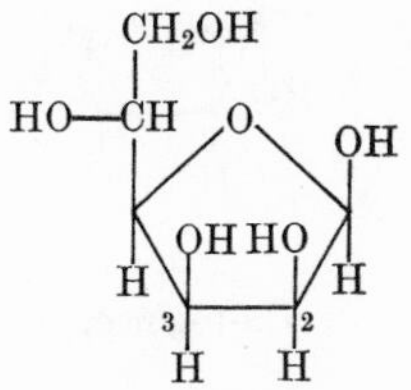

β-D-Mannofuranose
(CVII)

The increase in conductivity was found to be much greater for ketoses than for aldoses.[15] Both fructose (CVIII)[29,36] and sorbose (CIX),[37] even at low concentration, exhibited appreciable conductivity increments over that of boric acid as compared to the

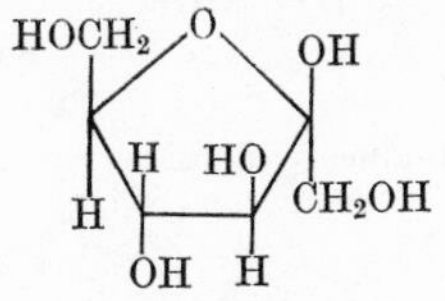

β-D-Fructofuranose
(CVIII)

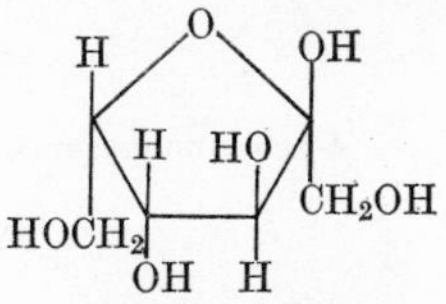

β-D-Sorbofuranose
(CIX)

aldoses (Table 15-4). There appears to be no logical explanation for this phenomenon other than the possibility that the equilibrium between pyranoses and furanoses lies further towards furanoses for the ketoses than it does for the aldoses.

The disaccharides (CX–CXIII)[15,22,24,29,161] and the trisaccharide (CXIV)[16,22] do not enhance the conductivity of boric acid solutions. This is consistent with the inability of the α-glucose unit of sucrose (CX), even after transformation to the furanoside, to form the necessary 1,2-bridge with boric acid due to the blocking glycoside linkage and the inability of the β-fructose unit to form the 2,3-bridge. For maltose (CXI), once again the necessary 1,2-bridge of one of the glucose units is prohibited, and due to the link at the 4-position, the possibility of furanoside formation is prohibited in the second glucose unit.[15] Similar arguments hold for α-lactose (CXII) and raffinose (CXIV). The arguments break down, however, for melibiose (CXIII) which has a glucose unit with free 1,2-hydroxyls capable of forming the necessary α-D-glucofuranose complex with boric acid.

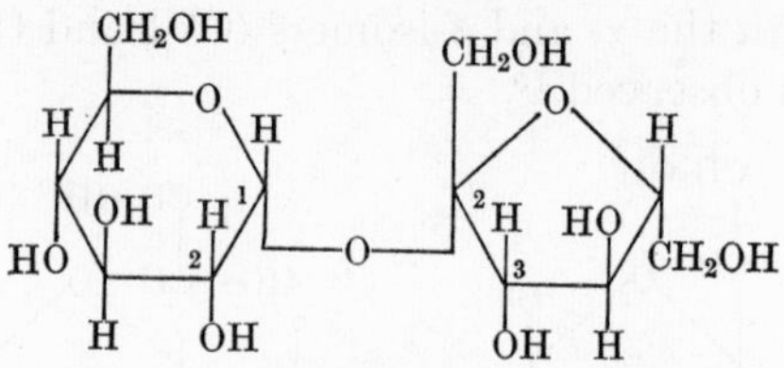

Sucrose

1-α-D-glucopyranosyl-β-D-fructofuranoside

(CX)

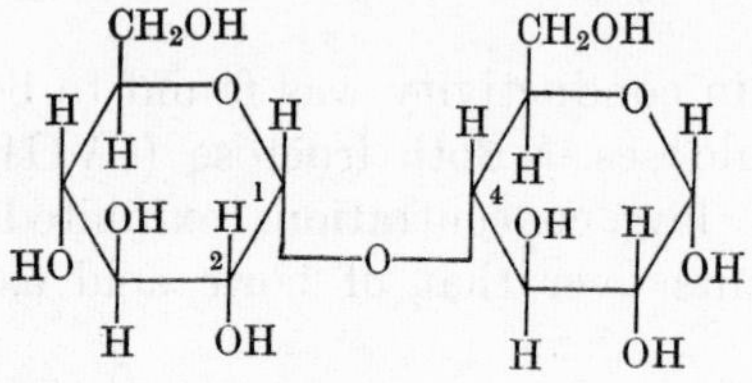

Maltose

4-α-D-glucopyranosyl-α-D-glucopyranoside

(CXI)

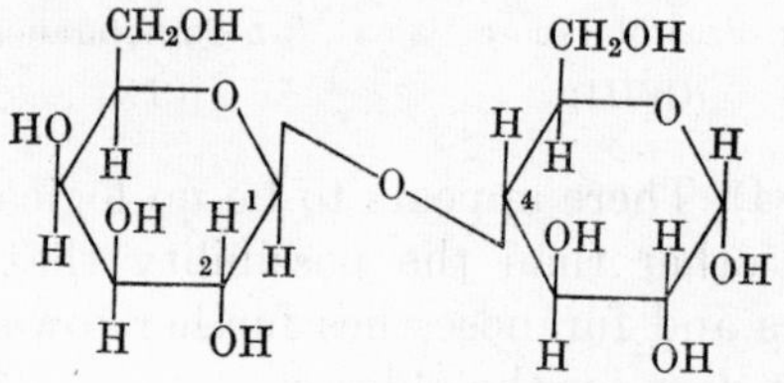

α-Lactose

4-α-D-glucopyranosyl-β-D-galactopyranoside

(CXII)

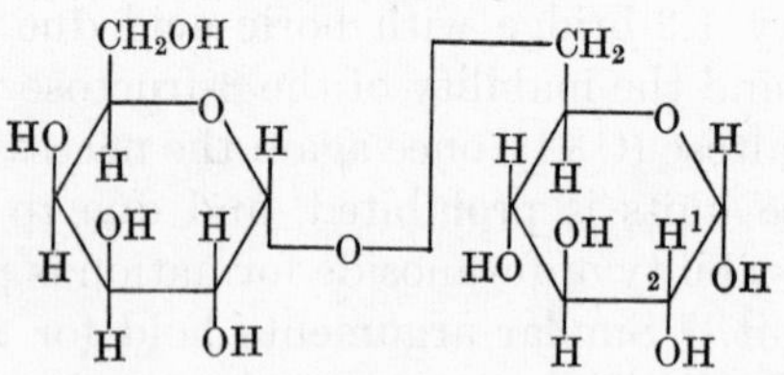

Melibiose

6-α-D-glucopyranosyl-α-D-galactopyranoside

(CXIII)

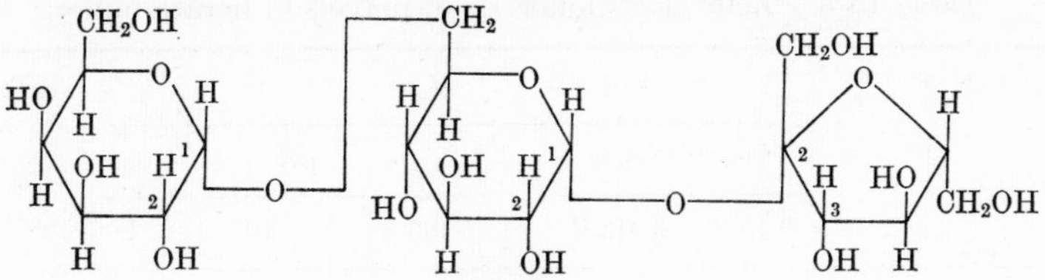

Raffinose

2-β-D-fructofuranosyl-6-α-D-glucopyranosyl-α-D-galactopyranoside

(CXIV)

C. *Ionophoretic Mobility Considerations*

1. INTRODUCTION

In 1942 it was observed that D-glucose and maltose migrated to the anode when subjected to an applied potential in an aqueous borax solution.[53] When the conducting solution and the migrating species are supported on a solid matrix, such as filter paper, the process is known as *zone electrophoresis*.[68] Clearly, the phenomenon of zone electrophoresis of neutral polyols in the presence of a borate is a direct consequence of the anionic species (CXV) and (CXVI) which actually undergo the migration. Thus the facility with which a neutral polyol migrates is a function of its ability to enter into the complexes (CXV) and (CXVI) which, as discussed in detail in the

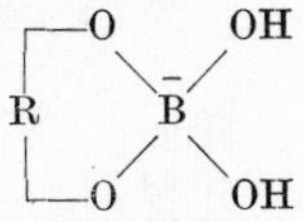

(CXV) 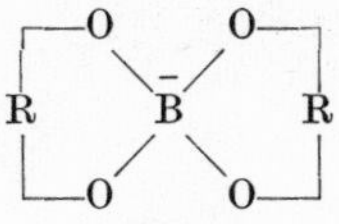 (CXVI)

preceding conductivity section, is a function of the stereochemical relationships within the polyol.*

Table 15-5 records the mobilities of a variety of polyols. The index of the mobility, the M_G value, is defined as the ratio of the true distance of migration of a substance to the true distance of migration of D-glucose.†

* Some care must be exercised in employing this generalization since the concentration of the ions (CXV) and (CXVI) are a function of the pH and thus the electrophoretic mobility increases with pH.[55]

† The true distances of migration are obtained by correcting for movement due to electroendosmotic flow, which in the case of borate solutions is toward the cathode. Electroendosmotic flow is determined by referring to the movement of substances which do not react with borate ions, such as *trans*-1,2-cyclohexanediol.[68]

Table 15-5. Zone electrophoresis of polyols in borate buffer.

Polyol	M_G					Reference
	Concentration		pH			
	0.15M	0.012M	9.2	10	?	
Acyclic polyols						
1,2-Diols						
threo-2,3-Butanediol			0.56			68, 79
erythro-2,3-Butanediol			0.14			68, 79
DL-Glyceraldehyde				0.79		49
1,3-Diols						
1,3-Pentanediol			0.05, 0.19			68, 79
2,4-Pentanediol			0.00, 0.35			68, 79
1,3-Dihydroxyacetone				0.78		49
1,4- and 1,5-Diols						
1,4-Butanediol			0.00			68, 79
1,5-Pentanediol			0.00			68, 79
Triols						
Glycerol				0.44		49
Tetrols						
meso-Erythritol				0.75		49
Pentitols						
D-Arabitol				0.90		49
Hexitols						
D-Sorbitol			0.92	0.89		49, 79
Dulcitol			0.76	0.98		49, 79
D-Mannitol			0.83	0.90		49, 79
Heptitols						
D-Glycero-D-galaheptitol				1.00		49
D-Glycero-D-mannoheptitol				0.92		49
Alicyclic polyols						
Five-membered rings						
1,4-Anhydrodulcitol				0.47		71
Six-membered rings						
cis-1,2-Cyclohexanediol	0.11	0.01				2
trans-1,2-Cyclohexanediol	0.00	0.00			0.00	2, 68
cis-1,3-Cyclohexanediol	0.01	0.00				2

(Table continued)

Table 15-5 (*continued*)

Polyol	M_G					Reference
	Concentration		pH			
	0.15M	0.012M	9.2	10	?	
trans-1,3-Cyclohexanediol	0.00	0.00				2
cis-1,2,3-Cyclohexanetriol	0.07	0.05		0.19		2, 69
trans-1,2,3-Cyclohexanetriol	0.00	0.00				2
cis-1,3,5-Cyclohexanetriol		0.11				2
cis,trans-1,2,3-Cyclohexanetriol	0.20	0.08		0.10		2, 69
1,5-Anhydro-D-xylitol				0.00		72, 73, 77
1,5-Anhydro-L-arabinitol				0.39		72, 73
1,5-Anhydroribitol				0.53		72, 73
1,5-Anhydro-D-glucitol				0.20		73, 77
1,5-Anhydro-D-galactitol				0.38		72, 73
1,5-Anhydro-D-mannitol				0.40		72, 73
1,5-Anhydro-L-rhamnitol				0.31		72, 73
1,5-Anhydro-2-deoxy-D-glucitol				0.20		77
(+)-Inositol	0.83	0.28		0.63	0.69	2, 69, 75
(−)-Inositol				0.63	0.69	69, 75
Ononitol (4-methyl-*myo*inositol)	0.60	0.45				2
meso-Inositol (CXXI)	0.60	0.30		0.51	0.53	2, 69, 75
(+)-Bornesitol (1-methyl-*myo*-inositol) (CXIX)	0.15	0.02		0.12		2, 75
Quebrachitol (2-methyl-(−)-inositol) (CXXII)	0.29	0.14		0.31		2, 75
Pinitol (3-methyl-*myo*inositol)	0.73	0.23		0.66		2, 75
Sequoyitol A (CXXIII)	0.24	0.05		0.18		2, 69
2-Methyl*myo*inositol (CXXIV)	0.62	0.29				2
epi-Inositol	0.74	1.50		0.73		2, 69
neo-Inositol (CXXVII)	0.77	0.30				2
allo-Inositol (CXXVIII)	0.96	0.54		0.88		2, 69
cis-Inositol	0.73	1.60				2
muco-Inositol	0.97	0.87		0.96		2, 69
1-Methyl-(−)-inositol	0.32					2
scyllo-Inositol		0.02		0.05		2, 69
Dambonitol (1,3-Dimethyl*myo*inositol)	0.00	0.00				2

(*Table continued*)

Table 15-5 (*continued*)

Polyol	M_G					Reference
	Concentration		pH			
	0.15*M*	0.012*M*	9.2	10	?	
scyllo-Quercitol (CXXIX)	0.23	0.05				2
proto-Quercitol	0.31	0.05				2
vibo-Quercitol	0.31	0.07				2
epi-Quercitol (CXXVI)	0.78	1.17				2
cis-Quercitol	0.80	1.60				2
Sugars						
Monosaccharides						
L-Arabinose				0.96		49
D-Ribose				0.77		49
D-Xylose				1.00		49
2-Deoxy-D-ribose				0.33		49, 76
L-Fucose				0.89		49
L-Rhamnose				0.52		49
D-Galactose				0.93		49
D-Glucose				1.00		49
D-Mannose				0.72		49
N-Acetyl-D-glucosamine				0.23		76
2-Deoxy-D-galactose				0.37		76
D-galacturonic acid-1-phosphate				1.63		76
D-glucoronic acid-1-phosphate				1.4		76
D-Galactose-1-phosphate				1.16		76
2-Deoxy-D-glucose				0.29, 0.24		74, 76
D-Galacturonic acid				1.17		76
D-Fructose				0.90		49
N-Acetyl-D-chondrosamine				0.35		76
L-Sorbose				0.95		49
L-Galaheptulose				0.89		49
3-Deoxy-D-mannose				0.76		74
D-Mannoheptulose				0.87		49
D-Glucose-1-phosphate				1.10		49
D-Glucuronic acid				1.20		49
1,2-*O*-Isopropylidene-α-D-glucofuranose				0.73		71
1,6-Anhydro-β-D-glucopyranose				0.00		77
Disaccharides						
β-D-Sophorose				0.33, 0.24		49, 77
β-D-Cellobiose				0.29, 0.23		49, 77
α-D-Nigerose				0.69		49, 68

(*Table continued*)

Table 15-5 (*continued*)

Polyol	M_G					Reference
	Concentration		pH			
	0.15M	0.012M	9.2	10	?	
α-D-Maltose				0.34, 0.32		49, 70
β-D-Gentiobiose				0.72, 0.75		49, 70
β-D-Lactose				0.38		70
Melibiose				0.80		70
α-D-Isomaltose				0.69		70
β-D-Laminaribiose				0.69		70
Sucrose				0.18		49
				0.17		77
α,α-Trehalose				0.19		49, 77
α,β-Trehalose				0.23		73, 77
β,β-Trehalose				0.19		73, 77
Trisaccharides						
Raffinose				0.28		49
Melezitose				0.22		49
Methylated monosaccharides						
Methyl α-D-arabofuranoside				0.035		71
Methyl β-D-arabofuranoside				0.035		71
Methyl α-D-arabinopyranoside				0.38		72
Methyl β-D-arabinopyranoside				0.38		72
Methyl α-D-xylofuranoside				0.30		77
				0.56		71
Methyl β-D-xylofuranoside				0.30		77
				0.33		71
Methyl α-D-xylopyranoside				0.00		72, 73, 77
Methyl β-D-xylopyranoside				0.00		72, 73, 77
Methyl α-D-lyxopyranoside (CXXXIV)				0.45		72, 73
Methyl β-D-lyxopyranoside (CXXX)				0.27		72, 73
Methyl β-D-ribopyranoside				0.53		72, 73
Methy l-2-deoxy-α,β-D-ribopyranoside				0.34		72
Methyl α-D-glucopyranoside				<0.09		70
				0.11		77

(*Table continued*)

Table 15-5 (*continued*)

Polyol	M_G					Reference
	Concentration		pH			
	0.15M	0.012M	9.2	10	?	
Methyl 2-deoxy-α-D-glucopyranoside				0.12		77
Methyl β-D-glucopyranoside				0.19		73, 77
Methyl α-D-glucofuranoside				0.73		71, 77
Methyl 4-*O*-Methyl-β-D-glucopyranoside				0.00		73, 77
2-*O*-Methyl-D-glucose				0.23		70, 76
3-*O*-Methyl-D-glucose				0.82		70, 76
4-*O*-Methyl-D-glucose				0.24		70
6-*O*-Methyl-D-glucose				0.82		70, 76
2,3-Di-*O*-methyl-D-glucose				0.12		70
2,4-Di-*O*-methyl-D-glucose				<0.05		70, 76
3,4-Di-*O*-methyl-D-glucose				0.31		70, 76
2,3,4-Tri-*O*-methyl-D-glucose				0.00		70, 76
2,3,6-Tri-*O*-methyl-D-glucose				0.00		70
3,5,6-Tri-*O*-methyl-D-glucose				0.71		70, 76
2,3,4,6-Tetra-*O*-methyl-D-glucose				0.00		68, 76
Methyl α-D-galactofuranoside				0.41		71
Methyl β-D-galactofuranoside				0.31		71
Methyl α-D-galactopyranoside				0.38		72, 73
Methyl β-D-galactopyranoside				0.38		72, 73
Methyl α-L-rhamnopyranoside (CXXXVII)				0.31		72, 73
Methyl β-L-rhamnopyranoside (CXXXIII)				0.14		72, 73
2,3-Di-*O*-methyl-L-rhamnose				<0.05		70, 76
2,4-Di-*O*-methyl-L-rhamnose				<0.05		70, 76
3,4-Di-*O*-methyl L-rhamnose				0.36		70, 76
Methyl α-D-mannopyranoside (CXXXV)				0.42		71, 72

(*Table continued*)

Table 15-5 (*continued*)

Polyol	M_G					Reference
	Concentration		pH			
	0.15*M*	0.012*M*	9.2	10	?	
Methyl β-D-mannopyranoside (CXXXI)				0.31		72, 73
Methyl α-D-fructofuranoside				0.60		71
Methyl β-D-fructofuranoside				0.04		71
Methyl α-D-fructopyranoside				0.71		71
Methyl β-D-fructopyranoside				0.59		71
Methyl α-D-gulopyranoside (CXXXII)				0.59		72, 73
Methyl β-D-gulopyranoside (CXXXVI)				0.72		71, 72
2-*O*-Methyl-D-galactose				0.32		76
4-*O*-Methyl-D-galactose				0.27		70
Ethylated monosaccharides						
Ethyl α-D-glucopyranoside				0.17		77
Ethyl α-D-glucofuranoside				0.70		77
Ethyl β-D-glucofuranoside				0.65		77
Ethyl 2-deoxy-α-D-glucopyranoside				0.17		77
Ethyl 2,3-dideoxy-α-D-glucopyranoside				0.10		77

2. ACYLIC POLYOLS

It is seen in Table 15-5, as in the case of the conductivity data, that 1,4-diols and 1,5-diols are without effect in aqueous borax solutions. However, in contrast to the conductivity data, simple 1,2- and 1,3-glycols do migrate.[68,79] Thus the sensitivity of zone electrophoresis to subtleties in the stereochemistry of the polyols appears to lie between that of conductivity measurements, which are highly sensitive, and non-aqueous synthetic techniques, which are the least sensitive to considerations of the disposition of hydroxyl groups.

The enhanced migration of *threo*-2,3-butanediol as compared to the *erythro* isomer is consistent with the more favorable conformation

(CXVII) as compared to the eclipsed methyl groups in conformation (CXVIII).[68]

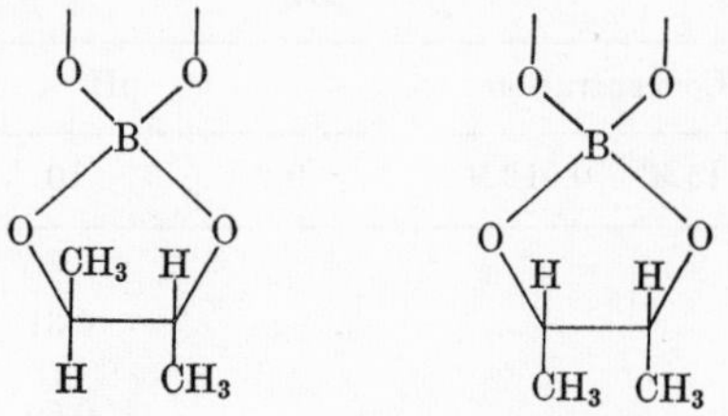

threo

(CXVII)

erythro

(CXVIII)

As in the case of conductivity data, the triols and higher polyols are effective complexing agents.[49,79]

3. ALICYCLIC POLYOLS

In contrast to the conductivity data, *cis*-1,2-cyclohexanediols are active. This loss of sensitivity to non-planarity of the hydroxyl groups does not apply to the *trans* isomer, however, and *trans*-1,2-cyclohexanediol is inactive. In contrast to some acyclic 1,3-diols[79] which do migrate in borate buffer, *cis*-1,3-cyclohexanediols do not.[2]

(+)-Bornesitol is a naturally occurring monomethyl ether of *meso*-inositol (CXXI). Since it is optically active, it is either (CXIX) or (CXX). Its structure was deduced by comparison of its rate of migration to those of (CXXII) and *meso*-inositol itself which possess, respectively, two and three vicinal *cis*-hydroxyl groups as are present in (CXIX and CXX). The M_G value of (+)-bornesitol was found to be closer to that of (CXXII) than (CXXI) and thus (+)-bornesitol was assigned the structure (CXIX).[75]

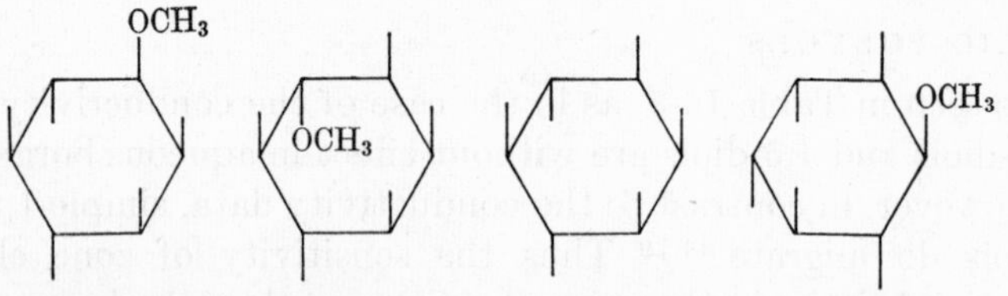

(CXIX) (CXX) (CXXI) (CXXII)

The lower M_G value in (CXIX) as compared to (CXXII) was believed to be due to the greater steric requirements in (CXIX) caused by the *cis*-methoxy group adjacent to the *cis*-hydroxyl groups. The inhibiting effect of a vicinal *cis*-methoxyl to vicinal *cis*-hydroxyl groups has been further demonstrated in a series of methyl pyranosides[72] discussed in Section VII-C-4.

Sequoyitol A, an optically inactive monomethyl ether of *meso*-inositol, exhibited an M_G value of 0.18 and was assigned the structure (CXXIII) and not (CXXIV) since (CXXIV) has no vicinal *cis*-

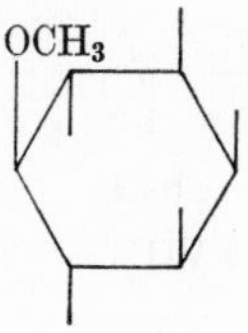

OCH_3 OCH_3

(CXXIII) 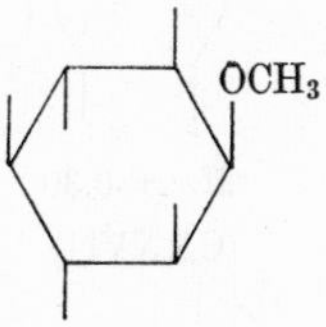 (CXXIV)

hydroxyl groups and could not be expected to migrate.[69] This conclusion, however, may be invalid since it subsequently was shown that cyclitols with *cis* oriented 1,3,5-hydroxyl groups, and specifically 2-O-methyl*myo*inositol (CXXIV), migrate in a borate buffer due to the formation of a "tridentate complex" (CXXV).*[2] Indeed, *epi*-

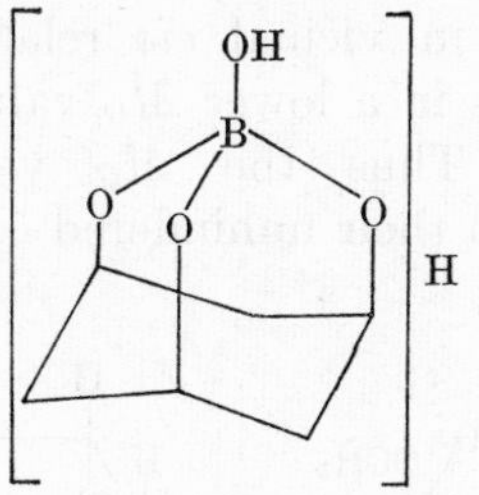

OH B O O O H

(CXXV)

quercitol (CXXVI) has a much higher mobility in a dilute buffer than *neo*- or *allo*inositol (CXXVII) and (CXXVIII), and both

* The ionophoretic migration of pentaerythritol[79] and the methyl and ethyl glucofuranosides[77] are believed to be due to tridentate complex formation.[2,65,77]

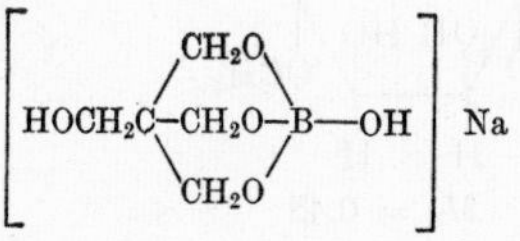

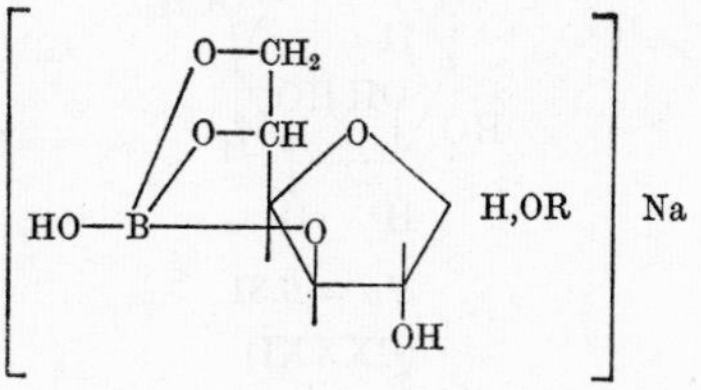

[$HOCH_2C(CH_2O)_3B$—OH] Na

[HO—B(O—CH_2)(O—CH)(O) ... H,OR, OH] Na

*scyllo*quercitol (CXXIX) and 2-*O*-methyl*myo*inositol (CXXIV) migrate ($M_G = 0.29$) although each pair of adjacent hydroxyl groups are *trans* oriented.

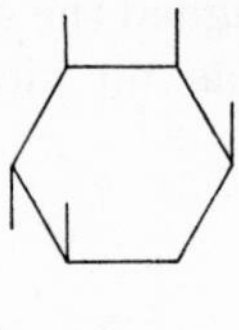

$M_G = 1.17$ (CXXVI) $M_G = 0.30$ (CXXVII) $M_G = 0.54$ (CXXVIII) $M_G = 0.05$ (CXXIX)

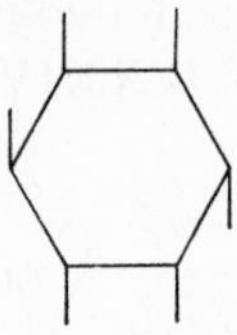

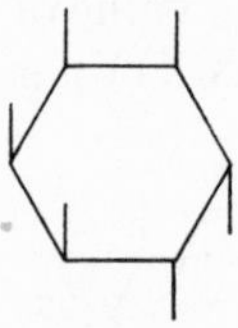

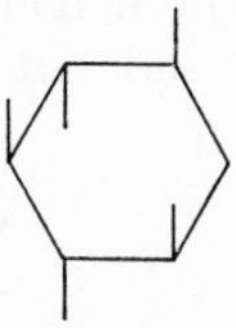

4. SUGARS

Essentially all mono-, di-, and trisaccharides migrate in a borate buffer (Table 15-5), presumably due to the presence of aldehydo forms.[68,76] As a result stereochemical implications cannot be drawn.

A study of methylated glucose derivatives revealed that the hydroxyl groups in the 1,2- and 4,6-positions play a dominant role.[70,76] The *cis*-1,2-hydroxyls would be active in the furanose and pyranose forms and the 4,6-hydroxyls in the aldehydo form.

A methoxy group in vicinal *cis* relationship to vicinal *cis*-hydroxyl groups reflects in a lower M_G value due to the increased steric requirements.[72] Thus the M_G values of (CXXX) to (CXXXIII) are less than their unhindered counterparts (CXXXIV–CXXXVII).

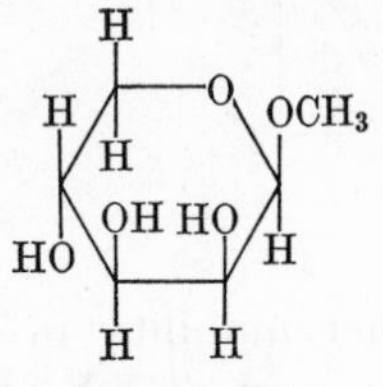

$M_G = 0.27$ (CXXX) $M_G = 0.45$ (CXXXIV)

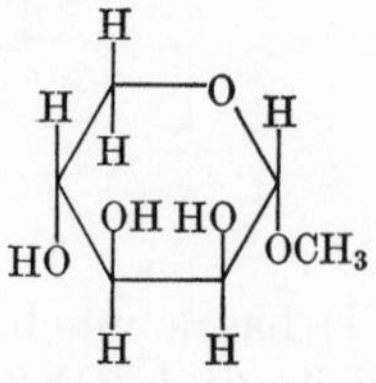

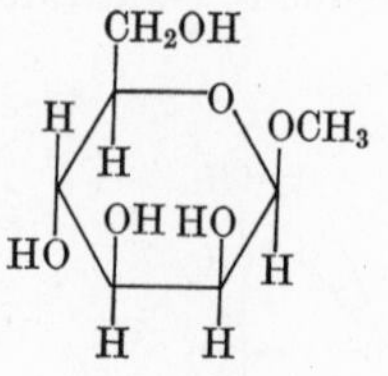

$M_G = 0.31$ (CXXXI) $M_G = 0.42$ (CXXXV)

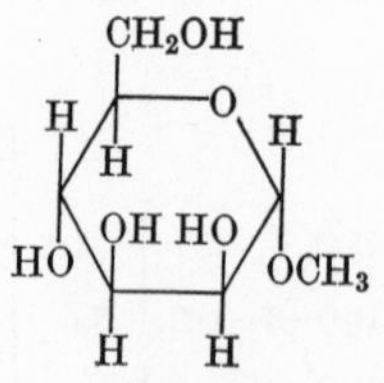

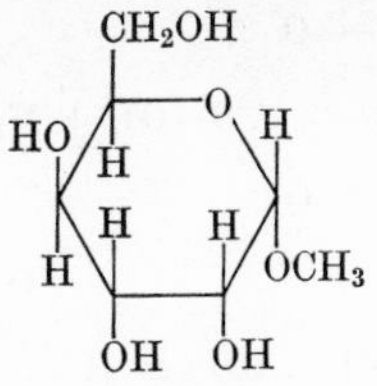

$M_G = 0.59$
(CXXXII)

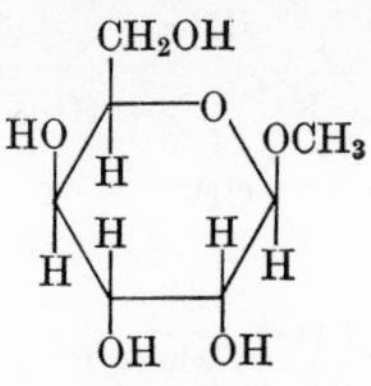

$M_G = 0.72$
(CXXXVI)

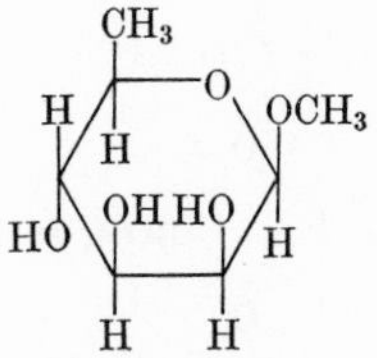

$M_B = 0.14$
(CXXXIII)

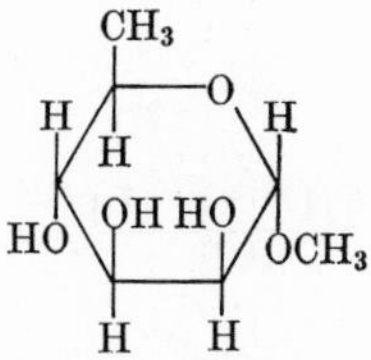

$M_G = 0.31$
(CXXXVII)

D. *Optical Rotation Considerations*

In a tetracoordinate complex of an alkali borate and a sugar or sugar alcohol, the asymmetric carbon atoms in the original carbohydrate are placed in a new molecular environment. This new environment may lead to changes in the magnitude of rotation, and indeed the effects of borates on the optical rotation of glucose,[16,88,118,120,126,153] fructose,[13,14,59,88,126,135] sucrose,[88,119] mannitol,[118,162] and a variety of other sugars[88] have been recorded.

Figure 15-3 represents a hypothetical equilibrium diagram for a tetraborate–diol system based on the equilibria 15-37 to 15-40 and the resulting mass action expressions 15-41 to 15-43.[89]

$$H_3BO_3 + H_2O \underset{}{\overset{K_1}{\rightleftharpoons}} B(OH)_4^- + H^+ \qquad (15\text{-}37)$$

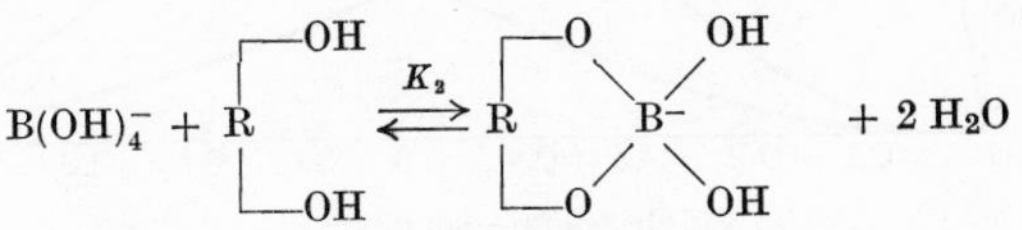

$$B(OH)_4^- + R\begin{matrix}-OH\\-OH\end{matrix} \overset{K_2}{\rightleftharpoons} R\begin{matrix}-O\\-O\end{matrix}\!\!>B^-\!\!<\!\begin{matrix}OH\\OH\end{matrix} + 2\,H_2O \qquad (15\text{-}38)$$

$$R\begin{matrix}-O\\-O\end{matrix}\!\!>B^-\!\!<\!\begin{matrix}OH\\OH\end{matrix} + R\begin{matrix}-OH\\-OH\end{matrix} \overset{K_3}{\rightleftharpoons} R\begin{matrix}-O\\-O\end{matrix}\!\!>B<\!\!\begin{matrix}O-\\O-\end{matrix}R^- + 2\,H_2O \qquad (15\text{-}39)$$

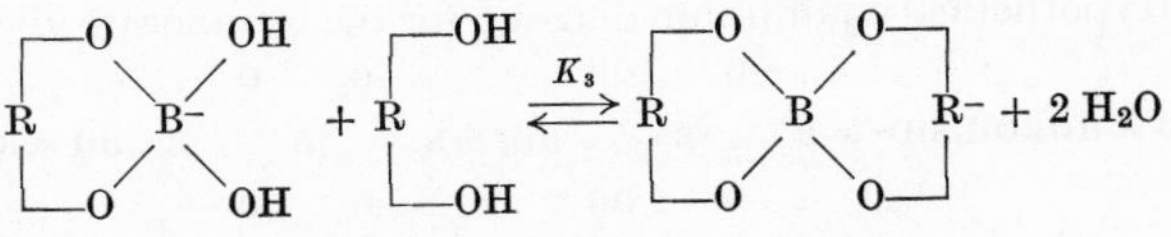

$$\mathrm{R}\begin{matrix}\text{—O} & & \text{OH}\\ & \mathrm{B^-} & \\ \text{—O} & & \text{OH}\end{matrix} + \mathrm{H^+} \overset{K_4}{\rightleftarrows} \mathrm{R}\begin{matrix}\text{—O} & \\ & \text{B—OH}\\ \text{—O} & \end{matrix} + \mathrm{H_2O} \tag{15-40}$$

$$[\mathrm{BD_2^-}] = \frac{K_3[\mathrm{BD^-}]^2}{K_2[\mathrm{B^-}]},\ \text{where } \mathrm{B^-} \equiv \mathrm{B(OH)_4^-},\ \mathrm{BD^-} \equiv \mathrm{R}\begin{matrix}\text{—O} & & \text{OH}\\ & \mathrm{B^-} & \\ \text{—O} & & \text{OH}\end{matrix}, \tag{15-41}$$

$$\mathrm{BD_2^-} \equiv \mathrm{R}\begin{matrix}\text{—O} & & \text{O—}\\ & \mathrm{B} & \\ \text{—O} & & \text{O—}\end{matrix}\mathrm{R^-}$$

$$[\mathrm{BD}] = \frac{K_2K_4[\mathrm{H^+}][\mathrm{B^-}][\mathrm{D}]}{[\mathrm{H_2O}]^3},\ \text{where BD} \equiv \mathrm{R}\begin{matrix}\text{—O} & \\ & \text{BOH}\\ \text{—O} & \end{matrix},\ \mathrm{D} \equiv \mathrm{R}\begin{matrix}\text{—OH}\\ \\ \text{—OH}\end{matrix} \tag{15-42}$$

$$[\mathrm{BD^-}] = \frac{K_4[\mathrm{BD}][\mathrm{H_2O}]}{[\mathrm{H^+}]} \tag{15-43}$$

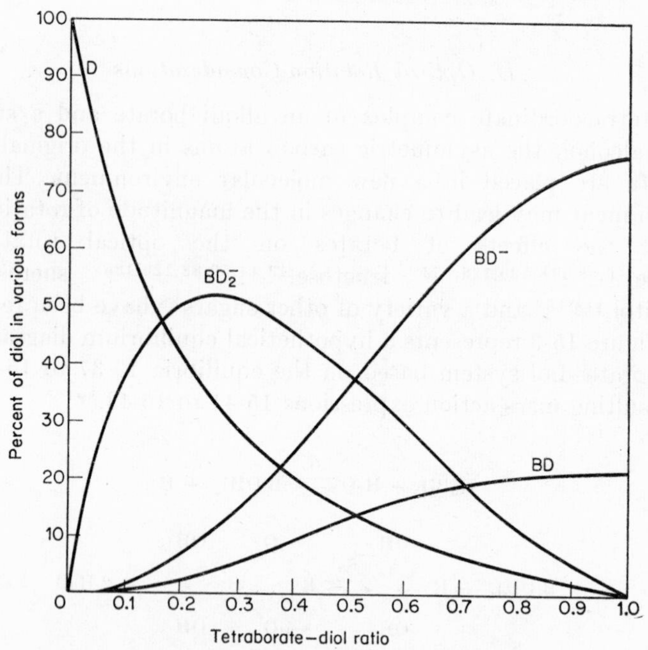

Fig. 15-3. Hypothetical equilibrium diagram for the tetraborate–diol system. $\mathrm{B^-} \equiv \mathrm{B(OH)_4^-}$, $\mathrm{D} \equiv \mathrm{HOROH}$, $\mathrm{BD^-} \equiv \mathrm{R}\begin{matrix}\text{—O} & & \text{OH}\\ & \mathrm{B^-} & \\ \text{—O} & & \text{OH}\end{matrix}$, $\mathrm{BD_2^-} \equiv \mathrm{R}\begin{matrix}\text{—O} & & \text{O—}\\ & \mathrm{B} & \\ \text{—O} & & \text{O—}\end{matrix}\mathrm{R^-}$, $\mathrm{BD} \equiv \mathrm{R}\begin{matrix}\text{—O} & \\ & \text{BOH}\\ \text{—O} & \end{matrix}$.

D-Glucose, D-fructose, L-sorbose and sorbitol, all of which possess vicinal *cis*-hydroxyl groups, were shown to form all three compounds of the type BD, BD^- and BD_2^-. Sucrose, which does not possess adjacent *cis*-hydroxyl groups, was believed to form a single complex of type BD, possibly involving the 4,6-hydroxyls of the pyranose ring (CXXXVIII). Presumably the corresponding complex involving the 4,6-hydroxyls of the furanose ring (CXXXIX) would be more difficult to form due to the relative planarity of the five-

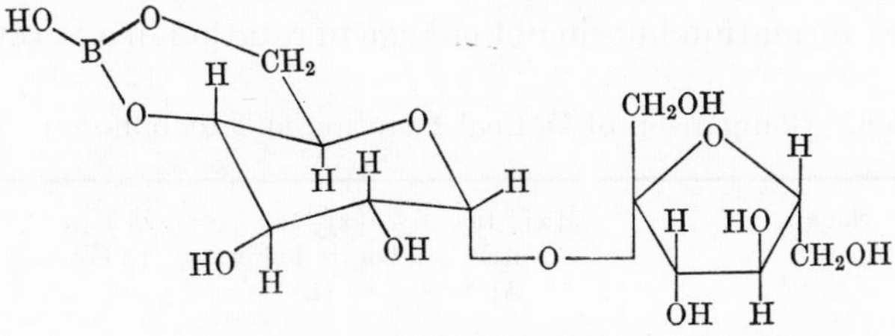

(CXXXVIII)

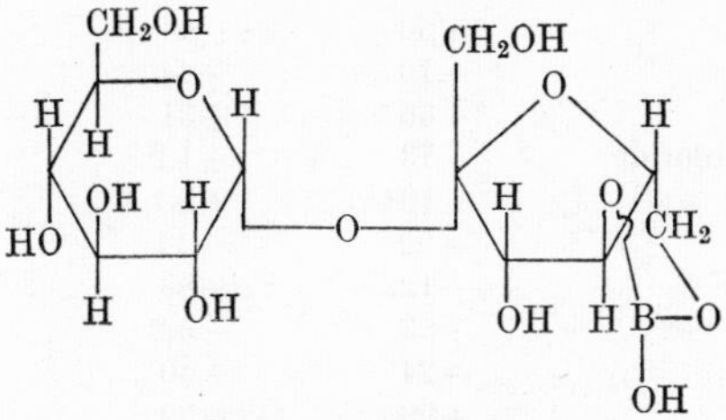

(CXXXIX)

membered ring. This conclusion is consistent with the fact that sucrose does not enhance the conductivity of a boric acid solution since it can only form an uncharged complex with boric acid.

Mannitol was believed to form the BD^- type compound (CXL) and the polymeric BD_2^- type compound (CXLI).[89]

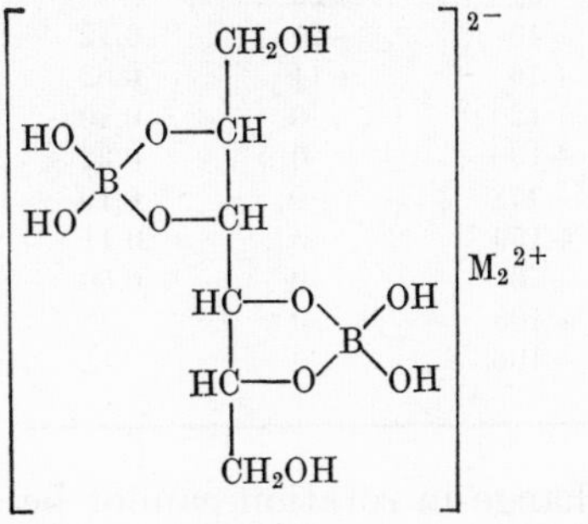

(CXL)

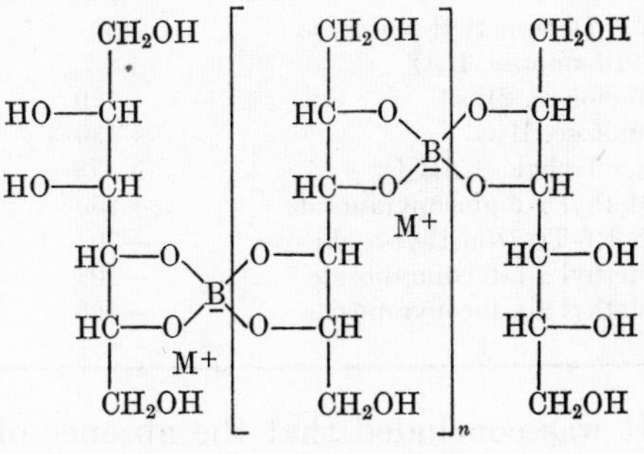

(CXLI)

The validity of the preceding stereochemical conclusions based on change in rotation has been challenged.[88] It was shown (Table 15-6) that there is no direct correlation between migration of a sugar during ionophoresis (M_G) in borate buffer at pH 10.0 and the change in molecular rotation ($\Delta[M]_D$). Substances with equal M_G values (isomaltose and laminaribiose) exhibit different $\Delta[M]_D$ values. Melibiose shows no change in $[M]_D$ and yet it has an M_G value of 0.80 and undoubtedly undergoes complex formation. Similarly, maltose and methyl α-glucoside exhibit finite M_G values indicative of complex formation but do not change in rotation in a borate buffer.

Table 15-6. Comparison of Optical Rotation and Ionophoretic Mobility

Sugar	$[\alpha]_D^{20}$ in water (A)	$[\alpha]_D^{20}$ in borate buffer (B)	$\Delta[M]_D$ (A–B)	M_G value
L-Fucose	−76	+60	−223	0.82
D-Galactose	+80	−44	+223	0.93
Laminaribiose	+19	−44	+215	0.69
3-*O*-Methyl-D-glucose	+56	−31	+169	0.80
D-Glucosamine hydrochloride	+73	+1.9	+153	—
L-Arabinose	+104	+3.1	+151	0.96
D-Fructose	−92	−14	+140	0.90
Isomaltose	+122	+88	+116	0.69
D-Glucose	+53	−5.2	+104	1.00
D-Ribose	−24	+40	+96	0.77
2-Deoxy-D-glucose	+90	+39	+84	0.29
N-Acetyl-D-glucosamine	+41	+5.0	+81	0.23
Sucrose	+67	+51	+55	0.17
Raffinose, $5H_2O$	+105	+98	+42	—
D-Glucoheptose	−20	−2.5	+37	—
Cellobiose	+35	+25	+34	0.23
2-*O*-Methyl-D-glucose	+65	+48	+33	0.23
D-Glucitol	−2.0	+15	−31	—
D-Mannose	+14	−2.5	+30	0.72
Leucrose	−7.5	0	−26	—
2:3-Di-*O*-methyl-D-glucose	+50	+40	+21	0.12
L-Rhamnose, H_2O	+8.2	+16	+14	0.52
Melibiose, $2H_2O$	+129	+129	0	0.80
Maltose, H_2O	+130	+130	0	0.32
α,α-Trehalose, $2H_2O$	+178	+178	0	0.19
Methyl α-D-glucopyranoside	+159	+159	0	0.11
2:3:6-Tri-*O*-methyl-D-glucose	+70	+70	0	0.00
Methyl α-L-fucofuranoside	−108	−108	0	—
Methyl α-L-fucopyranoside	−196	−196	0	—

It was concluded that the absence of change in rotation cannot be construed as meaning an absence of complex formation.

E. Acidity Considerations

1. INTRODUCTION

Polyols which are capable of entering into equilibria 15-44 and 15-45 convert the weak acid, boric acid (pK = 9.19), to the relatively

$$H_3BO_3 + R\begin{matrix}-OH\\ \\ -OH\end{matrix} \rightleftarrows \left[R\begin{matrix}-O\\ \\ -O\end{matrix}\overset{-}{B}\begin{matrix}OH\\ \\ OH\end{matrix} \right] H^+ + H_2O,\ K_1 \qquad (15\text{-}44)$$

(CXLII)

$$R\begin{matrix}-O\\ \\ -O\end{matrix}B{-}OH + R\begin{matrix}-OH\\ \\ -OH\end{matrix} \rightleftarrows \left[R\begin{matrix}-O\\ \\ -O\end{matrix}\overset{-}{B}\begin{matrix}O-\\ \\ O-\end{matrix}R \right] H^+ + H_2O,\ K_2 \qquad (15\text{-}45)$$

(CXLIII)

strong acids, (CXLII and CXLIII). The pH of a polyol–boric acid or polyol–borate solution is thus a measure of the ability of the polyol to form the necessary dioxaborolane and borinane rings. Table 15-7 records the equilibrium constants for the equilibria 15-44

Table 15-7. Equilibrium constants for the reactions of polyols and boric acid at 25°. (Values reported for the reaction with borate anion have been converted by multiplying by 6.4×10^{-10}, the acid constant for boric acid.)

Polyol	K_1	K_2	Reference
Acyclic			
Ethylene glycol	1.18×10^{-9}	6.4×10^{-11}	132
	8.31×10^{-10}		134[a]
Propylene glycol	1.98×10^{-9}	1.02×10^{-9}	132
	1.36×10^{-9}		134[a]
2,3-Butanediol (mixture of *meso* and *dl*)	2.21×10^{-9}	3.10×10^{-9}	132
meso-2,3-Butanediol	7.55×10^{-10}		134[a]
Phenylethylene glycol	4.77×10^{-9}	4.58×10^{-9}	132
3-Methoxy-1,2-propanediol	1.20×10^{-8}	8.56×15^{-9}	132
Glycerol	1.02×10^{-8}	2.64×10^{-8}	132
	2.89×10^{-8}	6.46×10^{-8}	5, 6
	8 to 10×10^{-8}	2.5×10^{-7}	17[a]
	9.46×10^{-9}		134[a]
Erythritol		$>10^{-7}$	135[b]
Pentaerythritol	1.54×10^{-7}	7.10×10^{-7}	132
Sorbitol	3.7×10^{-6}	2.11×10^{-4}	47[b], 17[b]

(*Table continued*)

Table 15-7 (*continued*)

Polyol	K_1	K_2	Reference
Mannitol	1.92×10^{-7}	3.3×10^{-5}	60[c]
		5.0×10^{-5}	4
	6.4×10^{-6}	5.3×10^{-5}	3
	8.04×10^{-6}	6.6×10^{-5}	6
		7.0×10^{-5}	135[b]
	3.58×10^{-7}	7.4×10^{-5}	149
		1.00×10^{-4}	131
	2.5×10^{-6}	1.10×10^{-4}	47[b], 17[b]
		1.70×10^{-4}	46[a]
		1.76×10^{-3}	155
Polyvinyl Alcohol	1.15×10^{-9}	2.75×10^{-9}	132
Alicyclic			
α-Mannitan	$4–5 \times 10^{-6}$	1.6×10^{-3}	17[a]
		2.0×10^{-3}	46[a]
cis-1,3,5-Cyclohexanetriol (phloroglucitol)		2.05×10^{-8}	3[d]
scyllo-Quercitol 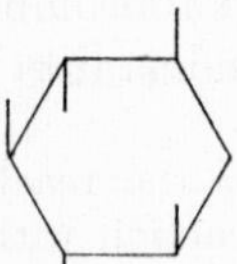		3.2×10^{-9}	1[d], 2[d]
myo-Inositol 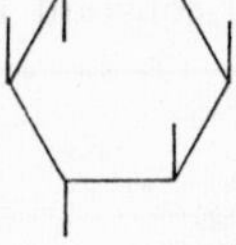		1.60×10^{-8}	1[d], 2[d]
epi-Quercitol 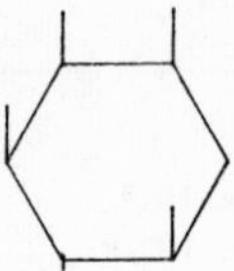		1.984×10^{-7}	1[d], 2[d]
cis-Quercitol 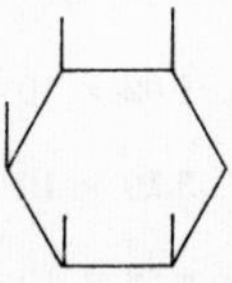		5.06×10^{-6}	1[d], 2[d]
epi-Inositol 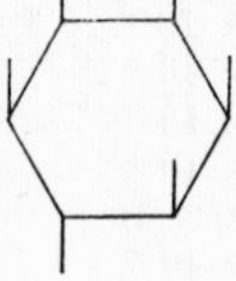		4.48×10^{-6}	1[d], 2[d]
cis-Inositol 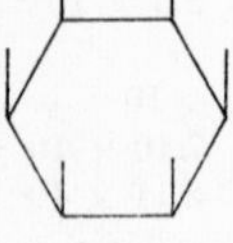		7.04×10^{-4}	1[d], 2[d]

(*Table continued*)

Table 15-7 (*continued*)

Polyol	K_1	K_2	Reference
Polyphenols			
Catechol		2.32×10^{-4}	155
	5.0×10^{-6}	9.10×10^{-5}	132
	ca. 1×10^{-4}		91
Pyrogallol		$>10^{-7}$	135[b]
Catechol-3,5-disulphonic acid	1×10^{-4}		121
Gallic acid	ca. 1×10^{-3}		91
Sugars			
D-Galactose	8.12×10^{-8}	1.91×10^{-7}	132
	1.64×10^{-7}	1.94×10^{-7}	6
		9.02×10^{-7}	155
D-Mannose	3.20×10^{-8}	3.14×10^{-7}	132
		2.63×10^{-5}	6
L-Arabinose	8.31×10^{-8}	4.32×10^{-7}	132
		9.27×10^{-6}	155
D-glucose	5.11×10^{-8}	4.93×10^{-7}	132
	2.36×10^{-7}	5.74×10^{-7}	6
Xylose		1.01×10^{-5}	155
Fructose	4.4×10^{-7}	5.3×10^{-5}	149
		6.07×10^{-5}	132
	3.75×10^{-6}	8.67×10^{-5}	6
	2.2×10^{-6}	9.0×10^{-5}	17[a], 47[a]
		1.1×10^{-4}	46[a]
		6.5×10^{-4}	135[b]
		1.76×10^{-3}	155

[a] Temperature not recorded
[b] 18°
[c] 23–25°
[d] 22°

and 15-45. It has been shown that the monodiol complex plays a noticeable part in volumetric analysis in dilute solution only and that the bisdiol complex predominates in most cases and is the only significant species in volumetric analysis of polyol-activated boric acid.[135]

2. ACYCLIC POLYOLS

In contrast to workers[93,97,120] who found that the simple glycols, ethylene glycol and propylene glycol, did not appreciably enhance the acidity of boric acid, it was shown[127] that both of these diols when present in large excess (mole ratio diol/boric acid of 60) permitted the titrimetric determination of boric acid to within one percent of the value obtained with the well established "activator," mannitol. Trimethylene glycol also was essentially without effect at the lower concentration (mole ratio to boric acid of 6.5). However, both dihydroxyacetone and glyceraldehyde were stronger activators than glycerol and essentially equivalent to mannitol.[97] Possibly the dioxaborole rings (CXLIV) derived from the enol form of the activator or the borolane ring with an exocyclic double bond (CXLV) or the six-membered unsaturated ring (CXLVI) have some inherent stability not present in the corresponding saturated rings.

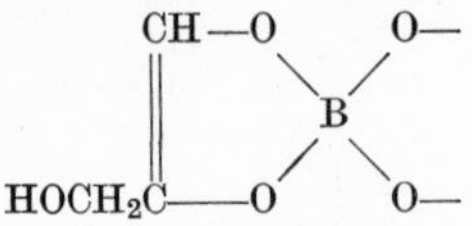

(CXLIV) 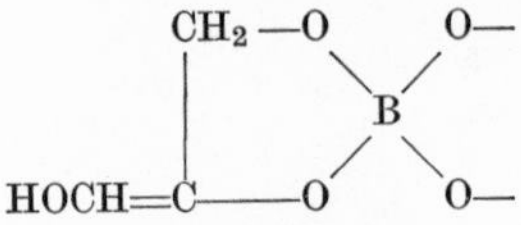 (CXLV) 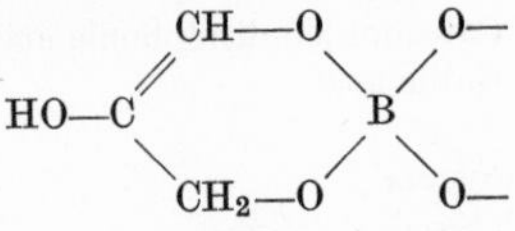 (CXLVI)

A rationale of the relative acidities of the complexes derived from 1,2- and 1,3-diols has been made.[58] It was stated that complexes from 1,2-diols (CXLVII) are more stable than those from comparable 1,3-diols (CXLVIII). This would be in contrast to the trend of stabilities in the hydroxy derivatives (CXLIX). Thus, secondary 1,2-diol esters such as (CXLVII) deposit boric acid in water; whereas secondary 1,3-diol esters such as (CXLVIII) can be formed by

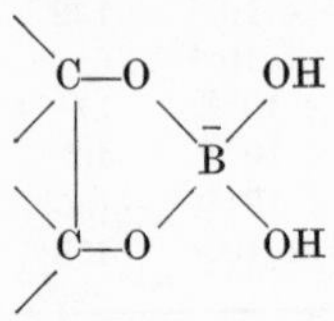

(CXLVII) 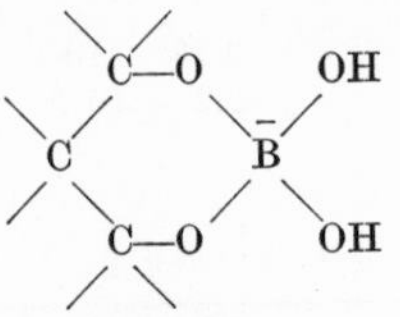 (CXLVIII) 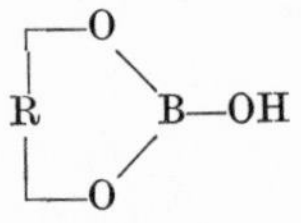 (CXLIX)

directly mixing the diol and boric acid in water solution (Chapter 7). However, if the structural requirements of the planar boric acid (or ester) system are considered, it is seen that to form a five-membered ring the angles, especially the BOC angles, have to be drastically reduced from the 120° required for maximal mesomeric interaction. When the tetrahedral anion is being formed, there is less mesomeric energy to lose and the strain can be completely removed. Thus, the possibility of forming a ring structure with tetrahedral boron which cannot easily be formed with trigonal boron is the driving force in the acidity increase of boric acid in the presence of 1,2-diols. In a six-membered ring both configurations of boron can be accommodated without strain; hence, there is no such strong driving force towards formation of the anion in the presence of 1,3-diols and the acidity of boric acid is not increased to a measurable extent.

Glycerol has long been a well-known and effective complexing agent for the determination of boric acid.[115,148,151] It is not, however, as effective as mannitol.[81,96] The tetrols, meso-erythritol and pentaerythritol, and the pentitol, i-adonitol, were approximately as effective as mannitol.[97]

Hexitols such as mannitol, dulcitol and sorbitol allow quantitative titrimetric determination of boric acid both potentiometrically and with indicators.[12,98,115,151] Mannitol, however, on the basis of availability, cost, and ease of handling, remains the most widely used reagent for this purpose.[96]

3. ALICYCLIC POLYOLS

The inability of *epi*-inositol (CL) to enhance the activity of boric acid[97] is consistent with the absence of a set of planar vicinal hydroxyl groups but is inconsistent with the ability of the cyclitol to form a tridentate complex (CLI).[1,2]

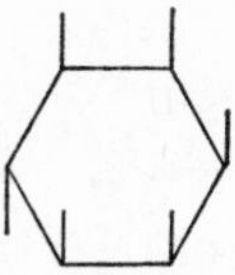

(CL) 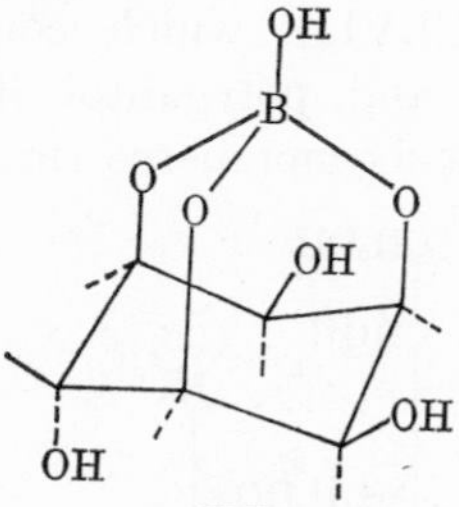 (CLI)

The tridentate complex does not increase the acidity of boric acid as much as might be expected due to the fact that the preferred conformation of a 1,3,5-*cis*-cyclohexanetriol is the chair form with

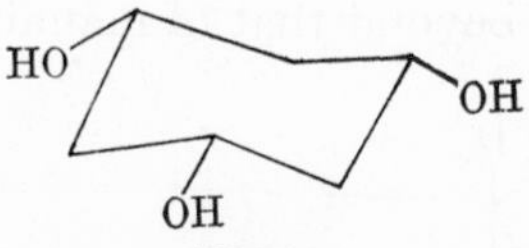

(CLII) 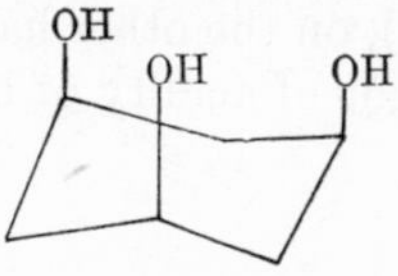 (CLIII)

three equatorial hydroxyl groups (CLII). Thus, to form the boric acid complex there must be an inversion to the less stable chair form with the three hydroxyl groups in the polar positions (CLIII).[2] In the case of *cis*-inositol (CLIV), a set of 1,3,5-*cis*-polar hydroxyl

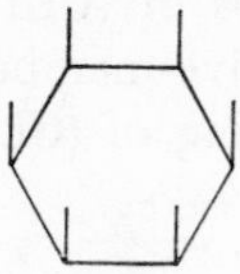

(CLIV)

groups are present in either chair form and an appreciable enhancement of the acidity results.[2]

The dihydrate of 3,3,5,5-tetramethyl-4-oxa-1,2-cyclopentadione (CLV) does not enhance the acidity of boric acid whereas the hemihydrate (CLVI) does.[133] Thus, *gem*-hydroxyl groups, at least on a

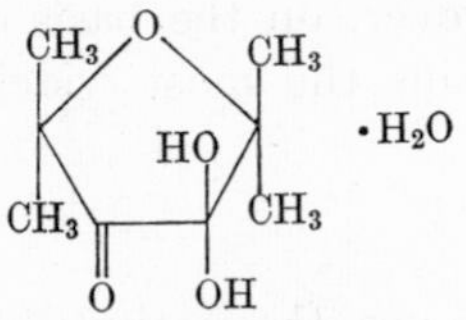

(CLV) 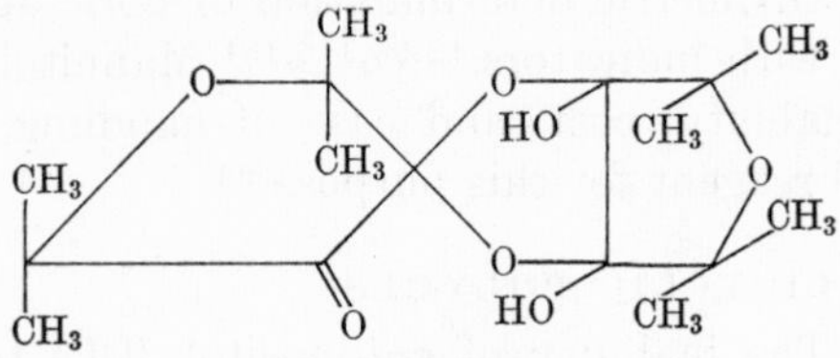 (CLVI)

five-membered ring, do not promote the formation of a dioxaboretane ring and enhancement of acidity.

Mannitan (CLVII), which contains *cis*-hydroxyls in a five-membered ring, and polygalitol (CLVIII), which has the same configuration in a six-membered ring, were ineffective.[97,98]* Erythri-

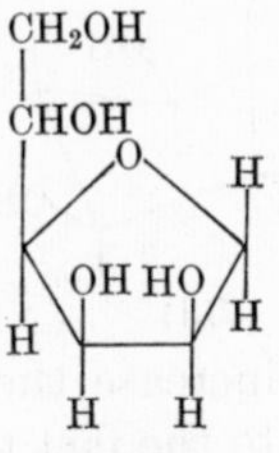

(CLVII) 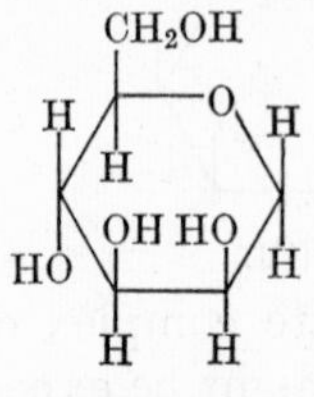 (CLVIII)

tan (CLIX), on the other hand, was extremely active and effected an enhancement of acidity of boric acid beyond that of mannitol itself.

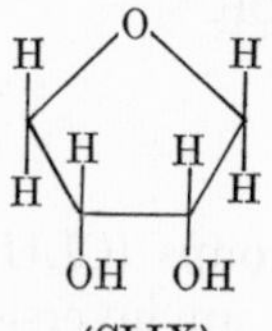

(CLIX)

The absence of substituents on (CLIX) in contrast to (CLVII) would leave the *cis*-hydroxyl groups of (CLIX) readily available for reaction with boric acid. The five-membered ring of (CLIX) as compared to the six-membered ring of (CLVIII) also is consistent with the observations of acidity.

* Very low molar ratios of polyol to boric acid (2.44) were employed.

Dulcitan (CLX), which has no vicinal *cis*-hydroxyl groups, mannide (CLXI), which is a 1,6-diol, and isomannide (CLXII), which at best is a 1,4-diol held in an unfavorable rigid conformation for complexing boric acid, showed no appreciable enhancement of the acidity of boric acid.[98]

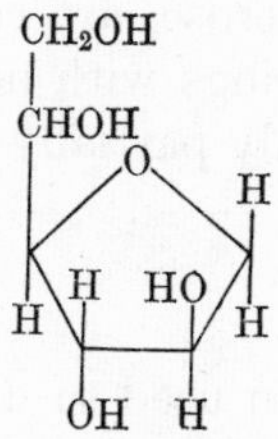

(CLX) 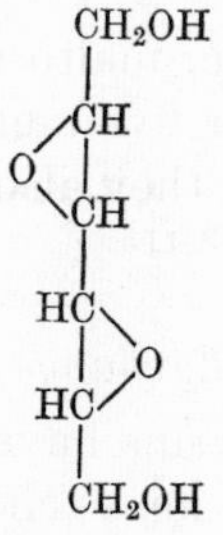 (CLXI) 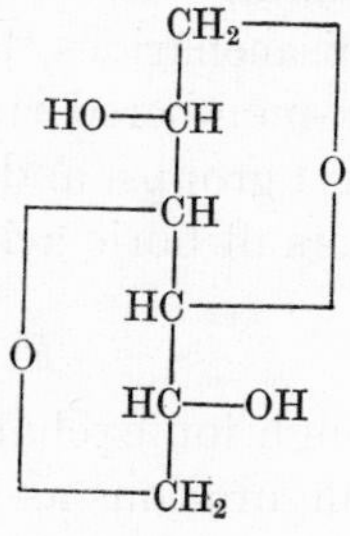 (CLXII)

4. AROMATIC DERIVATIVES

Polyphenols such as catechol and pyrogallol increase the acidity of boric acid solutions but not sufficiently to allow quantitative neutralization and determination of the acid.[115,116]

5. SUGARS

The pyranoses, xylose (CLXIII), rhamnose (CLXIV), mannose (CLXV), glucose (CLXVI), and galactose (CLXVII), increase the acidity of boric acid but not sufficiently to allow quantitative determination by titration of the acid with standard base.[12,13,115]

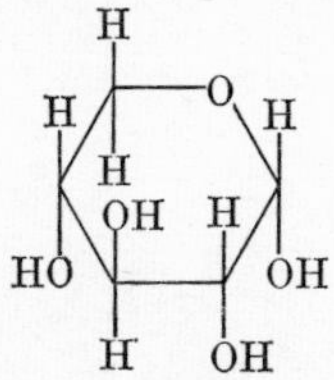

(CLXIII) 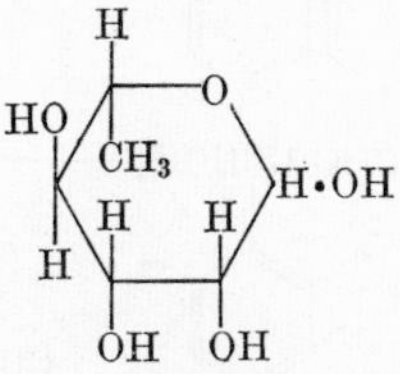 (CLXIV) 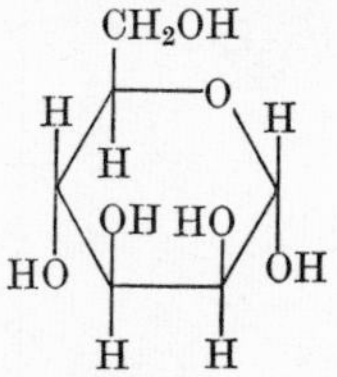 (CLXV)

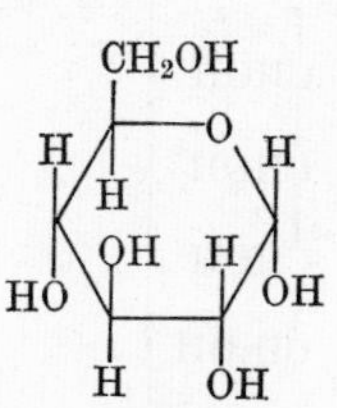

(CLXVI) 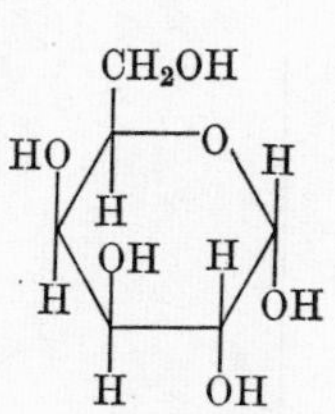 (CLXVII)

Fructose,[12,13,115] however, which in solution probably contains some ranose structure, allows quantitative determination of boric acid even more effectively than mannitol or sorbitol.[114] This again points out the superior complexing ability of vicinal *cis*-hydroxyl groups on a five-membered ring as compared to a six-membered ring or an aliphatic chain.

The disaccharides, lactose, maltose and sucrose, are composed only of six-membered rings or five-membered rings with no vicinal *cis*-hydroxyl groups, and thus they also were only partially effective as activators of boric acid.[12,13,115]

F. Ion-Exchange Resins

Although ion-exchange resins have not been used to determine polyol configurations as such, ion-exchange techniques in which the stereochemical relationships are implicit have been used to separate mixtures of polyols and to remove boric acid from aqueous solution. In polyol separation, an aqueous tetraborate solution of the polyol is passed through a quaternary ammonium derivative of a polystyrene resin.[92] Those polyols whose stereochemistry allows ready formation of the bisdiol complex are retained on the column as the quaternary ammonium salt and are the last to be eluted upon continuous washing with an aqueous borate solution.

Conversely, removal of boric acid from aqueous solution has been accomplished by incorporating a polyol structure into the

$CHCH_2CHCH_2$

$CHCH_2CHCH_2$

CH_2OH

$(CH_2)_nN$—CH

CH_3 $CHOH$

$CHOH$

$CHOH$

CH_2OH

$[\ ]_n$

(CLXVIII)

resin.[108] Passage of an aqueous boric acid solution through a resin similar to (CLXVIII) effectively removes the boric acid as either the mono or bisdiolborate complex.

IX. ANALYTICAL

Coordination compounds derived from catechol have been analyzed for boron by fusion with sodium carbonate, dissolution of the melt with hydrochloric acid, neutralization to methyl orange endpoint after elimination of the carbon dioxide, and final titration with standard base to phenolphthalein endpoint in the presence of mannitol.[99]

Potassium hydroxide[86] and potassium carbonate[137,138] have been used in place of the sodium carbonate. A fuming nitric acid digestion procedure led to erroneous results.[41]

A variety of sodium salts were analyzed by potentiometric titration first with hydrochloric acid to determine sodium, then with sodium hydroxide in the presence of mannitol to determine boron.[58]

For non-acidic polyol derivatives such as mannitol, the boron can be determined by solution of a sample in water, addition of more mannitol, and direct titration with standard base to the phenolphthalein endpoint.[78]

The boron content of (CLXIX) was determined by heating a

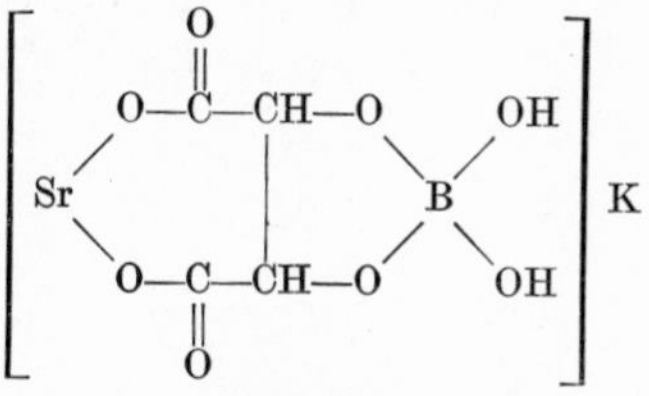

```
 [          O                      ]
 [          ‖                      ]
 [     O—C—CH—O        OH          ]
 [    /       |     \  /           ]
 [ Sr         |      B             ]  K
 [    \       |     /  \           ]
 [     O—C—CH—O        OH          ]
 [          ‖                      ]
 [          O                      ]
```

(CLXIX)

sample to 800° until all the carbon was consumed. The residue was dissolved in 0.1*N* hydrochloric acid, the carbon dioxide removed by boiling, and the excess acid titrated to methyl orange endpoint. Glycerol was added and the solution was titrated to the naphtholphthalein endpoint with standard base.[142]

X. PHYSICAL CONSTANTS

$\left[R\begin{matrix}O\\O\end{matrix}B\begin{matrix}O\\O\end{matrix}R\right]H$	M.p. (°C)	B.p. (°C)	d_4^t	n_D^t	Reference
1,2-Diols					
$[(CH_2O)_2B(OCH_2)_2]H$ — $\left[\begin{matrix}CH_2—O\\CH_2—O\end{matrix}B\begin{matrix}O—CH_2\\O—CH_2\end{matrix}\right]H$	135–143				40, 150
$\left[\begin{matrix}(CH_3)_2C—O\\(CH_3)_2C—O\end{matrix}B\begin{matrix}O—C(CH_3)_2\\O—C(CH_3)_2\end{matrix}\right]H$	70				147
$\left[\begin{matrix}CH_2—O\\C_4H_9—CH—O\end{matrix}B\begin{matrix}O—CH_2\\O—CH—C_4H_9\end{matrix}\right]H$	—	—	—	—	107
$\left[\begin{matrix}CH_2—O\\C_4H_9—C(C_2H_5)—O\end{matrix}B\begin{matrix}O—CH_2\\O—C(C_2H_5)—C_4H_9\end{matrix}\right]H$	—	—	—	—	107

1,3-Diols					
$[(CH_3)_2C(CH_2\text{—}O)_2B(O\text{—}CH_2)_2C(CH_3)_2]H$	—	—	—	—	106
$[(CH_3)_2C\text{—}O\text{—}B(\text{—}O\text{—}C(CH_3)_2\text{—}CH_2\text{—}CH(CH_3)\text{—}O\text{—})\text{—}O\text{—}CH(CH_3)\text{—}CH_2\text{—}]H$ (B bonded to O—C(CH₃)₂, CH₂, CH(CH₃)—O rings on both sides)	—	—	—	—	147
$[\{(CH_3)_2C\text{—}O\}_2\{CH_2\}\text{—}B\text{—}\{CH_2\}\{O\text{—}C(CH_3)_2\}_2]H$	120	228			147
$[\{(CH_3)_2C\text{—}O\}\{CH_2\}\{C_2H_5(CH_3)C\text{—}O\}\text{—}B\text{—}\{O\text{—}C(CH_3)_2\}\{CH_2\}\{O\text{—}C(CH_3)C_2H_5\}]H$	43–45				147

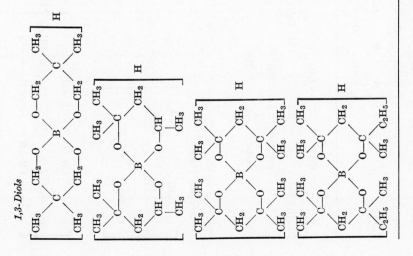

(Table continued)

$\left[\begin{matrix} R\!<\!(O)_2\!>\!B\!<\!(O)_2\!>\!R \end{matrix}\right]H$	M.p. (°C)	B.p. (°C)	d_4^t	n_D^t	Reference
$[C_2H_5\text{—}CH(CH_2\text{—}O)(CH(C_3H_7)\text{—}O)B(O\text{—}CH_2)(O\text{—}CH(C_3H_7))CH\text{—}C_2H_5]H$	—	—	—	—	107
Alicyclic Diols					
$[(C_6H_5)C_5H_7(O)_2B(O)_2C_5H_7(C_6H_5)]H$	129				109
$[cis\ (CH_2)_5(CH\text{—}O)(CH\text{—}O)B(O\text{—}CH)(O\text{—}CH)(CH_2)_5]H$		Oil			84

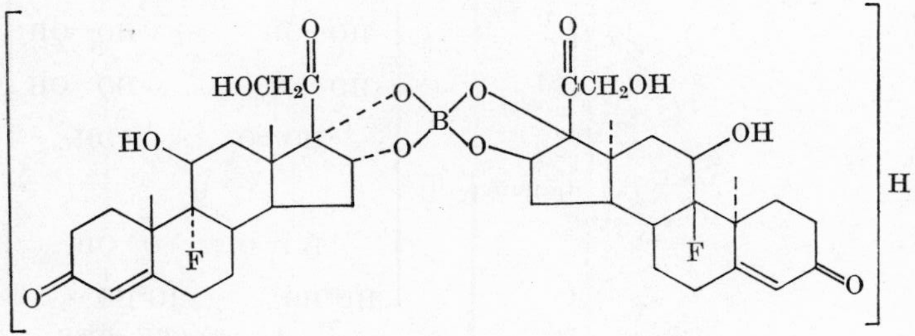 [$HOCH_2C(=O)$, HO, F, O; CCH_2OH, OH, F, O; B] H	Needles				103
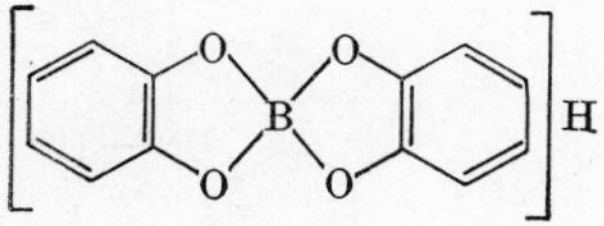 [$C_6H_4O_2$–B–$O_2C_6H_4$] H	92–104	227.5/4.2			125
		200°/vac. (sublimes)			84
		Sublimes			117
	—	—	—	—	138, 159
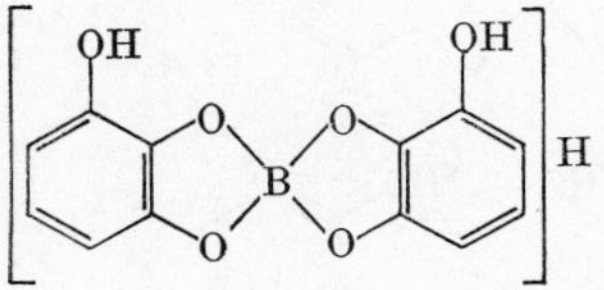 [OH, OH; B] H	Needles, does not melt	Sublimes			117
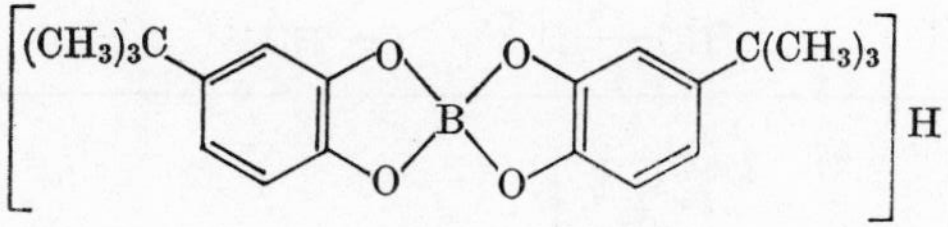 [$(CH_3)_3C$, $C(CH_3)_3$; B] H	Glass				147

(*Table continued*)

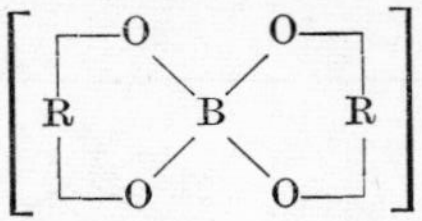 $[(RO_2)_2B]H$	M.p. (°C)	B.p. (°C)	d_4^t	n_D^t	Reference
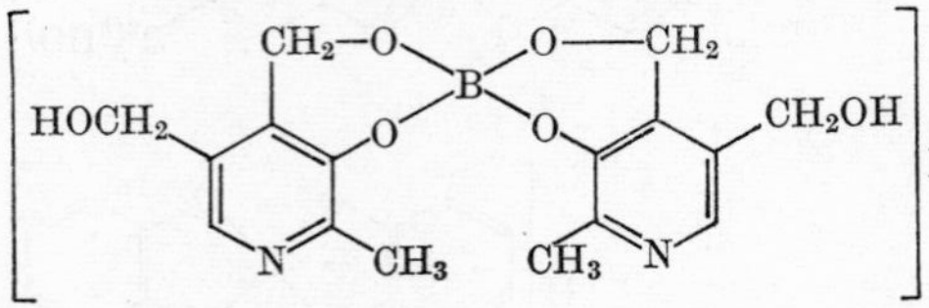 [bis(pyridoxine) borate structure] H	—	—	—	—	141
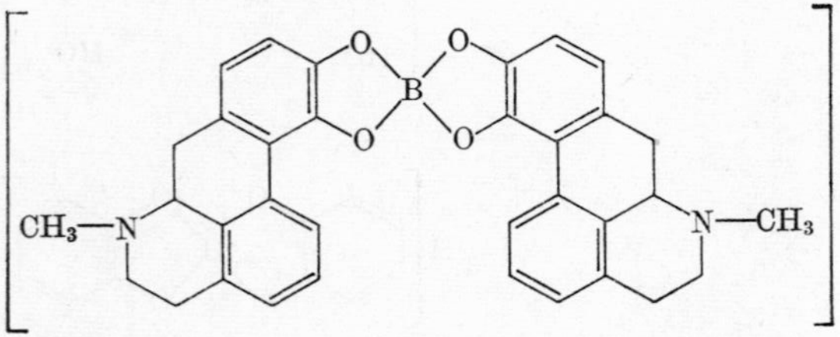 [bis(catecholic aporphine) borate structure, N—CH_3] H	Gelatinous				168
Sugar Alcohols					
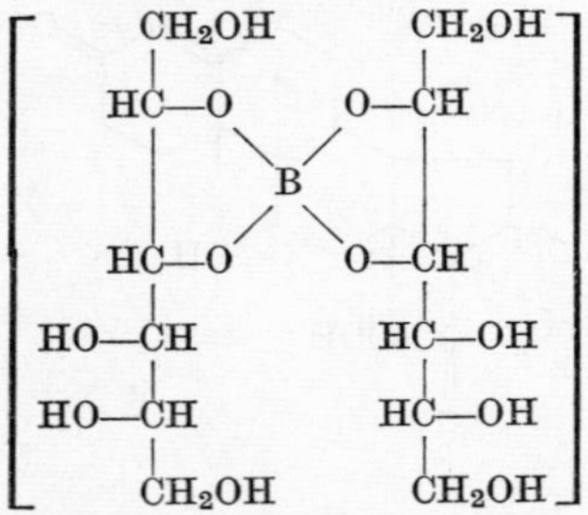 [mannitol borate structure] H (Mannitol)	146–148				155

Compound	M.p. (°C)	B.p. (°C)	d_4^t	n_D^t	Reference
Sugars					
$[\text{fructose residue}]_2$ B H (Fructose)	172–173				155
$[\text{xylose residue}]_2$ B H (Xylose)	132 (d)				155

$\left[R \begin{smallmatrix} O \\ O \end{smallmatrix} B \begin{smallmatrix} O \\ O \end{smallmatrix} R \right] M$	M.p. (°C)	B.p. (°C)	d_4^t	n_D^t	Reference
1,2-Diols					
$[(CH_2O)_2B(OCH_2)_2]\ C_6H_{11}NH_3$	Brown waxy solid				150
$[(CH_2O)_2B(OCH_2)_2]\ (HOCH_2CH_2)_3NH$	Brown semi-solid				150
$[(CH_2O)_2B(OCH_2)_2]\ C_{16}H_{33}NH_3$	60–69				64, 150

(*Table continued*)

[R(O)(O)B(O)(O)R] M	M.p. (°C)	B.p. (°C)	d_4^t	n^t	Reference
[CH_2—O O—CH_2 B CH_3CH—O O—$CHCH_3$] $C_{16}H_{33}NH_3$	Brown waxy solid				150
[CH_3OCCH—O O—$CHCOCH_3$ B CH_3OCCH—O O—$CHCOCH_3$] K (C=O on each ester carbon)	—	—	—	—	90
[C_2H_5OCCH—O O—$CHCOC_2H_5$ B C_2H_5OCCH—O O—$CHCOC_2H_5$] K (C=O on each ester carbon)	White crystalline solid				90
[CH_2—O O—CH_2 B $(C_2H_5O)_2CHCH$—O O—$CHCH(OC_2H_5)_2$] K	> 320				169

$[B\{OC(CH_3)_2C(CH_3)_2O\}_2]$	$Na \cdot 4H_2O$	Thin leaflets				58
	Na	Solid				58
$[B\{OCH_2CH(C_4H_9)O\}_2]$	$H_2NCH_2C_6H_4CH_2NH_3$	—	—	—	—	107
$[B\{OCH_2C(C_4H_9)(C_2H_5)O\}_2]$	$H_2NCH_2C_6H_4CH_2NH_3$	—	—	—	—	107
1,3-Diols						
$[B\{OCH_2CH_2CH_2O\}_2]$	$(HOCH_2CH_2)_3NH$	Brown semi-liquid				150
	$C_{16}H_{33}NH_3$	60–69				150

(*Table continued*)

$[(RO_2)B(O_2R)]M$	M.p. (°C)	B.p. (°C)	d_4^t	n_D^t	Reference
$[(CH_3)_2C(CH_2O)_2B(OCH_2)_2C(CH_3)_2]Na$	—	—	—	—	106
$[CH_2(CH(CH_3)O)_2B(OCH(CH_3))_2CH_2]Na$	> 350				57
$[C_2H_5CH(CH_2O)(CH(C_3H_7)O)B(OCH_2)(OCH(C_3H_7))CHC_2H_5]$ p-$H_3NCH_2C_6H_4CH_2NH_2$	—	—	—	—	107
m-$H_3NCH_2C_6H_4CH_2NH_2$	—	—	—	—	107

	$[(CH_3CH_2)_2NHCH_2CH_2]_2C_6H_3OH$	—	—	—	—	107
	$NH_2C_6H_5$ 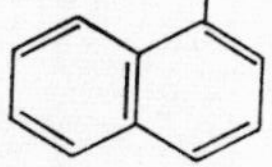 (1-naphthyl)		—	—	—	107
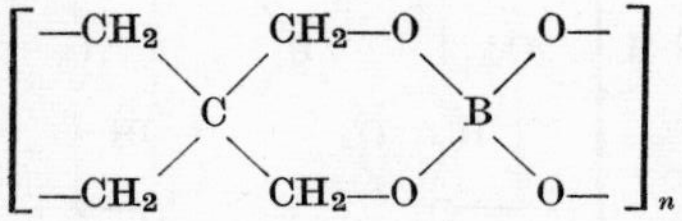 $[$—CH_2, CH_2—O, O—; C, B; —CH_2, CH_2—O, O—$]_n$	$Na_n \cdot 6H_2O$	Solid				58
	Na_n	Solid				58
Alicyclic Diols						
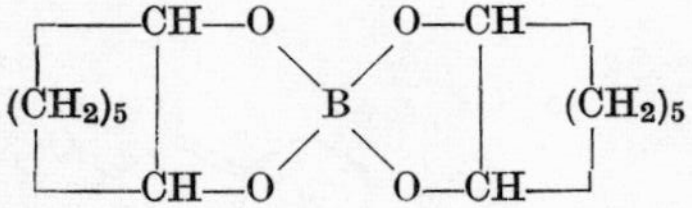 $(CH_2)_5$ CH—O, CH—O; B; O—CH, O—CH $(CH_2)_5$	$C_6H_5NH_3$	~50				84
[HOCH₂C(=O) … HO … F … O—B—O … CCH₂OH(=O) … OH … F]	Na	Solid				103
	NH_4	Solid				103

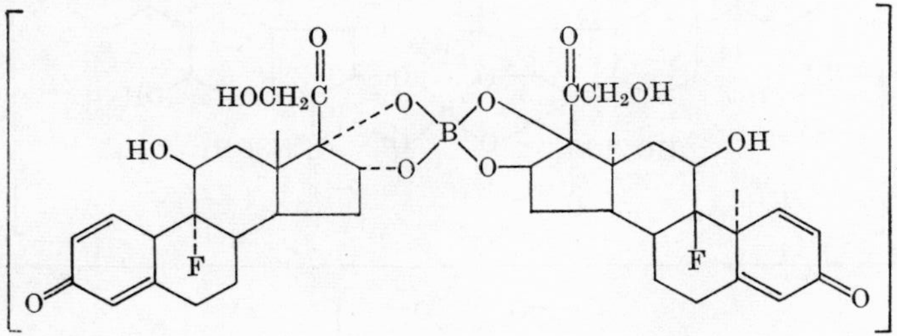

(*Table continued*)

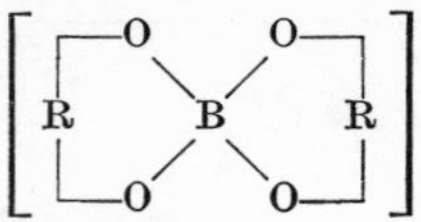 M	M.p. (°C)	B.p. (°C)	d_4^t	n_D^t	Reference
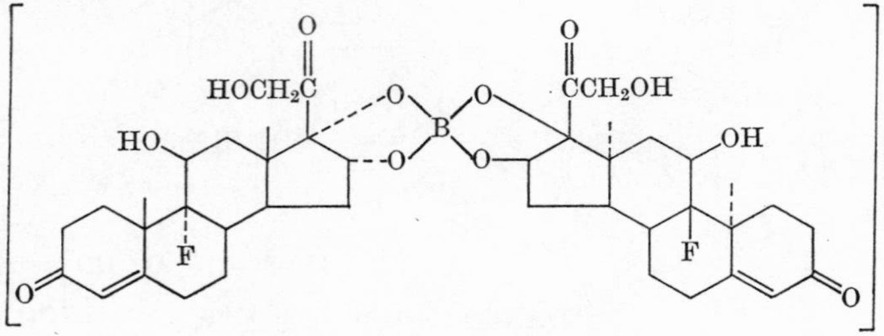 Na	Solid				103
NH_4	Solid				103
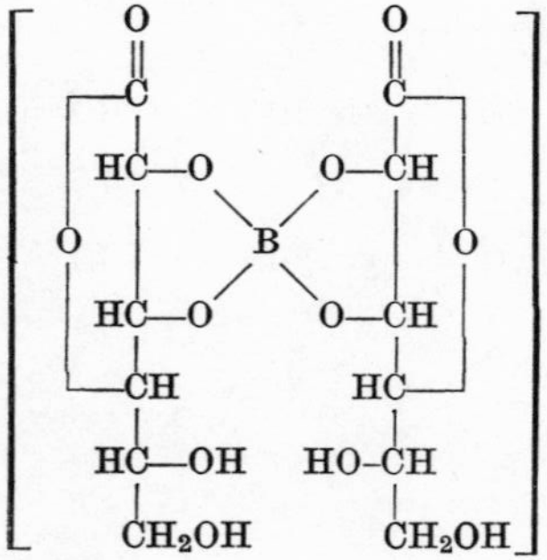 K (Ascorbic acid)	—		—	—	165

Aromatic Derivatives

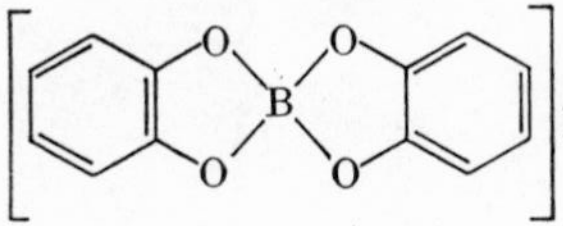 Na		Colorless crystals				136
		Transparent crystals				137
		Microscopic hexagonal leaflets				130
		Platelets				117
	K	Transparent crystals				137
		Lustrous leaves				41
		Lustrous leaflets				130
		—	—	—	—	86, 117, 125
	Rb	Transparent crystals				137
		Lustrous leaves				41
	Tl	Transparent crystals				137
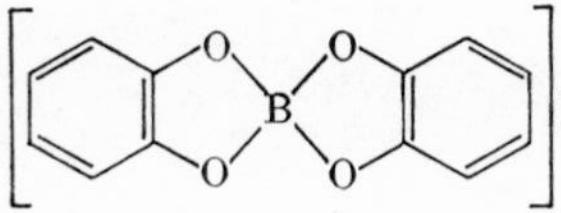 NH_4		Small square platelets	Sublimes at 130° in vacuo			117
		Transparent quadratic crystals	Sublimes			137
		Fine leaflets				130
		Lustrous leaves	Sublimes			41
		—	—	—	—	86, 125
	CH_3NH_3	Transparent quadratic crystals	Sublimes			137
	$HOCH_2CH_2NH_3$	—	—	—	—	166
	$C_4H_9NH_3$	232				166
	$(C_4H_9)_2NH_2$	163				166
	$(C_4H_9)_3NH$	134				166

(Table continued)

[R(O)₂B(O)₂R] M	M.p. (°C)	B.p. (°C)	d_4^t	n_D^t	Reference
NH_2	255				166
	305–306				138
CH_3, NH_2	238				166
$C_6H_5CH_2NH_3$	Hexagonal tablets and broad needles				137
$(HOCH_2CH_2)_3NH$	107–116				150
$C_{16}H_{33}NH_3$	146–152				150
NH	176–178				49
	179–180				138
	—	—	—	—	125
$-NH_3$	Needles				41, 117
	Needle-like				137

$Cl-C_6H_4-NH_3$	Needles				41
	—	—	—	—	117
$C_6H_5-NH(CH_3)_2$	Needle-like				137
	Needles Platelets or clusters				41 117
$C_6H_4(NH_3)(NH_2) \cdot \frac{1}{4} H_2O$	Needles				137
$CH_3C_6H_3(NH_3)(NH_2)$	227				166
$C_{10}H_7-NH_3$	Hexagonal tablets and broad needles				137

(Table continued)

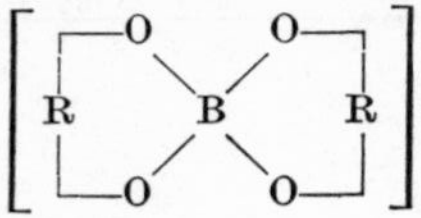 $\left[R\begin{smallmatrix}O\\O\end{smallmatrix}B\begin{smallmatrix}O\\O\end{smallmatrix}R\right]M$	M.p. (°C)	B.p. (°C)	d_4^t	n_D^t	Reference
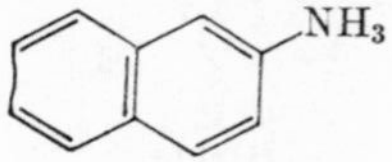 NH_3	206				166
	Hexagonal tablets and broad needles				137
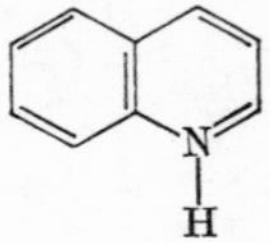 N–H	213				138
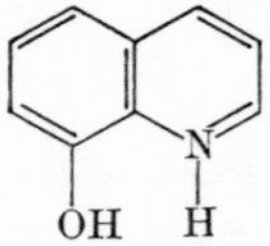 OH, N–H	203				138
Nicotine H+	171				138
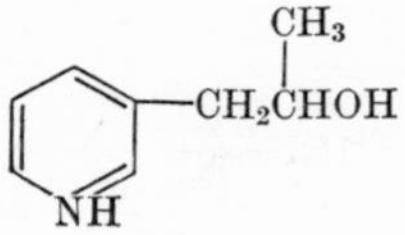 $CH_2CH(CH_3)OH$, NH	158.5				138

Nitron H^+, C_6H_5N—CH—N—C_6H_5, N—C_6H_5, C=N (ring structure)	H	179				137, 138
Methylene blue, $C_{16}H_{18}N_3S$		Small dark needles				137
$NH_2C(=NH_2)NH_2$		—	—	—	—	137
$C_6H_5NHC(=NH_2)NHC_6H_5$		230				166
		—	—	—	—	54, 67
$CH_3C_6H_4$—NHC(=NH_2)NH—$C_6H_4CH_3$ (di-o-tolyl)		167				166
[bis(3-hydroxy-1,2-phenylenedioxy)borate] $C_6H_5NH_3$						
		Crystalline				117
	C_5H_6N	~225				117

(*Table continued*)

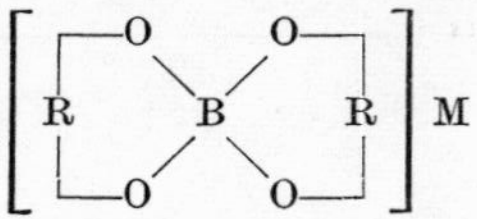 $[B(O_2R)_2]M$ — R	M	M.p. (°C)	B.p. (°C)	d_4^t	n_D^t	Reference
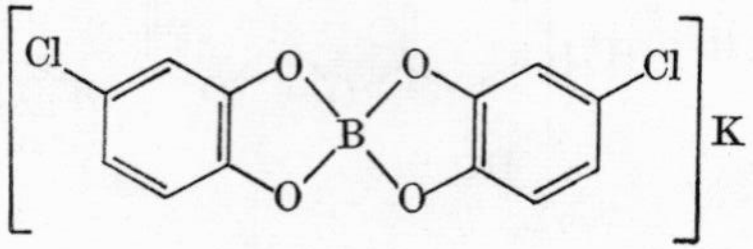 $[(Cl\text{-}C_6H_3O_2)_2B]K$		Microcrystalline				40
	NH_4	Microcrystalline				40
	$C_6H_5NH_3$	Long needles				40
	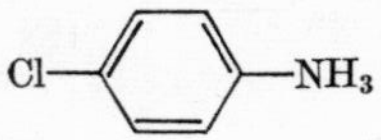 $Cl\text{-}C_6H_4\text{-}NH_3$	Long needles				40
	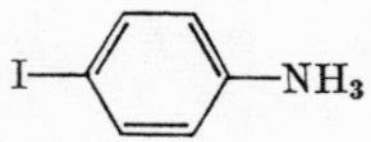 $I\text{-}C_6H_4\text{-}NH_3$	Long needles				40
	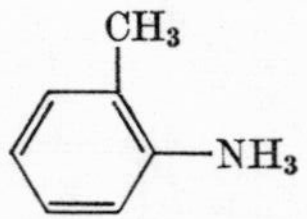 $CH_3\text{-}C_6H_4\text{-}NH_3$	Rectangular platelets				40
	Brucine H^+, $C_{21}H_{21}O_2N_2(OCH_3)_2 \cdot 6H_2O$	Needles				40

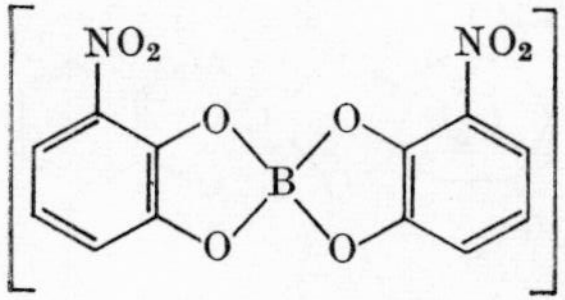 K		Yellow squares				117
	NH_4	Yellow squares				117
	$C_6H_5NH_3$	Small yellow needles				40
		Needles				117
	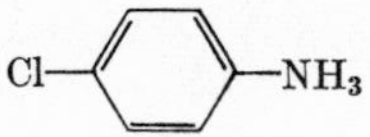 Cl–C_6H_4–NH_3	Small yellow needles				40
Brucine H^+, $C_{21}H_{21}O_2N_2(OCH_3)_2$		Small hard spheres				40
Strychnine H^+, $C_{21}H_{23}O_2N_2$		Small hard spheres				40
Quinine H^+, $C_{19}H_{21}N_2(OH)(OCH_3)$		Small hard spheres				40
Cinchonine H^+, $C_{19}H_{22}N_2(OH)$		Small hard spheres				40
Cinchonidine H^+, $C_{19}H_{22}N_2(OH)$		Small hard spheres				40
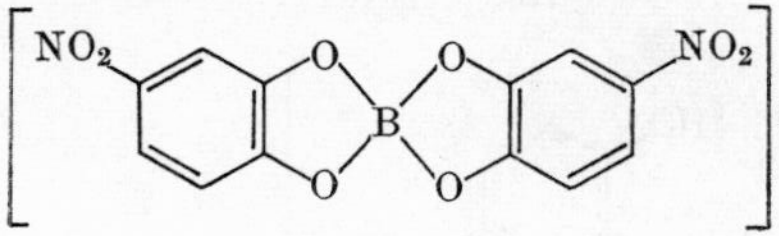 $C_6H_5NH_3$		Needles				117
	NH_4	—	—	—	—	117
	K	—	—	—	—	117
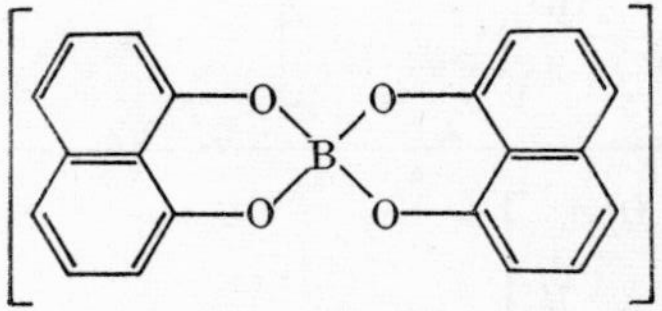 K		—	—	—	—	30

(Table continued)

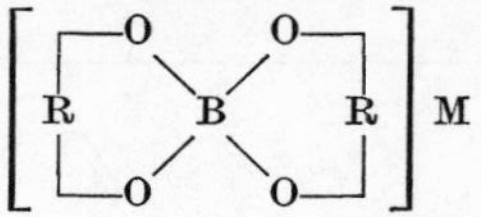 $[(R\langle O_2\rangle)_2B]M$	M.p. (°C)	B.p. (°C)	d_4^t	n_D^t	Reference
Vitamin B_6, [structure: bis(pyridoxine) borate; HOCH$_2$, CH$_2$, CH$_3$, N, CH$_2$OH] Na 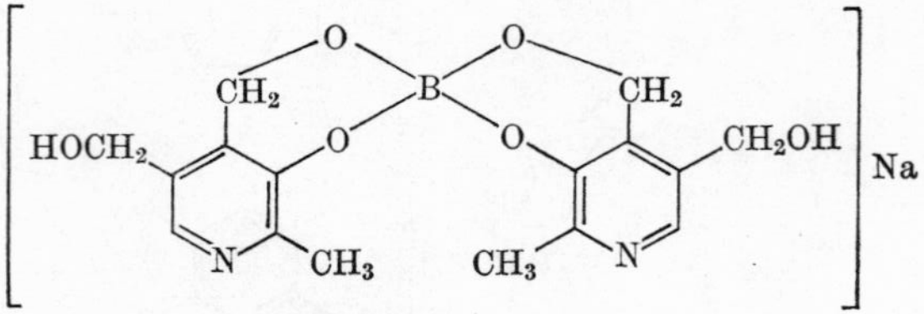	Grey crystals				140
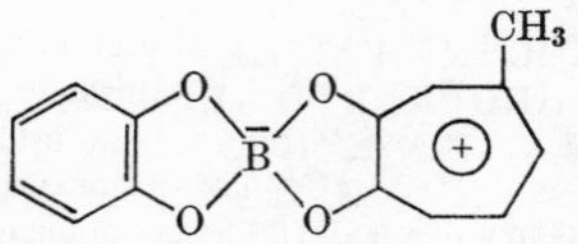 [structure: catechol borate of methyltropolone, CH$_3$]	210				8
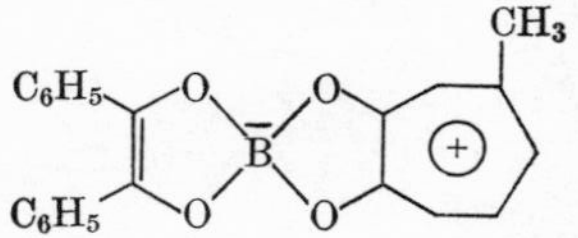 [structure: C_6H_5, C_6H_5 ene-diol borate of methyltropolone, CH$_3$]	262				8
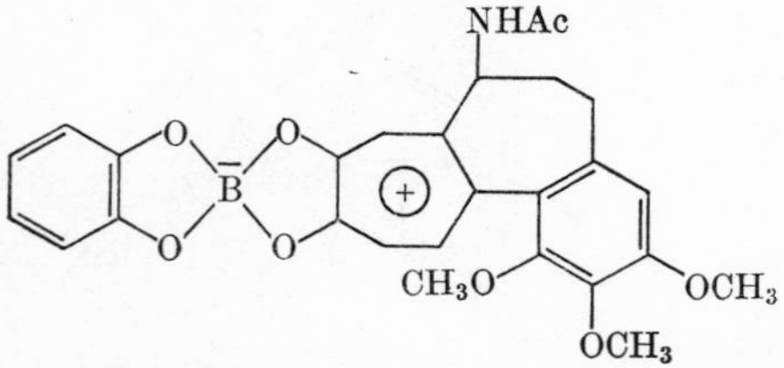 [structure: catechol borate of colchiceine type; NHAc, CH$_3$O, OCH$_3$, OCH$_3$]	Ca. 140				8

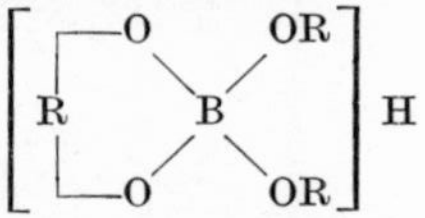 $[R(O)_2B(OR)_2]H$	M.p. (°C)	B.p. (°C)	d_4^t	n_D^t	Reference
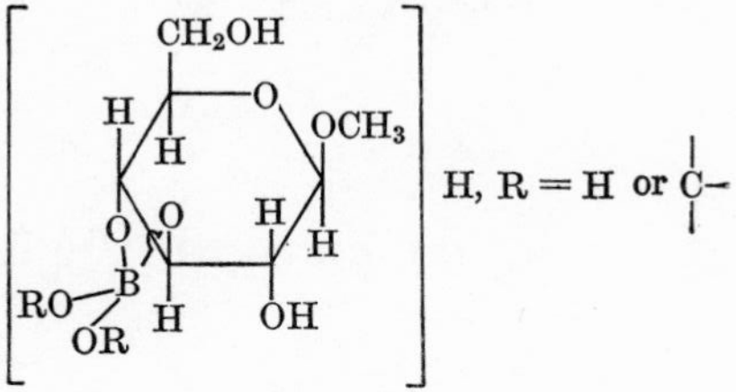 [methyl glycoside borate complex (CH₂OH, OCH₃, OH)] H, R = H or C—	—	—	—	—	146
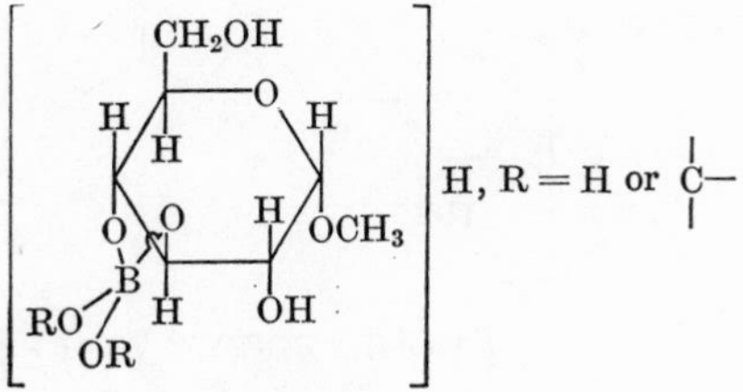 [methyl glycoside borate complex (CH₂OH, OCH₃, OH)] H, R = H or C—	—	—	—	—	146
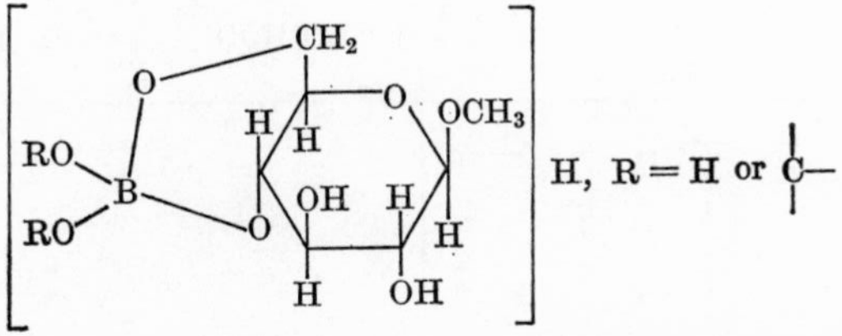 [methyl glycoside 4,6-borate complex (CH₂, OCH₃, OH, OH)] H, R = H or C—	—	—	—	—	146

(*Table continued*)

$\left[R(O)_2B(OR)_2 \right] M$	M.p. (°C)	B.p. (°C)	d_4^t	n_D^t	Reference
$[(CH_2O)_2B(OCH_2CH_2OH)_2]$ Na	—	—	—	—	113
$[(C_6H_4O_2)B(OC_6H_4OH)_2]$ $(C_2H_5)_3NH$	103–104				138
C_5H_5NH	122–123				117
	122–124				99
	125-126				138
Nitron H+	118				138

	M.p. (°C)	B.p. (°C)	d_4^t	n_D^t	Reference
$C_9H_6N(OH)\cdot H$ (OH, N–H)	—	—	—	—	138
$[R(O)_2B(OH)_2]H$	M.p. (°C)	B.p. (°C)	d_4^t	n_D^t	Reference
$[CH_2OH{-}CH(OH){-}CH(OH){-}CH(O){-}CH(O){-}CH_2OH \; B(OH)_2]H$	89.5				78
$[(CH_3)_2C(O{-}CH)(O{-}CH){-}CH(OH){-}CH(O){-}CH(O){-}CH_2OH \; B(OH)_2]H$	75–90				160

(*Table continued*)

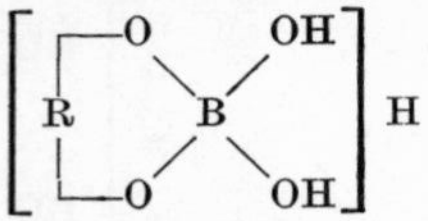 $[R(O)_2B(OH)_2]H$	M.p. (°C)	B.p. (°C)	d_4^t	n_D^t	Reference
$[(HO)_2B(O{-}CH(CH_2OH))(O{-}CH){-}(HC{-}O)(HC{-}O(CH_2OH))B(OH)_2]H_2$	—	—	—	—	50
$[HO{-}B(OH)(O)(O){-}CHCH_2OH$ (furanose, H, H, H, H; O, O–C(CH$_3$)$_2$)$]H$	90–110				159
	95–108				144

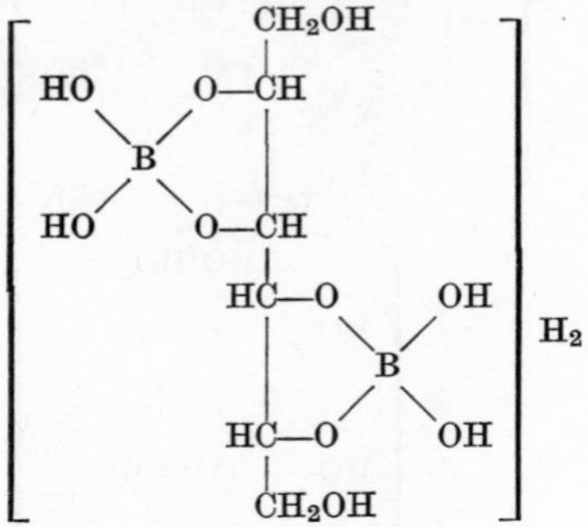

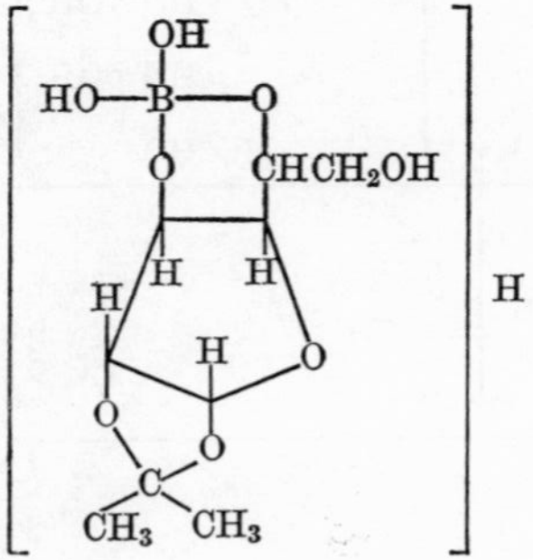

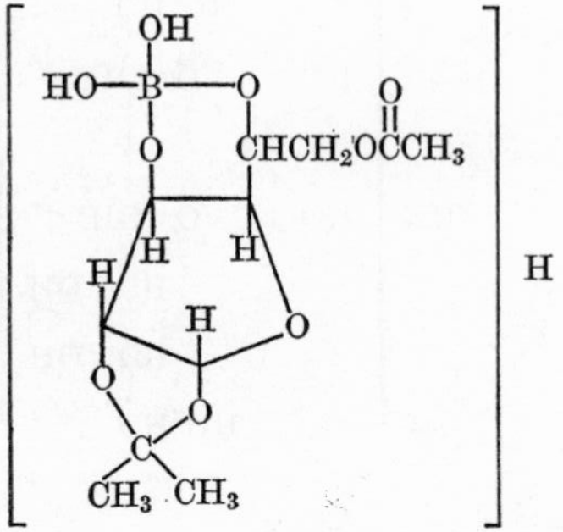 [HO—B(OH)(O—)—O—CHCH$_2$OC(=O)CH$_3$; H, H, H, H ; O ; O, O, C, CH$_3$ CH$_3$] H	120 (d.)				144
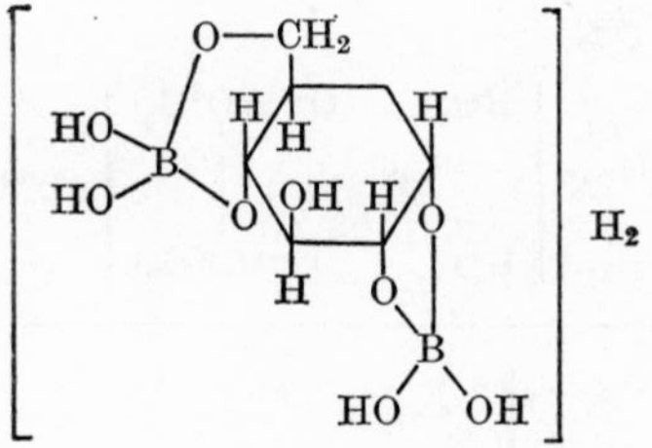 [O—CH$_2$; HO, HO, B ; H, H, H, H, OH, H ; O, O, O ; B, HO, OH] H_2	—	—	—	—	50

(*Table continued*)

$[R(O)_2B(OH)_2]M$	M.p. (°C)	B.p. (°C)	d_4^t	n_D^t	Reference
meso $[(CH_3CH{-}O)_2B(OH)_2]Na \cdot 3H_2O$	Thin flakes				58
Na	Solid				58
dl $[(CH_3CH{-}O)_2B(OH)_2]Na \cdot 3H_2O$	Hexagonal plates				58
Na	Solid				58
$[CH_2OH{-}CH(OH){-}CH(OH){-}CH(O){-}CH(O){-}CH_2OH \; B(OH)_2]NH_4$ (HC—O, HC—O bonded to B)	Crystalline solid				78

Ag	Crystalline powder				78
$\frac{1}{2}$ Ca	Crystalline powder				78
$\frac{1}{2}$ Ba	Crystalline powder				78
[cyclopentane ring –O, –O > B < OH, OH] $Na \cdot 3H_2O$	Irregular plates				58
[cyclopentane ring –O, –O > B < OK, OH] K	Needles				86
[cyclohexane ring –O, –O > B < OH, OH] $Na \cdot 3H_2O$	Thin flakes				58
[cyclohexane ring –O, –O > B < OK, OH] K	—	—	—	—	86

(Table continued)

$\left[R{<}^{O}_{O}{>}B{<}^{OH}_{OH}\right]M$	M.p. (°C)	B.p. (°C)	d_4^t	n_D^t	Reference
$\left[Sr{<}^{O-C(=O)-CH-O}_{O-C(=O)-CH-O}{>}B{<}^{OH}_{OH}\right]K\cdot 5H_2O$	White crystalline solid				142
$\left[C_6H_4{<}^{O}_{O}{>}B{<}^{OH}_{OH}\right]Na$	Plates				136
Li	Plates				136
Sr	Leaflets				136
$\frac{1}{2}$ Mg	Needles				136
meso $\left[CH_2{<}^{CH(CH_3)-O}_{CH(CH_3)-O}{>}B{<}^{OH}_{OH}\right]Na\cdot 3H_2O$	Thin flakes				58
Na	Solid				58

Compound	M.p. (°C)	B.p. (°C)	d_4^t	n_D^t	Reference
dl $\left[CH_3CH(-O-)CH_2CH(-O-)CH_3 \; B(OH)_2\right]Na\cdot 3H_2O$	Irregular crystals				58
$\left[(HO)_2B(OCH_2)_2C(CH_2O)_2B(OH)_2\right]Na_2\cdot 12H_2O$	> 350				58
Na_2	Solid				58

$\left[R(O-)_3B-OH\right]M$	M.p. (°C)	B.p. (°C)	d_4^t	n_D^t	Reference
$\left[CH_3C(CH_2O)_3BOH\right]Na\cdot 3H_2O$	Flakes				58
Na	Solid				58

(*Table continued*)

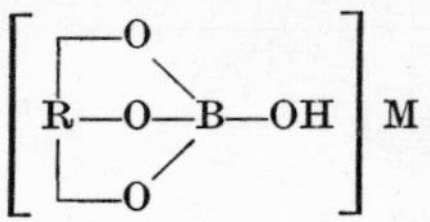 $\left[R{-}O{-}B(O)_2{-}OH \right]$	M	M.p. (°C)	B.p. (°C)	d_4^t	n_D^t	Reference
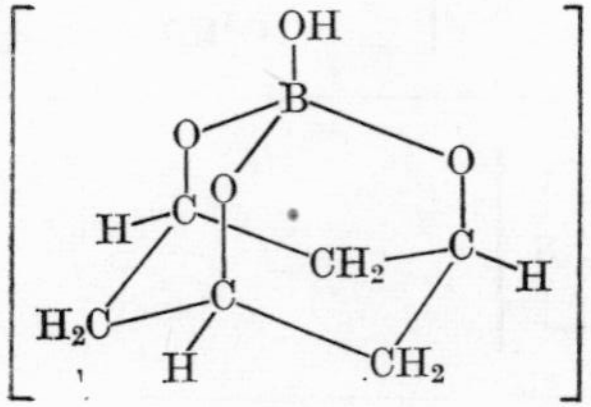	$Na \cdot 3H_2O$	Oblong flakes				58
	Na	Solid				58
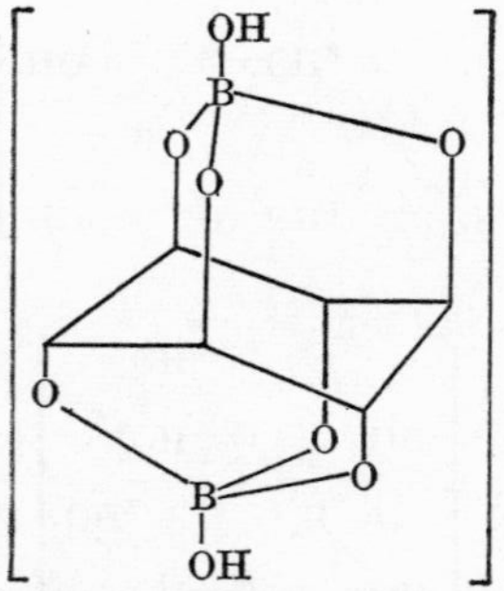	$Na \cdot 9H_2O$	White solid				164

XI. REFERENCES

1. Angyal, S. J., and D. J. McHugh, *Chem. & Ind.* (*London*), 1147 (1956).
2. Angyal, S. J., and D. J. McHugh, *J. Chem. Soc.*, 1423 (1957).
3. Antikainen, P. J., *Acta Chem. Scand.*, **9**, 1008 (1955).
4. Antikainen, P. J., *Ann. Acad. Sci. Fennicae, Ser. A. II*, **56**, (1954).
5. Antikainen, P. J., *Suomen Kemistilehti*, **B 29**, 179 (1956).
6. Antikainen, P. J., *Suomen Kemistilehti*, **B 31**, 255 (1958).
7. Austin, J. A., U.S. Pat. 2,007,786 (1935, to Jensen-Salsberg Laboratories, Inc.).
8. Balaban, A. T., G. Mihai, R. Antonescu, and P. T. Frangopol, *Tetrahedron*, **16**, 68 (1961).
9. Bancroft, W. D., and H. L. Davis, *J. Phys. Chem.*, **34**, 2479 (1930).
10. Barsky, G., U.S. Pat. 2,590,146 (1952, to Freeport Sulphur Co.).
11. Bell, D. J., *J. Chem. Soc.*, 175 (1935).
12. Berenshtein, F. I., *Biochem. Z.*, **215**, 344 (1929).
13. Berenshtein, F. I., and L. N. Aisenberg, *Ukr. Khim. Zh.*, **8**, 307 (1933); through *Chem. Abstracts*, **29**, 2054 (1935).
14. Berenshtein, F. I., and A. U. Shpakovskii, *Ukr. Khim. Zh.*, **11**, 433 (1936).
15. Böeseken, J., *Advan. Carbohydrate Chem.*, **4**, 189 (1949).
16. Böeseken, J., *Ber.*, **46**, 2612 (1913).
17. Böeseken, J., *Bull. Soc. Chim. France*, **53**, 1332 (1933).
18. Böeseken, J., *Chem. Weekblad*, **19**, 207 (1922).
19. Böeseken, J., *Inst. Intern. Chim. Solvay, Conseil Chim.*, 61 (1931).
20. Böeseken, J., *Proc. Acad. Sci. Amsterdam*, **26**, 97 (1923).
21. Böeseken, J., *Rec. Trav. Chim.*, **39**, 178 (1920).
22. Böeseken, J., *Rec. Trav. Chim.*, **40**, 553 (1921).
23. Böeseken, J., *Rec. Trav. Chim.*, **45**, 552 (1926).
24. Böeseken, J., *Rec. Trav. Chim.*, **61**, 82 (1942).
25. Böeseken, J., *Verslag Akad. Wetenschap. Amsterdam*, **24**, 1617 (1916).
26. Böeseken, J., *Verslag Akad. Wetenschap. Amsterdam*, **27**, 627 (1918).
27. Böeseken, J., *et al.*, *Rec. Trav. Chim.*, **34**, 96 (1915).
28. Böeseken, J., and J. Coops, *Rec. Trav. Chim.*, **45**, 407 (1926).
29. Böeseken, J., and H. Couvert, *Rec. Trav. Chim.*, **40**, 354 (1921); *Verslag Akad. Wetenschap. Amsterdam*, **29**, 924 (1920).
30. Böeseken, J., J. A. de Bruin, and W. E. van Rijswijk de Jong, *Rec. Trav. Chim.*, **58**, 3 (1939).
31. Böeseken, J., and H. G. Derx, *Rec. Trav. Chim.*, **40**, 529 (1921).
32. Böeseken, J., and J. P. Dommisse, *Rec. Trav. Chim.*, **45**, 491 (1926).
33. Böeseken, J., J. H. Gonngrijp, and A. E. A. van Rhijn, *Rec. Trav. Chim.*, **57**, 1356 (1938).
34. Böeseken, J., and P. H. Hermans, *Rec. Trav. Chim.*, **42**, 1104 (1923).
35. Böeseken, J., and G. V. D. Hoek Ostende, *Rec. Trav. Chim.*, **37**, 162 (1918).
36. Böeseken, J., and A. H. Kerstjens, *Proc. Acad. Sci. Amsterdam*, **18**, 1654 (1916).
37. Böeseken, J., and J. L. Leefers, *Rec. Trav. Chim.*, **54**, 861 (1935).
38. Böeseken, J., and J. Meulenhoff, *Proc. Acad. Sci. Amsterdam*, **27**, 174 (1924).

39. Böeseken, J., and J. C. Meuwissen, *Rec. Trav. Chim.*, **45**, 496 (1926).
40. Böeseken, J., and J. A. Mijs, *Rec. Trav. Chim.*, **44**, 758 (1925).
41. Böeseken, J., M. A. Obreen, and A. Van Haeften, *Rec. Trav. Chim.*, **37**, 184 (1918).
42. Böeseken, J., J. D. Ruys, and K. Brackmann, *Rec. Trav. Chim.*, **34**, 272 (1915).
43. Böeseken, J., W. Sturm, and G. Goettsch, *Rec. Trav. Chim.*, **37**, 144 (1918).
44. Böeseken, J., and J. Van. Giffen, *Rec. Trav. Chim.*, **39**, 183 (1920).
45. Böeseken, J., and A. Van Rossem, *Rec. Trav. Chim.*, **30**, 392 (1912).
46. Böeseken, J., N. Vermaas, and A. T. Küchlin, *Rec. Trav. Chim.*, **49**, 711 (1930).
47. Böeseken, J., N. Vermaas, W. H. Zaayer, and J. L. Leefers, *Rec. Trav. Chim.*, **54**, 853 (1935).
48. Bouchardat, G., *Compt. Rend.*, **80**, 120 (1875); *Ann. Chim. et phys.*, **6**, 100 (1875).
49. Bourne, E. J., A. B. Foster, and P. M. Grant, *J. Chem. Soc.*, 4311 (1956).
50. Brigl, P., and H. Gruner, *Ann.*, **495**, 60 (1932).
51. Brown, M. L., U.S. Pat. 2,442,677 (1948, to Merck and Company).
52. Carpeni, C., *Bull. Soc. Chim. France*, 1280 (1950).
53. Coleman, G. H., and A. Miller, *Proc. Iowa Acad. Sci.*, **49**, 257 (1942).
54. Collins, J. O., W. R. Goethel, and J. O. Hei, *Rubber Chem. and Technol.*, **33**, 237 (1960).
55. Consden, R., and W. M. Stanier, *Nature*, **169**, 783 (1952).
56. Curtis, D., U.S. Pat. 2,582,191 (1952).
57. Dale, J., *J. Chem. Soc.*, 910 (1961).
58. Dale, J., *J. Chem. Soc.*, 922 (1961).
59. Darmois, E., and R. Peyroux, *Compt. Rend.*, **193**, 1182 (1931).
60. Deutsch, A., and S. Osoling, *J. Am. Chem. Soc.*, **71**, 1637 (1949).
61. Dryerre, H., and J. R. Greig, *Vet. Record*, **15**, 546 (1935).
62. Edwards, J. O., and G. C. Morrison, V. F. Ross, and J. W. Schultz, *J. Am. Chem. Soc.*, **77**, 266 (1955).
63. Elving, P. J., and C. M. Callahan, *J. Am. Chem. Soc.*, **77**, 2077 (1955).
64. Fawcett, J. S., U.S. Pat. 2,492,562 (1949, to Gulf Research and Development Co.).
65. Ferrier, R. J., and W. G. Overend, *Quart. Rev.* (*London*), **13**, 265 (1959).
66. Fischer, E., and R. Stahel, *Ber.*, **24**, 2144 (1891).
67. Forman, D. B., R. R. Radcliff, and L. R. Mayo, *Ind. Eng. Chem.*, **42**, 686 (1950).
68. Foster, A. B., *Advan. Carbohydrate Chem.*, **12**, 81 (1957).
69. Foster, A. B., *Chem. & Ind.* (*London*), 591 (1953).
70. Foster, A. B., *J. Chem. Soc.*, 982 (1953).
71. Foster, A. B., *J. Chem. Soc.*, 1395 (1957).
72. Foster, A. B., *J. Chem. Soc.*, 4214 (1957).
73. Foster, A. B., E. F. Martlew, and M. Stacey, *Chem. & Ind.* (*London*), 825 (1953).
74. Foster, A. B., W. G. Overend, M. Stacey, and G. Vaughan, *J. Chem. Soc.*, 3308 (1953).
75. Foster, A. B., and M. Stacey, *Chem. & Ind.* (*London*), 279 (1953).
76. Foster, A. B., and M. Stacey, *J. Appl. Chem.* (*London*), **3**, 19 (1953).

77. Foster, A. B., and M. Stacey, *J. Chem. Soc.*, 1778 (1955).
78. Fox, J. J., and A. J. H. Gauge, *J. Chem. Soc.*, **99**, 1075 (1911).
79. Frahn, J. L., and J. A. Mills, *Chem. & Ind.* (*London*), 578 (1956).
80. Gatsis, J. G., U.S. Pat. 2,848,375 (1958, to Universal Oil Products Co.).
81. Gilmour, B., *Analyst*, **46**, 3 (1921).
82. Grün, A., and H. Nossowitch, *Monatsh.*, **37**, 409 (1916).
83. Heilbron, S. I., and H. M. Bunbury, *Dictionary of Organic Compounds*, Vol. III, Oxford University Press, New York, 1953, p. 658.
84. Hermans, P. H., *Proc. Acad. Sci. Amsterdam*, **26**, 32 (1923).
85. Hermans, P. H., *Theoretical Organic Chemistry*, Elsevier Publishing Co., New York, 1954, p. 360.
86. Hermans, P. H., *Z. Anorg. Allgem. Chem.*, **142**, 83 (1925).
87. Hubert, A. J., B. Hargitay, and J. Dale, *J. Chem. Soc.*, 931 (1961).
88. Hughes, R. C., and W. J. Whelan, *Chem. & Ind.* (*London*), 50 (1959).
89. Isbell, H. S., J. F. Brewster, N. B. Holt, and H. L. Frush, *J. Res. Nat. Bur. Std.*, *A*, **40**, 129 (1948).
90. Jones, B., *J. Chem. Soc.*, 951 (1933).
91. Khan, I. A., and D. Sen, *Proc. Indian Acad. Sci.*, *Sect. A*, **49**, 226 (1959).
92. Khym, J. X., and P. Zill, U.S. Pat. 2,818,851 (1958).
93. Kinoshita, Y., H. Koike, S. Kuriyama, Y. Asami, and M. Okamoto, *Nagoya Shiritsu Daigaku Yakugakubu Kiyo*, **5**, 32 (1957); *Chem. Abstracts*, **52**, 4397 (1958).
94. Klein, D., *Compt. Rend.*, **86**, 826 (1878); **97**, 1437 (1883); **99**, 144 (1884); *Bull Soc. Chim. France*, **29**, 357 (1878).
95. Kohlrausch, F., and L. Holborn, *Das Leitvermögen der Elektrolyte*, B. G. Teubner, Leipzig, 1916.
96. Kolthoff, I. M., and V. A. Stenger, *Volumetric Analysis*, Vol. II, 2nd ed., Interscience, New York, 1947, p. 115.
97. Krantz, J. C. Jr., C. J. Carr, and F. F. Beck, *J. Phys. Chem.*, **40**, 927 (1936).
98. Krantz, J. C. Jr., M. Oakley, and C. J. Carr, *J. Phys. Chem.*, **40**, 151 (1936).
99. Kuemmel, D. K., and M. G. Mellon, *J. Am. Chem. Soc.*, **78**, 4572 (1956).
100. Kuhn, L. P., *J. Am. Chem. Soc.*, **74**, 2492 (1952).
101. Kwart, H., and G. C. Gatos, *J. Am. Chem. Soc.*, **80**, 881 (1958).
102. Leeson, L. J., J. A. Lowery, G. M. Sieger, and C. Krieger, *J. Pharm. Sci.*, **50**, 856 (1961).
103. Leeson, L. J., J. A. Lowery, G. M. Sieger, and S. Muller, *J. Pharm. Sci.*, **50**, 193 (1961).
104. Leeson, L. J., J. A. Lowery, G. M. Sieger, and S. Muller, *J. Pharm. Sci.*, **50**, 606 (1961).
105. Leeson, L. J., S. A. Muller, and G. M. Sieger, U.S. Pat. 3,005,839 (1961, to American Cyanamid Company).
106. Liao, C. W., and M. B. Denny, 140th Meeting American Chemical Society, Chicago, September, 1961, Abstracts of Papers, p. 35-N.
107. Lowe, W., U.S. Pat. 2,883,412 and 2,902,450 (1959, to California Research Corp.).
108. Lyman, W. R., and A. F. Preuss, Jr., U.S. Pat. 2,813,838 (1957 to Rohm and Haas Co.).
109. Maan, C. J., *Rec. Trav. Chim.*, **48**, 332 (1929).

110. MacPherson, H. T., and J. Stewart, *Biochem. J.*, **32**, 76 (1938).
111. Magnanini, G., *Z. Physik. Chem.*, **6**, 58 (1890); **9**, 230 (1892); **11**, 281 (1893); *Gazz. Chim. Ital.*, **20**, I, 428 (1890); **21**, II, 134, 215 (1891).
112. Mark, H., *Chem. Rev.*, **26**, 169 (1940).
113. Meerwein, H., and T. Bersin, *Ann.*, **476**, 113 (1929).
114. Mehta, S. M., and K. V. Kantak, *J. Am. Chem. Soc.*, **74**, 3470 (1952).
115. Mellon, M. G., and V. N. Morris, *Ind. Eng. Chem.*, **16**, 123 (1924).
116. Mellon, M. G., and V. N. Morris, *Proc. Indiana Acad. Sci.*, **33**, 85 (1924).
117. Meulenhoff, J., *Rec. Trav. Chim.*, **44**, 150 (1925).
118. Muller, J. A., *Bull. Soc. Chim. France*, **11**, 329 (1894).
119. Müntz, A., *Z. Ver. Rüberzucher Ind.*, **26**, 735 (1876).
120. Murgier, M., and E. Darmois, *Atti Congr. Intern. Chim., 10, Rome, 1938*, **2**, 737 (1939).
121. Nasanen, R., *Suomen Kemistilehti*, **33B**, 1 (1960); *Chem. Abstracts*, **54**, 23628 (1960).
122. Onak, T. P., H. Landesman, R. E. Williams, and I. Shapiro, *J. Phys. Chem.*, **63**, 1533 (1959).
123. Owen, B. B., *J. Am. Chem. Soc.*, **56**, 1695 (1934).
124. Owen, B. B., and E. J. King, *J. Am. Chem. Soc.*, **65**, 1612 (1943).
125. Prochazka, J., and V. Ettel, *Przemysl Chem.*, **37**, 720 (1958).
126. Rimbach, E., and O. Weber, *Z. Physik. Chem.*, **51**, 473 (1905).
127. Rippere, R. E., and V. K. LaMer, *J. Phys. Chem.*, **47**, 204 (1943).
128. Ritchey, W. M., J. G. Gasselli, and C. W. Liao, 140th Meeting American Chemical Society, Chicago, September, 1961, Abstracts of Papers, p. 35-N.
129. Rodd, E. H., *Chemistry of Carbon Compounds*, Vol. II, Part A, Elsevier Publishing Co., New York, 1953, p. 133.
130. Rosenheim, A., and H. Vermehren, *Ber.*, **57**, 1337 (1924).
131. Ross, S. D., and A. J. Catotti, *J. Am. Chem. Soc.*, **71**, 3563 (1949).
132. Roy, G. L., A. L. Laferriere, and J. O. Edwards, *J. Inorg. Nucl. Chem.*, **4**, 106 (1957).
133. Sandris, C., and G. Owisson, *Bull. Soc. Chim. France*, 338 (1958).
134. Sargent, R., and W. Rieman III, *J. Phys. Chem.*, **60**, 1370 (1956).
135. Schäfer, H., *Z. Anorg. Allgem. Chem.*, **247**, 96 (1941).
136. Schäfer, H., *Z. Anorg. Allgem. Chem.*, **250**, 127 (1942).
137. Schäfer, H., *Z. Anorg. Allgem. Chem.*, **259**, 86 (1949).
138. Schäfer, H., *Z. Anorg. Allgem. Chem.*, **259**, 255 (1949).
139. Schiff, H., *Ann. Suppl.* **5**, 154 (1867).
140. Scudi, J. V., U.S. Pat. 2,261,188 (1941, to Merck and Co.).
141. Scudi, J. V., W. A. Bastedo, and T. J. Webb, *J. Biol. Chem.*, **136**, 399 (1940).
142. Shvarts, E. M., and A. F. Ievin'sh, *Zh. Neorgan. Khim.*, **2**, 1494 (1957).
143. Souchay, P., and Lourijsen, *Bull. Soc. Chim. France*, 893 (1956).
144. Stanek, J., and I. Hauzar, *Chem. Zvesti*, **8**, 337 (1954).
145. Stewart, J., and H. T. MacPherson, *Vet. J.*, **94**, 220 (1938).
146. Sugihara, J. M., and J. C. Peterson, *J. Am. Chem. Soc.*, **78**, 1760 (1956).
147. Thomas, J. R., and O. L. Harle, U.S. Pat. 2,795,548 (1957, to Calif. Research Corp.).
148. Thomson, R. T., *J. Soc. Chem. Ind.* (*London*), **12**, 432 (1893).
149. Torssell, K., *Arkiv Kemi*, **3**, 571 (1952).

150. Trautman, C. E., U.S. Pat. 2,497,521 (1950, to Gulf Research and Development Co.).
151. Treadwell, W. D., and L. Weiss, *Helv. Chim. Acta*, **3**, 433 (1920).
152. Tsuzuki, Y., *Bull. Chem. Soc. Japan*, **13**, 337 (1938).
153. Tsuzuki, Y., *Bull. Chem. Soc. Japan*, **16**, 23 (1941).
154. Tsuzuki, Y., and Y. Kimura, *Bull. Chem. Soc. Japan*, **15**, 27 (1940).
155. Tung, J. Y., and H. L. Chang, *J. Chinese Chem. Soc.*, **9**, 125 (1942).
156. Van Gilmour, G., *J. Chem. Soc.*, **121**, 1333 (1922).
157. Van Romburgh, P., and J. H. N. van der Burg, *Proc. Acad. Sci. Amsterdam*, **25**, 335 (1922).
158. Van't Hoff, J. H. *Die Lagerung der Atome im Raume*, 3rd ed., F. Vieweg and Son, Braunschweig, 1908, p. 90.
159. Vargha, L. V., *Ber.*, **66**, 704 (1933).
160. Vargha, L. V., *Ber.*, **66**, 1394 (1933).
161. Verschuur, R., *Rec. Trav. Chim.*, **47**, 123 (1928).
162. Vignon, L., *Compt. Rend.*, **78**, 148 (1874); *Ann. Chim. et Phys.*, **2**, 440 (1874).
163. Weil, H., and M. Adler, *Ber.*, **57**, 2091 (1924).
164. Weissbach, A., *J. Org. Chem.*, **23**, 329 (1958).
165. Willems, J. F., and A. E. Van Hoof, U.S. Pat. 2,967,772 (1961, to Gevaert Photo-Production N.V.).
166. Williams, I., and A. M. Neal, U.S. Pat. 1,975,890 (1934, to E. I. duPont de Nemours & Co.).
167. Winstein, S., and R. B. Henderson, "Ethylene and Trimethylene Oxides", in R. C. Elderfield, *Heterocyclic Compounds*, Vol. I, Wiley, New York, 1950, p. 59.
168. Witteboon, S., *Pharm. Weekblad*, **72**, 350 (1935); *Chem. Abstracts*, **29**, 6697 (1935).
169. Wohl, A., and C. Neuberg, **Ber.**, **32**, 3488 (1899).

16

COORDINATION COMPOUNDS DERIVED FROM HYDROXY ACIDS AND DIBASIC ACIDS

I. INTRODUCTION

The chemistry of coordination compounds derived from hydroxy acids and dibasic acids,* as was the case for coordination compounds derived from diols, is concentrated in two areas. On the one hand, under anhydrous or highly concentrated solution conditions, a few hydroxy acids have led to isolable compounds of type (I) in

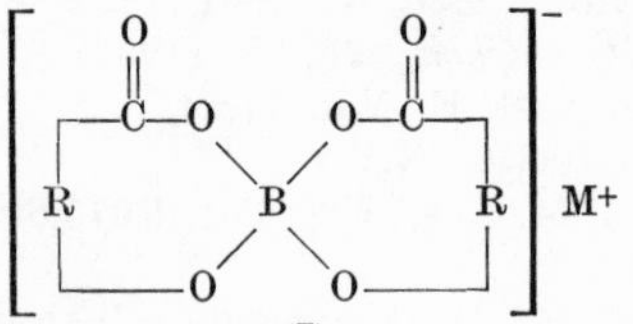

(I)

which the cation is a proton, a mono- or divalent metal, ammonium or an alkylammonium ion. A lesser number of derivatives in which only one hydroxy acid moiety (II) or a dibasic acid moiety (III) are involved have been reported.

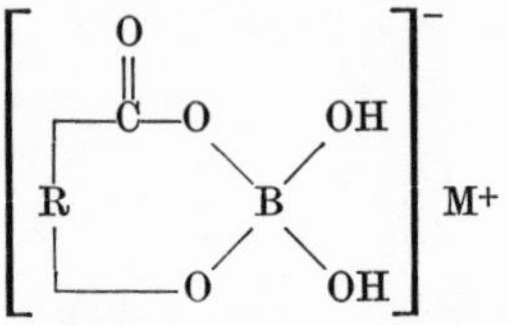

(II) 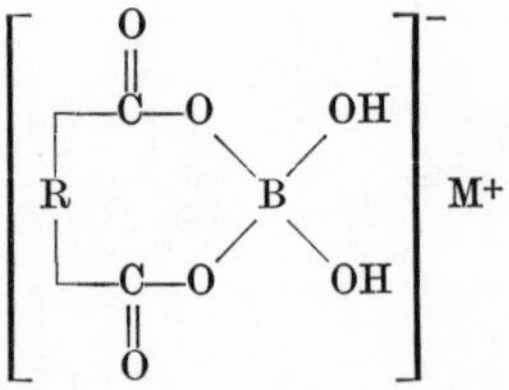 (III)

On the other hand, the aqueous chemistry of type (I) compounds has been pursued vigorously by the techniques of conductivity and polarimetry. This chapter is concerned with both of the areas of investigation.

* One example of a coordination compound derived from a monobasic acid has been reported.[42]

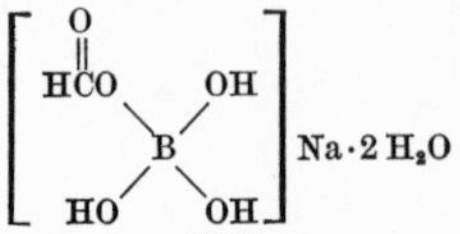

II. HISTORICAL

The first coordination compounds (IV) derived from hydroxy acids were isolated in 1878,[44] thirteen years before conductivity[50,54] and

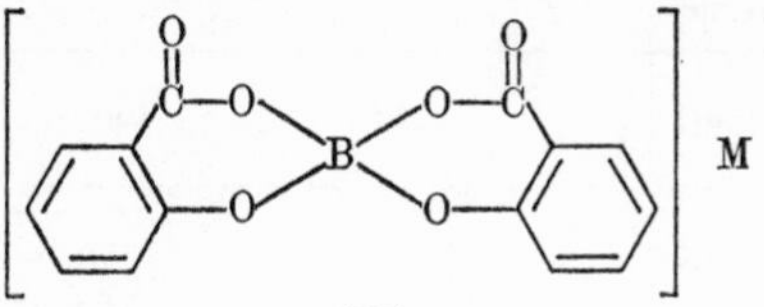

M

(IV)

acidity[56] effects were discussed and thirty-four years after rotatory effects were recorded.[4]

Barthe[3] in 1908 first isolated salts with a 1:1 mole ratio of hydroxy acid to boron (V).

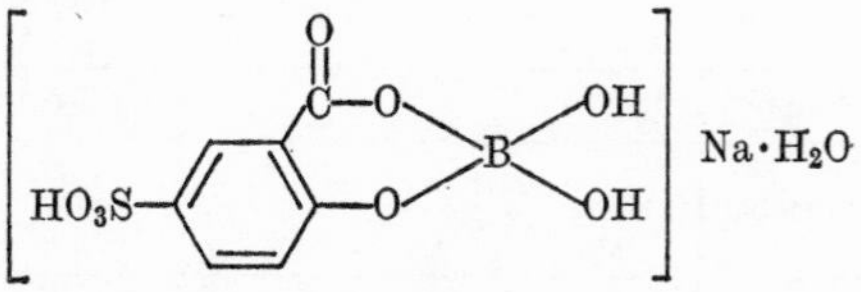

HO_3S $Na \cdot H_2O$

(V)

III. PROPERTIES

A. General

Hydrogen bissalicylatoborate[40] and the salts of various bis(hydroxy acid)borates[1,3,39,44,55,59] and bis(dibasic acid)borates[31] with the exception of barium, lead and silver bissalicylatoborate[44] are soluble in water. Solubilities in organic solvents are recorded in Table 16-1.

Hydrogen bissalicylatoborate and its salts have a bitter taste.[40,44,54] Sodium and ammonium bissalicylatoborate monohydrate burn with a green flame.[44]

B. Stereochemistry

The strychnine salt (VI) was separated into its enantiomorphs by fractional crystallization;[21,29,55] the brucine salts (VII and VIII)

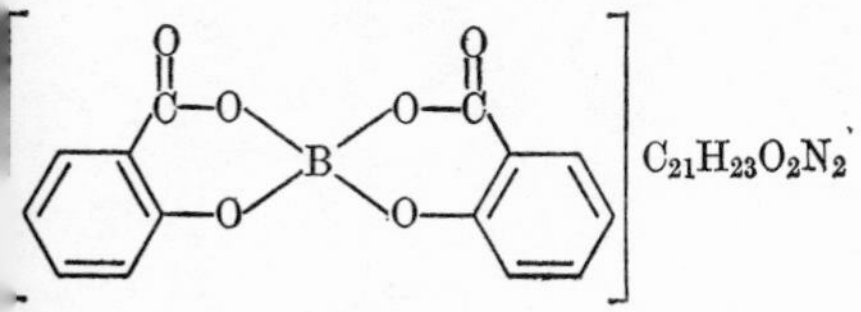

$C_{21}H_{23}O_2N_2$

(VI)

$C_{21}H_{21}O_2N_2(OCH_3)_2$

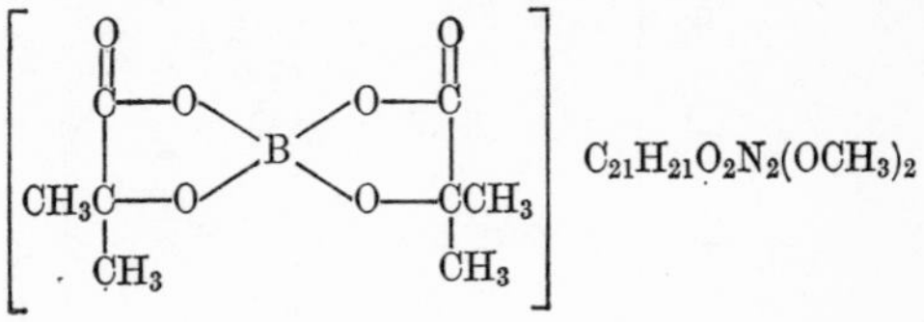

(VII)

Table 16-1. Solubility of coordination compounds derived from hydroxy acids and dibasic acids in organic solvents

	Methanol	Ethanol	Amyl alcohol	Glycerol	Ether	Acetone	Ethyl acetate	Acetic anhydride	Carbon disulfide	Chloroform	Carbon tetrachloride	Benzene	Nitrobenzene	Hexane	Ligroin	Mineral oil	Reference
$[B(O_2C{-}C_6H_4{-}O)_2]^-H^+$	S				VSS			VSS		VSS		VSS					35
	S	S		S		S											40
$Na\cdot{}^+H_2O$		S			I												44
Ca^{++}		S															57
$Ca\cdot{}^{++}10\ H_2O$		S															44
Zn^{++}	S	S															39
$C_{16}H_{33}NH_3^+$		S			S (hot)							S		I		S (hot)	62, 63
$(HOCH_2CH_2)_3NH^+$		S (hot)			I							I		I		SS	62, 63
Strychnine H^+					I	VSS			I	SS	I	I	S (hot)		I		55
$[B(O{-}CO{-}CH_2{-}O)_2]^-\ C_6H_{11}NH_3^+$		S				SS, S(hot)						SS (hot)		SS (hot)		SS	63

$[C_6H_4(COO)(O)B(OH)_2]^- Na^+$	S	S	S	S	I	S	S										1
$[(OC{=}O)_2B(OH)_2]^- K^+ \cdot H_2O$	Insoluble in common organic solvents																31

S = Soluble: SS = Slightly soluble: VSS = Very slightly soluble. I = Insoluble.

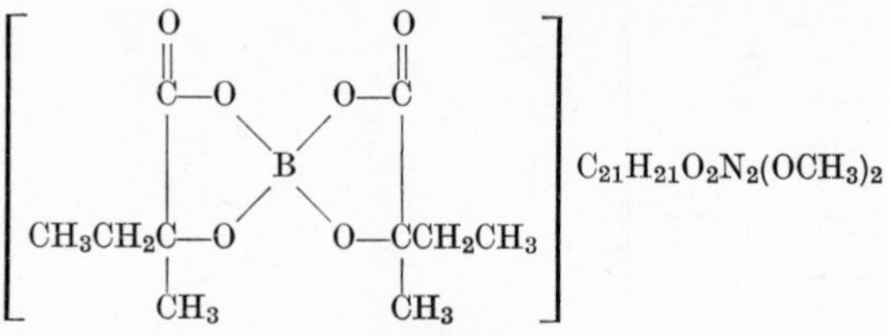

$$\left[\begin{array}{c} \text{spiro borate of two } CH_3CH_2C(CH_3)(O-)C(=O)O- \text{ ligands about } B \end{array}\right] C_{21}H_{21}O_2N_2(OCH_3)_2$$

(VIII)

were separated by extraction of a chloroform solution with petroleum ether, indicating that a spiro boron atom could possess asymmetry.*

IV. HYDROXY ACID DERIVATIVES

A. Methods of Preparation

1. SALTS WITH 1:1 MOLE RATIO HYDROXY ACID TO BORON

Hydrated lithium and potassium salts of the 1:1 complex of salicyclic acid and boric acid were obtained by concentration of a solution of boric acid and the metal salicylate.[59] Unequivocal structures were not presented; however, the dihydroxy derivatives of (IX), analogous to the mannitol and cycloheptanediol derivatives of Chapter 15, seem reasonable.

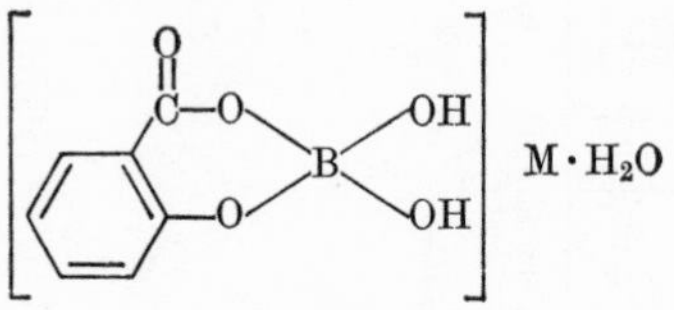

$$\left[C_6H_4(C(=O)O-)(O-)B(OH)_2 \right] M\cdot H_2O$$

(IX)

The magnesium, cobalt, nickel and zinc salts corresponding to (IX) were obtained by treatment of a solution of the sodium salt with magnesium chloride or cobalt, nickel or zinc sulfate. The sodium salt could be obtained only as an amorphous mass on concentration of an equimolar solution of sodium salicylate and boric acid.[1,54]

A concentrated equimolar aqueous solution of sodium salicylate and boric acid was reported to deposit microscopic plates of sodium bissalicylatoborate (X),[57] and a crystalline sodium salt of sulfo-

* Unsymmetrically substituted biscatecholborates (Chapter 15) also have been resolved.

salicylic acid (XI)* was obtained by refrigeration and evaporation of a dilute alcoholic solution containing a 2:1 mole ratio of sulfosalicylic acid and borax. The sulfonic acid derivative (XI) was

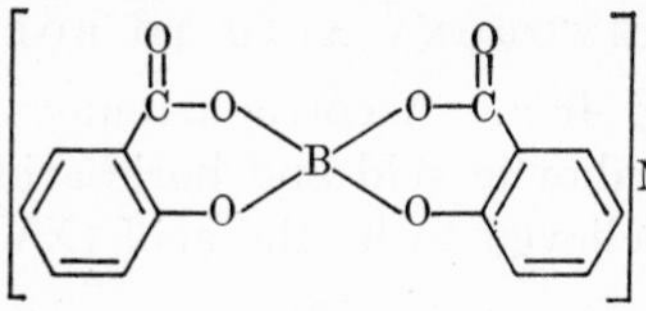

(X) 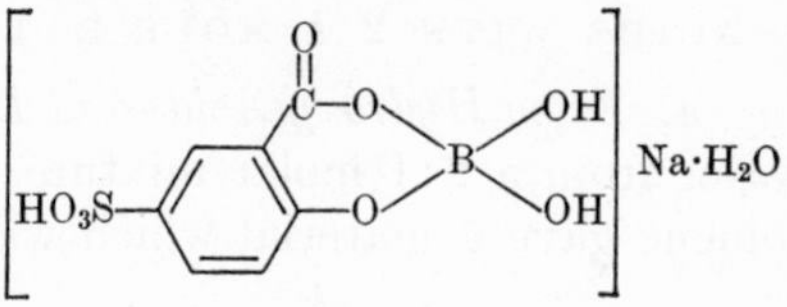 (XI)

converted to the potassium salt (XII) by evaporation of a solution of (XI) in hot aqueous alcoholic potassium hydroxide.[3]

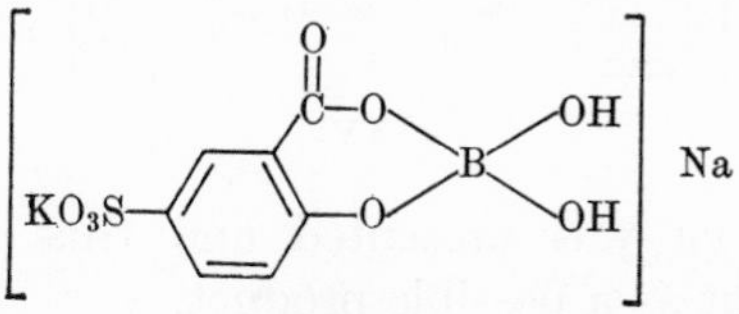

(XII)

The lithium, sodium, potassium, magnesium and ammonium salts of the 1:1 complex of citric acid and boric acid, presumably (XIII) or (XIV)† were obtained from water solutions containing

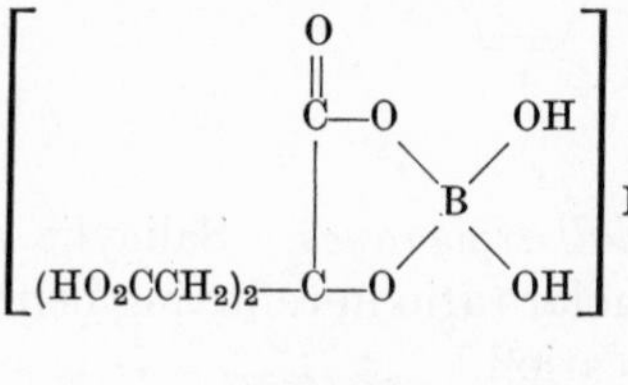

(XIII) 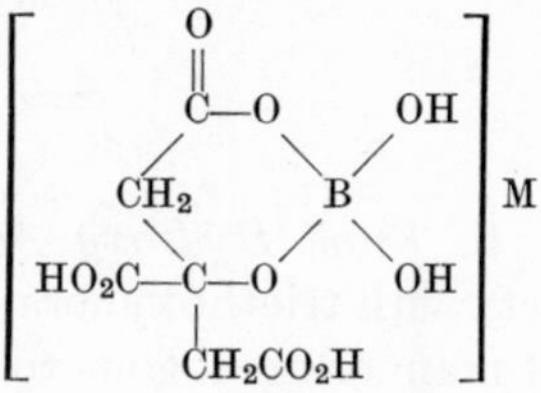 (XIV)

* The salt actually was formulated as the trihydrate,

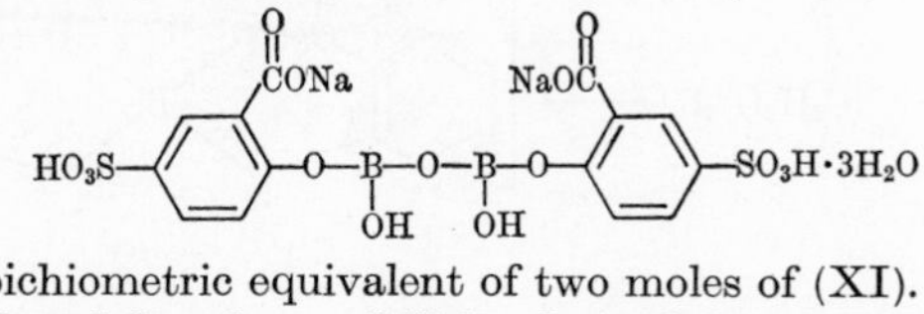

which is the stoichiometric equivalent of two moles of (XI).

† The third and fourth possibilities derived from reaction of citric acid as a dibasic acid are unlikely on the basis of the relatively unfavorable seven- and eight-membered rings.

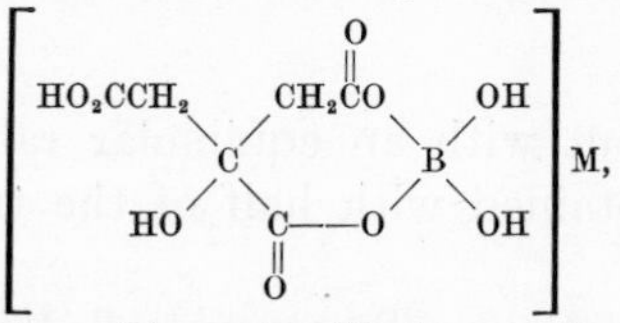

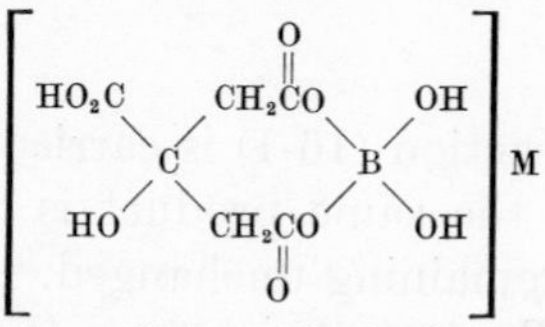

the theoretical stoichiometry of boric acid, citric acid and the appropriate carbonate or bicarbonate.[60]

2. ACIDS WITH 2:1 MOLE RATIO HYDROXY ACID TO BORON

a. *From Hydroxy Acids and Boric Acid.* Azeotropic removal of water from a 2:1 molar mixture of salicylic acid and boric acid in toluene gave a material which was believed to be the acid (XV).[63]

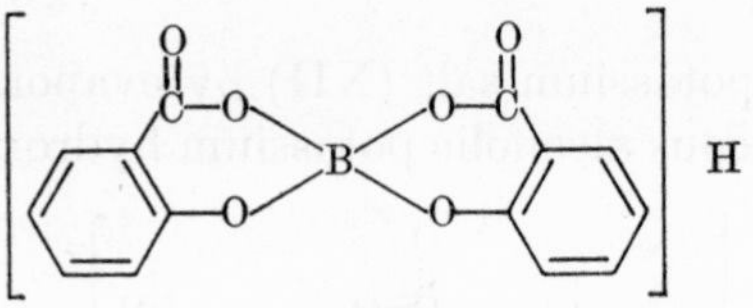

(XV)

No structural proof was presented and thus the isomer (XVI) cannot be ruled out as a possible product.

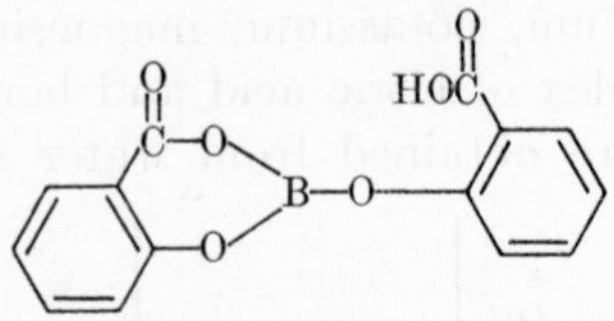

(XVI)

b. *From Hydroxy Acids and Trialkoxyboranes.* Salicylic acid reacts with triethoxyborane in a 1:2 molar ratio in refluxing benzene in a manner analogous to transesterification.

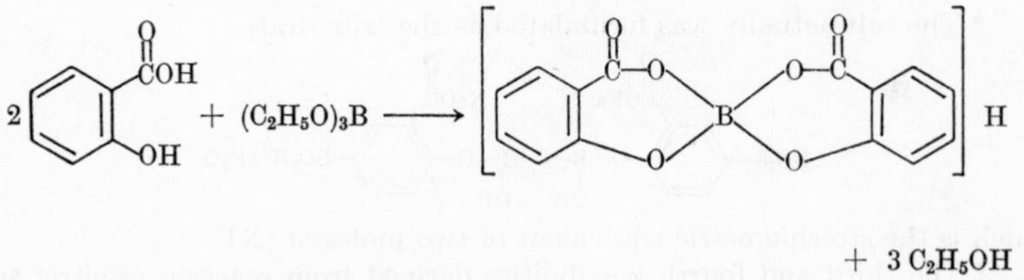

$$2\,C_6H_4(OH)COOH + (C_2H_5O)_3B \longrightarrow [B(O_2CC_6H_4O)_2]H + 3\,C_2H_5OH \qquad (16\text{-}1)$$

When reaction (16-1) is carried out with an equimolar ratio of reactants, the same product is obtained with half of the triethoxyborane remaining unchanged.[51]

c. *From Acetoxyborane Derivatives.* Treatment of (XVII) with wet acetic acid or reaction of salicylic acid with oxybis(diacetoxyborane) in either ether or benzene solution is reported to give the crystalline acid (XV).[35]

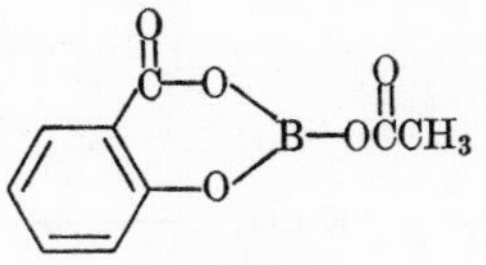

(XVII)

d. *From Salts with 2:1 Mole Ratio Hydroxy Acid to Boron.* Treatment of zinc bissalicylatoborate with hydrogen sulfide and removal of zinc sulfide resulted in the precipitation of hydrogen

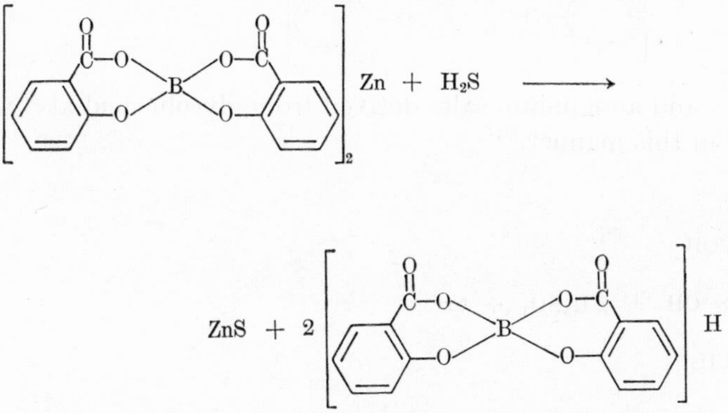

$$[\ldots]_2\text{Zn} + H_2S \longrightarrow ZnS + 2[\ldots]\text{H} \qquad (16\text{-}2)$$

bissalicylatoborate.[40] This work could not be confirmed.[54]

e. *From Other Sources.* The acid (XVIII) was referred to by Hermans[41] without experimental details.

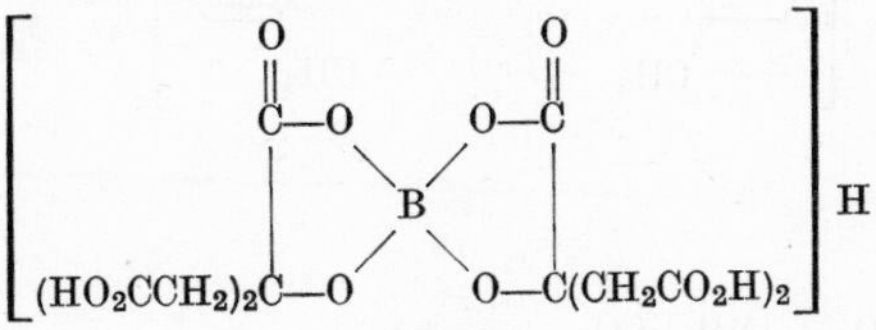

$(HO_2CCH_2)_2C$—O … O—$C(CH_2CO_2H)_2$ … H

(XVIII)

3. SALTS WITH 2:1 MOLE RATIO HYDROXY ACID TO BORON

a. *From Hydroxy Acid, Boric Acid and Base.* A variety of bissalicylatoborate salts were isolated by concentrating or cooling an aqueous solution of salicyclic acid, boric acid and the appropriate base or carbonate (16-3).[21,38,39,44,54,55,57] Ammonia in place of the carbonate led to the ammonium salt,[44] and borax instead of the boric acid and carbonate led to the sodium salt.[44,54] The anilinium,[54] pyridinium[54] and strychninium[21,29,55] salts were prepared similarly. The calcium salt derived from *o*-cresotic acid and the calcium,

$$4\ o\text{-}HOC_6H_4COOH + 2\ H_3BO_3 + K_2CO_3 \longrightarrow 2\left[B(O_2CC_6H_4O)_2\right]K + CO_2 + 7\ H_2O \qquad (16\text{-}3)$$

potassium and ammonium salts derived from glycolic acid also were prepared in this manner.[57]

$$4\ HO(CH_3)C_6H_3COOH + 2\ H_3BO_3 + CaCO_3 \longrightarrow \left[B(O_2CC_6H_3(CH_3)O)_2\right]_2 Ca\cdot 5H_2O + 2\ H_2O + CO_2 \qquad (16\text{-}4)$$

$$4\ HOC(=O)CH_2OH + 2\ H_3BO_3 + (NH_4)_2CO_3 \longrightarrow 2\left[B(O_2CCH_2O)_2\right]^{-} NH_4 + CO_2 + 7\ H_2O \qquad (16\text{-}5)$$

Sodium bisglycolatoborate was too soluble to isolate and formed a syrup on concentration of the reaction mixture.[57]

The aniline, *o*-toluidine and dimethylaniline salts (XIX) were prepared by evaporation of an aqueous solution of two moles of the hydroxy acid and one mole each of boric acid and the base. An alcohol solution was employed for the brucine salts (XIX) and (XX)[22] and the dimethylaniline salt (XXI).[23]

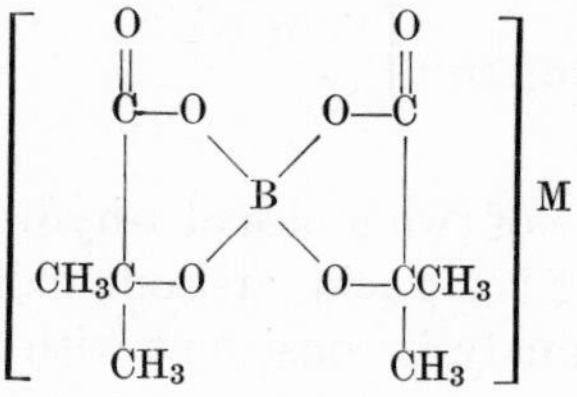

M (XIX)

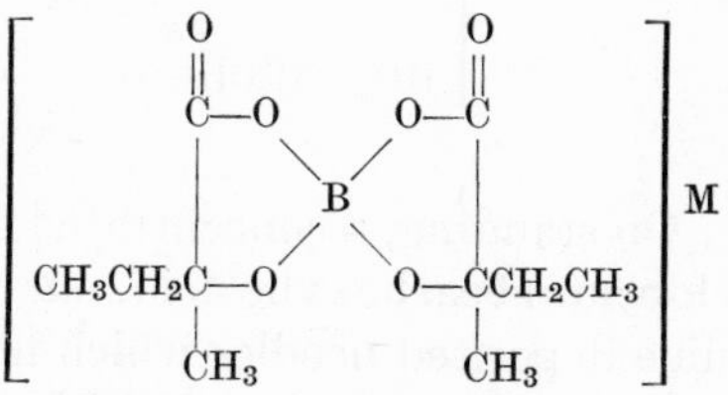

M (XX)

$C_6H_5NH(CH_3)_2$

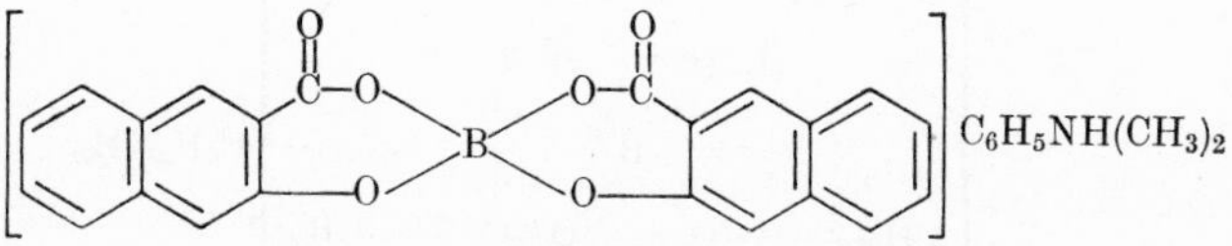

(XXI)

The potassium salt (XXII)* was precipitated from a solution of boric acid and potassium acid tartrate.[49] The monohydrate of the ammonium salt corresponding to (XXII) was obtained from a

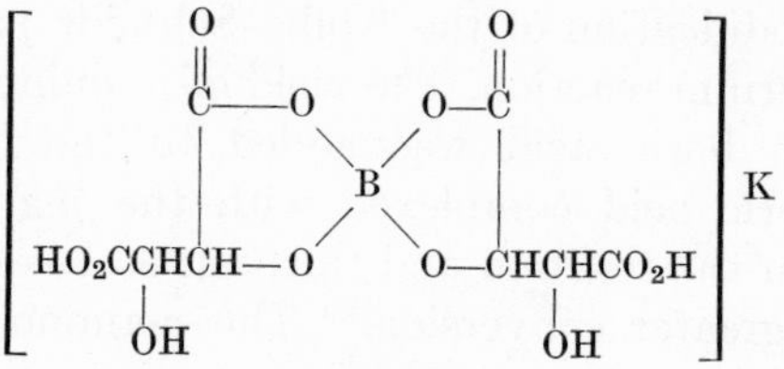

K

(XXII)

solution of tartaric acid, ammonium tartrate and boric acid. The

* The structure proposed in reference 57,

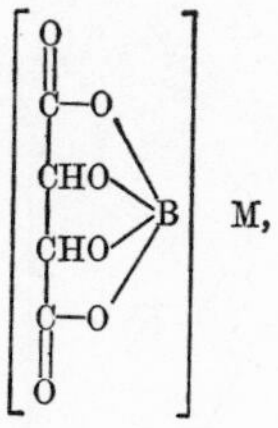

M,

clearly is sterically prohibited.

similar malic acid salt (XXIII) was obtained from a solution of malic acid, boric acid and potassium hydroxide.[45]

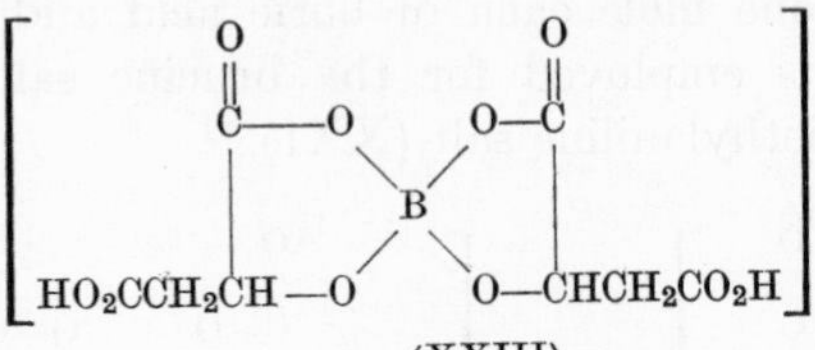

(XXIII)

On standing, a concentrated solution of two moles of 1-hydroxycyclopentanecarboxylic acid, one mole of boric acid, and one mole of aniline deposited needles which had an analysis consistent with that calculated for structure (XXIV).[42]

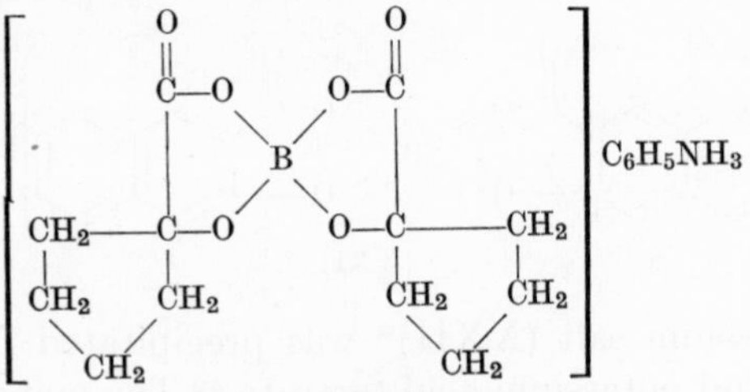

(XXIV)

The formation of *p*-aminosalicylic acid from *m*-aminophenol in the aqueous modification of the Kolbe–Schmidt process was shown to be an equilibrium reaction. The yield of *p*-aminosalicylic acid was increased when boric acid was added to the reaction mixture. Presumably boric acid complexed with the *p*-aminosalicylic acid (16-6) formed in the reaction and thus served to displace the equilibrium toward greater conversion.[36] The *p*-amino group would act as the necessary base.

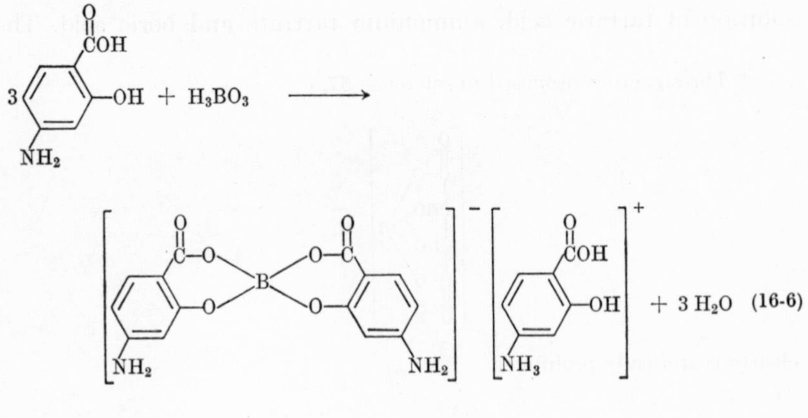

$+ 3\,H_2O$ (16-6)

b. *From Hydroxy Acid Salts and Boric Acid.* A concentrated equimolar solution of sodium salicylate and boric acid deposited the crystalline salt (X). The potassium salt is obtained similarly.[57]

c. *From Acids with* 2:1 *Mole Ratio Hydroxy Acid to Boron.* Amine salts such as (XXV) and (XXVI) were obtained by reaction of the acids (XIV) and (XXVII) with the appropriate amine in chloroform[63] or benzene[62] solution.

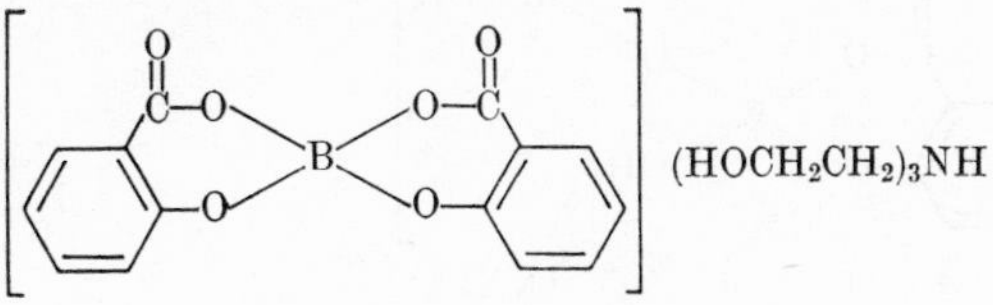

$(HOCH_2CH_2)_3NH$

(XXV)

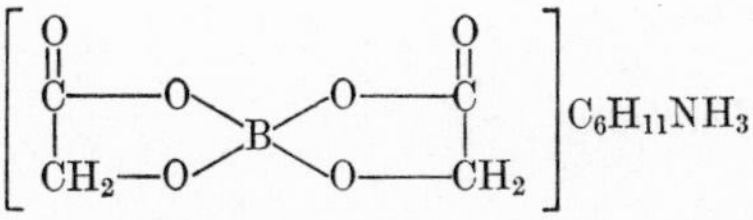

$C_6H_{11}NH_3$ H

(XXVI) 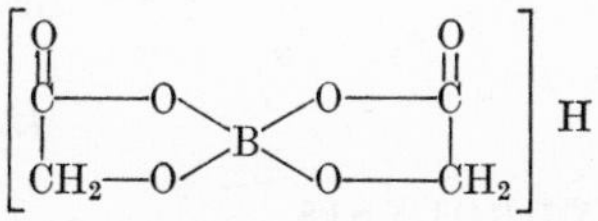 (XXVII)

The reaction of (XXVIIIa) with silver nitrate has been reported to give the silver salt (XXVIIIb);[54] no experimental details were given.

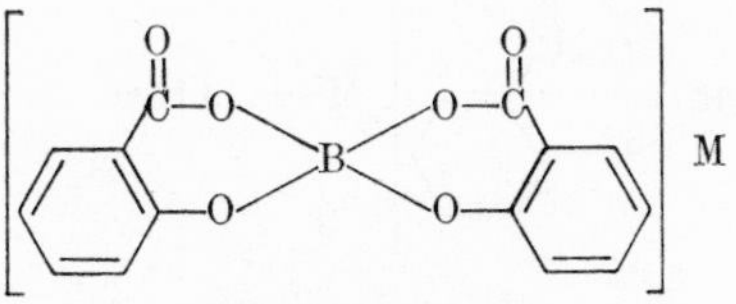

M

(XXVIIa, M = H)
(XXVIIb, M = Ag)

d. *From Other Salts with* 2:1 *Mole Ratio Hydroxy Acid to Boron.* The barium, lead and silver salts of bissalicylatoborate were precipitated from a water solution of the sodium salt on addition of soluble salts of the three metals. Zinc, mercury and copper salts could not be made by this method.[44]

The heavy metal salts of bisglycolatoborate could not be isolated from reaction mixtures with sodium bisglycolatoborate presumably due to hydrolysis of the products.[57]

4. SALTS WITH 2:3 MOLE RATIO HYDROXY ACID TO BORON

Hydrated sodium, cadmium and barium salts with a salicylic acid to boron mole ratio of 2:3 have been prepared by slow evaporation of solutions containing equimolar amounts of salicylic acid and boric acid and the appropriate cation. The salts were formulated as (XXIX).[59]

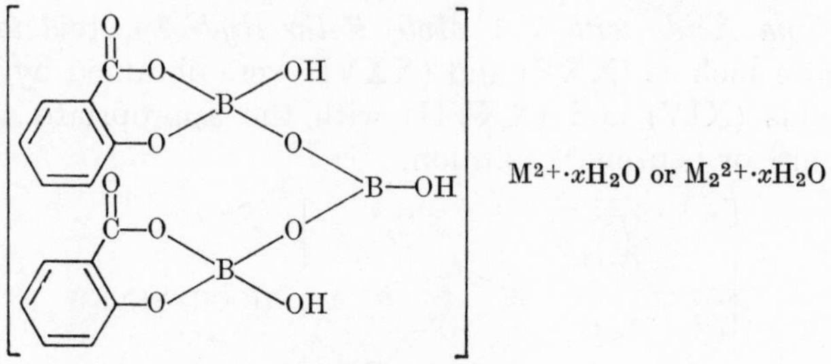

$M^{2+}\cdot xH_2O$ or $M_2{}^{2+}\cdot xH_2O$

(XXIX)

$M^+ = Na, x = 5$
$M^{2+} = Cd, x = 4$
$M^{2+} = Ba, x = 1$

B. Reactions

1. HYDROLYSIS

Hydrogen bissalicylatoborate[35] and its salts[39,44,54,57] (16-7) as well as salts of dihydroxysalicylatoborate derivatives[3] (16-8) hydrolyze in water to give salicylic acid, its salts, and boric acid.

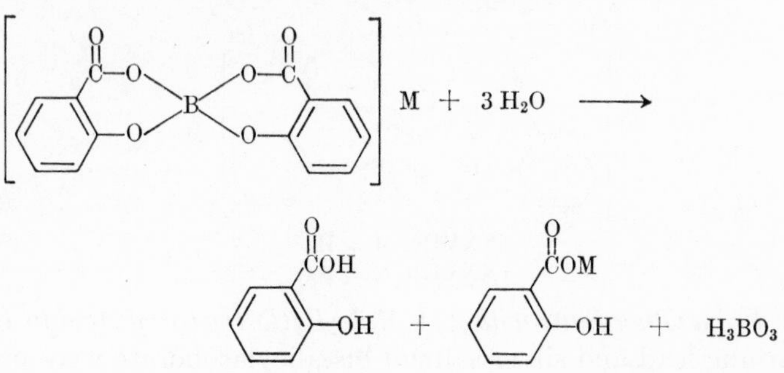

$$[\ldots]M + 3\,H_2O \longrightarrow (\text{salicylic acid}) + (\text{M salicylate}) + H_3BO_3 \quad (16\text{-}7)$$

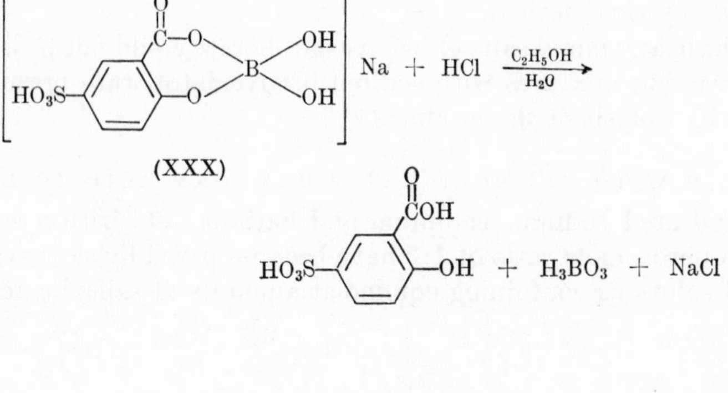

$$[\ldots]Na + HCl \xrightarrow[H_2O]{C_2H_5OH} HO_3S\text{-}(\text{salicylic acid}) + H_3BO_3 + NaCl \quad (16\text{-}8)$$

(XXX)

Treatment of (XXX) with ferric chloride solution produces a violet color.[3,44]

2. ALCOHOLYSIS

Some evidence is available indicating the inertness of sodium bissalicylatoborate to alcoholysis by ethanol. An ultraviolet spectrum of the complex in absolute ethanol solution differed from the spectrum of an ethanol solution of the components, salicylic acid, boric acid and sodium hydroxide.[2]

3. PYROLYSIS

The monohydrate of sodium bissalicylatoborate[44] loses its water of hydration when it is heated to 120°; the zinc monohydrate decomposes with evolution of phenol on melting at 110°.[39] The magnesium and calcium decahydrates require 150° for dehydration.[44]

Dihydroxysalicylatoborate derivatives can be converted to trigonal coplanar compounds (see Chapter 8) by thermal dehydration.[59]

$$[C_6H_4(COO)(O)B(OH)_2]M \xrightarrow{-H_2O} C_6H_4(COO)(O)BOM \qquad (16\text{-}9)$$

The tetrahydrate of the cadmium derivative (XXXI) loses four moles of water in the presence of phosphorus pentoxide at 75° and a fifth mole of water at 150°.[59] Presumably, this involves the formation of B–O–B type materials such as (XXXII).

$$[\{C_6H_4(COO)(O)B(OH)O\}_2B{-}OH]\ Cd\cdot 4H_2O$$

(XXXI)

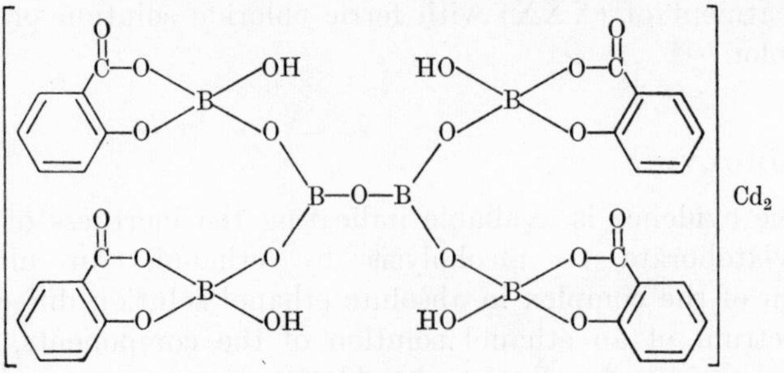

(XXXII)

4. WITH HYDROGEN SULFIDE

The treatment of zinc bissalicylatoborate with hydrogen sulfide has been discussed in Section III-A-2-d.

IV. DIBASIC ACID DERIVATIVES

A. Methods of Preparation

Sodium, potassium, lithium, ammonium and magnesium salts of the 2:1 complex of boric acid and citric acid reportedly were obtained from a water solution containing the appropriate carbonate or bicarbonate salt and a 1:2 mole ratio of citric acid to boric acid.[60] If the products indeed were discrete chemical species, there appears to be no logical way to accommodate the stoichiometry without recourse to a dibasic acid bidentate ligand with unlikely seven- and eight-membered rings (XXXIII or XXXIV).

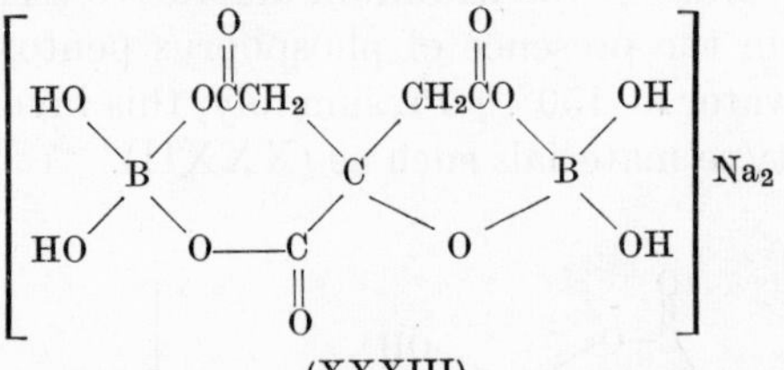

(XXXIII)

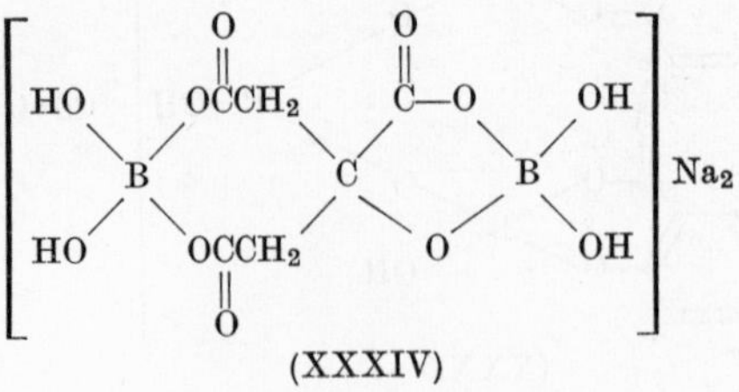

(XXXIV)

Fractional crystallization of a boiled and cooled equimolar solution of boric acid and potassium hydrogen oxalate resulted in a crystalline material with an analysis consistent with that of (XXXV).[31] Dipotassium oxalate instead of potassium hydrogen

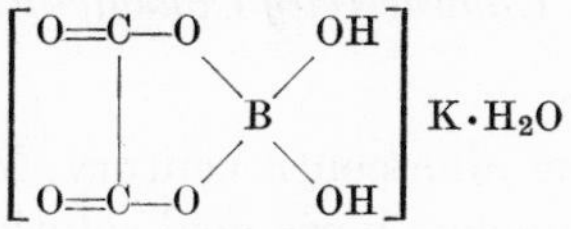

```
⎡O=C—O      OH⎤
⎢ |    \   /  ⎥
⎢ |      B    ⎥ K·H2O
⎢ |    /   \  ⎥
⎣O=C—O      OH⎦
```

(XXXV)

oxalate led to (XXXVI).

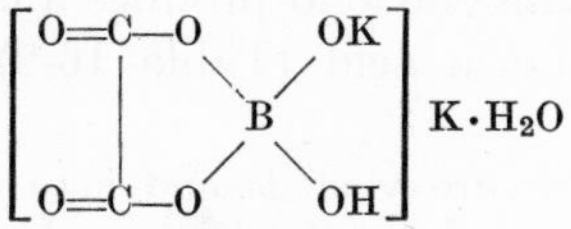

```
⎡O=C—O      OK⎤
⎢ |    \   /  ⎥
⎢ |      B    ⎥ K·H2O
⎢ |    /   \  ⎥
⎣O=C—O      OH⎦
```

(XXXVI)

B. Reactions

Hydrolysis of this class of compounds is indicated by the precipitation of barium oxalate on treatment of (XXXV) with a barium chloride solution. Alcoholysis is shown by the residue of potassium acid oxalate obtained on treatment of (XXXV) with ethanol.[31]

V. STEREOCHEMICAL CONSIDERATIONS

A. Introduction

As in the case of the coordination compounds derived from diols which is described in Chapter 15, the ability of hydroxy acids (XXXVII) and dibasic acids (XXXVIII) to form five- and six-

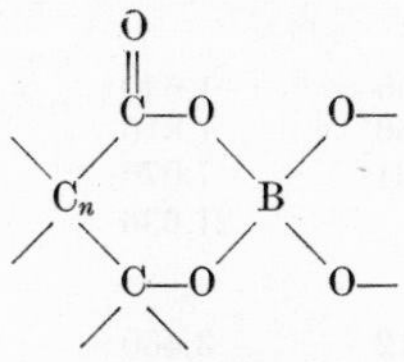

```
        O                                 O
        ‖                                 ‖
        C—O     O—                        C—O     O—
  \   /     \  /                    \   /     \  /
    Cn        B                       Cn        B
  /   \     /  \                    /   \     /  \
        C—O     O—                        C—O     O—
      /   \                                ‖
                                           O
```

(XXXVII) 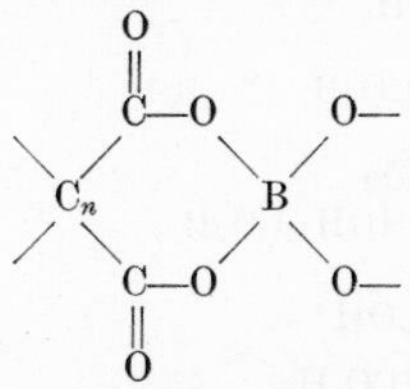 (XXXVIII)

membered rings with boric acid gives insight into the stereochemical relationships between the functional groups of the acid. The extent of the ability of the acid to form the rings (XXXVII) and

(XXXVIII) is measured, as in the case of the diols of Chapter 15, by observing the changes in conductivity, rotatory power and acidity of aqueous solutions of the organic acids and boric acid.*

B. Conductivity Considerations

1. HYDROXY ACIDS

At the close of the nineteenth century, Magnanini[50] found that the conductivity of aqueous boric acid solutions is enhanced by aliphatic α-hydroxy acids and aromatic *o*-hydroxy acids. β-Hydroxy acids and *m*- and *p*-hydroxy acids were without effect. Thus glycolic acid, lactic acid and salicylic acid produce a considerable increase in the conductivity of boric acid (Table 16-2); whereas β-hydroxy-

Table 16-2. Effects of hydroxy acids and keto acids on conductivity of aqueous 0.5 molar boric acid at 25°

Acid	Conc. (mole/l.)	Δ^a	Reference
α-Hydroxy acids			
$HOCH_2CO_2H$	0.0625	340	14
	0.5	441	5, 12, 15, 19
$HOCH_2CH(OH)CO_2H$	0.0625	2,180	14
	0.5	18,660	15, 30
	0.5	21,700	5, 12
$CH_3CH(OH)CO_2H$	0.05	1,465	14
	0.5	14,213	5, 12, 15, 18
$(CH_3)_2C(OH)CO_2H$	0.0625	5,655	14
	0.5	41,307	5
	0.5	41,370	10, 12, 15
$CH_3CH_2C(OH)(CH_3)CO_2H$	0.0156	1,630	20
	0.0156	1,810	26
	0.0634	7,070	14
$HOCH_2(CHOH)_4CO_2H$	0.5	21,636	5, 12, 15, 30
(S-ring)C(OH)CO_2H	0.0312	3,460	14

(*Table continued*)

* It has been proposed that the enhanced solubility of oxalic acid and tartaric acid in boric acid solution is due to complex formation.[43]

Table 16-2 (*continued*)

Acid	Conc. (mole/l.)	Δ[a]	Reference
$CH_3(CH_2)_5\overset{OH}{C}HCO_2H$	0.00781	370	14, 30
	0.00781	416	5, 12
$C_6H_5\overset{OH}{C}HCO_2H$	0.0625	2,510	14
	0.5	19,313	18
dl-$C_6H_5\overset{OH}{C}HCO_2H$	0.5	21,500	5, 12
	0.5	21,725	15, 27
d-$C_6H_5\overset{OH}{C}HCO_2H$	0.5	21,222	15, 27
$C_6H_5CH_2\overset{OH}{C}HCO_2H$	0.0625	1,990	14
	0.125	3,950	12, 15, 19
2,4,6-$(CH_3)_3C_6H_2\overset{OH}{C}HCO_2H$	0.04	1,200	17
	0.04	1,325	14
$(C_6H_5)_2\overset{OH}{C}CO_2H$	0.00781	555	5, 10, 12, 15
	0.00781	655	14
9-fluorenyl: $(C_6H_4)_2C(OH)CO_2H$	0.01	482	10, 12, 15
	0.01	600	14
α-Hydroxy dibasic acids			
$HO_2CCH_2\overset{OH}{C}HCO_2H$	0.0156	530	6
	0.05	1,730	14
$HO_2C(HO)C{=}C(OH)CO_2H$	0.00629	200	30
meso-$HO_2C\overset{OH}{C}H\text{—}\overset{OH}{C}HCO_2H$	0.0625	3,746	7
	0.0625	4,120	14

(*Table continued*)

Table 16-2 (*continued*)

Acid	Conc. (mole/l.)	Δ[a]	Reference
dl-$HO_2CCH(OH)—CH(OH)CO_2H$	0.0625	4,170	7
	0.5	17,107	15, 27
d-$HO_2CCH(OH)—CH(OH)CO_2H$	0.0625	4,158	7
	0.0625	4,390	14
	0.5	16,836	15, 27
$HO_2CCH_2C(OH)(CO_2H)CH_2CO_2H$	0.0124	842	20
	0.0495	4,020	14
β-Hydroxy acids			
$HOCH_2CH_2CO_2H$	0.5	0	5, 12
$CH_3CH(OH)CH_2CO_2H$	0.48	0	10, 12, 15
$Cl_3CCH(OH)CH_2CO_2H$	0.5	0	5, 12
$C_6H_5CH(OH)CH_2CO_2H$	0.5	0	5, 15, 19
Meconic acid (4-pyrone ring: C=O; HC, C—OH; HO_2C—C, C—CO_2H; O)	4.88×10^{-4}	0	65
γ-Hydroxy acids			
$CH_3CH(OH)CH_2CH_2CO_2H$	0.5	0	5, 12
δ-Hydroxy acids			
Comenic acid (4-pyrone ring: C=O; HO—C, CH; CH, C—CO_2H; O)	4.88×10^{-4}	0	65

(*Table continued*)

Table 16-2 (*continued*)

Acid	Conc. (mole/l.)	Δ[a]	Reference
Aromatic hydroxy acids			
CO_2H, OH	0.0156	1,264	5, 6, 9, 12
	0.0156	1,400	13
CO_2H, HO, OH	0.0156	1,501	5, 6, 12
	0.0156	1,605	13
HO, CO_2H, OH	0.0156	1,104	6, 12
	0.0156	1,245	13
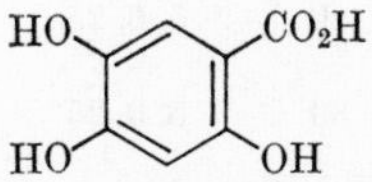 HO, CO_2H, HO, OH	0.0156	1,102	5
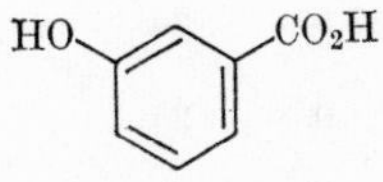 HO, CO_2H	?	0	6, 9, 12, 13
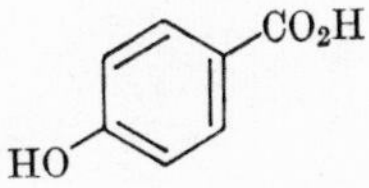 CO_2H, HO	?	0	6, 9, 12, 13
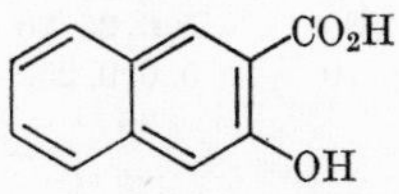 CO_2H, OH	5.53×10^{-4}	0	23
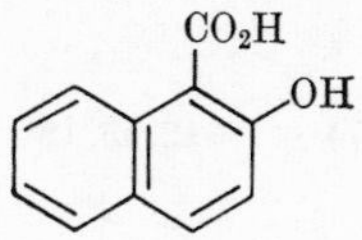 CO_2H, OH	7.45×10^{-4}	27	23
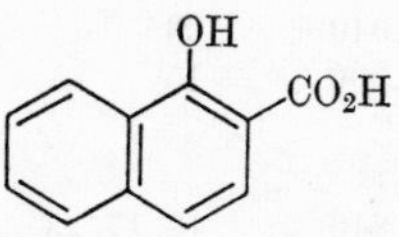 OH, CO_2H	9.52×10^{-4}	25	23

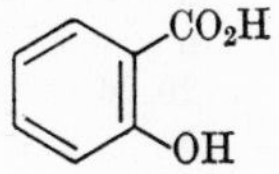

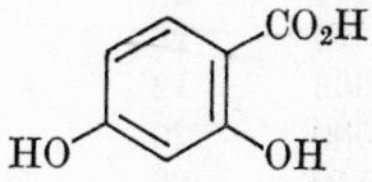

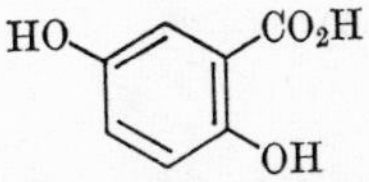

(*Table continued*)

Table 16-2 (*continued*)

Acid	Conc. (mole/l.)	Δ^a	Reference
Alicyclic α-hydroxy acids			
1-Hydroxycyclopropanecarboxylic acid	0.0156	66	8
	0.0156	104	6
1-Hydroxycyclobutanecarboxylic acid	0.0156	0	20, 26
	0.0156	± 125	8
	0.0156	± 200	6
1-Hydroxycyclopentanecarboxylic acid	0.0156	1,400	20
	0.0156	1,510	26
1-Hydroxycyclohexanecarboxylic acid	0.00781	656	12
	0.0156	1,500	20
	0.0156	1,540	26
1-Hydroxycycloheptanecarboxylic acid	0.0156	1,430	20
	0.0156	1,500	26
Alicyclic β-hydroxy acids			
cis-2-Hydroxycyclopentanecarboxylic acid	0.125	96	5, 6, 25
trans-2-Hydroxycyclopentanecarboxylic acid	0.125	0	5, 6, 25
cis-5-Methyl-2-hydroxycyclopentanecarboxylic acid	0.125	89	5, 6, 25
trans-5-Methyl-2-hydroxycyclopentanecarboxylic acid	0.125	0	5, 6
cis-2-Hydroxycyclohexanecarboxylic acid (structure in doubt)	0.0625	33.8	25
trans-2-Hydroxycyclohexanecarboxylic acid	0.125	0	25
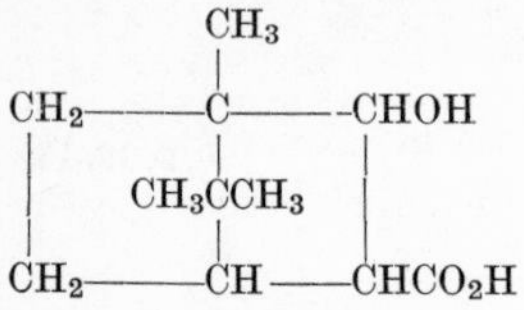 CH_3 CH_2—C—$CHOH$ CH_3CCH_3 CH_2—CH—$CHCO_2H$			
cis-Borneolcarboxylic acid	0.0156	530	5, 6, 25, 26
trans-Borneolcarboxylic acid	0.0156	0	5, 6, 9, 25, 26
Keto acids			
$CH_3\overset{O}{\overset{\|}{C}}CO_2H$	0.5	16,574	12, 15, 18
$(CH_3)_3C\overset{O}{\overset{\|}{C}}CO_2H$	0.5	902	12, 24
	0.25	1,940	23
	0.5	10,900	15
$C_6H_5\overset{O}{\overset{\|}{C}}CO_2H$	0.0667	840	12, 17, 23

(*Table continued*)

Table 16-2 (*continued*)

Acid	Conc. (mole/l.)	Δ^a	Reference
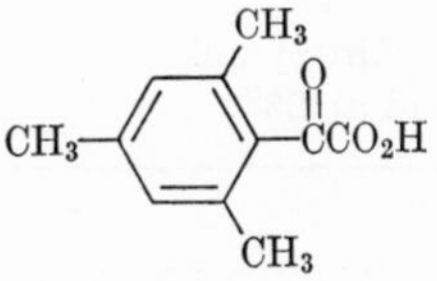 CH_3–$C_6H_2(CH_3)_2$–$\overset{O}{\overset{\Vert}{C}}CO_2H$ (2,4,6-trimethylphenyl)	0.0333	460	12, 17, 23
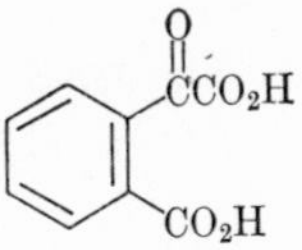 $C_6H_4(\overset{O}{\overset{\Vert}{C}}CO_2H)(CO_2H)$	0.2	1,940	12, 17, 23
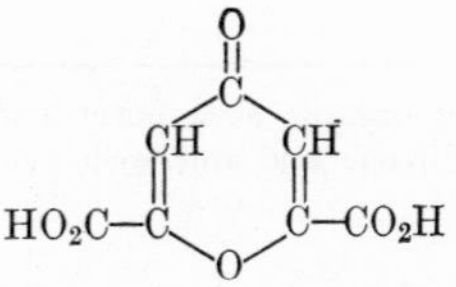 HO_2C–C=CH–C(=O)–CH=C–CO_2H (ring through O) (Chelidonic acid)	4.88×10^{-4}	0	65

[a] Δ = Conductivity increment = observed conductivity of organic acid–boric acid solution minus the sum of the conductivities of the individual organic acid and boric acid solutions in Kohlrausch–Holborn[46] units $\times 10^6$.

propionic acid and *m*-hydroxybenzoic acid do not. These observations, as discussed for the case of diols and diphenols in Chapter 15, are consistent with the planarity of the five-membered ring (XXXIX), the planarity of the six-membered ring (XL), the probable conformation of the β-hydroxy acid (XLI), and the non-planarity of the six-membered ring (XLII). The enhancement of

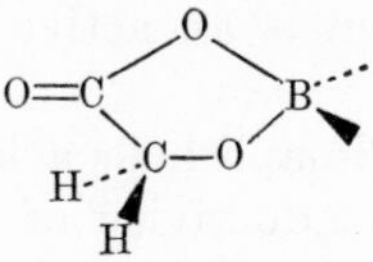

(XXXIX)

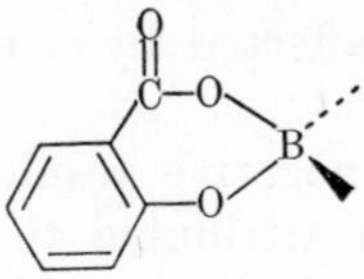

(XL)

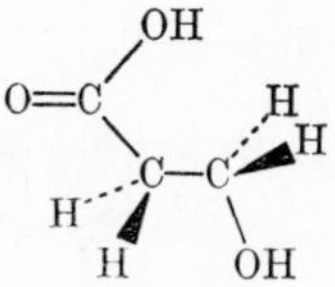

(XLI)

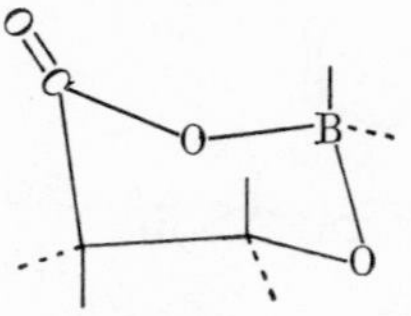

(XLII)

conductivity by a hydroxy acid is thus a diagnostic tool since it indicates an α- or an *o*-hydroxy configuration.[16] This is borne out by the data on a large number of derivatives (see Table 16-2).

It is seen in Table 16-3 (abstracted from Table 16-2) that the

Table 16-3. Effect of steric requirements of the hydroxy acid on conductivity of aqueous 0.5 molar boric acid at 25°

α-Hydroxy acid	Δ[a]
$HOCH_2CO_2H$	441
$CH_3CH(OH)CO_2H$	14,213
$(CH_3)_2C(OH)CO_2H$	41,307

[a] Δ = Conductivity increment = observed conductivity of organic acid–boric acid solution minus the sum of the conductivities of the individual dibasic acid and boric acid solutions in Kohlrausch–Holborn[46] units × 10^6.

values of Δ increase as the steric requirements of the α-hydroxy acid increase. This was attributed to the stabilization of the conformation with coplanar hydroxyl and carboxyl groups (XLIII); other con-

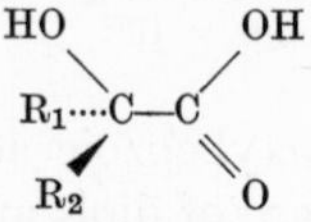

HO OH
R_1····C—C
R_2 O

(XLIII)

formations put one of the carboxyl oxygen atoms in opposition to a bulky R group.[20,26]

From work with racemic and active mandelic acid and tartaric acid it was concluded that the boric acid conductivity increment was not affected by a racemic mixture versus an active enantiomorph.[27]

The negative result with 3-hydroxy-β-naphthoic acid (Table 16-2) was attributed to the high initial conductivity of the acid itself which is decreased in the presence of boric acid by the formation of the neutral compound (XLIV), in contrast to the strong acids

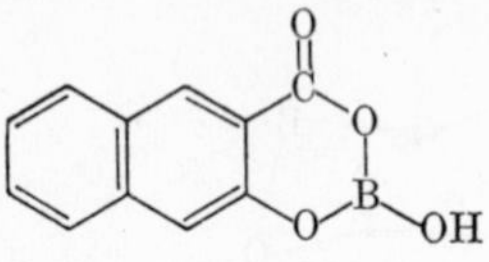

(XLIV)

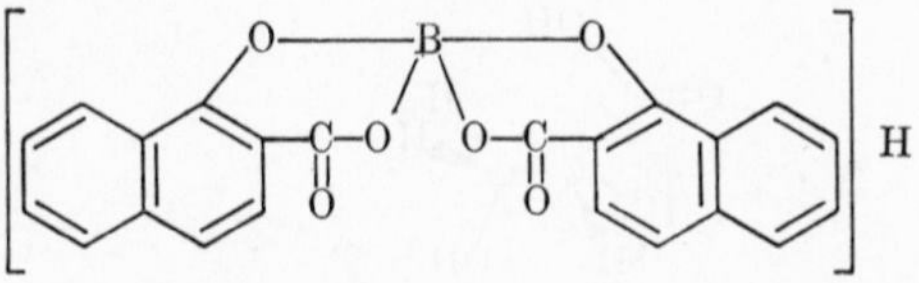

(XLV)

(XLV) and (XLVI) formed by the α-hydroxy-β-naphthoic and β-hydroxy-α-naphthoic acids which did effect a conductivity increment.[23]

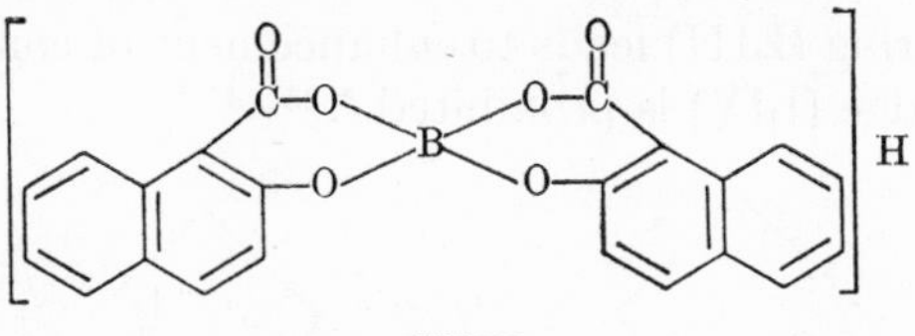

(XLVI)

Comparison of the high conductivity increment for the *o*-hydroxybenzoic acids with the relatively low value found for the catechol derivative (XLVII) (see Chapter 15) suggests that conductivity measurements in the presence of boric acid offer a means of distinguishing between compounds such as (XLVIII) and (XLIX).

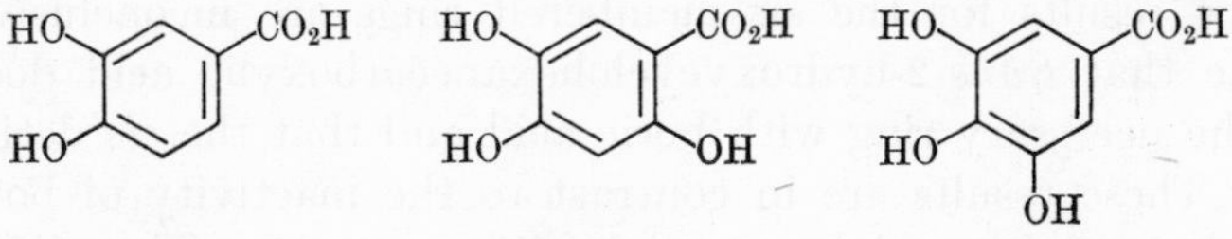

(XLVII) (XLVIII) (XLIX)

Five-, six- and seven-membered ring alicyclic α-hydroxy acids allow the spiran structure (L) to form with equal facility as evidenced by similar large Δ values (Table 16-2).

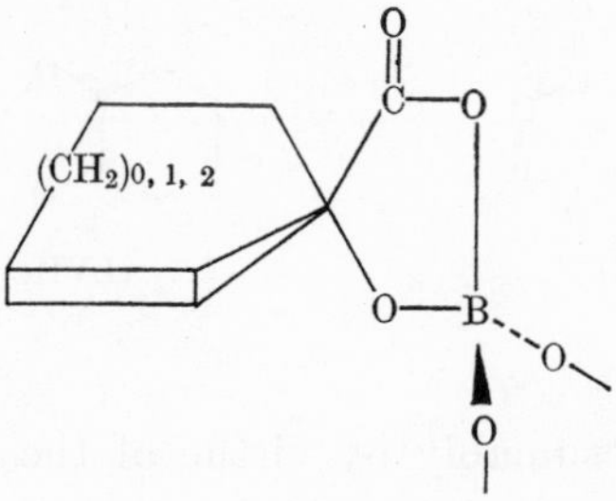

$(CH_2)_{0,\,1,\,2}$

(L)

In the cyclopropane (LI) and cyclobutane (LII) derivatives,

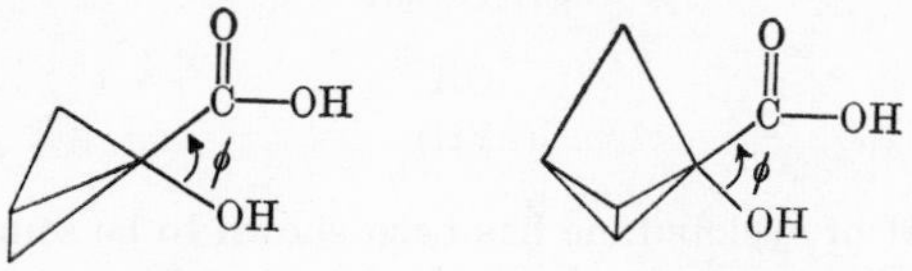

(LI) (LII)

however, the three- and four-membered rings have a larger angle ϕ* which prevents formation of the five-membered boron ring.[8,20,26]

For alicyclic β-hydroxy acids, as in the case of the alicyclic diols in Chapter 15, it is seen in Table 16-2 that a *cis*-bridge on a five-membered ring (LIII) leads to enhancement of conductivity and that a *trans*-bridge (LIV) is prohibited.[5,25,26]

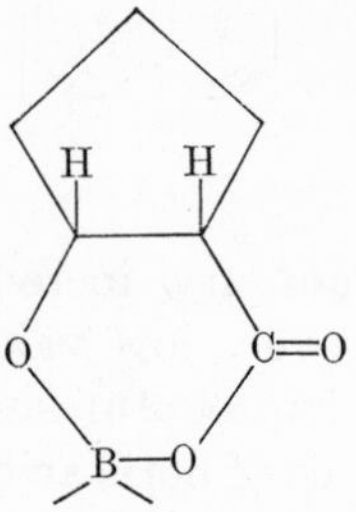

(LIII) 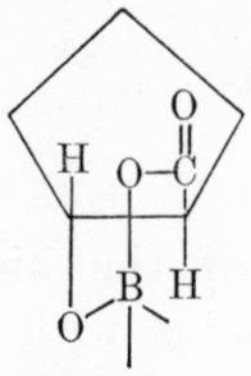 (LIV)

The results for the six-membered rings are inconclusive but indicate that *trans*-2-hydroxycyclohexanecarboxylic acid does not form the necessary ring with boric acid and that the *cis* derivative does.[25] These results are in contrast to the inactivity of both the *cis* and *trans*-1,2-cyclohexanediols (Chapter 15). The difference might be due to the greater ease of formation of a boron-containing six-membered ring (LV) as contrasted to the five-membered ring (LVI) from the *cis*-equatorial-polar hydroxyl substituents on a cyclohexane ring.

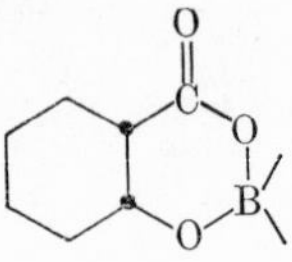

(LV) 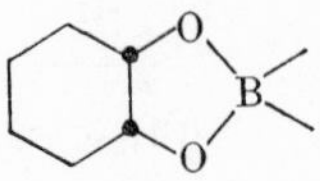 (LVI)

2. KETO ACIDS

Pyruvic acid, presumably by virtue of the hydrated carbonyl (LVII), gave a large enhancement of conductivity comparable to

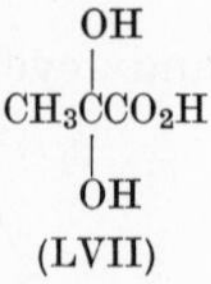

$$CH_3C(OH)_2CO_2H$$

(LVII)

* The ∠HCH of cyclobutane has been shown to be somewhat increased from the normal.[37]

that of lactic acid.[18] That the enhancement was due at least in part to hydration of the carbonyl group and not entirely due to enolization (LVIII) was shown by the conductivity increment of trimethylpyruvic acid (LIX)[15,24] and phenylglyoxylic acid (LX),[12,17] both of which are incapable of enolization.

$$\underset{\text{(LVIII)}}{CH_2{=}\overset{\overset{\large OH}{|}}{C}HCO_2H} \qquad \underset{\text{(LIX)}}{(CH_3)_3C\overset{\overset{\large O}{\|}}{C}CO_2H} \qquad \underset{\text{(LX)}}{C_6H_5\overset{\overset{\large O}{\|}}{C}CO_2H}$$

3. DIBASIC ACIDS

With the exception of oxalic acid, dibasic acids (Table 16-4) do

Table 16-4. Effect of dibasic acids on conductivity of aqueous 0.5 molar boric acid at 25°

Acid		Conc. (mole/l.)	Δ[a]	Reference
Oxalic	HO_2CCO_2H	0.1	2,270	15, 28
Malonic	$CH_2(CO_2H)_2$	0.167	0	28
Diethylmalonic	$(CH_3CH_2)_2C(CO_2H)_2$	0.5	0	11
Succinic	$(CH_2CO_2H)_2$	0.0417	0	28
Glutaric	$CH_2(CH_2CO_2H)_2$	0.0417	0	28
Diglycolic	$O(CH_2CO_2H)_2$	0.5	0	12, 19
Adipic	$(CH_2CH_2CO_2H)_2$	0.0417	0	28
Maleic	$CHCO_2H{=}CHCO_2H$ (cis)	0.125	0	28
Fumaric	$HO_2CCH{=}CHCO_2H$ (trans)	0.0417	0	28
Glutaconic	$HO_2CCH{=}CHCH_2CO_2H$	0.0417	0	28

[a] Δ = Conductivity increment = observed conductivity of organic acid–boric acid solution minus the sum of the conductivities of the individual dibasic acid and boric acid solutions in Kohlrausch–Holborn[46] units $\times 10^6$.

not produce a conductivity increment with boric acid solution.[28] Presumably the equilibria (16-10) and (16-11) involving six-membered

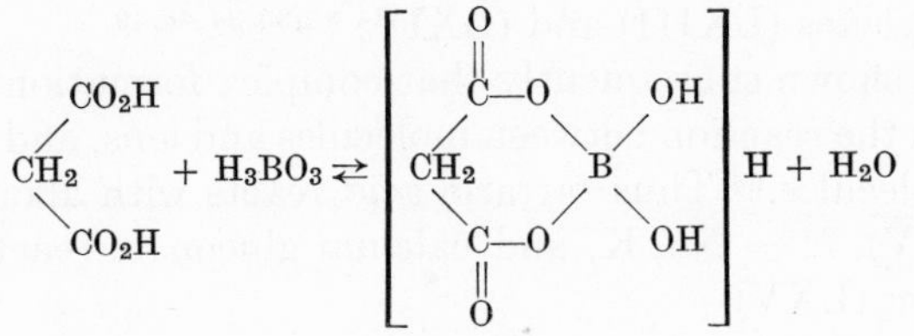

$$CH_2(CO_2H)_2 + H_3BO_3 \rightleftarrows \left[CH_2\begin{matrix} \diagup C(=O){-}O \diagdown \\ \diagdown C(=O){-}O \diagup \end{matrix} B \begin{matrix} OH \\ OH \end{matrix} \right] H + H_2O \qquad (16\text{-}10)$$

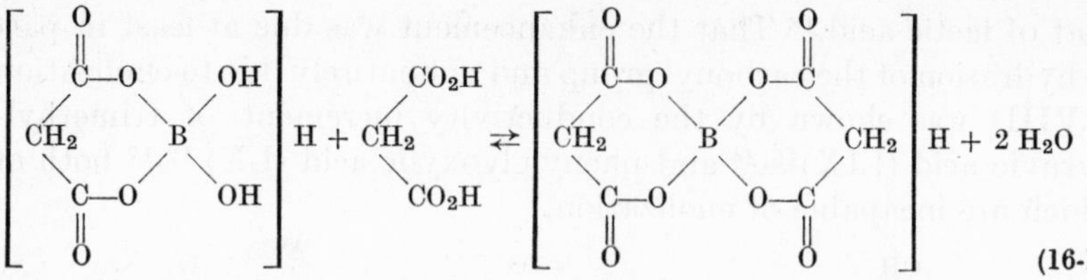

$$\left[\begin{array}{c} (CH_2(CO)_2O_2)B(OH)_2 \end{array}\right]H + CH_2(CO_2H)_2 \rightleftarrows \left[CH_2(CO)_2O_2 \, B \, O_2(CO)_2CH_2 \right]H + 2\,H_2O \qquad (16\text{-}11)$$

rings are not sufficiently displaced to the right in an aqueous boric acid–malonic acid solution to contribute to the conductivity. Higher molecular weight acids, succinic, glutaric, etc. would, of course, be even less likely to form the necessary ring systems and they also do not effect a conductivity increment. The positive effect of oxalic acid could be attributed either to the presence of an "α-hydroxy acid" (LXI) resulting from hydration of one of the carbonyl

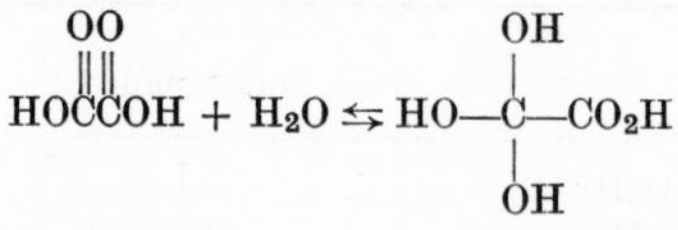

$$HOCOCOOH + H_2O \rightleftarrows HO\text{—}C(OH)_2\text{—}CO_2H$$

(LXI)

groups as was found for pyruvic acid,[18] or to the species (LXII).

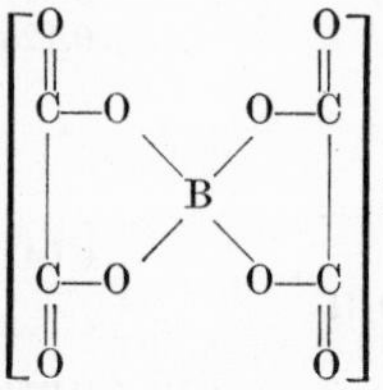

$$\left[(CO)_2O_2 \, B \, O_2(CO)_2 \right]H$$

(LXII)

C. Optical Rotation Considerations

The rotatory powers of optically active malic and tartaric acid and their salts are altered in the presence of boric acid by the formation of the complexes (LXIII) and (LXIV).[32,33,34,45,49]

It was shown subsequently that complex formation is in general based upon the reaction between molecules and ions, and not between neutral molecules.[64] Thus tartaric acid reacts with alkali borates to form (LXIV), M = Na, K, and calcium gluconate reacts with boric acid to form (LXV).

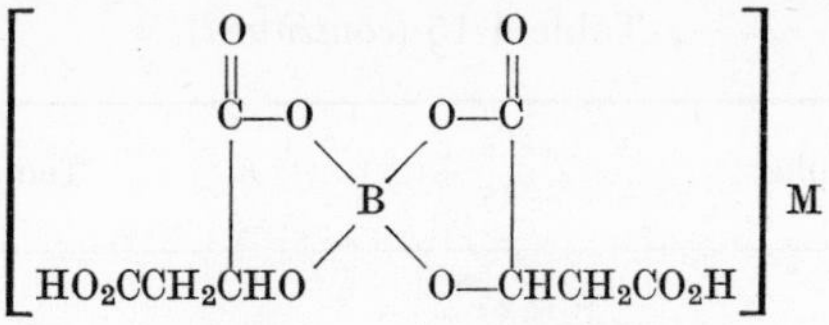

```
[      O            O      ]
       ‖            ‖
       C—O        O—C
       |   \    /   |
       |     B      |       M
       |   /    \   |
 HO2CCH2CHO       O—CHCH2CO2H
```

(LXIII, M = H, Na, K, NH_4)

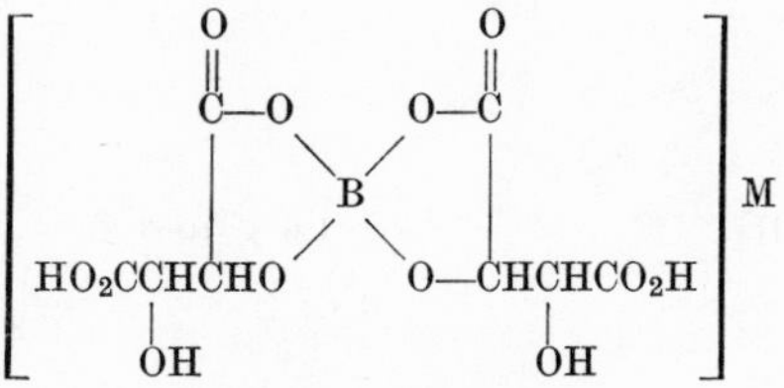

```
[      O            O      ]
       ‖            ‖
       C—O        O—C
       |   \    /   |
       |     B      |       M
       |   /    \   |
 HO2CCHCHO        O—CHCHCO2H
       |               |
       OH              OH
```

(LXIV, M = H, Na, K)

```
[             O              O                ]
              ‖              ‖
              C——O         O—C
              |     \     /   |
              |       B       |                  Ca
              |     /     \   |
 HOCH2(CHOH)3CH—O          O—CH(CHOH)3CH2OH  ]2
```

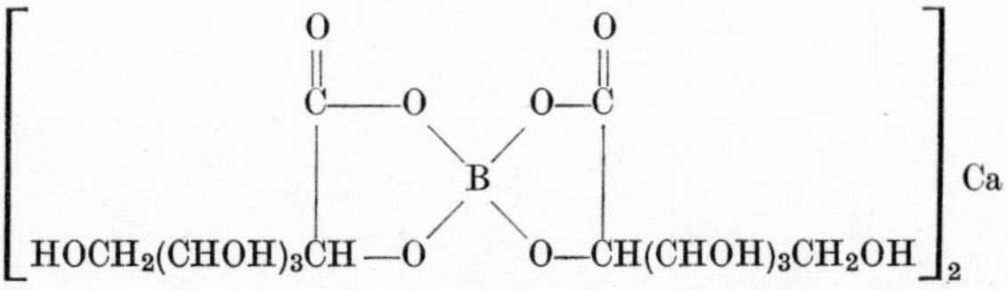

(LXV)

D. Acidity and Equilibrium Considerations

Glycolic, lactic, malic, tartaric and citric acid in the presence of boric acid have been shown to exhibit an increase in the hydrogen ion concentration over the calculated additive value. The effect of tartaric acid is most pronounced.[56] The enhancement of acidity, however, is not great enough to allow the quantitative titrimetric determination of boric acid.[52,53]

Table 16-5 records the dissociation constants of some boric acid–hydroxy acid complexes.

Table 16-5. Dissociation constants of some boric acid–hydroxy acid complexes

Complex	K	Temp. (°C)	Reference
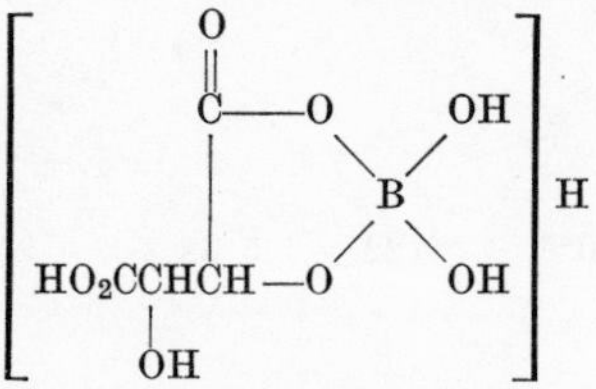 $[HO_2CCH(OH)CH–O–B(OH)_2–O–C(=O)]H$ (ring: C(=O)—O—B(OH)(OH)—O—CH)	2.15×10^{-2}	—	48

(*Table continued*)

Table 4-15 (*continued*)

Complex	K	Temp.(°C)	Reference
[O=C—O, OH, B, CH—O, OH, CH—O, OH, B, C—O, OH, O] H_2	1.9×10^{-3}	18	47
[O, C, O, OH, CH, C, B, OH, HO_2C—C, C, O, O, C, O] H	$\sim 4 \times 10^{-2}$	18	47
[O, O, O—C—CH_2, C, CH_2—C, O, HO—B—O—C, O—B, OH, O, HO, OH] H_2	1×10^{-3}	18	47
[O, C—O, OH, B, O, OH] H	435×10^{-2} 4.6×10^{-2}	22 18	58 47
[O, C—O, B, O—C, O, O, O] H	7.52×10^{-3}	22	58

VII. ANALYTICAL

Reported methods of analysis for boron involve an incineration or fusion in potassium carbonate,[31,59] sodium carbonate,[57] or potassium hydroxide[55] followed by the usual neutralization and titration of the boric acid in the presence of mannitol[42,57] or invert sugar.[59] The methanol–sulfuric acid distillation procedure also has been used.[51]

VIII. PHYSICAL CONSTANTS

Compound		M.p. (°C)	Reference
[Borodiester of R(CO–O)(O) with B]H (structure: two O=C–O–B–O rings bridged by R)			
[B bis-chelate of citric acid: $(HO_2CCH_2)_2C$–O / O–$C(CH_2CO_2H)_2$, with C(=O)–O]H		Crystalline	41
[B bis(salicylate): two C_6H_4(C(=O)–O)(O) rings on B]H		265–270	63
		Decomposed, no definite m.p.	35
		—	51
	$H \cdot H_2O$	110–120 (d.)	40

$\left[B \begin{matrix} O{-}C(=O){-}R \\ O{-}\!\!\!\!\!\!\!\!\quad \end{matrix} \right]_2 M$ — $[(RC(=O)O)(O)B(O)(OC(=O)R)]M$	M.p. (°C)	Reference
Aliphatic hydroxy acids		
$[B(OC(=O)CH_2O)_2]K$	Prisms	57
NH_4	Prisms	57
$C_6H_{11}NH_3$	Fluid at 60–70°	63
$[B(OC(=O)CH_2O)_2]_2Ca \cdot xH_2O$	Needles	57

(*Table continued*)

$\left[\begin{matrix} O=C{-}O & & O{-}C=O \\ R & B & R \\ O & & O \end{matrix} \right] M$	M.p. (°C)	Reference
$[(CH_3)_2C(O)C(=O)O{-}B{-}OC(=O)C(O)(CH_3)_2]\,C_6H_5NH_3$	Crystalline solid	22
$o\text{-}CH_3C_6H_5NH_3$	Needles	22
$C_6H_5NH(CH_3)_2$	Crystalline solid	22
$C_{21}H_{21}O_2N_2(OCH_3)_2$	Crystalline solid	22
$[CH_3CH_2C(CH_3)(O)C(=O)O{-}B{-}OC(=O)C(O)(CH_3)CH_2CH_3]\,C_{21}H_{21}O_2N_2(OCH_3)_2$	Crystalline solid	22
$[HO_2CCH_2CH(O)C(=O)O{-}B{-}OC(=O)CH(O)CH_2CO_2H]\,K \cdot H_2O$	White crystalline solid	45

$\left[\begin{matrix} \text{O} & & \text{O} \\ \text{HOCCHCH—O} & \text{B} & \text{O—CHCHCOH} \\ \text{OH} & & \text{OH} \end{matrix}\right]$ with C(=O)—O and O—C(=O) bound to B; K	Crystalline	34, 49
$NH_4 \cdot H_2O$	White solid	45
$\left[\begin{matrix} \text{C(=O)—O} & & \text{O—C(=O)} \\ & \text{B} & \\ (HO_2CCH_2)_2\text{C—O} & & \text{O—C}(CH_2CO_2H)_2 \end{matrix}\right]$K	—	61
$K \cdot 2H_2O$	Crystalline	42
$\left[\begin{matrix} \text{C(=O)—O} & & \text{O—C(=O)} \\ & \text{B} & \\ CH_2\text{—C—O} & & \text{O—C—}CH_2 \\ CH_2 \quad CH_2 & & CH_2 \quad CH_2 \\ CH_2 & & CH_2 \end{matrix}\right]C_6H_5NH_3$	225	42

(*Table continued*)

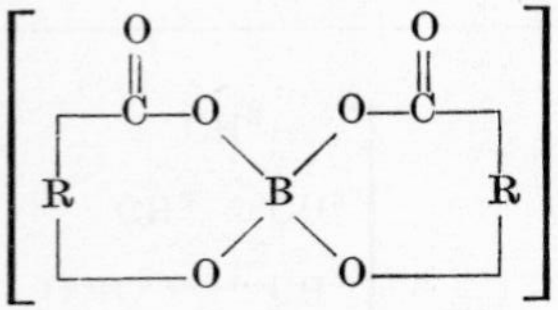 Compound (general formula: borate complex with counter-ion M)	M.p. (°C)	Reference
Aromatic hydroxy acids		
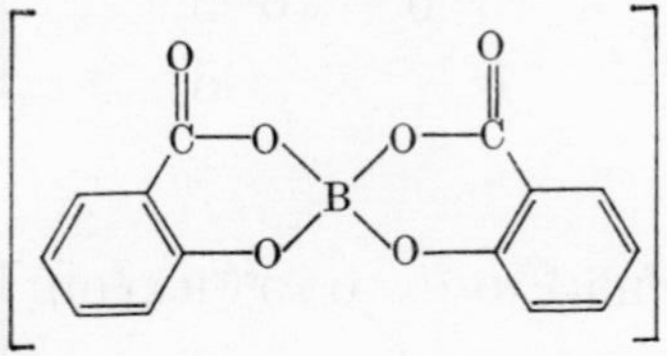 Na	Opaque crystals	21, 54, 55
	Microscopic plates	57
	—	44
K	Rectangular platelets	21, 54, 55
	Microscopic leaflets	57
	—	44
$NH_4 \cdot H_2O$	Melts at high temperature	44
	Rectangular platelets	21, 54, 55
Ag	Rectangular platelets	21, 54, 55
	—	44
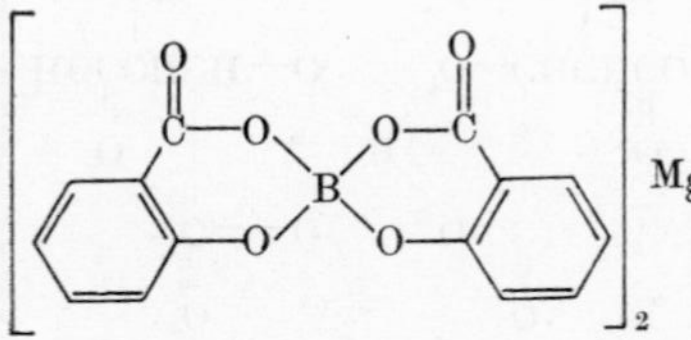 Mg (complex anion)$_2$	—	44

$Mg \cdot 10\ H_2O$	Tablet, melts on heating	44
	Solid	21, 54, 55
$Ca \cdot 6\ H_2O$	—	57
$Ca \cdot 10\ H_2O$	Transparent tabular crystals	44
	Long crystals	21, 54, 55
Sr	Crystalline	21, 54, 55
Ba	Many faced plates	21, 54, 55
	—	44
$Mn \cdot 10\ H_2O$	Light yellow solid	21, 54, 55
$Co \cdot 10\ H_2O$	Salmon solid	21, 54, 55
$Ni \cdot 10\ H_2O$	Solid	21
Cu	Green microscopic platelets	57
$Cu \cdot 10\ H_2O$	Blue-green solid	21, 54, 55
$Zn \cdot H_2O$	100–110 (d.)	38, 39
$Zn \cdot 10\ H_2O$	Solid	21, 42
Pb	Needles	21, 54, 55
	—	44
$C_5H_5NH \cdot H_2O$	82–83	21, 54, 55
$C_6H_5NH_3$	229–231	21, 54, 55
$(HOCH_2CH_2)_3NH$	107–116	62, 63
$C_{16}H_{33}NH_3$	57–85	62, 63
$C_{21}H_{23}O_2N_2$	Rods or needles	21, 29, 55
$[B(O-CO-C_6H_3(CH_3)-O)_2]_2$ Ca	Needles	57

(*Table continued*)

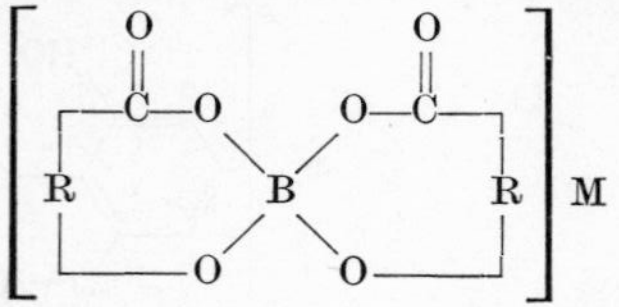 M	M.p. (°C)	Reference
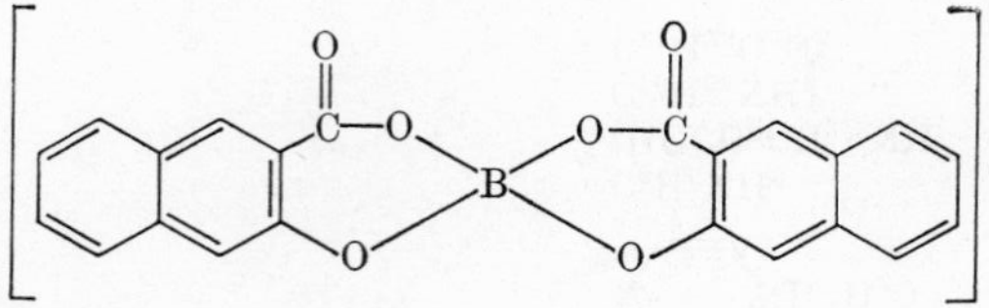 $C_6H_5NH(CH_3)_2$	Yellow needles	23
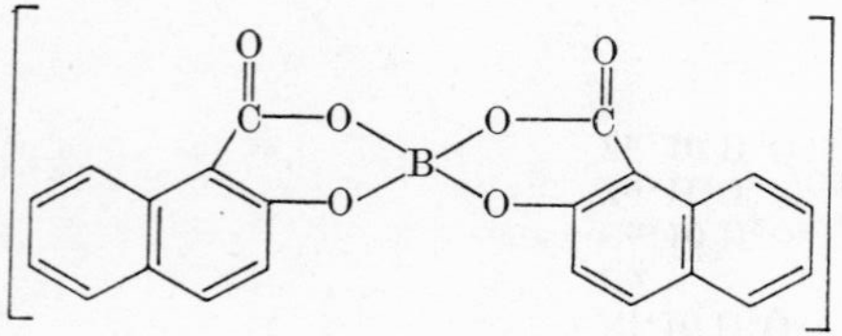 $C_6H_5NH(CH_3)_2$	White needles	23

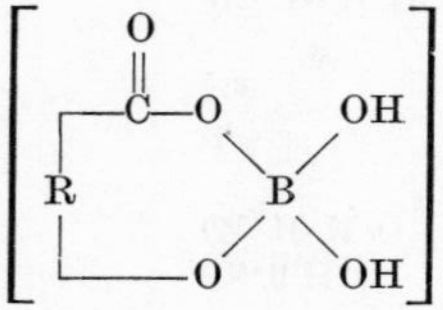 M	M.p. (°C)	Reference

Compound		Description	Reference
$\left[(HO_2CCH_2)_2C(-O-)\text{-}C(=O)\text{-}O\text{-}B(OH)_2\right]$ or $\left[HO_2C\text{-}C(CH_2CO_2H)(-O-)\text{-}CH_2\text{-}C(=O)\text{-}O\text{-}B(OH)_2\right]$	Li	Solid	60
	Na	Solid	60
	K	Solid	60
	NH_4	Solid	60
	$\frac{1}{2}$ Mg	Solid	60
$\left[C_6H_4(C(=O)\text{-}O\text{-})(\text{-}O\text{-})B(OH)_2\right]$	$Li\cdot H_2O$	Colorless rectangles	59
	Na	Amorphous mass	1, 54
	$K\cdot H_2O$	Flat needles	59
$\left[C_6H_4(C(=O)\text{-}O\text{-})(\text{-}O\text{-})B(OH)_2\right]_2$	$Mg\cdot 2\,H_2O$	Fine needles	59
	$Co\cdot 2H_2O$	Small pink needles	59
	$Ni\cdot 2H_2O$	Small green rods	59
	$Zn\cdot 2H_2O$	Needles	59

(Table continued)

	M.p. (°C)	Reference
$\left[R(C(=O)\text{–}O)(\text{–}O)B(OH)_2 \right] M$		
$\left[HO_3S\text{–}C_6H_3(C(=O)\text{–}O)(\text{–}O)B(OH)_2 \right] Na \cdot H_2O$	Brilliant white crystals	3
$\left[KO_3S\text{–}C_6H_3(C(=O)\text{–}O)(\text{–}O)B(OH)_2 \right] Na$	Tabular crystals	3

	M.p. (°C)	Reference
$\left[R(C(=O)\text{–}O)(C(=O)\text{–}O)B(OH)_2 \right] M$		

Compound	Cation	Properties	Ref.
$\left[\begin{array}{c}O{=}C{-}O \\ \vert \\ O{=}C{-}O\end{array}\!\!>B<\!\!\begin{array}{c}OH \\ OH\end{array}\right]$	$K\cdot H_2O$	Crystalline	31
$\left[\begin{array}{c}O{=}C{-}O \\ \vert \\ O{=}C{-}O\end{array}\!\!>B<\!\!\begin{array}{c}OK \\ OH\end{array}\right]$	$K\cdot H_2O$	Crystalline	31
$\left[(HO)_2B<\!\!\begin{array}{c}OC(=O)CH_2 \\ OC(=O)CH_2\end{array}\!\!>C<\!\!\begin{array}{c}C(=O)O \\ O\end{array}\!\!>B(OH)_2\right]$			
or $\left[(HO)_2B<\!\!\begin{array}{c}OC(=O)CH_2 \\ O{-}C(=O)\end{array}\!\!>C<\!\!\begin{array}{c}CH_2C(=O)O \\ O\end{array}\!\!>B(OH)_2\right]$	Li_2	Solid	60
	Na_2	Solid	60
	K_2	Solid	60
	$(NH_4)_2$	Solid	60
	Mg	Solid	60

(*Table continued*)

$\left[R\langle {}^{C(=O)-O}_{O} \rangle B(OH)-O-B(OH)-O-B(OH)\langle {}^{O-C(=O)}_{O} \rangle R \right] M_2$	M.p. (°C)	Reference
$[(C_6H_4(COO)(O))B(OH)-O-B(OH)-O-B(OH)((OOC)(O)C_6H_4)]$ $Na_2 \cdot 5H_2O$	Small needles	59
$Ba \cdot H_2O$	Microscopic cubes and rectangles	59
$Cd \cdot 4\ H_2O$	Small needles	59

IX. REFERENCES

1. Adam, F., *Boll. Chim. Farm.*, **55**, 263 (1916).
2. Andress, K., and W. Topf, *Z. Anorg. Allgem. Chem.*, **254**, 52 (1947).
3. Barthe, L., *Compt. Rend.*, **146**, 408 (1908).
4. Biot, *Ann. chim. et phys.*, **11**, 82 (1844); **29**, 341 (1850); **59**, 229 (1860).
5. Böeseken, J., *Advan. in Carbohydrate Chem.*, **4**, 189 (1949).
6. Böeseken, J., *Bull. Soc. Chim. France*, **53**, 1332 (1933).
7. Böeseken, J., *Chem. Weekblad*, **19**, 207 (1922).
8. Böeseken, J., *Chem. Weekblad.*, **33**, 206 (1936).
9. Böeseken, J., *Inst. Intern. Chim. Solvay, Conseil Chim.*, 61 (1931); *Chem. Abstracts*, **27**, 948 (1933).
10. Böeseken, J., *Rec. Trav. Chim.*, **35**, 211 (1915).
11. Böeseken, J., *Rec. Trav. Chim.*, **39**, 178 (1920).
12. Böeseken, J., *Rec. Trav. Chim.*, **40**, 553 (1921).
13. Böeseken, J., *Rec. Trav. Chim.*, **40**, 574 (1921).
14. Böeseken, J., *Rec. Trav. Chim.*, **40**, 578 (1921).
15. Böeseken, J., *Verslag Akad. Wetenschap. Amsterdam*, **26**, 3 (1918).
16. Böeseken, J., and J. Coops, *Rec. Trav. Chim.*, **45**, 407 (1926).
17. Böeseken, J., and B. B. C. Felix, *Rec. Trav. Chim.*, **40**, 568 (1921).
18. Böeseken, J., L. W. Hansen, and S. H. Bertram, *Rec. Trav. Chim.*, **35**, 309 (1916).
19. Böeseken, J., and H. Kalshoven, *Rec. Trav. Chim.*, **37**, 130 (1918).
20. Böeseken, J., and A. G. Lutgerhorst, *Rec. Trav. Chim.*, **51**, 159 (1932).
21. Böeseken, J., and J. Meulenhoff, *Proc. Acad. Sci. Amsterdam*, **27**, 174 (1924).
22. Böeseken, J., H. D. Muller, and R. T. Japhongjouw, *Rec. Trav. Chim.*, **45**, 919 (1926).
23. Böeseken, J., and A. Niks, *Rec. Trav. Chim.*, **59**, 1062 (1940).
24. Böeseken, J., and W. Root van Tonningen, *Rec. Trav. Chim.*, **39**, 187 (1920).
25. Böeseken, J., G. Slooff, J. M. Hoeffelman, and H. E. Hirsch, *Rec. Trav. Chim.*, **52**, 881 (1933).
26. Böeseken, J., G. Slooff, and A. G. Lutgerhorst, *Proc. Acad. Sci. Amsterdam*, **34**, 932 (1931).
27. Böeseken, J., and L. A. Van der Ent, *Rec. Trav. Chim.*, **37**, 178 (1918).
28. Böeseken, J., and P. E. Verkade, *Rec. Trav. Chim.*, **36**, 167 (1916).
29. Böeseken, J., and N. Vermaas, *J. Phys. Chem.*, **35**, 1477 (1931).
30. Böeseken, J., J. Weisfelt, J. v. D. Spek, C. v. Loon, and G. Goettsch, *Rec. Trav. Chim.*, **37**, 165 (1918).
31. Cretcher, L. H., and F. W. Hightower, *J. Am. Pharm. Assoc.*, **13**, 625 (1924).
32. Darmois, E., *J. Chim. Phys.*, **23**, 130 (1926).
33. Darmois, E., *J. Chim. Phys.*, **23**, 649 (1926).
34. Darmois, E., *J. Chim. Phys.*, **27**, 179 (1930).
35. Dimroth, O., *et al.*, *Ann.*, **446**, 97 (1925).
36. Doub, L., *et al.*, 131st Meeting American Chemical Society, Miami, April, 1957, *Abstracts of Papers*, p. 28-N.
37. Dunitz, J. D., and V. Schomaker, *J. Chem. Phys.*, **20**, 1703 (1952).
38. Foelsing, A., Brit. Pat. 1616 (1910).

39. Foelsing, A., Ger. Pat. 230,725 (1909).
40. Foelsing, A., Ger. Pat. 288,388 (1914).
41. Hermans, P. H., *Proc. Acad. Sci. Amsterdam*, **26**, 32 (1923).
42. Hermans, P. H., *Z. Anorg. Allgem. Chem.*, **142**, 83 (1925).
43. Herz, W., *Z. Anorg. Allgem. Chem.*, **66**, 93 (1910); **70**, 71 (1911).
44. Jahns, E., *Arch. Pharm.*, **12**, 212 (1878).
45. Jones, B., *J. Chem. Soc.*, 951 (1933).
46. Kohlrausch, F., and L. Holborn, *Das Leitvermögen der Elektrolyte*, B. G. Turner, Leipzig, 1916.
47. Kolthoff, I. M., *Rec. Trav. Chim.*, **45**, 607 (1926).
48. Lourijsen, M., *Bull. Soc. Chim. France*, 898 (1956).
49. Lowry, T. M., *J. Chem. Soc.*, 2853 (1929).
50. Magnanini, G., *Gazz. Chim. Ital.*, **21**, II, 215 (1891); **22**, I, 541 (1892); *Atti Acad. Gioenia Sci. Nat. Catania*, **5**, 1 (1892); *Z. Physik. Chem.*, **9**, 230 (1892); **11**, 281 (1893).
51. Mehrotra, R. C., and G. Srivastava, *J. Indian Chem. Soc.*, **38**, 1 (1961).
52. Mellon, M. G., and V. N. Morris, *Proc. Indiana Acad. Sci.*, **33**, 85 (1924).
53. Mellon, M. G., and V. N. Morris, *Ind. Eng. Chem.*, **16**, 123 (1924).
54. Meulenhoff, J., *Rec. Trav. Chim.*, **44**, 161 (1925).
55. Meulenhoff, J., *Z. Anorg. Allgem. Chem.*, **142**, 373 (1925).
56. Rimbach, E., and P. Ley, *Z. Physik. Chem.*, **100**, 393 (1922).
57. Rosenheim, A., and H. Vermehren, *Ber.*, **57**, 1337 (1924).
58. Schäfer, H., *Z. Anorg. Allgem. Chem.*, **250**, 82 (1942).
59. Schäfer, H., *Z. Anorg. Allgem. Chem.*, **250**, 96 (1942).
60. Scheibe, E., *Pharm.*, **11**, 389 (1880).
61. Scheibe, E., *Pharm. Z. für Russland*, **18**, 257, 289, 321 (1879); **19**, 513 (1880).
62. Trautman, C. E., U.S. Pat. 2,497,521 (1950, to Gulf Research and Development Co.).
63. Trautman, C. E., U.S. Pat. 2,568,472 (1951, to Gulf Research and Development Co.).
64. Tsuzuki, Y., *Bull. Chem. Soc. Japan*, **16**, 23 (1941).
65. Verkade, P. A., *Rec. Trav. Chim.*, **43**, 879 (1924).

17

TETRA(ALKOXYHYDRO)- AND TETRA(ACYLOXYHYDRO)BORATES

I. INTRODUCTION

Tetra(alkoxyhydro)borate salts are tetrahedral compounds of boron containing both alkoxyl and hydro ligands (I). The trialkoxy

$$[(RO)_xBH_{4-x}]M$$
$$(I,\ x = 1, 2 \text{ or } 3)$$

derivatives have been most thoroughly explored. Evidence for dialkoxy and monoalkoxy derivatives has been presented but has not been confirmed. Aromatic derivatives have not been reported.

A few structurally similar compounds which contain acyloxy ligands in place of the alkoxy ligands (II) have been reported and these also will be treated in this chapter.

$$\left[(R\overset{\overset{O}{\|}}{C}O)_xBH_{4-x}\right]M$$
$$(II,\ x = 1, 2 \text{ or } 3)$$

II. HISTORICAL

The first readily available publication of the synthesis of a tetra(alkoxyhydro)borate is in a patent issued to Schlesinger and Brown in 1949.[28] Sodium trimethoxyhydroborate was prepared by the reaction of sodium hydride with a slight excess of trimethoxyborane at reflux temperature.

$$NaH + (CH_3O)_3B \rightarrow [(CH_3O)_3BH]Na \qquad (17\text{-}1)$$

Reaction (17-1) and the decomposition reaction (17-2), however, actually were reported six years earlier in 1943 in a report to the

$$4\ NaBH(OCH_3)_3 \rightarrow NaBH_4 + 3\ (CH_3O)_3B + 3\ NaOCH_3 \qquad (17\text{-}2)$$

Government on methods of preparation of sodium borohydride.[32] In addition, sodium trimethoxyhydroborate was described as a reducing agent in a Master's thesis at the University of Chicago in 1944.[39]

Table 17-1. Solubility of tetra(alkoxyhydro)borates in organic solvents

Solubility, g./100 g. solvent (°C)	Compound				
	$[(CH_3O)_3BH]Na$	$[(CH_3O)_3BH]_2Ca$	$[(n\text{-}C_4H_9O)_3BH]Li$	$[(CH_3O)_2BH_2]Li$	$[C_2H_5OBH_3]_2Ca,Sr,Ba$
Ether	I[4]	I[18]	SS[43]	S[8]	
Dibutyl ether	I[4]				
Tetrahydrofuran	VS[4]	I[18]	S[43]		I[13]
	40(25)[13]				
	49.6(25)[32]				
Dioxane	1.6(25)[8,35]	I[18]	I[43]		
	4.5(75)[8,35]				
	36(25)[13]				
Glyme	22(25)[13]	I[18]			
Diglyme	2.6(25)[13]				
Triglyme	1.0(25)[13]				
Tetraglyme	2.3(25)[13]				
Hexane	7[24]				
Benzene			SS[43]		
Mineral oil	S[24]				
Liquid ammonia	5.6(−33)[8]	1.8(−33)[18]			
	5.6(25)[35]				
Ethylamine		VSS[18]			
Ethylenediamine	0.2(25)[22]				
	0.2(75)[22]				

Tetramethylethylenediamine	43(25)[13]	
Isopropylamine	9.0(25)[8]	VSS[18]
	9.0(28)[35]	
Pyridine	0.4(24)[8,35]	VSS[18]
	3.0(75)[8,35]	
	18(25)[13]	
Piperidine	16(25)[13]	
N-Methylpiperidine	5(25)[13]	
N,*N*-Dimethylaniline	1.4(25)[13]	
Morpholine	0.3(24)[8,35]	
	2.3(75)[8,35]	
N-methylmorpholine	22(25)[13]	

S = Soluble. VS = Very soluble. SS = Slightly soluble. VSS = Very slightly soluble. I = Insoluble.

26*

III. PROPERTIES

The properties of the tetra(alkoxyhydro)borates have not been extensively recorded. The most well described member, sodium trimethoxyhydroborate, is a white crystalline solid which is stable in dry air.[8,22,28,29] It must be stored in tightly sealed containers, however, since hydrogen gas is evolved when the compound is exposed to humid air.[22] Calcium methoxytrihydroborate burns with a green flame.[42] Solubilities of the salts in organic solvents are recorded in Table 17-1.

IV. TRIALKOXYHYDROBORATES

A. Methods of Preparation

The only known method of preparation of the monohydro derivatives involves the direct transformation of a trialkoxyborane to the salt by reaction with a metal hydride* (17-3) or trialkoxyhydroborate (17-4) [24] A small excess of the ester is employed to avoid the com-

$$(RO)_3B + MH \rightarrow [(RO)_3BH]M \tag{17-3}$$

$$[(i\text{-}C_3H_7O)_3BH]Na + (CH_3O)_3B \rightarrow [(CH_3O)_3BH]Na + (i\text{-}C_3H_7O)_3B \tag{17-4}$$

peting conversion (17-5) to the borohydride effected by an excess of of the hydride.

$$(RO)_3B + 4\,MH \rightarrow MBH_4 + 3\,ROM \tag{17-5}$$

Reaction 17-3 has been performed under reflux in the absence of solvent[8,24,28,29,32,33,38] and in tetrahydrofuran,[4,5,7] dioxane,[8] benzene,[29] diglyme,[5] triglyme[5] and mineral oil[24] solution. The mineral oil tends to moderate the reaction. Reactants have included sodium[4,5,7,8,24,28,29,33] and lithium[8,29] hydride and esters derived from primary,[4,5,7,8,28,29,32,33] secondary,[5,24] and tertiary[5] alcohols. Certain amines and ethers have been claimed to accelerate the reaction.[13]

The dry preparation of sodium hydrotrimethoxyborate is accompanied by a fivefold increase in volume of the reaction mixture and therefore a reaction vessel of adequate size must be employed.[4,8,28,33]

Calcium trimethoxyhydroborate was prepared from calcium hydride and excess trimethoxyborane in an autoclave reaction at 215°.[18]

* Sodium tetraisopropoxyborate could not be converted to triisopropoxyhydroborate by reaction with sodium hydride or sodium borohydride.[5]

The metal hydride may be prepared *in situ*. Treatment of metallic sodium with a mixture of hydrogen and trimethoxyborane at 225–250° under pressure gave good yields of sodium trimethoxyhydroborate (17-6).[29,35] Xylene and diglyme have been used as solvents.[17]

$$2\,Na + H_2 + 2\,(CH_3O)_3B \rightarrow 2\,[(CH_3O)_3BH]Na \qquad (17\text{-}6)$$

The rate of reaction of sodium hydride with a trialkoxyborane in tetrahydrofuran decreases sharply in the order methyl > ethyl ≫ isopropyl ≫ *t*-butyl.[5] This order is attributed to the increasing steric requirements of the alkyl groups which would deter the entry of the hydride ion to within bonding distance of the central boron atom. The mechanism of reaction (17-3) thus can be considered to be a nucleophilic attack of hydride ion on boron with attendant rehybridization of the boron from sp^2 to sp^3 configuration.

B. Reactions

1. HYDROLYSIS

Sodium trimethoxyhydroborate is slowly attacked by moist air[8,12,28,29] and must be stored in a tightly sealed container since hydrogen gas is evolved on exposure to humid air.[22] In cold water the salt dissolves with a short initial burst of hydrogen. Additional hydrogen is generated only slowly unless the solution is acidified. A possible explanation[8] for this observation is found in the fact that as the reaction proceeds the solution becomes basic due to the formation of sodium borate (17-7). The sodium borate would be

$$[(CH_3O)_3BH]Na + 4\,H_2O \rightarrow 3\,CH_3OH + Na^+ + B(OH)_4^- + H_2 \qquad (17\text{-}7)$$

expected to decrease the rate of hydrolysis since the hydrolysis of a borohydride is markedly affected by the hydrogen ion concentration.[20,34] In hot water, complete hydrolysis occurs rapidly with evolution of one mole of hydrogen per mole of salt.[8] Sodium tributoxyhydroborate in water rapidly evolves hydrogen.[43]

In contrast to sodium trimethoxyhydroborate, an aqueous solution of calcium trimethoxyhydroborate was stored for several days at 0° and only decomposed to the extent of three percent in ten hours at room temperature. At 55°, the active hydrogen content decreased ninety percent in ten hours. At 100°, it decomposed in a few minutes.[18]

2. ALCOHOLYSIS

In contrast to sodium borohydride, which requires treatment in boiling methanol for quantitative conversion to the tetraalkoxyborate, sodium trimethoxyhydroborate reacts rapidly and completely with methanol even in the cold, and without acidification, to free one mole of hydrogen per mole of salt (17-8).[8,29] Sodium tri-

$$[(CH_3O)_3BH]Na + CH_3OH \rightarrow [(CH_3O)_4B]Na + H_2 \qquad (17\text{-}8)$$

methoxyhydroborate and sodium tributoxyhydroborate also rapidly evolve hydrogen on treatment with ethanol.[22,43]

Sodium triisopropoxyhydroborate reacts slowly with isopropyl alcohol at 0° and rapidly at 60°;[5] whereas sodium borohydride is only moderately soluble in isopropyl alcohol and the solution can be heated under reflux for days without noticeable reaction.[6]

Thus the substitution of alkoxide for hydride on tetravalent boron appears to become progressively easier in the series BH_4^-, $ROBH_3^-$, $(RO)_2BH_2^-$, $(RO)_3BH^-$. This order is consistent with the increasing ease of abstraction of a hydride by an incipient proton which would be aided by coordination of the boron atom with the free electron pair on oxygen.

$$R\ddot{O}\!-\!\underset{OR}{\overset{OR}{\underset{|}{\overset{|}{B}}}}\!-\!H \quad H\!-\!\ddot{O}R \rightarrow \{(RO)_3B + RO^-\} + H_2 \rightarrow (RO)_4B^- + H_2 \qquad (17\text{-}9)$$

This explanation is consistent with the observed rates for the reaction of sodium borohydride with ketones in which it is postulated that the first transfer of hydride from the borohydride to the ketone is much slower than subsequent transfers.[5,16]

Calcium trimethoxyhydroborate lost 13% of its active hydrogen content in ten hours when treated with 50% methanol. Sixty percent ethanol effected a 25% loss in active hydrogen content.[18]

Treatment of sodium trimethoxyhydroborate with tetrakis-(β-hydroxyethyl)ammonium chloride resulted in displacement of both the hydride and a methoxy ligand. In addition sodium chloride was formed leaving the borate anion internally compensated by the tetraalkylammonium cation.[27]

$$2\,NaBH(OCH_3)_3 + 2\,[N(CH_2CH_2OH)_4]Cl \rightarrow 2\,NaCl + H_2 + CH_3OH$$

$$+ (HOCH_2CH_2)_3\overset{+}{N}CH_2CH_2O\overset{-}{B}(OCH_3)_3 + (HOCH_2CH_2)_3\overset{+}{N}CH_2CH_2O\overset{-}{B}H(OCH_3)_2 \qquad (17\text{-}10)$$

3. DISPROPORTIONATION

Sodium trimethoxyhydroborate disproportionates at 200–230° (17-11). To drive the reaction to completion the resulting sodium

$$4\,[(CH_3O)_3BH]Na \rightarrow 3\,[(CH_3O)_4B]Na + NaBH_4 \qquad (17\text{-}11)$$

tetramethoxyborate must be decomposed according to equation (17-12), and the trimethoxyborane which is produced must be con-

$$[(CH_3O)_4B]Na \rightarrow (CH_3O)_3B + NaOCH_3 \qquad (17\text{-}12)$$

tinuously removed by evacuation of the reaction vessel.[8,32,33,35] Even then the reaction is not exclusively as shown since dimethoxyborane is evolved along with the trimethoxyborane (17-13).[32,35]

$$[(CH_3O)_3BH]Na \rightarrow (CH_3O)_2BH + NaOCH_3 \qquad (17\text{-}13)$$

Lithium trimethoxyhydroborate gives dimethoxy- and trimethoxyborane when heated to 200°.[8] At 100°, the lithium salt is converted to $[(CH_3O)_2BH_2]Li$.[8]

The disproportionation of sodium trimethoxyhydroborate to sodium tetramethoxyborate and sodium borohydride (17-11) also can be effected by simple dissolution in tetrahydrofuran[5,7] (17-14)

$$4\,[(CH_3O)_3BH]Na\ (\text{soln.}) \xrightarrow{\text{Tetrahydrofuran}} \underline{NaBH_4} + 3\,[(CH_3O)_4B]Na\ (\text{soln.}) \qquad (17\text{-}14)$$

or diglyme (17-15).[7] The driving force for the reaction is the in-

$$4\,[(CH_3O)_3BH]Na\ (\text{soln.}) \xrightarrow{\text{Diglyme}} NaBH_4\ (\text{soln.}) + \underline{3\,[(CH_3O)_4B]Na} \qquad (17\text{-}15)$$

solubility of one of the products; sodium borohydride is insoluble in tetrahydrofuran and sodium tetramethoxyborate is insoluble in diglyme.

Sodium triethoxyhydroborate undergoes a similar disproportionation in tetrahydrofuran, but the isopropoxy and *t*-butoxy derivatives do not.[5] Presumably the greater steric requirements of the branched chain compounds prevent the exchange of alkoxide and hydride ligands.

The higher straight-chain alkoxyhydroborates, $[(C_2H_5O)_3BH]Na$ and $[(n\text{-}C_4H_9O)_3BH]Na$, disproportionate and decompose at temperatures in excess of 230° in a manner similar to that of the methoxy derivative.[35]

4. WITH HYDRIDIC MATERIALS

Sodium and lithium trimethoxyhydroborate are converted to the borohydride by reaction with sodium or lithium hydride[8,30,32,33,35]

(17-16), dimethoxyborane[37] (17-17), or diborane[7,8,28,33,37,38] (17-18).

$$[(CH_3O)_3BH]Na + 3\ NaH \rightarrow NaBH_4 + 3\ NaOCH_3 \qquad (17\text{-}16)$$

$$[(CH_3O)_3BH]Na + 3\ (CH_3O)_2BH \rightarrow NaBH_4 + 3\ (CH_3O)_3B \qquad (17\text{-}17)$$

$$[(CH_3O)_3BH]Na + \tfrac{1}{2}\ B_2H_6 \rightarrow NaBH_4 + (CH_3O)_3B \qquad (17\text{-}18)$$

The reaction with diborane proceeds so rapidly and so nearly quantitatively that trimethoxyhydroborate may be used to absorb diborane from a stream of gas.[37] In tetrahydrofuran, the reaction is quantitative.[7] Reaction (17-18) can be looked upon as a displacement of the weak Lewis acid, trimethoxyborane, from the reference base, H^-, by the comparatively strong Lewis acid, borane.[33]

5. WITH TRIMETHOXYBORANE

The reaction of sodium trimethoxyhydroborate with trimethoxyborane to give dimethoxyborane and sodium tetramethoxyborate (17-19) has been performed under a variety of conditions. Vapors of

$$[(CH_3O)_3BH]Na + (CH_3O)_3B \rightarrow (CH_3O)_2BH + [(CH_3O)_4B]Na \qquad (17\text{-}19)$$

trimethoxyborane were bubbled through molten sodium trimethoxyhydroborate maintained at 250° or through a solution of the hydroborate in tetraethylene glycol dimethyl ether heated to 230°. The dimethoxyborane formed was swept out with the trimethoxyborane. In another preparation, the reactants were heated at 70° in a packed distillation column. The distillate contained about seven percent dimethoxyborane.[11]

In contrast to reaction (17-1), the reaction of sodium triisopropoxyhydroborate with trimethoxyborane (17-4) resulted only in exchange of the methoxy and isopropoxy groups, or transfer of sodium hydride.[24]

6. WITH TRIMETHOXYBOROXINE

A small yield of dimethoxyborane was contained in the distillate of trimethoxyborane obtained from a refluxing mixture of trimethoxyboroxine and sodium trimethoxyhydroborate. The reaction was formulated as in equation (17-20).[10]

$$10\ (CH_3OBO)_3 + 6\ [(CH_3O)_3BH]Na \rightarrow 6\ (CH_3O)_2BH + 12\ (CH_3O)_3B + 3\ Na_2B_6O_{10} \qquad (17\text{-}20)$$

7. WITH TRIETHYLBORANE

A mixture of sodium triisopropoxyhydroborate and triethylborane which was refluxed for twenty-two hours resulted in a nonvolatile solid approximately equal in weight to that expected if the sodium triisopropoxyhydroborate had been converted to $[(i\text{-}C_3H_7O)_2BH(C_2H_5)]Na$. It is evident that the order of Lewis acid strength is $(i\text{-}C_3H_7O)_2BH > (C_2H_5)_3B > (i\text{-}C_3H_7O)_3B$.[24]

8. WITH BORON TRIHALIDES

Boron trichloride reacted with sodium triisopropoxyhydroborate in mineral oil at room temperature to give diborane and other boron hydrides. Seventy-two percent of the hydridic hydrogen from the original salt was converted to volatile hydrides.[24]

The treatment of sodium trimethoxyhydroborate with unsolvated boron trifluoride led to the liberation of trimethoxyborane without the formation of diborane (17-21).[36] However, the use of

$$[(CH_3O)_3BH]Na + BF_3 \rightarrow (CH_3O)_3B + NaBHF_3 \qquad (17\text{-}21)$$

boron trifluoride etherate or the addition compounds with methyl ether, *n*-butyl ether or dioxane led to the rapid evolution of diborane.[8,31,33,36,38]

$$6\,NaBH(OCH_3)_3 + 8\,(C_2H_5)_2O{:}BF_3 \rightarrow B_2H_6 + 6\,(CH_3O)_3B + 6\,NaBF_4 + 8\,(C_2H_5)_2O \qquad (17\text{-}22)^*$$

The above displacements of trimethoxyborane and diborane by boron trifluoride indicate that boron trifluoride is a stronger Lewis acid than either of these species.[33] This order, coupled with the displacement of trimethoxyborane from sodium trimethoxyhydroborate by diborane discussed in Section IV-B-4 above, leads to the series of decreasing Lewis acid strength $BF_3 > BH_3 > (CH_3O)_3B$. This order is consistent with the order obtained from the stability of addition products of boron compounds with dimethyl ether and trimethylamine.[33]

Other salts such as sodium triethoxyhydroborate and sodium tributoxyhydroborate react with other halides such as boron tribromide in a manner similar to the sodium trimethoxyhydroborate–boron trifluoride reaction but with an overall smaller percent conversion.[36]

Lithium trimethoxyhydroborate has been claimed to reduce tertiary amine complexes of boron trifluoride to amine–borane complexes.[21]

$$3\,LiBH(OCH_3)_3 + R_3N{:}BF_3 \rightarrow R_3N{:}BH_3 + 3\,LiF + 3\,(CH_3O)_3B \qquad (17\text{-}23)$$

* Twice the theoretical quantity of etherate was needed to effect reaction (17-22a)

$$(CH_3O)_3B + (C_2H_5)_2O:BF_3 \rightleftarrows (CH_3O)_2BF + CH_3OBF_2 + (C_2H_5)_2O \qquad (17\text{-}22a)$$

and avoid the loss of diborane by reaction (17-22b)[36]

$$B_2H_6 + 4\,(CH_3O)_3B \rightleftarrows 6\,(CH_3O)_2BH \qquad (17\text{-}22b)$$

9. WITH CHLOROBORAZINES

A preliminary statement has indicated that trialkoxyhydroborates reduce chloroborazines.[19]

$$\text{Cl-substituted borazine } (RN\text{—}BCl)_3 \xrightarrow{MBH(OR)_3} (RN\text{—}BH)_3 \qquad (17\text{-}24)$$

10. WITH HYDROGEN CHLORIDE

Very little hydrogen is generated when hydrogen chloride is passed through sodium trimethoxyhydroborate and the volatile products are trapped at $-80°$. The trapped material, however, does liberate hydrogen when warmed to room temperature. No diborane is generated. These observations are in accord with equation (17-25).[8]

$$[(CH_3O)_3BH]Na + HCl \rightarrow (CH_3O)_2BH + CH_3OH + NaCl \qquad (17\text{-}25)$$

This behavior is in marked contrast to that of the borohydrides which immediately liberate hydrogen when treated with hydrogen chloride (17-26). With the borohydride, the attack of the proton can

$$NaBH_4 + HCl \rightarrow NaCl + H_2 + \tfrac{1}{2} B_2H_6 \qquad (17\text{-}26)$$

only be on one of the four hydrogen atoms attached to boron (17-27). However, in the case of the trimethoxyhydroborate, the proton

$$H^+ \; H\text{—}BH_2\text{—}H \rightarrow H_2 + BH_3 \qquad (17\text{-}27)$$

could attack the more basic oxygen atom to give dimethoxyborane and methanol (17-28).[8]

$$H^+ + :\underset{CH_3}{O}\text{—}\overset{H}{\underset{OCH_3}{B^-}}\text{—}OCH_3 \rightarrow H\text{—}\overset{+}{\underset{CH_3}{O}}\text{—}\overset{H}{\underset{OCH_3}{B^-}}\text{—}OCH_3 \rightarrow (CH_3O)_2BH + CH_3OH \qquad (17\text{-}28)$$

11. WITH SILICON TETRACHLORIDE

Small quantities of diborane and silane were obtained when silicon tetrachloride reacted with sodium triisopropoxyhydroborate in tetrahydrofuran.[24]

12. WITH CARBON DIOXIDE

Passage of a stream of gaseous carbon dioxide through a tube filled with solid sodium trimethoxyhydroborate resulted in rapid exothermic absorption of the gas and production of trimethoxyborane and sodium formate.[8]

$$NaBH(OCH_3)_3 + CO_2 \rightarrow (CH_3O)_3B + H\overset{\overset{\displaystyle O}{\|}}{C}ONa \quad (17\text{-}29)$$

13. REDUCTION OF ORGANIC COMPOUNDS

The rapid reduction of carbon dioxide by sodium trimethoxyhydroborate suggested that it would be a powerful reducing agent for organic compounds containing a carbonyl group.[8] Indeed, sodium trimethoxyhydroborate at moderate temperatures readily reduces aldehydes, ketones, acid chlorides and acid anhydrides to the corresponding alcohols.[1,4] Calcium trimethoxyhydroborate has been reported to reduce a variety of aldehydes and ketones.[18] The stoichiometry is equimolar for aldehydes (17-30) and ketones (17-31)

$$R\overset{\overset{\displaystyle O}{\|}}{C}H + NaBH(OCH_3)_3 \rightarrow \{[RCH_2OB(OCH_3)_3]Na\} \xrightarrow{H_2O} RCH_2OH + 3\,CH_3OH + NaBO_2 \quad (17\text{-}30)$$

$$R\overset{\overset{\displaystyle O}{\|}}{C}R + NaBH(OCH_3)_3 \rightarrow \{[R_2CHOB(OCH_3)_3]Na\} \xrightarrow{H_2O} R_2CHOH + 3\,CH_3OH + NaBO_2 \quad (17\text{-}31)$$

and 2 : 1 for acid chlorides (17-32) and anhydrides (17-33).[4]

$$R\overset{\overset{\displaystyle O}{\|}}{C}Cl + 2\,NaBH(OCH_3)_3 \rightarrow \text{Complex} \xrightarrow{H_2O} RCH_2OH + 6\,CH_3OH + NaCl + \tfrac{1}{2}\,Na_2B_4O_7 \quad (17\text{-}32)$$

$$R\overset{\overset{\displaystyle O}{\|}}{C}O\overset{\overset{\displaystyle O}{\|}}{C}R + 2\,NaBH(OCH_3)_3 \rightarrow \text{Complex} \xrightarrow{H_2O} RCH_2OH + 6\,CH_3OH + R\overset{\overset{\displaystyle O}{\|}}{C}OH + 2\,NaBO_2 \quad (17\text{-}33)$$

At low temperatures (0 to −80°), reaction (17-32) results in 25–40% yields of aldehydes (17-34).[4]

$$\mathrm{RC(=O)Cl + NaBH(OCH_3)_3 \rightarrow RC(=O)H + (CH_3O)_3B + NaCl} \qquad (17\text{-}34)$$

Esters are reduced more slowly (17-35), even at higher temperatures (100–140°). Carboxylic acids are not attacked under these conditions.[4]

$$\mathrm{RC(=O)OR' + 2\,NaBH(OCH_3)_3 \rightarrow \{[RCH_2OB(OCH_3)_3]Na + [R'OB(OCH_3)_3]Na\}}$$
$$\xrightarrow{H_2O} \mathrm{RCH_2OH + R'OH + 6\,CH_3OH + 2\,NaBO_2} \qquad (17\text{-}35)$$

The mechanism of the reductions was believed to involve transfer of a hydride ion to the carbonyl carbon atom (17-36).[4,5]

$$\mathrm{(CH_3O)_3\bar{B}{-}H,\ \ {>}C{=}O \rightarrow (CH_3O)_3B + {-}\overset{|}{\underset{|}{C}}H{-}O^-} \qquad (17\text{-}36)$$

The resulting alkoxide ion and trimethoxyborane would be expected to form a complex (17-37) (see Chapter 14).

$$\mathrm{(CH_3O)_3B + {-}\overset{|}{\underset{|}{C}}HO^- \rightarrow \left[(CH_3O)_3BO\overset{|}{\underset{|}{C}}H\right]^-} \qquad (17\text{-}37)$$

If initial hydride transfer were the rate-determining step, it would be expected that trialkoxyhydroborates would be more rapid reducing agents than borohydrides. The transfer of hydride from the trialkoxyhydroborate would be promoted by the coordination of boron with the electron pair on oxygen and the resonance stabilization of the resulting trialkoxyborane (17-38) as compared to the

$$\mathrm{RO{-}\bar{B}(OR)(\ddot{O}R){-}H \rightarrow RO{-}\bar{B}({=}\overset{+}{O}R)(OR) + H^-} \quad \updownarrow \quad \mathrm{R\overset{+}{O}{=}\bar{B}(OR)_2} \qquad (17\text{-}38)$$

removal of hydride from the comparatively strong Lewis acid, borane.[4,5] Indeed, both acetone and ethyl benzoate are more readily reduced by sodium triisopropoxyhydroborate than by sodium borohydride.[5]

Other types of compounds reduced by sodium trimethoxyhydroborate include nitriles and nitro compounds; elevated temperatures are required. The products are not described. Double bonds are not reduced, even when conjugated with a carbonyl group.[4] However, thiamine (III) was reduced to dihydrothiamine I (IV) at −15° in aqueous methanol.[3]

```
                               CH3  CH2CH2OH
                               |    |
            N=CH          Cl̄   C====C
           /    \          \  /     |
      CH3C       CCH2N          |
          \\    //    +\\       |
           N----C       CH--S
                |
               NH2
                    (III)

                               CH3  CH2CH2OH
                               |    |
            N=CH               C====C
           /    \             /     |
      CH3C       CCH2N              |
          \\    /      \            |
           N----C       CH2--S
                |
               NH2
                    (IV)
```

The pyrimidine ring in (III) is not attacked by sodium trimethoxyhydroborate.[2,3]

14. REDUCTION OF INORGANIC SPECIES

Solutions of sodium trimethoxyhydroborate with silver nitrate, arsenious oxide, bismuth nitrate and antimony trichloride give dark precipitates which contain no boron. They probably consist largely of elemental silver, arsenic, bismuth or antimony. Mercuric chloride gives a mixture of mercurous chloride and free mercury. Copper sulfate solutions give dark brown precipitates which do not contain boron. White precipitates of the hydroxides are formed with lead nitrate and zinc nitrate. Bromine in carbon tetrachloride is immediately decolorized. Ferricyanide ion is reduced to ferrocyanide ion. Nickel, cobalt, and ferrous salts all yield black precipitates containing boron.[8,29] Potassium permanganate, ceric sulfate and hydrogen peroxide also are reduced by sodium trimethoxyhydroborate.[22]

V. DIALKOXYDIHYDROBORATES

Attempts to prepare lithium trimethoxyhydroborate in a sealed tube reaction at 100° resulted in the formation of a considerable amount of hydrogen and an impure 1:1 adduct of lithium hydride and trimethoxyborane. A disproportionation product believed to be the dihydro derivative $[(CH_3O)_2BH_2]Li$ also was isolated.[5,8]

VI. ALKOXYTRIHYDROBORATES

A. *Methods of Preparation*

1. FROM DIBORANE AND METAL ALKOXIDES

Calcium, strontium, and barium ethoxytrihydroborate reportedly are formed from the reaction of diborane with calcium, strontium or barium ethoxide at 70–80° (17-39).[42] The possibility that the pro-

$$B_2H_6 + M(OC_2H_5)_2 \rightarrow [C_2H_5OBH_3]_2M \qquad (17\text{-}39)$$

ducts are not the monoethoxy compound but rather a mixture of $[BH_4]_2M$ and $[(C_2H_5O)_4B]_2M$ in a 3:1 molar ratio was ruled out on the basis of their rapid solubility in water and insolubility in tetrahydrofuran. The tetraethoxyborates hydrolyze slowly and $[BH_4]_2M$ is soluble in tetrahydrofuran. In addition, the products were thermally stable to 320°; whereas alkaline earth tetraethoxyborates decompose at 145–200° (see Chapter 14).

The reaction of diborane and calcium methoxide reportedly gave a monomethoxy derivative.[42]

$$\tfrac{1}{2} B_2H_6 + Ca(OCH_3)_2 \rightarrow [CH_3OBH_3]CaOCH_3 \qquad (17\text{-}40)$$

2. FROM SODIUM BOROHYDRIDE AND PHENOLS

The kinetics of reaction (17-41) have been recorded for sodium and lithium borohydride and a variety of alcohols and phenols.[14,15] The infrared spectrum of sodium methoxytrihydroborate was determined but the products were not described.

$$MBH_4 + ArOH \rightarrow [ArOBH_3]M + H_2 \qquad (17\text{-}41)$$

B. *Reactions*

The alkaline earth ethoxytrihydroborates are stable *in vacuo* to 320°.[42] The methoxy derivative $[CH_3OBH_3]CaOCH_3$ when treated with acid reportedly was rapidly and completely hydrolyzed with the evolution of hydrogen.[42]

VII. TETRA(ACYLOXYHYDRO)BORATES

Sodium borohydride in dimethyl ether at room temperature takes up three moles of carbon dioxide to give a powdery white solid with a volume about six to eight times as great as the sodium borohydride originally used. Treatment of the solid with hydrochloric acid and sulfuric acid results in hydrogen, boric acid and formic acid in mole ratios consistent with that for structure (V).[25,40,41]

$$NaBH_4 + 3\,CO_2 \rightarrow \underset{\text{(V)}}{NaBH(O\overset{\overset{O}{\|}}{C}H)_3} \qquad (17\text{-}42)$$

When allowed to stand at room temperature, (V) slowly liberates methyl formate; appreciable quantities are evolved on heating to 125°. The decomposition is formulated in equations (17-43) and (17-44).[41]

$$NaBH(O\overset{\overset{O}{\|}}{C}H)_3 \rightarrow H\overset{\overset{O}{\|}}{C}ONa + \left\{HB(O\overset{\overset{O}{\|}}{C}H)_2\right\} \qquad (17\text{-}43)$$

$$2\left\{HB(O\overset{\overset{O}{\|}}{C}H)_2\right\} \rightarrow H\overset{\overset{O}{\|}}{C}OCH_3 + \text{other products} \qquad (17\text{-}44)$$

Addition of a dioxane solution of triacetoxyborane to a boiling suspension of sodium hydride in dioxane resulted in a solid white product formulated as (VI) containing small amounts of (VII).[23]

$$\underset{\text{(VI)}}{\left[(CH_3\overset{\overset{O}{\|}}{C}O)_3BH\right]Na} \qquad \underset{\text{(VII)}}{\left[(CH_3\overset{\overset{O}{\|}}{C}O)_2BH_2\right]Na}$$

Treatment of a tetrahydrofuran solution of sodium borohydride with acetic acid led to a white precipitate believed to be (VIII).

$$\underset{\text{(VIII)}}{\left[CH_3\overset{\overset{O}{\|}}{C}OBH_3\right]Na}$$

Rapid evolution of hydrogen was observed when the product was dissolved in water.[26]

Treatment of one mole of sodium borohydride in diglyme with one mole of propionic acid resulted in the formation of one mole of hydrogen and a product formulated as (IX). The same product was

$$\underset{\text{(IX)}}{\left[CH_3CH_2\overset{\overset{O}{\|}}{C}OBH_3\right]Na}$$

obtained from the reaction of diborane and sodium propionate.[9]

VIII. ANALYTICAL

Sodium trialkoxyhydroborates have been analyzed for both alkalinity and boron by titration of an aqueous solution with standard acid to the methyl red endpoint followed by addition of mannitol and titration to the phenolphthalein endpoint with carbonate-free base.[5,7,8]

Active hydrogen or hydride content was determined as hydrogen gas by hydrolysis of a separate sample[7,8] and by iodate titration.[5,7]

IX. PHYSICAL CONSTANTS

$[(RO)_3BH]$	M.p. (°C)	d_4^t	Reference
$[(CH_3O)_3BH]Na$	~230 (d.)		8, 28, 32
		1.24	22
$[(CH_3O)_3BH]Li$	—	—	8, 28
$[(CH_3O)_3BH]_2Ca$	White powder		18
$[(C_2H_5O)_3BH]Na$	>295		32
	—	—	5, 8
$[(i\text{-}C_3H_7O)_3BH]Na$	White solid		5, 24
$[(n\text{-}C_4H_9O)_3BH]Na$	—	—	8, 32
$[(n\text{-}C_4H_9O)_3BH]Li \cdot 0.5(C_2H_5)_2O$	Colorless rectangles		43
$[(t\text{-}C_4H_9O)_3BH]Na$	—	—	5

$[(RO)_2(R'O)BH]M$	M.p. (°C)	d_4^t	Reference
$(HOCH_2CH_2)_3\overset{+}{N}CH_2CH_2O\overset{-}{B}H(OCH_3)_2$	—	—	27

$[(RO)_2BH_2]M$	M.p. (°C)	d_4^t	Reference
$[(CH_3O)_2BH_2]Li$	—	—	8

$[ROBH_3]M$	M.p. (°C)	d_4^t	Reference
$[CH_3OBH_3]CaOCH_3$	—	—	42
$[C_2H_5OBH_3]_2Ca$	>320		42
$[C_2H_5OBH_3]_2Sr$	>320		42
$[C_2H_5OBH_3]_2Ba$	>320		42

(Table continued)

$[(RC(=O)O)_3BH]M$	M.p. (°C)	d_4^t	Reference
$[(HC(=O)O)_3BH]Na$	~125		40
$[(CH_3C(=O)O)_3BH]Na$	White solid		23

$[(RC(=O)O)_2BH_2]M$	M.p. (°C)	d_4^t	Reference
$[(CH_3C(=O)O)_2BH_2]Na$	Solid		23

$[RC(=O)OBH_3]M$	M.p. (°C)	d_4^t	Reference
$[CH_3C(=O)OBH_3]Na$	Solid		26
$[C_2H_5C(=O)OBH_3]Na$	—	—	9

X. REFERENCES

1. Beckett, A. H., N. J. Harper, A. D. J. Balon, and T. H. E. Watts, *Tetrahedron*, **6**, 319 (1959).
2. Bonvicino, G. E., and D. J. Hennessy, 117th Meeting American Chemical Society, Philadelphia, April, 1950, Abstracts of Papers, p. 48-C.
3. Bonvicino, G. E., and D. J. Hennessy, 122nd Meeting American Chemical Society, Atlantic City, Sept., 1952, Abstracts of Papers, p. 7-C.
4. Brown, H. C., and E. J. Mead, *J. Am. Chem. Soc.*, **75**, 6263 (1953).
5. Brown, H. C., E. J. Mead, and C. J. Shoaf, *J. Am. Chem. Soc.*, **78**, 3616 (1956).
6. Brown, H. C., E. J. Mead, and B. C. Subba Rao, *J. Am. Chem. Soc.*, **77**, 6209 (1955).
7. Brown, H. C., E. J. Mead, and P. A. Tierney, *J. Am. Chem. Soc.*, **79**, 5400 (1957).
8. Brown, H. C., H. I. Schlesinger, I. Sheft, and D. M. Ritter, *J. Am. Chem. Soc.*, **75**, 192 (1953).
9. Brown, H. C., and B. C. Subba Rao, *J. Am. Chem. Soc.*, **82**, 681 (1960).
10. Bush, J. D., U.S. Pat. 3,014,060 (1961, to Callery Chemical Company).

11. Bush, J. D., R. A. Carpenter, and W. H. Schechter, U.S. Pat. 3,014,059 (1961, to Callery Chemical Company).
12. Callery Chemical Company, Technical Data Sheet.
13. Carpenter, R. A., U.S. Pat. 2,895,985 (1959, to Callery Chemical Company); Can. Pat. 611,287 (1960, to Callery Chemical Company).
14. Dessy, R. E., and E. Grannen, Jr., *J. Am. Chem. Soc.*, **83**, 3953 (1961).
15. Dessy, R. E., E. Grannen, and Y. Okazumi, 138th Meeting American Chemical Society, New York, Sept., 1960, Abstracts of Papers, p. 32-P.
16. Garrett, E. R., and D. A. Lyttle, *J. Am. Chem. Soc.*, **75**, 6051 (1953).
17. Henle, W., Ger. Pat. 1,025,854 (1958, to Deutsche Gold und Silber).
18. Hesse, G., and H. Jäger, *Ber.*, **92**, 2022 (1959).
19. Hohnstedt, L. F., and D. T. Haworth, *J. Am. Chem. Soc.*, **82**, 89 (1960).
20. Kilpatrick, M., and C. D. McKinney, Jr., *J. Am. Chem. Soc.*, **72**, 5474 (1950).
21. Köster, R., Ger. Pat. 1,052,406 (1957, to Studiengesellschaft Kohle m.b.H.).
22. Metal Hydrides Incorporated, Technical Bulletin 504-C.
23. Nenitzeseu, C. D., and F. Badea, *Bul. Inst. Politeh. Bucuresti*, **20**, 93 (1958); through *Chem. Abstracts*, **55**, 2325 (1961).
24. Pearson, R. K., and L. J. Edwards, Callery Chemical Company, CCC-1024-TR-213, Dec. 13, 1956.
25. Pearson, R. K., and T. Wartik, U.S. Pat. 2,872,474 (1959, to Callery Chemical Co.).
26. Reetz, T., *J. Am. Chem. Soc.*, **82**, 5039 (1960).
27. Rudner, B., and M. S. Moores, U.S. Pat. 2,976,307 (1961, to Koppers Company, Inc.).
28. Schlesinger, H. I., and H. C. Brown, U.S. Pat. 2,461,661 (1949, to United States Atomic Energy Commission).
29. Schlesinger, H. I., and H. C. Brown, U.S. Pat. 2,494,968 (1950, to USA).
30. Schlesinger, H. I., and H. C. Brown, U.S. Pat. 2,534,533 (1950).
31. Schlesinger, H. I., and H. C. Brown, U.S. Pat. 2,543,511 (1951, to United States Atomic Energy Commission).
32. Schlesinger, H. I., H. C. Brown, *et al.*, Univ. of Chicago, 1943–1944 Final Report to Signal Corps Ground Signal Agency on Contract No. W-3434SC-174, File No. 1138-SCG-43 (ESL).
33. Schlesinger, H. I., H. C. Brown, *et al.*, *J. Am. Chem. Soc.*, **75**, 186 (1953).
34. Schlesinger, H. I., H. C. Brown, *et al.*, *J. Am. Chem. Soc.*, **75**, 215 (1953).
35. Schlesinger, H. I., H. C. Brown, and A. E. Finholt, *J. Am. Chem. Soc.*, **75**, 205 (1953).
36. Schlesinger, H. I., H. C. Brown, J. R. Gilbreath, and J. J. Katz, *J. Am. Chem. Soc.*, **75**, 195 (1953).
37. Schlesinger, H. I., H. C. Brown, H. R. Koekstra, and L. R. Rapp, *J. Am. Chem. Soc.*, **75**, 199 (1953).
38. Schlesinger, H. I., H. R. Hoekstra, and H. C. Brown, 115th Meeting American Chemical Society, San Francisco, March, 1960, Abstracts of Papers, p. 9-O.
39. Sheft, I., M. S. Dissertation, University of Chicago, March, 1944.
40. Wartik, T., and R. K. Pearson, *J. Am. Chem. Soc.*, **77**, 1075 (1955).
41. Wartik, T., and R. K. Pearson, *J. Inorg. Nucl. Chem.*, **7**, 404 (1958).
42. Wiberg, E., and R. Hartwimmer, *Z. Naturforsch.*, **10b**, 294 (1955).
43. Wittig, G., and P. Hornberger, *Ann.*, **577**, 11 (1952).

18

COORDINATION COMPOUNDS DERIVED FROM BORON TRIFLUORIDE AND ALCOHOLS, PHENOLS OR ACIDS

I. INTRODUCTION

This chapter is concerned with the tetracovalent compounds of boron which are derived from the coordination of boron trifluoride with alcohols and phenols (I and II), metal alkoxides (III), hydrogen tetraalkoxyborates (IV), and carboxylic acids (V and VI).

$[ROBF_3]^-H^+$ (I) $[ROBF_3]^-ROH_2^+$ (II) $[ROBF_3]^-M^+$ (III)

$[ROBF_3]^-(RO)_3BH^+$ (IV) $\left[\overset{O}{\overset{\|}{R C}}OBF_3\right]^- H^+$ (V) $\left[\overset{O}{\overset{\|}{R C}}OBF_3\right]^- \overset{O}{\overset{\|}{R C}}OH_2^+$ (VI)

The rapidity with which boron trichloride, boron tribromide and boron triiodide form hydrogen halide with hydroxylic organic compounds appears to exclude the possibility of stable chlorine, bromine and iodine analogs of (I) to (VI).[10,25,26]

The chemistry of the ether complexes of boron trifluoride,[3,5] for the most part, can be rationalized on the basis of a 1:1 complex in which boron assumes sp^3 hybridization but in which the ether moiety remains essentially intact (VII). Indeed, an electron diffrac-

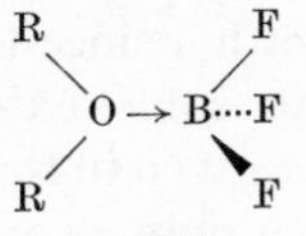

$$R_2O \rightarrow BF_3$$

(VII)

tion investigation[2] of the structure of dimethyl ether–boron trifluoride and the parachor[38] of both the dimethyl and diethyl ether complexes are consistent with this interpretation. In so far as structure (VII) is descriptive of the ether complexes of boron trifluoride, their chemistry is outside the stated scope of this chapter. However, the electrolysis of diethyl ether–boron trifluoride at potentials between 50 and 100 V. results in the liberation of hydrogen, ethyl ether and ethane at the cathode. In addition, the specific conductivity of the complex at 25° is 2.97×10^{-4} ohm^{-1} cm^{-1}. These data are consistent with an ionic interpretation for the structure of the complex in which heterolytic carbon–oxygen cleavage of the ether supplies the requisite ions (VIII).[15]

$$[C_2H_5OBF_3]^-C_2H_5^+$$
(VIII)

II. HISTORICAL

Although the chemistry of boron trifluoride and alcohols,[19,21,24] phenols,[9] and acids[22] has been explored since the early nineteenth century, it remained for Meerwein[27] in 1927 and Nieuwland[4] in 1931 to formulate the products as the coordination compounds (IX) and (X).*

$$[ROBF_3]H \qquad \left[CH_3\overset{\overset{O}{\|}}{C}OBF_3\right]H$$
(IX) (X)

III. PROPERTIES

A. *General*

The 1:1 boron trifluoride–alcohol complexes are low melting solids[2,4,13,42] which fume in air[29] and cannot be distilled without decomposition.[23,28,29] The ethylene glycol complex is soluble in ether and dioxane and insoluble in nitrobenzene and anisole.[29]

The 1:2 boron trifluoride–alcohol complexes, in the main, are colorless liquids which do not fume in air[29] and which can be distilled *in vacuo*.[28,29] The boiling points, however, are generally an unsatisfactory means of characterization since the complexes decompose or are thermally dissociated to some extent in the vapor phase.[14] Thus, the boiling point values given in the table of physical constants (Section VII) should be taken only as an indication of the temperature at which the vapor pressure above the liquid reaches a specific value, since the composition of the liquid and gaseous phases may differ appreciably.

* The compound actually was formulated as (Xa).[27] Subsequent workers[3] believed this was a misprint and felt it should be as shown in (X). Later workers[16] believed the original data was consistent with the 1:2 complex (Xb).

$$\left[CH_3\overset{\overset{O}{\|}}{C}OBF_3\right]_3H \qquad \left[CH_3\overset{\overset{O}{\|}}{C}OBF_3\right]CH_3\overset{\overset{O}{\|}}{C}OH_2$$
(Xa) (Xb)

The 1:2 alcohol complexes are soluble in ether, dioxane, anisole, and nitrobenzene and insoluble in petroleum ether and carbon tetrachloride.[29] The nitrobenzene solution of the 1:2 methanol complex is a good conductor of electricity.[28]

The 1:1 acid complexes are solids which fume in air.[17,27,29] They are soluble in nitrobenzene and anisole. The 1:2 acid complexes, with a few exceptions, are stable, colorless, oily liquids which fume in air.[18,28,29] They are soluble in ether and nitrobenzene.[29]

Molar refractivity data for a variety of 1:2 alcohol and acid complexes are summarized in Table 18-1.[29] Electrical conductivity

Table 18-1. Molar refractivities of 1:2 boron trifluoride–alcohol and acid complexes

Complex	$[R]_{He}$	Temp. (°C)
$[CH_3OBF_3]CH_3OH_2$	19.22	18
$[C_2H_5OBF_3]C_2H_5OH_2$	28.17	19.7
$[n\text{-}C_3H_7OBF_3]n\text{-}C_3H_7OH_2$	37.65	20
$[n\text{-}C_4H_9OBF_3]n\text{-}C_4H_9OH_2$	47.11	20.2
$[ClCH_2CH_2OBF_3]ClCH_2CH_2OH_2$	38.87	17
$[HC(=O)OBF_3]HC(=O)OH_2$	23.15	2.1
$[CH_3C(=O)OBF_3]CH_3C(=O)OH_2$	31.62[a]	21.1
$[C_2H_5C(=O)OBF_3]C_2H_5C(=O)OH_2$	40.83	21.6
$[n\text{-}C_3H_7C(=O)OBF_3]n\text{-}C_3H_7C(=O)OH_2$	50.14	21.8

[a] A value of 31.94 also has been recorded.[20]

data, electrical properties of molten complexes, and viscosity data also have been recorded.[12,13,14,23,41]

B. Structure

The structure originally postulated for the 1:2 complexes was explained in terms of hydrogen bonding (XI).[29] The properties of

$$\begin{array}{c} \quad\;\; Y \qquad\;\; Y \\ \quad\;\; | \qquad\;\;\; | \\ H\text{—}O\cdots H\text{—}O\cdots BF_3 \end{array}$$

(XI)

$$Y = R \text{ or } RC(=O)\text{—}$$

the complexes, however, are best explained by not mere dipole associations of the components[14] but by an ionic formulation in which boron trifluoride accepts a fourth ligand to become an anion, compensated by a proton in the case of the 1:1 complexes (I and V) or by an alkoxonium or carboxonium ion in the case of the 1:2 complexes (II and VI).[4,14,29] Thus boron trifluoride–methanol conducts ionically as $[CH_3OBF_3]H$.[13,32] A plot of melting point versus molar composition indicates definite compound formation between boron trifluoride and ethanol[4] as does the vapor pressure–composition isotherm for the system BF_3–$2CH_3OH$.[32] Electrical conductivity–composition isotherms have established stoichiometric compounds of boron trifluoride with one and two moles of methanol,[13,31] two moles of phenol,[36] and one mole of acetic acid,[16] and electrolytic data for molten boron trifluoride–alcohol systems were interpreted by assuming modes of ionization involving $[CH_3OBF_3]^-H^+$,[13] $[ROBF_3]^-ROH_2^+$,[11,13] and $[CH_3C(=O)OBF_3]^-H^+$.[16]

Infrared studies of $[CH_3OBF_3]H$ and $[C_2H_5OBF_3]H$ indicated the compounds to be polymeric with association through hydrogen bonds. The corresponding 1:2 complexes were described as an association of two complexes in which four hydrogen bonds formed a closed cycle.[1] In contrast, molecular weight determinations of some 1:2 alcohol complexes in nitrobenzene solution (Table 18-2) were found

Table 18-2. Molecular weights of 1:2 boron trifluoride–alcohol complexes in nitrobenzene solution

	Calculated	Found	% Dissociation
$[C_2H_5OBF_3]C_2H_5OH_2$	160	159, 160	0
$[C_4H_9OBF_3]C_4H_9OH_2$	216	217, 218	0
$[ClCH_2CH_2OBF_3]ClCH_2CH_2OH_2$	229	170	38.6
		179	32.8
$[Cl_3CCH_2OBF_3]Cl_3CCH_2OH_2$	336	178	77.1
		186	73.8

to be consistent with a monomeric formulation, at least for the ethyl and butyl alcohol derivatives. The low values for the chloroethyl alcohol complexes were rationalized by assuming dissociation of the complexes.[29]

IV. METHODS OF PREPARATION

A. *From Direct Reaction of Boron Trifluoride with Alcohols, Phenols or Acids*

The 1:1 (I and V) and 1:2 (II and VI) series of alcohol and acid complexes with boron trifluoride can be prepared by admixture of the components in the proper proportions.[13,16,17,18,23,28,29] It also has been stated that addition of a second mole of boron trifluoride to the 1:2 complexes yields the 1:1 complexes.[28,29] This transformation, however, does not take place with boron trifluoride and $[n\text{-}C_4H_9OBF_3]n\text{-}C_4H_9OH_2$.[23]

Benzyl alcohol forms a very unstable 1:2 complex which decomposes to boron trifluoride dihydrate and a higher molecular weight hydrocarbon.[29*]

$$2\ C_6H_5CH_2OH + BF_3 \rightarrow (C_6H_5CH_2OBF_3)C_6H_5CH_2OH_2 \rightarrow BF_3\cdot 2H_2O + (C_6H_5CH)_x \quad (18\text{-}1)$$

In condensation reactions of salicylic acid with propylene in the presence of boron trifluoride, it was suggested that the boron halide promoted the reaction by complexing with the carboxyl function in preference to the hydroxyl group. The stoichiometry of the complex was not reported.[7]

The 1:1:1 complex of boron trifluoride, tributoxyborane and butanol was assigned structure (XII). It was prepared directly from

$$[C_4H_9OBF_3](C_4H_9O)_3BH$$
(XII)

boron trifluoride, tributoxyborane and butanol and from tributoxyborane and the $BF_3\cdot 2C_4H_9OH$ complex.[23]

Reaction (18-2) has been claimed.[17]

$$\mathrm{H\overset{O}{\overset{\|}{C}}ONa} + BF_3 \rightarrow \left[\mathrm{H\overset{O}{\overset{\|}{C}}OBF_3}\right]Na \quad (18\text{-}2)$$

B. From Boron Trifluoride and Metal Alkoxides

Prolonged shaking of sodium or potassium methoxide with excess boron trifluoride etherate in ether solution resulted in the salts (XIII) and (XIV).[28,29]

$$[CH_3OBF_3]Na \qquad [CH_3OBF_3]K$$
(XIII) (XIV)

C. From Boron Trifluoride and Carboxylic Acid Anhydrides

In contrast to the reported 1:1 crystalline compound from the reaction of acetic anhydride and boron trifluoride,[4] a more complex reaction (18-3) resulting in the formation of (XV) and the 1:1 acetic

* Cannizzaro believed that the reaction of benzyl alcohol and boron trifluoride produced stilbene.[6]

acid complex has been reported.[28,30] Isobutyric anhydride behaved similarly.[30]

$$5\ CH_3\overset{O}{\overset{\|}{C}}O\overset{O}{\overset{\|}{C}}CH_3 + 7\ BF_3 \rightarrow \left[(CH_3\overset{O}{\overset{\|}{C}})_2CH\overset{O}{\overset{\|}{C}}\right]_2 0.3BF_3 + 4\left[CH_3\overset{O}{\overset{\|}{C}}OBF_3\right]H \quad \text{(18-3)}$$

(XV)

D. *From Alkoxydifluoroboranes*

Butoxydifluoroborane reacts with both butanol (18-4) and a limited amount of water (18-5) to produce the $BF_3 \cdot 2C_4H_9OH$ complex.[23]

$$3\ C_4H_9OBF_2 + 3\ C_4H_9OH \rightarrow [C_4H_9OBF_3]C_4H_9OH_2 + BF_3 \cdot (C_4H_9O)_3B \cdot C_4H_9OH \quad \text{(18-4)}$$

$$2\ C_4H_9OBF_2 + 3\ H_2O \rightarrow [C_4H_9OBF_3]C_4H_9OH_2 + H_3BO_3 + HF \quad \text{(18-5)}$$

E. *From Dihydroxyfluoboric Acid and Acetyl Chloride*

Acetylation of dihydroxyfluoboric acid with acetyl chloride was reported to result in the immediate formation of hydrogen chloride, the 1 : 2 acid complex (XVI), and a diboron compound formulated as (XVII).[20] In view of the recent elucidation of the chemistry of diboron compounds, the formation of (XVII) seems improbable.

$$\left[CH_3\overset{O}{\overset{\|}{C}}OBF_3\right]CH_3\overset{O}{\overset{\|}{C}}OH_2$$

(XVI)

$$CH_3\overset{O}{\overset{\|}{C}}O(F)B{-}B(F)O\overset{O}{\overset{\|}{C}}CH_3$$

(XVII)

F. *From* 1 : 1 *Boron Trifluoride–Carboxylic Acid Complex*

Attempted distillation of the 1 : 1 acid complex (XVIII) resulted in loss of half of the boron trifluoride leaving the 1 : 2 acid complex.[28]

$$\left[R\overset{O}{\overset{\|}{C}}OBF_3\right]H \rightarrow \tfrac{1}{2}\ BF_3 + \tfrac{1}{2}\left[R\overset{O}{\overset{\|}{C}}OBF_3\right]R\overset{O}{\overset{\|}{C}}OH_2 \quad \text{(18-6)}$$

(XVIII)

V. REACTIONS

A. *Thermal Stability*

1. ALCOHOL COMPLEXES

The 1 : 1 complexes derived from primary alcohols dissociate when heated (18-7). They may undergo further decomposition by elimination of water (18-8).[23,28,29] The olefins produced in this manner subsequently can polymerize under the catalytic influence of the boron trifluoride.

$$[ROBF_3]H \rightarrow BF_3 + ROH \quad (18\text{-}7)$$

$$[RCH_2CH_2OBF_3]H \rightarrow BF_3 \cdot H_2O + RCH{=}CH_2 \quad (18\text{-}8)$$

The 1:2 complexes generally are more stable than the 1:1 complexes and can be distilled *in vacuo.*[28,29] They can be decomposed, however, as evidenced by the thermal decomposition of $[C_4H_9OBF_3]C_4H_9OH_2$ to butene, and dissociation to boron trifluoride and butanol when heated with sodium hydroxide. The 1:1:1 complex (XII) is thermally degraded to n-butene when heated for fourteen hours at 180°.[23]

A variety of 1:1 and 1:2 complexes have been converted to dialkyl ethers at 200-225° in an autoclave.[34] Alkylbenzenes were formed in addition to the ethers when the reactions were run in benzene solvent.[34]

$$2\,[ROBF_3]H \rightarrow ROR + H_2O + 2\,BF_3 \quad (18\text{-}9)$$

$$[ROBF_3]ROH_2 \rightarrow ROR + H_2O + BF_3 \quad (18\text{-}10)$$

Complexes derived from secondary alcohols decompose on attempted distillation yielding hydrated boron trifluoride and olefin.[29]

2. ACID COMPLEXES

The 1:2 acid complexes, like the 1:2 alcohol complexes, can be distilled under vacuum without decomposition.[28,29] The formic acid complex, however, loses carbon monoxide at 75°.[29]

$$\left[\overset{\displaystyle O}{\overset{\|}{HC}}OBF_3\right]\overset{\displaystyle O}{\overset{\|}{HC}}OH_2 \rightarrow 2\,CO + BF_3 \cdot 2H_2O \quad (18\text{-}11)$$

Attempted distillation of the 1:1 acid complexes results in loss of half of their boron trifluoride and gives the 1:2 complex (18-12).[12,28] Thus, in general, the 1:1 acid complexes cannot be distilled without decomposition* even in vacuum.[29]

$$\left[\overset{\displaystyle O}{\overset{\|}{RC}}OBF_3\right]H \rightarrow \tfrac{1}{2}\,BF_3 + \tfrac{1}{2}\left[\overset{\displaystyle O}{\overset{\|}{RC}}OBF_3\right]\overset{\displaystyle O}{\overset{\|}{RC}}OH_2 \quad (18\text{-}12)$$

In the chloroacetic acid series, the stability of the 1:1 complex varies inversely with the strength of the acid.[28] Thus, (XIX) loses all of its boron trifluoride at 80°, (XX) is completely stripped of the

* Boiling points for the 1:1 acetic acid complex have been reported.[27,30]

boron halide at room temperature, and (XXI) does not form a complex at all.

$$\left[\mathrm{ClCH_2\overset{\overset{\displaystyle O}{\|}}{C}OBF}\right]\mathrm{H} \qquad \left[\mathrm{Cl_2CH\overset{\overset{\displaystyle O}{\|}}{C}OBF_3}\right]\mathrm{H} \qquad \mathrm{Cl_3C\overset{\overset{\displaystyle O}{\|}}{C}OH}$$

(XIX) (XX) (XXI)

B. Hydrolysis

The 1:1 complex with acetic acid is extremely unstable in moist air and hydrolyzes immediately with copious fuming.[16] Other members of this series probably are just as hydrolytically unstable since they also fume in air.[29] Definitive statements of hydrolytic stability are lacking in the 1:1 alcohol series, but they too fume in air.[29]

The 1:1:1 complex (XII) reacts vigorously with water to give boric acid, butanol, and the 1:2 butanol complex.[23]

C. With Alcohols

The propionic acid complex* has served as a ready source of propionic acid for the preparation of esters (18-13). The complex also serves as the catalyst.[18]

$$\left[\mathrm{CH_3CH_2\overset{\overset{\displaystyle O}{\|}}{C}OBF_3}\right]\mathrm{CH_3CH_2\overset{\overset{\displaystyle O}{\|}}{C}OH_2} + 2\,\mathrm{ROH} \rightarrow 2\,\mathrm{CH_3CH_2\overset{\overset{\displaystyle O}{\|}}{C}OR} + \mathrm{BF_3} + 2\,\mathrm{H_2O} \quad (18\text{-}13)$$

D. With Ammonia and Amines

Ammonia abstracts boron trifluoride from its methanol complex.[32]

$$[\mathrm{CH_3OBF_3}]\mathrm{H} + \mathrm{NH_3} \rightarrow \mathrm{BF_3{:}NH_3} + \mathrm{CH_3OH} \quad (18\text{-}14)$$

Pyridine reacts with the butanol complexes as shown in equations 18-15 and 18-16 to effect alcoholysis of the boron.[23]

$$4\,[\mathrm{C_4H_9OBF_3}]\mathrm{C_4H_9OH_2} + 3\,\mathrm{C_5H_5N} \rightarrow (\mathrm{C_4H_9O})_3\mathrm{B} + 3\,\mathrm{C_5H_5N\cdot BF_3\cdot HF} + 5\,\mathrm{C_4H_9OH} \quad (18\text{-}15)$$

$$4\,[\mathrm{C_4H_9OBF_3}](\mathrm{C_4H_9O})_3\mathrm{BH} + 3\,\mathrm{C_5H_5N} \rightarrow 5\,(\mathrm{C_4H_9O})_3\mathrm{B} + 3\,\mathrm{C_5H_5N\cdot BF_3\cdot HF} + \mathrm{C_4H_9OH} \quad (18\text{-}16)$$

The 1:1 acetic acid complex reacts with ammonia to give the ammonium salt.[17]

* The complex appeared to be 1:1 by the stoichiometry of the reaction and 1:2 by analysis.[4]

E. *With Olefins*

Propylene reacts with the 1:2 methanol complex at room temperature to give methyl isopropyl ether.[29]

$$[CH_3OBF_3]CH_3OH_2 + CH_3CH{=}CH_2 \rightarrow CH_3OCH(CH_3)_2{\cdot}BF_3 + CH_3OH \quad (18\text{-}17)$$

F. *With Alkali Halides*

The 1:2 boron trifluoride-acetic acid complex is degraded to its components when heated at 250° in the presence of one to two molar equivalents of sodium fluoride or chloride.[8]

$$\left[CH_3\overset{\overset{O}{\|}}{C}OBF_3\right]CH_3\overset{\overset{O}{\|}}{C}OH_2 + NaX \xrightarrow{250^\circ} 2\,CH_3\overset{\overset{O}{\|}}{C}OH + NaBF_3X \quad (18\text{-}18)$$

$$NaBF_3X \xrightarrow{300\text{–}500^\circ} BF_3 + NaX$$

G. *With Boron Trifluoride*

In contrast to $[C_4H_9OBF_3]C_4H_9OH_2$ which does not react with boron trifluoride, the reaction of the 1:1:1 complex (XII) was formulated as follows:[23]

$$2\,[C_4H_9OBF_3](C_4H_9O)_3BH + 3\,BF_3 \rightarrow [C_4H_9OBF_3]C_4H_9OH_2 + 6\,C_4H_9OBF_2 \quad (18\text{-}19)$$

H. *With Sodium*

Addition of metallic sodium to the 1:1 acetic acid complex results in evolution of hydrogen.[12]

I. *With Hydroxides and Oxides*

Incremental addition of mercuric oxide to (XXII) resulted in ultimate crystallization of the salt (XXIII).[32] The 1:1 acetic acid complex forms salts by reaction with potassium hydroxide, magnesium oxide, etc.[17]

$[CH_3OBF_3]H$ (XXII) $\qquad$ $[CH_3OBF_3]_2Hg$ (XXIII)

J. *Attempted Reaction with Sodium Methoxide*

The sodium salt (XXIV) could not be obtained from the reaction of (XXII) and sodium methoxide.[32]

$[CH_3OBF_3]Na$ (XXIV)

VI. ANALYTICAL

Alcohol and acid complexes were analyzed for boron with an average error of about six percent by decomposition of the sample with a mixture of fuming nitric acid, copper oxide and lead chromate in a sealed tube at 200° and titration of the boric acid thus formed by the standard procedure.[4]

A second method,[29] adapted from the procedure of Wherry and Chapin,[43] involved distillation of the complex with methanol. The distilled trimethoxyborane–methanol azeotrope was hydrolyzed, neutralized to methyl red endpoint, and titrated for boric acid to the phenolphthalein endpoint in the presence of glycerol. Boron values in the still residue were determined by precipitation of the fluorine as calcium fluoride and repetition of the methanol distillation.

A third procedure which has been applied to ester complexes of boron trifluoride appears to be applicable to the alcohol and acid complexes also. The complex is oxidized with a mixture of potassium chlorate, sodium peroxide and sugar in an electrically ignited Parr bomb. The fusion products are dissolved in water and neutralized with ammonium chloride. Calcium nitrate is added to remove the fluoride ion and the filtrate is titrated for boric acid in the usual manner.[33]

VII. PHYSICAL CONSTANTS

$[ROBF_3]H$	M.p. (°C)	B.p. (°C)	d_4^t	n_D^t	Reference
$[CH_3OBF_3]H$	−18.6		1.4081^{20}		13
	−19.4				32
		Decomposes	1.416		40, 41
			1.399^{20}		1
	−19				4
$[C_2H_5OBF_3]H$			1.272^{20}	1.3260^{20}	1
		Decomposes	1.353		40, 41
$[n\text{-}C_3H_7OBF_3]H$	—	—	—	—	37
$[HOCH_2CH_2OBF_3]H$	42–44				29
$[i\text{-}C_3H_7OBF_3]H$	—	—	—	—	34

$[ArOBF_3]H$	M.p. (°C)	B.p. (°C)	d_4^t	n_D^t	Reference
$[C_6H_5OBF_3]H$		Decomposes	1.244		40, 41

$[ROBF_3]M$	M.p. (°C)	B.p. (°C)	d_4^t	n_D^t	Reference
$[CH_3OBF_3]Na$	Solid				29
$[CH_3OBF_3]K$	Solid				29
$[CH_3OBF_3]_2Hg$	White needles				32

(Table continued)

$[ROBF_3]ROH_2$	M.p. (°C)	B.p. (°C)	d_4^t	n_D^t	Reference
$[CH_3OBF_3]CH_3OH_2$	−58.1		1.2120^{20}		13
		58–59/4	1.3115^{20}	1.3070^{18}_{He}	28, 29
			1.312^{20}	1.3074^{20}	1
	—	—	—	—	32
$[C_2H_5OBF_3]C_2H_5OH_2$		51–52/15	1.1638^{20}	$1.3344^{19.7}_{He}$	28
		60/4	1.1638^{20}	$1.3344^{19.7}_{He}$	29
			1.167^{20}	1.3350^{20}	1
$H_2\overset{+}{O}CH_2CH_2O\overset{-}{B}F_3$	42–44	Decomposes			28, 29
$[ClCH_2CH_2OBF_3]ClCH_2CH_2OH_2$		59/2.5	1.4009^{20}	1.4084^{17}_{He}	28, 29
$[Cl_3CCH_2OBF_3]Cl_3CCH_2OH_2$	40–42				29
$[n\text{-}C_3H_7OBF_3]n\text{-}C_3H_7OH_2$		56/2	1.1059^{20}	1.3615^{20}_{He}	28, 29
			1.0561^{20}		11
$[n\text{-}C_4H_9OBF_3]n\text{-}C_4H_9OH_2$		69–70/3	1.0442^{20}	$1.3732^{20.2}_{He}$	28, 29
		86/8, 92–93/16	1.041^{20}	1.3722^{20}	23
$[i\text{-}C_4H_9OBF_3]i\text{-}C_4H_9OH_2$	—	—	—	—	34
$[i\text{-}C_5H_{11}OBF_3]i\text{-}C_5H_{11}OH_2$	—	—	—	—	34
$[C_6H_5CH_2OBF_3]C_6H_5CH_2OH_2$	Unstable				29

$[ArOBF_3]ArOH_2$	M.p. (°C)	B.p. (°C)	d_4^t	n_D^t	Reference
$[C_6H_5OBF_3]C_6H_5OH_2$	—	—	—	—	9, 29, 36

$[ROBF_3](RO)_3BH$	M.p. (°C)	B.p. (°C)	d_4^t	n_D^t	Reference
$[n\text{-}C_4H_9OBF_3](n\text{-}C_4H_9O)_3BH$		67–70/16		1.3940^{20}	23

$\left[\overset{\displaystyle O}{\overset{\Vert}{R C}}OBF\right]H$	M.p. (°C)	B.p. (°C)	d_4^t	n_D^t	Reference
$\left[H\overset{\displaystyle O}{\overset{\Vert}{C}}OBF_3\right]H$	−20 to −21				29
		43/14			17
$\left[CH_3\overset{\displaystyle O}{\overset{\Vert}{C}}OBF_3\right]H$	23–24				29
	37.5				16
	38–39				39
		59/13			27
		62/11			30
		62/14			17
			$1.4736^{37.5}$		12
$\left[ClCH_2\overset{\displaystyle O}{\overset{\Vert}{C}}OBF_3\right]H$		95–100/18 (d.)			17
	—	—	—	—	28
$\left[Cl_2CH\overset{\displaystyle O}{\overset{\Vert}{C}}OBF_3\right]H$	—	—	—	—	28
$\left[HO\overset{\displaystyle O}{\overset{\Vert}{C}}\overset{\displaystyle O}{\overset{\Vert}{C}}OBF_3\right]H$	57–58 (d.)				29
$\left[C_2H_5\overset{\displaystyle O}{\overset{\Vert}{C}}OBF_3\right]H$	28–29				29

(Table continued)

$[RC(=O)OBF]H$	M.p. (°C)	B.p. (°C)	d_4^t	n_D^t	Reference
$[CH_3CH(OH)C(=O)OBF_3]H$		Oil			17
$[n\text{-}C_3H_7C(=O)OBF_3]H$	29–30				29
$[CH_3CH{=}CHC(=O)OBF_3]H$	35–36				29
$[HOC(=O)CH_2CH_2C(=O)OBF_3]H$	82–84 (d.)				29
$[HOC(=O)CH{=}CHC(=O)OBF_3]H$ (cis: both H on the same side of C=C)	75–82				29
$[C_6H_5CH_2C(=O)OBF_3]H$	56–59 (d.)				29
$[CH_3(CH_2)_7CH{=}CH(CH_2)_7C(=O)OBF_3]H$		Oil			17

$[RC(=O)OBF_3]M$	M.p. (°C)	B.p. (°C)	d_4^t	n_D^t	Reference
$[HC(=O)OBF_3]Na$	White powder				17

$[ArC(=O)OBF_3]H$	M.p. (°C)	B.p. (°C)	d_4^t	n_D^t	Reference
$[C_6H_5C(=O)OBF_3]H$	70				17
	90–91.5				29
	~98				4

$[RC(=O)OBF_3]RC(=O)OH_2$	M.p. (°C)	B.p. (°C)	d_4^t	n_D^t	Reference
$[HC(=O)OBF_3]HC(=O)OH_2$		43–44/11	1.5145^{20}	$1.3572^{21.1}$	29
$[CH_3C(=O)OBF_3]CH_3C(=O)OH_2$		53–54/10	1.3421^{20}	$1.3692^{21.1}$	29
		64–66/15		1.3735^{25}	20
		140/746	1.351^{21}		4
		142			35

(Table continued)

$[\mathrm{RC(=O)OBF_3}]$ $\mathrm{RC(=O)OH_2}$	M.p. (°C)	B.p. (°C)	d_4^t	n_D^t	Reference
$[\mathrm{ClCH_2C(=O)OBF_3}]$ $\mathrm{ClCH_2C(=O)OH_2}$	40–42				29
$\mathrm{H_2^+OC(=O)C(=O)O\bar{B}F_3}$	57–58 (d.)				29
$[\mathrm{C_2H_5C(=O)OBF_3}]$ $\mathrm{C_2H_5C(=O)OH_2}$		60–60.5/12	1.2283^{20}	$1.3807^{21.6}$	29
		62–63/17	1.238^{23}		4
$[\mathrm{n\text{-}C_3H_7C(=O)OBF_3}]$ $\mathrm{n\text{-}C_3H_7C(=O)OH_2}$		64/11	1.1506^{20}	$1.3884^{21.8}$	29
$[\mathrm{i\text{-}C_3H_7C(=O)OBF_3}]$ $\mathrm{i\text{-}C_3H_7C(=O)OH_2}$		68–70/15			30
$[\mathrm{CH_3CH{=}CHC(=O)OBF_3}]$ $\mathrm{CH_3CH{=}CHC(=O)OH_2}$		81–82/12.5 (d.)			29
$\mathrm{H_2^+OC(=O)CH_2CH_2C(=O)O\bar{B}F_3}$	82–84 (d.)				29
$\mathrm{H_2^+OC(=O)CH{=}CHC(=O)O\bar{B}F_3}$	75–82 (d.)				29

VIII. REFERENCES

1. Babushkin, A. A., L. A. Gribov, N. G. Guseva, and V. M. Emel'yanova, *Opt. i Spektroskopiya*, **5**, 256 (1958); through *Chem. Abstracts*, **53**, 1919 (1959).
2. Bauer, S. H., G. R. Finlay, and A. W. Laubengayer, *J. Am. Chem. Soc.*, **65**, 889 (1943).
3. Booth, H. S., and D. R. Martin, *Boron Trifluoride and its Derivatives*, Wiley, New York, 1949, p. 65; 3a. p. 68.
4. Bowlus, H., and J. A. Nieuwland, *J. Am. Chem. Soc.*, **53**, 3835 (1931).
5. Brown, H. C., and R. M. Adams, *J. Am. Chem. Soc.*, **64**, 2557 (1942).
6. Cannizzaro, S., *Ann.*, **92**, 113 (1854).
7. Croxall, W. J., F. J. Sowa, and J. A. Nieuwland, *J. Am. Chem. Soc.*, **56**, 2054 (1934).
8. DuPont de Nemours & Company, Brit. Pat. 486,887 (1938).
9. Gasselin, M. V., *Ann. Chim. et Phys.*, **3**, 5 (1894).
10. Gerrard, W., and M. F. Lappert, *Chem. Rev.*, **58**, 1081 (1958).
11. Greenwood, N. N. in N. N. Greenwood, and R. L. Martin, *Quart. Rev. (London)*, **8**, 1 (1954).
12. Greenwood, N. N., and R. L. Martin, *J. Chem. Soc.*, 1795 (1951).
13. Greenwood, N. N., and R. L. Martin, *J. Chem. Soc.*, 757 (1953).
14. Greenwood, N. N., and R. L. Martin, *Quart. Rev.* (*London*), **8**, 1 (1954).
15. Greenwood, N. N., R. L. Martin, and H. J. Emeléus, *J. Chem. Soc.*, 3030 (1950).
16. Greenwood, N. N., R. L. Martin, and H. J. Emeléus, *J. Chem. Soc.*, 1328 (1951).
17. Hardtmann, M., E. Tietze, and W. Schepss, Ger. Pat. 551,513 (1932, to I.G. Farbenindustrie Akt.-Ges.).
18. Hinton, H. D., and J. A. Nieuwland, *J. Am. Chem. Soc.*, **54**, 2017 (1932).
19. Knop, W., *J. Prakt. Chem.*, **74**, 41 (1858).
20. Kroeger, J. W., F. J. Sowa, and J. A. Nieuwland, *J. Am. Chem. Soc.*, **59**, 965 (1937).
21. Kuhlman, F., *Ann.*, **33**, 205 (1840).
22. Landolph, F., *Compt. Rend.*, **85**, 39 (1877); *Ber.*, **10**, 1312 (1877).
23. Lappert, M. F., *J. Chem. Soc.*, 784 (1955).
24. Liebig, J., and F. Wöhler, *Pogg. Ann.*, **24**, 171 (1832).
25. Martin, D. R., *Chem. Rev.*, **34**, 461 (1944).
26. Martin, D. R., *Chem. Rev.*, **42**, 581 (1948).
27. Meerwein, H., *Ann.*, **455**, 227 (1927).
28. Meerwein, H., *Ber.*, **66**, 411 (1933).
29. Meerwein, H., and W. Pannwitz, *J. Prakt. Chem.*, **141**, 123 (1934).
30. Meerwein, H., and D. Vossen, *J. Prakt. Chem.*, **141**, 149 (1934).
31. Nieuwland, J. A., R. R. Vogt, and W. L. Foohey, *J. Am. Chem. Soc.*, **52**, 1018 (1930).
32. O'Leary, L. A., and H. H. Wenzke, *J. Am. Chem. Soc.*, **55**, 2117 (1933).
33. Pflaum, D. J., and H. H. Wenzke, *Ind. Eng. Chem., Anal. Ed.*, **4**, 392 (1932).
34. Romadane, I., and J. Pelchers, *Izv. Vysshykh Uchebn. Zavedenii, Khim. i Khim. Tekhnol.*, **2**, No. 3, 381 (1959); through *Chem. Abstracts*, **54**, 4357 (1960).

35. Sowa, F. J., *J. Am. Chem. Soc.*, **60**, 654 (1938).
36. Sowa, F. J., H. D. Hinton, and J. A. Nieuwland, *J. Am. Chem. Soc.*, **55**, 3402 (1933).
37. Studiengesellschaft Kohle m.b.H., Brit. Pat. 880,788 (1961).
38. Sugden, S., and M. Waloff, *J. Chem. Soc.*, 1492 (1932).
39. Swinehart, C. F., in Ref. 3, p. 67.
40. Topchiev, A. V., and A. M. Paushkin, *Usp. Khim.*, **16**, 664 (1947).
41. Topchiev, A. V., Ya. M. Paushkin, T. P. Vishnyakova, and M. V. Kurashov, *Dokl. Akad. Nauk S.S.S.R.*, **80**, 381 (1951).
42. Vaugh, T. H., H. Bowlus, and J. A. Nieuwland, *Proc. Indiana Acad. Sci.*, **40**, 203 (1931).
43. Wherry, E. T., and W. H. Chapin, *J. Am. Chem. Soc.*, **30**, 1687 (1908).

19

BORONIUM SALTS

I. INTRODUCTION AND HISTORICAL

The reaction of a β-diketone capable of enolization such as acetylacetone with boron trifluoride results in the elimination of one mole of hydrogen fluoride with the formation of an alkoxydifluoroborane (19-1, see Chapter 12).[2] There is no evidence for further reaction

```
CH3           CH3                      CH3
   \             \                        \
    C=O           C—OH                     C—O      F
   /             //                       //   \   /
CH2        ⇄ CH              + BF3 → CH         B        + HF        (19-1)
   \             \                        \   /   \
    C=O           C=O                      C=O      F
   /             /                        /
CH3           CH3                      CH3
```

with a second mole of diketone. With boron trichloride, however, a second mole of diketone reacts to yield a spiran type compound in which boron is the spiro atom (I).* The third halogen on boron is freed as the anion by virtue of coordination of the boron atom with

```
┌CH3                       CH3┐
│   \                     /    │
│    C—O           O—C         │
│   //   \       /    \\       │
│ CH        B         CH       │ +Cl⁻
│   \     ↗   ↖      /         │
│    C=O          O=C          │
│   /                 \        │
└CH3                    CH3┘
```

(I)

* Even though structure (I) has been accepted in numerous subsequent publications, there seems to be no actual proof for its existence. Indeed, it is possible to ignore the intramolecular complex with the carbonyl oxygens and write the simple dialkoxyhaloborane structure. Six-membered rings involving

```
CH3        Cl        CH3
   \        |        /
    C—O—B—O—C
   //            \\
CH                 CH
   \               /
    C=O       O=C
   /               \
CH3                 CH3
```

a boron–carbonyl oxygen interaction have no special validity *per se*, as shown by numerous examples of unsuccessful attempts to prepare compounds with such a configuration (see Chapter 8).

the two carbonyl groups. The boron-containing ion thus bears a formal unit positive charge. This unique type of compound was first prepared and named as a boronium salt* by Dilthey[1] in 1906.† Actual formulation as the spiran (I) was first recorded by Sidgwick.[5]

II. PROPERTIES

Bis(acetylacetone)boronium chloride is soluble in chloroform and acetic acid and insoluble in ether and ligroin. It is unstable in air and therefore difficult to purify. The iodide is too unstable to undergo recrystallization. Bis(acetylacetone)boronium salts with complex anions are stable in air and can be purified. The sulfate is extremely deliquescent. Bis(benzoylacetone)boronium chloride is soluble in chloroform and acetic acid. It is unstable in air.[1]

III. METHODS OF PREPARATION

A. From Boron Trichloride and β-Diketones

Bis(acetylacetone)-, bis(benzoylacetone)-, and bis(dibenzoylmethane)boronium chloride were prepared in ether solution by reaction of the diketones and boron chloride.[1]

$$2\ \mathrm{R{-}C(OH){=}CH{-}C({=}O){-}R'} + \mathrm{BCl_3} \rightarrow \left[\mathrm{(R{-}C{-}O)(CH)(R'{-}C{-}O)B(O{-}C{-}R)(CH)(O{-}C{-}R')}\right]\mathrm{Cl} + 2\ \mathrm{HCl} \qquad (19\text{-}2)$$

$$\rightleftharpoons\ 2\ \mathrm{R{-}C({=}O){-}CH_2{-}C({=}O){-}R'}$$

* It is interesting that the boronium compounds derived from neutral trigonal coplanar boron compounds are stabilized in a tetrahedral configuration; whereas carbonium compounds are trigonal coplanar in their positive state and tetrahedral in their neutral counterparts.

† Workers three years prior to this date had observed the reactions of boron trichloride with both acetylacetone and acetoacetic ester. The products, however, were not formulated as boronium salts but rather as trialkoxy borane hydrochlorides, $(C_6H_9O_3)_3B\cdot 2HCl$.[3]

B. From Boronium Chlorides and Iodides

Bis(acetylacetone)boronium chloride and bis(benzoylacetone)-boronium chloride were converted to a series of salts with more complex anions by simple addition of a variety of metal chlorides to the boronium chlorides in chloroform or acetic acid solution.[1]

$$[(CH_3COCHCOCH_3)_2B]Cl + MCl_x \rightarrow [(CH_3COCHCOCH_3)_2B]MCl_{x+1} \qquad (19\text{-}3)$$

The boronium chlorides also were converted to the iodides by treatment with hydriodic acid in chloroform solution. The iodides in turn were converted to the triiodides by treatment with iodine in acetic acid solution.[1]

$$[(CH_3COCHCOC_6H_5)_2B]Cl \xrightarrow{HI} [(CH_3COCHCOC_6H_5)_2B]I \xrightarrow{I_2} [(CH_3COCHCOC_6H_5)_2B]I_3 \qquad (19\text{-}4)$$

Treatment of bis(acetylacetone)boronium chloride with concentrated sulfuric acid gave the sulfate.[1]

Bis(dibenzoylmethane)boronium chloride was converted to the iron tetrachloride salt by treatment with ferric chloride in chloroform solution.[1]

C. *From Hydroxyketones*

The borate–aureomycin complex which formed in 78% sulfuric acid was formulated as the cationic species (II).[4] The salt was not isolated.

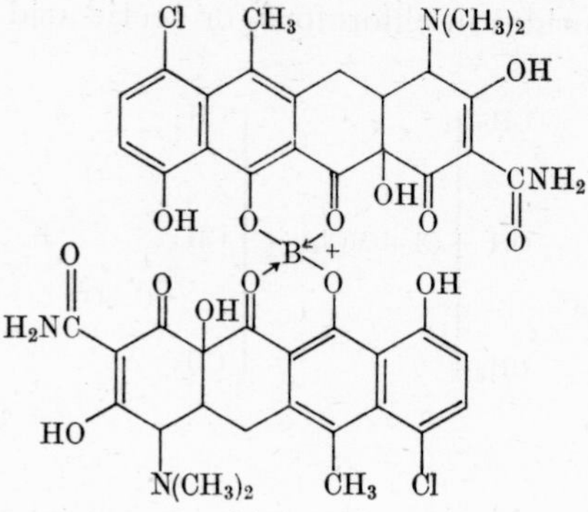

(II)

IV. REACTIONS

Boronium salts rapidly hydrolyze in water to give diketone, boric acid and halogen acid.[5] The salts with a simple halide anion are attacked by atmospheric moisture.[1]

Reactions of the boronium chlorides with metal chlorides, hydriodic acid and sulfuric acid as well as the reaction of the iodides with iodine are discussed in Section III-B.

V. ANALYTICAL

The ferric chloride and zinc chloride complex salts of bis(acetylacetone)boronium chloride and bis(benzoylacetone)boronium chloride were analyzed for boron by decomposition in molten sodium carbonate, followed by separation of the metal salts by filtration or decantation, and titration of the filtrate or decantate with standard base after acidification and removal of carbon dioxide.[1]

VI. PHYSICAL CONSTANTS

		M.p. (°C)	Reference
$[(CH_3C(O)CHC(O)CH_3)_2B]^+Cl^-$		(Structure in doubt)	
		Microcrystals	3
		Yellowish white solid	1
	$FeCl_4^-$	137 (d).	1
	$AuCl_4^-$	135	1
	$\frac{1}{2}PtCl_6^{2-}$	> 300	1
	$ZnCl_3^-$	206 (d.)	1
	$\frac{1}{2}SnCl_6^{2-}$	210–212	1
	I^-	Yellow crystals	1
	I_3^-	Reddish brown crystals	1
	$\frac{1}{2}SO_4^{2-}$	Crystalline mass	1
$[(CH_3C(O)CHC(O)OC_2H_5)_2B]^+Cl^-$		(Structure in doubt)	
		Needles	3
$[(CH_3C(O)CHC(O)C_6H_5)_2B]^+Cl^-$		Yellowish white solid	1
	$FeCl_4^-$	180–182	1
	$\frac{1}{2}PtCl_6^{2-}$	Solid	1
	$ZnCl_3^-$	208, 223–225	1
	$\frac{1}{2}SnCl_6^{2-}$	Solid	1
	I^-	210	1
	I_3^-	Violet brown prisms	1
$[(C_6H_5C(O)CHC(O)C_6H_5)_2B]^+Cl^-$		White crystals	1
	$FeCl_4^-$	Yellow needles	1

VII. REFERENCES

1. Dilthey, W., F. Eduardoff, and F. J. Schumacher, *Ann.*, **344**, 300 (1906).
2. Morgan, G. T., and R. B. Tunstall, *J. Chem. Soc.*, **125**, 1963 (1924).
3. Rosenheim, A., W. Loewenstamm, and L. Singer, **Ber.**, **36**, 1833 (1903).
4. Sakaguchi, T., and A. Hanaki, *J. Pharm. Soc., Japan*, **76**, 176 (1956).
5. Sidgwick, N. V., *The Chemical Elements and Their Compounds*, Vol. I, Oxford University Press, New York, 1950, p. 408.

20

BORON–SULFUR COMPOUNDS

I. INTRODUCTION

Relatively few boron–sulfur compounds have been reported in comparison to the boron–oxygen derivatives. Reported types include mono-,[7] di-[29] and trialkylthioboranes[7,10,18,19,29,40] (I–III), the sulfur counterparts of the alkoxyhaloboranes (IV and V),[18] and the 2-halo-1,3,2-dithiaborolanes and borinanes (VI).[9]

$RSBH_2$* (I) $(RS)_2BH$ (II) $(RS)_3B$ (III) $RSBX_2$† (IV) $(RS)_2BX$ (V)

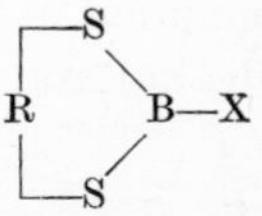

(VI): cyclic R bridging two S atoms, both bonded to B—X

Mixed boron–oxygen–sulfur compounds derived from monohydric alcohols and thiols (VII and VIII) have not been reported;

$(RO)_2BSR$ (VII) $ROB(SR)_2$ (VIII)

however cyclic systems containing both types of bondings (IX[15] and X[37,48,49]) are known.

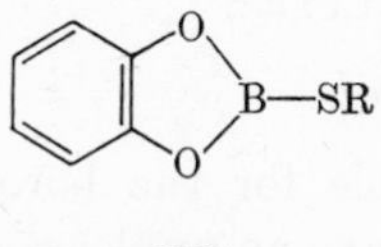

(IX): benzene ring fused to O, O, which are bonded to B—SR

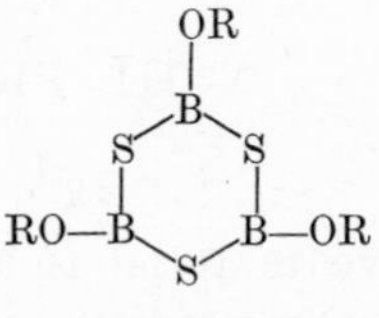

(X): six-membered ring of alternating B and S atoms, each B bearing OR

In addition to the partial sulfur analogs of the metaborates (X), one example of the complete sulfur analog (XI) has been reported.[51]

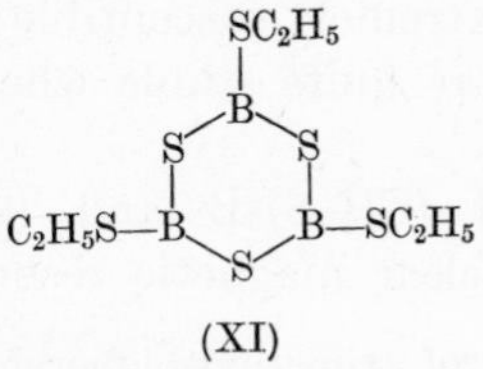

(XI): six-membered ring of alternating B and S atoms, each B bearing SC_2H_5

* Exists as a monomer only when complexed with a tertiary amine.

† Reported to exist as a dimer.

One example of a tetracovalent compound containing a boron–sulfur bond (XII) has been reported.[38]

$$[CH_3SBCl_3]H$$
(XII)

No silylthioboranes have been reported. In contrast to the ready cleavage of (XIII) with boron trifluoride or trichloride to give silyloxyborane products (Chapter 12), the sulfur analog (XIV)

$$(CH_3SiH_2)_2O \qquad (CH_3SiH_2)_2S$$
(XIII) (XIV)

required elevated temperature to react with these halides and no Si–S–B products could be isolated.[12]

Thiol and dialkylsulfide complexes of boron compounds are not included in this chapter, in keeping with the absence of discussion of alcohol and ether complexes in earlier chapters.

II. HISTORICAL

In 1878 Councler[10] isolated an impure yellow substance from the reaction of triisobutoxyborane and phosphorus pentasulfide. On the basis of its hydrolysis to isobutyl mercaptan and boric acid, he assigned it the structure triisobutylthioborane (XV).

$$(i\text{-}C_4H_9S)_3B$$
(XV)

III. PROPERTIES

A. General

Little descriptive material is available for the boron–sulfur compounds. As might be predicted they have an unpleasant odor.[49,51] In general, trialkylthioboranes are clear, mobile, high-boiling liquids* which have low freezing points and a tendency to supercool. They are fairly stable when exposed to elevated temperatures in the absence of air, but are extremely susceptible to hydrolysis by atmospheric moisture. They are quite stable when stored in sealed containers.[54]

Raman spectra of $(CH_3S)_3B$ and $(CH_3S)_2BBr$ have been recorded.[18] The ^{11}B nuclear magnetic resonance chemical shift of

* With the exception of trimethylthioborane, their boiling points at atmospheric pressure are approximately 120° greater than the corresponding trialkoxyboranes.

trimethylthioborane also has been recorded, -47.9 p.p.m. relative to trimethoxyborane.[20]

Solubilities in organic solvents are summarized in Table 20-1.

Table 20-1. Solubilities of boron–sulfur compounds

	Ether	Acetone	Dioxane	Chloroform	Carbon tetrachloride
$(CH_3S)_3B$	S				S
$(C_6H_5S)_3B$	S (hot)	S (hot)	S (hot)		I
$(CH_3SBH_2)_x$	I			I	
$(CH_3SBCl_2)_2$	SS				
$(CH_3OBS)_3$				S	S
$(C_2H_5SBS)_2$					

	Carbon disulfide	Benzene	Hexane	Reference
$(CH_3S)_3B$	S	S		18
$(C_6H_5S)_3B$		S (hot)	I	14
$(CH_3SBH_2)_x$		I		7
$(CH_3SBCl_2)_2$	SS	SS		18
$(CH_3OBS)_3$	S	S		49
$(C_2H_5SBS)_2$	S	S		51

S = Soluble. SS = Slightly soluble. I = Insoluble.

B. Structure

The trialkylthioboranes, like the trialkoxyboranes, are monomeric in nature in both the gaseous[7] and liquid[18,39,40] states. Methylthioborane (XVI), similar to its oxygen analog, is polymeric with x varying from slightly greater than two in the vapor state to slightly greater than three in the liquid state.[7] A trimeric composition (XVII), however, has been reported in benzene solution.[32]

$$(CH_3SBH_2)_x \qquad \text{(XVI)} \qquad\qquad (CH_3SBH_2)_3 \qquad \text{(XVII)}$$

The complex of methylthioborane with trimethylamine tends to be stabilized in the monomeric form, at least in dilute ether solution.[7]

In contrast to the oxygen analog, dichloro(methylthio)borane is dimeric in boiling benzene; the bromo derivative was reported to be

85% dimerized in this medium. Bridged sulfur atoms were proposed as the basis for the dimeric structure (XVIII).[18]

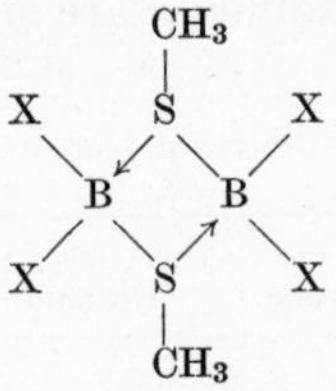

$$\begin{array}{ccccc} & & CH_3 & & \\ & & | & & \\ X & & S & & X \\ & \diagdown & \swarrow \quad \diagdown & \diagup & \\ & B & & B & \\ & \diagup & \diagdown \quad \nearrow & \diagdown & \\ X & & S & & X \\ & & | & & \\ & & CH_3 & & \end{array}$$

(XVIII)

A comparison of Pauling's[36] electronegativity values for the halogens and sulfur (Table 20-2) indicates an increased tendency for

Table 20-2. Structure of dihalo(methylthio)boranes as a function of difference in halogen and sulfur electronegativities

	$X_{Halogen} - X_{Sulfur}$	Structure
F	+1.5	No examples, dimer predicted
Cl	+0.5	Dimeric
Br	+0.3	85% Dimeric
I	0	No examples, unstable monomer predicted

dimer formation as the difference between the halogen and sulfur values increases.[17] The states of aggregation of the dihalo(methoxy)-boranes also appear to be consistent with the halogen–oxygen electronegativity differences (Table 20-3).

Table 20-3. Structure of dihalo(methoxy)boranes as a function of the difference in halogen and oxygen electronegativities

	$X_{Halogen} - X_{Oxygen}$	Structure
F	+0.5	Dimeric
Cl	−0.5	Monomeric
Br	−0.7	Unstable monomer
I	−1.0	No examples, unstable monomer predicted

Molecular weights for trimethoxyborthiin (XIX)[48,49] and triethylthioborthiin (XX)[46] are consistent with trimeric structures.

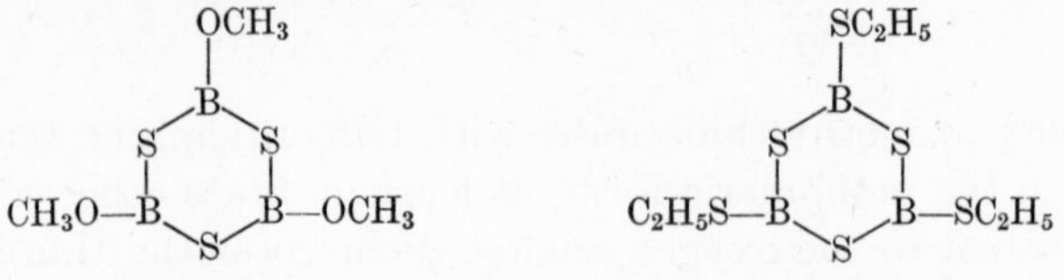

$$\begin{array}{ccccc} & & OCH_3 & & \\ & & | & & \\ & & B & & \\ & S & & S & \\ & | & & | & \\ CH_3O{-}B & & & & B{-}OCH_3 \\ & & S & & \end{array} \qquad \begin{array}{ccccc} & & SC_2H_5 & & \\ & & | & & \\ & & B & & \\ & S & & S & \\ & | & & | & \\ C_2H_5S{-}B & & & & B{-}SC_2H_5 \\ & & S & & \end{array} \qquad (20\text{-}56)$$

(XIX) (XX)

The mixed sulfur–oxygen derivatives (XXI) showed no infrared absorption band normally associated with the boron–sulfur bond. This was believed due to the contribution of structures such as (XXII).[3]

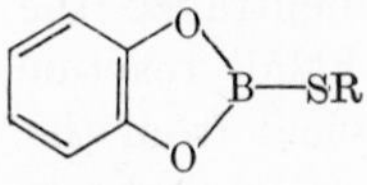

(XXI) 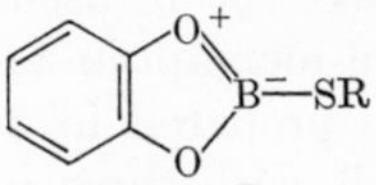 (XXII)

IV. TRIALKYL- AND TRIARYLTHIOBORANES

A. Methods of Preparation

1. FROM MERCAPTANS

a. *And Boron Trihalides.* The feasibility of reaction (20-1) was

$$BX_3 + 3\,RSH \rightarrow (RS)_3B + 3\,HX \qquad (20\text{-}1)$$

proposed without experimental details in 1939.[44] However, early attempts to effect the reaction of boron trichloride or boron tribromide with three moles of methyl mercaptan, even under conditions of elevated temperature and pressure and the use of excess mercaptan, in every case, resulted in the mono substitution product.[18] Similarly, the reaction of boron trichloride and thiophenol could not be forced to completion.[14] The inordinate stability of these intermediates was attributed to their dimeric structure (XXIII).[18] In contrast to these

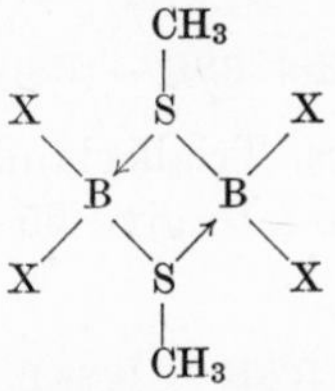

(XXIII, X = Cl, Br)

results, complete conversions have been reported. A convenient direct preparation of the higher alkylthioboranes involves the addition of boron trichloride to a solution of n-amyl mercaptan in decane solution at −20°. The solution is refluxed and the product recovered in 57% yield by distillation (20-2). The method may be

$$BCl_3 + 3\,n\text{-}C_5H_{11}SH \rightarrow (n\text{-}C_5H_{11}S)_3B + 3\,HCl \qquad (20\text{-}2)$$

limited to boron trichloride, however, since the reaction of n-amyl mercaptan and boron tribromide stopped after approximately two moles of hydrogen bromide were evolved.[40]

The direct reaction of boron tribromide and thiophenol resulted in the phenylthio ester.[14,53]

$$BBr_3 + 3\,C_6H_5SH \rightarrow (C_6H_5S)_3B + 3\,HBr \qquad (20\text{-}3)$$

Amines have been used to neutralize the hydrogen halide produced in the mercaptan–boron halide reaction. Thus, trimethylthioborane was prepared in 34% yield from the thioalcoholysis of boron trichloride with three moles of methyl mercaptan in pentane solution in the presence of trimethylamine (20-4). The n-amyl

$$BCl_3 + 3\,CH_3SH + 3\,(CH_3)_3N \rightarrow (CH_3S)_3B + 3\,(CH_3)_3N \cdot HCl \qquad (20\text{-}4)$$

derivative was prepared in 27% yield by a similar process involving boron tribromide, n-amyl mercaptan, and pyridine.[39,40] Triphenylthioborane was obtained from boron triiodide, thiophenol and n-propylamine.[39]

b. *And Boron Sulfide.* The thioalcoholysis of boron sulfide (20-5), in direct analogy to the alcoholysis of boric oxide (20-6), has been claimed, without experimental details, to be a preparative method for trialkylthioboranes.[44]

$$6\,RSH + B_2S_3 \rightarrow 2\,(RS)_3B + 3\,H_2S \qquad (20\text{-}5)$$

$$6\,ROH + B_2O_3 \rightarrow 2\,(RO)_3B + 3\,H_2O \qquad (20\text{-}6)$$

c. *And Dialkylthioboranes.* The reaction of dialkylthioboranes with mercaptans to produce trialkylthioboranes[29] proceeds in a manner analogous to the alcoholysis of dialkoxyboranes (Chapter 4).

$$(RS)_2BH + RSH \rightarrow (RS)_3B + H_2 \qquad (20\text{-}7)$$

d. *And Amine Boranes.* Trialkylamine–boranes can be treated with high boiling mercaptans to give 65–70% yields of the trialkylthioboranes.[13,19,20,24]

$$R_3N{:}BH_3 + 3\,R'SH \rightarrow (R'S)_3B + R_3N + 3\,H_2 \qquad (20\text{-}8)$$

e. *And Tris(alkylamino)boranes.* Treatment of a tris(alkylamino)borane with a mercaptan in the presence of hydrogen chloride in ether solution results in complete replacement of the amino residues by alkylthio residues.[4,40]

$$3\,CH_3SH + [(CH_3)_2N]_3B + 3\,HCl \rightarrow (CH_3S)_3B + 3\,(CH_3)_2NH \cdot HCl \qquad (20\text{-}9)$$

f. *And Alkylthiodiboranes.* The reaction of a mercaptan with a tetraalkylthiodiborane begins at 50–60° and proceeds vigorously at the boiling point of the mercaptan to yield the trialkylthioborane.[30]

$$2\,RSH + (RS)_2BHBH(SR)_2 \rightarrow 2\,(RS)_3B + 2\,H_2 \qquad (20\text{-}10)$$

Conversion of a trialkylthiodiborane to a trialkylthioborane also has been recorded.[42]

$$3\ C_2H_5SH + (C_2H_5S)_2BHBH_2(SC_2H_5) \rightarrow 2\ (C_2H_5S)_3B + 3\ H_2 \qquad (20\text{-}11)$$

2. FROM MERCAPTIDES AND BORON TRIHALIDES

The problems of incomplete reaction and hydrogen halide removal, as sometimes experienced in the preparation of trialkylthioboranes from mercaptans and boron halides, are obviated in preparations utilizing metal mercaptides. Thus, the simplest member of the family was obtained by refluxing a benzene solution of boron tribromide with an excess of either silver or lead mercaptide (20-12).[18] The reaction failed with potassium mercaptide and boron

$$BBr_3 + 3\ AgSCH_3 \rightarrow (CH_3S)_3 + 3\ AgBr \qquad (20\text{-}12)$$

tribromide in benzene solution, or boron trifluoride in ether solution;[18] however it proceeded in 45% yield with sodium mercaptide and boron tribromide without solvent.[7]

$$BBr_3 + 3\ NaSCH_3 \rightarrow (CH_3S)_3B + 3\ NaBr \qquad (20\text{-}13)$$

Trimethylthioborane also was obtained, in undisclosed yield, from the reaction of methyl mercaptan and boron trichloride in the presence of sodium methyl mercaptide. The mercaptide was used to react with the hydrogen chloride generated in the reaction; however, it was recovered apparently unchanged. The ethyl derivative also was prepared by the reaction of ethyl mercaptan and boron trichloride. The last traces of unreacted chloroboranes were converted by a final treatment with sodium ethyl mercaptide.[54] The n-butyl derivative was obtained in good yield from lead mercaptide and boron trichloride in pentane solution.[26]

Treatment of boron tribromide with excess silver thiocyanate in benzene solution was reported to give boron thiocyanate (20-14).[8]

$$BBr_3 + 3\ AgSCN \rightarrow B(SCN)_3 + 3\ AgBr \qquad (20\text{-}14)$$

Subsequent workers suggested the product may be an isothiocyanate, $B(NCS)_3$.[27]

3. FROM ALKYLTHIOHALOBORANES AND HYDROGEN SULFIDE

The attempted preparation of triethylthioborthiin by treatment of dibromo(ethylthio)borane with hydrogen sulfide resulted in triethylthioborane instead (20-15).[46] Since the desired borthiin

$$3\ C_2H_5SBBr_2 + 3\ H_2S \rightarrow (C_2H_5S)_3B + B_2S_3 + 6\ HBr \qquad (20\text{-}15)$$

(XXIV) does not readily disproportionate,[51] it was felt that the disproportionation products $(C_2H_5S)_3B$ and B_2S_3 arose from the monomer, $C_2H_5SB{=}S$.[46] Disproportionation of the intermediates $C_2H_5SBBr(SH)$ and $C_2H_5SB(SH)_2$ was not suggested.

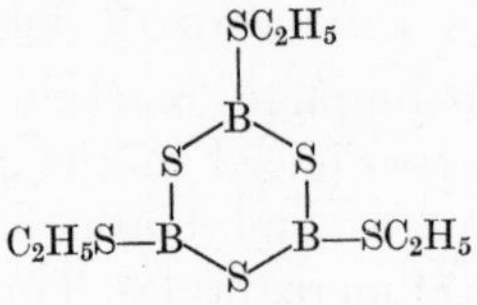

```
              SC2H5
                |
                B
              /   \
             S     S
             |     |
    C2H5S—B       B—SC2H5
              \   /
                S
```

(XXIV)

4. FROM TRIALKOXYBORANES AND PHOSPHORUS PENTASULFIDE

The conversion of a trialkoxyborane to the sulfur analog by gently warming with an excess of phosphorus pentasulfide has been reported for the isobutoxy derivative.[10]

5. FROM TRIPHENYLTHIOALUMINUM AND POTASSIUM FLUOBORATE

Triphenylthioborane was prepared by the reaction of potassium fluoborate and triphenylthioaluminum at 260°.[22]

$$KBF_4 + (C_6H_5S)_3Al \rightarrow (C_6H_5S)_3B + AlF_3 + KF \quad (20\text{-}16)$$

6. BY DISPROPORTIONATION OF METHYLTHIOBORANE

The heating of polymeric methylthioborane at 140° in a closed system resulted in disproportionation to trimethylthioborane and diborane (20-17).[7] The trimethylthio derivative also was obtained in

$$3\,(CH_3SBH_2)_x \rightarrow x\,(CH_3S)_3B + x\,B_2H_6 \quad (20\text{-}17)$$

small yield from the disproportionation of the trimethylamine complex of methylthioborane at 145°.[7]

$$3\,CH_3SBH_2{:}N(CH_3)_3 \rightarrow (CH_3S)_3B + 2\,(CH_3)_3N{:}BH_3 + (CH_3)_3N \quad (20\text{-}18)$$

7. BY DISPROPORTIONATION OF ALKYL(ALKYLTHIO)BORANES

Methyl(methylthio)boranes disproportionate when heated in the presence of a catalytic amount of diborane to give small yields of trimethylthioborane.[6]

$$2\,(CH_3S)_2BCH_3 \rightleftharpoons (CH_3S)_3B + CH_3SB(CH_3)_2 \quad (20\text{-}19)$$

$$3\,CH_3SB(CH_3)_2 \rightleftharpoons (CH_3S)_3B + 2\,(CH_3)_3B \quad (20\text{-}20)$$

The reaction of triethylthiodiborane and 1-octene gave some triethylthioborane and trioctylborane, presumably by redistribution reactions of intermediate ethylthioctylboranes.[42]

$$(C_2H_5S)_2BHBH_2(SC_2H_5) + 3\ CH_2{=}CHC_6H_{13} \rightarrow$$
$$C_8H_{17}B(SC_2H_5)_2 + (C_8H_{17})_2BSC_2H_5 \rightarrow (C_2H_5S)_3B + (C_8H_{17})_3B \quad (20\text{-}21)$$

8. ATTEMPTED PREPARATIONS

In contrast to the ready methanolysis of boric oxide (Chapter 4) the reaction of methyl mercaptan and boric oxide did not proceed even after five hours at 100°. In further contrast to the relatively facile cleavage of ethers with boron tribromide, dimethyl sulfide and boron tribromide when heated at 250° for four hours did not undergo a more deep seated transformation than formation of the 1:1 addition complex.[18] Di-n-butyl sulfide and boron trichloride also formed a 1:1 complex and could not be made to undergo carbon–sulfur fission on heating at 215° for thirty-two hours.[25] The boron trichloride complexes of diethyl and diisobutyl sulfide appear to be less thermally stable than the di-n-butyl sulfide derivative, but still did not appear to produce alkylthioborane products.[41]

Small amounts of methyl chloride were obtained from the reaction of diboron tetrachloride and dimethyl sulfide; however, no methylthioborane products were isolated.[45]

Treatment of triisobutoxyborane with carbon disulfide or phosphorus pentasulfide up to 200° did not result in triisobutylthioborane.[10]

B. Reactions

1. HYDROLYSIS

Trialkylthioboranes hydrolyze in a manner analogous to that of the trialkoxyboranes to give boric acid and mercaptans.[7,10,18,19,20]

$$(RS)_3B + 3\ H_2O \rightarrow H_3BO_3 + 3\ RSH \quad (20\text{-}22)$$

2. ALCOHOLYSIS

Ethanolysis of trimethylthioborane was stated, without experimental details, to yield triethoxyborane and methyl mercaptan (see Chapter 4).[18]

$$(CH_3S)_3B + 3\ C_2H_5OH \rightarrow (C_2H_5O)_3B + 3\ CH_3SH \quad (20\text{-}23)$$

3. WITH AMINES

Triethylthioborane reacts with one, two or three moles of a primary or secondary aliphatic amine to give aminothioboranes (20-24 and 20-25) or trisalkylaminoboranes (20-26). Reaction (20-24)

$$(C_2H_5S)_3B + R_2NH \rightarrow (C_2H_5S)_2BNR_2 + C_2H_5SH \qquad (20\text{-}24)$$

$$(C_2H_5S)_3B + 2\ R_2NH \rightarrow C_2H_5SB(NR_2)_2 + 2\ C_2H_5SH \qquad (20\text{-}25)$$

$$(C_2H_5S)_3B + 3\ R_2NH \rightarrow (R_2N)_3B + 3\ C_2H_5SH \qquad (20\text{-}26)$$

also has been carried out with aniline.[43]

An equimolar reaction of triethylthioborane and ethylenediamine resulted in a polymer containing no ethylmercapto groups. Structure (XXV) was suggested.[43]

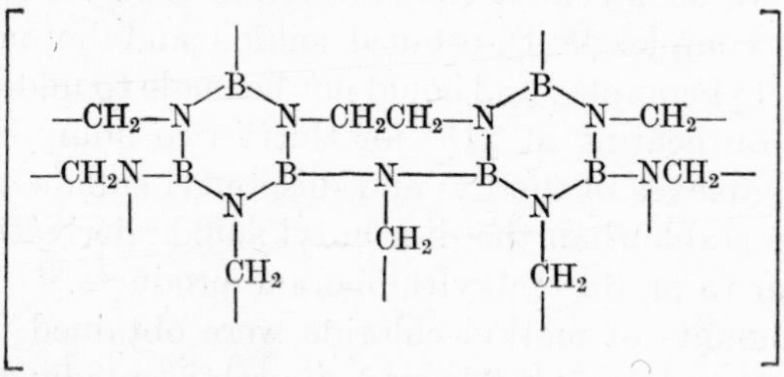

```
 [            |                         |              ]
 [            B                         B              ]
 [  —CH2—N        N—CH2CH2—N                N—CH2—     ]
 [       |        |                |        |          ]
 [ —CH2N—B        B————N————B               B—NCH2—    ]
 [       |    N        |             N      |          ]
 [            |       CH2            |                 ]
 [           CH2       |            CH2                ]
 [            |                      |                 ]n
```

(XXV)

Addition of pyridine to an equimolar amount of triethylthioborane resulted in an exothermic reaction and the formation of an orange-colored solution. A 1:1 complex was postulated.[43]

4. WITH BORON TRIHALIDES

Reactions of trialkylthioboranes with boron halides are described in Section VI-A-2.

5. WITH ALKOXY(ALKYL)BORANES

Reactions (20-27) and (20-28) have been recorded without experimental detail.[34]

$$2\ (RS)_3B + 3\ R'B(OR'')_2 \rightarrow 3\ R'B(SR)_2 + 2\ (R''O)_3B \qquad (20\text{-}27)$$

$$(RS)_3B + 3\ R'_2BOR'' \rightarrow 3\ R'_2BSR + (R''O)_3B \qquad (20\text{-}28)$$

6. WITH THIOMETABORIC ACID

The reaction of a trialkylthioborane and thiometaboric acid results in a borthiin derivative. See Section X-A.

7. WITH TRIALKYLBORANES

Trialkylthioboranes equilibrate with trialkylboranes in a 2:1 molar reaction at 250° to give alkyldialkylthioboranes.[31] For the n-butyl derivative, reaction (20-29) can be performed at 130–140° in the presence of a catalytic amount of tetrabutyldiborane.[33]

$$2\,(RS)_3B + R'_3B \rightarrow 3\,R'B(SR)_2 \qquad (20\text{-}29)$$

Trimethylthioborane equilibrates with trimethylborane or dimethyl(methylthio)borane in a similar manner. Reactions (20-30) and (20-31) require heat and a catalytic amount of diborane.[6,23]

$$(CH_3S)_3B + 2\,(CH_3)_3B \rightleftarrows 3\,CH_3SB(CH_3)_2 \qquad (20\text{-}30)$$

$$(CH_3S)_3B + CH_3SB(CH_3)_2 \rightleftarrows 2\,(CH_3S)_2BCH_3 \qquad (20\text{-}31)$$

V. ALKYLTHIOBORANES

A. Methods of Preparation

Polymeric methylthioborane was obtained by allowing the methyl mercaptan–borane complex which formed at −78° to warm to room temperature (20-32).[7,32] It also was obtained by the decomposition of

$$2x\,CH_3SH + x\,B_2H_6 \rightarrow 2x\,CH_3SH{:}BH_3 \rightarrow 2\,(CH_3XBH_2)_x + 2x\,H_2 \qquad (20\text{-}32)$$

methylthiodiborane at 21° (20-33),[7] the cleavage of dimethyldisulfide with diborane at room temperature (20-34),[7] and the reduced pressure disproportionation of methyl(methylthio)borane at 85–95° (20-35).[5]

$$2x\,CH_3SB_2H_5 \rightarrow 2\,(CH_3SBH_2)_x + x\,B_2H_6 \qquad (20\text{-}33)$$

$$x\,CH_3SSCH_3 + x\,B_2H_6 \rightarrow 2\,(CH_3SBH_2)_x + x\,H_2 \qquad (20\text{-}34)$$

$$2x\,CH_3SBHCH_3 \rightarrow (CH_3SBH_2)_x + x\,CH_3SB(CH_3)_2 \qquad (20\text{-}35)$$

Ethyl and n-butyl mercaptan also react with diborane in ether to give vitreous polymers, $(C_2H_5SBH_2)_x$ and $(n\text{-}C_4H_9SBH_2)_x$. On standing at room temperature, these polymers are converted to the trimers, $(C_2H_5SBH_2)_3$ and $(n\text{-}C_4H_9SBH_2)_3$. Polymeric methylthioborane, $(CH_3SBH_2)_x$, is converted to the trimer on dissolution in tetrahydrofuran.[32]

Diborane reacts with the methylsulfenylamines (XXVI) to give the adducts (XXVII). The ethyl derivative (XXVII) is transformed into (XXVIII) on warming to room temperature. The methyl derivative (XXVII) requires 110° for the transformation.

CH_3SNR_2	$CH_3SNR_2{:}BH_3$	$CH_3SBH_2{:}NH(C_2H_5)_2$
(XXVI, R = CH_3, C_2H_5)	(XXVII, R = CH_3, C_2H_5)	(XXVIII)

The adducts (XXVII) were believed to involve sulfur as the donor atom. The mechanism of the transformation to (XXVIII) would then require a 1–3 hydride shift.[35]

$$\begin{array}{ccccccc} \overset{+}{\ddot{S}} & & & \overset{+}{N} & & & \\ CH_3-\underset{\substack{| \\ H-B^{-}-H \\ | \\ H}}{\ddot{S}}-\ddot{N}R_2 & \rightleftarrows & CH_3-\underset{\substack{| \\ H-B^{-}-H \\ | \\ H}}{\ddot{S}}=NR_2 & \rightarrow & CH_3-\underset{\substack{| \\ H-B \\ | \\ H}}{\ddot{S}}: & + HNR_2 \rightarrow CH_3SBH_2{:}HNR_2 \end{array} \quad (20\text{-}36)$$

Di-n-propyl and di-n-butylthioborane were prepared in 50% yield by the direct thioalcoholysis of diborane (20-37).[29] Amine boranes also can be thioalcoholyzed (20-38).[13,24]

$$B_2H_6 + 4\ RSH \rightarrow 2\ (RS)_2BH + 4\ H_2 \quad (20\text{-}37)$$

$$(C_2H_5)_3N{:}BH_3 + 2\ C_{12}H_{25}SH \rightarrow (C_{12}H_{25}S)_2BH + (C_2H_5)_3N + 2\ H_2 \quad (20\text{-}38)$$

Reaction (20-39) has been recorded.[42] The products were not isolated.

$$(C_2H_5S)_2BHBH_2(SC_2H_5) + 2\ C_2H_5NH_2 \rightarrow C_2H_5SBH_2{:}NH_2C_2H_5 + (C_2H_5S)_2BH{:}NH_2C_2H_5 \quad (20\text{-}39)$$

B. Reactions

1. THERMAL

When heated *in vacuo* at 100°, polymeric methylthioborane is depolymerized and results in slightly volatile liquids and solids and a less volatile glassy liquid, all of the same empirical composition as the starting material. Heating of polymeric methylthioborane at 140° for six hours in a closed system resulted in disproportionation to trimethylthioborane and diborane.[7]

$$3\ (CH_3SBH_2)_x \rightarrow x\ (CH_3S)_3B + x\ B_2H_6 \quad (20\text{-}40)$$

The diethylamine complex of methylthioborane dissociates slowly on heating (20-41). Prolonged heating at 280° results in the loss of hydrogen and the formation of a covalent boron–nitrogen bond (20-42).[35]

$$CH_3SBH_2 : NH(C_2H_5)_2 \underset{}{\overset{\Delta}{\rightleftarrows}} CH_3SBH_2 + NH(C_2H_5)_2 \quad (20\text{-}41)$$

$$CH_3SBH_2 : NH(C_2H_5)_2 \xrightarrow[12\ hr.]{280^\circ} CH_3SBHN(C_2H_5)_2 + H_2 \quad (20\text{-}42)$$

2. HYDROLYSIS

All of the fractions of polymeric methylthioborane readily hydrolyzed to give one volume of methyl mercaptan, two volumes of hydrogen, and one equivalent of boric acid.[7]

$$(CH_3SBH_2)_x + 3x\ H_2O \rightarrow x\ CH_3SH + 2x\ H_2 + x\ H_3BO_3 \quad (20\text{-}43)$$

Trimeric alkylthioboranes, $(RSBH_2)_3$, have been stated to have considerable stability to water.[32]

3. WITH AMINES

Depolymerization of polymeric methylthioborane is effected by complex formation with trimethylamine.[7]

$$(CH_3SBH_2)_x + x\ (CH_3)_3N \rightarrow x\ CH_3SBH_2{:}N(CH_3)_3 \quad (20\text{-}44)$$

4. WITH DIBORANE

Depolymerization of polymeric methylthioborane at 90° in a stream of diborane results in the production of methylthiodiborane. The same reaction proceeds even more efficiently with the trimethylamine complex of methylthioborane.[7]

$$CH_3SBH_2{:}N(CH_3)_3 + B_2H_6 \rightarrow CH_3SB_2H_5 + (CH_3)_3N{:}BH_3 \quad (20\text{-}45)$$

5. WITH MERCAPTANS

The conversion of a dialkylthioborane to a trialkylthioborane by thioalcoholysis with a mercaptan is discussed in Section IV-A-1-c.

VI. ALKYLTHIOHALOBORANES

A. Methods of Preparation

1. FROM MERCAPTANS AND BORON TRIHALIDES

The feasibility of partial reaction of a mercaptan and a boron halide (20-46) was stated in an early publication.[44] Still earlier the

$$BX_3 + RSH \rightarrow RSBX_2 + HX \quad (20\text{-}46)$$

reaction involving boron tribromide and methyl mercaptan was formulated as proceeding via a 1:1 addition complex which lost hydrogen bromide when gently heated.[52] It subsequently was shown that the reaction of boron tribromide or trichloride with methyl mercaptan, with or without solvent and at elevated temperatures and pressures, always stopped at the mono substitution stage even in the presence of excess mercaptan. The inertness of the initial intermediate to further reaction was attributed to its dimeric nature (XXIII).[18]

Evidence for a disubstituted product was obtained, but its disproportionation (20-47) was too facile to allow isolation of a pure product.[18]

$$4\,(CH_3S)_2BBr \rightarrow 2\,CH_3SBBr_2 + 2\,(CH_3S)_3B \qquad (20\text{-}47)$$

The reaction of boron trichloride and thiophenol resulted in a greenish slimy product which lost hydrogen chloride at room temperature and appeared to form $C_6H_5SBCl_2$ and $(C_6H_5S)_2BCl$.[38]

2. FROM TRIALKYLTHIOBORANES AND BORON TRIHALIDES

The equilibration of trialkylthioboranes with boron trichloride was stated to proceed in a manner analogous to the reaction of trialkoxyboranes with boron trichloride.[26]

$$(RS)_3B + 2\,BCl_3 \rightarrow 3\,RSBCl_2 \qquad (20\text{-}48)$$

$$2\,(RS)_3B + BCl_3 \rightarrow 3\,(RS)_2BCl \qquad (20\text{-}49)$$

B. Reactions

Dimeric dichloro(methylthio)borane is slowly hydrolyzed in water or damp air to boric acid, methyl mercaptan and hydrochloric acid.[18]

$$(CH_3SBCl_2)_2 + 6\,H_2O \rightarrow 2\,H_3BO_3 + 2\,CH_3SH + 4\,HCl \qquad (20\text{-}50)$$

VII. 2-HALO-1,3,2-DITHIABOROLANES

The feasibility of reaction (20-51) with 1,2- and 1,3-dithiols and the

$$R\begin{cases}SH\\SH\end{cases} + BCl_3 \rightarrow R\begin{cases}S\\S\end{cases}BCl + 2\,HCl \qquad (20\text{-}51)$$

preparation of (XXIX) by this method have been recorded. The conversion of (XXIX) in ether solution to the dimethylamino

$$\begin{matrix}CH_2\text{—}S\\ |\qquad\quad \diagdown\\ |\qquad\qquad BCl\\ |\qquad\quad \diagup\\ CH_2\text{—}S\end{matrix}$$

(XXIX)

derivative (20-52) also has been described.[9]

$$\begin{matrix}CH_2\text{—}S\\ |\qquad \diagdown\\ |\qquad\quad BCl\\ |\qquad \diagup\\ CH_2\text{—}S\end{matrix} + 2\,(CH_3)_2NH \rightarrow \begin{matrix}CH_2\text{—}S\\ |\qquad \diagdown\\ |\qquad\quad BN(CH_3)_2\\ |\qquad \diagup\\ CH_2\text{—}S\end{matrix} + (CH_3)_2NH\cdot HCl \qquad (20\text{-}52)$$

VIII. 2-ALKYLTHIO-1,3,2-DIOXABOROLANES

A. Methods of Preparation

The *o*-phenylene derivatives (XXX)[15] and the ethylenedioxy derivative (XXXI)[2] represent the only authenticated examples* of boron–

$$\text{o-C}_6\text{H}_4\text{O}_2\text{BSR} \qquad \begin{matrix} CH_2—O \\ | \\ CH_2—O \end{matrix} \!\!> BS\text{-n-}C_4H_9$$

(XXX, R = n-C_4H_9, n-C_8H_{17}) (XXXI)

oxygen, boron–sulfur bonded compounds other than the alkoxyborthiins (see Section IX). They were prepared in 79, 94 and 54% yield, respectively, by the thioalcoholysis of (XXXII) with n-butyl mercaptan at 150–160° or n-octyl mercaptan at 200–220° and the prolonged reaction of (XXXIII) with butyl mercaptan under reflux. The reactions proceeded slowly at room temperature. The benzo derivatives (XXX) could not be prepared by "transesterification" of (XXXIV) with either n-butyl or n-octyl mercaptan, and it was

$$\text{o-C}_6\text{H}_4\text{O}_2\text{BCl} \qquad \begin{matrix} CH_2—O \\ | \\ CH_2—O \end{matrix} \!\!> BCl \qquad \text{o-C}_6\text{H}_4\text{O}_2\text{BOR}$$

(XXXII) (XXXIII) (XXXIV, R = C_2H_5, n-C_4H_9)

generalized that a thioalkoxy group could not replace an alkoxy group on boron.[15]†

B. Reactions

The 2-alkylthio-1,3,2-benzodioxaboroles (XXX) are readily hydrolyzed by cold water (20-53) or alcoholyzed by n-octyl alcohol (20-54).[15]

$$\text{o-C}_6\text{H}_4\text{O}_2\text{BSR} + 3\,H_2O \rightarrow \text{o-C}_6\text{H}_4(OH)_2 + H_3BO_3 + RSH \qquad (20\text{-}53)$$

$$\text{o-C}_6\text{H}_4\text{O}_2\text{BS-n-}C_4H_9 + \text{n-}C_8H_{17}OH \rightarrow \text{o-C}_6\text{H}_4\text{O}_2\text{BO-n-}C_8H_{17} + \text{n-}C_4H_9SH \qquad (20\text{-}54)$$

* Trialkylthioboroxines have been prophesied without experimental documentation.[11]

$$3\,RSH + 3\,HBO_2 \rightarrow (RSBO)_3 + 3\,H_2O$$
$$3\,RSH + 3\,H_3BO_3 \rightarrow (RSBO)_3 + 6\,H_2O$$

† Such generalizations with regard to the inability of amino groups replacing alkoxy groups[15,16] have been proven inadequate,[28] and it most likely that the analogous transformation of B–O to B–S also can be made under certain conditions.

IX. TRIALKOXYBORTHIINS

A. Methods of Preparation

Trimethoxyborthiin (XXXV) has been prepared from the reaction of trimethoxyborane and metathioboric acid (20-55),[48] a reaction reminiscent of the preparation of trialkoxyboroxines from trialkoxyboranes and metaboric acid (see Chapter 9). It also has been prepared by air oxidation of trimethylborthiin (20-56).[50]

$$(CH_3O)_3B + 2\ HBS_2 \rightarrow CH_3O{-}\overline{B{-}S{-}B(OCH_3){-}S{-}B{-}S}{-}OCH_3 + H_2S^* \qquad (20\text{-}55)$$

(XXXV)

$$CH_3{-}\overline{B{-}S{-}B(CH_3){-}S{-}B{-}S}{-}CH_3 \xrightarrow{[O]} CH_3O{-}\overline{B{-}S{-}B(OCH_3){-}S{-}B{-}S}{-}OCH_3$$

An attempt to prepare (XXXV) by exchange of bromine and methoxyl groups between tribromoborthiin and trimethoxyborane (20-57) led to carbon–oxygen cleavage (20-58) and the formation of a complex product. The product was formulated as a dimethoxyboryloxy substituted borthiin (XXXVI) on the basis of its ebullioscopic

$$Br{-}\overline{B{-}S{-}B(Br){-}S{-}B{-}S}{-}Br + (CH_3O)_3B \rightarrow CH_3O{-}\overline{B{-}S{-}B(OCH_3){-}S{-}B{-}S}{-}OCH_3 + BBr_3 \qquad (20\text{-}57)$$

$$(BrBS)_3 + 3\ (CH_3O)_3B \rightarrow 3\ CH_3Br + (CH_3O)_2BO\overline{B{-}S{-}B(OB(OCH_3)_2){-}S{-}B{-}S}OB(OCH_3)_2 \qquad (20\text{-}58)$$

(XXXVI)

molecular weight in carbon disulfide.[37] A second attempt to prepare trimethoxyborthiin via the bromine–methoxy exchange of reaction (20-57) was successful.[49]

* The reaction also has been formulated as follows:[11]

$$(RO)_3B + 3\ HBS_2 \rightarrow (ROBS)_3 + B(SH)_3$$

Triethoxyborthiin was prepared in the form of the ethyl etherate from the room temperature reaction of tribromoborthiin and ethyl ether (20-59).[37] The cleavage of the ether by the B–Br portion of the

$$(BrBS)_3 + 4\,(C_2H_5)_2O \rightarrow (C_2H_5OBS)_3 \cdot (C_2H_5)_2O + 3\,C_2H_5Br \qquad (20\text{-}59)$$

borthiin is not unexpected in view of the ready cleavage of ethers by boron tribromide (see Chapters 4 and 12).

An attempt to prepare triethoxyborthiin by the ethanolysis of tribromoborthiin was unsuccessful.[37]

B. Reactions

Trimethoxyborthiin is readily hydrolyzed and alcoholized.[48,49] It reacts in an undescribed fashion with acetone and ether and disproportionates (20-60) when heated at 100° at reduced pressure.[49]

$$(CH_3OBS)_3 \rightarrow (CH_3O)_3B + B_2S_3 \qquad (20\text{-}60)$$

X. TRIALKYLTHIOBORTHIINS

A. Methods of Preparation

The formal analogy of the trialkylthioborthiins (XXXVII) as the sulfur analogs of the trialkoxyboroxines (XXXVIII) indicates their

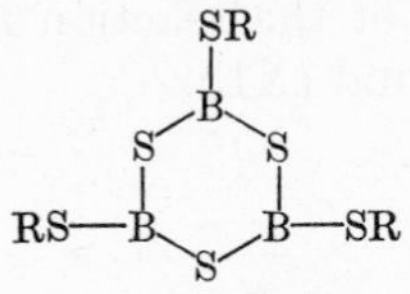

(XXXVII) 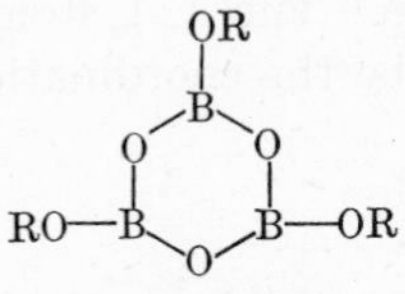 (XXXVIII)

possible preparation from the reaction of mercaptans and boron sulfide (20-61) or thiometaboric acid (20-62). These methods have been prophesied.[11,44]

$$6\,RSH + 3\,B_2S_3 \rightarrow 2\,(RSBS)_3 + 3\,H_2S \qquad (20\text{-}61)$$

$$3\,RSH + 3\,HBS_2 \rightarrow (RSBS)_3 + 3\,H_2S \qquad (20\text{-}62)$$

The only experimentally documented method of preparation also is analogous to a method of synthesis of trialkoxyboroxines.

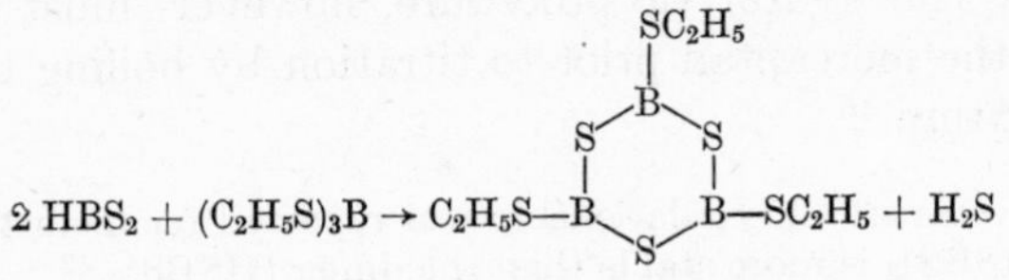

$$2\,HBS_2 + (C_2H_5S)_3B \rightarrow (C_2H_5SBS)_3 + H_2S \qquad (20\text{-}63)$$

Triethylthioborthiin was prepared from the prolonged reaction of thiometaboric acid and triethylthioborane in refluxing carbon disulfide.[51]

B. Reactions

Attempted distillation of triethylthioborthiin under high vacuum at 150–160° was reported to result in a distillate of a dithiodiboretane (XXXIX)*.[51] Four-membered ring structures such as (XXXIX)

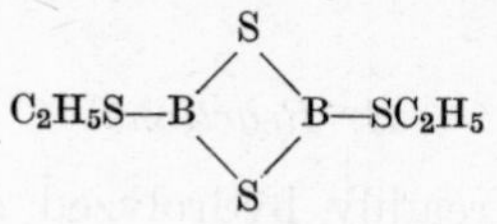

$$C_2H_5S{-}B\overset{S}{\underset{S}{\diamond}}B{-}SC_2H_5$$

(XXXIX)

have no well-characterized oxygen counterparts.

The dithiodiboretane derivative (XXXIX), like the alkoxyborthiins, is readily hydrolyzed and alcoholyzed. It reacts with acetone and ether in an unknown fashion. Unlike the alkoxyborthiins, it does not tend to disproportionate when heated to 150°.[51]

XI. ALKYLTHIOTRIHALOBORATES

Mercaptans have been used to remove boron trifluoride from a gaseous mixture.[1] The 1:1 stoichiometry of the reaction indicates the product to be the coordination compound (XL).

$$[RSBF_3]\,H$$

(XL)

Reaction of boron trichloride and methyl mercaptan in the cold resulted in an adduct, presumably $[CH_3SBCl_3]H$.[38]

XII. ANALYTICAL

Trialkylthioboranes cannot be analyzed for boron by the usual reaction with sodium peroxide, potassium chlorate, and benzoic acid in a Parr bomb since they are explosively oxidized by this mixture.[40]

The carbonate fusion method[21] or simple hydrolysis may be employed.[40] The hydrolytic procedure, however, must involve the removal of the mercaptan prior to titration by boiling the acidified reaction mixture.[40]

* The reverse stability relationship was reported for metathioboric acid; the trimer $(HSBS)_3$ is more stable than the dimer $(HSBS)_2$.[47]

XIII. PHYSICAL CONSTANTS

$(RS)_3B$	M.p. (°C)	B.p. (°C)	d_4^t	n_D^t	Reference
$(CH_3S)_3B$	3.5–4.0	59/2	1.09		54
		102–103/18		1.5755^{24}	39, 40
		213–216		1.5601^{24}	4
	3.2	216.8–218.2	1.127^{20}	1.5788^{20}	18
	4.1–4.9				7
$(NCS)_3B$	Crystalline				8
$(C_2H_5S)_3B$	−46	64–67/0.5	1.06^{24}		54
		87–89/1		1.5440^{20}	43
		93–96/2	1.0191^{20}	1.5465^{20}	42
	—	—	—	—	46, 51
$(C_2H_5S)_3B \cdot C_5H_5N$			1.1098^{20}	1.5872^{20}	43
$(n\text{-}C_3H_7S)_3B$		135–135.5/4	0.9952^{20}	1.5312^{20}	30
$(n\text{-}C_4H_9S)_3B$		147/1.0			19, 20
		150–152/1	0.9082^{20}	1.5205^{20}	29
		150–152/1	0.9684^{20}	1.5205^{20}	30
	—	—	—	—	26
$(i\text{-}C_4H_9S)_3B$	Impure				10
$(n\text{-}C_5H_{11}S)_3B$		145–147/0.1		1.5140^{25}	39
		164/0.4			19, 20
		168–173/0.2		1.5145^{24}	40
$(n\text{-}C_6H_{13}S)_3B$		Liquid			4
$(C_6H_5CH_2S)_3B$	Solid				4
$(n\text{-}C_{12}H_{25}S)_3B$		Decomposes			24

$(ARS)_3B$	M.p. (°C)	B.p. (°C)	d_4^t	n_D^t	Reference
$(C_6H_5S)_3B$	59	190–195 (high vac.)			22
	129–143	193–194/0.02			53
	Solid				39
	Needles				14

$RSBH_2$	M.p. (°C)	B.p. (°C)	d_4^t	n_D^t	Reference
$(CH_3SBH_2)_3$		80–81/1.5	1.0121^{20}	1.5483^{20}	32
$(CH_3SBH_2)_x$	65–80				7
	—	—	—	—	32
$CH_3SBH_2{:}NH(CH_3)_2$		Colorless liquid			35
$CH_3SBH_2{:}NH(C_2H_5)_2$	1				35
$CH_3SBH_2{:}N(CH_3)_3$	13–15				7
$(C_2H_5SBH_2)_3$		94–96/1	0.9772^{20}	1.5323^{20}	32
$(C_2H_5SBH_2)_x$	Vitreous				32
$(n\text{-}C_4H_9SBH_2)_3$		Decomposes	0.9376^{20}	1.5130^{20}	32
$(n\text{-}C_4H_9SBH_2)_x$	Vitreous				32

$(RS)_2BH$	M.p. (°C)	B.p. (°C)	d_4^t	n_D^t	Reference
$(n\text{-}C_3H_7S)_2BH$		90/4	0.9809^{20}	1.5265^{20}	29
$(n\text{-}C_4H_9S)_2BH$		95/2	0.9561^{20}	1.5170^{20}	29
$(n\text{-}C_{12}H_{25}S)_2BH$	Ca. 45				24
	White solid				13

(*Table continued*)

$RSBX_2$	M.p. (°C)	B.p. (°C)	d_4^t	n_D^t	Reference
$(CH_3SBBr_2)_2$	112.3	71–73/8			18
	—	—	—	—	52
$(CH_3SBCl_2)_2$	72.7	50.5–53/25			18

$(RS)_2BX$	M.p. (°C)	B.p. (°C)	d_4^t	n_D^t	Reference
$(CH_3S)_2BBr$	Impure				18

S R B—X S	M.p. (°C)	B.p. (°C)	d_4^t	n_D^t	Reference
CH_2—S BCl CH_2—S	—	—	—	—	9

O R BSR O	M.p. (°C)	B.p. (°C)	d_4^t	n_D^t	Reference
CH_2—O BS-n-C_4H_9 CH_2—O		26/0.002		1.4872^{22}	2
	—	—	—	—	3
CH_2—O BS-n-C_8H_{17} CH_2—O		—	—	—	3

(o-phenylene)O BSR O	M.p. (°C)	B.p. (°C)	d_4^t	n_D^t	Reference
(o-phenylene)O BS-n-C_4H_9 O		80–84/0.1		1.5334^{20}	15
	—	—	—	—	3
(o-phenylene)O BS-n-C_8H_{17} O		142/0.05		1.5198^{20}	15
	—	—	—	—	3

(*Table continued*)

(RO-substituted B_3S_3 ring: trialkoxyboroxine-type structure, RO—B ring with S)	M.p. (°C)	B.p. (°C)	d_4^t	n_D	Reference
$(CH_3OBS)_3$	24				48
	27.5				49
$(C_2H_5OBS)_3 \cdot (C_2H_5)_2O$		Viscous yellow oil			37
$[(CH_3O)_2BOBS]_3$		Oil			37

(RS-substituted B_3S_3 ring: RS—B ring with S)	M.p. (°C)	B.p. (°C)	d_4^t	n_D^t	Reference
$(C_2H_5SBS)_2$		Heavy oil			51

(RSB(S)₂BSR ring)	M.p. (°C)	B.p. (°C)	d_4^t	n_D^t	Reference
$(C_2H_5SBS)_2$	4				51

$[RSBX_3]H$	M.p. (°C)	B.p. (°C)	d_4^t	n_D^t	Reference
$[CH_3SBCl_3]H$	−20 (d.)				38

XIV. REFERENCES

1. Axe, W. N., U.S. Pat. 2,378,968 (1945, to Phillips Petroleum Company).
2. Blau, J. A., W. Gerrard, and M. F. Lappert, *J. Chem. Soc.*, 667 (1960).
3. Blau, J. A., W. Gerrard, M. F. Lappert, B. A. Mountfield, and H. Pyszora, *J. Chem. Soc.*, 380 (1960).
4. Brotherton, R. J., and L. L. Petterson, U.S. Pat. 2,960,530 (1960, to United States Borax and Chemical Corporation); Can. Pat. 622,990.
5. Burg, A. B., Studies on Boron Hydrides, Tenth Annual Technical Report of Investigations on Water-Reactive Chemical Compounds to the Office of Naval Research, Project No. NR 052 050, Contract No. N6onr-238-TO-I, November 1, 1956.
6. Burg, A. B., and F. M. Graber, *J. Am. Chem. Soc.*, **78**, 1523 (1956).
7. Burg, A. B., and R. I. Wagner, *J. Am. Chem. Soc.*, **76**, 3307 (1954).
8. Cocksedge, H. E., *J. Chem. Soc.*, **93**, 2177 (1908).

9. Conklin, G. W., and R. C. Morris, Brit. Pat. 790,090 (1958, to N.V. De Bataafsche Petroleum Maatschappi); U.S. Pat. 2,886,575 (1959, to Shell Development Co.).
10. Councler, C., *J. Prakt. Chem.*, **18**, 371 (1878).
11. Dykstra, F. J., U.S. Pat. 2,862,879 (1958, to Ethyl Corporation).
12. Emeléus, H. J., and M. Onyszchuk, *J. Chem. Soc.*, 604 (1958).
13. Farbenfabriken Bayer Aktiengesellschaft, Brit. Pat. 884,650 (1961).
14. Funk, H., and H. J. Koch, *Z. Univ. Halle*, **8**, 1025 (1959).
15. Gerrard, W., M. F. Lappert, and B. A. Mountfield, *J. Chem. Soc.*, 1529 (1959).
16. Gerrard, W., M. F. Lappert, and C. A. Pearce, *J. Chem. Soc.*, 381 (1957).
17. Goubeau, J., H. J. Becker, and F. Griffel, *Z. Anorg. Allgem. Chem.*, **282**, 86 (1955).
18. Goubeau, J., and H. W. Wittmeier, *Z. Anorg. Allgem. Chem.*, **270**, 16 (1952).
19. Hawthorne, M. F., *J. Am. Chem. Soc.*, **82**, 784 (1960).
20. Hawthorne, M. F., *J. Am. Chem. Soc.*, **83**, 1345 (1961).
21. Hunter, D. L., L. L. Petterson, and H. Steinberg, *Anal. Chim. Acta*, **21**, 523 (1959).
22. Jenkner, H., Ger. Pat. 950,640 (1956, to Kali-Chemie Aktiengesellschaft).
23. Lang, K., Ger. Pat. 1,079,634 (1960, to Farbenfabriken Bayer Aktiengesellschaft).
24. Lang, K. Ger. Pat. 1,092,463 (1960, to Farbenfabriken Bayer Aktiengesellschaft).
25. Lappert, M. F., *J. Chem. Soc.*, 2784 (1953).
26. Lappert, M. F., in W. Gerrard, and M. F. Lappert, *Chem. Rev.*, **58**, 1081 (1958).
27. Lappert, M. F., and H. Pyszora, *Proc. Chem. Soc.*, 350 (1960).
28. McCloskey, A. L., H. Goldsmith, R. J. Brotherton, H. Steinberg, and G. W. Willcockson, 135th Meeting American Chemical Society, Boston, April, 1959, Abstracts of Papers, p. 34-M.
29. Mikhailov, B. M., and T. A. Shchegoleva, *Izv. Akad. Nauk S.S.S.R., Otd. Khim. Nauk*, 1868 (1959); *Bull Acad. Sci. U.S.S.R., Div. Chem. Sci.*, 1787 (1959).
30. Mikhailov, B. M., and T. A. Shchegoleva, *Proc. Acad. Sci. U.S.S.R., Chem. Sect.*, **131**, 321 (1960).
31. Mikhailov, B. M., T. A. Shchegoleva, and E. M. Shashkova, *Izv. Akad. Nauk. S.S.S.R., Otd. Khim. Nauk*, 916 (1961).
32. Mikhailov, B. M., T. A. Shchegoleva, E. M. Shashkova, and V. D. Sheludyakov, *Izv. Akad. Nauk. S.S.S.R., Otd. Khim. Nauk*, 1163 (1961).
33. Mikhailov, B. M., and L. S. Vasil'ev, *Dokl. Akad. Nauk S.S.S.R.*, **139**, 385 (1961).
34. Mikhailov, B. M., and L. S. Vasil'ev, *Izv. Akad. Nauk S.S.S.R., Otd. Khim. Nauk*, 2102 (1961).
35. Nöth, H., and G. Mikulaschek, *Ber.*, **94**, 634 (1961).
36. Pauling, L., *The Nature of the Chemical Bond*, 2nd ed., Cornell Univ. Press, Ithaca, 1948, p. 60.
37. Paulis, R. C., and T. Wartik, Pennsylvania State University, Report No. CCC-1024-TR-46, Sept. 30, 1954.
38. Peach, M. E., and T. C. Waddington, *J. Chem. Soc.*, 1238 (1961).

39. Petterson, L. L., and J. L. Boone, Can. Pat. 622,991 (1961, to United States Borax and Chemical Corporation).
40. Petterson, L. L., R. J. Brotherton, and J. L. Boone, *J. Org. Chem.*, **26**, 3030 (1961).
41. Phillips, G. M., J. S. Hunter, and L. E. Sutton, *J. Chem. Soc.*, 146 (1945).
42. Shchegoleva, T. A., and E. M. Belyavskaya, *Proc. Acad. Sci. U.S.S.R., Chem. Sect.*, **136**, 123 (1961).
43. Shchegoleva, T. A., E. M. Shashkova, and B. M. Mikhailov, *Izv. Akad. Nauk S.S.S.R., Otd. Khim. Nauk*, 918 (1961).
44. Shoemaker, B. H., and C. M. Loane, U.S. Pat. 2,160,917 (1939, to Standard Oil Co., Indiana).
45. Wartik, T., and E. F. Apple, *J. Am. Chem. Soc.*, **80**, 6155 (1958).
46. Wiberg, E., and W. Sturm, *Angew. Chem.*, **67**, 483 (1955).
47. Wiberg, E., and W. Sturm, *Z. Naturforsch.*, **8b**, 530 (1953).
48. Wiberg, E., and W. Sturm, *Z. Naturforsch.*, **8b**, 689 (1953).
49. Wiberg, E., and W. Sturm, *Z. Naturforsch.*, **10b**, 108 (1955).
50. Wiberg, E., and W. Sturm, *Z. Naturforsch.*, **10b**, 112 (1955).
51. Wiberg, E., and W. Sturm, *Z. Naturforsch.*, **10b**, 114 (1955).
52. Wiberg, E., and W. Sütterlin, *Z. Anorg. Allgem. Chem.*, **202**, 37 (1931).
53. Young, D. M., and C. D. Anderson, *J. Org. Chem.*, **26**, 5235 (1961).
54. Zletz, A., and D. R. Carmody, U.S. Pat. 2,896,404 (1959, to Standard Oil Company, Indiana).

21

HYDROLYTIC STABILITY

I. INTRODUCTION

Boron–oxygen compounds, as a general class, are hydrolytically unstable. However, by proper selection of certain steric and electronic factors, species with phenomenal hydrolytic stability have been produced.

This chapter will be mainly concerned with those classes of compounds for which quantitative hydrolytic rate data are available. The qualitative aspects of the reaction for the remainder of the boron–oxygen and boron–sulfur species are recorded in the appropriate sections of Chapters 5 through 20.

II. HISTORICAL

In 1846, Ebelmen and Bouquet, the original workers in the organoboron field, described the ready reaction of methyl, ethyl and amyl borate with water to produce boric acid and the starting alcohols.[12,13] In 1867, Schiff[60] converted glyceryl borate to glycerol and boric acid by treatment with water, and a few years later Copaux[8] stated that the immediate hydrolysis of ethyl borate was a fundamental property of the ester.

III. ORTHOBORATES

A. General Background

Isolated and qualitative statements as to the instability of various esters such as the *t*-butyl,[39] 2-chloroethyl,[34] benzyl,[7] methylisobutylcarbinyl,[69] *o*-cresyl,[51] 4-butylphenyl,[52] 2-cyclohexylphenyl,[53] and *l*-menthyl[48] derivatives, or the relative stability of others such as the trans-α-decalyl,[30] cyclohexyl,[7] 1,1,1,3,3,3-hexachloro-2-propyl,[21] diisobutylcarbinyl,[37] and 2,6-dimethylphenyl[1] derivatives, have been made. The first attempt of a general nature to correlate the structure and hydrolytic stability of a variety of trialkoxyboranes in aqueous media led to the conclusion, on the basis of qualitative observations, that stability was a function of the bulk of the alkyl groups involved.[57] Thus, neopentyl borate was the most stable ester derived from a primary alcohol, and diisopropylcarbinyl borate was the most stable secondary alkyl ester tested. Secondary esters were more stable than primary esters. Tertiary alkyl esters were not included in the study; however tri-*t*-butoxyborane subsequently was shown to be somewhat more stable than either the n-butyl or *s*-butyl derivatives.[18]

Heats of formation and boron–oxygen bond energies of the lower trialkoxyboranes have been calculated from measurements of their heats of hydrolysis.[5]

B. Useful Aspects of Instability

In certain instances the hydrolytic instability of the esters of boric acid has been used to advantage. Thus, the hydrolysis of butyl borate in the presence of diamylamine oleate has been claimed as a means of preparing a useful coloidal solution.[70] The ready hydrolysis of butyl, amyl and benzyl borate has been utilized to prepare anhydrous alcoholic solutions of hydrogen peroxide (21-1).[38] Other

$$B(OR)_3 + [3\,H_2O + n\,H_2O_2] \rightarrow 3\,ROH + H_3BO_3 + n\,H_2O_2 \qquad (21\text{-}1)$$

esters have been claimed as desiccants for drying gases,[77] and the hydrolysis of an ester in hydrocarbon solution was claimed as a means of preparing dispersions of boric acid in oils.[25]

The ready reaction of a trialkoxyborane with water also has been used to promote reactions in which water is formed, such as the esterification of benzoic acid and various amino acids,[35] the formation of acetals,[35] the condensation of alcohols in the Guerbert reaction,[29] and the formation of silicones.[3,55,67]

C. Mechanism of the Hydrolysis

The rate of hydrolysis of boric acid esters was believed to be a function of the relative steric hindrance of the alkyl groups to the approach of a water molecule.[57] Thus, the attack by a water molecule to give transition state (I) or intermediate (II) would be rate determining. The actual mechanism of the hydrolysis, however, has not

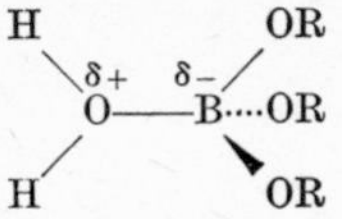

$$\underset{H}{\overset{H}{}}\!\!>\overset{\delta+}{O}\text{——}\overset{\delta-}{B}(OR)_3 \qquad \left[HO\text{—}B(OR)_3\right]H$$

(I) 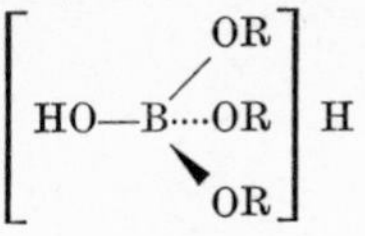 (II)

been elucidated. The S_N2 displacement of an alkoxyl group by water with either a concerted or subsequent loss of proton (21-2)[17,18,73]

$$\begin{matrix} H \\ \quad\diagdown \\ \quad O \\ \quad\diagup \\ H \end{matrix} + \begin{matrix} RO \\ \diagdown \\ B\text{—}OR \\ \diagup \\ RO \end{matrix} \rightarrow \begin{matrix} H \quad\quad OR \\ \diagdown^{\delta+} \quad | \quad ^{\delta-} \\ O\cdots B\cdots OR \\ \diagup \quad\quad | \\ H \quad\quad OR \end{matrix} \rightarrow HO\text{—}B\begin{matrix} OR \\ \diagup \\ \\ \diagdown \\ OR \end{matrix} + ROH \qquad (21\text{-}2)$$

seems a logical path for the three reactions necessary for complete hydrolysis. An S_N1 reaction (21-3) is conceivable; but no evidence

$$B(OR)_3 \xrightarrow{H_2O} RO^- + \overset{+}{B}(OR)_2 \xrightarrow{H_2O} ROH + HOB(OR)_2 \qquad (21\text{-}3)$$

for boronium ions (III) exists. Also, bulky R groups would be expected to accelerate reaction (21-3), which is contrary to the observed facts.

Boric acid ester hydrolyses were shown to involve boron–oxygen and not alkyl–oxygen cleavage.[57] Neopentyl borate gave rise to neopentyl alcohol and not rearranged alcohol which would be expected if alkyl–oxygen fission were operative.[75] In addition, complete optical activity was retained in the diol from the hydrolysis of tri-D-(−)-2,3-butanediol biborate.[16] Further indication of the absence of alkyl–oxygen cleavage was shown by the isolation of (+)-2-octanol and (+)-1-phenylethanol from the steam distillation of their optically active borates.[22]

D. Partial Hydrolysis

1. TRIALKOXY- AND TRIARYLOXYBORANES

Although the partially hydrolyzed species (IV) is known[48] (Chapter 7), it and its assumed precursor (V) have not been isolated

$$\underset{(IV)}{ROB(OH)_2} \qquad\qquad \underset{(V)}{(RO)_2BOH}$$

from the hydrolysis of a trialkoxy- or triaryloxyborane. The apparent absence of these species under conditions of hydrolysis indicates their rapid hydrolysis to boric acid. Consequently, the displacement of the first alkoxyl group (21-2) appears to be the rate determining step. In addition, the steric requirements of the transition state (VI)

$$\begin{matrix} H \quad\quad\quad\quad OH \\ \diagdown^{\delta+} \quad ^{\delta-}\diagup \\ O\text{——}B\cdots OR \\ \diagup \quad\quad\quad \blacktriangledown \\ H \quad\quad\quad\quad OR \end{matrix}$$

(VI)

with an alkoxy group replaced by a hydroxyl would not be as great as in (I), and it would be expected that the formation and collapse of (VI) would be kinetically more favorable than the formation and collapse of (I).

Controlled partial hydrolysis of trimethoxyborane[58] or triisopropoxyborane[42] has provided a means of preparing trimethoxy- and triisopropoxyboroxine (21-4).

$$3\,B(OR)_3 + 3\,H_2O \rightarrow (ROBO)_3 \text{ [cyclic boroxine: B–O six-membered ring, each B bearing OR]} + 6\,ROH \qquad (21\text{-}4)$$

The trimethoxyborane hydrolysis was carried out in the presence of 2-methylpentane which forms a low boiling azeotrope with methanol and its removal acted as the driving force for the reaction. Trimethoxyborane–methanol azeotrope also has been partially hydrolyzed (21-5).[58]

$$3\,[B(OCH_3)_3 + CH_3OH] + 3\,H_2O \rightarrow (CH_3OBO)_3 + 9\,CH_3OH \qquad (21\text{-}5)$$

2. GLYCOL BIBORATES

Glycol biborates are readily hydrolyzed to free glycol and boric acid (21-6).[11,16,20,23,44,50,63] However, in aqueous medium the hydrolysis products are in equilibrium with the cyclic compound (VII) (see Chapter 7), and depending upon the equilibrium point and the solubility of (VII), the hydrolysis products may be free glycol and (VII) (21-8).[9,63]

$$R\!<\!\!{}^{O}_{O}\!\!>\!B\text{—ORO—}B\!<\!\!{}^{O}_{O}\!\!>\!R + 6\,H_2O \rightarrow 3\,HOROH + 2\,H_3BO_3 \qquad (21\text{-}6)$$

$$HOROH + H_3BO_3 \rightleftarrows R\!<\!\!{}^{O}_{O}\!\!>\!BOH + 2\,H_2O \qquad (21\text{-}7)$$

$$R\!<\!\!{}^{O}_{O}\!\!>\!B\text{—ORO—}B\!<\!\!{}^{O}_{O}\!\!>\!R + 2\,H_2O \rightarrow 2\,\underset{\text{(VII)}}{R\!<\!\!{}^{O}_{O}\!\!>\!BOH} + HOROH \qquad (21\text{-}8)$$

3. UNSYMMETRICAL ORTHOBORATES

With the exception of the hindered phenolic borates (see Section IV), and the species (VIII)[76] and (IX),[46] the unsymmetrical esters

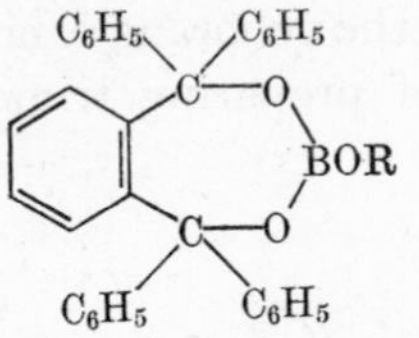

(VIII, R = C_2H_5, C_4H_9)

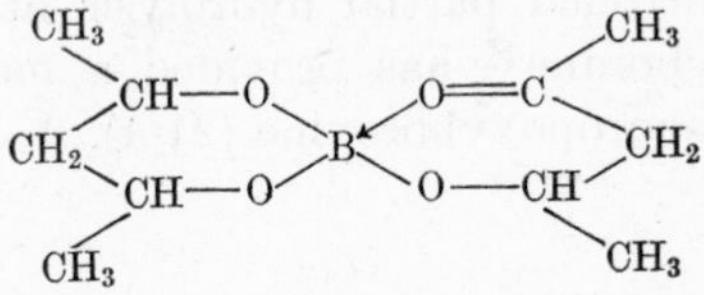

(IX)

derived from mono and dihydric alcohols and phenols[43] are readily hydrolyzed to boric acid and their respective alcohols, phenols, or glycols.

Compound (VIII) is partially hydrolyzed to (X) in boiling aqueous dioxane;[76] when exposed to moist air, (IX) is partially hydrolyzed to 2-hydroxy-4-pentanone and (XI).[46]

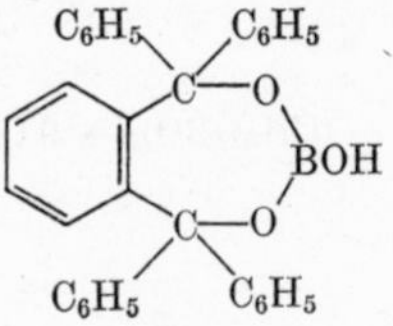

(X)

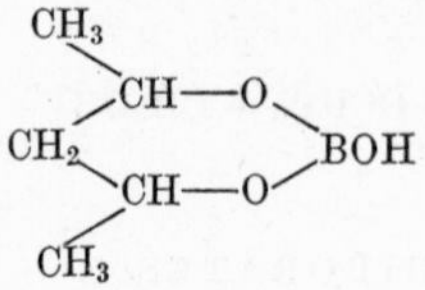

(XI)

The latter reaction is not surprising in view of the isolation of (XII)

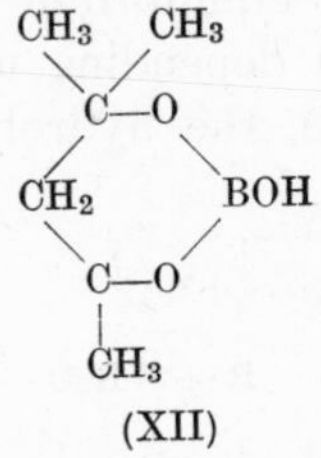

(XII)

from the hydrolysis of hexylene glycol biborate,[63] but it is remarkable that (X) could withstand further attack of water in boiling dioxane. Complete hydrolysis of (VIII) to (XIII) and sodium borate

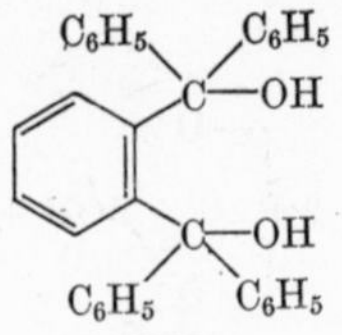

(XIII)

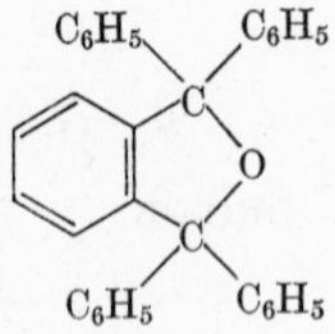

(XIV)

was effected by boiling sodium hydroxide. Hydrochloric acid also effects complete hydrolysis; in this case to give (XIV).

Reaction (21-9) has been recorded.[56]

$$2\ \mathrm{ROB}\begin{array}{c}\diagup\ \mathrm{O\underset{|}{\overset{CH_3}{C}}HCH_2}\ \diagdown \\ \\ \diagdown\ \mathrm{O\overset{|}{\underset{CH_3}{C}}HCH_2}\ \diagup\end{array}\mathrm{NCH_2CH_2N}\begin{array}{c}\diagup\ \mathrm{CH_2\underset{|}{\overset{CH_3}{C}}HO}\ \diagdown \\ \\ \diagdown\ \mathrm{CH_2\overset{|}{\underset{CH_3}{C}}HO}\ \diagup\end{array}\mathrm{BOR} + 8\ \mathrm{H_2O}$$

$$\rightarrow 4\ \mathrm{ROH} + (\mathrm{HO\overset{CH_3}{\overset{|}{C}}HCH_2})_2\mathrm{NCH_2CH_2N(CH_2\overset{CH_3}{\overset{|}{C}}HOH)_2}$$

$$+ \left[\mathrm{(HO)_2BO\overset{CH_3}{\overset{|}{C}}HCH_2}\right]_2\mathrm{NCH_2CH_2N}\left[\mathrm{CH_2\overset{CH_3}{\overset{|}{C}}HOB(OH)_2}\right]_2 \qquad (21\text{-}9)$$

E. Rates of Hydrolysis

1. STERIC FACTORS[63,66]

The most obvious single rate-determining factor in the transformation of a boron atom from an sp^2 trigonal coplanar configuration in an ester to sp^3 hybridization in a tetrahedral intermediate is the steric requirements of the tetrahedral species (I) and (II). If the R group is of sufficient size so as to hinder the formation of (I), the hydrolysis proceeds slowly. It is assumed throughout this discussion that the initial displacement is rate determining in the overall process and that all subsequent alkoxyhydroxyborane intermediates proceed to boric acid relatively fast.

Table 21-1 summarizes the base-catalyzed rate data for a series

Table 21-1. Base catalyzed rate of hydrolysis of boric acid esters of straight chain primary alcohols in 60% aqueous dioxane at 21°

Ester	Half-life (sec.)
Trimethyl borate	Too fast to measure
Triethyl borate	Too fast to measure
Tri-n-propyl borate	Too fast to measure
Tri-n-butyl borate	Too fast to measure
Tri-n-amyl borate	1.0
Tri-n-hexyl borate	2.9
Tri-n-octyl borate	16.0
Tri-n-dodecyl borate	21.3
Tristearyl borate	21.7

of straight chain esters prepared from alcohols with one to eighteen carbon atoms. The half-lives calculated from the pseudo-unimolecular reaction rate constants increase with the steric requirements and there appears to be a leveling of the steric effect at about twelve carbon atoms. Branching of the alkyl group introduces a further increment of stability.

The stability of esters derived from straight-chain secondary alcohols is dependent not only upon the bulk of the alkyl group, as seen in the first three entries of Table 21-2, but also on the distribution of the bulk above and below the BO_3 plane. Thus 3-pentyl borate and 3-heptyl borate are both more stable than 2-octyl borate. In every case studied, esters derived from tertiary alcohols are more stable than their secondary alcohol counterparts, which, in turn, are more slowly hydrolyzed than primary alkyl borates of comparable molecular weight (Table 21-3). Within the tertiary series itself, *t*-amyl borate is more stable than *t*-butyl borate.

Table 21-2. Base catalyzed rate of hydrolysis of boric acid esters of straight chain secondary alcohols in 60% aqueous dioxane at 21°

$[(R_1)(R_2)CHO]_3B$	Half-life (sec.)
$R_1 = R_2 = CH_3$	Too fast to measure
$R_1 = CH_3, R_2 = C_2H_5$	3.5
$R_1 = CH_3, R_2 = C_6H_{13}$	136
$R_1 = R_2 = C_2H_5$	1220
$R_1 = C_2H_5, R_2 = C_4H_9$	1416

Table 21-3. Base catalyzed rate of hydrolysis of boric acid esters of primary, secondary and tertiary alcohols in 60% aqueous dioxane at 21°

Ester	Half-life (sec.)
Tri-n-octyl borate	16.0
Tri-2-octyl borate	136
Tri-n-butyl borate	Too fast to measure
Tri-*s*-butyl borate	3.5
Tri-*t*-butyl borate	428
Tri-n-amyl borate	1.0
Tri-3-pentyl borate	1220
Tri-*t*-amyl borate	1320

Glycol biborates follow the secondary–tertiary trend (Table 21-4). Tri-hexylene glycol biborate (XV), with one secondary and

Table 21-4. Base catalyzed rate of hydrolysis of biborates and structurally similar esters in 60% aqueous dioxane at 21°

Ester	Half-life (sec.)
Tri-hexylene glycol biborate (XV)	Too fast to measure
Tri-octylene glycol biborate (XVI)	1.5
Methylisobutylcarbinyl borate (XVII)	242

one tertiary oxygen-bearing carbon, hydrolyzes more rapidly than tri-octylene glycol biborate (XVI) which possesses two tertiary

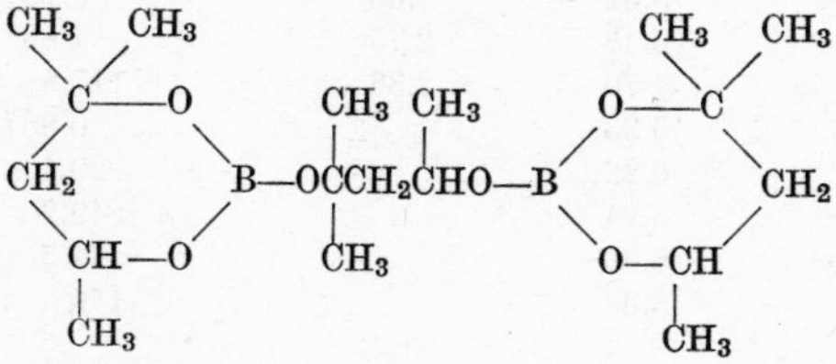

```
CH3   CH3                            CH3   CH3          ┌CH3   CH3┐
  \   /                                \   /            │  \   /  │
   C——O        CH3 CH3            O——C                 │   C—O—  │
  /     \       |   |            /      \               │  /      │
CH2      B—OCCH2CHO—B               CH2            │CH2      │
  \     /       |                \      /               │  |      │
   CH—O        CH3                O—CH                 │ CH2     │ B2
   |                                  |                 │   \     │
   CH3                               CH3                │   C—O—  │
                                                        │  /   \  │
                                                        └CH3   CH3┘3
              (XV)                                         (XVI)
```

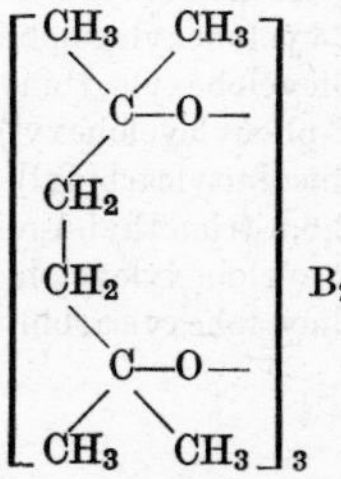

linkages. In addition, hexylene glycol biborate, with the alkylene chain tied in a ring, is more susceptible to hydrolysis than the analogous open-chain methylisobutylcarbinyl borate (XVII).

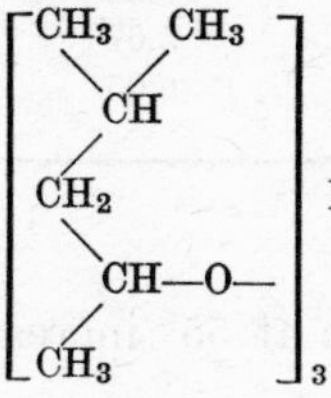

```
┌CH3   CH3 ┐
│  \   /   │
│   CH     │
│  /       │
│CH2       │ B
│  \       │
│   CH—O—  │
│  /       │
└CH3       ┘3
   (XVII)
```

Cis-2-phenylcyclohexyl borate[31] (half-life = 11.7 hr. in 91% aqueous dioxane at 21°) hydrolyzes more slowly than the *trans* isomer (half-life = 8.32 hr.). These results are in accord with data showing the *cis*-2-cyclohexylcyclohexyl succinate saponifies more slowly than the *trans* isomer.[71]

a. *Effect of Base.*[63,66] The hydrolysis of esters of inorganic acids in general is accelerated by alkali, but the effect is not very marked.[45] The basic catalysis of boric acid ester hydrolysis was shown with a series of relatively stable borates of large steric requirements (Table 21-5). In the presence of 0.5 equivalent of sodium

Table 21-5. Effect of base on rate of hydrolysis of sterically hindered boric acid esters in 91% aqueous dioxane

Ester	Initial conc. reactants (mmole/liter)		Half-life (hr.)
	Ester	Sodium hydroxide	
	55°C		
Tri-(2-phenylcyclohexyl) borate[a]	5.63	2.82	0.522
Tri-(diisobutylcarbinyl) borate	5.97	2.97	3.03
Tri-(2,6,8-trimethyl-4-nonyl) borate	5.32	2.66	3.70
Tri-(2-cyclohexylcyclohexyl) borate[a]	5.48	2.75	4.86
Tri-(dicyclohexylcarbinyl) borate	4.70	2.36	17.8
Tri-(2-phenylcyclohexyl) borate[a]	5.33		0.867
Tri-(diisobutylcarbinyl) borate	5.22		29.4
Tri-(2,6,8-trimethyl-4-nonyl) borate	5.14		49.2
Tri-(2-cyclohexylcyclohexyl) borate[a]	6.56		74.5
Tri-(dicyclohexylcarbinyl) borate	5.38		170
	21°C		
Tri-(*trans*-2-phenylcyclohexyl) borate	5.04	2.53	8.32
Tri-(2-phenylcyclohexyl) borate[a]	4.90	2.47	9.72
Tri-(*cis*-2-phenylcyclohexyl) borate	5.60	2.79	11.7
Tri-(2,6,8-trimethyl-4-nonyl) borate	4.71	2.35	33.9
Tri-*t*-amyl borate	10.0		1.15
Tri-(*trans*-2-phenylcyclohexyl) borate	5.24		14.6
Tri-(2-phenylcyclohexyl) borate[a]	5.00		17.2
Tri-(*cis*-2-phenylcyclohexyl) borate	5.67		20.4
Tri-(2,6,8-trimethyl-4-nonyl) borate	6.05		167

[a] *Cis–trans* mixture.

hydroxide, the average rate at 55° increased by a factor of 9.9, and at 21° by a factor of 2.6.

Although the exact function of the base was not elucidated, its function does not appear to be simply to compete with water as a nucleophile. Such behavior would be expected to lead to an acceleration in the rate of hydrolysis with increased concentration of base. In actuality, there was a tendency toward inverse proportionality of the rate constant and base concentration. This behavior would be expected if increases in base concentration in the $0.003M$ region effected significant decreases in the dielectric constant of the medium. The decrease in dielectric constant of the medium would then reflect in a decrease in rate of hydrolysis since the hydrolysis of an ester involves the formation of a transition state with a charge separation from two previously neutral molecules (21-10), a transformation aided by polar solvents.[33]

$$H_2O + (RO)_3B \rightarrow \begin{matrix} H & & OR & \\ & \diagdown^{\delta+} & | & ^{\delta-} \\ & O \cdots & B & \cdots OR \\ & \diagup & | & \\ H & & OR & \end{matrix} \qquad (21\text{-}10)$$

b. *Conclusions.* The data of Tables 21-1 through 21-5 indicate a primary requisite for hydrolytic stability in aliphatic and alicyclic esters to be the presence of groups of large steric requirements dispersed both above and below the BO_3 plane.

Cyclohexylcyclohexyl[31] groups meet this criterion, as do isobutyl or larger groups. The symmetry of the dicyclohexylcarbinyl group compared to the 2-cyclohexylcyclohexyl grouping allows for equal distribution of the bulk below and above the BO_3 plane, and, indeed, the ester derived from dicyclohexylcarbinol is more stable than 2-cyclohexylcyclohexyl borate. In turn, the 2-cyclohexylcyclohexyl group affords more protection than the less bulky 2-phenylcyclohexyl group and, therefore, leads to a hydrolytically more stable ester. Comparison of the half-lives of the entire spectrum of esters (Table 21-6) reveals that steric factors can result in a difference in rate of hydrolysis of about 10^6.

Table 21-6. Relative rates of hydrolysis of boric acid esters in aqueous dioxane

Ester	Relative rate
Trimethyl borate	$>5.87 \times 10^5$
Triethyl borate	$>5.87 \times 10^5$
Tri-n-propyl borate	$>5.87 \times 10^5$
Triisopropyl borate	$>5.87 \times 10^5$
Tri-(1,3-dichloro-2-propyl) borate	$>5.87 \times 10^5$
Tri-n-butyl borate	$>5.87 \times 10^5$
Triisobutyl borate	$>5.87 \times 10^5$
Tri-(β,β,β-trichloro-*t*-butyl) borate	$>5.87 \times 10^5$
Tri-(hexylene glycol) biborate	$>5.87 \times 10^5$
Triphenyl borate	$>5.87 \times 10^5$
Tri-*o*-chlorophenyl borate	$>5.87 \times 10^5$
Tri-*o*-cresyl borate	$>5.87 \times 10^5$
Tri-(*o*-phenylphenyl) borate	$>5.87 \times 10^5$
Tri-(*o*-cyclohexylphenyl) borate	$>5.87 \times 10^5$
Tri-n-amyl borate	5.87×10^5
Tri-(octylene glycol) biborate	3.92×10^5

(*Table continued*)

Table 21-6 (*continued*)

Ester	Relative rate
Tri-n-hexyl borate	2.02×10^5
Tri-*s*-butyl borate	1.68×10^5
Tri-(1-ethynylcyclohexyl) borate	4.29×10^4
Tri-n-octyl borate	3.67×10^4
Trioleyl borate	3.53×10^4
Tri-n-dodecyl borate	2.77×10^4
Tristearyl borate	2.71×10^4
Tri-2-octyl borate	4.33×10^3
Tri-(2-ethylhexyl) borate	2.77×10^3
Tri-(methylisobutylcarbinyl) borate	2430
Tri-*t*-butyl borate	1370
Tri-3-pentyl borate	483
Tri-*t*-amyl borate	449
Tri-3-heptyl borate	415
Tri-(*trans*-2-phenylcyclohexyl) borate	40.0
Tri-(2-phenylcyclohexyl) borate[a]	34.1
Tri-(*cis*-2-phenylcyclohexyl) borate	28.2
Tri-(diisobutylcarbinyl) borate	5.86
Tri-(2,6,8-trimethyl-4-nonyl) borate	4.83
Tri-(2-cyclohexylcyclohexyl) borate[a]	3.67
Tri-(dicyclohexylcarbinyl) borate	1

[a] *Cis–trans* mixture.

2. ELECTRONIC FACTORS[63,66]

Electronic effects can substantially affect hydrolysis rates; they may be more important than steric factors. Thus β,β,β-trichloro-*t*-butyl borate (XVIII), which obviously has much greater steric

$$\left[\begin{array}{c} CH_3 \\ | \\ CH_3—C—O— \\ | \\ Cl—C—Cl \\ | \\ Cl \end{array}\right]_3 B$$

(XVIII)

requirements than *t*-butyl borate itself, hydrolyzes at a rate too fast to measure as compared to a 428 sec. half-life for *t*-butyl borate. The inductive effect of the nine chlorine atoms decreases the electron density on the boron atom and leads to rapid nucleophilic attack.

Complexing of a trialkoxyborane with an amine, which in effect completely eliminates the electron deficiency of the boron atom, does not preclude hydrolysis. Thus both pyridine–triphenoxyborane[19] and ammonia–trimethoxyborane[59] are easily hydrolyzed.

Aromatic esters hydrolyze at a rate too rapid to measure (Table 21-6). They also are subject to electronic control.* In an aliphatic ester the shift of the electrons from oxygen to boron (XIX) deters the entry of a nucleophile. In aromatic esters the benzene ring is an electron sink (XX), and the entry of water is aided by the shift of

R—O, R—O B—ÖR (XIX) Ar—O, Ar—O B—Ö—C_6H_5 (XX)

electrons away from boron.[6] This effect is strikingly evident in the data of Table 21-7. It is seen that hindered phenyl esters, similar in

Table 21-7. Comparison of hydrolysis rates of alicyclic and aromatic borates in 91% aqueous dioxane at 55°

	Half-life (sec.)
[(S)–(S)–O–]$_3$B	17,500
[C_6H_5–(S)–O–]$_3$B	1,800
[(S)–C_6H_4–O–]$_3$B	<1
[C_6H_5–C_6H_4–O–]$_3$B	<1

* Tri-(2,6-diisopropylphenoxy)borane is an exception. A base catalyzed half-life of 118 sec. in 90% aqueous acetone at 25° has been reported.[78]

bulk to cyclohexyl esters, possess no stability at all; whereas the cyclohexyl esters are among the most hydrolytically stable known.

F. Equilibrium Constants

Equilibrium constants have been recorded in Table 21-8 for reaction (21-11) in anhydrous acetone at 0°.[2]

$$(RO)_3B + 3\,H_2O \rightarrow H_3BO_3 + 3\,ROH \qquad (21\text{-}11)$$

Table 21-8. Equilibrium constants for reaction (21-11) in anhydrous acetone at 0°

$(RO)_3B$	*K*	% Hydrolysis
$(CH_3O)_3B$	16.0	67
$(n\text{-}C_3H_7O)_3B$	2.7	56
$(n\text{-}C_4H_9O)_3B$	2.1	54.5
$(n\text{-}C_5H_{11}O)_3B$	1.8	53.5

IV. HINDERED PHENOLIC BORATES

The unsymmetrical esters derived from a 2,6-di-*t*-butylphenol and the lower alcohols (XXI) possess structural features which would

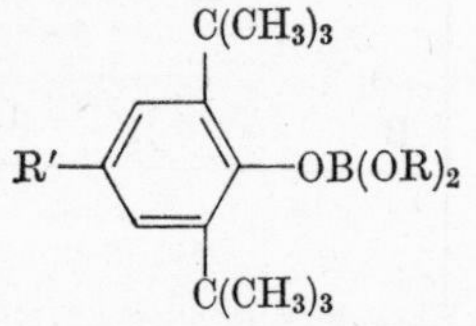

$C(CH_3)_3$

R′— [ring] —$OB(OR)_2$

$C(CH_3)_3$

(XXI, $R' = H, CH_3$; $R = CH_3$ to C_8H_{17})

not be expected to contribute to hydrolytic stability. The phenyl group makes them subject to electronic shifts as indicated in structure (XX), and, in addition, the small alkyl groups, R, afford little if any steric protection. Yet the hindered phenolic borates, as a class, are phenomenally stable with half-lives ranging up to greater than two years (Table 21-9).[32,54,66,72] The diisopropyl derivative (XXII) is the most hydrolytically stable borate derived from mono-

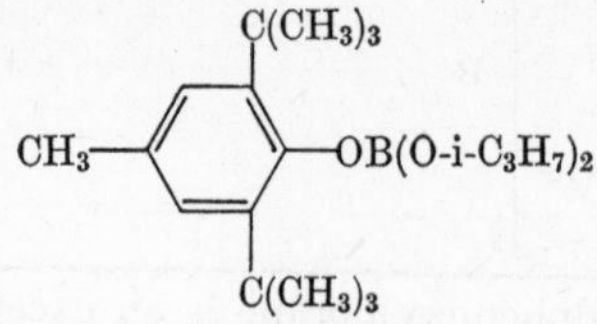

$C(CH_3)_3$

CH_3— [ring] —$OB(O\text{-}i\text{-}C_3H_7)_2$

$C(CH_3)_3$

(XXII)

Table 21-9. Rate of hydrolysis of hindered phenolic borates in 90% aqueous dioxane at 25°

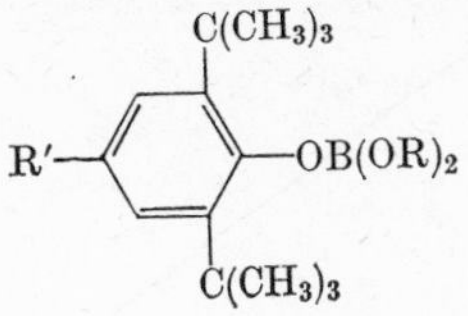

$C(CH_3)_3$

R′— [benzene ring] —$OB(OR)_2$

$C(CH_3)_3$

R	Half-life (days)	
	R′ = H	R′ = CH_3
C_2H_5	1.98	
n-C_8H_{17}	3.50	
n-C_4H_9	38.3	48.5
CH_3	73.7	
$(CH_3)_2\overset{\vert}{C}CH_2\overset{\vert}{C}HCH_3$		90
n-C_3H_7	78.1	98.0
i-C_3H_7	379	851[a]

[a] An infinite half-life in 37.5% aqueous acetone has been reported.[73]

hydric alcohols and phenols yet reported.* It is greater than seventy-four million times as stable as triisopropyl borate.[66]

The hydrolytic stability of the hindered phenolic borates must be due to the two *ortho* *t*-butyl groups. The bulk of these groups tends to twist the dialkoxyboryl group with respect to the plane of the phenyl ring, thereby shielding the boron atom from nucleophilic attack. The situation apparently is complex, however, since the results in Table 21-9 show a rather unexpected order of stability as the alkoxy substituent is varied. If the effect were totally steric, the hydrolysis rate would be expected to decrease as the steric requirement of the alkoxy group increases. However, the n-propyl derivative is more stable than the bulkier butyl and octyl derivatives and the methyl derivative is inordinately stable.

It is instructive to plot the logarithm of the hydrolysis rate constant (calculated from the half-life values) versus twice the aliphatic steric substituent constant, E_S,[68] for each alkyl group.† The parameter $2E_S$ is used, since two steric interactions are involved

* Tri-n-propanolamine borate has been stated to be completely inert to water at 25°.[24]

† The author is indebted to Dr. W. G. Woods for the following discussion.

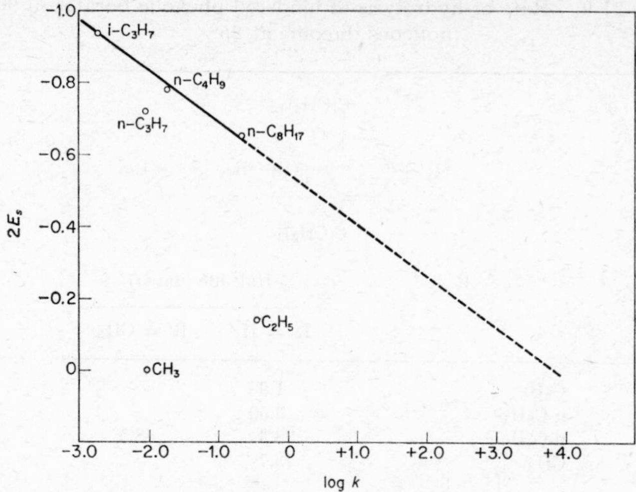

Fig. 21-1. **Steric substituent constants as a function of log $k_{\text{hydrolysis}}$.**

in the dialkoxyboryl-*t*-butyl group interference. The plot is shown in Fig. 21-1, using the data given in Table 21-10.

If the effect of varying the alkyl group were totally steric, a linear relationship would be anticipated. If the points for the n-C_8H_{17}, n-C_4H_9 and i-C_3H_7 groups are taken as reference, it is seen that the n-C_3H_7, C_2H_5 and CH_3 groups are progressively further removed from the line. This suggests that an electronic effect is operating to stabilize the lower members of the series.

A possible rationale of the observations lies in a type of "pseudo-

Table 21-10. **Comparison of rate of hydrolysis of hindered phenolic borates and steric substituent constants**

R in [benzene ring bearing $C(CH_3)_3$, $OB(OR)_2$, $C(CH_3)_3$]	log k	$2E_S$
CH_3	−2.029	0.00
C_2H_5	−0.459	−0.14
n-C_3H_7	−2.054	−0.72
n-C_4H_9	−1.745	−0.78
n-C_8H_{17}	−0.706	−0.66
i-C_3H_7	−2.740	−0.94

homobenzylic" resonance. The smaller alkyl groups might allow the dialkoxyboryl group to assume a position in which delocalization can take place between the empty $2p$-orbital of boron and the π-electron cloud of the aromatic ring (Fig. 21-2). Such an effect would be

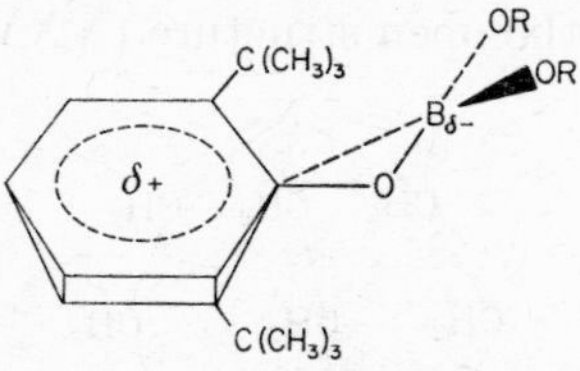

Fig. 21-2. Orbital overlap in hindered phenolic borates.

expected to decrease as the steric requirements of R increase. Just such an order is observed; n-C_3H_7 is too slow in rate by about $10^{0.85}$, C_2H_5 by $10^{3.3}$ and CH_3 by $10^{5.85}$ (see extrapolation in Fig. 21-1). As a test of reasonableness, stabilization energies of 1.2, 4.5 and 8.0 kcal/mole, respectively, can be calculated. Simonetta and Winstein[61] have calculated a maximum delocalization energy of 17.2 kcal/mole for an unstrained homobenzylic carbonium ion. This value can serve as an approximate upper limit for the type of overlap proposed for the hindered phenolic borates; the values found are well within this limit.

V. TRIALKANOLAMINE BORATES

Internal coordination of boron with available electrons, as suspected for the hindered phenolic borates, plays an important role in the kinetics of the hydrolysis of triethanolamine borate (XXIII) and triisopropanolamine borate (XXIV).

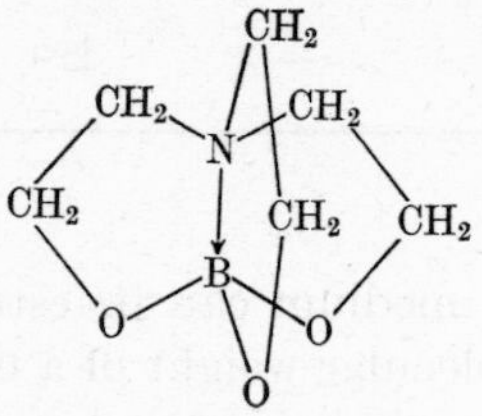

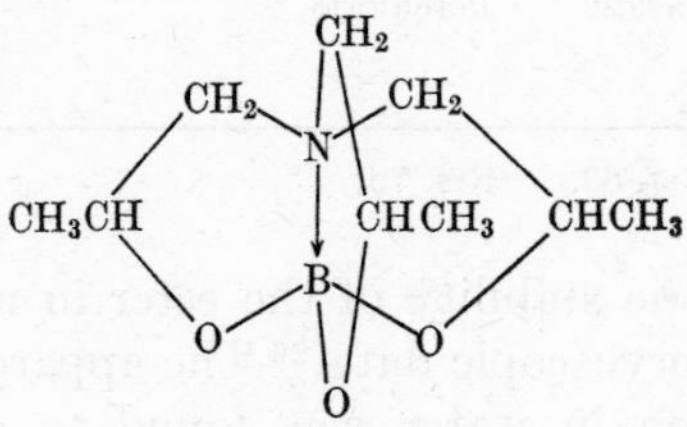

A. *Triethanolamine Borate*

The attempted titration of triethanolamine borate in water with hydrochloric acid or in nitrobenzene with methanesulfonic acid revealed that the neutralization took place at a slow, measurable rate; whereas triethanolamine itself is rapidly titrated with strong acids in both aqueous and non-aqueous media. It was concluded on the basis of this and other evidence (Chapter 5) that triethanolamine borate possesses the transannular B–N bond of structure (XXIII) and does not exist in the open structure (XXV), since (XXV) would

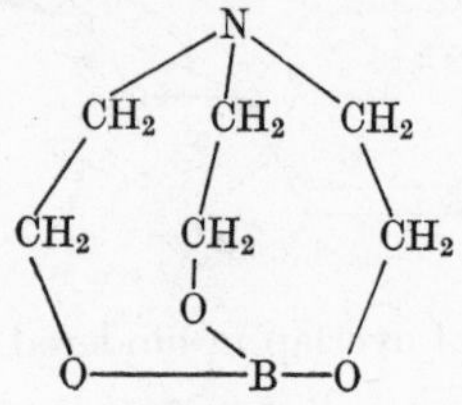

N

CH_2 CH_2 CH_2

CH_2 CH_2 CH_2

O

O——B—O

(XXV)

be expected to undergo rapid neutralization with strong acid. The slow neutralization was thus the result of a rate-determining hydrolysis of the ester (Table 21-11).[4]

Table 21-11. Rate of hydrolysis of triethanolamine borate

Solvent	Acid	Initial concentration of reactants (mole/l.)		Half-life (sec.)	
		Triethanolamine borate	Acid	25°	0°
Water	Hydrochloric	0.0357	0.0179	181	1,680
,,	,,	0.0241	0.0121	184	1,624
,,	,,	0.0182	0.0091	187	—
,,	,,	0.00459	0.00459	130[a]	—
,,	,,	—	—	191[b]	—
Nitrobenzene	Methanesulfonic	0.025	0.0125	1,950	—
Glacial acetic acid	Perchloric	—	—	220	—

[a] Ref. 63. [b] Ref. 79.

The stability of the ester in neutral medium can be estimated from cryoscopic data.[26] The apparent molecular weight of a $0.107M$ solution in water was found to change with time and reach an equilibrium value after 271 minutes (Table 21-12). It subsequently was shown that triethanolamine borate in water equilibrates with its hydrolysis products and contains about 20% of the transannular bonded structure (XXIII) at equilibrium.[40] Thus, the equilibrium point is sufficiently removed from the initial point to allow the use

Table 21-12. Hydrolytic equivalent of cryoscopic molecular weight of triethanolamine borate in water, 0.107 molar

Time (min.)	No. of Particles	% Hydrolyzed
0		0
8	1.17	28
22	1.28	47
35	1.39	62
55	1.38	63
77	1.41	68
88	1.37	62
106	1.41	68
221	1.45	75
271	1.48	80
341	1.47	78
24 hr.	1.46	77

of the usual kinetic expression for an irreversible first order process, $\log (a-x) = -kt/2.303 + \log a$. Assuming 80% hydrolysis after 271 minutes, a plot of $\log (a-x)$ versus t describes an initial straight line with a slope equivalent to a half life of 1,440 seconds. This value is in fair agreement with the half life of 1,624 seconds at 0° determined in the presence of 0.5 equivalent of acid and would tend to bear out the conclusion that the rate of hydrolysis of triethanolamine borate is independent of the acid concentration.[4] The first order nature of the hydrolysis has been confirmed.[79]

B. Triisopropanolamine Borate

Triisopropanolamine borate[63] as prepared from commercially available triisopropanolamine has been shown to exist as a mixture of diastereomers. The configuration about the asymmetric carbon atoms either are identical (XXVI) or the configuration of one carbon atom is inverted (XXVII).[64]

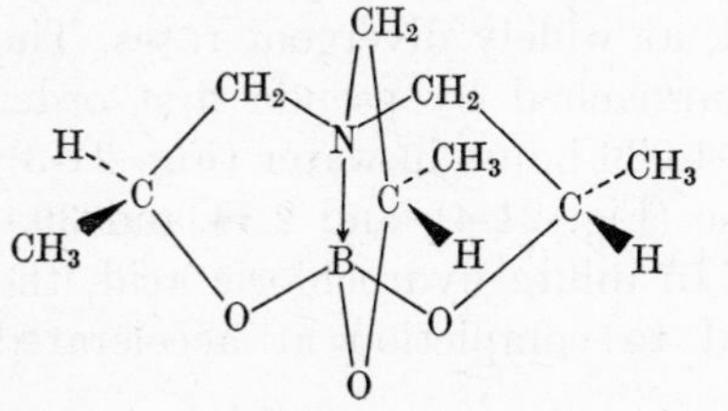

(XXVI) 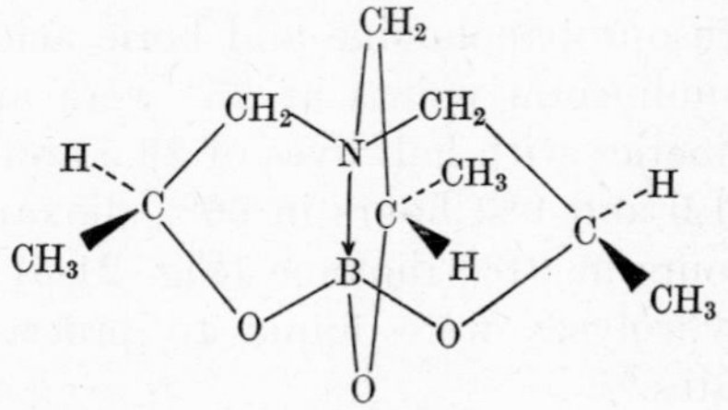 (XXVII)

Examination of Fisher–Hershfelder–Taylor atomic models indicates a decided interference of methyl and methylene groups in the unsymmetrical racemate (XXVII). The alleviation of the strain produced by this interference would be expected to alter the extent of the nitrogen–boron interaction, which in turn would be expected to reflect in a difference in rate of hydrolysis of the two diastereomeric borates (XXVI) and (XXVII). Indeed, the borates equilibrate

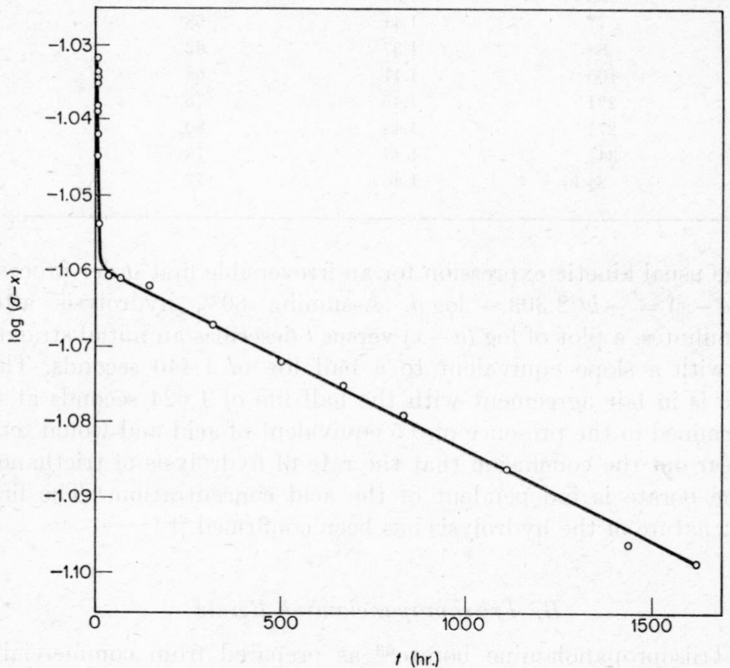

Fig. 21-3. Rate of hydrolysis of triisopropanolamine borate (mixture of racemates) in water at 25°.

in water or aqueous dioxane with their products of hydrolysis, triisopropanolamine and boric acid, at widely divergent rates. The equilibrium points at 25° were approached by pseudo first order kinetics with half-lives of 29.5 and 4,080 hours in water (Fig. 21-3), 11.0 and 983 hours in 60% dioxane (Fig. 21-4), and 2.74 and 39.0 hours in 91% dioxane (Fig. 21-5). In dilute hydrochloric acid, the hydrolyses were found to proceed to completion at accelerated rates.[64]

In Table 21-13, which contains a summary of the rate data,[64]

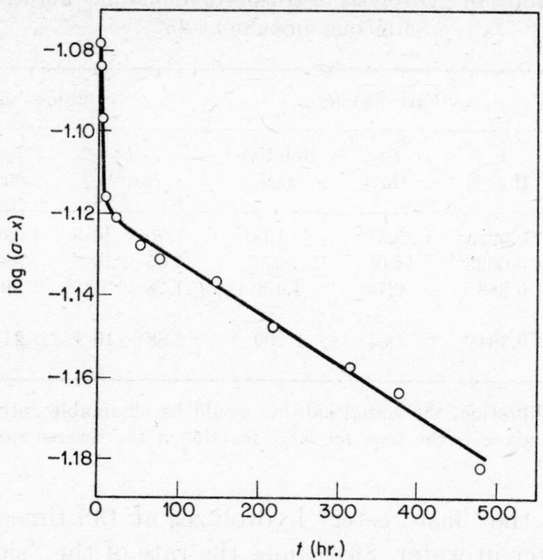

Fig. 21-4. Rate of hydrolysis of triisopropanolamine borate (mixture of racemates) in 60% aqueous dioxane at 25°.

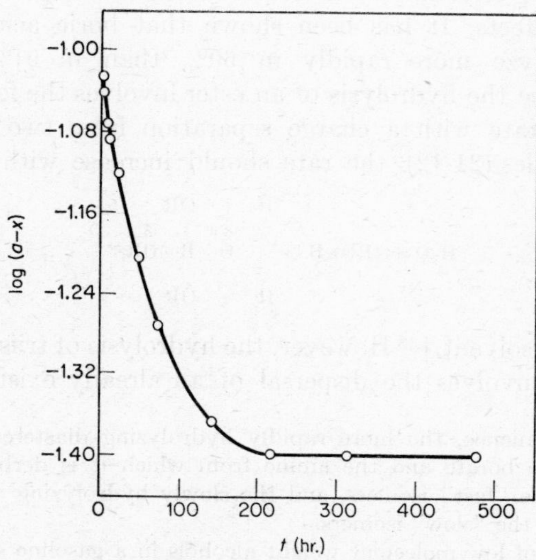

Fig. 21-5. Rate of hydrolysis of triisopropanolamine borate (mixture of racemates) in 91% dioxane at 25°.

Table 21-13. Rates of hydrolysis of triisopropanolamine borate in water and aqueous dioxane at 25°

Medium	"Fast" isomer			"Slow" isomer		
	k (hr.$^{-1}$)	$t_{1/2}$ (hr.)	Relative rate	k (hr.$^{-1}$)	$t_{1/2}$ (hr.)	Relative rate
Water	0.0235	29.5[a]	138	1.70×10^{-4}	4,080	1.0
60% Dioxane	0.0628	11.0[a]	371	7.05×10^{-4}	983	4.15
91% Dioxane	0.253	2.74[a]	1,490	1.78×10^{-2}	39.0	105
Water, 1.0 equiv. HCl	0.384	1.81	2,260	2.88×10^{-3}	241	16.9

[a] Due to equilibration, the actual half-life would be obtainable only in dilute solution. The half-life given is the time for 50% reaction if the reverse reaction were not operative.

it is seen that the "fast" ester* hydrolyzes at 138 times the rate of the "slow" ester in water, 89.4 times the rate of the "slow" ester in 60% dioxane, and 14.2 times the rate in 91% dioxane. It is further seen that for the neutral hydrolyses the rates for both isomers increase with decreasing polarity of the solvent. Although it is possible that dioxane may catalyze the reaction by forming a complex (dioxanate) with the ester which is more susceptible to hydrolyses than the original intramolecular complex, a more probable explanation can be found by a consideration of charge distribution and solvent effects. It has been shown that boric acid esters in general hydrolyze more rapidly in 60% than in 91% aqueous dioxane.[63] Since the hydrolysis of an ester involves the formation of a transition state with a charge separation from two previously neutral molecules (21-12), the rate should increase with increasing

$$H_2O + (RO)_3B \rightarrow \begin{matrix} H & & OR & & \\ & \diagdown^{\delta+} & | & & ^{\delta-} \\ & O\cdots & B & \cdots & OR \\ & \diagup & | & & \\ H & & OR & & \end{matrix} \qquad (21\text{-}12)$$

polarity of the solvent.†[33] However, the hydrolysis of triisopropanolamine borate involves the dispersal of an already existing charge

* For convenience, the more rapidly hydrolyzing diastereomer of triisopropanolamine borate and the amine from which it is derived shall be referred to as the "fast" isomers, and the slowly hydrolyzing diastereomer and its amine as the "slow" isomers.

† Inclusion of low molecular weight alcohols in a gasoline solution of a trialkoxyborane decreased the hydrolytic stability of the ester. Inclusion of a fatty alcohol increased the hydrolytic stability.[47]

separation (21-13), and consequently an increase in polarity of the solvent should result in a decrease in the rate of hydrolysis.[33] Furthermore, it would be expected that the isomer with the greater nitrogen–boron interaction and consequently the greater initial charge separation would be more sensitive to a change in solvent polarity. Thus, the "slow" isomer whose rate of hydrolysis in water

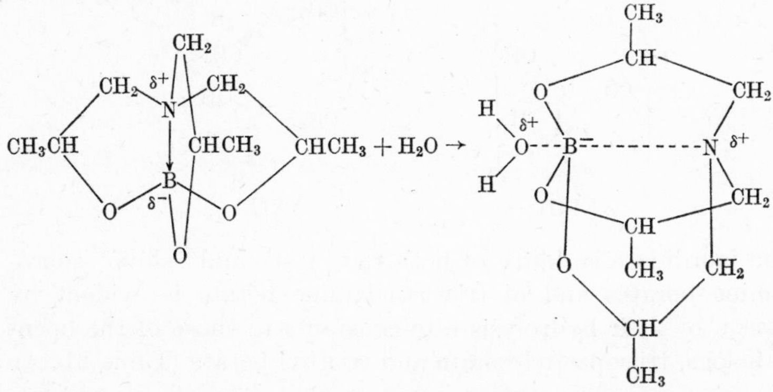

$$CH_3CH \quad CH_2 \; CH_2 \; CH_2 \; \overset{\delta+}{N} \; \overset{\delta-}{B} \; CHCH_3 \; CHCH_3 \; O \; O \; O + H_2O \rightarrow \qquad (21\text{-}13)$$

is increased by factors of 4 and 105 in 60 and 91% dioxane as compared to factors of 2.7 and 11 for the "fast" isomer might be expected to have the greater transannular interaction.*

An unequivocal assignment of diastereomers (XXVI) and (XXVII) to the "fast" and "slow" esters cannot be made. It is not obvious from examination of atomic models whether the methyl–methylene interference tends to increase or decrease the transannular interaction. However, if in the production of triisopropanolamine from propylene oxide and ammonia, the purely statistical possibilities of isomer distribution are not too greatly altered by the asymmetry present in the intermediate mono- and diisopropanolamines, a mixture containing 25% of the symmetrical (XXVIII) and 75% of the unsymmetrical (XXIX) amines would be expected. Thus the "fast" amine, which was found to comprise 38.1% of the mixture of amines, might be assigned the symmetrical configuration (XXVIII), and the "slow" amine the unsymmetrical configuration

* Acid catalysis would also be expected to be more pronounced in the isomer with the greatest nitrogen–boron interaction since protonization of the amino nitrogen would destroy the transannular interaction and leave the boron atom in an electron deficient state, a condition already at least partially present in the other isomer. The acceleration of "slow" isomer rate in acid medium by a factor of 16.9 versus the factor of 16.3 for the "fast" isomer does not bear out this contention.

(XXIX).[64] The consequences of such an assignment are that the methyl–methylene interference present in structure (XXVII) leads to a greater interaction of the nitrogen and boron orbitals and consequently decreases the rate of hydrolysis as compared to the symmetrical ester (XXVI).

$$\mathrm{N}\left[-\mathrm{CH_2}-\mathrm{C}(\mathrm{OH})(\mathrm{H})(\mathrm{CH_3})\right]_3 \qquad \text{(XXVIII)}$$

$$\mathrm{N}\left[\mathrm{CH_2}-\mathrm{C}(\mathrm{OH})(\mathrm{H})(\mathrm{CH_3})\right]_2\left[\mathrm{CH_2}-\mathrm{C}(\mathrm{OH})(\mathrm{CH_3})(\mathrm{H})\right] \qquad \text{(XXIX)}$$

The inordinate stability of both the "fast" and "slow" isopropanolamine borates and of triethanolamine borate is evident by comparison of their hydrolysis rate constants to those of the open-chain analogs, triisopropyl borate and triethyl borate (Table 21-14).

Table 21-14. Relative rates of hydrolysis of triisopropanolamine borate and structurally analogous compounds at 25°

Ester	$t_{1/2}$	Relative rate
$B(OC_2H_5)_3$	<1 sec.	$>1.47 \times 10^7$
$B[OCH(CH_3)_2]_3$	<1 sec.	$>1.47 \times 10^7$
$B(OCH_2CH_2)_3N$	181 sec.	8.11×10^4
"Fast" $B(OCH(CH_3)CH_2)_3N$	29.5 hr.	138
"Slow" $B(OCH(CH_3)CH_2)_3N$	170 days	1

Neglecting the solvent effects of water and 60% aqueous dioxane, isopropyl borate[63] hydrolyzes greater than ten million times as fast as the "fast" isomer and greater than one hundred thousand times as fast as the "slow" isomer. This is true even though the steric requirements for the attack of water on the boron atom are greater in the open-chain ester (XXX) which has freely rotating isopropyl groups as compared to the bicyclic structure (XXXI) in which the isopropyl groups are tied back into a cage. The accessibility of the boron atom in the cage structure (XXXI) to attack by water would indicate a rate of hydrolysis at least comparable in order of magnitude to that of the open-chain analog (XXX). That this situation does not hold provides independent support for the existence of a transannular bond in molecules of this kind.

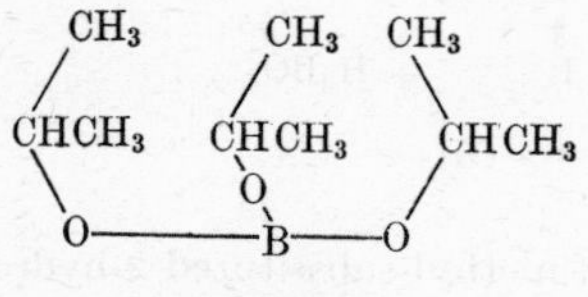

(XXX) 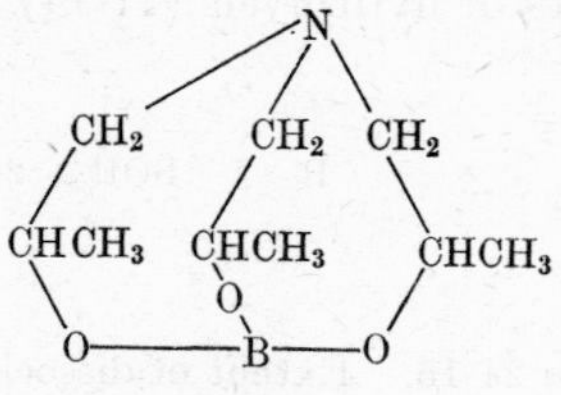 (XXXI)

Comparison of the half-lives of 181 seconds for triethanolamine borate and 170 days for triisopropanolamine borate indicates the latter to hydrolyze 8.11×10^4 times slower than the triethanolamine borate. This deceleration of rate in proceeding from a primary to secondary alcohol far surpasses any decreases observed in the open-chain esters: n-octyl > 2-octyl by a factor of 8.5, n-amyl > 3-pentyl by a factor of 1,220, and n-hexyl > 3-heptyl by a factor of 487.[63]

C. Tri-n-propanolamine Borate

Tri-n-propanolamine borate appears to be the most hydrolytically stable boric acid ester known. No measurable hydrolysis occurred in water solution after forty-three days at 25°.[24] Examination of atomic models indicates that the compactness of the transannular form (XXXII) completely precludes inversion to the necessary tetrahedral configuration on entry of water.

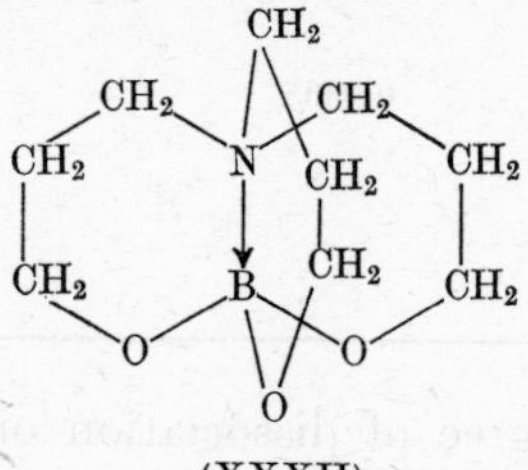

(XXXII)

VI. 2-HYDROXY-1,3,2-DIOXABOROLANES AND BORINANES AND THEIR SALTS AND ANHYDRIDES

Most hydroxyborolanes and borinanes are quantitatively converted to their corresponding glycol and boric acid on dissolution in water.

However, at least three of the methyl-substituted derivatives have been shown by cryoscopic measurements to equilibrate with their products of hydrolysis (21-14). See Table 21-15.

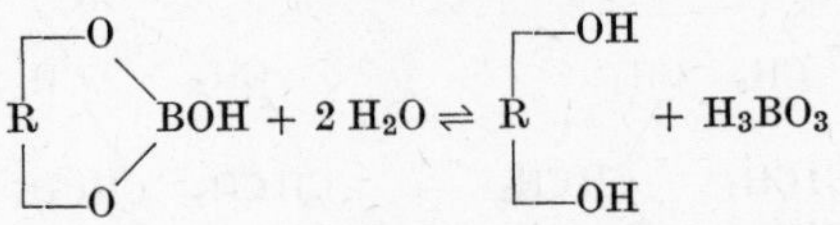

$$R\begin{cases}-O\\ -O\end{cases}BOH + 2\,H_2O \rightleftharpoons R\begin{cases}-OH\\ -OH\end{cases} + H_3BO_3 \qquad (21\text{-}14)$$

Table 21-15. Extent of dissociation of methyl-substituted 2-hydroxy-1,3,2-dioxaborolanes and borinanes in water at ca. 0°

	Concentration, mole/l.	% Dissociated	Reference
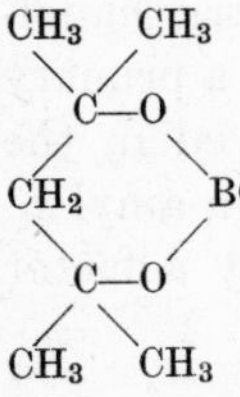 $(CH_3)_2C$—O—B(OH)—O—$C(CH_3)_2$ with CH_2 (ring: $(CH_3)_2C$–CH_2–$C(CH_3)_2$)	0.1542	74.3	28
	0.1404	74.7	28
	0.0348	85.6	28
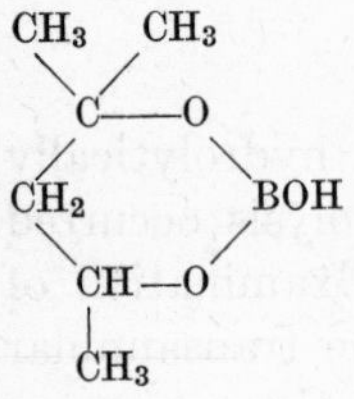 $(CH_3)_2C$—O—B(OH)—O—$CH(CH_3)$ with CH_2 (ring: $(CH_3)_2C$–CH_2–$CH(CH_3)$)	0.492	62.5	49
	0.0995	84.0	49
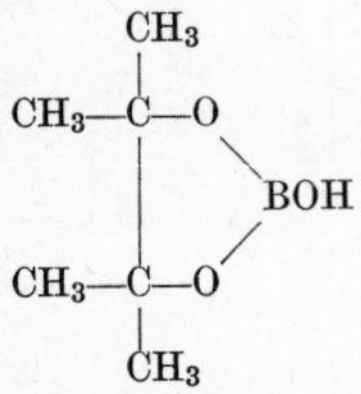 $(CH_3)_2C$—O—B(OH)—O—$C(CH_3)_2$ (ring: $(CH_3)_2C$–$C(CH_3)_2$)	0.0965	97.0	49

It is seen that the degree of dissociation or extent of hydrolysis increases with decreasing concentration of the hydroxyborane, which is consistent with equilibrium considerations. It is also seen that the six-membered ring compounds are more stable than the five-membered derivative.[9] It is difficult, however, to rationalize the cryoscopic molecular weight data determined by Watt[74] (Table 21-16) which indicate complete stability of the three-carbon-membered hydroxyborolane and borinane in water, particularly in

Table 21-16. Cryoscopic molecular weight data of 2-hydroxy 4-methyl-1,3,2-dioxaborolane and 2-hydroxy-1,3,2-dioxaborinane

	Concentration, mole/1000 g.	Mol. wt.	
		Found	Calculated
CH_3CH—O, CH_2—O ring with BOH (2-hydroxy-4-methyl-1,3,2-dioxaborolane)	0.0632	102	101.9
	0.0261	101	101.9
CH_2—O, CH_2, CH_2—O ring with BOH (2-hydroxy-1,3,2-dioxaborinane)	0.0522	102	101.9
	0.0313	104	101.9

view of the inability of Hermans[27,28] to prepare either the ethylene glycol or the trimethylene glycol borate in water solution.

The potassium salts of the hydroxyborolanes from both *cis*-1-methyl-1,2-dihydroxycyclopentane and *cis*-1-methyl-1,2-dihydroxy-cyclohexane undergo hydrolysis in water solution to give potassium metaborate and the corresponding diols. Both diols can be extracted from solution with chloroform. The cyclopentane derivative evidently is somewhat more hydrolytically stable than the cyclohexane derivative since it requires twelve days of continuous extraction with chloroform for complete diol removal as compared to only one day for the six-membered ring compound. This relationship is confirmed in aqueous cryoscopic data for the two esters which indicated 50% hydrolysis for the cyclopentane compound and 90% hydrolysis for the cyclohexane compound.[41]

The anhydrides of the hydroxy derivatives can be partially[9,10,14,15,49,62,74] hydrolyzed to the hydroxy derivative (21-15) or completely hydrolyzed to boric acid (21-16).[23]

$$R(O)_2B{-}O{-}B(O)_2R + H_2O \rightarrow 2\ R(O)_2BOH \qquad (21\text{-}15)$$

$$R(O)_2B{-}O{-}B(O)_2R + 5\ H_2O \rightarrow 2\ H_3BO_3 + 2\ R(OH)_2 \qquad (21\text{-}16)$$

VII. METABORATES

With the exception of the hindered phenolic metaborates, it appears that all alkyl and aryl metaborates hydrolyze rapidly regardless of the bulk of the organic groups (Table 21-17).*[65] This loss of steric

Table 21-17. Rate of hydrolysis of various metaborates in 60% aqueous dioxane at 25°

Metaborate	Base catalyzed 90% life (sec.)	60% life (min.)
Cresyl	<11	
Phenyl	<2	
Methyl	<3	
Cyclohexyl	<3	
Isopropyl	3	
2,6,8-Trimethyl-4-nonyl	3	
Methylisobutylcarbinyl	3–4	
2,6-Di-*t*-butyl phenyl		6[a]
2,6-Di-*t*-butyl-4-methylphenyl		6[a]

[a] The remaining 40% hydrolyzed at a much slower rate.

control is not unpredictable if one examines molecular models of the metaborates. The boroxine ring serves to separate the three organic substituents to the farthest possible distance and leaves each boron atom shielded by at most one of the organic residues. This shielding is insufficient to deter the entry of an attacking water molecule or seriously prevent the formation of a tetrahedral transition state.

It is apparent from the data of Table 21-17 that in the presence of an excess of water, orthoborates are not intermediates in the hydrolysis of metaborates (21-17) since the rate of hydrolysis of the

$$(ROBO)_3 + 3\ H_2O \rightarrow (RO)_3B + 2\ H_3BO_3 \qquad (21\text{-}17)$$

resulting sterically hindered orthoborate (such as 2,6,8-trimethyl-4-nonyl, $t_{1/2} = 167$ hr.) would then become rate determining. This clearly is not the case.

The mixed kinetics experienced with the hindered phenolic metaborates (Table 21-17) may be the result of competing mechan-

* Hindered phenolic metaborates are not easily wet by water and, therefore, are relatively stable in water alone. Thus a sample of 2,6-di-*t*-butylphenyl metaborate was only 20% hydrolyzed after a twenty minute treatment in boiling water.[32]

isms of hydrolysis. If the substituted phenoxy group is displaced as the initial reaction (21-18), the resulting hydroxy derivative is

$$(ArOBO)_3 + H_2O \rightarrow ArOH + HO\text{—}B_3O_3(OAr)_2 \qquad (21\text{-}18)$$

rapidly converted to at least one molecule of boric acid (21-19).

$$HO\text{—}B_3O_3(OAr)_2 + 2\,H_2O \rightarrow (HO)_3B + (ArO)(HO)B\text{—}O\text{—}B(OAr)(OH) \qquad (21\text{-}19)$$

The formation of boric acid in this manner might be responsible for the measured six minute 60% life. Alternatively, initial ring rupture (21-20) would result in the aryloxyhydroxyborane species (XXXIII).

$$(ArOBO)_3 + 2\,H_2O \rightarrow \underset{(XXXIII)}{ArOB(OH)_2} + (ArO)(HO)B\text{—}O\text{—}B(OAr)(OH) \qquad (21\text{-}20)$$

This species precipitates from water solution (see Chapter 7) indicating a higher order of hydrolytic stability. It is conceivable that the existence of these species is responsible for the decreased rates experienced in the latter 40% of the hydrolysis.

If insufficient water for complete hydrolysis is used in an inert solvent such as ether, boric acid may be removed by filtration leaving the orthoborate in the filtrate (21-21).[36]

$$(C_4H_9OBO)_3 + 3\,H_2O \rightarrow 2\,H_3BO_3 + (C_4H_9O)_3B \qquad (21\text{-}21)$$

With *l*-menthyl metaborate, the intermediate dihydroxymenthyloxyborane (XXXIV) was isolated by allowing the metaborate to stand in air for several hours.[48]

$$\text{cyclohexane ring with } CH(CH_3)_2,\ \text{—}OB(OH)_2,\ CH_3$$

(XXXIV)

VIII. REFERENCES

1. Bastin, E. L., *et al.*, Shell Development Company, Chemical Corps, Procurement Agency, Final Report, April 30, 1954, Contract No. CML-4564, Project No. 4-08-03-001.
2. Bradley, J. A., and P. M. Christopher, 129th Meeting American Chemical Society, Dallas, April 1956, Abstracts of Papers, p. 39-N.
3. British Thomson-Houston Company, Ltd., Brit. Pat. 549,081 (1942).
4. Brown, H. C., and E. A. Fletcher, *J. Am. Chem. Soc.*, **73**, 2808 (1951).
5. Charnley, T., H. A. Skinner, and N. B. Smith, *J. Chem. Soc.*, 2288 (1952).
6. Colclough, T., W. Gerrard, and M. F. Lappert, *J. Chem. Soc.*, 907 (1955).
7. Cook, H. G., J. D. Ilett, B. C. Saunders, and G. J. Stacey, *J. Chem. Soc.*, 3125 (1950).
8. Copaux, H., *Compt. Rend.*, **127**, 719 (1898).
9. Dale, J., *J. Chem. Soc.*, 910 (1961).
10. Darling, S. M., P. S. Fay, and L. S. Szabo, U.S. Pat. 2,741,548 (1956, to The Standard Oil Company, Ohio).
11. Dupire, A., *Compt. Rend.*, **202**, 2086 (1936).
12. Ebelman, J. J., *Ann.*, **57**, 319 (1846); *Ann. chim. et phys.*, **16**, 129 (1846).
13. Ebelman, J. J., and M. Bouquet, *Ann. chim. et phys.*, **17**, 54 (1846); *Ann.*, **60**, 251 (1846).
14. Fay, P. S., and L. S. Szabo, U.S. Pat. 2,767,069 (1956, to The Standard Oil Company, Ohio).
15. Fay, P. S., and L. S. Szabo, U.S. Pat. 2,961,380 (1960, to The Standard Oil Company, Ohio).
16. Garner, H. K., and H. J. Lucas, *J. Am. Chem. Soc.*, **72**, 5497 (1950).
17. Gel'perin, N. I., and K. N. Solopenkov, *Khim. Nauka i Promy.*, **1**, 324 (1956).
18. George, P. D., and J. R. Ladd, *J. Am. Chem. Soc.*, **77**, 1900 (1955).
19. Gerrard, W., *Chem. & Ind.* (*London*), 25 (1956).
20. Gerrard, W., *J. Oil & Colour Chemists' Assoc.*, **42**, 625 (1959).
21. Gerrard, W., and B. K. Howe, *J. Chem. Soc.*, 505 (1955).
22. Gerrard, W., and M. F. Lappert, *J. Chem. Soc.*, 1020 (1951).
23. Gerrard, W., M. F. Lappert, and B. A. Mountfield, *J. Chem. Soc.*, 1529 (1959).
24. Groszos, S. J., and N. E. Day, U.S. Pat. 2,942,021 (1960, to American Cyanamid Company).
25. Hartley, J., and E. C. Lumb, Brit. Pat. 818,047 (1959, to Shell Research Ltd.).
26. Hein, Fr., and R. Burkhardt, *Z. Anorg. Allgem. Chem.*, **268**, 159 (1952).
27. Hermans, P. H., *Proc. Acad. Sci., Amsterdam*, **26**, 32 (1923).
28. Hermans, P. H., *Z. Anorg. Allgem. Chem.*, **142**, 83 (1925).
29. Herzenberg, J., G. Cevidalli, and A. Nenz, U.S. Pat. 2,861,110 (1958, to Sicedison S.p.A.).
30. Hückel, W., O. Neunhoeffer, A. Gercke, and E. Frank, *Ann.*, **477**, 99 (1929).
31. Hunter, D. L., and E. W. Fajans, U.S. Pat. 2,878,256 (1959, to United States Borax and Chemical Corporation).
32. Hunter, D. L., and H. Steinberg, Fr. Pat. 1,203,698 (1960, to United States Borax and Chemical Corporation).

33. Ingold, C. K., *Structure and Mechanism in Organic Chemistry,* Cornell Univ. Press, Ithaca, 1953, p. 346.
34. Jones, W. J., L. H. Thomas, E. H. Pritchard, and S. T. Bowden, *J. Chem. Soc.*, 824 (1946).
35. Kollonitsch, J., and T. Vita, *Nature*, **178**, 1306 (1956).
36. Lappert, M. F., *J. Chem. Soc.*, 3256 (1958).
37. Levens, E., and R. M. Washburn, U.S. Pat. 2,875,236 (1959, to American Potash and Chemical Corp.).
38. Levitan, N. I., and R. Kuoch, U.S. Pat. 2,386,484 (1945, to Buffalo Electrochemical Co., Inc.).
39. Lippincott, S. B., U.S. Pat. 2,642,453 (1953, to Standard Oil Development Co.).
40. Lucchesi, C. A., Univ. Microfilms Publ. No. 13,109; *Dissertation Abstr.*, **15**, 2007 (1955); Ph.D. Thesis, Northwestern Univ., (D. D. DeFord) (1955).
41. Maan, C. J., *Rec. Trav. Chim.*, **48**, 332 (1929).
42. May, F. H., U.S. Pat. 2,839,565 (1958, to American Potash and Chemical Corp.).
43. Mehrotra, R. C., and G. Srivastava, *J. Chem. Soc.*, 4045 (1961).
44. Morell, S. A., and E. C. Lathrop, *J. Am. Chem. Soc.*, **67**, 879 (1945).
45. Noller, C. R., *Chemistry of Organic Compounds*, W. B. Saunders, Philadelphia, 1951, p. 95.
46. Nöth, H., and L. P. Winter, *Angew. Chem.*, **71**, 651 (1959).
47. Nottes, G., C. Schuster, and K. Ehrmann, Ger. Pat. 1,033,457 (1958, to Badische Anilin- & Soda-Fabrik Aktiengesellschaft).
48. O'Connor, G. L., and H. R. Nace, *J. Am. Chem. Soc.*, **77**, 1578 (1955).
49. Petterson, L. L., and H. Steinberg, Unpublished results.
50. Pictet, A., and A. Geleznoff, *Ber.*, **36**, 2219 (1903).
51. Prescott, R. F., R. C. Dosser, and J. J. Sculati, U.S. Pat. 2,260,336 (1941, to Dow Chemical Company).
52. Prescott, R. F., R. C. Dosser, and J. J. Sculati, U.S. Pat. 2,260,338 (1941, to Dow Chemical Co.).
53. Prescott, R. F., R. C. Dosser, and J. J. Sculati, U.S. Pat. 2,260,339 (1941, to Dow Chemical Co.).
54. Pruett, R. L., Can. Pat. 631,434 (1961, to Union Carbide Corporation).
55. Rochow, E. G., U.S. Pat. 2,371,068 (1945, to General Electric Co.).
56. Rudner, B., M. S. Moores, and J. J. Harris, 140th Meeting American Chemical Society, Chicago, Sept. 1961, Abstracts of Papers, p. 103-Q.
57. Scattergood, A., W. H. Miller, and J. Gammon, Jr., *J. Am. Chem. Soc.*, **67**, 2150 (1945).
58. Schechter, W. H., U.S. Pat. 2,891,086 (1959, to Callery Chemical Co.).
59. Schechter, W. H., Private communication.
60. Schiff, H., *Ann. Suppl.*, **5**, 154 (1897).
61. Simonetta, M., and S. Winstein, *J. Am. Chem. Soc.*, **76**, 18 (1954).
62. Standard Oil Company, Ohio, Brit. Pat. 822,279 (1959).
63. Steinberg, H., and D. L. Hunter, *Ind. Eng. Chem.*, **49**, 174 (1957).
64. Steinberg, H., and D. L. Hunter, *J. Am. Chem. Soc.*, **82**, 853 (1960).
65. Steinberg, H., and D. L. Hunter, Unpublished results.
66. Steinberg, H., D. L. Hunter, and A. L. McCloskey, 135th Meeting American Chemical Society, Boston, April, 1959, Abstracts of Papers, p. 41-O.

67. Swiss, J., and C. E. Arntzen, U.S. Pat. 2,595,722 (1952, to Westinghouse Electric Corp.).
68. Taft, R. W., Jr., "Separation of Polar, Steric, and Resonance Effects in Reactivity," in M. S. Newman, *Steric Effects in Organic Chemistry*, Wiley, New York, 1956, p. 556.
69. Thomas, L. H., *J. Chem. Soc.*, 820 (1946).
70. Vaughan, T. H., U.S. Pat. 2,058,844 (1936, to Carbide and Carbon Chemicals Corp.).
71. Vavon, G., and A. Herynk, *Bull. Soc. Chim. France*, **39**, 1138 (1926).
72. Washburn, R. M., E. Levens, C. F. Albright, and F. A. Billig, 131st Meeting American Chemical Society, Miami, April 1957, Abstracts of Papers, p. 12-L.
73. Washburn, R. M., E. Levens, C. F. Albright, and F. A. Billig, "Preparation, Properties, and Uses of Borate Esters," in *Advances in Chemistry Series No. 23, Metal–Organic Compounds*, American Chemical Society, Washington, 1959, p. 129.
74. Watt, W. J., Ph.D. Thesis, Cornell Univ. (A. W. Laubengayer), 1956.
75. Whitmore, F. C., *J. Am. Chem. Soc.*, **54**, 3274 (1932).
76. Wittig, G., and M. Leo, *Ber.*, **64**, 2395 (1931).
77. Young, D. M., Can. Pat. 630,611 (1961, to The Dow Chemical Company).
78. Young, D. M., and C. D. Anderson, *J. Org. Chem.*, **26**, 1669 (1961).
79. Zimmerman, H. K., Jr., and H. Weidmann, *Ann.*, **628**, 37 (1959).

APPENDIX A

I. INFRARED ASSIGNMENTS

Infrared absorption bands (stretching) associated with boron, oxygen, sulfur, hydrogen, and chlorine are recorded in order of complexity of the various types of compounds. The samples were liquids (neat or in solution) unless otherwise noted.

The range (μ) of absorption is as follows:

Type of compound	B–O	B–S	B–H	B–D	B–Cl	C–O	O–H
Aliphatic	6.89–7.69						
Alicyclic		10.3–11.2			11.0–11.05		2.90–2.98
Aromatic	6.92–7.49				10.17–10.6	8.03–8.33	
Methyl			3.98	5.25	10.4	9.20–10.03	
Primary alkyl			3.99	5.29	10.64–11.0	9.19–9.73	
Secondary alkyl						8.68–9.33	
Tertiary alkyl						8.79	
Cyclohexyl						9.26–9.46	

$(RO)_3B$	B–O (asym.)	C–O	Reference
$(CH_3O)_3B$	7.42	9.69	30
	7.34[a]	9.69[a]	24
	7.38	9.71	24
	7.35[a]	9.64[a]	4
	7.43	9.70	27
	7.40		28
$(CH_3O)_3B^{10}$	7.22[a]		24
$(CH_3O)_3B \cdot CH_3OH$	7.42		7
$(C_2H_5O)_3B$	7.51	9.52	13
	7.02[a]	9.73[a]	21
	7.49		28
$(C_2H_5O)_3B^{10}$	6.92[a]	9.73[a]	21
$(CH_3OCH_2CH_2O)_3B$	7.50		28
C_2H_5O (on CH)			
$(CH_3OCH_2CHO)_3B$	7.50		28
$(ClCH_2CH_2O)_3B$	7.45	9.65	3
$(n\text{-}C_3H_7O)_3B$	7.50		28
	7.50	9.33	30
$(i\text{-}C_3H_7O)_3B$	7.14[a]	8.87[a]	22
	7.53		27
	7.55	8.90	5

(*Table continued*)

$(RO)_3B$	B–O (asym.)	C–O	Reference
$(i\text{-}C_3H_7O)_3B^{10}$	6.98[a]	8.87[a]	22
	7.54		28
$(n\text{-}C_4H_9O)_3B$	7.48	9.34	30
	7.50	9.32	27
	7.49		28
		9.34	5
$(i\text{-}C_4H_9O)_3B$	7.52	9.72	27
$(s\text{-}C_4H_9O)_3B$	7.52	8.84	30
	7.51		28
$(t\text{-}C_4H_9O)_3B$	7.45		13
$(n\text{-}C_5H_{11}O)_3B$	7.46	9.47	30
	7.55	9.50	27
$(C_5H_9\text{–}O)_3B$ (cyclopentyl)	7.50		28
$(n\text{-}C_6H_{13}O)_3B$	7.52	9.45	27
$(CH_3CH(CH_3)CH_2CH(CH_3)O)_3B$	7.52		28
$[(CH_3)_2CHCH_2CH(CH_3)O]_3B$		8.58	22
$(C_6H_{11}\text{–}O\text{–})_3B$ (cyclohexyl)	7.51[b]	9.41[b]	30
	7.55		28
$[(CH_3CH)_2CH(CH_3)O]_3B$	7.50		28
$(n\text{-}C_8H_{17}O)_3B$	7.52	9.35	27
	7.48		28
$(n\text{-}C_6H_{13}CH(CH_3)O)_3B$	7.51	8.90	30
$(n\text{-}C_5H_{11}CH(C_2H_5)O)_3B$	7.50		28
$[(CH_3CH(CH_3)CH_2)_2CHO]_3B$	7.48	8.76	27
	7.46		28
$((CH_3)_2(CH_3)C_6H_8\text{–}O\text{–})_3B$ (3,3,5-trimethylcyclohexyl)	7.47		28
$(n\text{-}C_{10}H_{21}O)_3B$	7.48		28
$(n\text{-}C_{12}H_{25}O)_3B$	7.48		28

(*Table continued*)

$(RO)_3B$	B–O (asym.)	C–O	Reference
$(C_5H_9S\text{–}C_5H_8S\text{–}O\text{–})_3B$	7.42[c]	9.26[c] or 9.46[c]	27
$[(CH_3CH(CH_3)CH_2CH(CH_3)CH_2)(CH_3CH(CH_3)CH_2)CHO]_3B$	7.47[c]	8.79[c]	27
	7.49		28
$(C_{14}H_{29}O)_3B$	7.52		28

$(ArO)_3B$	B–O (asym.)	C–O	Reference
$(C_6H_5\text{–}O\text{–})_3B$	7.41	8.22	30
	7.39		28
$(CH_3\text{–}C_6H_4\text{–}O\text{–})_3B$	7.43	8.22	30
$(m\text{-}CH_3C_6H_4\text{–}O\text{–})_3B$	7.45	8.15	27
	7.37		28
$(o\text{-}CH_3C_6H_4\text{–}O\text{–})_3B$	7.40		28
$(CH_3\text{–}C_6H_4\text{–}O\text{–})_3B$ (para)	7.39		28

(Table continued)

$(ArO)_3B$	B–O (asym.)	C–O	Reference
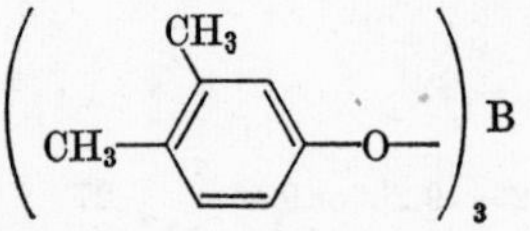 CH_3, CH_3, —O—, B, 3	7.40		28
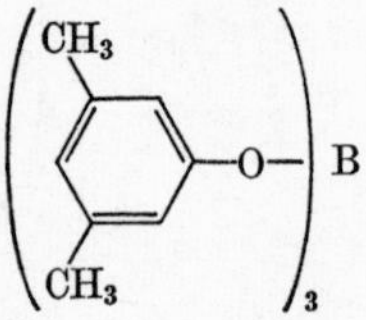 CH_3, —O—, B, CH_3, 3	7.37		28
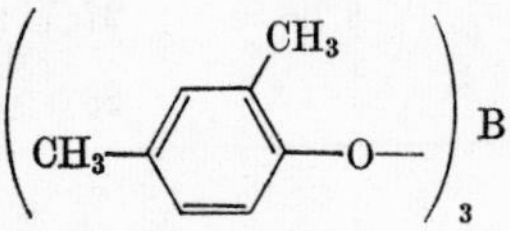 CH_3, CH_3, —O—, B, 3	7.40		28
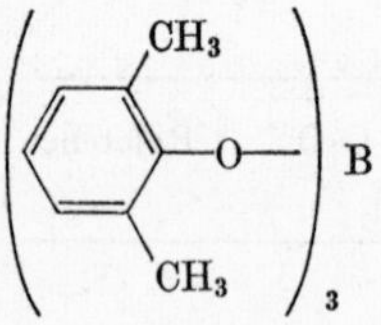 CH_3, —O—, B, CH_3, 3	7.36		28
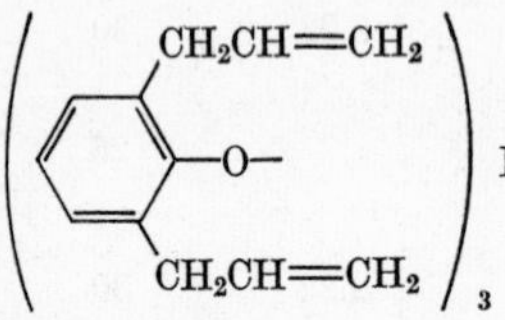 $CH_2CH{=}CH_2$, —O—, B, $CH_2CH{=}CH_2$, 3	7.39		28
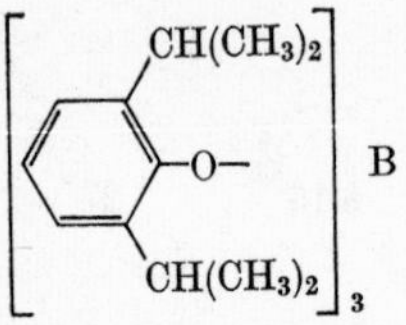 $CH(CH_3)_2$, —O—, B, $CH(CH_3)_2$, 3	7.39		28

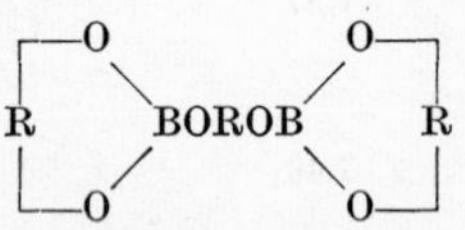 O, O, R, BOROB, R, O, O	B–O (asym.)	C–O	Reference
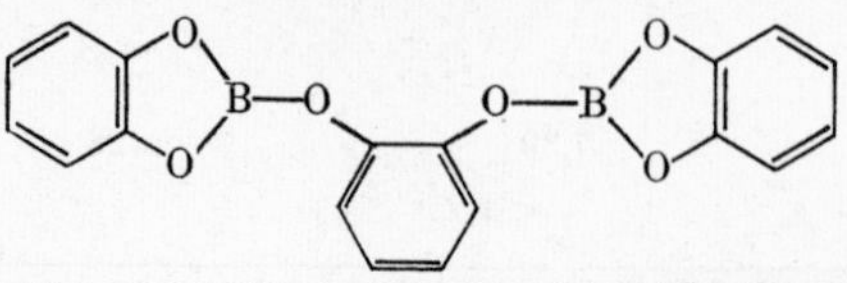 O, O, B—O, O—B, O, O	6.92 ± .20	8.03 ± .13	6

(*Table continued*)

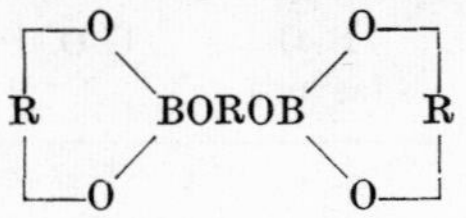 $R(O)_2BOB(O)_2R$ (cyclic: R bridging two O atoms on each B)	B–O (asym.)	C–O	Reference
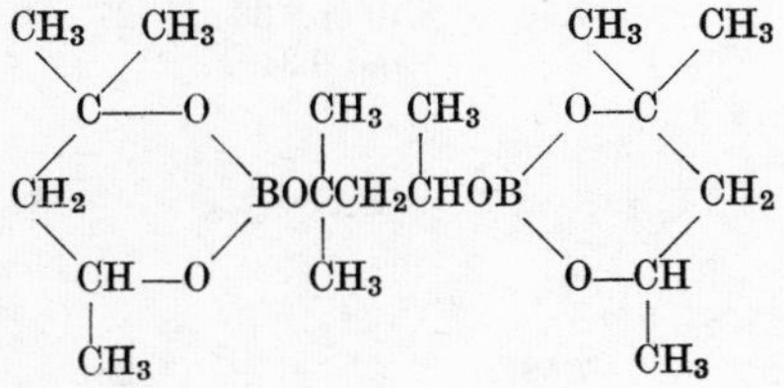 $(CH_3)_2C\text{—}O\text{—}B\text{—}O\text{—}CH(CH_3)\text{—}CH_2$ ring: $BOC(CH_3)_2CH_2CH(CH_3)OB$ linking two rings of $(CH_3)_2C(O)CH_2CH(CH_3)(O)$	7.69	8.68	27
	7.64		28

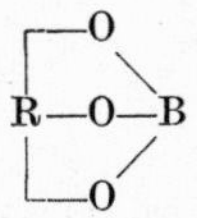 $R(O)_3B$ (cyclic: R—O—B, with R bridging the three O atoms)	B–O (asym.)	C–O	Reference
$N(CH_2CH_2O)_3B$	7.35	9.33	29
$N(CH_2CH(CH_3)O)_3B$	7.25	9.33	29
	7.26[c]	9.25[c]	25

$(RO)_2BOR'$	B–O (asym.)	C–O	Reference
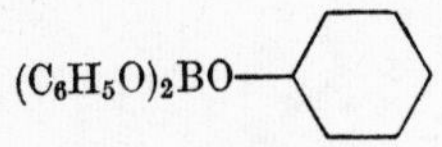 $(C_6H_5O)_2BO\text{—}C_6H_{11}$ (cyclohexyl)	7.50	9.61	31
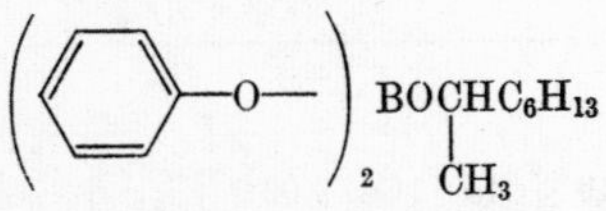 $(C_6H_5O)_2BOCH(CH_3)C_6H_{13}$ (phenyl rings drawn)	7.52	9.43	31
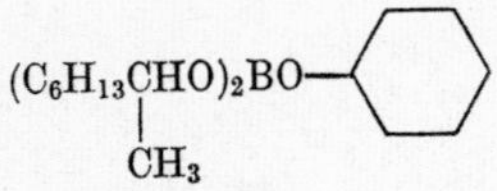 $(C_6H_{13}CH(CH_3)O)_2BO\text{—}C_6H_{11}$ (cyclohexyl)	7.51	8.86	31
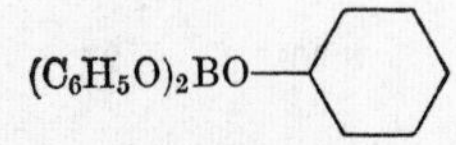 $(C_6H_5O)_2BO\text{—}C_6H_{11}$ (cyclohexyl)	7.34	9.35	31
$(C_6H_5O)_2BOCH(CH_3)C_6H_{13}$	7.48	9.34	31

(Table continued)

$(RO)_2BOR'$	B–O (asym.)	C–O	Reference
2,6-di-$C(CH_3)_3$-C_6H_3–$OB(OC_4H_9)_2$	7.50	8.10 or 8.33 and 9.34	27
4-CH_3-2,6-di-$C(CH_3)_3$-C_6H_2–$OB(O\text{-}i\text{-}C_3H_7)_2$	7.58[c]		28
4-CH_3-2,6-di-$C(CH_3)_3$-C_6H_2–$OB(OCH_2CH{=}CH_2)_2$	7.52		28
4-CH_3-2,6-di-$C(CH_3)_3$-C_6H_2–$OB(OC_4H_9)_2$	7.50		29

R(O)(O)BOR (cyclic)	B–O (asym.)	C–O	Reference
CH_2—O / CH_2—O ring BOR	7.49 ± .45	Ca. 9.09	6
$(CH_3)_2C$—O, CH_2, $CH(CH_3)$—O ring, BO–2,6-di-$C(CH_3)_3$-C_6H_3	7.40[c]	8.90[c]	27

(*Table continued*)

Compound (cyclic R(O)(O)BOR, boron ester)	B–O (asym.)	C–O	Reference
Catechol borate, $C_6H_4O_2BOR$	$C_{aromatic}$ 6.92 ± .20	8.03 ± .13	6
	$C_{aliphatic}$ 7.45 ± .05		6
$C_6H_4O_2BOC_6H_5$		8.03	6

$(R'O)_2BOROB(OR')_2$	B–O (asym.)	C–O	Reference
$[(R'O)_2BOCH_2]_2$	7.49 ± .45	Ca. 9.09	6
$[(i\text{-}C_4H_9O)_2BOCH_2]_2$		9.65	6
$[(C_6H_5O)_2BOCH_2]_2$		9.35	6

Compound (cyclic R(O)(O)B—OH)	B–O (asym.)	C–O	O–H	Reference
$(CH_3)_2C(O)CH_2CH(CH_3)O$B—OH (six-membered ring)	7.55	9.08	2.90	27
$CH_3C(CH_3)(O)C(CH_3)(CH_3)O$B—OH (pinacol ring)	7.53	8.77	2.96	27
$(CH_3)_3CCH(O)CH(O)C(CH_3)_3$B—OH			2.98	9

(*Table continued*)

$R(O)_2BOB(O)_2R$ (cyclic)	B–O (asym.)	C–O	Reference
$[(CH_3)_2C(O)–C(CH_3)_2(O)>B]_2O$	7.46	8.76	27
$[(CH_3)_2C(O)–CH_2–CH(CH_3)(O)>B]_2O$	7.23	9.07	27

$RC(=O)OB<$	B–O (asym.)	C–O	C=O Free	C=O Associated	Reference
$(CH_2O)_2BOC(=O)R$		9.07–9.65			6
$(CH_2O)_2BOC(=O)CH_3$			5.78	6.23	6
$(CH_2O)_2BOC(=O)CH_2Cl$			5.74	6.20	6
$(CH_2O)_2BOC(=O)CHCl_2$			5.70	6.12	6
$(CH_2O)_2BOC(=O)CCl_3$			5.68	6.11	6

(Table continued)

$RO\overset{O}{\overset{\|}{C}}B\langle$	B–O (asym.)	C–O	C=O Free	C=O Associated	Reference
$\begin{matrix}CH_2-O\\ \vert\\ CH_2-O\end{matrix}\rangle BO\overset{O}{\overset{\|}{C}}CF_3$			5.61		6
$(CH_3\overset{O}{\overset{\|}{C}}O)_2BOB(O\overset{O}{\overset{\|}{C}}CH_3)_2$			5.82[b]	6.23[b]	11
$(F_3\overset{O}{\overset{\|}{C}}CO)_2BOB(O\overset{O}{\overset{\|}{C}}CF_3)_2$			5.65[b]	6.04[b]	11
$(CH_3\overset{O}{\overset{\|}{C}}O\underset{Cl}{\underset{\vert}{B}})_2O$				6.30[b]	11
$(F_3C\overset{O}{\overset{\|}{C}}O)_3B$			5.63[b]	6.02[b]	11
$(CH_3\overset{O}{\overset{\|}{C}}O)_3B$	7.07		5.85		3

$(ROBO)_3$	B–O (asym.)	C–O	B_3O_6 (out of plane)		Reference
$(CH_3OBO)_3$		9.22	13.58	13.93	16
	7.42	9.20		13.94	27
$(C_2H_5OBO)_3$		9.26	13.59	13.85	16
$(BrCH_2CH_2OBO)_3$		9.10–9.52	13.6	13.9	8
$(n\text{-}C_3H_7OBO)_3$		9.23	13.62	13.85	16
$(i\text{-}C_3H_7OBO)_3$		8.94	13.64	13.83	16
	7.52	8.92	13.65	13.87	27
$(n\text{-}C_4H_9OBO)_3$		9.19	13.62	13.83	16
	7.50	9.19		13.86	27

$(ROBO)_3$	B–O (asym.)	C–O	B_3O_6 (out of plane)		Reference
$(i\text{-}C_4H_9OBO)_3$		9.23	13.59	13.81	16
	7.51	9.23		13.82	27
$(s\text{-}C_4H_9OBO)_3$		9.05	13.61	13.81	16
$(C_6H_5OBO)_3$		8.16	14.29	14.49	16
$(CH_3\overset{OBO}{\overset{\vert}{\underset{CH_3}{\underset{\vert}{C}}}}CH_2CH_2\overset{OBO}{\overset{\vert}{\underset{CH_3}{\underset{\vert}{C}}}}CH_3)_x$		8.79			27

(Table continued)

$(ROBO)_3$	B–O (asym.)	C–O	B_3O_6 (out of plane)		Reference
$[(CH_3CH(CH_3)CH_2CH(CH_3)CH_2)(CH_3CH(CH_3)CH_2)CHOBO]_3$	7.50	8.80	13.65	13.86	27
$[2,6\text{-}(C(CH_3)_3)_2C_6H_3\text{–}OBO]_3$	7.40	8.20	13.98	14.17	27

$ROOB\langle$	B–O (asym.)	Reference
$(n\text{-}C_4H_9OO)_3B$	7.42	10
$(t\text{-}C_4H_9OO)_3B$	7.48	10
$(t\text{-}C_4H_9OO)_2BOH$	7.47	10

$(RO)_2BH$	B–O		C–O	B–H	Reference
	asym.	Sym.			
$(CH_3O)_2BH$	7.35[a]	7.87[a]	10.03[a]	3.98[a]	18
$(CH_3O)_2BD$	7.35[a]	7.94[a]	9.61[a]	5.25[a]	18
$(C_2H_5O)_2BH$	7.00[a]		9.68[a]	3.99[a]	21
$(C_2H_5O)_2BD$	7.02[a]		9.50[a]	5.29[a]	21
$(C_2H_5O)_2B^{10}H$	6.89[a]		9.68[a]	3.99[a]	21
$(i\text{-}C_3H_7O)_2B^{10}H$	6.92[a]		8.87[a]	4.02[a]	22

$ROBX_2$, $(RO)_2BX$, and $R\langle^{O}_{O}\rangle B\text{—}X$	B–O		C–O	B–X		Reference
	Asym.	Sym.		Asym.	Sym.	
CH_3OBCl_2		7.38[a]	9.71[a]	10.4[a]		19
					18.5[a]	20
$CH_3OB^{10}Cl_2$				10.03[a]		19
$(CH_3O)_2BCl$	7.29[a]	7.84[a]	9.73[a]		~15.9[a]	19
$ClCH_2OCH_2CH_2OBCl_2$				10.64		8
$(ClCH_2OCH_2CH_2O)_2BCl$				11.0		8

(Table continued)

$ROBX_2$, $(RO)_2BX$, and $R(O)_2B{-}X$ (cyclic)	B–O Asym.	B–O Sym.	C–O	B–X Asym.	B–X Sym.	Reference
$ClCH_2\overset{+}{S}(CH_3){-}\overset{-}{B}(Cl){=}O$	6.90–7.14					17
$C_6H_5OBCl_2$, $(C_6H_5O)_2BCl$	7.41				13.5–14.1	23
$CH_2O{-}CH_2O{>}B{-}Cl$ (cyclic)				11.05		6
$CH_2(CH_2O)_2B{-}Cl$ (cyclic)	7.36		9.40	11.0		3
					18.2	12
2,6-$[C(CH_3)_3]_2C_6H_3OBCl_2$				10.17 or 10.6		26
$(CH_3OBF_2)_2$	7.24		9.50			14
CH_3OBF_2	7.24		9.34			14
$(CH_3O)_2BF$	7.31[a]		9.59[a]			14

$R_3SiOB{<}$	B–O (asym.)	Reference
$(R_3SiO)_3B$	7.50 ± 0.03	1
$(R_3SiOBO)_3$	7.25	1

$[(RO)_xBH_{4-x}]M$	B–O	Reference
$[(CH_3O)_4B]Na$	7.92, 8.37	28
$C_6H_4O_2\overset{-}{B}O_2C_6H_6CH_3{}^{+}$ (spiro, with CH_3 on the cyclohexadienyl ⊕ ring)	6.88, 8.06, ~9.10	2
$[(CH_3O)_3BH]Na$	7.98, 8.45	28

(Table continued)

RSB<	?	?	B–S	C–O	Reference
CH_2—O, CH_2—O >BSR (cyclic)			10.30–11.20[d]	9.07 ± 0.03	6
$(RS)_3B$	10–11	13.25–13.50			15

[a] Vapor. [b] Solid. [c]KBr pellet. [d] Triplet.

II. REFERENCES

1. Abel, E. W., and A. Singh, *J. Chem. Soc.*, 690 (1959).
2. Balaban, A. T., G. Mihai, R. Antonescu, and P. T. Frangopol, *Tetrahedron*, **16**, 68 (1961).
3. Bastin, E. L., *et al.*, Shell Development Company, Final Report on Potential CW Agents, Task 5, Boron Compounds as Toxicants for Chemical Corps Procurement Agency, Contract No. CML-4564, April 30, 1954.
4. Becker, H. J., *Z. Physik. Chem.*, **2**, 276 (1954).
5. Bell, J. V., J. Heisler, H. Tannenbaum, and J. Goldenson, *Anal. Chem.*, **25**, 1720 (1953).
6. Blau, J. A., W. Gerrard, M. F. Lappert, B. A. Mountfield, and H. Pyszora, *J. Chem. Soc.*, 380 (1960).
7. Christopher, P. M., *J. Phys. Chem.*, **64**, 1336 (1960).
8. Cooper, S., M. J. Frazer, and W. Gerrard, *J. Chem. Soc.*, 5545 (1961).
9. Dale, J., *J. Chem. Soc.*, 910 (1961).
10. Davies, A. G., and R. B. Moodie, *Chem. & Ind.* (*London*), 1622 (1957).
11. Duncanson, L. A., W. Gerrard, M. F. Lappert, H. Pyszora, and R. Shafferman, *J. Chem. Soc.*, 3652 (1958).
12. Finch, A., J. C. Lockhart, and J. Pearn, *J. Org. Chem.*, **26**, 3250 (1961).
13. George, P. D., and J. R. Ladd, *J. Am. Chem. Soc.*, **77**, 1900 (1955).
14. Goubeau, J., and D. Hummel, *Z. Physik. Chem.*, **20**, 15 (1959).
15. Hawthorne, M. F., *J. Am. Chem. Soc.*, **83**, 1345 (1961).
16. Lappert, M. F., *J. Chem. Soc.*, 2790 (1958).
17. Lappert, M. F., and J. K. Smith, *J. Chem. Soc.*, 3224 (1961).
18. Lehmann, W. J., T. P. Onak, and I. Shapiro, *J. Chem. Phys.*, **30**, 1215 (1959).
19. Lehmann, W. J., T. P. Onak, and I. Shapiro, *J. Chem. Phys.*, **30**, 1219 (1959).
20. Lehmann, W. J., T. P. Onak, and I. Shapiro, Olin Mathieson Chemical Corporation, Technical Research Report OMCC-HEF-180, Feb. 24, 1959.
21. Lehmann, W. J., H. G. Weiss, and I. Shapiro, *J. Chem. Phys.*, **30**, 1222 (1959).
22. Lehmann, W. J., H. G. Weiss, and I. Shapiro, *J. Chem. Phys.*, **30**, 1226 (1959).

23. Peach, M. E., and T. C. Waddington, *J. Chem. Soc.*, 1238 (1961).
24. Servoss, R. R., and H. M. Clark, *J. Chem. Phys.*, **26**, 1179 (1957).
25. Steinberg, H., and D. L. Hunter, *J. Am. Chem. Soc.*, **82**, 853 (1960).
26. Steinberg, H., and D. L. Hunter, Unpublished results.
27. Steinberg, H., D. L. Hunter, and L. L. Petterson, Unpublished results.
28. Washburn, R. M., E. Levens, C. F. Albright, and F. A. Billig, "Preparation, Properties, and Uses of Borate Esters," in *Metal–Organic Compounds, Advances in Chemistry Series No. 23*, American Chemical Society, Washington, 1959, p. 129.
29. Weidmann, H., and H. K. Zimmerman, Jr., *Ann.*, **620**, 4 (1959).
30. Werner, R. L., and K. G. O'Brien, *Australian J. Chem.*, 8, 355 (1955).
31. Werner, R. L., and K. G. O'Brien, *Australian J. Chem.*, **9**, 137 (1956).

APPENDIX B

I. BOND ENERGIES AND BOND DISTANCES

Compound	Bond energy (kcal)			Bond distance (Å)		Reference
	B–O	B–S	B–H	B–O	C–O	
$(CH_3O)_3B$	115					4
	116.5					6
	125					7
				1.38		8
				1.38 ± 0.02	1.43 ± 0.03	2
$(C_2H_5O)_3B$	104					1
	119 ± 5					1
	119.3					9, 10
	128					7
$(n\text{-}C_3H_7O)_3B$	129					7
$(n\text{-}C_4H_9O)_3B$	130					7
$(RO)_3B$	110 ± 5					5
$(CH_3O)_2BH$			9.25			6
\\B—S— /		68.5				3
		83				1

II. REFERENCES

1. Altshuller, A. P., NACA Research Memorandum E55127a, National Advisory Committee for Aeronautics, Washington, Nov. 18, 1955.
2. Bauer, S. H., and J. Y. Beach, *J. Am. Chem. Soc.*, **63**, 1394 (1941).
3. Brown, C. A., and L. J. Schupp, Western Reserve University, Technical Research Report, Boron–Nitrogen Compounds, MCC-1023-TR-65, August, 1954.
4. Brown, C. A., and L. J. Schupp, Western Reserve University, Technical Report No. 2, ONR Contract No. Nonr 1439(02), Project No. NR-052-55, Nov. 1, 1955.
5. Charnley, T., H. A. Skinner, and N. B. Smith, *J. Chem. Soc.*, 2288 (1952).
6. Cooper, W. J., and J. F. Masi, *J. Phys. Chem.*, **64**, 682 (1960).
7. Cottrell, T. L., *The Strengths of Chemical Bonds*, 2nd ed., Butterworths Scientific Publications, London, 1958, p. 241.
8. Laubengayer, A. W., R. P. Ferguson, and A. E. Newkirk, *J. Am. Chem. Soc.*, **63**, 559 (1941).
9. Pritchard, H. O., and H. A. Skinner, *Chem. Rev.*, **55**, 745 (1955).
10. Skinner, H. A., and N. B. Smith, *Trans. Faraday Soc.*, **51**, 19 (1955).

APPENDIX C

I. HEATS OF FORMATION

Compound	ΔH_f (kcal/mole, 25°)	Reference
$(CH_3O)_3B$	−215.3(g)	6
	−215.7(g)	3
	−215.7 ± 1.0(g)	1
	−223.60(l)	6
	−223.98(l)	3
	−224.0 ± 0.8(l)	1
	−255.9(c)	3
$(C_2H_5O)_3B$	−240.8(g)	3, 6
	−240.8 ± 1.2(g)	1, 5
	−251.26(l)	3
	−251.30(l)	6
	−251.3 ± 1.0(l)	1, 5
$(n\text{-}C_3H_7O)_3B$	−258.6(g)	3, 6
	−260.9 ± 2.4(g)	1
	−270.86(l)	6
	−271.06(l)	3
	−272.7 ± 1.4(l)	1
$(n\text{-}C_4H_9O)_3B$	−274.7(g)	3
	−275.3(g)	6
	−279.4 ± 2.5(g)	1
	−289.10(l)	6
	−289.19(l)	3
	−291.9 ± 1.5(l)	1
$(CH_3O)_2BH$	−139.2(g)	2
	−145.3 ± 1.5(l)	2
CH_3OBCl_2	−141.0(g)[a]	4
$(CH_3O)_2BCl$	−178.8 ± 0.5(g)	4
	−186.9 ± 0.4(l)	4
$C_2H_5OBCl_2$	−149.6(g)	3
	−149.9 ± 1.4(g)	5
	−158.0(l)	3
	−158.3 ± 1.2(l)	5
$(C_2H_5O)_2BCl$	−196.4(g)	3
	−197.0 ± 1.4(g)	5
	−206.0(l)	3
	−206.3 ± 1.2(l)	5

[a] Estimated.

II. REFERENCES

1. Charnley, T., H. A. Skinner, and N. B. Smith, *J. Chem. Soc.*, 2288 (1952).
2. Cooper, W. J., and J. F. Masi, *J. Phys. Chem.*, **64**, 682 (1960).

3. Evans, W. H., D. D. Wagman, and E. J. Prosen, Thermodynamic Properties of Some Boron Compounds, NBS Report No. 4943, NBS Project 0509-40-3283, August 31, 1956.
4. Kilday, M. V., W. H. Johnson, and E. J. Prosen, *J. Res. Nat. Bur. Std.*, *A*, **65**, 435 (1961).
5. Skinner, H. A., and N. B. Smith, *J. Chem. Soc.*, 3930 (1954).
6. Wagman, D. D., T. R. Munson, W. H. Evans, and E. J. Prosen, Thermodynamic Properties of Boron Compounds, NBS Report No. 3456, NBS Project 0509-10-3256, August 30, 1954.

AUTHOR INDEX

Italic numbers refer to the list of references at the end of each chapter

SUBJECT INDEX